QA
47
.M315
1996

AVALON

Chicago Public Library

P9-DNJ-946

CRC standard mathematical tables.

AVALON BRANCH LIBRARY
9828 SO. STONY ISLAND AVE

.CARD

CRC
STANDARD MATHEMATICAL TABLES AND FORMULAE

Editor-in-Chief
DANIEL ZWILLINGER

CRC Press
Boca Raton   Boston   London   New York   Washington, D.C.

Library of Congress Cataloging-in-Publication Data

Catalog information is available from the Library of Congress.

This book contains information obtained from authentic and highly regarded sources. Reprinted material is quoted with permission, and sources are indicated. A wide variety of references are listed. Reasonable efforts have been made to publish reliable data and information, but the author and the publisher cannot assume responsibility for the validity of all materials or for the consequences of their use.

Neither this book nor any part may be reproduced or transmitted in any form or by any means, electronic or mechanical, including photocopying, microfilming, and recording, or by any information storage or retrieval system, without prior permission in writing from the publisher.

All rights reserved. Authorization to photocopy items for internal or personal use, or the personal or internal use of specific clients, may be granted by CRC Press LLC, provided that $.50 per page photocopied is paid directly to Copyright Clearance Center, 27 Congress Street, Salem, MA 01970 USA. The fee code for users of the Transactional Reporting Service is ISBN 0-8493-9469-4/97/$0.00+$.50. The fee is subject to change without notice. For organizations that have been granted a photocopy license by the CCC, a separate system of payment has been arranged.

The consent of CRC Press LLC does not extend to copying for general distribution, for promotion, for creating new works, or for resale. Specific permission must be obtained in writing from CRC Press LLC for such copying.

Direct all inquiries to CRC Press LLC, 2000 Corporate Blvd., N.W., Boca Raton, Florida 33431.

Trademark Notice: Product or corporate names may be trademarks or registered trademarks, and are used only for identification and explanation, without intent to infringe.

© 1996 by CRC Press LLC

No claim to original U.S. Government works
International Standard Book Number 0-8493-2479-3
Library of Congress Card Number 30-4052
Printed in the United States of America   3 4 5 6 7 8 9 0
Printed on acid-free paper

AVALON BRANCH LIBRARY
9828 SO. STONY ISLAND AVE
CHICAGO, IL 60617

Editor-in-Chief

Daniel Zwillinger
Rensselaer Polytechnic Institute
Troy, New York

Associate Editors

Steven G. Krantz
Washington University
St. Louis, Missouri

Kenneth H. Rosen
AT&T Bell Laboratories
Holmdel, New Jersey

AVALON BRANCH LIBRARY
9828 SO. STONY ISLAND AVE
CHICAGO, IL 60617

Editorial Advisory Board

George E. Andrews
Pennsylvania State University
University Park, Pennsylvania

William H. Beyer
The University of Akron
Akron, Ohio

Robert Borrelli
Harvey Mudd College
Claremont, California

Michael F. Bridgland
Center for Computing Sciences
Bowie, Maryland

Courtney Coleman
Harvey Mudd College
Claremont, California

J. Douglas Faires
Youngstown State University
Youngstown, Ohio

Gerald B. Folland
University of Washington
Seattle, Washington

Ben Fusaro
Salisbury State University
Salisbury, Maryland

Alan F. Karr
National Institute Statistical Sciences
Research Triangle Park, North Carolina

Steve Landsburg
University of Rochester
Rochester, New York

Al Marden
University of Minnesota
Minneapolis, Minnesota

Cleve Moler
The MathWorks
Natick, Massachusetts

William H. Press
Harvard University
Cambridge, Massachusetts

Preface

It has long been the established policy of CRC Press to publish, in handbook form, the most up-to-date, authoritative, logically arranged, and readily usable reference material available. Prior to the preparation of this *30th Edition* of the *CRC Standard Mathematical Tables and Formulae*, the content of such a book was reconsidered. Previous editions were carefully reviewed, and input obtained from practitioners in the many branches of mathematics, engineering, and the physical sciences. The content selected for this *Handbook* provides the basic mathematical reference materials required for each of these disciplines.

While much material was retained, several topics were completely reworked, and many new topics were added. New and completely revised topics include: partial differential equations, scientific computing, integral equations, group theory, and graph theory. For each topic, old and new, the contents have been completely rewritten and retypeset. A more comprehensive index has been added.

The same successful format which has characterized earlier editions of the *Handbook* is retained, while its presentation is updated and more consistent from page to page. Material is presented in a multi-sectional format, with each section containing a valuable collection of fundamental reference material—tabular and expository.

In line with the established policy of CRC Press, the *Handbook* will be kept as current and timely as is possible. Revisions and anticipated uses of newer materials and tables will be introduced as the need arises. Suggestions for the inclusion of new material in subsequent editions and comments concerning the accuracy of stated information are welcomed.

No book is created in a vacuum, and this one is no exception. Not only did we start with an excellent previous edition, but our editorial staff was superb, and the contributors did an amazingly good job. I wholeheartedly thank them all. There were also many proofreaders, too many to name individually; again, thank you for your efforts.

Lastly, this book would not have been possible without the support of my loving wife, Janet Taylor.

Daniel Zwillinger
zwilling@world.std.com

Contributors

Karen Bolinger
Clarion University
Clarion, Pennsylvania

Patrick J. Driscoll
U.S. Military Academy
West Point, New York

M. Lawrence Glasser
Clarkson University
Potsdam, New York

Jeff Goldberg
University of Arizona
Tucson, Arizona

Rob Gross
Boston College
Chestnut Hill, Massachusetts

Melvin Hausner
Courant Institute (NYU)
New York, New York

Christopher Heil
Georgia Tech
Atlanta, Georgia

Paul Jameson
BBN
Cambridge, Massachusetts

Victor J. Katz
MAA
Washington, DC

Silvio Levy
Geometry Center
University of Minnesota
Minneapolis, Minnesota

Michael Mascagni
Supercomputing Research Center
Bowie, Maryland

Ray McLenaghan
University of Waterloo
Waterloo, Ontario

John Michaels
SUNY Brockport
Brockport, New York

William C. Rinaman
LeMoyne College
Syracuse, New York

Catherine Roberts
Northern Arizona University
Flagstaff, Arizona

John S. Robertson
Georgia College
Milledgeville, Georgia

Joseph J. Rushanan
MITRE Corporation
Burlington, Massachusetts

Neil J. A. Sloane
AT&T Bell Labs
Murray Hill, New Jersey

Mike Sousa
MITRE Corporation
Burlington, Massachusetts

Gary L. Stanek
Youngstown State University
Youngstown, Ohio

Michael T. Strauss
Zwillinger & Associates
Newton, Massachusetts

Nico M. Temme
CWI
Amsterdam, The Netherlands

George K. Tzanetopoulos
University of Rhode Island
Kingston, Rhode Island

Brad Wilson
SUNY Brockport
Brockport, New York

Ahmed I. Zayed
University of Central Florida
Orlando, Florida

Table of Contents

Chapter **1**

Analysis

0-8493-2479-3/96/$0.00+$.50
© 1996 CRC Press, Inc.

1.1 CONSTANTS

1.1.1 TYPES OF NUMBERS

Natural numbers

The *natural numbers* are customarily denoted by $\mathbb{N}$. They are the set $\{0, 1, 2, \dots\}$. Many authors do not consider 0 to be a natural number.

Integers

The *integers* are customarily denoted by $\mathbb{Z}$. They are the set $\{0, \pm 1, \pm 2, \dots\}$.

Rational numbers

The *rational numbers* are customarily denoted by $\mathbb{Q}$. They are the set $\{\frac{p}{q} \mid p, q \in \mathbb{Z}, q \neq 0\}$. Two fractions $\frac{p}{q}$ and $\frac{r}{s}$ are equal if $ps = qr$.

Addition of fractions is defined by $\frac{p}{q} + \frac{r}{s} = \frac{ps+qr}{qs}$. Multiplication of fractions is defined by $\frac{p}{q} \cdot \frac{r}{s} = \frac{pr}{qs}$.

Real numbers

The real numbers are customarily denoted by $\mathbb{R}$. Real numbers are defined to be converging sequences of rational numbers or as decimals that might or might not repeat.

Real numbers are often divided into two subsets. One subset, the *algebraic numbers*, are real numbers which solve a polynomial equation in one variable with integer coefficients. For example; $\frac{1}{\sqrt{2}}$ is an algebraic number because it solves the polynomial equation $2x^2 - 1 = 0$, and rational numbers are algebraic. Real numbers that are not algebraic numbers are called *transcendental numbers*. Examples of transcendental numbers include π and e.

Complex numbers

The *complex numbers* are customarily denoted by $\mathbb{C}$. They are numbers of the form $a + bi$, where $i^2 = -1$, and a and b are real numbers. See Section 1.5.

The sum of two complex numbers $a + bi$ and $c + di$ is $a + c + (b + d)i$. The product of two complex numbers $a + bi$ and $c + di$ is $ac - bd + (ad + bc)i$. The reciprocal of the complex number $a + bi$ is $\frac{a}{a^2+b^2} - \frac{b}{a^2+b^2}i$. If $z = a + bi$, the complex conjugate of z is $\overline{z} = a - bi$. Properties include: $\overline{z + w} = \overline{z} + \overline{w}$ and $\overline{zw} = \overline{z}\,\overline{w}$.

1.1.2   REPRESENTATION OF NUMBERS

Numerals as usually written have radix or base 10, because the numeral $a_n a_{n-1} \ldots a_2 a_1 a_0$ represents the number $a_n 10^n + a_{n-1} 10^{n-1} + \cdots + a_2 10^2 + a_1 10 + a_0$. However, other bases can be used, particularly bases 2, 8, and 16 (called *binary*, *octal*, and *hexadecimal*, respectively). When another base is used, it is indicated by a subscript:

$$543_7 = 5 \times 7^2 + 4 \times 7 + 3 = 276,$$
$$10111_2 = 1 \times 2^4 + 0 \times 2^3 + 1 \times 2^2 + 1 \times 2 + 1 = 23,$$
$$A3_{16} = 10 \times 16 + 3 = 163.$$

When writing a number in base b, the digits used can range from 0 to $b-1$. If $b > 10$, then the digit A stands for 10, B for 11, etc.

The above algorithm can be used to convert a numeral from base b to base 10. To convert a numeral from base 10 to base b, divide the numeral by b, and the remainder will be the last digit. Then divide the quotient by b, using the remainder as the previous digit. Continue dividing the quotient by b until a quotient of 0 is arrived at.

For example, to convert 574 to base 12, divide, yielding a remainder of 10 and a quotient of 47. Hence, the last digit of the answer is A. Divide 47 by 12, giving a remainder of 11 again and a quotient of 3. Divide 3 by 12, giving a remainder of 3 and a quotient of 0. Therefore, $575_{10} = 3BA_{12}$.

In general, to convert from base b to base r, it is simplest to convert to base 10 as an intermediate step. However, it is simple to convert from base b to base b^a. For example, to convert 110111101_2 to base 16, group the digits in fours (because 16 is 2^4), yielding 1 1011 1101, and then convert each group of 4 to base 16 directly, yielding $1BD_{16}$.

1.1.3 DECIMAL MULTIPLES AND PREFIXES

The prefix and symbols below are taken from Conference Générale des Poids et Mesures, 1991. The common names are for the U.S.

Multiple	Prefix	Symbol	Common name
$10^{(10^{100})}$			googolplex
10^{100}			googol
10^{24}	yotta	Y	heptillion
10^{21}	zetta	Z	hexillion
10^{18}	exa	E	quintillion
10^{15}	peta	P	quadrillion
10^{12}	tera	T	trillion
10^{9}	giga	G	billion
10^{6}	mega	M	million
10^{3}	kilo	K	thousand
10^{2}	hecto	h	hundred
10^{1}	deca	da	ten
10^{-1}	deci	d	tenth
10^{-2}	centi	c	hundreth
10^{-3}	milli	m	thousandth
10^{-6}	micro	μ (Greek mu)	millionth
10^{-9}	nano	n	billionth
10^{-12}	pico	p	trillionth
10^{-15}	femto	f	quadrillionth
10^{-18}	atto	a	quintillionth
10^{-21}	zepto	z	hexillionth
10^{-24}	yocto	y	heptillionth

1.1.4 ROMAN NUMERALS

The major symbols in Roman numerals are I $= 1$, V $= 5$, X $= 10$, L $= 50$, C $= 100$, D $= 500$, and M $= 1,000$. The rules for constructing Roman numerals are

1. A symbol following one of equal or greater value adds its value (for example, II $= 2$, XI $= 11$, DV $= 505$).

2. A symbol following one of lesser value has the lesser value subtracted from the larger value (for example, IV $= 4$, IX $= 9$, VM $= 995$).

3. When a symbol stands between two of greater value, its value is subtracted from the second and the result is added to the first (for example, XIV $= 10 + (5 - 1) = 14$, CIX $= 100 + (10 - 1) = 109$, DVL $= 500 + (50 - 5) = 545$).

4. When two ways exist for representing a number, the one in which the symbol of larger value occurs earlier in the string is preferred (for example, 14 is represented as XIV, not as VIX).

Decimal number	1	2	3	4	5	6	7	8	9
Roman numeral	I	II	III	IV	V	VI	VII	VIII	IX

10	14	50	200	400	500	600	999	1000
X	XIV	L	CC	CD	D	DC	CMXCIX	M

1950	1960	1970	1980	1990
MCML	MCMLX	MCMLXX	MCMLXXX	MCMXC

1996	1997	1998	1999	2000
MCMXCVI	MCMXCVII	MCMXCVIII	MCMXCIX	MM

1.1.5   DECIMAL EQUIVALENTS OF COMMON FRACTIONS

		1/64	0.015625			33/64	0.515625
	1/32	2/64	0.03125		17/32	34/64	0.53125
		3/64	0.046875			35/64	0.546875
1/16	2/32	4/64	0.0625	9/16	18/32	36/64	0.5625
		5/64	0.078125			37/64	0.578125
	3/32	6/64	0.09375		19/32	38/64	0.59375
		7/64	0.109375			39/64	0.609375
1/8	4/32	8/64	0.125	5/8	20/32	40/64	0.625
		9/64	0.140625			41/64	0.640625
	5/32	10/64	0.15625		21/32	42/64	0.65625
		11/64	0.171875			43/64	0.671875
3/16	6/32	12/64	0.1875	11/16	22/32	44/64	0.6875
		13/64	0.203125			45/64	0.703125
	7/32	14/64	0.21875		23/32	46/64	0.71875
		15/64	0.234375			47/64	0.734375
1/4	8/32	16/64	0.25	3/4	24/32	48/64	0.75
		17/64	0.265625			49/64	0.765625
	9/32	18/64	0.28125		25/32	50/64	0.78125
		19/64	0.296875			51/64	0.796875
5/16	10/32	20/64	0.3125	13/16	26/32	52/64	0.8125
		21/64	0.328125			53/64	0.828125
	11/32	22/64	0.34375		27/32	54/64	0.84375
		23/64	0.359375			55/64	0.859375
3/8	12/32	24/64	0.375	7/8	28/32	56/64	0.875
		25/64	0.390625			57/64	0.890625
	13/32	26/64	0.40625		29/32	58/64	0.90625
		27/64	0.421875			59/64	0.921875
7/16	14/32	28/64	0.4375	15/16	30/32	60/64	0.9375
		29/64	0.453125			61/64	0.953125
	15/32	30/64	0.46875		31/32	62/64	0.96875
		31/64	0.484375			63/64	0.984375
1/2	16/32	32/64	0.5	1/1	32/32	64/64	1

1.1.6 HEXADECIMAL ADDITION AND SUBTRACTION TABLE

A = 10, B = 11, C = 12, D = 13, E = 14, F = 15.
Example: $6 + 2 = 8$; hence $8 - 6 = 2$ and $8 - 2 = 6$.
Example: $4 + E = 12$; hence $12 - 4 = E$ and $12 - E = 4$.

	1	2	3	4	5	6	7	8	9	A	B	C	D	E	F
1	02	03	04	05	06	07	08	09	0A	0B	0C	0D	0E	0F	10
2	03	04	05	06	07	08	09	0A	0B	0C	0D	0E	0F	10	11
3	04	05	06	07	08	09	0A	0B	0C	0D	0E	0F	10	11	12
4	05	06	07	08	09	0A	0B	0C	0D	0E	0F	10	11	12	13
5	06	07	08	09	0A	0B	0C	0D	0E	0F	10	11	12	13	14
6	07	08	09	0A	0B	0C	0D	0E	0F	10	11	12	13	14	15
7	08	09	0A	0B	0C	0D	0E	0F	10	11	12	13	14	15	16
8	09	0A	0B	0C	0D	0E	0F	10	11	12	13	14	15	16	17
9	0A	0B	0C	0D	0E	0F	10	11	12	13	14	15	16	17	18
A	0B	0C	0D	0E	0F	10	11	12	13	14	15	16	17	18	19
B	0C	0D	0E	0F	10	11	12	13	14	15	16	17	18	19	1A
C	0D	0E	0F	10	11	12	13	14	15	16	17	18	19	1A	1B
D	0E	0F	10	11	12	13	14	15	16	17	18	19	1A	1B	1C
E	0F	10	11	12	13	14	15	16	17	18	19	1A	1B	1C	1D
F	10	11	12	13	14	15	16	17	18	19	1A	1B	1C	1D	1E

1.1.7 HEXADECIMAL MULTIPLICATION TABLE

Example: $2 \times 4 = 8$.
Example: $2 \times F = 1E$.

	1	2	3	4	5	6	7	8	9	A	B	C	D	E	F
1	01	02	03	04	05	06	07	08	09	0A	0B	0C	0D	0E	0F
2	02	04	06	08	0A	0C	0E	10	12	14	16	18	1A	1C	1E
3	03	06	09	0C	0F	12	15	18	1B	1E	21	24	27	2A	2D
4	04	08	0C	10	14	18	1C	20	24	28	2C	30	34	38	3C
5	05	0A	0F	14	19	1E	23	28	2D	32	37	3C	41	46	4B
6	06	0C	12	18	1E	24	2A	30	36	3C	42	48	4E	54	5A
7	07	0E	15	1C	23	2A	31	38	3F	46	4D	54	5B	62	69
8	08	10	18	20	28	30	38	40	48	50	58	60	68	70	78
9	09	12	1B	24	2D	36	3F	48	51	5A	63	6C	75	7E	87
A	0A	14	1E	28	32	3C	46	50	5A	64	6E	78	82	8C	96
B	0B	16	21	2C	37	42	4D	58	63	6E	79	84	8F	9A	A5
C	0C	18	24	30	3C	48	54	60	6C	78	84	90	9C	A8	B4
D	0D	1A	27	34	41	4E	5B	68	75	82	8F	9C	A9	B6	C3
E	0E	1C	2A	38	46	54	62	70	7E	8C	9A	A8	B6	C4	D2
F	0F	1E	2D	3C	4B	5A	69	78	87	96	A5	B4	C3	D2	E1

1.1.8 HEXADECIMAL–DECIMAL FRACTION CONVERSION TABLE

Hex	Decimal	Hex	Decimal	Hex	Decimal	Hex	Decimal
.00	0	.40	0.250000	.80	0.500000	.C0	0.750000
.01	0.003906	.41	0.253906	.81	0.503906	.C1	0.753906
.02	0.007812	.42	0.257812	.82	0.507812	.C2	0.757812
.03	0.011718	.43	0.261718	.83	0.511718	.C3	0.761718
.04	0.015625	.44	0.265625	.84	0.515625	.C4	0.765625
.05	0.019531	.45	0.269531	.85	0.519531	.C5	0.769531
.06	0.023437	.46	0.273437	.86	0.523437	.C6	0.773437
.07	0.027343	.47	0.277343	.87	0.527343	.C7	0.777343
.08	0.031250	.48	0.281250	.88	0.531250	.C8	0.781250
.09	0.035156	.49	0.285156	.89	0.535156	.C9	0.785156
.0A	0.039062	.4A	0.289062	.8A	0.539062	.CA	0.789062
.0B	0.042968	.4B	0.292968	.8B	0.542968	.CB	0.792968
.0C	0.046875	.4C	0.296875	.8C	0.546875	.CC	0.796875
.0D	0.050781	.4D	0.300781	.8D	0.550781	.CD	0.800781
.0E	0.054687	.4E	0.304687	.8E	0.554687	.CE	0.804687
.0F	0.058593	.4F	0.308593	.8F	0.558593	.CF	0.808593
.10	0.062500	.50	0.312500	.90	0.562500	.D0	0.812500
.11	0.066406	.51	0.316406	.91	0.566406	.D1	0.816406
.12	0.070312	.52	0.320312	.92	0.570312	.D2	0.820312
.13	0.074218	.53	0.324218	.93	0.574218	.D3	0.824218
.14	0.078125	.54	0.328125	.94	0.578125	.D4	0.828125
.15	0.082031	.55	0.332031	.95	0.582031	.D5	0.832031
.16	0.085937	.56	0.335937	.96	0.585937	.D6	0.835937
.17	0.089843	.57	0.339843	.97	0.589843	.D7	0.839843
.18	0.093750	.58	0.343750	.98	0.593750	.D8	0.843750
.19	0.097656	.59	0.347656	.99	0.597656	.D9	0.847656
.1A	0.101562	.5A	0.351562	.9A	0.601562	.DA	0.851562
.1B	0.105468	.5B	0.355468	.9B	0.605468	.DB	0.855468
.1C	0.109375	.5C	0.359375	.9C	0.609375	.DC	0.859375
.1D	0.113281	.5D	0.363281	.9D	0.613281	.DD	0.863281
.1E	0.117187	.5E	0.367187	.9E	0.617187	.DE	0.867187
.1F	0.121093	.5F	0.371093	.9F	0.621093	.DF	0.871093

Hex	Decimal	Hex	Decimal	Hex	Decimal	Hex	Decimal
.20	0.125000	.60	0.375000	.A0	0.625000	.E0	0.875000
.21	0.128906	.61	0.378906	.A1	0.628906	.E1	0.878906
.22	0.132812	.62	0.382812	.A2	0.632812	.E2	0.882812
.23	0.136718	.63	0.386718	.A3	0.636718	.E3	0.886718
.24	0.140625	.64	0.390625	.A4	0.640625	.E4	0.890625
.25	0.144531	.65	0.394531	.A5	0.644531	.E5	0.894531
.26	0.148437	.66	0.398437	.A6	0.648437	.E6	0.898437
.27	0.152343	.67	0.402343	.A7	0.652343	.E7	0.902343
.28	0.156250	.68	0.406250	.A8	0.656250	.E8	0.906250
.29	0.160156	.69	0.410156	.A9	0.660156	.E9	0.910156
.2A	0.164062	.6A	0.414062	.AA	0.664062	.EA	0.914062
.2B	0.167968	.6B	0.417968	.AB	0.667968	.EB	0.917968
.2C	0.171875	.6C	0.421875	.AC	0.671875	.EC	0.921875
.2D	0.175781	.6D	0.425781	.AD	0.675781	.ED	0.925781
.2E	0.179687	.6E	0.429687	.AE	0.679687	.EE	0.929687
.2F	0.183593	.6F	0.433593	.AF	0.683593	.EF	0.933593
.30	0.187500	.70	0.437500	.B0	0.687500	.F0	0.937500
.31	0.191406	.71	0.441406	.B1	0.691406	.F1	0.941406
.32	0.195312	.72	0.445312	.B2	0.695312	.F2	0.945312
.33	0.199218	.73	0.449218	.B3	0.699218	.F3	0.949218
.34	0.203125	.74	0.453125	.B4	0.703125	.F4	0.953125
.35	0.207031	.75	0.457031	.B5	0.707031	.F5	0.957031
.36	0.210937	.76	0.460937	.B6	0.710937	.F6	0.960937
.37	0.214843	.77	0.464843	.B7	0.714843	.F7	0.964843
.38	0.218750	.78	0.468750	.B8	0.718750	.F8	0.968750
.39	0.222656	.79	0.472656	.B9	0.722656	.F9	0.972656
.3A	0.226562	.7A	0.476562	.BA	0.726562	.FA	0.976562
.3B	0.230468	.7B	0.480468	.BB	0.730468	.FB	0.980468
.3C	0.234375	.7C	0.484375	.BC	0.734375	.FC	0.984375
.3D	0.238281	.7D	0.488281	.BD	0.738281	.FD	0.988281
.3E	0.242187	.7E	0.492187	.BE	0.742187	.FE	0.992187
.3F	0.246093	.7F	0.496093	.BF	0.746093	.FF	0.996093

1.2   SPECIAL NUMBERS

1.2.1   POSITIVE POWERS OF 2

n	2^n	n	2^n
1	2	6	64
2	4	7	128
3	8	8	256
4	16	9	512
5	32	10	1024

n	2^n	n	2^n
11	2048	51	2251799813685248
12	4096	52	4503599627370496
13	8192	53	9007199254740992
14	16384	54	18014398509481984
15	32768	55	36028797018963968
16	65536	56	72057594037927936
17	131072	57	144115188075855872
18	262144	58	288230376151711744
19	524288	59	576460752303423488
20	1048576	60	1152921504606846976
21	2097152	61	2305843009213693952
22	4194304	62	4611686018427387904
23	8388608	63	9223372036854775808
24	16777216	64	18446744073709551616
25	33554432	65	36893488147419103232
26	67108864	66	73786976294838206464
27	134217728	67	147573952589676412928
28	268435456	68	295147905179352825856
29	536870912	69	590295810358705651712
30	1073741824	70	1180591620717411303424
31	2147483648	71	2361183241434822606848
32	4294967296	72	4722366482869645213696
33	8589934592	73	9444732965739290427392
34	17179869184	74	18889465931478580854784
35	34359738368	75	37778931862957161709568
36	68719476736	76	75557863725914323419136
37	137438953472	77	151115727451828646838272
38	274877906944	78	302231454903657293676544
39	549755813888	79	604462909807314587353088
40	1099511627776	80	1208925819614629174706176
41	2199023255552	81	2417851639229258349412352
42	4398046511104	82	4835703278458516698824704
43	8796093022208	83	9671406556917033397649408
44	17592186044416	84	19342813113834066795298816
45	35184372088832	85	38685626227668133590597632
46	70368744177664	86	77371252455336267181195264
47	140737488355328	87	154742504910672534362390528
48	281474976710656	88	309485009821345068724781056
49	562949953421312	89	618970019642690137449562112
50	1125899906842624	90	1237940039285380274899124224

1.2.2 NEGATIVE POWERS OF 2

n	2^{-n}
1	0.5
2	0.25
3	0.125
4	0.0625
5	0.03125
6	0.015625
7	0.0078125
8	0.00390625
9	0.001953125
10	0.0009765625
11	0.00048828125
12	0.000244140625
13	0.0001220703125
14	0.00006103515625
15	0.000030517578125
16	0.0000152587890625
17	0.00000762939453125
18	0.000003814697265625
19	0.0000019073486328125
20	0.00000095367431640625
21	0.000000476837158203125
22	0.0000002384185791015625
23	0.00000011920928955078125
24	0.000000059604644775390625
25	0.0000000298023223876953125
26	0.00000001490116119384765625
27	0.000000007450580596923828125
28	0.0000000037252902984619140625
29	0.00000000186264514923095703125
30	0.000000000931322574615478515625
31	0.0000000004656612873077392578125
32	0.00000000023283064365386962890625
33	0.000000000116415321826934814453125
34	0.0000000000582076609134674072265625
35	0.00000000002910383045673370361328125
36	0.000000000014551915228366851806640625
37	0.0000000000072759576141834259033203125
38	0.00000000000363797880709171295166015625
39	0.000000000001818989403545856475830078125
40	0.0000000000009094947017729282379150390625

1.2.3   POWERS OF 16 IN DECIMAL SCALE

$n =$	$16^n =$	$16^{-n} =$
0	1	1
1	16	0.0625
2	256	0.00390625
3	4096	0.000244140625
4	65536	0.0000152587890625
5	1048576	0.00000095367431640625
6	16777216	0.000000059604644775390625
7	268435456	0.0000000037252902984619140625
8	4294967296	0.00000000023283064365386962890625
9	68719476736	0.0000000000145519152283668518066640625
10	1099511627776	0.00000000000090949470177292823791503906250
11	17592186044416	
12	281474976710656	
13	4503599627370496	
14	72057594037927936	
15	1152921504606846976	
16	18446744073709551616	
17	295147905179352825856	
18	4722366482869645213696	
19	75557863725914323419136	
20	1208925819614629174706176	

1.2.4   POWERS OF 10 IN HEXADECIMAL SCALE

$n =$	$10^n =$	$10^{-n} =$
0	1	1
1	A	0.19999999999999999999 . . .
2	64	0.028F5C28F5C28F5C28F5 . . .
3	3E8	0.004189374BC6A7EF9DB2 . . .
4	2710	0.00068DB8BAC710CB295E . . .
5	186A0	0.0000A7C5AC471B478423 . . .
6	F4240	0.000010C6F7A0B5ED8D36 . . .
7	989680	0.000001AD7F29ABCAF485 . . .
8	5F5E100	0.0000002AF31DC4611873 . . .
9	3B9ACA00	0.000000044B82FA09B5A5 . . .
10	2540BE400	0.000000006DF37F675EF6 . . .
11	174876E800	0.000000000AFEBFF0BCB2 . . .
12	E8D4A51000	0.00000000119799812DE . . .
13	9184E72A000	0.00000000001C25C26849 . . .
14	5AF3107A4000	0.000000000002D09370D4 . . .
15	38D7EA4C68000	0.000000000000480EBE7B . . .
16	2386F26FC10000	0.0000000000000734ACA5 . . .

1.2.5 SPECIAL CONSTANTS

The constant π

The transcedental number π is defined as the ratio of the circumference of a circle to the diameter. It is also the ratio of the area of a circle to the square of the radius (r) and appears in several other formulas from elementary geometry (see Section 4.6)

$$C(\text{circle}) = 2\pi r, \qquad\qquad V(\text{sphere}) = \frac{4}{3}\pi r^3,$$

$$A(\text{circle}) = \pi r^2, \qquad\qquad SA(\text{sphere}) = 4\pi r^2.$$

One method of computing π is to use the infinite series for the function $\tan^{-1} x$ and one of the identities

$$\pi = 4 \tan^{-1} 1 = 6 \tan^{-1} \frac{1}{\sqrt{3}}$$

$$= 2 \tan^{-1} \frac{1}{2} + 2 \tan^{-1} \frac{1}{3} + 8 \tan^{-1} \frac{1}{5} - 2 \tan^{-1} \frac{1}{239}$$

$$= 24 \tan^{-1} \frac{1}{8} + 8 \tan^{-1} \frac{1}{57} + 4 \tan^{-1} \frac{1}{239}$$

$$= 48 \tan^{-1} \frac{1}{18} + 32 \tan^{-1} \frac{1}{57} - 20 \tan^{-1} \frac{1}{239}$$

There are many other identities involving π. See Section 1.4.3. For example:
$\frac{\pi^3}{32} = \sum_{n=0}^{\infty} \frac{(-1)^n}{(2n+1)^3} = 1 - \frac{1}{27} + \frac{1}{125} - \frac{1}{343} + \cdots.$

To 200 decimal places:

$\pi \approx 3.$ 14159 26535 89793 23846 26433 83279 50288 41971 69399 37510
58209 74944 59230 78164 06286 20899 86280 34825 34211 70679
82148 08651 32823 06647 09384 46095 50582 23172 53594 08128
48111 74502 84102 70193 85211 05559 64462 29489 54930 38196

To 50 decimal places:

$\pi/20 \approx$ 0.15707 96326 79489 66192 31321 69163 97514 42098 58469 96876
$\pi/15 \approx$ 0.20943 95102 39319 54923 08428 92218 63352 56131 44626 62501
$\pi/12 \approx$ 0.26179 93877 99149 43653 85536 15273 29190 70164 30783 28126
$\pi/11 \approx$ 0.28559 93321 44526 65804 20584 89389 04571 67451 97218 12501
$\pi/10 \approx$ 0.31415 92653 58979 32384 62643 38327 95028 84197 16939 93751
$\pi/9 \approx$ 0.34906 58503 98865 91538 47381 53697 72254 26885 74377 70835
$\pi/8 \approx$ 0.39269 90816 98724 15480 78304 22909 93786 05246 46174 92189
$\pi/7 \approx$ 0.44879 89505 12827 60549 46633 40468 50041 20281 67057 05359
$\pi/6 \approx$ 0.52359 87755 98298 87307 71072 30546 58381 40328 61566 56252
$\pi/5 \approx$ 0.62831 85307 17958 64769 25286 76655 90057 68394 33879 87502
$\pi/4 \approx$ 0.78539 81633 97448 30961 56608 45819 87572 10492 92349 84378
$\pi/3 \approx$ 1.04719 75511 96597 74615 42144 61093 16762 80657 23133 12504
$\pi/2 \approx$ 1.57079 63267 94896 61923 13216 91639 75144 20985 84699 68755
$2\pi/3 \approx$ 2.09439 51023 93195 49230 84289 22186 33525 61314 46266 25007
$3\pi/2 \approx$ 4.71238 89803 84689 85769 39650 74919 25432 62957 54099 06266
$5\pi/2 \approx$ 7.85398 16339 74483 09615 66084 58198 75721 04929 23498 43776
$\sqrt{\pi} \approx$ 1.77245 38509 05516 02729 81674 83341 14518 27975 49456 12239

The constant e

The transcedental number e is the base of natural logarithms. It is given by

$$e = \lim_{n \to \infty} \left(1 + \frac{1}{n}\right)^n = \sum_{n=0}^{\infty} \frac{1}{n!}.$$

To 200 decimal places:

$e \approx 2.$ 71828 18284 59045 23536 02874 71352 66249 77572 47093 69995
95749 66967 62772 40766 30353 54759 45713 82178 52516 64274
27466 39193 20030 59921 81741 35966 29043 57290 03342 95260
59563 07381 32328 62794 34907 63233 82988 07531 95251 01901

To 50 decimal places:

$e/8 \approx$ 0.33978 52285 57380 65442 00359 33919 08281 22196 55886 71249
$e/7 \approx$ 0.38832 59754 94149 31933 71839 24478 95178 53938 92441 95714
$e/6 \approx$ 0.45304 69714 09840 87256 00479 11892 11041 62928 74515 61666
$e/5 \approx$ 0.54365 63656 91809 04707 20574 94270 53249 95514 49418 73999
$e/4 \approx$ 0.67957 04571 14761 30884 00718 67838 16562 44393 11773 42499
$e/3 \approx$ 0.90609 39428 19681 74512 00958 23784 22083 25857 49031 23332
$e/2 \approx$ 1.35914 09142 29522 61768 01437 35676 33124 88786 23546 84998
$2e/3 \approx$ 1.81218 78856 39363 49024 01916 47568 44166 51714 98062 46664

The function e^x is defined by $e^x = \sum_{n=0}^{\infty} \frac{x^n}{n!}$. The numbers e and π are related by the formula $e^{\pi i} = -1$.

To 50 decimal places:

$$e^\pi \approx 23.14069\ 26327\ 79269\ 00572\ 90863\ 67948\ 54738\ 02661\ 06242\ 60021$$
$$\pi^e \approx 22.45915\ 77183\ 61045\ 47342\ 71522\ 04543\ 73502\ 75893\ 15133\ 99669$$

The constant γ

Euler's constant γ is defined by

$$\gamma = \lim_{n \to \infty} \left(\sum_{k=1}^{n} \frac{1}{k} - \log n \right).$$

To 200 decimal places:

$\gamma \approx 0.$ 57721 56649 01532 86060 65120 90082 40243 10421 59335 93992
35988 05767 23488 48677 26777 66467 09369 47063 29174 67495
14631 44724 98070 82480 96050 40144 86542 83622 41739 97644
92353 62535 00333 74293 73377 37673 94279 25952 58247 09492

It is not known whether γ is rational or irrational.

The constant ϕ

The golden ratio ϕ is defined as the positive root of the equation $\frac{\phi}{1} = \frac{1+\phi}{\phi}$; that is $\phi = \frac{1+\sqrt{5}}{2}$.

To 200 decimal places:

$\phi \approx 1.$ 61803 39887 49894 84820 45868 34365 63811 77203 09179 80576
28621 35448 62270 52604 62818 90244 97072 07204 18939 11374
84754 08807 53868 91752 12663 38622 23536 93179 31800 60766
72635 44333 89086 59593 95829 05638 32266 13199 28290 26788

1.2.6 FACTORIALS

The factorial of n, denoted $n!$, is the product of all integers less than or equal to n. $n! = n \cdot (n-1) \cdot (n-2) \cdots 2 \cdot 1$. The double factorial of n, denoted $n!!$, is the product of every other integer: $n!! = n \cdot (n-2) \cdot (n-4) \cdots$, where the last element in the product is either 2 or 1, depending on whether n is even or odd. The generalization of the factorial function is the gamma function (see Section 6.11). When n is an integer, $\Gamma(n) = (n-1)!$.

The shifted factorial (also called the falling factorial and Pochhammer's symbol) is denoted by $(a)_n$ (sometimes $a^{\underline{n}}$) and is defined as

$$(a)_n = \underbrace{a \cdot (a+1) \cdot (a+2) \cdots}_{n \text{ terms}} = \frac{(a+n-1)!}{(a-1)!} = \frac{\Gamma(a+n)}{\Gamma(a)}. \tag{1.2.1}$$

The q-shifted factorial is defined as

$$(a; q)_0 = 1, \qquad (a; q)_n = (1 - a)(1 - aq)\dots(1 - aq^{n-1}).$$

$$(1.2.2)$$

n	$n!$	$\log_{10} n!$	$n!!$	$\log_{10} n!!$
0	1	0.00000	1	0.00000
1	1	0.00000	1	0.00000
2	2	0.30103	2	0.30103
3	6	0.77815	3	0.47712
4	24	1.38021	8	0.90309
5	120	2.07918	15	1.17609
6	720	2.85733	48	1.68124
7	5040	3.70243	105	2.02119
8	40320	4.60552	384	2.58433
9	3.6288×10^5	5.55976	945	2.97543
10	3.6288×10^6	6.55976	3840	3.58433
11	3.9917×10^7	7.60116	10395	4.01682
12	4.7900×10^8	8.68034	46080	4.66351
13	6.2270×10^9	9.79428	1.3514×10^5	5.13077
14	8.7178×10^{10}	10.94041	6.4512×10^5	5.80964
15	1.3077×10^{12}	12.11650	2.0270×10^6	6.30686
16	2.0923×10^{13}	13.32062	1.0322×10^7	7.01376
17	3.5569×10^{14}	14.55107	3.4459×10^7	7.53731
18	6.4024×10^{15}	15.80634	1.8579×10^8	8.26903
19	1.2165×10^{17}	17.08509	6.5473×10^8	8.81606
20	2.4329×10^{18}	18.38612	3.7159×10^9	9.57006
21	5.1091×10^{19}	19.70834	1.3749×10^{10}	10.13828
22	1.1240×10^{21}	21.05077	8.1750×10^{10}	10.91249
23	2.5852×10^{22}	22.41249	3.1623×10^{11}	11.50001
24	6.2045×10^{23}	23.79271	1.9620×10^{12}	12.29270
25	1.5511×10^{25}	25.19065	7.9059×10^{12}	12.89795
30	2.6525×10^{32}	32.42366	4.2850×10^{16}	16.63195
40	8.1592×10^{47}	47.91165	2.5511×10^{24}	24.40672
50	3.0414×10^{64}	64.48307	5.2047×10^{32}	32.71640
60	8.3210×10^{81}	81.92017	2.8481×10^{41}	41.45456
70	1.1979×10^{100}	100.07841	3.5504×10^{50}	50.55028
80	7.1569×10^{118}	118.85473	8.9711×10^{59}	59.95284
90	1.4857×10^{138}	138.17194	4.2088×10^{69}	69.62416
100	9.3326×10^{157}	157.97000	3.4243×10^{79}	79.53457
110	1.5882×10^{178}	178.20092	4.5744×10^{89}	89.66033
120	6.6895×10^{198}	198.82539	9.5934×10^{99}	99.98197
130	6.4669×10^{219}	219.81069	3.0428×10^{110}	110.48328
140	1.3462×10^{241}	241.12911	1.4142×10^{121}	121.15050
150	5.7134×10^{262}	262.75689	9.3726×10^{131}	131.97186
500	1.2201×10^{1134}	1134.0864	5.8490×10^{567}	567.76709
1000	4.0239×10^{2567}	2567.6046	3.9940×10^{1284}	1284.6014

1.2.7 IMPORTANT NUMBERS IN DIFFERENT BASES

Base 2	$\pi =$	$11.0010010000111111011010101010001\ldots$
	$e =$	$10.10110111110000101010100101100\ldots$
	$\gamma =$	$0.10010011110001000110011111111000\ldots$
	$\sqrt{2} =$	$1.0110101000001001111100110011001\ldots$
	$\log 2 =$	$0.1011000101110010000101111111101\ldots$
Base 8	$\pi =$	$3.110375524210264302151423063050\ldots$
	$e =$	$2.557605213050535512465277342542\ldots$
	$\gamma =$	$0.447421477067666061722321574376\ldots$
	$\sqrt{2} =$	$1.324047463177167462204262766115\ldots$
	$\log 2 =$	$0.542710277575071736325711707316\ldots$
Base 12	$\pi =$	$3.184809493B918664573A6211BB1515\ldots$
	$e =$	$2.8752360698219BA71971009B388AA8\ldots$
	$\gamma =$	$0.6B15188A6760B381B754334520434A\ldots$
	$\sqrt{2} =$	$1.4B79170A07B85737704B0854868535\ldots$
	$\log 2 =$	$0.839912483369AB213742A346792537\ldots$
Base 16	$\pi =$	$3.243F6A8885A308D313198A2E037073\ldots$
	$e =$	$2.B7E151628AED2A6ABF7158809CF4F3\ldots$
	$\gamma =$	$0.93C467E37DB0C7A4D1BE3F810152CB\ldots$
	$\sqrt{2} =$	$1.6A09E667F3BCC908B2FB1366EA957D\ldots$
	$\log 2 =$	$0.B17217F7D1CF79ABC9E3B39803F2F6\ldots$

1.2.8 BERNOULLI POLYNOMIALS AND NUMBERS

The Bernoulli polynomials $B_n(x)$ are defined by the generating function

$$\frac{te^{xt}}{e^t - 1} = \sum_{n=0}^{\infty} B_n(x)\frac{t^n}{n!}. \tag{1.2.3}$$

These polynomials can also be defined recursively by means of $B_0(x) = 1$, $B'_n(x) = nB_{n-1}(x)$, and $\int_0^1 B_n(x)\,dx = 0$ for $n \geq 1$. The identity $B_{k+1}(x+1) - B_{k+1}(x) = (k+1)x^k$ means that

$$1^k + 2^k + \cdots + n^k = \frac{B_{k+1}(n+1) - B_{k+1}(0)}{k+1}. \tag{1.2.4}$$

n	$B_n(x)$
0	1
1	$(2x-1)/2$
2	$(6x^2 - 6x + 1)/6$
3	$(2x^3 - 3x^2 + x)/2$
4	$(30x^4 - 60x^3 + 30x^2 - 1)/30$
5	$(6x^5 - 15x^4 + 10x^3 - x)/6$

The Bernoulli numbers are the Bernoulli polynomials evaluated at 0: $B_n = B_n(0)$. A generating function for the Bernoulli numbers is

$\sum_{n=0}^{\infty} B_n \frac{t^n}{n!} = \frac{t}{e^t-1}$. In the following table each Bernoulli number is written as a fraction of integers: $B_n = N_n/D_n$. Note that $B_{2m+1} = 0$ for $m \geq 1$.

n	N_n	D_n	B_n
0	1	1	1.000000000×10^0
1	-1	2	$-5.000000000 \times 10^{-1}$
2	1	6	$1.666666667 \times 10^{-1}$
4	-1	30	$-3.333333333 \times 10^{-2}$
6	1	42	$2.380952381 \times 10^{-2}$
8	-1	30	$-3.333333333 \times 10^{-2}$
10	5	66	$7.575757576 \times 10^{-2}$
12	-691	2730	$-2.531135531 \times 10^{-1}$
14	7	6	1.166666667×10^0
16	-3617	510	-7.092156863×10^0
18	43867	798	5.497117794×10^1
20	-174611	330	-5.291242424×10^2
22	854513	138	6.192123188×10^3
24	-236364091	2730	-8.658025311×10^4
26	8553103	6	1.425517167×10^6
28	-23749461029	870	-2.729823107×10^7
30	8615841276005	14322	6.015808739×10^8
32	-7709321041217	510	$-1.511631577 \times 10^{10}$
34	2577687858367	6	$4.296146431 \times 10^{11}$
36	-26315271553053477373	1919190	$-1.371165521 \times 10^{13}$
38	2929993913841559	6	$4.883323190 \times 10^{14}$
40	-261082718496449122051	13530	$-1.929657934 \times 10^{16}$

1.2.9 EULER POLYNOMIALS AND NUMBERS

The Euler polynomials $E_n(x)$ are defined by the generating function

$$\frac{2e^{xt}}{e^t + 1} = \sum_{n=0}^{\infty} E_n(x) \frac{t^n}{n!}. \tag{1.2.5}$$

n	$E_n(x)$
0	1
1	$(2x - 1)/2$
2	$x^2 - x$
3	$(4x^3 - 6x^2 + 1)/4$
4	$x^4 - 2x^3 + x$
5	$(2x^5 - 5x^4 + 5x^2 - 1)/2$

Alternating sums of powers can be computed in terms of Euler polynomials

$$\sum_{i=1}^{n}(-1)^{n-i}i^k = n^k - (n-1)^k + \cdots \mp 2^k \pm 1^k = \frac{E_k(n+1) + (-1)^n E_k(0)}{2}.$$
(1.2.6)

The Euler numbers are the Euler polynomials evaluated at $1/2$, and scaled: $E_n = 2^n E_n(\frac{1}{2})$. A generating function for the Euler numbers is

$$\sum_{n=0}^{\infty} E_n \frac{t^n}{n!} = \frac{2e^t}{e^{2t}+1}$$

n	E_n
2	−1
4	5
6	−61
8	1385
10	−50521
12	2702765
14	−199360981
16	19391512145
18	−2404879675441
20	370371188237525
22	−69348874393137901
24	15514534163557086905
26	−4087072509293123892361
28	1252259641403629865468285
30	−441543893249023104553682821
32	177519391579539289436664789665
34	−80723299235887898062168247453281
36	41222060339517702122347079671259045
38	−23489580527043108252017828576198947741
40	14851150718114980017877156781405826684425
42	−10364622733519612119397957304745185976310201
44	7947579422597592703608040510088070619519273805
46	−6667537516685544977435028474773748197524107684661
48	6096278645568542158691685742876843153976539044435185

1.2.10 FIBONACCI NUMBERS

The Fibonacci numbers $\{F_n\}$ are defined by the recurrence:

$$F_1 = 1, \qquad F_2 = 1, \qquad F_{n+2} = F_n + F_{n+1}.$$

An exact formula is available: $F_n = \frac{1}{\sqrt{5}}\left[\left(\frac{1+\sqrt{5}}{2}\right)^n - \left(\frac{1-\sqrt{5}}{2}\right)^n\right]$. Note that $\lim\limits_{n\to\infty}\frac{F_{n+1}}{F_n} = \phi$, the golden ratio. Also, $F_n \sim \phi^n/\sqrt{5}$ as $n \to \infty$.

n	F_n	n	F_n	n	F_n	n	F_n
1	1	14	377	27	196418	40	102334155
2	1	15	610	28	317811	41	165580141
3	2	16	987	29	514229	42	267914296
4	3	17	1597	30	832040	43	433494437
5	5	18	2584	31	1346269	44	701408733
6	8	19	4181	32	2178309	45	1134903170
7	13	20	6765	33	3524578	46	1836311903
8	21	21	10946	34	5702887	47	2971215073
9	34	22	17711	35	9227465	48	4807526976
10	55	23	28657	36	14930352	49	7778742049
11	89	24	46368	37	24157817	50	12586269025
12	144	25	75025	38	39088169	51	20365011074
13	233	26	121393	39	63245986	52	32951280099

1.2.11   POWERS OF INTEGERS

n	n^3	n^4	n^5	n^6	n^7	n^8	n^{10}
1	1	1	1	1	1	1	1
2	8	16	32	64	128	256	1024
3	27	81	243	729	2187	6561	59049
4	64	256	1024	4096	16384	65536	1048576
5	125	625	3125	15625	78125	390625	9765625
6	216	1296	7776	46656	279936	1679616	60466176
7	343	2401	16807	117649	823543	5764801	282475249
8	512	4096	32768	262144	2097152	16777216	1073741824
9	729	6561	59049	531441	4782969	43046721	3486784401
10	1000	10000	100000	1000000	10000000	100000000	10000000000
11	1331	14641	161051	1771561	19487171	214358881	25937424601
12	1728	20736	248832	2985984	35831808	429981696	61917364224

1.2.12   SUMS OF POWERS OF INTEGERS

Define $s_k(n) = 1^k + 2^k + \cdots + n^k = \sum_{m=1}^{n} m^k$. Properties include:

- $s_k(n) = (k+1)^{-1}\left[B_{k+1}(n+1) - B_{k+1}(0)\right]$
  (where the B_k are Bernoulli polynomials, see Section 1.2.8).

• Writing $s_k(n)$ as $\sum_{m=1}^{k+1} a_m n^{k-m+2}$ there is the recursion formula:

$$s_{k+1}(n) = \left(\frac{k+1}{k+2}\right) a_1 n^{k+2} + \cdots + \left(\frac{k+1}{k}\right) a_3 n^k$$

$$+ \cdots + \left(\frac{k+1}{2}\right) a_{k+1} n^2 + \left[1 - (k+1) \sum_{m=1}^{k+1} \frac{a_m}{k+3-m}\right] n. \quad (1.2.7)$$

$$s_1(n) = 1 + 2 + 3 + \cdots + n = \frac{1}{2}n(n+1).$$

$$s_2(n) = 1^2 + 2^2 + 3^2 + \cdots + n^2$$

$$= \frac{1}{6}n(n+1)(2n+1).$$

$$s_3(n) = 1^3 + 2^3 + 3^3 + \cdots + n^3$$

$$= \frac{1}{4}(n^2(n+1)^2) = [s_1(n)]^2.$$

$$s_4(n) = 1^4 + 2^4 + 3^4 + \cdots + n^4$$

$$= \frac{1}{5}(3n^2 + 3n - 1)s_2(n).$$

$$s_5(n) = 1^5 + 2^5 + 3^5 + \cdots + n^5$$

$$= \frac{1}{12}n^2(n+1)^2(2n^2 + 2n - 1).$$

$$s_6(n) = 1^6 + 2^6 + 3^6 + \cdots + n^6$$

$$= \frac{n}{42}(n+1)(2n+1)(3n^4 + 6n^3 - 3n + 1).$$

$$s_7(n) = 1^7 + 2^7 + 3^7 + \cdots + n^7$$

$$= \frac{n^2}{24}(n+1)^2(3n^4 + 6n^3 - n^2 - 4n + 2).$$

$$s_8(n) = 1^8 + 2^8 + 3^8 + \cdots + n^8$$

$$= \frac{n}{90}(n+1)(2n+1)(5n^6 + 15n^5 + 5n^4 - 15n^3 - n^2 + 9n - 3).$$

$$s_9(n) = 1^9 + 2^9 + 3^9 + \cdots + n^9$$

$$= \frac{n^2}{20}(n+1)^2(2n^6 + 6n^5 + n^4 - 8n^3 + n^2 + 6n - 3).$$

$$s_{10}(n) = 1^{10} + 2^{10} + 3^{10} + \cdots + n^{10}$$

$$= \frac{n}{66}(n+1)(2n+1)(3n^8 + 12n^7 + 8n^6 - 18n^5$$

$$- 10n^4 + 24n^3 + 2n^2 - 15n + 5).$$

n	$\sum_{k=1}^{n} k$	$\sum_{k=1}^{n} k^2$	$\sum_{k=1}^{n} k^3$	$\sum_{k=1}^{n} k^4$	$\sum_{k=1}^{n} k^5$
1	1	1	1	1	1
2	3	5	9	17	33
3	6	14	36	98	276
4	10	30	100	354	1300
5	15	55	225	979	4425
6	21	91	441	2275	12201
7	28	140	784	4676	29008
8	36	204	1296	8772	61776
9	45	285	2025	15333	120825
10	55	385	3025	25333	220825
11	66	506	4356	39974	381876
12	78	650	6084	60710	630708
13	91	819	8281	89271	1002001
14	105	1015	11025	127687	1539825
15	120	1240	14400	178312	2299200
16	136	1496	18496	243848	3347776
17	153	1785	23409	327369	4767633
18	171	2109	29241	432345	6657201
19	190	2470	36100	562666	9133300
20	210	2870	44100	722666	12333300
21	231	3311	53361	917147	16417401
22	253	3795	64009	1151403	21571033
23	276	4324	76176	1431244	28007376
24	300	4900	90000	1763020	35970000
25	325	5525	105625	2153645	45735625

1.2.13   NEGATIVE INTEGER POWERS

Riemann's zeta function is $\zeta(n) = \sum_{k=1}^{\infty} \frac{1}{k^n}$. Related functions are

$$\alpha(n) = \sum_{k=1}^{\infty} \frac{(-1)^{k+1}}{k^n}, \qquad \beta(n) = \sum_{k=0}^{\infty} \frac{(-1)^k}{(2k+1)^n}, \qquad \gamma(n) = \sum_{k=0}^{\infty} \frac{1}{(2k+1)^n}.$$

Properties include:

$$\alpha(n) = (1 - 2^{1-n})\zeta(n),$$
$$\gamma(n) = (1 - 2^{-n})\zeta(n),$$
$$\zeta(2k) = \frac{(2\pi)^{2k}}{2(2k)!} |B_{2k}|, \tag{1.2.8}$$
$$\beta(2k+1) = \frac{(\pi/2)^{2k+1}}{2(2k)!} |E_{2k}|.$$

The series $\beta(1) = 1 - \frac{1}{3} + \frac{1}{5} - \cdots = \pi/4$ is known as Gregory's series. Catalan's constant is $\mathbf{G} = \beta(2)$.

$$\zeta(2) = \pi^2/6 \qquad \beta(1) = \pi/4$$
$$\zeta(4) = \pi^4/90 \qquad \beta(3) = \pi^3/32$$
$$\zeta(6) = \pi^6/945 \qquad \beta(5) = 5\pi^5/1536$$
$$\zeta(8) = \pi^8/9450 \qquad \beta(7) = 61\pi^7/184320$$
$$\zeta(10) = \pi^{10}/93555 \qquad \beta(9) = 277\pi^9/8257536$$

n	$\zeta(n) = \displaystyle\sum_{k=1}^{\infty} \dfrac{1}{k^n}$	$\displaystyle\sum_{k=1}^{\infty} \dfrac{(-1)^{k+1}}{k^n}$	$\displaystyle\sum_{k=0}^{\infty} \dfrac{1}{(2k+1)^n}$	$\displaystyle\sum_{k=0}^{\infty} \dfrac{(-1)^k}{(2k+1)^n}$
1	∞	0.6931471805	∞	0.7853981633
2	1.6449340669	0.8224670334	1.2337005501	0.9159655941
3	1.2020569032	0.9015426773	1.0517997903	0.9689461463
4	1.0823232337	0.9470328294	1.0146780316	0.9889445517
5	1.0369277551	0.9721197705	1.0045237628	0.9961578281
6	1.0173430620	0.9855510912	1.0014470766	0.9986852222
7	1.0083492774	0.9925938199	1.0004715487	0.9995545079
8	1.0040773562	0.9962330018	1.0001551790	0.9998499902
9	1.0020083928	0.9980942975	1.0000513452	0.9999496842
10	1.0009945752	0.9990395075	1.0000170414	0.9999831640
11	1.0004941886	0.9995171435	1.0000056661	0.9999943749
12	1.0002460866	0.9997576851	1.0000018858	0.9999981224
13	1.0001227133	0.9998785428	1.0000006281	0.9999993736
14	1.0000612482	0.9999391703	1.0000002092	0.9999997911
15	1.0000305882	0.9999695512	1.0000000697	0.9999999303
16	1.0000152823	0.9999847642	1.0000000232	0.9999999768
17	1.0000076372	0.9999923783	1.0000000077	0.9999999923
18	1.0000038173	0.9999961879	1.0000000026	0.9999999974
19	1.0000019082	0.9999980935	1.0000000009	0.9999999991
20	1.0000009540	0.9999990466	1.0000000003	0.9999999997

1.2.14 INTEGER SEQUENCES

These sequences are arranged in numerical order (disregarding any leading zeros or ones). Note that $C(n, k) = \binom{n}{k}$.

1. 1, −1, −1, 0, −1, 1, −1, 0, 0, 1, −1, 0, −1, 1, 1, 0, −1, 0, −1, 0, 1, 1, −1, 0, 0, 0, −1, −1, −1, 0, 1, 1, 1, 0, −1, 1, 1, 0, −1, −1, −1, 0, 0, 1, −1, 0, 0, 0, 1, 0, −1, 0, 1, 0   **Möbius function** $\mu(n), n \geq 1$

2. 1, 1, 0, 1, 1, 0, 0, 1, 1, 1, 0, 0, 1, 0, 0, 1, 1, 1, 0, 1, 0, 0, 0, 0, 2, 1, 0, 0, 1, 0, 0, 1, 0, 1, 0, 1, 1, 0, 0, 1, 1, 0, 0, 0, 1, 0, 0, 0, 1, 2, 0, 1, 1, 0, 0, 0, 0, 1, 0, 0, 1, 0, 0, 1, 2, 0, 0, 1, 0   **Number of ways of writing n as a sum of 2 squares**, $n \geq 0$

3. 0, 1, 1, 1, 1, 2, 1, 1, 1, 2, 1, 2, 1, 2, 2, 1, 1, 2, 1, 2, 2, 2, 1, 2, 1, 2, 1, 2, 1, 3, 1, 1, 2, 2, 2, 2, 1, 2, 2, 2, 1, 3, 1, 2, 2, 2, 1, 2, 1, 2, 2, 2, 1, 2, 2, 2, 2, 2, 1, 3, 1, 2, 2, 1, 2, 3, 1, 2, 2   **Number of distinct primes dividing n**, $n \geq 1$

4. 1, 1, 1, 2, 1, 1, 1, 3, 2, 1, 1, 2, 1, 1, 1, 5, 1, 2, 1, 2, 1, 1, 1, 3, 2, 1, 3, 2, 1, 1, 1, 7, 1, 1, 1, 4, 1, 1, 1, 3, 1, 1, 1, 2, 2, 1, 1, 5, 2, 2, 1, 2, 1, 3, 1, 3, 1, 1, 1, 2, 1, 1, 2, 11, 1, 1, 1, 2   **Number of Abelian groups of order n**, $n \geq 1$

5. 1, 1, 1, 2, 1, 2, 1, 5, 2, 2, 1, 5, 1, 2, 1, 14, 1, 5, 1, 5, 2, 2, 1, 15, 2, 2, 5, 4, 1, 4, 1, 51, 1, 2, 1, 14, 1, 2, 2, 14, 1, 6, 1, 4, 2, 2, 1, 52, 2, 5, 1, 5, 1, 15, 2, 13, 2, 2, 1, 13, 1, 2, 4, 267   **Number of groups of order n, $n \geq 1$**

6. 0, 1, 1, 2, 1, 2, 2, 3, 1, 2, 2, 3, 2, 3, 3, 4, 1, 2, 2, 3, 2, 3, 3, 4, 2, 3, 3, 4, 3, 4, 4, 5, 1, 2, 2, 3, 2, 3, 3, 4, 2, 3, 3, 4, 3, 4, 4, 5, 2, 3, 3, 4, 3, 4, 4, 5, 3, 4, 4, 5, 4, 5, 5, 6, 1, 2, 2, 3, 2   **Number of 1's in binary expansion of n, $n \geq 0$**

7. 1, 2, 1, 2, 3, 6, 9, 18, 30, 56, 99, 186, 335, 630, 1161, 2182, 4080, 7710, 14532, 27594, 52377, 99858, 190557, 364722, 698870, 1342176, 2580795, 4971008
Number of binary irreducible polynomials of degree n, or n-bead necklaces, $n \geq 0$

8. 1, 1, 1, 2, 1, 3, 1, 4, 2, 3, 1, 8, 1, 3, 3, 8, 1, 8, 1, 8, 3, 3, 1, 20, 2, 3, 4, 8, 1, 13, 1, 16, 3, 3, 3, 26, 1, 3, 3, 20, 1, 13, 1, 8, 8, 3, 1, 48, 2, 8, 3, 8, 1, 20, 3, 20, 3, 3, 1
Number of perfect partitions of n, or ordered factorizations of $n + 1$, $n \geq 0$

9. 1, 2, 2, 1, 2, 1, 1, 2, 2, 1, 1, 1, 2, 1, 2, 2, 1, 2, 1, 1, 1, 2, 1, 2, 2, 1, 1, 2, 2, 1, 2, 1, 1, 2, 2, 1, 1, 2, 1, 2, 2, 1, 1, 2, 2, 1, 2, 1, 1, 2, 1, 2, 2, 1, 2, 1, 1, 2, 2, 1, 1, 2, 1, 2, 2, 1, 2, 1, 1, 2, 1   **Thue–Morse nonrepeating sequence**

10. 1, 2, 1, 4, 1, 2, 1, 8, 1, 2, 1, 4, 1, 2, 1, 9, 1, 2, 1, 4, 1, 2, 1, 8, 1, 2, 1, 4, 1, 2, 1, 10, 1, 2, 1, 4, 1, 2, 1, 8, 1, 2, 1, 4, 1, 2, 1, 9, 1, 2, 1, 4, 1, 2, 1, 8, 1, 2, 1, 4, 1, 2, 1, 12, 1, 2, 1, 4   **Hurwitz–Radon numbers**

11. 1, 2, 2, 3, 2, 4, 2, 4, 3, 4, 2, 6, 2, 4, 4, 5, 2, 6, 2, 6, 4, 4, 2, 8, 3, 4, 4, 6, 2, 8, 2, 6, 4, 4, 4, 9, 2, 4, 4, 8, 2, 8, 2, 6, 6, 4, 2, 10, 3, 6, 4, 6, 2, 8, 4, 8, 4, 4, 2, 12, 2, 4, 6, 7, 4, 8, 2, 6 $d(n)$, **the number of divisors of n, $n \geq 1$**

12. 0, 1, 2, 2, 3, 3, 4, 4, 4, 4, 5, 5, 6, 6, 6, 6, 7, 7, 8, 8, 8, 8, 9, 9, 9, 9, 9, 9, 10, 10, 11, 11, 11, 11, 11, 11, 12, 12, 12, 12, 13, 13, 14, 14, 14, 14, 15, 15, 15, 15, 15, 15, 16, 16, 16, 16 $\pi(n)$, **the number of primes $\leq n$, for $n \geq 1$**

13. 1, 1, 2, 2, 3, 4, 5, 6, 8, 10, 12, 15, 18, 22, 27, 32, 38, 46, 54, 64, 76, 89, 104, 122, 142, 165, 192, 222, 256, 296, 340, 390, 448, 512, 585, 668, 760, 864, 982, 1113, 1260, 1426   **Number of partitions of n into distinct parts, $n \geq 1$**

14. 1, 1, 2, 2, 4, 2, 6, 4, 6, 4, 10, 4, 12, 6, 8, 8, 16, 6, 18, 8, 12, 10, 22, 8, 20, 12, 18, 12, 28, 8, 30, 16, 20, 16, 24, 12, 36, 18, 24, 16, 40, 12, 42, 20, 24, 22, 46, 16, 42
Euler totient function $\phi(n)$: count numbers $\leq n$ and prime to n, for $n \geq 1$

15. 1, 1, 1, 0, 1, 1, 2, 2, 4, 5, 10, 14, 26, 42, 78, 132, 249, 445, 842, 1561, 2988, 5671, 10981, 21209, 41472, 81181, 160176, 316749, 629933, 1256070, 2515169, 5049816
Number of series-reduced trees with n unlabeled nodes, $n \geq 0$

16. 1, 2, 3, 4, 5, 7, 8, 9, 11, 13, 16, 17, 19, 23, 25, 27, 29, 31, 32, 37, 41, 43, 47, 49, 53, 59, 61, 64, 67, 71, 73, 79, 81, 83, 89, 97, 101, 103, 107, 109, 113, 121, 125, 127, 128, 131   **Prime powers**

17. 1, 2, 3, 4, 6, 8, 10, 12, 16, 18, 20, 24, 30, 36, 42, 48, 60, 72, 84, 90, 96, 108, 120, 144, 168, 180, 210, 216, 240, 288, 300, 336, 360, 420, 480, 504, 540, 600, 630, 660
Highly abundant numbers: where sum-of-divisors function increases

18. 1, 2, 3, 4, 6, 8, 11, 13, 16, 18, 26, 28, 36, 38, 47, 48, 53, 57, 62, 69, 72, 77, 82, 87, 97, 99, 102, 106, 114, 126, 131, 138, 145, 148, 155, 175, 177, 180, 182, 189, 197, 206, 209   **Ulam numbers: next is uniquely the sum of 2 earlier terms**

19. 2, 3, 5, 7, 11, 13, 17, 19, 23, 29, 31, 37, 41, 43, 47, 53, 59, 60, 61, 67, 71, 73, 79, 83, 89, 97, 101, 103, 107, 109, 113, 127, 131, 137, 139, 149, 151, 157, 163, 167, 168, 173   **Orders of simple groups**

20. 2, 3, 5, 7, 11, 13, 17, 19, 23, 29, 31, 37, 41, 43, 47, 53, 59, 61, 67, 71, 73, 79, 83, 89, 97, 101, 103, 107, 109, 113, 127, 131, 137, 139, 149, 151, 157, 163, 167, 173, 179, 181   **Prime numbers**

21. 1, 2, 3, 5, 7, 11, 15, 22, 30, 42, 56, 77, 101, 135, 176, 231, 297, 385, 490, 627, 792, 1002, 1255, 1575, 1958, 2436, 3010, 3718, 4565, 5604, 6842, 8349, 10143, 12310, 14883   **Number of partitions of n, $n \geq 1$**

22. 2, 3, 5, 7, 13, 17, 19, 31, 61, 89, 107, 127, 521, 607, 1279, 2203, 2281, 3217, 4253, 4423, 9689, 9941, 11213, 19937, 21701, 23209, 44497, 86243, 110503, 132049, 216091, 756839, 859433   **Mersenne primes: p such that $2^p - 1$ is prime**

23. 1, 1, 2, 3, 5, 8, 13, 21, 34, 55, 89, 144, 233, 377, 610, 987, 1597, 2584, 4181, 6765, 10946, 17711, 28657, 46368, 75025, 121393, 196418, 317811, 514229, 832040, 1346269   **Fibonacci numbers: $F(n) = F(n-1) + F(n-2)$**

24. 1, 2, 3, 6, 10, 20, 35, 70, 126, 252, 462, 924, 1716, 3432, 6435, 12870, 24310, 48620, 92378, 184756, 352716, 705432, 1352078, 2704156, 5200300, 10400600, 20058300   **Central binomial coefficients: $C(n, [n/2])$, $n \geq 1$**

25. 1, 1, 2, 3, 6, 11, 20, 40, 77, 148, 285, 570, 1120, 2200, 4323, 8498, 16996, 33707, 66844, 132568, 262936, 521549, 1043098, 2077698, 4138400, 8243093   **Stern's sequence: $a(n+1)$ is sum of $1 + [n/2]$ preceding terms, $n \geq 1$**

26. 1, 1, 2, 3, 6, 11, 22, 42, 84, 165, 330, 654, 1308, 2605, 5210, 10398, 20796, 41550, 83100, 166116, 332232, 664299, 1328598, 2656866, 5313732, 10626810 **Narayana–Zidek–Capell numbers: $a(2n) = 2a(2n-1)$, $a(2n+1) = 2a(2n) - a(n)$**

27. 1, 1, 1, 2, 3, 6, 11, 23, 46, 98, 207, 451, 983, 2179, 4850, 10905, 24631, 56011, 127912, 293547, 676157, 1563372, 3626149, 8436379, 19680277, 46026618, 107890609   **Wedderburn–Etherington numbers: interpretations of X^n, $n \geq 1$**

28. 1, 1, 1, 2, 3, 6, 11, 23, 47, 106, 235, 551, 1301, 3159, 7741, 19320, 48629, 123867, 317955, 823065, 2144505, 5623756, 14828074, 39299897, 104636890, 279793450   **Number of trees with n unlabeled nodes, $n \geq 1$**

29. 2, 3, 6, 20, 168, 7581, 7828354, 2414682040998, 56130437228687557907788 **Dedekind numbers: number of monotone Boolean functions of n variables, $n \geq 0$**

30. 1, 1, 2, 3, 7, 16, 54, 243, 2038, 33120, 1182004, 87723296, 12886193064, 3633057074584, 1944000150734320, 1967881448329407496   **Number of Euler graphs or 2-graphs with n nodes, $n \geq 1$**

31. 0, 0, 1, 1, 2, 3, 7, 18, 41, 123, 367, 1288, 4878   **Number of alternating prime knots with n crossings, $n \geq 1$**

32. 0, 0, 1, 1, 2, 3, 7, 21, 49, 165, 552, 2176, 9988   **Number of prime knots with n crossings, $n \geq 1$**

33. 1, 1, 2, 3, 8, 14, 42, 81, 262, 538, 1828, 3926, 13820, 30694, 110954, 252939, 933458, 2172830, 8152860, 19304190, 73424650, 176343390, 678390116, 1649008456   **Meandric numbers: ways a river can cross a road n times, $n \geq 1$**

34. 0, 1, 2, 4, 5, 8, 9, 10, 13, 16, 17, 18, 20, 25, 26, 29, 32, 34, 36, 37, 40, 41, 45, 49, 50, 52, 53, 58, 61, 64, 65, 68, 72, 73, 74, 80, 81, 82, 85, 89, 90, 97, 98, 100, 101, 104, 106   **Numbers that are sums of 2 squares**

35. 1, 2, 4, 5, 8, 10, 14, 15, 16, 21, 22, 25, 26, 28, 33, 34, 35, 36, 38, 40, 42, 46, 48, 49, 50, 53, 57, 60, 62, 64, 65, 70, 77, 80, 81, 83, 85, 86, 90, 91, 92, 100, 104, 107   **MacMahon's prime numbers of measurement, or segmented numbers**

36. 1, 2, 4, 6, 10, 14, 20, 26, 36, 46, 60, 74, 94, 114, 140, 166, 202, 238, 284, 330, 390, 450, 524, 598, 692, 786, 900, 1014, 1154, 1294, 1460, 1626, 1828, 2030, 2268, 2506   **Binary partitions (partitions of $2n$ into powers of 2), $n \geq 0$**

37. 1, 2, 4, 8, 16, 32, 64, 128, 256, 512, 1024, 2048, 4096, 8192, 16384, 32768, 65536, 131072, 262144, 524288, 1048576, 2097152, 4194304, 8388608, 16777216, 33554432, 67108864   **Powers of 2**

38. 1, 1, 2, 4, 9, 20, 48, 115, 286, 719, 1842, 4766, 12486, 32973, 87811, 235381, 634847, 1721159, 4688676, 12826228, 35221832, 97055181, 268282855, 743724984, 2067174645   **Number of rooted trees with n unlabeled nodes, $n \geq 1$**

39. 1, 1, 2, 4, 9, 21, 51, 127, 323, 835, 2188, 5798, 15511, 41835, 113634, 310572, 853467, 2356779, 6536382, 18199284, 50852019, 142547559, 400763223, 1129760415   **Motzkin numbers: ways to join n points on a circle by chords**

40. 1, 1, 2, 4, 9, 22, 59, 167, 490, 1486, 4639, 14805, 48107, 158808, 531469, 1799659, 6157068, 21258104, 73996100, 259451116, 951695102, 3251073303   **Number of different scores in n-team round-robin tournament, $n \geq 1$**

41. 1, 1, 2, 4, 11, 34, 156, 1044, 12346, 274668, 12005168, 1018997864, 165091172592, 50502031367952, 29054155657235488, 31426485969804308768   **Number of graphs with n unlabeled nodes, $n \geq 0$**

42. 0, 1, 2, 5, 12, 29, 70, 169, 408, 985, 2378, 5741, 13860, 33461, 80782, 195025, 470832, 1136689, 2744210, 6625109, 15994428, 38613965, 93222358, 225058681, 543339720   **Pell numbers: $a(n) = 2a(n-1) + a(n-2)$**

43. 1, 1, 2, 5, 12, 35, 108, 369, 1285, 4655, 17073, 63600, 238591, 901971, 3426576, 13079255, 50107909, 192622052, 742624232, 2870671950, 11123060678, 43191857688   **Polyominoes with n cells, $n \geq 1$**

44. 1, 1, 2, 4, 12, 56, 456, 6880, 191536, 9733056, 903753248, 154108311168, 48542114686912, 28401423719122304, 31021002160355166848   **Number of outcomes of n-team round-robin tournament, $n \geq 1$**

45. 1, 1, 2, 5, 14, 38, 120, 353, 1148, 3527, 11622, 36627, 121622, 389560, 1301140, 4215748, 13976335, 46235800, 155741571, 512559185, 1732007938, 5732533570   **Number of ways to fold a strip of n blank stamps, $n \geq 1$**

46. 1, 1, 2, 5, 14, 42, 132, 429, 1430, 4862, 16796, 58786, 208012, 742900, 2674440, 9694845, 35357670, 129644790, 477638700, 1767263190, 6564120420, 24466267020   **Catalan numbers: $C(2n, n)/(n+1), n \geq 0$**

47. 1, 1, 2, 5, 15, 52, 203, 877, 4140, 21147, 115975, 678570, 4213597, 27644437, 190899322, 1382958545, 10480142147, 82864869804, 682076806159, 5832742205057   **Bell or exponential numbers: expansion of $e^{(e^x - 1)}$**

48. 1, 1, 1, 2, 5, 16, 61, 272, 1385, 7936, 50521, 353792, 2702765, 22368256, 199360981, 1903757312, 19391512145, 209865342976, 2404879675441, 29088885112832   **Euler numbers: expansion of $\sec x + \tan x$**

49. 0, 2, 6, 12, 20, 30, 42, 56, 72, 90, 110, 132, 156, 182, 210, 240, 272, 306, 342, 380, 420, 462, 506, 552, 600, 650, 702, 756, 812, 870, 930, 992, 1056, 1122, 1190, 1260, 1332   **Pronic numbers: $n(n+1), n \geq 0$**

50. 1, 2, 6, 20, 70, 252, 924, 3432, 12870, 48620, 184756, 705432, 2704156, 10400600, 40116600, 155117520, 601080390, 2333606220, 9075135300, 35345263800   **Central binomial coefficients: $C(2n, n), n \geq 0$**

51. 1, 1, 1, 2, 6, 21, 112, 853, 11117, 261080, 11716571, 1006700565, 164059830476, 50335907869219, 29003487462848061, 31397381142761241960   **Number of connected graphs with n unlabeled nodes, $n \geq 0$**

52. 1, 2, 6, 22, 101, 573, 3836, 29228, 250749, 2409581, 25598186, 296643390, 3727542188, 50626553988, 738680521142   **Kendall–Mann numbers: maximal inversions in permutation of n letters, $n \geq 1$**

53. 1, 1, 2, 6, 24, 120, 720, 5040, 40320, 362880, 3628800, 39916800, 479001600, 6227020800, 87178291200, 1307674368000, 20922789888000, 355687428096000, 6402373705728000   **Factorial numbers: $n!, n \geq 0$**

54. 1, 2, 7, 42, 429, 7436, 218348, 10850216, 911835460, 129534272700,
    31095744852375, 12611311859677500, 8639383518297652500

    Robbins numbers: $\prod_{k=0}^{n-1}(3k+1)!/(n+k)!, n \geq 1$

55. 1, 2, 8, 42, 262, 1828, 13820, 110954, 933458, 8152860, 73424650, 678390116,
    6405031050, 61606881612, 602188541928, 5969806669034, 59923200729046

    Closed meandric numbers: ways a loop can cross a road $2n$ **times,** $n \geq 1$

56. 1, 2, 8, 48, 384, 3840, 46080, 645120, 10321920, 185794560, 3715891200, 81749606400,
    1961990553600, 51011754393600, 1428329123020800,
    428498736906224000   **Double factorial numbers:** $(2n)!! = 2^n n!, n \geq 0$

57. 0, 1, 2, 9, 44, 265, 1854, 14833, 133496, 1334961, 14684570, 176214841, 2290792932,
    32071101049, 481066515734, 7697064251745, 130850092279664

    Derangements: permutations of n **elements with no fixed points,** $n \geq 1$

58. 1, 2, 16, 272, 7936, 353792, 22368256, 1903757312, 209865342976,
    29088885112832, 4951498053124096, 1015423886506852352,
    246921480190207983616   **Tangent numbers: expansion of** $\tan x$

59. 1, 3, 4, 7, 6, 12, 8, 15, 13, 18, 12, 28, 14, 24, 24, 31, 18, 39, 20, 42, 32, 36, 24, 60,
    31, 42, 40, 56, 30, 72, 32, 63, 48, 54, 48, 91, 38, 60, 56, 90, 42, 96, 44, 84, 78, 72, 48,
    124    $\sigma(n)$**, sum of the divisors of** n**,** $n \geq 1$

60. 1, 3, 4, 7, 9, 12, 13, 16, 19, 21, 25, 27, 28, 31, 36, 37, 39, 43, 48, 49, 52, 57, 61, 63,
    64, 67, 73, 75, 76, 79, 81, 84, 91, 93, 97, 100, 103, 108, 109, 111, 112, 117, 121, 124,
    127   **Numbers of the form** $x^2 + xy + y^2$

61. 1, 3, 4, 7, 11, 18, 29, 47, 76, 123, 199, 322, 521, 843, 1364, 2207, 3571, 5778, 9349,
    15127, 24476, 39603, 64079, 103682, 167761, 271443, 439204, 710647, 1149851,
    1860498   **Lucas numbers:** $L(n) = L(n-1) + L(n-2)$

62. 1, 1, 1, 3, 4, 12, 27, 82, 228, 733, 2282, 7528, 24834, 83898, 285357, 983244, 3412420,
    11944614, 42080170, 149197152, 531883768, 1905930975, 6861221666, 24806004996

    Number of ways to cut an n**-sided polygon into triangles,** $n \geq 1$

63. 1, 3, 6, 10, 15, 21, 28, 36, 45, 55, 66, 78, 91, 105, 120, 136, 153, 171, 190, 210, 231,
    253, 276, 300, 325, 351, 378, 406, 435, 465, 496, 528, 561, 595, 630, 666, 703, 741,
    780   **Triangular numbers:** $n(n+1)/2, n \geq 1$

64. 1, 3, 6, 11, 17, 25, 34, 44, 55, 72, 85, 106, 127, 151

    Shortest Golomb ruler with n **marks,** $n \geq 2$

65. 1, 3, 6, 13, 24, 48, 86, 160, 282, 500, 859, 1479, 2485, 4167, 6879, 11297, 18334, 29601,
    47330, 75278, 118794, 186475, 290783, 451194, 696033, 1068745, 1632658

    Number of planar partitions of n**,** $n \geq 1$

66. 1, 3, 7, 9, 13, 15, 21, 25, 31, 33, 37, 43, 49, 51, 63, 67, 69, 73, 75, 79, 87, 93, 99,
    105, 111, 115, 127, 129, 133, 135, 141, 151, 159, 163, 169, 171, 189, 193, 195, 201,
    205   **Lucky numbers (defined by sieve similar to prime numbers)**

67. 1, 3, 7, 19, 47, 130, 343, 951, 2615, 7318, 20491, 57903, 163898, 466199, 1328993,
    3799624, 10884049, 31241170, 89814958, 258604642

    Number of mappings from n **unlabeled points to themselves,** $n \geq 1$

68. 1, 3, 9, 25, 65, 161, 385, 897, 2049, 4609, 10241, 22529, 49153, 106497, 229377,
    491521, 1048577, 2228225, 4718593, 9961473, 20971521, 44040193,
    92274689   **Cullen numbers:** $n \cdot 2^n + 1, n \geq 1$

69. 1, 3, 9, 27, 81, 243, 729, 2187, 6561, 19683, 59049, 177147, 531441, 1594323, 4782969,
    14348907, 43046721, 129140163, 387420489, 1162261467, 3486784401, 10460353203

    Powers of 3

70. 1, 3, 9, 33, 139, 718, 4535
Number of topologies or transitive-directed graphs with n unlabeled nodes, $n \geq 1$

71. 1, 1, 3, 11, 45, 197, 903, 4279, 20793, 103049, 518859, 2646723, 13648869, 71039373, 372693519, 1968801519, 10463578353, 55909013009, 300159426963
Schroeder's second problem: ways to interpret $X_1 X_2 \ldots X_n, n \geq 1$

72. 1, 3, 11, 50, 274, 1764, 13068, 109584, 1026576, 10628640, 120543840, 1486442880, 19802759040, 283465647360, 4339163001600, 70734282393600, 1223405590579200
Stirling numbers of first kind: $\begin{bmatrix} n \\ 2 \end{bmatrix}, n \geq 2.$

73. 1, 3, 13, 75, 541, 4683, 47293, 545835, 7087261, 102247563, 1622632573, 28091567595, 526858348381, 10641342970443, 230283190977853, 5315654681981355
Preferential arrangements of n things, $n \geq 1$

74. 1, 3, 15, 105, 945, 10395, 135135, 2027025, 34459425, 654729075, 13749310575, 316234143225, 7905853580625, 213458046676875, 6190283353629375
Double factorial numbers: $(2n + 1)!! = 1 \cdot 3 \cdot 5 \cdots (2n + 1), n \geq 1$

75. 1, 3, 16, 125, 1296, 16807, 262144, 4782969, 100000000, 2357947691, 61917364224, 1792160394037, 56693912375296, 1946195068359375, 72057594037927936
Number of trees with n labeled nodes: $n^{n-2}, n \geq 2$

76. 1, 3, 16, 218, 9608, 1540944, 882033440, 1793359192848, 13027956824399552, 341260431952972580352, 3252290938505588611197440
Directed graphs with n unlabeled nodes, $n \geq 1$

77. 1, 1, 3, 17, 155, 2073, 38227, 929569, 28820619, 1109652905, 51943281731, 2905151042481, 191329672483963, 14655626154768697, 1291885088448017715
Genocchi numbers: expansion of $\tan(x/2)$

78. 0, 1, 4, 5, 16, 17, 20, 21, 64, 65, 68, 69, 80, 81, 84, 85, 256, 257, 260, 261, 272, 273, 276, 277, 320, 321, 324, 325, 336, 337, 340, 341, 1024, 1025, 1028, 1029, 1040, 1041
Moser–de Bruijn sequence: sums of distinct powers of 4

79. 4, 7, 8, 9, 10, 11, 12, 12, 13, 13, 14, 15, 15, 16, 16, 16, 17, 17, 18, 18, 19, 19, 19, 20, 20, 20, 21, 21, 21, 22, 22, 22, 23, 23, 23, 24, 24, 24, 24, 25, 25, 25, 25, 26, 26, 26
Chromatic number of surface of genus $n, n \geq 0$

80. 1, 4, 9, 16, 25, 36, 49, 64, 81, 100, 121, 144, 169, 196, 225, 256, 289, 324, 361, 400, 441, 484, 529, 576, 625, 676, 729, 784, 841, 900, 961, 1024, 1089, 1156, 1225, 1296
The squares

81. 1, 4, 10, 19, 31, 46, 64, 85, 109, 136, 166, 199, 235, 274, 316, 361, 409, 460, 514, 571, 631, 694, 760, 829, 901, 976, 1054, 1135, 1219, 1306, 1396, 1489, 1585, 1684, 1786
Centered triangular numbers: $(3n^2 + 3n + 2)/2, n \geq 1$

82. 1, 4, 10, 20, 35, 56, 84, 120, 165, 220, 286, 364, 455, 560, 680, 816, 969, 1140, 1330, 1540, 1771, 2024, 2300, 2600, 2925, 3276, 3654, 4060, 4495, 4960, 5456, 5984
Tetrahedral numbers: $C(n + 3, 3), n \geq 0$

83. 1, 1, 4, 26, 236, 2752, 39208, 660032, 12818912, 282137824, 6939897856, 188666182784, 5617349020544, 181790703209728, 6353726042486272
Schroeder's fourth problem: families of subsets of an n set, $n \geq 1$

84. 1, 4, 29, 355, 6942, 209527, 9535241, 642779354, 63260289423, 8977053873043, 1816846038736192, 519355571065774021
Number of transitive-directed graphs with n labeled nodes, $n \geq 1$

85. 1, 5, 12, 22, 35, 51, 70, 92, 117, 145, 176, 210, 247, 287, 330, 376, 425, 477, 532, 590, 651, 715, 782, 852, 925, 1001, 1080, 1162, 1247, 1335, 1426, 1520, 1617, 1717, 1820
Pentagonal numbers: $n(3n - 1)/2, n \geq 1$

86. 1, 5, 13, 25, 41, 61, 85, 113, 145, 181, 221, 265, 313, 365, 421, 481, 545, 613, 685, 761, 841, 925, 1013, 1105, 1201, 1301, 1405, 1513, 1625, 1741, 1861, 1985, 2113, 2245   **Centered square numbers:** $n^2 + (n-1)^2, n \geq 1$

87. 1, 5, 14, 30, 55, 91, 140, 204, 285, 385, 506, 650, 819, 1015, 1240, 1496, 1785, 2109, 2470, 2870, 3311, 3795, 4324, 4900, 5525, 6201, 6930, 7714, 8555, 9455, 10416   **Square pyramidal numbers:** $n(n+1)(2n+1)/6, n \geq 1$

88. 1, 5, 25, 125, 625, 3125, 15625, 78125, 390625, 1953125, 9765625, 48828125, 244140625, 1220703125, 6103515625, 30517578125, 152587890625, 762939453125, 3814697265625   **Powers of 5**

89. 1, 5, 52, 1522, 145984, 48464496, 56141454464, 229148550030864, 3333310786076963968, 1746952727466749919580928   **Number of possible relations on n unlabeled points,** $n \geq 1$

90. 1, 1, 5, 61, 1385, 50521, 2702765, 199360981, 19391512145, 2404879675441, 370371188237525,   69348874393137901,   15514534163557086905, 4087072509293123892361   **Euler numbers: expansion of** $\sec x$

91. 1, 5, 109, 32297, 2147321017, 9223372023970362989, 170141183460469231667123699502996689125   **Number of ways to cover an n set,** $n \geq 1$

92. 1, 6, 15, 28, 45, 66, 91, 120, 153, 190, 231, 276, 325, 378, 435, 496, 561, 630, 703, 780, 861, 946, 1035, 1128, 1225, 1326, 1431, 1540, 1653, 1770, 1891, 2016, 2145, 2278   **Hexagonal numbers:** $n(2n-1), n \geq 1$

93. 1, 6, 25, 90, 301, 966, 3025, 9330, 28501, 86526, 261625, 788970, 2375101, 7141686, 21457825, 64439010, 193448101, 580606446, 1742343625, 5228079450, 15686335501   **Stirling numbers of second kind:** $\left\{ {n \atop 3} \right\}, n \geq 3$

94. 6, 28, 496, 8128, 33550336, 8589869056, 137438691328, 2305843008139952128, 2658455991569831744654692615953842176   **Perfect numbers: equal to the sum of their proper divisors**

95. 1, 8, 21, 40, 65, 96, 133, 176, 225, 280, 341, 408, 481, 560, 645, 736, 833, 936, 1045, 1160, 1281, 1408, 1541, 1680, 1825, 1976, 2133, 2296, 2465, 2640, 2821, 3008, 3201   **Octagonal numbers:** $n(3n-2), n \geq 1$

96. 1, 8, 27, 64, 125, 216, 343, 512, 729, 1000, 1331, 1728, 2197, 2744, 3375, 4096, 4913, 5832, 6859, 8000, 9261, 10648, 12167, 13824, 15625, 17576, 19683, 21952, 24389   **The cubes**

97. 1, -24, 252, -1472, 4830, -6048, -16744, 84480, -113643, -115920, 534612, -370944, -577738, 401856, 1217160, 987136, -6905934, 2727432, 10661420   **Ramanujan τ function**

98. 341, 561, 645, 1105, 1387, 1729, 1905, 2047, 2465, 2701, 2821, 3277, 4033, 4369, 4371, 4681, 5461, 6601, 7957, 8321, 8481, 8911, 10261, 10585, 11305, 12801, 13741, 13747   **Sarrus numbers: pseudo-primes to base 2**

99. 561, 1105, 1729, 2465, 2821, 6601, 8911, 10585, 15841, 29341, 41041, 46657, 52633, 62745, 63973, 75361, 101101, 115921, 126217, 162401, 172081, 188461, 252601, 278545   **Carmichael numbers**

100. 1, 744, 196884, 21493760, 864299970, 20245856256, 333202640600, 4252023300096, 44656994071935, 401490886656000, 3176440229784420, 22567393309593600   **Coefficients of the modular function** j

For more information about all of these sequences including formulae and references, see N.J.A. Sloane and S. Plouffe, *Encyclopedia of Integer Sequences,* Academic Press, 1995, where over 5000 other sequences are also described.

1.2.15   DE BRUIJN SEQUENCES

A sequence of length q^n over an alphabet of size q is a *de Bruijn sequence* if every possible n-tuple occurs in the sequence (allowing wraparound to the start of the sequence). There are de Bruijn sequences for any q and n. The table below gives some small examples.

q	n	Length	Sequence
2	2	4	0110
2	3	8	01110100
3	2	9	001220211
4	2	16	0011310221203323

1.3   SERIES AND PRODUCTS

1.3.1   DEFINITIONS

If $\{a_n\}$ is a sequence of numbers or functions, then

- $S_N = \sum_{n=1}^{N} a_n = a_1 + a_2 + \ldots + a_N$.
- S_N is the Nth partial sum of S.
- The series is said to converge if the limit exists and diverge if it does not.
- For an infinite series: $S = \lim_{N \to \infty} S_N = \sum_{n=1}^{\infty} a_n$ (when the limit exists).
- If $a_n = b_n x^n$, where b_n is independent of x, then S is called a *power series*.
- If $a_n = (-1)^n |a_n|$, then S is called an alternating series.
- If $\sum |a_n|$ converges, then the series converges absolutely.
- If S converges, but not absolutely, then it converges conditionally.

For example, the harmonic series $S = 1 + \frac{1}{2} + \frac{1}{3} + \ldots$ diverges. The corresponding alternating series (called the alternating harmonic series) $S = 1 - \frac{1}{2} + \frac{1}{3} + \cdots + (-1)^{n-1}\frac{1}{n} + \ldots$ converges (conditionally) to $\log 2$.

1.3.2   GENERAL PROPERTIES

1. Adding or removing a finite number of terms does not affect the convergence or divergence of an infinite series.
2. The terms of an absolutely convergent series may be rearranged in any manner without affecting its value.

3. A conditionally convergent series can be made to converge to any value by suitably rearranging its terms.

4. If the component series are convergent, then $\sum(\alpha a_n + \beta b_n) = \alpha \sum a_n + \beta \sum b_n$.

5. $\left(\sum_{n=0}^{\infty} a_n\right)\left(\sum_{n=0}^{\infty} b_n\right) = \sum_{n=0}^{\infty} c_n$ where $c_n = a_0 b_n + a_1 b_{n-1} + \cdots + a_n b_0$.

6. Summation by parts: let $\sum a_n$ and $\sum b_n$ converge. Then

$$\sum a_n b_n = \sum S_n (b_n - b_{n+1})$$

where S_n is the nth partial sum of $\sum a_n$.

7. A power series may be integrated and differentiated term by term within its interval of convergence.

8. *Schwarz inequality*:

$$\sum |a_n| |b_n| \le \left(\sum a_n^2\right)^{1/2} \left(\sum b_n^2\right)^{1/2}$$

9. *Holder's inequality*:

$$\sum |a_n b_n| \le \sum |a_n|^{1/p} \sum |b_n|^{1/q}$$
$$\text{when } 1/p + 1/q = 1 \text{ and } p, q > 1$$

10. *Minkowski's inequality*:

$$\left(\sum |a_n + b_n|^p\right)^{1/p} \le \left(\sum |a_n|^p\right)^{1/p} + \left(\sum |b_n|^p\right)^{1/p}$$
$$\text{when } p \ge 1$$

For example:

1. Let T be the alternating harmonic series S rearranged so that each positive term is followed by the next two negative terms. By combining each positive term of T with the succeeding negative term, we find that $T_{3N} = \frac{1}{2} S_{2N}$. Hence, $T = \frac{1}{2} \log 2$.

2. The series $1 + \frac{1}{2} - \frac{1}{3} + \frac{1}{4} + \frac{1}{5} - \frac{1}{6} + \frac{1}{7} + \frac{1}{8} - \frac{1}{9} + \ldots$ diverges, whereas

$$1 + \frac{1}{3} - \frac{1}{2} + \frac{1}{5} + \frac{1}{7} - \frac{1}{4} + \cdots + \frac{1}{4n-3} + \frac{1}{4n-1} - \frac{1}{2n} + \ldots$$

converges to $\log(2\sqrt{2})$.

1.3.3   CONVERGENCE TESTS

1. *Comparison test*: If $|a_n| \leq b_n$ and $\sum b_n$ converges, then $\sum a_n$ converges.
2. *Limit test*: If $\lim_{n \to \infty} a_n \neq 0$, then $\sum a_n$ is divergent.
3. *Ratio test*: Let $\rho = \lim_{n \to \infty} |\frac{a_{n+1}}{a_n}|$. If $\rho < 1$, the series converges absolutely. If $\rho > 1$, the series diverges.
4. *Cauchy root test*: Let $\sigma = \lim_{n \to \infty} |a_n|^{1/n}$. If $\sigma < 1$, the series converges. If $\sigma > 1$, it diverges.
5. *Integral test*: Let $|a_n| = f(n)$ with $f(x)$ being monotone decreasing, and $\lim_{x \to \infty} f(x) = 0$. Then $\int_A^\infty f(x)\,dx$ and $\sum a_n$ both converge or both diverge for any $A > 0$.
6. *Gauss's test*: If $\left| \dfrac{a_{n+1}}{a_n} \right| = 1 - \dfrac{p}{n} + \dfrac{A_n}{n^q}$ where $q > 1$ and the sequence $\{A_n\}$ is bounded, then the series is absolutely convergent if and only if $p > 1$.
7. *Alternating series test*: If $|a_n|$ tends monotonically to 0, then $\sum (-1)^n |a_n|$ converges.

For example:

1. For $S = \sum_{n=1}^{\infty} n^c x^n$, $\rho = \lim_{n \to \infty}(1 + \frac{1}{n})^c x = x$. Hence, using the ratio test, S converges for $0 < x < 1$ and any value of c.
2. For $S = \sum_{n=1}^{\infty} \frac{5^n}{n^{20}}$, $\sigma = \lim_{n \to \infty}(\frac{5^n}{n^{20}})^{1/n} = 5$. Therefore the series diverges.
3. For $S = \sum_{n=1}^{\infty} n^{-s}$, let $f(x) = x^{-s}$. Then

$$\int_1^\infty f(x)\,dx = \int_1^\infty \frac{dx}{x^s} = \frac{1}{s-1}$$

for $s > 1$, and the integral diverges for $s \leq 1$. Hence, S converges for $s > 1$.
4. The sum $\sum_{n=2}^{\infty} \frac{1}{n(\log n)^s}$ converges for $s > 1$ by the integral test.
5. Let $a_n = \frac{(c)_n}{n!} = \frac{c(c+1)...(c+n-1)}{n!}$ where c is not 0 or a negative integer. Then $|a_{n+1}/a_n| = 1 - (c+1)/n + (c+1)/n^2(1+1/n)$. By Gauss's test, the series converges absolutely if and only if $c > 0$.

1.3.4   TYPES OF SERIES

Bessel series

1. *Fourier–Bessel series*:

$$\sum_{n=0}^{\infty} a_n J_v(j_{v,n} z)$$

2. *Neumann series*:

$$\sum_{n=0}^{\infty} a_n J_{v+n}(z)$$

3. *Kapteyn series*:

$$\sum_{n=0}^{\infty} a_n J_{v+n}[(v+n)z]$$

4. *Schlömilch series*:

$$\sum_{n=1}^{\infty} a_n J_v(nz)$$

For example;

- $\sum_{n=0}^{\infty} \frac{1}{n!} J_{v+n}(2) = \frac{1}{\Gamma(v+1)}$
- $\sum_{n=1}^{\infty} J_n(nz) = \frac{1}{2} \frac{z}{1-z}$ for $0 < z < 1$
- $\sum_{n=1}^{\infty} (-1)^{n+1} J_0(nz) = \frac{1}{2}$ for $0 < z < \pi$

Dirichlet series

These are series of the form $\sum_{n=1}^{\infty} \frac{a_n}{n^x}$. They converge for $x > x_0$, where x_0 is the *abscissa of convergence*. Assuming the limits exist:

If $\sum a_n$ diverges, then $x_0 = \lim_{n\to\infty} \frac{\log |a_1 + \cdots + a_n|}{\log n}$.

If $\sum a_n$ converges, then $x_0 = \lim_{n\to\infty} \frac{\log |a_{n+1} + a_{n+2} + \ldots|}{\log n}$.

For example:

- *Riemann zeta function*:

$$\zeta(x) = \sum_{n=1}^{\infty} \frac{1}{n^x}, \quad x_0 = 1$$

- $\sum_{n=1}^{\infty} \frac{\mu(n)}{n^x} = \frac{1}{\zeta(x)}, \quad x_0 = 1$ ($\mu(n)$ denotes the Möbius function)
- $\sum_{n=1}^{\infty} \frac{d(n)}{n^x} = [\zeta(x)]^2, \quad x_0 = 1$ ($d(n)$ is the number of divisors of n)

Fourier series

If $f(x)$ satisfies certain properties, then (see page 46 for details)

$$f(x) = \frac{a_0}{2} + \sum_{n=1}^{\infty} \left(a_n \cos \frac{n\pi x}{L} + b_n \sin \frac{n\pi x}{L} \right) \qquad (1.3.1)$$

- If $f(x)$ has the Laplace transform $F(k)$, then

$$\sum_{k=1}^{\infty} F(k)\cos(kt) = \frac{1}{2}\int_0^{\infty} \frac{\cos(t)-e^{-x}}{\cosh(x)-\cos(t)} f(x)\,dx,$$

$$\sum_{k=1}^{\infty} F(k)\sin(kt) = \frac{1}{2}\int_0^{\infty} \frac{f(x)}{\cosh(x)-\cos(t)}\,dx. \qquad (1.3.2)$$

- Since the cosine transform of $(\cosh(x)-\cos(t))^{-1}$ with respect to x is $\pi\csc(t)$ $\operatorname{csch}(\pi y)\sinh(\pi - t)y$, we find that

$$\sum_{k=1}^{\infty} \frac{k\sin(kt)}{k^2+y^2} = \frac{\pi}{2}\frac{\sinh(\pi - t)y}{\sinh(\pi y)}.$$

- $\sum_{n=1}^{\infty} \frac{\sin(2n\pi x)}{n^{2k+1}} = \frac{(-1)^{k-1}}{2}\frac{(2\pi)^{2k+1}}{2k+1} B_{2k+1}(x)$, for $0 < x < \frac{1}{2}$

- $\sum_{n=1}^{\infty} \frac{\cos(2n\pi x)}{n^{2k}} = \frac{(-1)^{k-1}}{2}\frac{(2\pi)^{2k}}{(2k)!} B_{2k}(x)$ for $0 < x < \frac{1}{2}$

- $\sum_{n=1}^{\infty} \frac{\sin((2n+1)\pi x - \pi k/2)}{(2n+1)^{k+1}} = \frac{\pi^{k+1}}{4k!} E_k(x)$

- $\sum_{n=1}^{\infty} a^n \sin(nx) = \frac{a\sin(x)}{1-2a\cos(x)+a^2}$ for $|a| < 1$

- $\sum_{n=0}^{\infty} a^n \cos(nx) = \frac{1-a\cos(x)}{1-2a\cos(x)+a^2}$ for $|a| < 1$

Hypergeometric series

The hypergeometric function is

$$_pF_q\left(\begin{matrix} a_1 & a_2 & \cdots & a_p \\ b_1 & b_2 & \cdots & b_q \end{matrix}\,\middle|\,x\right) = \sum_{n=0}^{\infty} \frac{(a_1)_n(a_2)_n\cdots(a_p)_n}{(b_1)_n(b_2)_n\cdots(b_q)_n}\frac{x^n}{n!}$$

where $(a)_n = \Gamma(a+n)/\Gamma(a)$ is the shifted factorial. Any infinite series $\sum A_n$ with A_{n+1}/A_n a rational function of n is of this type. These include series of products and quotients of binomial coefficients. For example:

$$_2F_1\left(\begin{matrix} a, & b \\ & c \end{matrix}\,\middle|\,1\right) = \frac{\Gamma(c)\Gamma(c-a-b)}{\Gamma(c-a)\Gamma(c-b)} \quad \text{(Gauss)}$$

$$_3F_2\left(\begin{matrix} -n, & a, & b \\ c, & 1+a+b-c-n & \end{matrix}\,\middle|\,1\right) = \frac{(c-a)_n(c-b)_n}{(c)_n(c-a-b)_n} \quad \text{(Saalschutz)}$$

$$_4F_3\left(\begin{matrix} a, & 1+a/2, & b, & -n \\ a/2, & 1+a-b, & 1+2b-n & \end{matrix}\,\middle|\,1\right) = \frac{(a-2b)_n(-b)_n}{(1+a-b)_n(-2b)_n} \quad \text{(Bailey)}$$

$$\sum_{m=0}^{2n} (-1)^m \frac{\binom{2n}{m}\binom{2n+m+1}{m}}{\binom{4n+2m+2}{2m}}(3+2\sqrt{2})^m = \frac{(3/4)_n(5/4)_n}{(7/8)_n(9/8)_n}$$

Power series

1. The values of x for which the power series $\sum_{n=0}^{\infty} a_n x^n$ converges, form an interval (*interval of convergence*) which may or may not include one or both endpoints.

2. A power series may be integrated and differentiated term-by-term within its interval of convergence.

3. Note that $[1 + \sum_{n=1}^{\infty} a_n x^n]^{-1} = 1 - \sum_{n=1}^{\infty} b_n x^n$, where $b_1 = a_1$ and $b_n = a_n + \sum_{k=1}^{n-1} b_{n-k} a_k$ for $n \geq 2$.

4. *Inversion of power series*: If $s = \sum_{n=1}^{\infty} a_n x^n$, then $x = \sum_{n=1}^{\infty} A_n s^n$, where $A_1 = 1/a_1$, $A_2 = -a_2/a_1^3$, $A_3 = (2a_2^2 - a_1 a_3)/a_1^5$, $A_4 = (5a_1 a_2 a_3 - a_1^2 a_4 - 5a_2^3)/a_1^7$, $A_5 = (6a_1^2 a_2 a_4 + 3a_1^2 a_3^2 + 14a_2^4 - a_1^3 a_5 - 21a_1 a_2^2 a_3)/a_1^9$.

Taylor series

1. Taylor series in 1 variable:

$$f(a + x) = \sum_{n=0}^{N} \frac{x^n}{n!} f^{(n)}(a) + R_N.$$

2. Lagrange's form of the remainder:

$$R_N = \frac{x^{N+1}}{(N+1)!} f^{(N+1)}(\theta a), \qquad \text{for some } 0 < \theta < 1.$$

3. Taylor series in 2 variables:

$$f(a + x, b + y) = f(a, b) + x f_x(a, b) + y f_y(a, b) +$$
$$\frac{1}{2!} \left[x^2 f_{xx}(a, b) + 2xy f_{xy}(a, b) + y^2 f_{yy}(a, b) \right] + \dots.$$

4. Taylor series for vectors:

$$f(\mathbf{a} + \mathbf{x}) = \sum_{n=0}^{N} \frac{[(\mathbf{x} \cdot \nabla)^n f](\mathbf{a})}{n!} + R_N(\mathbf{a}) = f(\mathbf{a}) + \mathbf{x} \cdot \nabla f(\mathbf{a}) + \dots.$$

For example (see also page 40):

- *Binomial series*:

$$(x + y)^\nu = \sum_{n=0}^{\infty} \frac{\Gamma(\nu + 1)}{\Gamma(\nu - n + 1)} \frac{x^n y^{\nu-n}}{n!}.$$

When ν is a positive integer, the series terminates at $n = \nu$.

- $\frac{1}{\sqrt{1-4x}} = \sum_{k=0}^{\infty} \frac{(2k)!}{(k!)^2} x^k$ for $|x| < 1/4$

- $\frac{x e^{xt}}{e^x - 1} = \sum_{n=0}^{\infty} B_n(t) \frac{x^n}{n!}$

- $\frac{2 e^{xt}}{e^x + 1} = \sum_{n=0}^{\infty} E_n(t) \frac{x^n}{n!}$

- $\sum_{n=1}^{\infty} \frac{x^n}{(n+1)(n+3)} = \frac{1}{x^3}\int_0^x u\, du \int_0^u dt \sum_{0}^{\infty} t^n$
  $$= \frac{1}{2x^3}\left[x + \tfrac{1}{2}x^2 + (1 - x^2)\log(1 - x)\right] \text{ for } |x| < 1$$
- $\sum_{k=1}^{\infty} \frac{x^k}{k^n} = \mathrm{Li}_n(x)$ (polylogarithm)

Telescoping series

If $\lim_{n\to\infty} F(n) = 0$, then $\sum_{n=1}^{\infty}[F(n) - F(n + 1)] = F(1)$. For example,

$$\sum_{n=1}^{\infty} \frac{1}{(n+1)(n+2)} = \sum_{n=1}^{\infty}\left[\frac{1}{n+1} - \frac{1}{n+2}\right] = \frac{1}{2}.$$

The GWZ symbolic computer algorithm expresses a proposed identity in the form of a telescoping series $\sum_k[F(n + 1, k) - F(n, k)] = 0$, then searches for a $G(n, k)$ that satisfies $F(n + 1, k) - F(n, k) = G(n, k + 1) - G(n, k)$ and $G(n, \pm\infty) = 0$. The search assumes that $G(n, k) = R(n, k)F(n, k - 1)$ where $R(n, k)$ is a rational expression in n and k. When R is found, the proposed identity is verified. For example, the Pfaff–Saalschutz identity has the following proof:

$$\sum_{k=-\infty}^{\infty} \frac{(a + k)!(b + k)!(c - a - b + n - 1 - k)!}{(k + 1)!(n - k)!(c + k)!} = \frac{(c - a + n)!(c - b + n)!}{(n + 1)!(c + n)!},$$

$$R(n, k) = -\frac{(b + k)(a + k)}{(c - b + n + 1)(c - a + n + 1)}.$$

Other types of series

1. Arithmetic series:

$$\sum_{n=1}^{N}(a + nd) = Na + \frac{1}{2}N(N + 1)d.$$

2. Arithmetic power series:

$$\sum_{n=1}^{N}(a + nb)x^n = \frac{a - (a + bN)x^{N+1}}{1 - x} + \frac{bx(1 - x^N)}{(1 - x)^2}, \qquad (x \neq 1).$$

3. Geometric series:

$$1 + x + x^2 + x^3 + \cdots = \frac{1}{1 - x}, \qquad (|x| < 1).$$

4. Arithmetic–geometric series:

$$a + (a + b)x + (a + 2b)x^2 + (a + 3b)x^3 + \cdots = \frac{a}{1 - x} + \frac{bx}{(1 - x)^2},$$
$$(|x| < 1).$$

5. Combinatorial sums:

- $\sum_{k=0}^{n} \binom{x-k}{n-k} = \binom{x+1}{n}$

- $\sum_{k=-\infty}^{m} (-1)^k \binom{x}{k} = (-1)^m \binom{x-1}{m}$

- $\sum_{k=0}^{n} \binom{k+m}{k} = \binom{m+n+1}{n}$

- $\sum_{k=-\infty}^{m} (-1)^k \binom{x+m}{k} = \binom{-x}{m}$

- $\sum_{k=-\infty}^{\infty} \binom{x}{m+k}\binom{y}{n-k} = \binom{x+y}{m+n}$

- $\sum_{k=-\infty}^{\infty} \binom{l}{m+k}\binom{x}{n+k} = \binom{l+x}{l-m+n}$

- $\sum_{k=-\infty}^{\infty} (-1)^k \binom{l}{m+k}\binom{x+k}{n} = (-1)^{l+m}\binom{x-m}{n-l}$

- $\sum_{k=-\infty}^{l} (-1)^k \binom{l-k}{m}\binom{x}{k-n} = (-1)^{l+m}\binom{x-m-l}{l-m-n}$

- $\sum_{k=0}^{l} \binom{l-k}{m}\binom{q+k}{n} = \binom{l+q+1}{m+n+1}$ $(m \geq q)$

6. Generating functions:

- Bessel functions: $\sum_{k=-\infty}^{\infty} J_k(x) z^k = \exp(\frac{1}{2}x\frac{z^2-1}{z})$

- Chebyshev polynomials: $\sum_{n=1}^{\infty} T_n(x) z^n = \frac{z(z+2x)}{2xz-z^2-1}$

- Hermite polynomials: $\sum_{n=0}^{\infty} \frac{H_n(x)}{n!} z^n = \exp(2xz - z^2)$

- Laguerre polynomials: $\sum_{n=0}^{\infty} L_n^{(\alpha)}(x) z^n = (1-z)^{-\alpha-1} \exp[\frac{xz}{z-1}]$

- Legendre polynomials: $\sum_{n=0}^{\infty} P_n(z) x^n = \frac{1}{\sqrt{1-xz+x^2}}$, for $|x| < 1$

7. Multiple series:

- $\sum \frac{(-1)^{l+m+n}}{\sqrt{(l+1/6)^2+(m+1/6)^2+(n+1/6)^2}} = \sqrt{3}$ for $-\infty < l, m, n < \infty$ not all zero

- $\sum \frac{1}{(m^2+n^2)^z} = 4\beta(z)\zeta(z)$ for $-\infty < m, n < \infty$ not both zero

- $\sum_{m,n=0}^{\infty} \frac{(-1)^n}{n!} \frac{\Gamma(n+1/2)}{\Gamma(m+n+1/2)} z^{m+n} = \sqrt{\pi} e^z \frac{\mathrm{erf}(\sqrt{z-z})}{\sqrt{z-z}}$ for $z > 0$

- $\sum_{m,n=1}^{\infty} \frac{m^2-n^2}{(m^2+n^2)^2} = \frac{\pi}{4}$

- $\sum \frac{1}{k_1^2 k_2^2 \ldots k_n^2} = \frac{\pi^{2n}}{(2n+1)!}$ for $1 \leq k_1 < \cdots < k_n < \infty$

1.3.5 SUMMATION FORMULAE

1. *Euler–Maclaurin summation formula*: As $n \to \infty$,

$$\sum_{k=0}^{n} f(k) \sim \frac{1}{2} f(n) + \int_0^n f(x)\,dx + C + \sum_{j=1}^{\infty} (-1)^{j+1} B_{j+1} \frac{f^{(j)}(n)}{(j+1)!}$$

where

$$C = \lim_{m\to\infty}\left[\sum_{j=1}^{m}(-1)^j B_{j+1}\frac{f^{(j)}(0)}{(j+1)!} + \frac{1}{2}f(0)\right.$$

$$\left. + \frac{(-1)^m}{(m+1)!}\int_0^\infty B_{m+1}(x - \lfloor x\rfloor)f^{(m+1)}(x)\,dx\right].$$

2. *Poisson summation formula*: If f is continuous,

$$\frac{1}{2}f(0) + \sum_{n=1}^{\infty}f(n) = \int_0^\infty f(x)\,dx + 2\sum_{n=1}^{\infty}\left[\int_0^\infty f(x)\cos(2n\pi x)dx\right].$$

For example:

- $\sum_{k=1}^{n}\frac{1}{k} \sim \log n + \gamma + \frac{1}{2n} - \frac{B_2}{2n^2} - \ldots$ where γ is Euler's constant.
- $1 + 2\sum_{n=1}^{\infty}e^{-n^2 x} = \sqrt{\frac{\pi}{x}}[1 + 2\sum_{n=1}^{\infty}e^{-\pi^2 n^2/x}]$ (Jacobi)

1.3.6 IMPROVING CONVERGENCE: SHANKS TRANSFORMATION

Let s_n be the nth partial sum. The sequences $\{S(s_n)\}$, $\{S(S(s_n))\}$, $\ldots$ often converge successively more rapidly to the same limit as $\{s_n\}$, where

$$S(s_n) = \frac{s_{n+1}s_{n-1} - s_n^2}{s_{n+1} + s_{n-1} - 2s_n}. \tag{1.3.3}$$

For example, for $s_n = \sum_{k=0}^{n}(-1)^k z^k$, we find $S(s_n) = \frac{1}{1+z}$ for all n.

1.3.7 SUMMABILITY METHODS

Unique values can be assigned to divergent series in a variety of ways which preserve the values of convergent series.

1. Abel summation: $\sum_{n=0}^{\infty}a_n = \lim_{r\to 1^-}\sum_{n=0}^{\infty}a_n r^n$.
2. Cesaro $(C, 1)$-summation: $\sum_{n=0}^{\infty}a_n = \lim_{N\to\infty}\frac{s_0 + s_1 + \ldots s_N}{N+1}$ where $s_n = \sum_{m=0}^{n}a_m$.

For example:

- $1 - 1 + 1 - 1 + \cdots = \frac{1}{2}$ (in the sense of Abel summation)
- $1 - 1 + 0 + 1 - 1 + 0 + 1 - \cdots = \frac{1}{3}$ (in the sense of Cesaro summation)

1.3.8 OPERATIONS WITH SERIES

Let $y = a_1x + a_2x^2 + a_3x^3 + \ldots$, and let $z = z(y) = b_1x + b_2x^2 + b_3x^3 + \ldots$.

$z =$	b_0	b_1	b_2	b_3
$\dfrac{1}{1-y}$	1	a_1	$a_1^2 + a_2$	$a_1^3 + 2a_1a_2 + a_3$
$\sqrt{1+y}$	1	$\frac{1}{2}a_1$	$-\frac{1}{8}a_1^2 + \frac{1}{2}a_2$	$\frac{1}{16}a_1^3 - \frac{1}{4}a_1a_2 + \frac{1}{2}a_3$
$(1+y)^{-1/2}$	1	$-\frac{1}{2}a_1$	$\frac{3}{8}a_1^2 - \frac{1}{2}a_2$	$-\frac{5}{16}a_1^3 + \frac{3}{4}a_1a_2 - \frac{1}{2}a_3$
e^y	1	a_1	$\frac{1}{2}a_1^2 + a_2$	$\frac{1}{6}a_1^3 + a_1a_2 + a_3$
$\log(1+y)$	0	a_1	$a_2 - \frac{1}{2}a_1^2$	$a_3 - a_1a_2 + \frac{1}{3}a_1^3$
$\sin y$	0	a_1	a_2	$-\frac{1}{6}a_1^3 + a_3$
$\cos y$	1	0	$-\frac{1}{2}a_1^2$	$-a_1a_2$
$\tan y$	0	a_1	a_2	$\frac{1}{3}a_1^3 + a_3$

1.3.9 MISCELLANEOUS SUMS AND SERIES

- $\sum_{n=1}^{N}(-1)^{n+1}n^k = \frac{1}{2}(-1)^{N+1}[E_k(N+1) + (-1)^N E_k]$
- $\sum_{k=1}^{n} \frac{1}{k(k+1)(k+2)} = \frac{1}{4} - \frac{1}{2(n+1)(n+2)}$
- $\sum_{k=1}^{n} \frac{km^k}{(k+m)!} = \frac{1}{(m-1)!} - \frac{m^{n+1}}{(m+n)!}$
- $\sum_{k=0}^{2n}(-1)^k \binom{2n}{k}^{-1} = \frac{2n+1}{n+1}$
- $\sum_{k=0}^{n} \binom{m}{k}\binom{n}{k}\binom{m+n+k}{m+n} = \binom{m+n}{m}^2$
- $\sum_{k=0}^{n-1} \frac{1}{4^k}\operatorname{sech}^2 \frac{x}{2^k} = \frac{1}{4^n}\operatorname{csch}^2 \frac{x}{2^n} - \operatorname{csch}^2 x$
- $\sum_{k=0}^{n-1}(-1)^k \cos^n \frac{\pi k}{n} = \frac{n}{2^{n-1}}, \qquad \sum_{k=0}^{n} \sec \frac{\pi k}{n} = 0, \qquad (k \ne n/2)$
- $\sum_{k=-\infty}^{\infty} \frac{1}{(k+a)(k+b)} = \frac{\pi}{b-a}(\cot \pi a - \cot \pi b)$
- $\sum_{k=0}^{\infty} \frac{1}{k^4+a^4} = \frac{1}{2a^4} + \frac{\pi}{2a^3\sqrt{2}} \frac{\sinh(a\pi\sqrt{2})+\sin(a\pi\sqrt{2})}{\cosh(a\pi\sqrt{2})-\cos(a\pi\sqrt{2})}$
- $\sum_{k=1}^{\infty} \frac{k}{e^{2\pi k}-1} = \frac{1}{24} - \frac{1}{8\pi}$
- The series $\displaystyle\sum_{n=3}^{\infty} \frac{1}{n \log n (\log\log n)^2}$ converges to $38.43\ldots$ so slowly that it requires $10^{3.14 \cdot 10^{86}}$ terms to give two-decimal accuracy
- The series $\displaystyle\sum_{n=3}^{\infty} \frac{1}{n \log n (\log\log n)}$ diverges, but the partial sums exceed 10 only after a googolplex of terms have appeared

1.3.10   INFINITE SERIES

Algebraic functions

$$(x + y)^n = x^n + \binom{n}{1}x^{n-1}y + \binom{n}{2}x^{n-2}y^2 + \dots .$$

$$(1 \pm x)^n = 1 \pm \binom{n}{1}x + \binom{n}{2}x^2 \pm \binom{n}{3}x^3 + \dots , \qquad (x^2 < 1).$$

$$(1 \pm x)^{-n} = 1 \mp \binom{n}{1}x + \binom{n+1}{2}x^2 \mp \binom{n+2}{3}x^3 + \dots , \qquad (x^2 < 1).$$

$$\sqrt{1+x} = 1 + \frac{1}{2}x - \frac{1}{8}x^2 + \frac{1}{16}x^3 - \frac{5}{128}x^4 + \dots , \qquad (x^2 < 1).$$

$$(1+x)^{-1/2} = 1 - \frac{1}{2}x + \frac{3}{8}x^2 - \frac{5}{16}x^3 + \frac{35}{128}x^4 + \dots , \qquad (x^2 < 1).$$

$$(1 \pm x)^{-1} = 1 \mp x + x^2 \mp x^3 + x^4 \mp x^5 + \dots , \qquad (x^2 < 1).$$

$$(1 \pm x)^{-2} = 1 \mp 2x + 3x^2 \mp 4x^3 + 5x^4 \mp 6x^5 + \dots , \qquad (x^2 < 1).$$

Exponential functions

$$e = 1 + \frac{1}{1!} + \frac{1}{2!} + \dots + \frac{1}{n!} + \dots .$$

$$e^x = 1 + \frac{x}{1!} + \frac{x^2}{2!} + \dots + \frac{x^n}{n!} + \dots , \qquad \text{(all real values of } x\text{)}$$

$$= e^a \left[1 + (x - a) + \frac{(x-a)^2}{2!} + \dots + \frac{(x-a)^n}{n!} + \dots \right].$$

$$a^x = 1 + x \log_e a + \frac{(x \log_e a)^2}{2!} + \dots + \frac{(x \log_e a)^n}{n!} + \dots .$$

Logarithmic functions

$$\log x = \frac{x-1}{x} + \frac{1}{2}\left(\frac{x-1}{x}\right)^2 + \cdots + \frac{1}{n}\left(\frac{x-1}{x}\right)^n + \cdots, \qquad (x > 1/2),$$

$$= (x-1) - \frac{1}{2}(x-1)^2 + \frac{1}{3}(x-1)^3 - \cdots, \qquad (2 \geq x > 0),$$

$$= 2\left[\frac{x-1}{x+1} + \frac{1}{3}\left(\frac{x-1}{x+1}\right)^3 + \frac{1}{5}\left(\frac{x-1}{x+1}\right)^5 + \cdots\right], \qquad (x > 0).$$

$$= \log a + \frac{(x-a)}{a} - \frac{(x-a)^2}{2a^2} + \frac{(x-a)^3}{3a^2} - \cdots, \qquad (0 < x \leq 2a).$$

$$\log(1+x) = x - \frac{x^2}{2} + \frac{x^3}{3} - \frac{x^4}{4} + \cdots, \qquad -1 < x \leq 1.$$

$$\log(n+1) = \log(n-1) + 2\left[\frac{1}{n} + \frac{1}{3n^3} + \frac{1}{5n^5} + \cdots\right].$$

$$\log(a+x) = \log a + 2\left[\frac{x}{2a+x} + \frac{1}{3}\left(\frac{x}{2a+x}\right)^3 + \frac{1}{5}\left(\frac{x}{2a+x}\right)^5 + \cdots\right],$$

$$(a > 0, -a < x).$$

$$\log\frac{1+x}{1-x} = 2\left[x + \frac{x^3}{3} + \cdots + \frac{x^{2n-1}}{2n-1} + \cdots\right], \qquad (-1 < x < 1).$$

Trigonometric functions

$$\sin x = x - \frac{x^3}{3!} + \frac{x^5}{5!} - \frac{x^7}{7!} + \cdots. \qquad \text{(all real values of } x\text{)}.$$

$$\cos x = 1 - \frac{x^2}{2!} + \frac{x^4}{4!} - \frac{x^6}{6!} + \cdots. \qquad \text{(all real values of } x\text{)}.$$

$$\tan x = x + \frac{x^3}{3} + \frac{2x^5}{15} + \cdots + \frac{(-1)^{n-1}2^{2n}(2^{2n}-1)B_{2n}}{(2n)!}x^{2n-1} + \cdots$$

$$(x^2 < \pi^2/4, \ B_n \text{ is the } n^{\text{th}} \text{ Bernoulli number}).$$

$$\cot x = \frac{1}{x} - \frac{x}{3} - \frac{x^3}{45} - \frac{2x^5}{945} - \frac{x^7}{4725} - \cdots + \frac{(-1)^{n+1}2^{2n}B_{2n}}{(2n)!}x^{2n-1} + \cdots$$

$$(x^2 < \pi^2, \ B_n \text{ is the } n^{\text{th}} \text{ Bernoulli number}).$$

$$\sec x = 1 + \frac{x^2}{2} + \frac{5}{24}x^4 + \frac{61}{720}x^6 + \frac{277}{8064}x^8 + \cdots + \frac{(-1)^n E_{2n}}{(2n)!}x^{2n} + \cdots$$

$$(x^2 < \pi^2/4, \ E_n \text{ is the } n^{\text{th}} \text{ Euler number}).$$

$$\csc x = \frac{1}{x} + \frac{x}{6} + \frac{7x^3}{360} + \frac{31x^5}{15120} + \cdots + \frac{(-1)^{n+1}2(2^{2n-1}-1)B_{2n}}{(2n)!}x^{2n-1} + \cdots$$

$(|x| < \pi$, B_n is the nth Bernoulli number$)$.

$$\log \sin x = \log x - \frac{x^2}{6} - \frac{x^4}{180} - \frac{x^6}{2835} - \cdots \qquad (x^2 < \pi^2).$$

$$\log \cos x = -\frac{x^2}{2} - \frac{x^4}{12} - \frac{x^6}{45} - \frac{17x^6}{2520} - \cdots \qquad (x^2 < \pi^2/4).$$

$$\log \tan x = \log x + \frac{x^2}{3} + \frac{7x^4}{90} + \frac{62x^6}{2835} + \cdots \qquad (x^2 < \pi^2/4).$$

$$e^{\sin x} = 1 + x + \frac{x^2}{2!} - \frac{3x^4}{4!} - \frac{8x^5}{5!} - \frac{3x^6}{6!} + \frac{56x^7}{7!} + \cdots.$$

$$e^{\cos x} = e\left(1 - \frac{x^2}{2!} + \frac{4x^4}{4!} - \frac{31x^6}{6!} + \cdots\right).$$

$$e^{\tan x} = 1 + x + \frac{x^2}{2!} + \frac{3x^3}{3!} + \frac{9x^4}{4!} + \frac{37x^5}{5!} + \cdots \qquad (x^2 < \pi^2/4).$$

$$\sin x = \sin a + (x - a)\cos a - \frac{(x - a)^2}{2!}\sin a - \frac{(x - a)^3}{3!}\cos a + \cdots.$$

Inverse trigonometric functions

$$\sin^{-1} x = x + \frac{1}{2 \cdot 3}x^3 + \frac{1 \cdot 3}{2 \cdot 4 \cdot 5}x^5 + \frac{1 \cdot 3 \cdot 5}{2 \cdot 4 \cdot 6 \cdot 7}x^7 + \cdots$$

$$(x^2 < 1, -\tfrac{\pi}{2} < \sin^{-1} x < \tfrac{\pi}{2}).$$

$$\cos^{-1} x = \frac{\pi}{2} - \left(x + \frac{1}{2 \cdot 3}x^3 + \frac{1 \cdot 3}{2 \cdot 4 \cdot 5}x^5 + \frac{1 \cdot 3 \cdot 5}{2 \cdot 4 \cdot 6 \cdot 7}x^7 + \cdots\right)$$

$$(x^2 < 1, 0 < \cos^{-1} x < \pi).$$

$$\tan^{-1} x = x - \frac{x^3}{3} + \frac{x^5}{5} - \frac{x^7}{7} + \cdots \qquad (x^2 < 1),$$

$$= \frac{\pi}{2} - \frac{1}{x} + \frac{1}{3x^3} - \frac{1}{5x^5} + \frac{1}{7x^7} - \cdots \qquad (x > 1),$$

$$= -\frac{\pi}{2} - \frac{1}{x} + \frac{1}{3x^3} - \frac{1}{5x^5} + \frac{1}{7x^7} - \cdots \qquad (x < -1).$$

$$\cot^{-1} x = \frac{\pi}{2} - x + \frac{x^3}{3} - \frac{x^5}{5} + \frac{x^7}{7} - \cdots \qquad (x^2 < 1).$$

Hyperbolic functions

$$\sinh x = x + \frac{x^3}{3!} + \frac{x^5}{5!} + \frac{x^7}{7!} + \cdots + \frac{x^{(2n+1)}}{(2n+1)!} + \cdots.$$

$$\sinh ax = \frac{2}{\pi} \sinh \pi a \left[\frac{\sin x}{a^2 + 1^2} - \frac{2 \sin 2x}{a^2 + 2^2} + \frac{3 \sin 3x}{a^2 + 3^2} + \cdots \right] \qquad (|x| < \pi).$$

$$\cosh x = 1 + \frac{x^2}{2!} + \frac{x^4}{4!} + \frac{x^6}{6!} + \cdots + \frac{x^{2n}}{(2n)!} + \cdots.$$

$$\cosh ax = \frac{2a}{\pi} \sinh \pi a \left[\frac{1}{2a^2} - \frac{\cos x}{a^2 + 1^2} + \frac{\cos 2x}{a^2 + 2^2} - \frac{\cos 3x}{a^2 + 3^2} + \cdots \right] \quad (|x| < \pi).$$

$$\tanh x = x - \frac{1}{3}x^3 + \frac{2}{15}x^5 - \cdots + \frac{2^{2n}(2^{2n} - 1)B_{2n}}{(2n)!}x^{2n-1} + \cdots \qquad (|x| < \pi/2),$$

$$= 1 - 2e^{-2x} + 2e^{-4x} - 2e^{-6x} + \cdots \qquad (\text{Re } x > 0),$$

$$= 2x \left[\frac{1}{\left(\frac{\pi}{2}\right)^2 + x^2} + \frac{1}{\left(\frac{3\pi}{2}\right)^2 + x^2} + \frac{1}{\left(\frac{5\pi}{2}\right)^2 + x^2} + \cdots \right].$$

$$\coth x = \frac{1}{x} + \frac{x}{3} - \frac{x^3}{45} + \frac{2x^5}{945} + \cdots + \frac{2^{2n}B_{2n}}{(2n)!}x^{2n-1} + \cdots \qquad (0 < |x| < \pi),$$

$$= 1 + 2e^{-2x} + 2e^{-4x} + 2e^{-6x} + \cdots \qquad (\text{Re } x > 0),$$

$$= \frac{1}{x} + 2x \left[\frac{1}{\pi^2 + x^2} + \frac{1}{(2\pi)^2 + x^2} + \frac{1}{(3\pi)^2 + x^2} + \cdots \right] \qquad (\text{Re } x > 0).$$

$$\text{sech } x = 1 - \frac{1}{2!}x^2 + \frac{5}{4!}x^4 - \frac{61}{6!}x^6 + \cdots + \frac{E_{2n}}{(2n)!}x^{2n} + \cdots$$

$$(|x| < \pi/2, \ E_n \text{ is the } n^{\text{th}} \text{ Euler number}),$$

$$= 2 \left(e^{-x} - e^{-3x} + e^{-5x} - e^{-7x} + \cdots \right) \qquad (\text{Re } x > 0),$$

$$= 4\pi \left[\frac{1}{\pi^2 + 4x^2} - \frac{3}{(3\pi)^2 + 4x^2} + \frac{5}{(5\pi)^2 + 4x^2} + \cdots \right].$$

$$\text{csch } x = \frac{1}{x} - \frac{x}{6} + \frac{7x^3}{360} + \cdots + \frac{2(2^{2n-1} - 1)B_{2n}}{(2n)!}x^{2n-1} + \cdots \qquad (0 < |x| < \pi),$$

$$= 2 \left(e^{-x} + e^{-3x} + e^{-5x} + e^{-7x} + \cdots \right) \qquad (\text{Re } x > 0),$$

$$= \frac{1}{x} - \frac{2x}{\pi^2 + x^2} + \frac{2x}{(2\pi)^2 + x^2} - \frac{2x}{(3\pi)^2 + x^2} + \cdots.$$

$$\sinh nu = \sinh u \left[(2\cosh u)^{n-1} - \frac{(n-2)}{1!}(2\cosh u)^{n-3} \right.$$

$$+ \frac{(n-3)(n-4)}{2!}(2\cosh u)^{n-5}$$

$$\left. - \frac{(n-4)(n-5)(n-6)}{3!}(2\cosh u)^{n-7} + \cdots \right].$$

$$\cosh nu = \frac{1}{2}\Big[(2\cosh u)^n - \frac{n}{1!}(2\cosh u)^{n-2} + \frac{n(n-3)}{2!}(2\cosh u)^{n-4}$$
$$- \frac{n(n-4)(n-5)}{3!}(2\cosh u)^{n-6} + \cdots\Big].$$

Inverse hyperbolic functions

$$\sinh^{-1} x = x - \frac{1}{2\cdot 3}x^3 + \frac{1\cdot 3}{2\cdot 4\cdot 5}x^5 - \frac{1\cdot 3\cdot 5}{2\cdot 4\cdot 6\cdot 7}x^7 + \cdots \qquad (|x| < 1),$$

$$= \log(2x) + \frac{1}{2}\cdot\frac{1}{2x^2} + \frac{1\cdot 3}{2\cdot 4}\cdot\frac{1}{4x^4} + \frac{1\cdot 3\cdot 5}{2\cdot 4\cdot 6}\cdot\frac{1}{6x^6} + \cdots \qquad (|x| > 1).$$

$$\cosh^{-1} x = \pm\Big[\log(2x) - \frac{1}{2}\cdot\frac{1}{2x^2} - \frac{1\cdot 3}{2\cdot 4}\cdot\frac{1}{4x^4} + \cdots\Big] \qquad (x > 1).$$

$$\operatorname{csch}^{-1} x = \frac{1}{x} - \frac{1}{2}\cdot\frac{1}{3x^3} - \frac{1\cdot 3}{2\cdot 4}\cdot\frac{1}{5x^5} - \frac{1\cdot 3\cdot 5}{2\cdot 4\cdot 6}\cdot\frac{1}{7x^7} + \cdots \qquad (|x| > 1),$$

$$= \log\frac{2}{x} + \frac{1}{2}\cdot\frac{x^2}{2} - \frac{1\cdot 3}{2\cdot 4}\cdot\frac{x^4}{4} + \frac{1\cdot 3\cdot 5}{2\cdot 4\cdot 6}\cdot\frac{x^6}{6} - \cdots \qquad (0 < x < 1).$$

$$\operatorname{sech}^{-1} x = \log\frac{2}{x} - \frac{1}{2}\cdot\frac{x^2}{2} - \frac{1\cdot 3}{2\cdot 4}\cdot\frac{x^4}{4} - \frac{1\cdot 3\cdot 5}{2\cdot 4\cdot 6}\cdot\frac{x^6}{6} - \cdots \qquad (0 < x < 1).$$

$$\tanh^{-1} x = x + \frac{x^3}{3} + \frac{x^5}{5} + \frac{x^7}{7} + \cdots + \frac{x^{2n+1}}{2n+1} + \cdots \qquad (|x| < 1).$$

$$\coth^{-1} x = \frac{1}{x} + \frac{1}{3x^3} + \frac{1}{5x^5} + \frac{1}{7x^7} + \cdots + \frac{1}{(2n+1)x^{2n+1}} + \cdots \qquad (|x| > 1).$$

$$\operatorname{gd} x = x - \frac{1}{6}x^3 + \frac{1}{24}x^5 + \cdots + \frac{E_{2n}}{(2n+1)!}x^{2n+1} + \cdots \qquad (|x| < 1).$$

1.3.11   INFINITE PRODUCTS

For the sequence of complex numbers $\{a_k\}$, the infinite product is defined as $\prod_{k=1}^{\infty}(1 + a_k)$. A necessary condition for convergence is that $\lim_{n\to\infty} a_n = 0$. A necessary and sufficient condition for convergence is that $\sum_{k=1}^{\infty}\log(1 + a_k)$ converges. Examples:

- $$z! = \prod_{k=1}^{\infty}\frac{(1 + \frac{1}{k})^z}{1 + \frac{z}{k}}$$

- $$\sin z = z\prod_{k=1}^{\infty}\cos\frac{z}{2^k}$$

- $$\sin \pi z = \pi z\prod_{k=1}^{\infty}\Big(1 - \frac{z^2}{k^2}\Big)$$

- $$\cos \pi z = \prod_{k=1}^{\infty}\Big(1 - \frac{z^2}{(k - \frac{1}{2})^2}\Big)$$

- $\sin(a+z) = (\sin a) \displaystyle\prod_{k=0,\pm1,\pm2,\ldots}^{\infty} \left(1 + \dfrac{z}{a+k\pi}\right)$

- $\cos(a+z) = (\cos a) \displaystyle\prod_{k=\pm1,\pm3,\pm5,\ldots}^{\infty} \left(1 + \dfrac{2z}{2a+k\pi}\right)$

- $\sinh z = z \displaystyle\prod_{k=1}^{\infty} \left(1 + \dfrac{z^2}{k^2\pi^2}\right)$

- $\cosh z = \displaystyle\prod_{k=0}^{\infty} \left(1 + \dfrac{4z^2}{(2k+1)^2\pi^2}\right)$

Weierstrass theorem

Define $E(w,m) = (1-w)\exp\left(w + \dfrac{w^2}{2} + \cdots + \dfrac{w^m}{m}\right)$. For $k = 1, 2, \ldots$ let $\{b_k\}$ be a sequence of complex numbers such that $|b_k| \to \infty$. Then the infinite product $P(z) = \displaystyle\prod_{k=1}^{\infty} E\left(\dfrac{z}{b_k}, k\right)$ is an entire function with zeros at b_k and at these points only. The multiplicity of the root at b_n is equal to the number of indices j such that $b_j = b_n$.

1.3.12 INFINITE PRODUCTS AND INFINITE SERIES

1. The Rogers–Ramanujan identities (for $a = 0$ or $a = 1$) are

$$1 + \sum_{k=1}^{\infty} \frac{q^{k^2+ak}}{(1-q)(1-q^2)\cdots(1-q^k)}$$
$$= \prod_{j=0}^{\infty} \frac{1}{(1-q^{5j+a+1})(1-q^{5j-a+4})}. \tag{1.3.4}$$

2. Jacobi's triple product identity is

$$\sum_{k=-\infty}^{\infty} q^{\binom{k}{2}} x^k = \prod_{j=1}^{\infty} (1-q^j)(1+x^{-1}q^j)(1+xq^{j-1}). \tag{1.3.5}$$

3. The quintuple product identity is

$$\sum_{k=-\infty}^{\infty} (-1)^k q^{(3k^2-k)/2} x^{3k}(1+xq^k)$$
$$= \prod_{j=1}^{\infty} (1-q^j)(1+x^{-1}q^j)(1+xq^{j-1})(1+x^{-2}q^{2j-1})(1+x^2q^{2j-1}). \tag{1.3.6}$$

1.4 FOURIER SERIES

If $f(x)$ is a bounded periodic function of period $2L$ (that is, $f(x + 2L) = f(x)$) and satisfies the Dirichlet conditions,

1. In any period, $f(x)$ is continuous, except possibly for a finite number of jump discontinuities.
2. In any period $f(x)$ has only a finite number of maxima and minima.

Then $f(x)$ may be represented by the Fourier series,

$$f(x) = \frac{a_0}{2} + \sum_{n=1}^{\infty} \left(a_n \cos \frac{n\pi x}{L} + b_n \sin \frac{n\pi x}{L} \right), \tag{1.4.1}$$

where $\{a_n\}$ and $\{b_n\}$ are determined as follows:

$$
\begin{aligned}
a_n &= \frac{1}{L} \int_{\alpha}^{\alpha+2L} f(x) \cos \frac{n\pi x}{L} \, dx \qquad \text{for } n = 0, 1, 2, \ldots, \\
&= \frac{1}{L} \int_{0}^{2L} f(x) \cos \frac{n\pi x}{L} \, dx, \\
&= \frac{1}{L} \int_{-L}^{L} f(x) \cos \frac{n\pi x}{L} \, dx;
\end{aligned}
\tag{1.4.2}
$$

$$
\begin{aligned}
b_n &= \frac{1}{L} \int_{\alpha}^{\alpha+2L} f(x) \sin \frac{n\pi x}{L} \, dx \qquad \text{for } n = 1, 2, 3, \ldots, \\
&= \frac{1}{L} \int_{0}^{2L} f(x) \sin \frac{n\pi x}{L} \, dx, \\
&= \frac{1}{L} \int_{-L}^{L} f(x) \sin \frac{n\pi x}{L} \, dx,
\end{aligned}
\tag{1.4.3}
$$

where α is any real number (the second and third lines of each formula represent $\alpha = 0$ and $\alpha = L$ respectively).

The series in Equation (1.4.1) will converge (in the Cesaro sense) to every point where $f(x)$ is continuous, and to $\dfrac{f(x^+) + f(x^-)}{2}$ (i.e., the average of the left hand and right hand limits) at every point where $f(x)$ has a jump discontinuity.

1.4.1 SPECIAL CASES

1. If, in addition to the Dirichlet conditions, $f(x)$ is an even function (i.e., $f(x) = f(-x)$), then the Fourier series becomes

$$f(x) = \frac{a_0}{2} + \sum_{n=1}^{\infty} a_n \cos \frac{n\pi x}{L}. \tag{1.4.4}$$

That is, every $b_n = 0$. In this case, the $\{a_n\}$ may be determined from

$$a_n = \frac{2}{L} \int_0^L f(x) \cos \frac{n\pi x}{L} \, dx \qquad n = 0, 1, 2, \dots. \qquad (1.4.5)$$

If, in addition to the above requirements, $f(x) = f(L-x)$, then a_n will be zero for all even values of n. In this case the expansion becomes

$$f(x) = \sum_{m=1}^{\infty} a_{2m-1} \cos \frac{(2m-1)\pi x}{L}. \qquad (1.4.6)$$

2. If, in addition to the Dirichlet conditions, $f(x)$ is an odd function (i.e., $f(x) = -f(-x)$), then the Fourier series becomes

$$f(x) = \sum_{n=1}^{\infty} b_n \sin \frac{n\pi x}{L}. \qquad (1.4.7)$$

That is, every $a_n = 0$. In this case, the $\{b_n\}$ may be determined from

$$b_n = \frac{2}{L} \int_0^L f(x) \sin \frac{n\pi x}{L} \, dx \qquad n = 1, 2, 3, \dots. \qquad (1.4.8)$$

If, in addition to the above requirements, $f(x) = f(L-x)$, then b_n will be zero for all even values of n. In this case the expansion becomes

$$f(x) = \sum_{m=1}^{\infty} b_{2m-1} \sin \frac{(2m-1)\pi x}{L}. \qquad (1.4.9)$$

The series in Equation (1.4.6) and Equation (1.4.9) are known as odd harmonic series, since only the odd harmonics appear. Similar rules may be stated for even harmonic series, but when a series appears in even harmonic form, it means that $2L$ has not been taken to be the smallest period of $f(x)$. Since any integral multiple of a period is also a period, series obtained in this way will also work, but, in general, computation is simplified if $2L$ is taken as the least period.

Writing the trigonometric functions in terms of complex exponentials, we obtain the complex form of the Fourier series known as the *complex Fourier series* or as the *exponential Fourier series*. It is represented by

$$f(x) = \sum_{n=-\infty}^{\infty} c_n e^{i\omega_n x} \qquad (1.4.10)$$

where $\omega_n = \dfrac{n\pi}{L}$ for $n = 0, \pm 1, \pm 2, \dots$ and the $\{c_n\}$ are determined from

$$c_n = \frac{1}{2L} \int_{-L}^{L} f(x) e^{-i\omega_n x} \, dx. \qquad (1.4.11)$$

The set of coefficients $\{c_n\}$ is often referred to as the *Fourier spectrum*.

1.4.2   ALTERNATE FORMS

The Fourier series in Equation (1.4.1) may be represented in the alternate forms:

1. When $\phi_n = \tan^{-1}(-a_n/b_n)$, $a_n = c_n \sin \phi_n$, $b_n = -c_n \cos \phi_n$, and $c_n = \sqrt{a_n^2 + b_n^2}$, then

$$f(x) = \frac{a_0}{2} + \sum_{n=1}^{\infty} c_n \sin \left(\frac{n\pi x}{L} + \phi_n \right). \tag{1.4.12}$$

2. When $\phi_n = \tan^{-1}(a_n/b_n)$, $a_n = c_n \sin \phi_n$, $b_n = c_n \cos \phi_n$, and $c_n = \sqrt{a_n^2 + b_n^2}$, then

$$f(x) = \frac{a_0}{2} + \sum_{n=1}^{\infty} c_n \cos \left(\frac{n\pi x}{L} + \phi_n \right). \tag{1.4.13}$$

1.4.3   USEFUL SERIES

$$1 = \frac{4}{\pi} \left[\sin \frac{\pi x}{k} + \frac{1}{3} \sin \frac{3\pi x}{k} + \frac{1}{5} \sin \frac{5\pi x}{k} + \dots \right] \qquad [0 < x < k].$$

$$x = \frac{2k}{\pi} \left[\sin \frac{\pi x}{k} - \frac{1}{2} \sin \frac{2\pi x}{k} + \frac{1}{3} \sin \frac{3\pi x}{k} + \dots \right] \qquad [-k < x < k].$$

$$x = \frac{k}{2} - \frac{4k}{\pi^2} \left[\cos \frac{\pi x}{k} + \frac{1}{3^2} \cos \frac{3\pi x}{k} + \frac{1}{5^2} \cos \frac{5\pi x}{k} + \dots \right] \qquad [0 < x < k].$$

$$x^2 = \frac{2k^2}{\pi^3} \left[\left(\frac{\pi^2}{1} - \frac{4}{1} \right) \sin \frac{\pi x}{k} - \frac{\pi^2}{2} \sin \frac{2\pi x}{k} + \left(\frac{\pi^2}{3} - \frac{4}{3^3} \right) \sin \frac{3\pi x}{k} \right.$$
$$\left. - \frac{\pi^2}{4} \sin \frac{4\pi x}{k} + \left(\frac{\pi^2}{5} - \frac{4}{5^3} \right) \sin \frac{5\pi x}{k} \dots \right] \qquad [0 < x < k].$$

$$x^2 = \frac{k^2}{3} - \frac{4k^2}{\pi^2} \left[\cos \frac{\pi x}{k} - \frac{1}{2^2} \cos \frac{2\pi x}{k} + \frac{1}{3^2} \cos \frac{3\pi x}{k} - \frac{1}{4^2} \cos \frac{4\pi x}{k} + \dots \right]$$
$$[-k < x < k]$$

$$1 - \frac{1}{3} + \frac{1}{5} - \frac{1}{7} + \dots = \frac{\pi}{4}.$$
$$1 + \frac{1}{2^2} + \frac{1}{3^2} + \frac{1}{4^2} + \dots = \frac{\pi^2}{6}.$$
$$1 - \frac{1}{2^2} + \frac{1}{3^2} - \frac{1}{4^2} + \dots = \frac{\pi^2}{12}. \tag{1.4.14}$$
$$1 + \frac{1}{3^2} + \frac{1}{5^2} + \frac{1}{7^2} + \dots = \frac{\pi^2}{8}.$$
$$\frac{1}{2^2} + \frac{1}{4^2} + \frac{1}{6^2} + \frac{1}{8^2} + \dots = \frac{\pi^2}{24}.$$

1.4.4 EXPANSIONS OF BASIC PERIODIC FUNCTIONS

- $f(x) = \dfrac{4}{\pi} \displaystyle\sum_{n=1,3,5,\ldots} \dfrac{1}{n} \sin \dfrac{n\pi x}{L}$

- $f(x) = \dfrac{2}{\pi} \displaystyle\sum_{n=1}^{\infty} \dfrac{(-1)^n}{n} \left(\cos \dfrac{n\pi c}{L} - 1\right) \sin \dfrac{n\pi x}{L}$

- $f(x) = \dfrac{c}{L} + \dfrac{2}{\pi} \displaystyle\sum_{n=1}^{\infty} \dfrac{(-1)^n}{n} \sin \dfrac{n\pi c}{L} \cos \dfrac{n\pi x}{L}$

- $f(x) = \dfrac{2}{L} \displaystyle\sum_{n=1}^{\infty} \sin \dfrac{n\pi}{2} \dfrac{\sin(n\pi c/2L)}{n\pi c/2L} \sin \dfrac{n\pi x}{L}$

- $f(x) = \dfrac{2}{\pi} \displaystyle\sum_{n=1}^{\infty} \dfrac{(-1)^{n+1}}{n} \sin \dfrac{n\pi x}{L}$

- $f(x) = \dfrac{1}{2} - \dfrac{4}{\pi^2} \displaystyle\sum_{n=1,3,5,\ldots} \dfrac{1}{n^2} \cos \dfrac{n\pi x}{L}$

- $f(x) = \dfrac{8}{\pi^2} \displaystyle\sum_{n=1,3,5,\ldots} \dfrac{(-1)^{(n-1)/2}}{n^2} \sin \dfrac{n\pi x}{L}$

- $f(x) = \dfrac{1}{2} - \dfrac{1}{\pi} \displaystyle\sum_{n=1}^{\infty} \dfrac{1}{n} \sin \dfrac{n\pi x}{L}$

- $f(x) = \dfrac{1+a}{2} + \dfrac{2}{\pi^2(1-a)} \displaystyle\sum_{n=1}^{\infty} \dfrac{1}{n^2} \left[(-1)^n \cos n\pi a - 1\right] \cos \dfrac{n\pi x}{L}$ $\qquad \left(a = \dfrac{c}{2L}\right)$

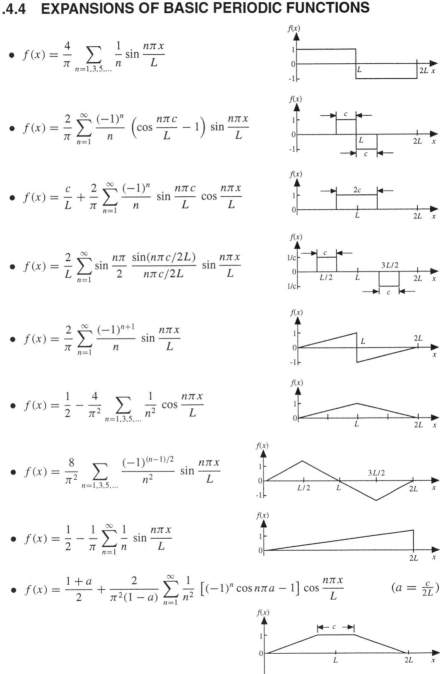

- $f(x) = \dfrac{2}{\pi} \sum_{n=1}^{\infty} \dfrac{(-1)^{n-1}}{n} \left[1 + \dfrac{\sin n\pi a}{n\pi(1-a)} \right] \sin \dfrac{n\pi x}{L}$ $\left(a = \dfrac{c}{2L} \right)$

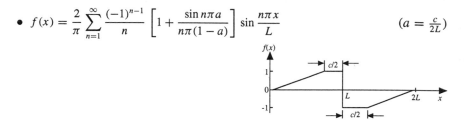

- $f(x) = \dfrac{1}{2} - \dfrac{4}{\pi^2(1-2a)} \sum_{n=1,3,5,\ldots} \dfrac{1}{n^2} \cos n\pi a \, \cos \dfrac{n\pi x}{L}$ $\left(a = \dfrac{c}{2L} \right)$

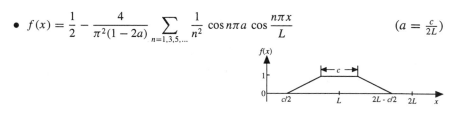

- $f(x) = \dfrac{2}{\pi} \sum_{n=1}^{\infty} \dfrac{(-1)^n}{n} \left[1 + \dfrac{1+(-1)^n}{n\pi(1-2a)} \sin n\pi a \right] \sin \dfrac{n\pi x}{L}$ $\left(a = \dfrac{c}{2L} \right)$

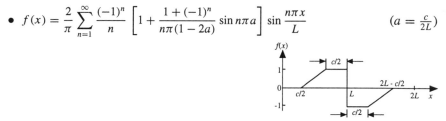

- $f(x) = \dfrac{4}{\pi} \sum_{n=1}^{\infty} \dfrac{1}{n} \sin \dfrac{n\pi}{4} \sin n\pi a \, \sin \dfrac{n\pi x}{L}$ $\left(a = \dfrac{c}{2L} \right)$

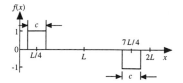

- $f(x) = \dfrac{9}{\pi^2} \sum_{n=1}^{\infty} \dfrac{1}{n^2} \sin \dfrac{n\pi a}{3} \sin \dfrac{n\pi x}{L}$ $\left(a = \dfrac{c}{2L} \right)$

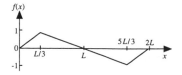

- $f(x) = \dfrac{32}{3\pi^2} \sum_{n=1}^{\infty} \dfrac{1}{n^2} \sin \dfrac{n\pi a}{4} \sin \dfrac{n\pi x}{L}$ $\left(a = \dfrac{c}{2L} \right)$

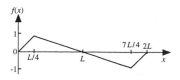

- $f(x) = \dfrac{1}{\pi} + \dfrac{1}{2} \sin \omega t - \dfrac{2}{\pi} \displaystyle\sum_{n=2,4,6,\dots} \dfrac{1}{n^2 - 1} \cos n\omega t$

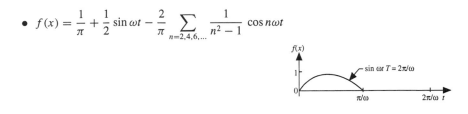

1.5 COMPLEX ANALYSIS

1.5.1 DEFINITIONS

A complex number z has the form $z = x + iy$ where x and y are real numbers, and $i = \sqrt{-1}$; the number i is sometimes called the imaginary unit. We write $x = \text{Re } z$ and $y = \text{Im } z$. The number x is called the *real* part of z and y is called the *imaginary* part of z. This form is also called the *Cartesian form* of the complex number.

Complex numbers can also be written in *polar form*, $z = re^{i\theta}$, where r, called the *modulus*, is given by $r = |z| = \sqrt{x^2 + y^2}$, and θ is called the *argument*: $\theta = \arg z = \tan^{-1}\frac{y}{x}$. The geometric relationship between Cartesian and polar forms is shown below

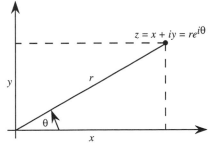

The *complex conjugate* of z, denoted $\bar{z}$, is defined as $\bar{z} = x - iy = re^{-i\theta}$. Note that $|z| = |\bar{z}|$, $\arg \bar{z} = -\arg z$, and $|z| = \sqrt{z\bar{z}}$. In addition, $\bar{\bar{z}} = z$, $\overline{z_1 + z_2} = \bar{z}_1 + \bar{z}_2$, and $\overline{z_1 z_2} = \bar{z}_1 \bar{z}_2$.

1.5.2 OPERATIONS ON COMPLEX NUMBERS

Addition and subtraction:

$$z_1 \pm z_2 = (x_1 + iy_1) \pm (x_2 + iy_2) = (x_1 \pm x_2) + i(y_1 \pm y_2).$$

Multiplication:

$$z_1 z_2 = (x_1 + iy_1)(x_2 + iy_2) = (x_1 x_2 - y_1 y_2) + i(x_1 y_2 + x_2 y_1) = r_1 r_2 e^{i(\theta_1 + \theta_2)}.$$

$$|z_1 z_2| = |z_1||z_2|, \qquad \arg(z_1 z_2) = \arg z_1 + \arg z_2 = \theta_1 + \theta_2.$$

Division:

$$\frac{z_1}{z_2} = \frac{z_1 \bar{z}_2}{z_2 \bar{z}_2} = \frac{(x_1 x_2 + y_1 y_2) + i(x_2 y_1 - x_1 y_2)}{x_2^2 + y_2^2} = \frac{r_1}{r_2} e^{i(\theta_1 - \theta_2)}.$$

$$\left|\frac{z_1}{z_2}\right| = \frac{|z_1|}{|z_2|}, \qquad \arg\left(\frac{z_1}{z_2}\right) = \arg z_1 - \arg z_2 = \theta_1 - \theta_2.$$

1.5.3   POWERS AND ROOTS OF COMPLEX NUMBERS

Powers:
$z^n = r^n e^{in\theta} = r^n (\cos n\theta + i \sin n\theta)$ *DeMoivre's Theorem.*

Roots:

$$z^{1/n} = r^{1/n} e^{i\theta/n} = r^{1/n}\left(\cos\frac{\theta + 2k\pi}{n} + i \sin\frac{\theta + 2k\pi}{n}\right), \quad k = 0, 1, 2, \ldots, n-1.$$

The *principal root* has $-\pi < \theta \leq \pi$ and $k = 0$.

1.5.4   FUNCTIONS OF A COMPLEX VARIABLE

A complex function

$$w = f(z) = u(x, y) + iv(x, y) = |w|e^{i\phi},$$

where $z = x + iy$, associates one or more values of the complex dependent variable w with each value of the complex independent variable z for those values of z in a given domain.

1.5.5   CAUCHY–RIEMANN EQUATIONS

A function $w = f(z)$ is said to be *analytic* at a point z_0 if it is differentiable in a neighborhood (i.e., at each point of a circle centered on z_0 with an arbitrarily small radius) of z_0. That is, $\lim_{h\to 0} \frac{f(z_0+h)-f(z_0)}{h}$ exists. A function is called *analytic* in a connected domain if it is analytic at every point in that domain.

A necessary and sufficient condition for $f(z) = u(x, y) + iv(x, y)$ to be analytic is that it satisfy the Cauchy–Riemann equations,

$$\frac{\partial u}{\partial x} = \frac{\partial v}{\partial y}, \quad \text{and} \quad \frac{\partial u}{\partial y} = -\frac{\partial v}{\partial x}. \tag{1.5.1}$$

Examples:

1. $f(z) = z^n$ is analytic everywhere when n is a nonnegative integer. If n is a negative integer, then $f(z)$ is analytic except at the origin.
2. $f(z) = \bar{z}$ is nowhere analytic.
3. $f(z) = e^z$ is analytic everywhere.

1.5.6 CAUCHY INTEGRAL THEOREM

If $f(z)$ is analytic at all points within and on a simple closed curve C, then

$$\int_C f(z)\,dz = 0. \qquad (1.5.2)$$

1.5.7 CAUCHY INTEGRAL FORMULA

If $f(z)$ is analytic inside and on a simple closed contour C and if z_0 is interior to C, then

$$f(z_0) = \frac{1}{2\pi i} \int_C \frac{f(z)}{z - z_0}\,dz. \qquad (1.5.3)$$

Moreover, if the derivatives $f'(z)$, $f''(z)$, ... of all orders exist, then

$$f^{(n)}(z_0) = \frac{n!}{2\pi i} \int_C \frac{f(z)}{(z - z_0)^{n+1}}\,dz. \qquad (1.5.4)$$

1.5.8 TAYLOR SERIES EXPANSIONS

If $f(z)$ is analytic inside of and on a circle C of radius r centered at the point z_0, then a unique and uniformly convergent series expansion exists in powers of $(z - z_0)$ of the form

$$f(z) = \sum_{n=0}^{\infty} a_n(z - z_0)^n, \quad |z - z_0| < r, \quad z_0 \neq \infty, \qquad (1.5.5)$$

where

$$a_n = \frac{1}{n!} f^{(n)}(z_0) = \frac{1}{2\pi i} \int_C \frac{f(z)}{(z - z_0)^{n+1}}\,dz. \qquad (1.5.6)$$

If $M(r)$ is an upper bound of $|f(z)|$ on C, then

$$|a_n| = \frac{1}{n!}|f^{(n)}(z_0)| \le \frac{M(r)}{r^n} \quad \text{(Cauchy's inequality).} \qquad (1.5.7)$$

If the series is truncated with the term $a_n(z - z_0)^n$, the remainder $R_n(z)$ is given by

$$R_n(z) = \frac{(z - z_0)^{n+1}}{2\pi i} \int_C \frac{f(s)}{(s - z)(s - z_0)^{n+1}}\,ds, \qquad (1.5.8)$$

and

$$|R_n(z)| \le \left(\frac{|z - z_0|}{r} \right)^n \frac{r M(r)}{r - |z - z_0|}. \qquad (1.5.9)$$

1.5.9   LAURENT SERIES EXPANSIONS

If $f(z)$ is analytic inside the annular domain between the concentric circles C_1 and C_2 centered at z_0 with radii r_1 and r_2 ($r_1 < r_2$), respectively, then a unique series expansion exists in terms of positive and negative powers of $z - z_0$ of the following form:

$$f(z) = \sum_{n=1}^{\infty} b_n (z - z_0)^{-n} + \sum_{n=0}^{\infty} a_n (z - z_0)^n,$$

$$= \cdots + \frac{b_2}{(z - z_0)^2} + \frac{b_1}{z - z_0} + a_0 + a_1(z - z_0) + a_2(z - z_0)^2 + \cdots$$

$$(1.5.10)$$

where

$$a_n = \frac{1}{2\pi i} \int_C \frac{f(s)}{(s - z_0)^{n+1}} \, ds, \quad n = 0, 1, 2, \ldots, \tag{1.5.11}$$

and

$$b_n = \frac{1}{2\pi i} \int_C f(s)(s - z_0)^{n-1} \, ds, \quad n = 1, 2, 3, \ldots. \tag{1.5.12}$$

1.5.10   ZEROS AND SINGULARITIES

The points z for which $f(z) = 0$ are called *zeros* of $f(z)$. A function $f(z)$ which is analytic at z_0 has a zero of order m there, where m is a positive integer, if and only if the first m coefficients $a_0, a_1, \ldots, a_{m-1}$ in the Taylor expansion about z_0 vanish.

A singular point or *singularity* of the function $f(z)$ is any point at which $f(z)$ is not analytic. An *isolated singularity* of $f(z)$ at z_0 may be classified in one of three ways:

1. A *removable* singularity if and only if all coefficients b_n in the Laurent series expansion of $f(z)$ about z_0 vanish.

2. A *pole* of order m if and only if $(z - z_0)^m f(z)$, but not $(z - z_0)^{m-1} f(z)$, is analytic at z_0, (i.e., if and only if $b_m \neq 0$ and $0 = b_{m+1} = b_{m+2} = \ldots$ in the Laurent series expansion of $f(z)$ about z_0). Equivalently, $f(z)$ has a pole of order m if $1/f(z)$ is analytic at z_0 and has a zero of order m there.

3. An isolated *essential singularity* if and only if the Laurent series expansion of $f(z)$ about z_0 has an infinite number of terms involving negative powers of $z - z_0$.

1.5.11 RESIDUES

Given a point z_0 where $f(z)$ is either analytic or has an isolated singularity, the *residue* of $f(z)$ is the coefficient of $(z - z_0)^{-1}$ in the Laurent series expansion of $f(z)$ about z_0, or

$$\text{Res}(z_0) = b_1 = \frac{1}{2\pi i} \int_C f(z)\, dz. \tag{1.5.13}$$

If $f(z)$ is either analytic or has a removable singularity at z_0, then $b_1 = 0$ there. If z_0 is a pole of order m, then

$$b_1 = \frac{1}{(m-1)!} \frac{d^{m-1}}{dz^{m-1}} \left[(z - z_0)^m f(z) \right]\big|_{z=z_0}. \tag{1.5.14}$$

For every simple closed contour C enclosing at most a finite number of singularities $z_1, z_2, \ldots, z_n$ of an analytic function continuous on C,

$$\int_C f(z)\, dz = 2\pi i \sum_{k=1}^{n} \text{Res}(z_k), \tag{1.5.15}$$

where $\text{Res}(z_k)$ is the residue of $f(z)$ at z_k.

1.5.12 THE ARGUMENT PRINCIPLE

Let $f(z)$ be analytic on a simple closed curve C with no zeros on C and analytic everywhere inside C except possibly at a finite number of poles. Let $\Delta_C \arg f(z)$ denote the change in the argument of $f(z)$ (final value − initial value) as z transverses the curve once in the positive sense. Then

$$\frac{1}{2\pi} \Delta_C \arg f(z) = N - P, \tag{1.5.16}$$

where N is number of zeros of $f(z)$ inside C, and P is the number of poles inside C. The zeros and poles are counted according to their multiplicities.

1.5.13   TRANSFORMATIONS AND MAPPINGS

A function $w = f(z) = u(z) + iv(z)$ maps points of the z-plane into corresponding points of the w-plane. At every point z such that $f(z)$ is analytic and $f'(z) \neq 0$, the mapping is *conformal*, i.e., the angle between two curves in the z-plane through such a point is reproduced in magnitude and sense by the angle between the corresponding curves in the w-plane. A table giving real and imaginary parts, zeros, and singularities for frequently used functions of a complex variable and a table illustrating a number of special transformations of interest are at the end of this section.

A function is said to be simple in a domain D if it is analytic in D and assumes no value more than once in D. *Riemann's mapping theorem* states

> If D is a simply connected domain in the complex z plane, which is neither the z plane nor the extended z plane, then there is a simple function $f(z)$ such that $w = f(z)$ maps D onto the disc $|w| < 1$.

1.5.14   BILINEAR TRANSFORMATIONS

The *bilinear* transformation is defined by $w = \dfrac{az + b}{cz + d}$, where a, b, c, and d are complex numbers and $ad \neq bc$. It is also known as the *Möbius* or *linear fractional* transformation. The bilinear transformation is defined for all $z \neq -d/c$. The bilinear transformation is conformal and maps circles and lines into circles and lines.

The inverse transformation is given by $z = \dfrac{-dw + b}{cw - a}$, which is also a bilinear transformation. Note that $w \neq a/c$.

The *cross ratio* of four distinct complex numbers z_k (for $k = 1, 2, 3, 4$) is given by

$$(z_1, z_2, z_3, z_4) = \frac{(z_1 - z_2)(z_3 - z_4)}{(z_1 - z_4)(z_3 - z_2)}.$$

If any of the z_k is complex infinity, the cross ratio is redefined so that the quotient of the two terms on the right containing z_k is equal to 1. Under the bilinear transformation, the cross ratio of four points is invariant: $(w_1, w_2, w_3, w_4) = (z_1, z_2, z_3, z_4)$.

1.5.15 TABLE OF TRANSFORMATIONS

$f(z) = w(x,y)$	$u(x,y) = \operatorname{Re} w(x,y)$	$v(x,y) = \operatorname{Im} w(x,y)$	Zeros (and order m)	Singularities (and order m)
z	x	y	$z=0,\ m=1$	Pole ($m=1$) at $z=\infty$
z^2	x^2-y^2	$2xy$	$z=0,\ m=2$	Pole ($m=2$) at $z=\infty$
$\dfrac{1}{z}$	$\dfrac{x}{x^2+y^2}$	$\dfrac{-y}{x^2+y^2}$	$z=\infty,\ m=1$	Pole ($m=1$) at $z=0$
$\dfrac{1}{z^2}$	$\dfrac{x^2-y^2}{(x^2+y^2)^2}$	$\dfrac{-2xy}{(x^2+y^2)^2}$	$z=\infty,\ m=2$	Pole ($m=2$) at $z=0$
$\dfrac{1}{z-(a+ib)}$ a,b real	$\dfrac{x-a}{(x-a)^2+(y-b)^2}$	$\dfrac{-(y-b)}{(x-a)^2+(y-b)^2}$	$z=\infty,\ m=1$	Pole ($m=1$) at $z=a+ib$
$\sqrt{z}$	$\pm\left(\dfrac{x+\sqrt{x^2+y^2}}{2}\right)^{1/2}$	$\pm\left(\dfrac{-x+\sqrt{x^2+y^2}}{2}\right)^{1/2}$	$z=0,\ m=1$	Branch point ($m=1$) at $z=0$ Branch point ($m=1$) at $z=\infty$
e^z	$e^x\cos y$	$e^x\sin y$	None	Essential singularity at $z=\infty$
$\sin z$	$\sin x \cosh y$	$\cos x \sinh y$	$z=k\pi,\ m=1$ $(k=0,\pm1,\pm2,\dots)$	Essential singularity at $z=\infty$
$\cos z$	$\cos x \cosh y$	$-\sin x \sinh y$	$z=(k+1/2)\pi,\ m=1$ $(k=0,\pm1,\pm2,\dots)$	Essential singularity at $z=\infty$
$\sinh z$	$\sinh x \cos y$	$\cosh x \sin y$	$z=k\pi i,\ m=1$ $(k=0,\pm1,\pm2,\dots)$	Essential singularity at $z=\infty$
$\cosh z$	$\cosh x \cos y$	$\sinh x \sin y$	$z=(k+1/2)\pi i,\ m=1$ $(k=0,\pm1,\pm2,\dots)$	Essential singularity at $z=\infty$
$\tan z$	$\dfrac{\sin 2x}{\cos 2x+\cosh 2y}$	$\dfrac{\sinh 2y}{\cos 2x+\cosh 2y}$	$z=k\pi,\ m=1$ $(k=0,\pm1,\pm2,\dots)$	Essential singularity at $z=\infty$ Poles ($m=1$) at $z=(k+1/2)\pi$ $(k=0,\pm1,\pm2,\dots)$
$\tanh z$	$\dfrac{\sinh 2x}{\cosh 2x+\cos 2y}$	$\dfrac{\sin 2y}{\cosh 2x+\cos 2y}$	$z=k\pi i,\ m=1$ $(k=0,\pm1,\pm2,\dots)$	Essential singularity at $z=\infty$ Poles ($m=1$) at $z=(k+1/2)\pi i$ $(k=0,\pm1,\pm2,\dots)$
$\log z$	$\log(x^2+y^2)/2$	$\tan^{-1}\dfrac{y}{x}+2k\pi$ $(k=0,\pm1,\pm2,\dots)$	$z=1,\ m=1$	Branch points at $z=0,\ z=\infty$

1.5.16   TABLE OF CONFORMAL MAPPINGS

In the following functions $z = x + iy$ and $w = u + iv = \rho e^{i\phi}$.

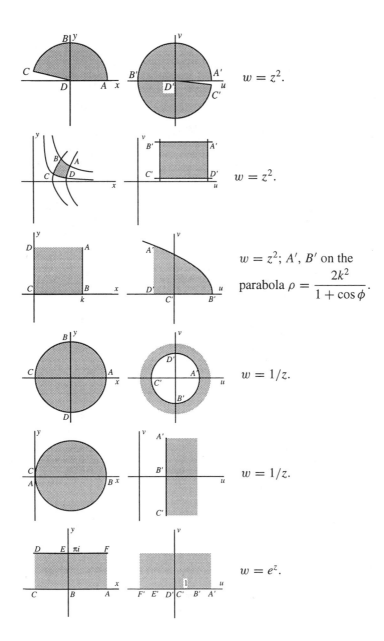

$w = z^2$.

$w = z^2$.

$w = z^2$; A', B' on the parabola $\rho = \dfrac{2k^2}{1 + \cos\phi}$.

$w = 1/z$.

$w = 1/z$.

$w = e^z$.

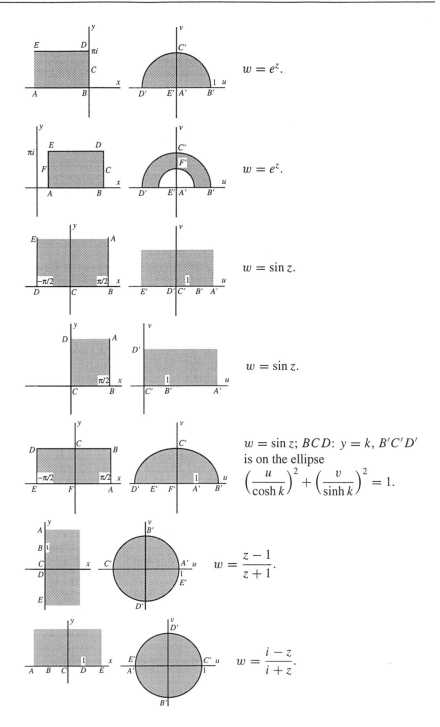

$w = e^z.$

$w = e^z.$

$w = \sin z.$

$w = \sin z.$

$w = \sin z$; BCD: $y = k$, $B'C'D'$ is on the ellipse
$$\left(\frac{u}{\cosh k}\right)^2 + \left(\frac{v}{\sinh k}\right)^2 = 1.$$

$w = \dfrac{z-1}{z+1}.$

$w = \dfrac{i-z}{i+z}.$

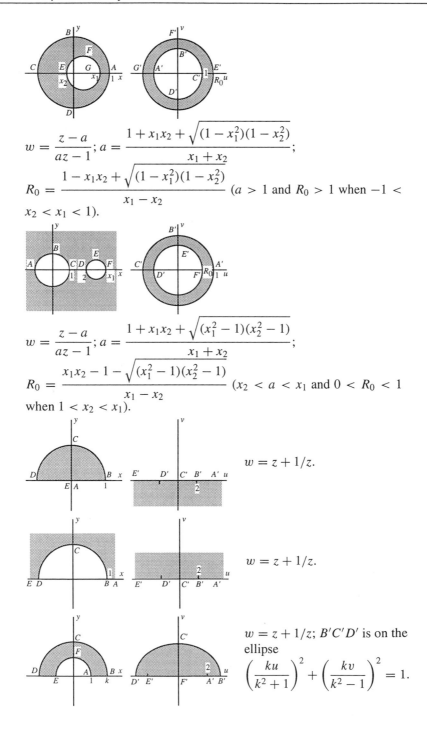

$$w = \frac{z - a}{az - 1}; \quad a = \frac{1 + x_1 x_2 + \sqrt{(1 - x_1^2)(1 - x_2^2)}}{x_1 + x_2};$$

$$R_0 = \frac{1 - x_1 x_2 + \sqrt{(1 - x_1^2)(1 - x_2^2)}}{x_1 - x_2} \quad (a > 1 \text{ and } R_0 > 1 \text{ when } -1 <$$
$$x_2 < x_1 < 1).$$

$$w = \frac{z - a}{az - 1}; \quad a = \frac{1 + x_1 x_2 + \sqrt{(x_1^2 - 1)(x_2^2 - 1)}}{x_1 + x_2};$$

$$R_0 = \frac{x_1 x_2 - 1 - \sqrt{(x_1^2 - 1)(x_2^2 - 1)}}{x_1 - x_2} \quad (x_2 < a < x_1 \text{ and } 0 < R_0 < 1$$
$$\text{when } 1 < x_2 < x_1).$$

$$w = z + 1/z.$$

$$w = z + 1/z.$$

$w = z + 1/z$; $B'C'D'$ is on the ellipse
$$\left(\frac{ku}{k^2 + 1}\right)^2 + \left(\frac{kv}{k^2 - 1}\right)^2 = 1.$$

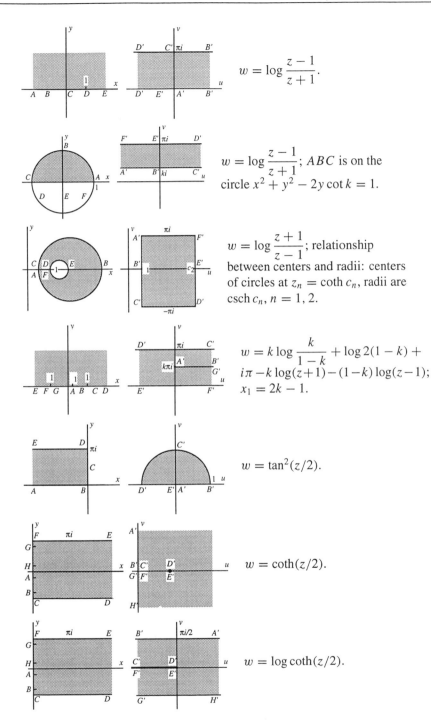

$$w = \log \frac{z-1}{z+1}.$$

$w = \log \dfrac{z-1}{z+1}$; ABC is on the circle $x^2 + y^2 - 2y \cot k = 1$.

$w = \log \dfrac{z+1}{z-1}$; relationship between centers and radii: centers of circles at $z_n = \coth c_n$, radii are $\operatorname{csch} c_n$, $n = 1, 2$.

$w = k \log \dfrac{k}{1-k} + \log 2(1-k) + i\pi - k \log(z+1) - (1-k)\log(z-1)$; $x_1 = 2k - 1$.

$w = \tan^2(z/2)$.

$w = \coth(z/2)$.

$w = \log \coth(z/2)$.

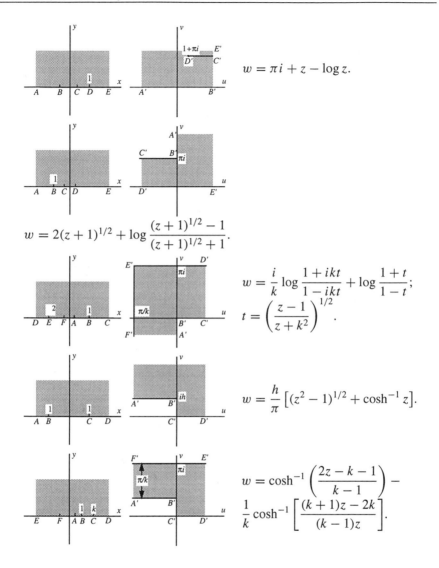

$$w = \pi i + z - \log z.$$

$$w = 2(z+1)^{1/2} + \log \frac{(z+1)^{1/2} - 1}{(z+1)^{1/2} + 1}.$$

$$w = \frac{i}{k} \log \frac{1 + ikt}{1 - ikt} + \log \frac{1 + t}{1 - t};$$
$$t = \left(\frac{z - 1}{z + k^2} \right)^{1/2}.$$

$$w = \frac{h}{\pi} \left[(z^2 - 1)^{1/2} + \cosh^{-1} z \right].$$

$$w = \cosh^{-1} \left(\frac{2z - k - 1}{k - 1} \right) - \frac{1}{k} \cosh^{-1} \left[\frac{(k+1)z - 2k}{(k-1)z} \right].$$

1.6   REAL ANALYSIS

1.6.1   RELATIONS

For two sets A and B, the *product* $A \times B$ is the set of all ordered pairs (a, b) where a is in A and b is in B. Any subset of the product $A \times B$ is called a *relation*. A relation R on a product $A \times A$ is called an *equivalence relation* if the following three properties hold:

1. *Reflexive*: (a, a) is in R for every a in A.
2. *Symmetric*: If (a, b) is in R, then (b, a) is in R.
3. *Transitive*: If (a, b) and (b, c) are in R, then (a, c) is in R.

When R is an equivalence relation then the *equivalence class* of an element a in A is the set of all b in A such that (a, b) is in R.

Example: The set of rational numbers has an equivalence relation "=" defined by the requirement that an ordered pair $(\frac{a}{b}, \frac{c}{d})$ belongs in the relation if and only if $ad = bc$. The equivalence class of $\frac{1}{2}$ is the set $\{\frac{1}{2}, \frac{2}{4}, \frac{3}{6}, \ldots \frac{-1}{-2}, \frac{-2}{-4}, \ldots\}$.

1.6.2   FUNCTIONS (MAPPINGS)

A relation f on a set $X \times Y$ is a *function* (or *mapping*) from X into Y if (x, y) and (x, z) in the relation implies that $y = z$, and each $x \in X$ has a $y \in Y$ such that (x, y) is in the relation. The last condition means that there is a unique pair in f whose first element is x. We write $f(x) = y$ to mean that (x, y) is in the relation f, and emphasize the idea of mapping by the notation $f : X \to Y$. The *domain* of a function f is the set of all x for which there is a pair (x, y) in the relation. The *range* of a function f is a set containing all the y for which there is a pair (x, y) in the relation. The *image* of a set A in the domain of a function f is the set of y in Y such that $y = f(x)$ for some x in A. The notation for the image of A under f is $f[A]$. The *inverse image* of a set B in the range of a function f is the set of all x in X such that $f(x) = y$ for some y in B. The notation is $f^{-1}[B]$.

A function f is *one-to-one* (or *univalent*, or *injective*) if $f(x_1) = f(x_2)$ implies $x_1 = x_2$. A function $f : X \to Y$ is *onto* (or *surjective*) if for every y in Y there is some x in X such that $f(x) = y$. A function is *bijective* if it is both one-to-one and onto.

Examples:

- $f(x) = e^x$, as a mapping from $\mathbb{R}$ to $\mathbb{R}$, is one-to-one because $e^{x_1} = e^{x_2}$ implies $x_1 = x_2$ (by taking the natural logarithm). It is not onto because -1 is not the value of e^x for any x in $\mathbb{R}$.

- $g(x) = x^3 - x$, as a mapping from $\mathbb{R}$ to $\mathbb{R}$, is onto because every real number is attained as a value of $g(x)$, for some x. It is not one-to-one because $g(-1) = g(0) = g(1)$.

- $h(x) = x^3$, as a mapping from $\mathbb{R}$ to $\mathbb{R}$, is bijective.

For an injective function f mapping X into Y, there is an *inverse function* f^{-1} mapping the range of f into X which is defined by: $f^{-1}(y) = x$ if and only if $f(x) = y$. Example: The function $f(x) = e^x$ mapping $\mathbb{R}$ into $\mathbb{R}^+$ (the set of positive reals) is bijective. Its inverse is $f^{-1}(x) = \ln(x)$ which maps $\mathbb{R}^+$ into $\mathbb{R}$.

For functions $f: X \rightarrow Y$ and $g: Y \rightarrow Z$, with the range of f contained in the domain of g, the *composition* $(g \circ f): X \rightarrow Z$ is a function defined by $(g \circ f)(x) = g(f(x))$ for all x in the domain of f.

1. Note that $g \circ f$ may not be the same as $f \circ g$. For example, for $f(x) = x + 1$, and $g(x) = 2x$, we have $(g \circ f)(x) = g(f(x)) = 2f(x) = 2(x + 1) = 2x + 2$. However $(f \circ g)(x) = f(g(x)) = g(x) + 1 = 2x + 1$.

2. For every function f and its inverse f^{-1}, we have $(f \circ f^{-1})(x) = x$, for all x in the domain of f^{-1}, and $(f^{-1} \circ f)(x) = x$ for all x in the domain of f. Note that the inverse function f^{-1} is not the same as $\frac{1}{f}$ (unless $f(x) = x$).

1.6.3   SETS OF REAL NUMBERS

A *sequence* is the range of a function having the natural numbers as its domain. It can be denoted by $\{x_n \mid n$ is a natural number$\}$ or simply $\{x_n\}$. For a chosen natural number N, a *finite* sequence is the range of a function having natural numbers less than N as its domain. Sets A and B are in a *one-to-one correspondence* if there is a bijective function from A into B. Two sets A and B have the same cardinality if there is a one-to-one correspondence between them. A set which is equivalent to the set of natural numbers is *denumerable* (or *countably infinite*). A set which is empty or is equivalent to a finite sequence is *finite* (or *finite countable*).

Examples: The set of letters in the English alphabet is finite. The set of rational numbers is denumerable. The set of real numbers is uncountable.

Axioms of order

1. There is a subset P (positive numbers) of $\mathbb{R}$ for which $x + y$ and xy are in P for every x and y in P.

2. Exactly one of the following conditions can be satisfied by a number x in $\mathbb{R}$ (*trichotomy*): $x \in P$, $-x \in P$, or $x = 0$.

Definitions

A number b is an *upper (lower) bound* of a subset S in $\mathbb{R}$ if $x \leq b$ ($x \geq b$) for every x in S. A number c is a *least upper bound* (*lub*, *supremum*, or *sup*) of a subset S in $\mathbb{R}$ if c is an upper bound of S and $b \geq c$ for every upper bound b of S. A number c is a *greatest lower bound (glb, infimum,* or *inf)* if c is a lower bound of S and $c \geq b$ for every lower bound b of S.

Completeness (or least upper bound) axiom

If a nonempty set of real numbers has an upper bound, then it has a least upper bound.

Characterization of the real numbers

The real numbers are the smallest complete ordered field that contain the rationals. Alternatively, the properties of a field, the order properties, and the least upper bound axiom characterize the set of real numbers. The least upper bound axiom distinguishes the set of real numbers from other ordered fields.

Archimedean property of $\mathbb{R}$: For every real number x, there is an integer N such that $x < N$. For every pair of real numbers x and y with $x < y$, there is a rational number r such that $x < r < y$. This is sometimes stated: The set of rational numbers is dense in $\mathbb{R}$.

Definitions

The *extension* of $\mathbb{R}$ by $+\infty$ is accomplished by including the symbols ∞ and $-\infty$ with the following definitions (for all $x \in \mathbb{R}$)

- $-\infty < x < \infty$, for all x in $\mathbb{R}$
- $x + \infty = \infty$, for all x in $\mathbb{R}$
- $x - \infty = -\infty$, for all x in $\mathbb{R}$
- $\frac{x}{\infty} = \frac{x}{-\infty} = 0$, for all x in $\mathbb{R}$
- $x \cdot \infty = \infty$, if $x > 0$
- $x \cdot (-\infty) = -\infty$, if $x > 0$
- $\infty + \infty = \infty$
- $-\infty - \infty = -\infty$
- $\infty \cdot \infty = \infty$
- $-\infty \cdot (-\infty) = \infty$

1.6.4 TOPOLOGY

A *topology* on a set X is a collection T of subsets of X (called open sets) having the following properties:

1. The empty set and X are in T.
2. The union of elements in an arbitrary subcollection of T is in T.
3. The intersection of elements in a finite subcollection of T is in T.

The complement of an open set is a closed set. A set is compact if every open cover has a finite subcover.

Notes

1. A subset E of X is closed if and only if E contains all its limit points.
2. The union of finitely many closed sets is closed.
3. The intersection of an arbitrary collection of closed sets is closed.
4. The image of a compact set under a continuous function is compact.

1.6.5   METRIC SPACE

A *norm* on a vector space E with scalar field $\mathbb{R}$ is a function $||\cdot||$ from E into $\mathbb{R}$ that satisfies the following conditions:

1. *Positive definiteness*: $||x|| \geq 0$ for all x in E, and $||x|| = 0$ if and only if $x = 0$.
2. *Scalar homogeneity*: For every x in E and a in $\mathbb{R}, ||ax|| = |a|\,||x||$.
3. *Triangle inequality*: $||x + y|| \leq ||x|| + ||y||$ for all x, y in E.

A *metric* (or *distance function*) on a set E is a function $\rho : E \times E \to \mathbb{R}$ that satisfies the following conditions:

1. *Positive definiteness*: $\rho(x, y) > 0$ for all x, y in E, and $\rho(x, y) = 0$ if and only if $x = y$.
2. *Symmetry*: $\rho(x, y) = \rho(y, x)$ for all x, y in E.
3. *Triangle inequality*: $\rho(x, y) \leq \rho(x, z) + \rho(z, y)$ for all x, y, z in E.

Every norm $||\cdot||$ gives rise to a metric ρ by defining: $\rho(x, y) = ||x - y||$. Examples:

1. $\mathbb{R}$ with absolute value as norm has metric $\rho(x, y) = |x - y|$.
2. $\mathbb{R} \times \mathbb{R}$ (denoted $\mathbb{R}^2$) with Euclidean norm $||(x, y)|| = \sqrt{x^2 + y^2}$, has metric $\rho((x_1, y_1), (x_2, y_2)) = \sqrt{(x_1 - x_2)^2 + (y_1 - y_2)^2}$

A δ *neighborhood* of a point x in a metric space E is the set of all y in E such that $\rho(x, y) < \delta$. For example, a δ neighborhood of x in $\mathbb{R}$ is the interval centered at x with radius δ, $(x - \delta, x + \delta)$. In a metric space the topology is generated by the δ neighborhoods.

1. A subset G of $\mathbb{R}$ is *open* if, for every x in G, there is a $\delta > 0$ such that every y in $\mathbb{R}$ with $|x - y| < \delta$ is in G also. For example, intervals (a,b), (a,∞), $(-\infty,b)$ are open in $\mathbb{R}$.
2. A number x is a *limit* (or a *point of closure,* or an *accumulation point*) of a set F if, for every $\delta > 0$, there is a point y in F such that $|x - y| < \delta$.

3. A subset F of $\mathbb{R}$ is *closed* if it contains all of its limits. For example, intervals $[a,b]$, $(-\infty, b]$, and $[a, \infty)$ are closed in $\mathbb{R}$.

4. A subset F is *dense* in $\mathbb{R}$ if every element of $\mathbb{R}$ is a limit point of F.

5. A metric space is *separable* if it contains a denumerable dense set. For example, $\mathbb{R}$ is separable because the subset of rationals is a denumerable dense set.

- (*Bolzano–Weierstrass theorem*) Any bounded infinite set of real numbers has a limit point in $\mathbb{R}$.

- (*Heine–Borel theorem*) A closed, bounded subset of $\mathbb{R}$ is compact.

1.6.6 CONVERGENCE IN $\mathbb{R}$

A number L is a *limit point* of a sequence $\{x_n\}$ if, for every $\epsilon > 0$, there is a natural number N such that $|x_n - L| < \epsilon$ for all $n > N$. If it exists, a limit point of a sequence is unique. A sequence is said to *converge* if it has a limit. A number L is a *cluster point* of a sequence $\{x_n\}$ if, for every $\epsilon > 0$, there is an index N such that $|x_n - L| < \epsilon$ for some $n > N$.

Example: The limit of a sequence is a cluster point, as in $\{\frac{1}{n}\}$, which converges to 0. However, cluster points are not necessarily limits, as in $\{(-1)^n\}$, which has cluster points $+1$ and -1 but no limit.

Limits

Let $\{x_n\}$ be a sequence. A number L is the *limit superior (limsup)* if, for every $\epsilon > 0$, there is a natural number N such that $x_n > L - \epsilon$ for infinitely many $n \geq N$, and $x_n > L + \epsilon$ for only finitely many terms. An equivalent definition of the limit superior is given by

$$\overline{\lim} \, x_n = \inf_N \sup_{k \geq N} x_k.$$

The *limit inferior (liminf)* is defined in a similar way by

$$\underline{\lim} \, x_n = \sup_N \inf_{k \geq N} x_k.$$

For example, the sequence $\{x_n\}$ with $x_n = 1 + (-1)^n + \frac{1}{2^n}$ has $\overline{\lim} \, x_n = 2$, and $\underline{\lim} \, x_n = 0$.

(*Theorem*) Every bounded sequence $\{x_n\}$ in $\mathbb{R}$ has a $\overline{\lim}$ and a $\underline{\lim}$. In addition, if $\overline{\lim} \, x_n = \underline{\lim} \, x_n$, then the sequence converges to their common value.

A sequence $\{x_n\}$ is a *Cauchy* sequence if, for any $\epsilon > 0$, there exists a positive integer N such that $|x_n - x_m| < \epsilon$ for every $n > N$ and $m > N$.

(*Theorem*) A sequence $\{x_n\}$ in $\mathbb{R}$ converges if and only if it is a Cauchy sequence. A metric space, in which every Cauchy sequence converges to a point in the space, is called *complete*. For example, $\mathbb{R}$ with the metric $\rho(x, y) = |x - y|$ is complete.

A number L is a *limit* of a function f as x approaches a number a if, for every $\epsilon > 0$, there is a $\delta > 0$ such that $|f(x) - L| < \epsilon$ for all x with $|x - a| < \delta$. This is represented by the notation $\lim_{x \to a} f(x) = L$. The symbol ∞ is the limit of a function f as x approaches a number a if, for every positive number M, there is a $\delta > 0$ such that $f(x) > M$ for all x with $|x - a| < \delta$. Notation is $\lim_{x \to a} f(x) = \infty$. A number L is a limit of a function f as x approaches ∞ if, for every $\epsilon > 0$, there is a positive number M such that $|f(x) - L| < \epsilon$ for all $x > M$; this is written $\lim_{x \to \infty} f(x) = L$. The number L is said to be the *limit at infinity*.

For example, $\lim_{x \to 2} 3x - 1 = 5$, $\lim_{x \to 0} \dfrac{1}{x^2} = \infty$, and $\lim_{x \to \infty} \dfrac{1}{x} = 0$.

Pointwise and uniform convergence

A sequence of functions $\{f_n(x)\}$ is said to *converge pointwise* to the function $f(x)$ on a set E if for every $\epsilon > 0$ and $x \in E$ there is a positive integer N such that $|f(x) - f_n(x)| < \epsilon$ for every $n \geq N$. A sequence of functions $\{f_n(x)\}$ is said to *converge uniformly* to the function f on a set E if, for every $\epsilon > 0$, there exists a positive integer N such that $|f(x) - f_n(x)| < \epsilon$ for all x in E and $n \geq N$.

Note that these formulations of convergence are not equivalent. For example, the functions $f_n(x) = x^n$ on the interval $[0, 1]$ converge pointwise to the function $f(x) = 0$ for $0 \leq x < 1$, $f(1) = 1$. They do not converge uniformly because, for $\epsilon = 1/2$, there is no N such that $|f_n(x) - f(x)| < 1/2$ for all x in $[0, 1]$ and every $n \geq N$.

A function f is *Lipschitz* if there exists $k > 0$ in $\mathbb{R}$ such that $|f(x) - f(y)| \leq k|x - y|$ for all x and y in its domain. The function is a *contraction* if $0 < k < 1$.

(*Fixed point or contraction mapping theorem*) If the function $f : [a, b] \to [a, b]$ is a contraction, then there is a unique point x in $[a, b]$ such that $f(x) = x$. The point x is called a *fixed point* of f.

Example: Newton's method for finding a zero of $f(x) = (x + 1)^2 - 2$ on the interval $[0, 1]$ produces $x_{n+1} = g(x_n)$ with the contraction $g(x) = \frac{x}{2} - \frac{1}{2} + \frac{1}{x+1}$. This has the unique fixed point $\sqrt{2} - 1$ in $[0, 1]$.

1.6.7 CONTINUITY IN $\mathbb{R}$

A function $f : \mathbb{R} \to \mathbb{R}$ is *continuous at a point a* if f is defined at a and $\lim_{x \to a} f(x) = f(a)$. The function f is *continuous on a set E* if it is continuous at every point of E. A function f is *uniformly continuous* on a set E if, for every $\epsilon > 0$, there exists a $\delta > 0$ such that $|f(x) - f(y)| < \epsilon$ for every x and y in its domain with $|x - y| < \delta$. A sequence $\{f_n(x)\}$ of continuous functions on the interval $[a, b]$ is *equicontinuous* if, for every $\epsilon > 0$, there exists a $\delta > 0$ such that $|f_n(x) - f_n(y)| < \epsilon$ for every n and for all x and y in $[a, b]$ with $|x - y| < \delta$. Examples:

1. A function can be continuous without being uniformly continuous. The function $g(x) = \frac{1}{x}$ is continuous but not uniformly continuous on the open interval $(0, 1)$.

2. A collection of continuous functions can be bounded on a closed interval without having a uniformly convergent sub-sequence. The continuous functions $f_n(x) = \frac{x^2}{x^2 + (1 - nx)^2}$ are each bounded by 1 in the closed interval $[0, 1]$ and for every x there is the limit: $\lim_{n \to \infty} f_n(x) = 0$. However, $f_n(\frac{1}{n}) = 1$ for every n, so

that no sub-sequence can converge uniformly to 0 everywhere on [0, 1]. This sequence is not equicontinuous.

(*Theorem*) Let $\{f_n(x)\}$ be a sequence of functions mapping $\mathbb{R}$ into $\mathbb{R}$ which converges uniformly to a function f. If each $f_n(x)$ is continuous at a point a, then $f(x)$ is also continuous at a.

(*Theorem*) If a function f is continuous on a closed bounded set E, then it is uniformly continuous on E.

(*Ascoli–Arzela theorem*) Let K be a compact set in $\mathbb{R}$. If $\{f_n(x)\}$ is uniformly bounded and equicontinuous on K, then $\{f_n(x)\}$ contains a uniformly convergent sub-sequence on K.

1.6.8 CONVERGENCE IN L_p

In the context of elementary measure theory, two measurable functions f and g are *equivalent* if they are equal except on a set of measure zero. They are said to be equal *almost everywhere*. This is denoted by $f = g$ a.e.

The (vector) space of measurable functions f on $[a, b]$, for which $\int_a^b |f(x)|^p dx < \infty$ with $0 < p < \infty$, is denoted by $L_p[a, b]$ or simply L_p. The space of bounded measurable functions on $[a, b]$ is denoted by L_∞.

The L_p *norm* for $0 < p < \infty$ is defined by $\|f\|_p = \left(\int_a^b |f(x)|^p dx\right)^{1/p}$. The L_∞ norm is defined by

$$\|f\|_\infty = \operatorname*{ess\ sup}_{a \leq x \leq b} |f(x)|, \tag{1.6.1}$$

where

$$\operatorname*{ess\ sup}_{a \leq x \leq b} |f(x)| = \inf\{M | m\{t : f(t) > M\} = 0\}. \tag{1.6.2}$$

Let $\{f_n(x)\}$ be a sequence of functions in L_p $(1 \leq p < \infty)$ and f be some function in L_p. We say that $\{f_n\}$ *converges in the mean of order p* to f if $\lim_{n\to\infty} \|f_n - f\|_p = 0$.

(*Riesz–Fischer theorem*) The L_p spaces are complete.

Inequalities

1. *Minkowski inequality*: If f and g are in L_p with $1 \leq p \leq \infty$, then $\|f + g\|_p \leq \|f\|_p + \|g\|_p$. That is,

$$\left(\int_a^b |f + g|^p\right)^{1/p} \leq \left(\int_a^b |f|^p\right)^{1/p} + \left(\int_a^b |g|^p\right)^{1/p} \quad \text{for } (1 \leq p < \infty), \tag{1.6.3}$$

$$\operatorname{ess\ sup} |f + g| \leq \operatorname{ess\ sup} |f| + \operatorname{ess\ sup} |g|.$$

2. *Hölder inequality*: If p and q are nonnegative extended real numbers such that $1/p + 1/q = 1$ and $f \in L_p$ and $g \in L_q$, then $\|fg\|_1 \leq \|f\|_p \|g\|_q$. That is

$$\int_a^b |fg| \leq \left(\int_a^b |f|^p \right)^{1/p} \left(\int_a^b |g|^q \right)^{1/q} \quad \text{for } (1 \leq p < \infty),$$
$$(1.6.4)$$

$$\int_a^b |fg| \leq (\text{ess sup } |f|) \int_a^b |g|. \tag{1.6.5}$$

3. *Schwartz* (or *Cauchy–Schwartz*) *inequality*: If f and g are in L_2, then $\|fg\|_1 \leq \|f\|_2 \|g\|_2$. This is the special case of Hölder's inequality with $p = q = 2$.

1.6.9 CONVERGENCE IN L_2

Two functions f and g in $L_2[a, b]$ are *orthogonal* if $\int_a^b fg = 0$. A set of L_2 functions $\{\phi_n\}$ are *orthogonal* if $\int_a^b \phi_m \phi_n = 0$ for $m \neq n$. The set is *orthonormal* if, in addition, each member has norm 1. That is, $\|\phi_n\|_2 = 1$. For example, the functions $\{\sin nx\}$ are mutually orthogonal on $(-\pi, \pi)$. The functions $\{\frac{\sin nx}{\sqrt{\pi}}\}$ form an orthonormal set on $(-\pi, \pi)$.

Let ϕ_n be an orthonormal set in L_2 and f be in L_2. The numbers $c_n = \int_a^b f\phi_n dx$ are the *generalized Fourier coefficients* of f with respect to $\{\phi_n\}$, and the series $\sum_{n=1}^{\infty} c_n \phi_n(x)$ is called the *generalized Fourier series* of f with respect to $\{\phi_n\}$.

For a function f in L_2, the *mean square error* of approximating f by the sum $\sum_{n=1}^{N} a_n \phi_n$ is $\frac{1}{b-a} \int_a^b |f(x) - \sum_{n=1}^{N} a_n \phi_n(x)|^2 dx$. An orthonormal set $\{\phi_n\}$ is *complete* if the only measurable function f that is orthogonal to every ϕ_n is zero. That is, $f = 0$ a.e.

(*Theorem*) The generalized Fourier series of f in L_2 converges in the mean (of order 2) to f.

(*Theorem*) Parseval's identity holds:

$$\int_a^b |f(x)|^2 dx = \sum_{n=1}^{\infty} c_n^2.$$

Bessel's inequality: For a function f in L_2 having generalized Fourier coefficients $\{c_n\}$, $\sum_{n=1}^{\infty} c_n^2 \leq \int_a^b |f(x)|^2 dx$.

(*Theorem*) The mean square error of approximating f by the series $\sum_{n=1}^{\infty} a_n \phi_n$ is minimum when all coefficients a_n are the Fourier coefficients of f with respect to $\{\phi_n\}$.

(*Riesz–Fischer theorem*) Let $\{\phi_n\}$ be an orthonormal set in L_2 and let $\{c_n\}$ be constants such that $\sum_{n=1}^{\infty} c_n^2$ converges. Then a unique function f in L_2 exists such that the c_n are the Fourier coefficients of f with respect to $\{\phi_n\}$ and $\sum_{n=1}^{\infty} c_n \phi_n$ converges in the mean (or order 2) to f.

Example: suppose that the series $\frac{a_0}{2} + \sum_{n=1}^{\infty} (a_n^2 + b_n^2)$ converges. Then the trigonometric series $\frac{a_0}{2} + \sum_{n=1}^{\infty} (a_n \cos nx + b_n \sin nx)$ is the Fourier series of some function in L_2.

1.6.10 ASYMPTOTIC RELATIONSHIPS

Asymptotic relationships are indicated by the symbols O, Ω, Θ, o, and $\sim$.

1. The symbol O (pronounced "big-oh"): $f(x) \in O(g(x))$ as $x \to x_0$ if a positive constant C exists such that $|f(x)| \leq C|g(x)|$ for all x sufficiently close to x_0. Note that $O(g(x))$ is a class of functions. Sometimes the statement $f(x) \in O(g(x))$ is written (imprecisely) as $f = O(g)$.

2. The symbol Ω : $f(x) \in \Omega(g(x))$ as $x \to x_0$ if a positive constant C exists such that $g(x) \leq Cf(x)$ for all x sufficiently close to x_0.

3. The symbol Θ : $f(x) \in \Theta(g(x))$ as $x \to x_0$ if positive constants c_1 and c_2 exist such that $c_1 g(x) \leq f(x) \leq c_2 g(x)$ for all x sufficiently close to x_0. This is equivalent to: $f(x) = O(g(x))$ and $g(x) = O(f(x))$. The symbol $\approx$ is often used for Θ.

4. The symbol o (pronounced "little-oh"): $f(x) \in o(g(x))$ as $x \to x_0$ if, given any $\mu > 0$, we have $|f(x)| < \mu|g(x)|$ for all x sufficiently close to x_0.

5. The symbol $\sim$ (pronounced "asymptotic to"): $f(x) \sim (g(x))$ as $x \to x_0$ if $f(x) = g(x)[1 + o(1)]$ as $x \to x_0$.

6. Two functions, $f(x)$ and $g(x)$, are *asymptotically equivalent* as $x \to x_0$ if $f(x)/g(x) \sim 1$ as $x \to x_0$.

7. A sequence of functions, $\{g_k(x)\}$, forms an *asymptotic series* at x_0 if $g_{k+1}(x) = o(g_k(x))$ as $x \to x_0$.

8. Given a function $f(x)$ and an asymptotic series $\{g_k(x)\}$ at x_0, the formal series $\sum_{k=0}^{\infty} a_k g_k(x)$ is an *asymptotic expansion* of $f(x)$ if $f(x) - \sum_{k=0}^{m} a_k g_k(x) = o(g_n(x))$ as $x \to x_0$ for every n; this is expressed as $f(x) \sim \sum_{k=0}^{\infty} a_k g_k(x)$. Partial sums of this formal series are called *asymptotic approximations* to $f(x)$. This formal series need not converge.

Think of O being an upper bound on a function, Ω being a lower bound, and Θ being both an upper and lower bound. For example: $\sin x \in O(x)$ as $x \to 0$, $\log n \in o(n)$ as $n \to \infty$, and $n^9 \in \Omega(n^9 + n^2)$ as $n \to \infty$.

1.7 GENERALIZED FUNCTIONS

Dirac's delta function is defined by $\delta(x) = \begin{cases} 0 & x \neq 0 \\ \infty & x = 0 \end{cases}$, and is normalized so that $\int_{-\infty}^{\infty} \delta(x)\, dx = 1$. Properties include (assuming that $f(x)$ is continuous):

1. $\int_{-\infty}^{\infty} f(x)\delta(x - a)\, dx = f(a)$.
2. $\int_{-\infty}^{\infty} f(x)\frac{d^m \delta(x)}{dx^m}\, dx = (-1)^m \frac{d^m f(0)}{dx^m}$.

3. $x\delta(x)$, as a distribution, equals zero

4. $\delta(ax) = \frac{1}{|a|}\delta(x)$ when $a \neq 0$.

5. $\delta(x^2 - a^2) = \frac{1}{2a}[\delta(x+a) + \delta(x-a)]$.

6. $\delta(x) = \frac{1}{2L} + \frac{1}{L}\sum_{n=1}^{\infty} \cos\frac{n\pi x}{L}$ (Fourier series).

7. $\delta(x) = \frac{2}{L}\sum_{n=1}^{\infty} \sin\frac{n\pi\xi}{L} \sin\frac{n\pi x}{L}$ for $0 < \xi < L$ (Fourier sine series).

8. $\delta(x) = \frac{1}{2\pi}\int_{-\infty}^{\infty} e^{ikx}\,dk$ (Fourier transform).

9. $\delta(\rho - \rho') = \rho \int_0^{\infty} k J_m(k\rho) J_m(k\rho')\,dk$.

Sequences of functions $\{\phi_n\}$ that approximate the delta function as $n \to \infty$ are known as delta sequences. For example:

- $\phi_n(x) = \frac{n}{\pi}\frac{1}{a+n^2x^2}$

- $\phi_n(x) = \frac{n}{\sqrt{\pi}}e^{-n^2x^2}$

- $\phi_n(x) = \frac{1}{n\pi}\frac{\sin^2 nx}{x^2}$

- $\phi_n(x) = \begin{cases} 0 & |x| \geq 1/n \\ n/2 & |x| < 1/n \end{cases}$

The Heaviside function, or step function, is defined as

$H(x) = \int_{-\infty}^{x}\delta(t)\,dt = \begin{cases} 0 & x < 0 \\ 1 & x > 1 \end{cases}$. Sometimes $H(0)$ is stated to be $1/2$. This function has the representations:

1. $H(x) = \frac{1}{2} + \frac{2}{\pi}\sum_{n=\text{odd}}^{\infty}\frac{1}{n}\sin\frac{n\pi x}{L}$

2. $H(x) = \frac{1}{2\pi i}\int_{-\infty}^{\infty}\frac{e^{ikx}}{k}\,dk$

The related signum function gives the sign of its argument:

$$\text{sgn}(x) = 2H(x) - 1 = \begin{cases} -1 & \text{if } x < 0 \\ 1 & \text{if } x > 0 \end{cases} \tag{1.7.1}$$

The delta function $\delta(\mathbf{x} - \mathbf{x}') = \delta(x_1 - x_1')\delta(x_2 - x_2')\delta(x_3 - x_3')$ in terms of the coordinates (ξ_1, ξ_2, ξ_3), related to (x_1, x_2, x_3), via the Jacobian $J(x_i, \xi_j)$, is written

$$\delta(\mathbf{x} - \mathbf{x}') = \frac{1}{|J(x_i, \xi_j)|}\delta(\xi_1 - \xi_1')\delta(\xi_2 - \xi_2')\delta(\xi_3 - \xi_3'). \tag{1.7.2}$$

For example, in spherical polar coordinates

$$\delta(\mathbf{x} - \mathbf{x}') = \frac{1}{r^2}\delta(r - r')\delta(\phi - \phi')\delta(\cos\theta - \cos\theta'). \tag{1.7.3}$$

The solutions to differential equations involving delta functions are called Green's functions (see Sections 5.6.5 and 5.7.4).

References

1. L. B. W. Jolley, *Summation of Series*, Dover Publications, New York, 1961.
2. S. G. Krantz, *Real Analysis and Foundations,* CRC Press, Boca Raton, FL, 1991.
3. S. G. Krantz, *The Elements of Advanced Mathematics,* CRC Press, Boca Raton, FL, 1995.
4. N. J. A. Sloane and S. Plouffe, *Encyclopedia of Integer Sequences*, Academic Press, New York, 1995.

Chapter 2

Algebra

0-8493-2479-3/96/$0.00+$.50
© 1996 CRC Press, Inc.

2.1 ELEMENTARY ALGEBRA

2.1.1 BASIC ALGEBRA

Algebraic equations

A polynomial equation in one variable is an equation of the form

$$f(x) = a_n x^n + a_{n-1} x^{n-1} + \cdots + a_1 x + a_0.$$

The degree of the equation is n (where $a_n \neq 0$).

A complex number z is a root of the polynomial $f(x)$ if $f(z) = 0$. A complex number z is a root of multiplicity k if $f(z) = f'(z) = f''(z) = \cdots = f^{(k-1)}(z) = 0$, but $f^{(k)}(z) \neq 0$. A root of multiplicity 1 is called a simple root. A root of multiplicity 2 is called a double root, and a root of multiplicity 3 is called a triple root.

Fundamental theorem of algebra

A polynomial equation of degree n has exactly n complex roots, where a double root is counted twice, a triple root three times, and so on. If the n roots of the polynomial $f(x)$ are $z_1, z_2, \ldots, z_n$ (where a double root is listed twice, a triple root three times, and so on), then

$$f(x) = a_n(x - z_1)(x - z_2) \cdots (x - z_n). \tag{2.1.1}$$

If the coefficients $a_0, a_1, \ldots a_n$ are real numbers, then the polynomial will always have an even number of complex roots occurring in pairs. That is, if z is a complex root, then so is $\bar{z}$. If the polynomial has an odd degree and the coefficients are real, then it must have at least one real root.

The coefficients of the polynomial may be expressed as symmetric functions of the roots. For example, the elementary symmetric functions are

$$s_1 = z_1 + z_2 + \cdots + z_n = -\frac{a_{n-1}}{a_n},$$

$$s_2 = z_1 z_2 + z_1 z_3 + z_2 z_3 + \cdots = \sum_{i>j} z_i z_j = \frac{a_{n-2}}{a_n},$$

$$\vdots \tag{2.1.2}$$

$$s_n = z_1 z_2 z_3 \cdots z_n = (-1)^n \frac{a_0}{a_n}.$$

where s_k is the sum of $\binom{n}{k}$ products, each product combining k factors without repetition.

The *discriminant* of the polynomial is defined by $\prod_{i>j}(z_i - z_j)^2$, where the ordering of the roots is irrelevant. The discriminant can always be written as a polynomial combination of $a_0, a_1, \ldots, a_n$, divided by a_n.

Resultants

Let $f(x) = a_n x^n + a_{n-1} x^{n-1} + \cdots + a_1 x + a_0$ and $g(x) = b_m x^m + b_{m-1} x^{m-1} + \cdots + b_1 x + b_0$, where $a_n \neq 0$ and $b_m \neq 0$. The resultant of f and g is the determinant of the $(m+n) \times (m+n)$ matrix

$$\det \begin{bmatrix} a_n & a_{n-1} & \cdot & \cdot & a_0 & 0 & \cdots & 0 \\ 0 & a_n & a_{n-1} & \cdot & a_1 & a_0 & & 0 \\ \cdots\cdots\cdots\cdots\cdots\cdots\cdots\cdots\cdots\cdots\cdots\cdots\cdots\cdots \\ \cdot & \cdot & 0 & a_n & a_{n-1} & \cdot & a_1 & a_0 \\ b_m & b_{m-1} & \cdot & b_0 & 0 & \cdots & \cdot & 0 \\ 0 & b_m & b_{m-1} & \cdot & b_0 & 0 & \cdots & 0 \\ \cdots\cdots\cdots\cdots\cdots\cdots\cdots\cdots\cdots\cdots\cdots\cdots\cdots\cdots \\ \cdot & \cdot & \cdot & 0 & b_m & \cdot & b_1 & b_0 \end{bmatrix} \qquad (2.1.3)$$

The resultant of $f(x)$ and $g(x)$ is 0 if and only if $f(x)$ and $g(x)$ have a common root. The resultant of $f(x)$ and $f'(x)$ is zero if and only if $f(x)$ has a multiple root. For example:

1. If $f(x) = x^2 + 2x + 3$ and $g(x; \alpha) = 4x^3 + 5x^2 + 6x + (7 + \alpha)$, then the resultant of $f(x)$ and $g(x; \alpha)$ is

$$\det \begin{bmatrix} 1 & 2 & 3 & 0 & 0 \\ 0 & 1 & 2 & 3 & 0 \\ 0 & 0 & 1 & 2 & 3 \\ 4 & 5 & 6 & 7+\alpha & 0 \\ 0 & 4 & 5 & 6 & 7+\alpha \end{bmatrix} = (16 + \alpha)^2$$

   Note that $g(x, -16) = (4x - 3)(x^2 + 2x + 3) = (4x - 3)f(x)$.

2. The resultant of $ax + b$ and $cx + d$ is $da - bc$.

3. The resultant of $(x + a)^5$ and $(x + b)^5$ is $(b - a)^{25}$.

Algebraic identities

$$(a \pm b)^2 = a^2 \pm 2ab + b^2.$$
$$(a \pm b)^3 = a^3 \pm 3a^2b + 3ab^2 \pm b^3.$$
$$(a \pm b)^4 = a^4 \pm 4a^3b + 6a^2b^2 \pm 4ab^3 + b^4.$$
$$(a + b)^n = \sum_{k=0}^{n} \binom{n}{k} a^k b^{n-k} \text{ where } \binom{n}{k} = \frac{n!}{k!(n-k)!}.$$
$$a^2 + b^2 = (a + bi)(a - bi).$$
$$a^4 + b^4 = (a^2 + \sqrt{2}ab + b^2)(a^2 - \sqrt{2}ab + b^2).$$
$$a^2 - b^2 = (a - b)(a + b).$$
$$a^3 - b^3 = (a - b)(a^2 + ab + b^2).$$
$$a^n - b^n = (a - b)(a^{n-1} + a^{n-2}b + \cdots + ab^{n-2} + b^{n-1}).$$
$$(a + b + c)^2 = a^2 + b^2 + c^2 + 2ab + 2ac + 2bc.$$
$$(a + b + c)^3 = a^3 + b^3 + c^3 + 3(a^2b + ab^2 + a^2c + ac^2 + b^2c + bc^2) + 6abc.$$

Laws of exponents

Assuming all quantites are real, then

$$a^x a^y = a^{x+y}, \qquad \frac{a^x}{a^y} = a^{x-y}, \qquad (ab)^x = a^x b^x,$$

$$a^0 = 1 \text{ if } a \neq 0, \qquad a^{-x} = \frac{1}{a^x}, \qquad \left(\frac{a}{b}\right)^x = \frac{a^x}{b^x},$$

$$(a^x)^y = a^{xy}, \qquad a^{\frac{1}{x}} = \sqrt[x]{a}, \qquad \sqrt[x]{ab} = \sqrt[x]{a}\sqrt[x]{b},$$

$$\sqrt[x]{\sqrt[y]{a}} = \sqrt[xy]{a}, \qquad a^{\frac{x}{y}} = \sqrt[y]{a^x} = (\sqrt[y]{a})^x, \qquad \sqrt[x]{\frac{a}{b}} = \frac{\sqrt[x]{a}}{\sqrt[x]{b}}.$$

Proportion

If $\frac{a}{b} = \frac{c}{d}$, then $\frac{a}{c} = \frac{b}{d}$, $ad = bc$, $\frac{a+b}{b} = \frac{c+d}{d}$, $\frac{a-b}{b} = \frac{c-d}{d}$, and $\frac{a-b}{a+b} = \frac{c-d}{c+d}$.

    If $\frac{a}{b} = \frac{c}{d}$, where a, b, c, and d are all positive numbers and a is the largest of the four numbers, then $a + d > b + c$.

2.1.2 PROGRESSIONS

Arithmetic progression

An arithmetic progression is a sequence of numbers such that the difference of any two consecutive numbers is constant. If the sequence is $a_1, a_2, \ldots a_n$, where $a_{i+1} - a_i = d$, then $a_k = a_1 + (k - 1)d$ and

$$a_1 + a_2 + \cdots a_n = \frac{n}{2}(2a_1 + (n - 1)d).$$

In particular, the sequence $1, 2, \ldots n$ is an arithmetic progression with sum $n(n+1)/2$.

Geometric progression

A geometric progression is a sequence of numbers such that the ratio of any two consecutive numbers is constant. If the sequence is $a_1, a_2, \ldots a_n$, where $a_{i+1}/a_i = r$, then $a_k = a_1 r^{k-1}$.

$$a_1 + a_2 + \cdots a_n = \begin{cases} a_1 \frac{1-r^n}{1-r} & r \neq 1 \\ na_1 & r = 1. \end{cases} \tag{2.1.4}$$

If $|r| < 1$, then the infinite geometric series $a_1(1 + r + r^2 + r^3 + \cdots)$ converges to $\frac{a_1}{1-r}$. For example, $1 + \frac{1}{2} + \frac{1}{4} + \frac{1}{8} + \cdots = 2$.

Means

The arithmetic mean of a and b is given by $\frac{a+b}{2}$. More generally, the arithmetic mean of $a_1, a_2, \ldots, a_n$ is given by $(a_1 + a_2 + \cdots + a_n)/n$.

The geometric mean of a and b is given by $\sqrt{ab}$. More generally, the geometric mean of $a_1, a_2, \ldots, a_n$ is given by $\sqrt[n]{a_1 a_2 \cdots a_n}$. The geometric mean of n numbers is less than the arithmetic mean, unless all of the numbers are equal.

The harmonic mean of a and b is given by $\frac{2ab}{a+b}$. If A, G, and H represent the arithmetic, geometric, and harmonic means of a and b, then $AH = G^2$.

2.1.3   DEMOIVRE'S THEOREM

A complex number $a + bi$ can be written in the form $re^{i\theta}$, where $r^2 = a^2 + b^2$ and $\tan \theta = b/a$. Because $e^{i\theta} = \cos \theta + i \sin \theta$,

$$(a + bi)^n = r^n(\cos n\theta + i \sin n\theta),$$
$$\text{and } \sqrt[n]{1} = \cos \frac{2k\pi}{n} + i \sin \frac{2k\pi}{n}, \qquad k = 0, 1, \ldots, n - 1.$$

2.1.4   PARTIAL FRACTIONS

The technique of partial fractions allows a quotient of two polynomials to be written as a sum of simpler terms.

Given the fraction $\frac{f(x)}{g(x)}$, where both $f(x)$ and $g(x)$ are polynomials, begin by dividing $f(x)$ by $g(x)$ to produce a quotient $q(x)$ and a remainder $r(x)$, where the degree of $r(x)$ is less than the degree of $g(x)$, so that $\frac{f(x)}{g(x)} = q(x) + \frac{r(x)}{g(x)}$. Therefore, assume that the rational function has the form $\frac{r(x)}{g(x)}$, where the degree of the numerator is less than the degree of the denominator.

The techniques used depend on the factorization of $g(x)$.

Single linear factor

Suppose that $g(x) = (x - a)h(x)$, where $h(a) \neq 0$. Then

$$\frac{r(x)}{g(x)} = \frac{A}{x - a} + \frac{s(x)}{h(x)},$$

where the number A is given by $r(a)/h(a)$. For example,

$$\frac{2x}{x^2 - 1} = \frac{1}{x - 1} + \frac{1}{x + 1}.$$

Repeated linear factor

Suppose that $g(x) = (x - a)^k h(x)$, where $h(a) \neq 0$. Then

$$\frac{r(x)}{g(x)} = \frac{A_1}{x - a} + \frac{A_2}{(x - a)^2} + \cdots + \frac{A_k}{(x - a)^k} + \frac{s(x)}{h(x)},$$

where

$$A_k = \frac{r(a)}{h(a)},$$

$$A_{k-1} = \frac{d}{dx}\left(\frac{r(x)}{g(x)}\right)\bigg|_{x=a},$$

$$A_{k-2} = \frac{1}{2!}\frac{d^2}{dx^2}\left(\frac{r(x)}{g(x)}\right)\bigg|_{x=a},$$

$$A_{k-j} = \frac{1}{j!}\frac{d^j}{dx^j}\left(\frac{r(x)}{g(x)}\right)\bigg|_{x=a}.$$

Single quadratic factor

Suppose that $g(x) = (x^2 + bx + c)h(x)$, where $b^2 - 4c < 0$ (so that $x^2 + bx + c$ does not factor into real linear factors) and $h(x)$ is relatively prime to $x^2 + bx + c$. Then

$$\frac{r(x)}{g(x)} = \frac{Ax + B}{x^2 + bx + c} + \frac{s(x)}{h(x)}.$$

In order to determine A and B, multiply the equation by $g(x)$ so that there are no denominators remaining, and substitute any two values for x, yielding two equations for A and B.

Repeated quadratic factor

Suppose that $g(x) = (x^2 + bx + c)^k h(x)$, where $b^2 - 4c < 0$ (so that $x^2 + bx + c$ does not factor into real linear factors) and $h(x)$ is relatively prime to $x^2 + bx + c$. Then

$$\frac{r(x)}{g(x)} = \frac{A_1 x + B_1}{x^2 + bx + c} + \frac{A_2 x + B_2}{(x^2 + bx + c)^2} + \frac{A_3 x + B_3}{(x^2 + bx + c)^3}$$

$$+ \cdots + \frac{A_k x + B_k}{(x^2 + bx + c)^k} + \frac{s(x)}{h(x)}.$$

In order to determine A_i and B_i, multiply the equation by $g(x)$ so that there are no denominators remaining, and substitute any $2k$ values for x, yielding $2k$ equations for A_i and B_i.

2.2   POLYNOMIALS

2.2.1   QUADRATIC POLYNOMIALS

The solution of the equation $ax^2 + bx + c = 0$, where $a \neq 0$, is given by

$$x = \frac{-b \pm \sqrt{b^2 - 4ac}}{2a}. \tag{2.2.1}$$

The discriminant of this equation is $b^2 - 4ac$. Suppose that a, b, and c are all real. If the discriminant is negative, then the two roots are complex numbers which are conjugate. If the discriminant is positive, then the two roots are unequal real numbers. If the discriminant is 0, then the two roots are equal.

2.2.2   CUBIC POLYNOMIALS

To solve the equation $ax^3 + bx^2 + cx + d = 0$, where $a \neq 0$, begin by making the substitution $y = x + \frac{b}{3a}$. That gives the equation $y^3 + 3py + q = 0$, where $p = \frac{3ac - b^2}{9a^2}$ and $q = \frac{2b^3 - 9abc + 27a^2 d}{27a^3}$. The discriminant of this polynomial is $4p^3 + q^2$.

The solutions are given by $\sqrt[3]{\alpha} - \sqrt[3]{\beta}$, $e^{\frac{2\pi i}{3}} \sqrt[3]{\alpha} - e^{\frac{4\pi i}{3}} \sqrt[3]{\beta}$, and $e^{\frac{4\pi i}{3}} \sqrt[3]{\alpha} - e^{\frac{2\pi i}{3}} \sqrt[3]{\beta}$, where

$$\alpha = \frac{-q + \sqrt{q^2 + 4p^3}}{2} \quad \text{and} \quad \beta = \frac{-q - \sqrt{q^2 + 4p^3}}{2}.$$

Suppose that p and q are real numbers. If the discriminant is positive, then one root is real, and two are complex conjugates. If the discriminant is 0, then there are three real roots, of which at least two are equal. If the discriminant is negative, then there are three unequal real roots.

Trigonometric solution of cubic polynomials

In the event that the roots of the polynomial $y^3 + 3py + q = 0$ are all real, meaning that $q^2 + 4p^3 \leq 0$, then the expressions above involve complex numbers. In that case one can also express the solution in terms of trigonometric functions. Define r and θ by

$$r = \sqrt{-p^3} \quad \text{and} \quad \theta = \cos^{-1} \frac{-q}{2r}.$$

Then the three roots are given by

$$2\sqrt[3]{r}\cos\frac{\theta}{3}, \qquad 2\sqrt[3]{r}\cos\frac{\theta+2\pi}{3}, \qquad \text{and} \qquad 2\sqrt[3]{r}\cos\frac{\theta+4\pi}{3}$$

2.2.3 QUARTIC POLYNOMIALS

To solve the equation $ax^4 + bx^3 + cx^2 + dx + e = 0$, where $a \neq 0$, start with the substitution $y = x + \frac{b}{4a}$. That gives $y^4 + py^2 + qy + r = 0$, where $p = \frac{8ac-3b^2}{8a^2}$, $q = \frac{b^3-4abc+8a^2d}{8a^3}$, and $r = \frac{16ab^2c+256a^3e-3b^4-64a^2bd}{256a^4}$.

The *cubic resolvent* of this polynomial is defined as $t^3 - pt^2 - 4rt + (4pr - q^2) = 0$. If u is a root of the cubic resolvent, then the solutions of the original quartic are given by the solutions of

$$y^2 \pm \sqrt{u-p}\left(y - \frac{q}{2(u-p)}\right) + \frac{u}{2} = 0.$$

2.2.4 QUINTIC POLYNOMIALS

Some quintic equations are solvable by radicals. If the function $f(x) = x^5 + ax + b$ (with a and b rational) is irreducible, then $f(x) = 0$ is solvable by radicals if, and only if, numbers ϵ, c, and e exist (with $\epsilon = \pm 1$, $c \geq 0$, and $e \neq 0$) such that

$$a = \frac{5e^4(3-4\epsilon c)}{c^2+1} \quad \text{and} \quad b = \frac{-4e^5(11\epsilon+2c)}{c^2+1}.$$

In this case, the roots are given by $x = e\left(\omega^j u_1 + \omega^{2j} u_2 + \omega^{3j} u_3 + \omega^{4j} u_4\right)$ for $j = 0, 1, 2, 3, 4$, where ω is a fifth root of unity ($\omega = \exp(2\pi i/5)$) and

$$u_1 = \left(\frac{v_1^2 v_3}{D^2}\right), \quad u_2 = \left(\frac{v_3^2 v_4}{D^2}\right), \quad u_3 = \left(\frac{v_2^2 v_1}{D^2}\right), \quad u_4 = \left(\frac{v_4^2 v_2}{D^2}\right),$$

$$v_1 = \sqrt{D} + \sqrt{D - \epsilon\sqrt{D}}, \qquad v_2 = -\sqrt{D} - \sqrt{D + \epsilon\sqrt{D}},$$

$$v_3 = -\sqrt{D} + \sqrt{D + \epsilon\sqrt{D}}, \qquad v_4 = \sqrt{D} - \sqrt{D - \epsilon\sqrt{D}}, \quad \text{and}$$

$$D = c^2 + 1.$$

EXAMPLE 2.2.1

The quintic $f(x) = x^5 + 15x + 12$ has the values $\epsilon = -1$, $c = 4/3$, and $e = 1$. Hence the unique real root is given by

$$x = \left(\frac{-75 + 21\sqrt{10}}{125}\right)^{1/5} + \left(\frac{-75 - 21\sqrt{10}}{125}\right)^{1/5}$$

$$+ \left(\frac{225 + 72\sqrt{10}}{125}\right)^{1/5} + \left(\frac{225 - 72\sqrt{10}}{125}\right)^{1/5}.$$

2.2.5   TSCHIRNHAUS' TRANSFORMATION

The nth degree polynomial equation

$$a_n x^n + a_{n-1} x^{n-1} + \cdots + a_1 x + a_0 = 0$$

can be transformed to one with up to three fewer terms,

$$z^n + b_{n-4} z^{n-4} + \cdots + b_1 z + b_0 = 0$$

by making a transformation of the form

$$z_j = \gamma_4 x_j^4 + \gamma_3 x_j^3 + \gamma_2 x_j^2 + \gamma_1 x_j + \gamma_0$$

for $j = 1, \ldots, n$ where the $\{\gamma_i\}$ can be computed, in terms of radicals, from the $\{a_i\}$. Hence, the general quintic polynomial can be transformed to the form $z^5 + az + b = 0$.

2.2.6   POLYNOMIAL NORMS

The polynomial $P(x) = \displaystyle\sum_{j=0}^{n} a_j x^j$ has the norms:

$$\|P\|_1 = \int_0^{2\pi} \left| P\left(e^{i\theta}\right) \right| \frac{d\theta}{2\pi} \qquad\qquad |P|_1 = \sum_{j=0}^{n} |a_j| . \qquad (2.2.2)$$

$$\|P\|_2 = \left(\int_0^{2\pi} \left| P\left(e^{i\theta}\right) \right|^2 \frac{d\theta}{2\pi} \right)^{1/2} \qquad |P|_2 = \left(\sum_{j=1}^{n} |a_j|^2 \right)^{1/2} . \qquad (2.2.3)$$

$$\|P\|_\infty = \max_{|z|=1} |P(z)| \qquad\qquad |P|_\infty = \max_j |a_j| . \qquad (2.2.4)$$

For the double bar norms, P is considered as a function on the unit circle; for the single bar norms, P is identified with its coefficients. These norms are comparable:

$$|P|_\infty \leq \|P\|_1 \leq |P|_2 = \|P\|_2 \leq \|P\|_\infty \leq |P|_1 \leq n|P|_\infty.$$
$$(2.2.5)$$

2.2.7   GALOIS GROUP OF A POLYNOMIAL

Consider the polynomial $P(x) = a_n x^n + a_{n-1} x^{n-1} + \cdots + a_0 = a_n (x - z_1)(x - z_2) \ldots (x - z_n)$.

There are certain relations among the roots that do not depend on how the roots are numbered. For example, this is true of the elementary symmetric functions; see Equation (2.1.2). The set of permutations that leave all polynomials with rational coefficients, $H(z_1, \ldots, z_n)$, invariant is the Galois group of the equation.

For example, consider the polynomial $f(x) = (x^2 - 2)(x^2 - 3)$, with roots $\{z_1 = -\sqrt{2}, z_2 = \sqrt{2}, z_3 = -\sqrt{3}, z_4 = \sqrt{3}\}$. There are four permutations that leave all allowable relationships between the roots invariant:

$$\pi = \begin{pmatrix} 1 & 2 & 3 & 4 \\ 1 & 2 & 3 & 4 \end{pmatrix} \qquad p_1 = \begin{pmatrix} 1 & 2 & 3 & 4 \\ 2 & 1 & 3 & 4 \end{pmatrix}$$

$$p_2 = \begin{pmatrix} 1 & 2 & 3 & 4 \\ 1 & 2 & 4 & 3 \end{pmatrix} \qquad p_3 = \begin{pmatrix} 1 & 2 & 3 & 4 \\ 2 & 1 & 4 & 3 \end{pmatrix}$$

That is, all permutations that switch z_1 and z_2, or switch z_3 and z_4, or both, will leave allowable relations invariant. To demonstrate that neither z_1 nor z_2 can be switched with z_3 or z_4, consider the expressions $H_1(z_i) = z_1 z_2 + 2$ and $H_2(z_i) = z_3 z_4 + 3$.

2.2.8 OTHER POLYNOMIAL PROPERTIES

1. For the polynomial $P(x) = \sum_{j=0}^{n} a_j x^j$, with $a_0 \neq 0$, Jensen's inequality is

$$\int_0^{2\pi} \log \left| P\left(e^{i\theta}\right) \right| \frac{d\theta}{2\pi} \geq \log |a_0|$$

2. The polynomial $P(x_1, \ldots, x_n) = \sum_{|\alpha|=m} a_\alpha x_1^{\alpha_1} x_2^{\alpha_2} \ldots x_N^{\alpha_N}$, where $\alpha = (\alpha_1, \ldots, \alpha_N)$ can be written in the symmetric form

$$P(x_1, \ldots, x_n) = \sum_{i_1, \ldots, i_m = 1}^{N} c_{i_1, \ldots, i_m} x_{i_1} x_{i_2} \ldots x_{i_m}$$

with $c_{i_1, \ldots, i_m} = \frac{\partial^m P}{\partial x_{i_1} \ldots \partial x_{i_m}}$. This means that the $x_1 x_2$ term is written as $\frac{1}{2}(x_1 x_2 + x_2 x_1)$, the term $x_1 x_2^2$ becomes $\frac{1}{3}(x_1 x_2 x_2 + x_2 x_1 x_2 + x_2 x_2 x_1)$.

3. A valuation of the polynomial $P(x) = a_n x^n + a_{n-1} x^{n-1} + \cdots + a_0 = a_n(x - z_1)(x - z_2) \ldots (x - z_n)$ is given by $M(P) = a_n \prod_{i=1}^{n} \max(1, |z_i|)$. This valuation satisfies the properties:

   • $M(P) M(Q) = M(PQ)$
   • $M(P(x)) = M(P(x^k))$ for $k \geq 1$
   • $M(x^n P(x^{-1})) = M(P(x))$

2.3 NUMBER THEORY

2.3.1 CONGRUENCES

Definitions

1. If the integers a and b leave the same remainder when divided by the number n, then a and b are *congruent* modulo n. This is written $a \equiv b \pmod{n}$.

2. If the congruence $x^2 \equiv a \pmod{p}$ has a solution, then a is a *quadratic residue* of p. Otherwise, a is a *quadratic nonresidue* of p.

   - Let p be a prime. *Legendre's symbol* $\left(\frac{a}{p}\right)$ has the value $+1$ if a is a quadratic residue of p, and the value -1 if a is a quadratic nonresidue of p.

   - The *Jacobi symbol* generalizes the Legendre symbol to non-prime moduli. If $n = \prod_{i=1}^{k} p_i^{b_i}$ then the Jacobi symbol can be written in terms of the Legendre symbol

$$\left(\frac{a}{n}\right) = \prod_{i=1}^{k} \left(\frac{a}{p_i}\right)^{b_i} \tag{2.3.1}$$

3. Carmichael numbers are composite numbers $\{n\}$ that satisfy $a^{n-1} \equiv 1 \pmod{n}$ for every a $(1 < a < n)$ relatively prime to n.

Properties

1. If $a \equiv b \pmod{n}$, then $b \equiv a \pmod{n}$.

2. If $a \equiv b \pmod{n}$, and $b \equiv c \pmod{n}$, then $a \equiv c \pmod{n}$.

3. If $a \equiv a' \pmod{n}$, and $b \equiv b' \pmod{n}$, then $a \pm b \equiv a' \pm b' \pmod{n}$.

4. If $a \equiv a' \pmod{n}$, then $a^2 \equiv (a')^2 \pmod{n}$, $a^3 \equiv (a')^3 \pmod{n}$, etc.

5. If $(k, m) = d$, then the congruence $kx \equiv n \pmod{m}$ is solvable if and only if d divides n. It then has d solutions.

6. If p is a prime, then $a^p \equiv a \pmod{p}$.

7. If p is a prime, and p does not divide a, then $a^{p-1} \equiv 1 \pmod{p}$.

8. If $(a, m) = 1$ then $a^{\phi(m)} \equiv 1 \pmod{m}$. (See Section 2.3.16 for $\phi(m)$.)

9. If p is an odd prime and a is not a multiple of p, then $(p-1)! \equiv -\left(\frac{a}{p}\right) a^{(p-1)/2} \pmod{p}$.

10. If p and q are odd primes, then the law of quadratic reciprocity states that
$$\left(\frac{p}{q}\right)\left(\frac{q}{p}\right) = (-1)^{(p-1)(q-1)/4}.$$

11. The number -1 is a quadratic residue of primes of the form $4k + 1$ and a nonresidue of primes of the form $4k + 3$.

12. The number 2 is a quadratic residue of primes of the form $8k \pm 1$ and a nonresidue of primes of the form $8k \pm 3$.

13. The number -3 is a quadratic residue of primes of the form $6k + 1$ and a nonresidue of primes of the form $6k + 5$.

14. The number 3 is a quadratic residue of primes of the form $12k \pm 1$ and a nonresidue of primes of the form $12k \pm 5$.

Values

There are infinitely many Carmichael numbers. There are 32 Carmichael numbers less than one million; they are 561, 1105, 1729, 2465, 2821, 6601, 8911, 10585, 15841, 29341, 41041, 46657, 52633, 62745, 63973, 75361, 101101, 115921, 126217, 162401, 172081, 188461, 252601, 278545, 294409, 314821, 334153, 340561, 399001, 410041, 449065, and 488881.

2.3.2 CHINESE REMAINDER THEOREM

Let $m_1, m_2, \ldots, m_r$ be pairwise relatively prime integers. Then the system of congruences

$$x \equiv a_1 \quad (\text{mod } m_1)$$
$$x \equiv a_2 \quad (\text{mod } m_2)$$
$$\vdots$$
$$x \equiv a_r \quad (\text{mod } m_r)$$

has a unique solution modulo $M = m_1 m_2 \cdots m_r$. This unique solution can be written as

$$x = a_1 M_1 y_1 + a_2 M_2 y_2 + \cdots + a_r M_r y_r \qquad (2.3.2)$$

where $M_k = M/m_k$, and y_k is the inverse of M_k (modulo m_k).

Example: For the system of congruences

$$x \equiv 1 \quad (\text{mod } 3)$$
$$x \equiv 2 \quad (\text{mod } 5)$$
$$x \equiv 3 \quad (\text{mod } 7)$$

we have $M = 3 \cdot 5 \cdot 7 = 105$. Hence $M_1 = 35$, $M_2 = 21$, and $M_3 = 15$. The equation for y_1 is $M_1 y_1 = 35 y_1 \equiv 1 \ (\text{mod } 3)$ with solution $y_1 \equiv 2 \ (\text{mod } 3)$. Likewise, $y_2 \equiv 1$ (mod 5) and $y_3 \equiv 1 \ (\text{mod } 7)$. This results in $x = 1 \cdot 35 \cdot 2 + 2 \cdot 21 \cdot 1 + 3 \cdot 15 \cdot 1 \equiv 52$ (mod 105).

2.3.3   CONTINUED FRACTIONS

The symbol $[a_0, a_1, \ldots, a_N]$ (with N finite or infinite and the $\{a_i\}$ being positive integers) represents the simple *continued fraction*,

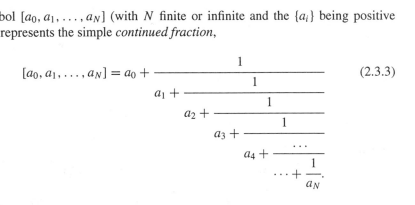

$$[a_0, a_1, \ldots, a_N] = a_0 + \cfrac{1}{a_1 + \cfrac{1}{a_2 + \cfrac{1}{a_3 + \cfrac{1}{a_4 + \cfrac{\cdots}{\cdots + \cfrac{1}{a_N}}}}}}. \qquad (2.3.3)$$

The nth *convergent* (with $0 < n < N$) of $[a_0, a_1, \ldots, a_N]$ is defined to be $[a_0, a_1, \ldots, a_n]$. If $\{p_n\}$ and $\{q_n\}$ are defined by

$$p_0 = a_0, \quad p_1 = a_1 a_0 + 1, \quad p_n = a_n p_{n-1} + p_{n-2} \quad (2 \leq n \leq N)$$
$$q_0 = 1, \quad q_1 = a_1, \quad q_n = a_n q_{n-1} + q_{n-2} \quad (2 \leq n \leq N)$$

then $[a_0, a_1, \ldots, a_n] = p_n/q_n$. The continued fraction is convergent if and only if the infinite series $\sum^{\infty} a_i$ is divergent.

If the positive rational number x can be represented by a simple continued fraction with an odd (even) number of terms, then it is also representable by one with an even (odd) number of terms. (Specifically, if $a_n = 1$ then $[a_0, a_1, \ldots, a_{n-1}, 1] = [a_0, a_1, \ldots, a_{n-1} + 1]$, and if $a_n \geq 2$, then $[a_0, a_1, \ldots, a_n] = [a_0, a_1, \ldots, a_n - 1, 1]$.) Aside from this indeterminacy, the simple continued fraction of x is unique. The error in approximating by a convergent is bounded by

$$\left| x - \frac{p_n}{q_n} \right| \leq \frac{1}{q_n q_{n+1}} < \frac{1}{q_n^2}. \qquad (2.3.4)$$

The algorithm for finding a continued fraction expansion of a number is to remove the integer part of the number (this becomes a_i), take the reciprocal, and repeat. For the number π:

$$\beta_0 = \pi \approx 3.14159 \qquad\qquad a_0 = \lfloor \beta_0 \rfloor = 3$$
$$\beta_1 = 1/(\beta_0 - a_0) \approx 7.062 \qquad\qquad a_1 = \lfloor \beta_1 \rfloor = 7$$
$$\beta_2 = 1/(\beta_1 - a_1) \approx 15.997 \qquad\qquad a_2 = \lfloor \beta_2 \rfloor = 15$$
$$\beta_3 = 1/(\beta_2 - a_2) \approx 1.0034 \qquad\qquad a_3 = \lfloor \beta_3 \rfloor = 1$$
$$\beta_4 = 1/(\beta_3 - a_3) \approx 292.6 \qquad\qquad a_4 = \lfloor \beta_4 \rfloor = 292$$

Approximations to π and e may be found from $\pi = [3, 7, 15, 1, 292, 1, 1, 1, 2, 1, 3, 1, 14, 2, \ldots]$ and $e = [2, 1, 2, 1, 1, 4, 1, 1, 6, \ldots, 1, 1, 2n, \ldots]$. The convergents for π are $\frac{22}{7}, \frac{333}{106}, \frac{355}{113}, \frac{103993}{33102}, \ldots$. The convergents for e are $\frac{8}{3}, \frac{11}{4}, \frac{19}{7}, \frac{87}{32}, \ldots$.

A periodic continued fraction is an infinite continued fraction in which $a_l = a_{l+k}$ for all $l \geq L$. The set of partial quotients $a_L, a_{L+1}, \ldots, a_{L+k-1}$ is the period. A periodic continued fraction may be written as

$$\left[a_0, a_1, \ldots, a_{L-1}, \dot{a}_L, a_{L+1}, \ldots, \dot{a}_{L+k-1} \right]. \tag{2.3.5}$$

For example, $\sqrt{2} = [1, \dot{2}]$, $\sqrt{3} = [1, \dot{1}, \dot{2}]$, $\sqrt{5} = [2, \dot{4}]$, and $\sqrt{7} = [2, \dot{1}, 1, 1, \dot{4}]$. If $x = [\dot{b}, \dot{a}]$ then $x = \frac{1}{2}(b + \sqrt{b^2 + \frac{4b}{a}})$. For example, $[\dot{1}] = (1 + \sqrt{5})/2$, $[\dot{2}] = 1 + \sqrt{2}$, and $[\dot{2}, \dot{1}] = 1 + \sqrt{3}$.

Functions can be represented as continued fractions. Using the notation

$$b_0 + \cfrac{a_1}{b_1 + \cfrac{a_2}{b_2 + \cfrac{a_3}{b_3 + \cfrac{a_4}{b_4 + \ldots}}}} = b_0 + \frac{a_1}{b_1 +} \frac{a_2}{b_2 +} \frac{a_3}{b_3 +} \frac{a_4}{b_4 +} \cdots \tag{2.3.6}$$

then (allowable values of z may be restricted in the following)

- $\ln(1 + z) = \frac{z}{1+} \frac{z}{2+} \frac{z}{3+} \frac{4z}{4+} \frac{4z}{5+} \frac{9z}{6+} \cdots$
- $e^z = \frac{1}{1-} \frac{z}{1+} \frac{z}{2-} \frac{z}{3+} \frac{z}{2-} \frac{z}{5+} \frac{z}{2-} \cdots = 1 + \frac{z}{1-} \frac{z}{2+} \frac{z}{3-} \frac{z}{2+} \frac{z}{5-} \frac{z}{2+} \frac{z}{7-} \cdots$
- $\tan z = \frac{z}{1-} \frac{z^2}{3-} \frac{z^2}{5-} \frac{z^2}{7-} \cdots$
- $\tanh z = \frac{z}{1+} \frac{z^2}{3+} \frac{z^2}{5+} \frac{z^2}{7+} \cdots$

2.3.4 DIOPHANTINE EQUATIONS

A diophantine equation is one which requires the solutions to come from the set of integers.

Apart from the trivial solutions (with $x = y = 0$ or $x = u$), the general solution to the equation $x^3 + y^3 = u^3 + v^3$ is given by

$$x = \lambda \left[1 - (a - 3b)(a^2 + 3b^2) \right] \qquad y = \lambda \left[(a + 3b)(a^2 + 3b^2) - 1 \right]$$
$$u = \lambda \left[(a + 3b) - (a^2 + 3b^2)^2 \right] \qquad v = \lambda \left[(a^2 + 3b^2)^2 - (a - 3b) \right] \tag{2.3.7}$$

where $\{\lambda, a, b\}$ are any rational numbers except that $\lambda \neq 0$.

A parametric solution to $x^4 + y^4 = u^4 + v^4$ is given by

$$\begin{aligned}
x &= a^7 + a^5 b^2 - 2a^3 b^4 + 3a^2 b^5 + ab^6 \\
y &= a^6 b - 3a^5 b^2 - 2a^4 b^3 + a^2 b^5 + b^7 \\
u &= a^7 + a^5 b^2 - 2a^3 b^4 - 3a^2 b^5 + ab^6 \\
v &= a^6 b + 3a^5 b^2 - 2a^4 b^3 + a^2 b^5 + b^7
\end{aligned} \tag{2.3.8}$$

Fermat's last theorem states that there are no integer solutions to $x^n + y^n = z^n$, when $n > 2$. This was proven by Andrew Wiles in 1995.

Pell's equation

Pell's equation is $x^2 - My^2 = 1$. The solutions, integral values of (x, y), arise from continued fraction convergents of $\sqrt{M}$ (see page 88).

The number $\sqrt{2}$ has the continued fraction expansion $[1, 2, 2, 2, 2, \dots]$. Hence, the first few convergents are $\frac{3}{2}, \frac{7}{5}, \frac{17}{12}, \frac{41}{29}, \frac{99}{70}, \dots$ In this case, every second convergent represents a solution:

$$3^2 - 2 \cdot 2^2 = 1,$$
$$17^2 - 2 \cdot 12^2 = 1, \text{ and}$$
$$99^2 - 2 \cdot 70^2 = 1.$$

Pythagorean triples

If the positive integers A, B, and C satisfy the relationship $A^2 + B^2 = C^2$, then the triplet (A, B, C) is a Pythagorean triple. It is possible to construct a right triangle with sides of length A and B and a hypotenuse of C.

There are infinitely many Pythagorean triples. The most general solution to $A^2 + B^2 = C^2$, with $(A, B) = 1$ and A even, is given by

$$A = 2xy \qquad B = x^2 - y^2 \qquad C = x^2 + y^2, \tag{2.3.9}$$

where x and y are relatively prime integers of opposite parity with $x > y > 0$. The following shows some Pythagorean triples with the associated (x, y) values.

x	y	A	B	C
2	1	4	3	5
4	1	8	15	17
6	1	12	35	37
8	1	16	63	65
10	1	20	99	101
3	2	12	5	13
5	2	20	21	29
7	2	28	45	51
4	3	24	7	25

Waring's problem

If each positive integer can be expressed as a sum of n k^{th} powers, then there is a least value of n for which this is true: this is the number $g(k)$. For all sufficiently large numbers, however, a smaller value of n may suffice: this is the number $G(k)$. Lagrange's theorem states: "Every positive integer is the sum of four squares;" this is equivalent to the statement $g(2) = 4$. The following identity shows how a product can be written as the sum of four squares:

$$(x_1^2 + x_2^2 + x_3^2 + x_4^2)(y_1^2 + y_2^2 + y_3^2 + y_4^2) =$$
$$(x_1 y_1 + x_2 y_2 + x_3 y_3 + x_4 y_4)^2 + (x_1 y_2 - x_2 y_1 + x_3 y_4 - x_4 y_3)^2$$
$$+ (x_1 y_3 - x_3 y_1 + x_4 y_2 - x_2 y_4)^2 + (x_1 y_4 - x_4 y_1 + x_2 y_3 - x_3 y_2)^2 \tag{2.3.10}$$

Consider $k = 3$; all numbers can be written as the sum of not more than 9 cubes, so that $g(3) = 9$. However, only the two numbers

$$23 = 2^3 + 2^3 + 1^3 + 1^3 + 1^3 + 1^3 + 1^3 + 1^3 + 1^3,$$
$$239 = 4^3 + 4^3 + 3^3 + 3^3 + 3^3 + 3^3 + 1^3 + 1^3 + 1^3,$$

require the use of 9 cubes; so $G(3) \leq 8$.

The current known values of $g(k)$ include: $g(3) = 9$, $g(4) \geq 19$, $g(5) = 37$ and

$$g(k) = \left\lfloor \left(\frac{3}{2}\right)^k \right\rfloor + 2^k - 2 \text{ for } 6 \leq k \leq 471600000.$$

The value of $G(k)$ is only known for two values of k, $G(2) = 4$ and $G(4) = 16$. It is known that: $4 \leq G(3) \leq 7$, $G(5) \leq 23$, $G(6) \leq 36$, $G(7) \leq 137$, and $G(8) \leq 163$. It is also known that

$$G(k) \leq 6k \log k + \left(4 + 3\log\left(3 + \frac{2}{k}\right)\right) k + 3. \tag{2.3.11}$$

2.3.5 GREATEST COMMON DIVISOR

The greatest common divisor (GCD) of the integers n and m is the largest integer that evenly divides both n and m. The Euclidean algorithm is frequently used for computing the GCD of two numbers; it utilizes the fact that $a = \lfloor \frac{a}{b} \rfloor b + c$ where $0 \leq c < b$. For example, consider 78 and 21. Since $78 = 3 \cdot 21 + 15$, the largest integer that evenly divides both 78 and 21 is also the largest integer that evenly divides both 21 and 15. Iterating results in

$$78 = 3 \cdot 21 + 15$$
$$21 = 1 \cdot 15 + 6$$
$$15 = 2 \cdot 6 + 3$$
$$6 = 2 \cdot 3 + 0$$

Hence GCD(78,21) = GCD(6,3) = 3. A common notation for GCD(n, m) is (n, m).

Two numbers, a and b, are said to be *relatively prime* if they have no divisors in common; i.e., if GCD$(a, b) = 1$. The probability that two integers chosen randomly are relatively prime is $\pi/6$.

2.3.6 LEAST COMMON MULTIPLE

The least common multiple of the integers a and b (denoted LCM(a, b)) is the smallest integer r that is divisible by both a and b. The simplest way to find the LCM of a and b is via the formula LCM$(a, b) = ab/\text{GCD}(a, b)$. For example, LCM$(10, 4) = \frac{10 \cdot 4}{\text{GCD}(10,4)} = \frac{10 \cdot 4}{2} = 20$.

2.3.7   FAREY SEQUENCES

The Farey series of order n, $\mathcal{F}_n$, is the ascending series of irreducible fractions between zero and one whose denominators do not exceed n. The fraction k/m belongs to $\mathcal{F}_n$ if $0 \le k \le m \le n$ and k and m are relatively prime. If k/m and k'/m' are two successive terms of $\mathcal{F}_n$ then $mk' - km' = 1$. $\mathcal{F}_{n-1}$ can be obtained from $\mathcal{F}_n$ by deleting terms with denominators of n.

$$\mathcal{F}_3 = \left(\frac{0}{1}, \frac{1}{3}, \frac{1}{2}, \frac{2}{3}, \frac{1}{1} \right),$$

$$\mathcal{F}_5 = \left(\frac{0}{1}, \frac{1}{5}, \frac{1}{4}, \frac{1}{3}, \frac{2}{5}, \frac{1}{2}, \frac{3}{5}, \frac{2}{3}, \frac{3}{4}, \frac{4}{5}, \frac{1}{1} \right).$$

2.3.8   MÖBIUS FUNCTION

The Möbius function is defined by

- $\mu(1) = 1$
- $\mu(n) = 0$ if n has a squared factor
- $\mu(p_1 p_2 \ldots p_k) = (-1)^k$ if all the primes $\{p_1, \ldots, p_k\}$ are distinct

The Möbius inversion formula states that, if $g(n) = \sum_{d|n} f(d)$, then

$$f(n) = \sum_{d|n} \mu\left(\frac{n}{d}\right) g(d) = \sum_{d|n} \mu(d) g\left(\frac{n}{d}\right).$$

For example, $\phi(n) = n \sum_{d|n} \frac{\mu(d)}{d}$.

The generalized Möbius formula in one dimension is that: if $g(x) = \sum_{n=1}^{\infty} f(n^\alpha x)$, then $f(x) = \sum_{n=1}^{\infty} \mu(n) g(n^\alpha x)$, for any real α except 0.

The table below can be derived from the table in Section 2.3.13 (For example, $\mu(2) = -1$, $\mu(4) = 0$, and $\mu(6) = 1$).

	_0	_1	_2	_3	_4	_5	_6	_7	_8	_9
0_		1	−1	−1	0	−1	1	−1	0	0
1_	1	−1	0	−1	1	1	0	−1	0	−1
2_	0	1	1	−1	0	0	1	0	0	−1
3_	−1	−1	0	1	1	1	0	−1	1	1
4_	0	−1	−1	−1	0	0	1	−1	0	0
5_	0	1	0	−1	0	1	0	1	1	−1
6_	0	−1	1	0	0	1	−1	−1	0	1
7_	−1	−1	0	−1	1	0	0	1	−1	−1
8_	0	0	1	−1	0	1	1	1	0	−1
9_	0	1	0	1	1	1	0	−1	0	0
10_	0	−1	−1	−1	0	−1	1	−1	0	−1
11_	−1	1	0	−1	−1	1	0	0	1	1
12_	0	0	1	1	0	0	0	−1	0	1
13_	−1	−1	0	1	1	0	0	−1	−1	−1
14_	0	1	1	1	0	1	1	0	0	−1
15_	0	−1	0	0	−1	1	0	−1	1	1
16_	0	1	0	−1	0	−1	1	−1	0	0
17_	−1	0	0	−1	−1	0	0	1	1	−1
18_	0	−1	−1	1	0	1	−1	1	0	0
19_	−1	−1	0	−1	1	−1	0	−1	0	−1

2.3.9 PRIME NUMBERS

- A *prime number* is a positive integer greater than 1 with no positive, integral divisors other than 1 and itself. There are infinitely many prime numbers, $2, 3, 5, 7, \ldots$.

- *Twin primes* are prime numbers that differ by two: $(3, 5)$, $(5, 7)$, $(11, 13)$, $(17, 19), \ldots$. It is not known whether there are infinitely many twin primes.

- For every integer $n \geq 2$, the numbers $\{n! + 2, n! + 3, \ldots, n! + n\}$ are a sequence of $n - 1$ consecutive composite numbers.

The function $\pi(x)$ represents the number of primes less than x. The prime number theorem states that $\pi(x) \sim x/\log x$ as $x \to \infty$.

x	100	1000	10000	10^5	10^6	10^7
$\pi(x)$	25	168	1229	9592	78498	664579

Prime formula

The set of prime numbers is identical with the set of positive values taken on by the polynomial of degree 25 in the 26 variables $\{a, b, \ldots, z\}$:

$$(k+2)\{1 - [wz+h+j-q]^2 - [(gk+2g+k+1)(h+j)+h-z]^2 - [2n+p+q+z-e]^2$$
$$- [16(k+1)^3(k+2)(n+1)^2+1-f^2]^2 - [e^3(e+2)(a+1)^2+1-o^2]^2 - [(a^2-1)y^2+1-x^2]^2$$
$$- [16r^2y^4(a^2-1)+1-u^2]^2 - [((a+u^2(u^2-a))^2-1)(n+4dy)^2+1-(x+cu)^2]^2 - [n+l+v-y]^2$$
$$- [(a^2-1)l^2+1-m^2]^2 - [ai+k+1-l-i]^2 - [p+l(a-n-1)+b(2an+2a-n^2-2n-2)-m]^2$$
$$- [q+y(a-p-1)+s(2ap+2a-p^2-2p-2)-x]^2 - [z+pl(a-p)+t(2ap-p^2-1)-pm]^2\}.$$

$$(2.3.12)$$

Although this polynomial appears to factor, the factors are improper, $P = P \cdot 1$. Note that this formula will also take on negative values, such as -76.

There also exists a prime representing polynomial which contains 12 variables.

Dirichlet's theorem on primes in arithmetic progressions: Let a and b be relatively prime positive integers. Then the arithmetic progression $an + b$ (for $n = 1, 2, \ldots$) contains infinitely many primes.

Proofs of primality

Lucas–Lehmer primality test: Define the sequence, $r_1 = 3$, $r_{m+1} = r_m^2 - 2$. If p is a prime of the form $4n+3$ and $M_p = 2^p - 1$, then M_p will be prime (called a Mersenne prime) if, and only if, M_p divides r_{p-1}.

This simple test is the reason that the largest known prime numbers are Mersenne primes. For example, consider $p = 7$ and $M_7 = 127$. The $\{r_n\}$ sequence is $\{3, 7, 47, 2207 \equiv 48, 2302 \equiv 16, 254 \equiv 0\}$; hence M_7 is prime.

It is also possible to give, for a general number p, a "certificate" that p is prime. It is easy to use the certificate to verify that a given number is prime (easier than it was to determine that it was prime in the first place). There are several types of certificates that can be given. Pratt's certificate consists of a number a and the factorization of the number $p - 1$. This method is feasible if $p - 1$ is easy to factor.

The number p will be prime if there exists a primitive root a in the field GF$[p]$. This primitive root must satisfy the conditions $a^{p-1} = 1$ (mod p) and $a^{(p-1)/q} \neq 1$ (mod p) for any prime q that divides p. For example, the number $p = 31$ has $p - 1 = 30 = 2 \cdot 3 \cdot 5$, and a primitive root is given by $a = 3$. Hence, to verify that $p = 31$ is prime, we compute

$$3^{(31-1)/2} = 3^{15} \equiv 14348907 \equiv -1 \neq 1 \qquad \text{(mod 31),}$$
$$3^{(31-1)/3} = 3^{10} \equiv 59049 \equiv 25 \neq 1 \qquad \text{(mod 31),}$$
$$3^{(31-1)/5} = 3^6 \equiv 719 \equiv 16 \neq 1 \qquad \text{(mod 31),}$$
$$3^{(31-1)} = \left(3^{(31-1)/2}\right)^2 \equiv (-1)^2 = 1 \qquad \text{(mod 31).}$$

Probabilistic primality test

Let n be a number whose primality is to be determined. Probabilistic primality tests can return one of two results: either a proof that the number n is composite or a statement of the form, "The probability that the number n is not prime is less than ϵ", where ϵ can be specified by the user. Typically, we take $\epsilon = 2^{-200} < 10^{-60}$.

From Fermat's theorem, if $b \neq 0$, then $b^{n-1} = 1 \pmod{n}$ whenever n is prime. If this holds, then n is a *probable prime to the base* b. Given a value of n, if a value of b can be found such that this does not hold, then n cannot be prime. It can happen, however, that a probable prime is not prime.

Let $P(x)$ be the probability that n is composite under the hypotheses:

1. n is an odd integer chosen randomly from the range $[2, x]$;

2. b is an integer chosen randomly from the range $[2, n - 2]$;

3. n is a probable prime to the base b.

Then $P(x) \leq (\log x)^{-197}$ for $x \geq 10^{10000}$.

A different test can be obtained from the following theorem. Given the number n, find s and t with $n - 1 = 2^s t$, with t odd. Then choose a random integer b from the range $[2, n - 2]$. If either

$$b^t = 1 \pmod{n} \qquad \text{or} \qquad b^{2^i t} = -1 \pmod{n}, \quad \text{for some } i < s,$$

then n is a *strong probable prime to the base* b. Every odd prime must pass this test. If $n > 1$ is an odd composite, then the probability that it is a strong probable prime to the base b, when b is chosen randomly, is less than $1/4$.

A stronger test can be obtained by choosing k independent values for b in the range $[2, n - 2]$ and checking the above relation for each value of b. Let $P_k(x)$ be the probability that n is found to be a strong probable prime to each base b. Then $P_k(x) \leq 4^{-(k-1)} P(x)/(1 - P(x))$.

2.3.10 PRIME NUMBERS LESS THAN 10,000

The prime number p_{10n+k} is found by looking at the row begining with $n\_$ and at the column beginning with $\_k$.

	_0	_1	_2	_3	_4	_5	_6	_7	_8	_9
		2	3	5	7	11	13	17	19	23
1_	29	31	37	41	43	47	53	59	61	67
2_	71	73	79	83	89	97	101	103	107	109
3_	113	127	131	137	139	149	151	157	163	167
4_	173	179	181	191	193	197	199	211	223	227
5_	229	233	239	241	251	257	263	269	271	277
6_	281	283	293	307	311	313	317	331	337	347
7_	349	353	359	367	373	379	383	389	397	401
8_	409	419	421	431	433	439	443	449	457	461
9_	463	467	479	487	491	499	503	509	521	523
10_	541	547	557	563	569	571	577	587	593	599
11_	601	607	613	617	619	631	641	643	647	653
12_	659	661	673	677	683	691	701	709	719	727
13_	733	739	743	751	757	761	769	773	787	797
14_	809	811	821	823	827	829	839	853	857	859
15_	863	877	881	883	887	907	911	919	929	937

	_0	_1	_2	_3	_4	_5	_6	_7	_8	_9
16_	941	947	953	967	971	977	983	991	997	1009
17_	1013	1019	1021	1031	1033	1039	1049	1051	1061	1063
18_	1069	1087	1091	1093	1097	1103	1109	1117	1123	1129
19_	1151	1153	1163	1171	1181	1187	1193	1201	1213	1217
20_	1223	1229	1231	1237	1249	1259	1277	1279	1283	1289
21_	1291	1297	1301	1303	1307	1319	1321	1327	1361	1367
22_	1373	1381	1399	1409	1423	1427	1429	1433	1439	1447
23_	1451	1453	1459	1471	1481	1483	1487	1489	1493	1499
24_	1511	1523	1531	1543	1549	1553	1559	1567	1571	1579
25_	1583	1597	1601	1607	1609	1613	1619	1621	1627	1637
26_	1657	1663	1667	1669	1693	1697	1699	1709	1721	1723
27_	1733	1741	1747	1753	1759	1777	1783	1787	1789	1801
28_	1811	1823	1831	1847	1861	1867	1871	1873	1877	1879
29_	1889	1901	1907	1913	1931	1933	1949	1951	1973	1979
30_	1987	1993	1997	1999	2003	2011	2017	2027	2029	2039
31_	2053	2063	2069	2081	2083	2087	2089	2099	2111	2113
32_	2129	2131	2137	2141	2143	2153	2161	2179	2203	2207
33_	2213	2221	2237	2239	2243	2251	2267	2269	2273	2281
34_	2287	2293	2297	2309	2311	2333	2339	2341	2347	2351
35_	2357	2371	2377	2381	2383	2389	2393	2399	2411	2417
36_	2423	2437	2441	2447	2459	2467	2473	2477	2503	2521
37_	2531	2539	2543	2549	2551	2557	2579	2591	2593	2609
38_	2617	2621	2633	2647	2657	2659	2663	2671	2677	2683
39_	2687	2689	2693	2699	2707	2711	2713	2719	2729	2731
40_	2741	2749	2753	2767	2777	2789	2791	2797	2801	2803
41_	2819	2833	2837	2843	2851	2857	2861	2879	2887	2897
42_	2903	2909	2917	2927	2939	2953	2957	2963	2969	2971
43_	2999	3001	3011	3019	3023	3037	3041	3049	3061	3067
44_	3079	3083	3089	3109	3119	3121	3137	3163	3167	3169
45_	3181	3187	3191	3203	3209	3217	3221	3229	3251	3253
46_	3257	3259	3271	3299	3301	3307	3313	3319	3323	3329
47_	3331	3343	3347	3359	3361	3371	3373	3389	3391	3407
48_	3413	3433	3449	3457	3461	3463	3467	3469	3491	3499
49_	3511	3517	3527	3529	3533	3539	3541	3547	3557	3559
50_	3571	3581	3583	3593	3607	3613	3617	3623	3631	3637
51_	3643	3659	3671	3673	3677	3691	3697	3701	3709	3719
52_	3727	3733	3739	3761	3767	3769	3779	3793	3797	3803
53_	3821	3823	3833	3847	3851	3853	3863	3877	3881	3889
54_	3907	3911	3917	3919	3923	3929	3931	3943	3947	3967
55_	3989	4001	4003	4007	4013	4019	4021	4027	4049	4051
56_	4057	4073	4079	4091	4093	4099	4111	4127	4129	4133
57_	4139	4153	4157	4159	4177	4201	4211	4217	4219	4229
58_	4231	4241	4243	4253	4259	4261	4271	4273	4283	4289
59_	4297	4327	4337	4339	4349	4357	4363	4373	4391	4397
60_	4409	4421	4423	4441	4447	4451	4457	4463	4481	4483
61_	4493	4507	4513	4517	4519	4523	4547	4549	4561	4567
62_	4583	4591	4597	4603	4621	4637	4639	4643	4649	4651
63_	4657	4663	4673	4679	4691	4703	4721	4723	4729	4733
64_	4751	4759	4783	4787	4789	4793	4799	4801	4813	4817
65_	4831	4861	4871	4877	4889	4903	4909	4919	4931	4933
66_	4937	4943	4951	4957	4967	4969	4973	4987	4993	4999

	_0	_1	_2	_3	_4	_5	_6	_7	_8	_9
67_	5003	5009	5011	5021	5023	5039	5051	5059	5077	5081
68_	5087	5099	5101	5107	5113	5119	5147	5153	5167	5171
69_	5179	5189	5197	5209	5227	5231	5233	5237	5261	5273
70_	5279	5281	5297	5303	5309	5323	5333	5347	5351	5381
71_	5387	5393	5399	5407	5413	5417	5419	5431	5437	5441
72_	5443	5449	5471	5477	5479	5483	5501	5503	5507	5519
73_	5521	5527	5531	5557	5563	5569	5573	5581	5591	5623
74_	5639	5641	5647	5651	5653	5657	5659	5669	5683	5689
75_	5693	5701	5711	5717	5737	5741	5743	5749	5779	5783
76_	5791	5801	5807	5813	5821	5827	5839	5843	5849	5851
77_	5857	5861	5867	5869	5879	5881	5897	5903	5923	5927
78_	5939	5953	5981	5987	6007	6011	6029	6037	6043	6047
79_	6053	6067	6073	6079	6089	6091	6101	6113	6121	6131
80_	6133	6143	6151	6163	6173	6197	6199	6203	6211	6217
81_	6221	6229	6247	6257	6263	6269	6271	6277	6287	6299
82_	6301	6311	6317	6323	6329	6337	6343	6353	6359	6361
83_	6367	6373	6379	6389	6397	6421	6427	6449	6451	6469
84_	6473	6481	6491	6521	6529	6547	6551	6553	6563	6569
85_	6571	6577	6581	6599	6607	6619	6637	6653	6659	6661
86_	6673	6679	6689	6691	6701	6703	6709	6719	6733	6737
87_	6761	6763	6779	6781	6791	6793	6803	6823	6827	6829
88_	6833	6841	6857	6863	6869	6871	6883	6899	6907	6911
89_	6917	6947	6949	6959	6961	6967	6971	6977	6983	6991
90_	6997	7001	7013	7019	7027	7039	7043	7057	7069	7079
91_	7103	7109	7121	7127	7129	7151	7159	7177	7187	7193
92_	7207	7211	7213	7219	7229	7237	7243	7247	7253	7283
93_	7297	7307	7309	7321	7331	7333	7349	7351	7369	7393
94_	7411	7417	7433	7451	7457	7459	7477	7481	7487	7489
95_	7499	7507	7517	7523	7529	7537	7541	7547	7549	7559
96_	7561	7573	7577	7583	7589	7591	7603	7607	7621	7639
97_	7643	7649	7669	7673	7681	7687	7691	7699	7703	7717
98_	7723	7727	7741	7753	7757	7759	7789	7793	7817	7823
99_	7829	7841	7853	7867	7873	7877	7879	7883	7901	7907
100_	7919	7927	7933	7937	7949	7951	7963	7993	8009	8011
101_	8017	8039	8053	8059	8069	8081	8087	8089	8093	8101
102_	8111	8117	8123	8147	8161	8167	8171	8179	8191	8209
103_	8219	8221	8231	8233	8237	8243	8263	8269	8273	8287
104_	8291	8293	8297	8311	8317	8329	8353	8363	8369	8377
105_	8387	8389	8419	8423	8429	8431	8443	8447	8461	8467
106_	8501	8513	8521	8527	8537	8539	8543	8563	8573	8581
107_	8597	8599	8609	8623	8627	8629	8641	8647	8663	8669
108_	8677	8681	8689	8693	8699	8707	8713	8719	8731	8737
109_	8741	8747	8753	8761	8779	8783	8803	8807	8819	8821
110_	8831	8837	8839	8849	8861	8863	8867	8887	8893	8923
111_	8929	8933	8941	8951	8963	8969	8971	8999	9001	9007
112_	9011	9013	9029	9041	9043	9049	9059	9067	9091	9103
113_	9109	9127	9133	9137	9151	9157	9161	9173	9181	9187
114_	9199	9203	9209	9221	9227	9239	9241	9257	9277	9281
115_	9283	9293	9311	9319	9323	9337	9341	9343	9349	9371
116_	9377	9391	9397	9403	9413	9419	9421	9431	9433	9437
117_	9439	9461	9463	9467	9473	9479	9491	9497	9511	9521

	.0	.1	.2	.3	.4	.5	.6	.7	.8	.9
118_	9533	9539	9547	9551	9587	9601	9613	9619	9623	9629
119_	9631	9643	9649	9661	9677	9679	9689	9697	9719	9721
120_	9733	9739	9743	9749	9767	9769	9781	9787	9791	9803
121_	9811	9817	9829	9833	9839	9851	9857	9859	9871	9883
122_	9887	9901	9907	9923	9929	9931	9941	9949	9967	9973

2.3.11   PRIME NUMBERS OF SPECIAL FORMS

1. As of September 1996, the largest known prime numbers, in descending order, are

Number	Number of digits
$2^{1257787} - 1$	[a]378,632
$2^{859433} - 1$	258,716
$2^{756839} - 1$	227,832
$391581 \cdot 2^{216193} - 1$	[b]65,087
$2^{216091} - 1$	65,050
$3 \cdot 2^{157169} + 1$	47,314
$9 \cdot 2^{149143} + 1$	44,898
$9 \cdot 2^{147073} + 1$	44,275
$9 \cdot 2^{145247} + 1$	43,725
$2^{132049} - 1$	39,751
$9 \cdot 2^{127003} + 1$	38,233
$5 \cdot 2^{125413} + 1$	37,754
$9 \cdot 2^{114854} + 1$	34,576
$13 \cdot 2^{114296} + 1$	34,408
$2^{110503} - 1$	33,265

[a]Largest known prime of the form $2^n - 1$, a Mersenne prime.
[b]Largest known non-Mersenne prime.

Other large primes include:

- $134088 \cdot 10^{15030} + 1$ (largest prime of the form $k \cdot 10^n + 1$, has 15,036 digits)

- $10^{11810} + 1465641 \cdot 10^{5902} + 1$ (largest palindromic prime, has 11,811 digits)

- $3610! - 1$ (largest prime factorial minus 1, has 11,277 digits)

- $2 \cdot 3^{13782} + 1$ (largest prime of the form $k \cdot 3^n + 1$, has 6,576 digits)

- $3476!! - 1$ (largest double factorial minus one, has 5,402 digits)

2. All of the known Mersenne primes of the form $2^n - 1$ are given by the values (note that n must be prime itself), $n = 2, 3, 5, 7, 13, 17, 19, 31, 61, 89, 107,$ $127, 521, 607, 1279, 2203, 2281, 3217, 4253, 4423, 9689, 9941, 11213, 19937,$ $21701, 23209, 44497, 86243, 110503, 132049, 216091, 756839, 859433,$ and 1257787.

3. The largest known twin primes are: $242206083 \cdot 2^{38880} \pm 1$ (with 11,713 digits), $570918348 \cdot 10^{5120} \pm 1$ (with 5,129 digits), and $697053813 \cdot 2^{16352} \pm 1$ (with 4,932 digits).

4. The nth repunit is $R_n = (10^n - 1)/9 = 11 \ldots 11$. The only known prime repunits correspond to $n = 2, 19, 23, 317, 1031$.

5. Prime numbers of the forms $2^n \pm a$ and $10^n \pm b$: Large prime numbers of a specified size are sometimes needed. In the following table, for a given n, $a_\pm$ and $b_\pm$ are the least values such that $2^n + a_\pm$ and $10^n + b_\pm$ are probably primes (a probabilistic primality test was used). For example, for $n = 3$, the numbers $2^3 - 1 = 7$, $2^3 + 3 = 11$, $10^3 - 3 = 997$, and $10^3 + 9 = 1009$ are all prime.

n	$2^n + a$		$10^n + b$	
	a_-	a_+	b_-	b_+
2	-1	1	-3	1
3	-1	3	-3	9
4	-3	1	-27	7
5	-1	5	-9	3
6	-3	3	-17	3
7	-1	3	-9	19
8	-5	1	-11	7
9	-3	9	-63	7
10	-3	7	-33	19
11	-9	5	-23	3
12	-3	3	-11	39
13	-1	17	-29	37
14	-3	27	-27	31
15	-19	3	-11	37
16	-15	1	-63	61
17	-1	29	-3	3
18	-5	3	-11	3
19	-1	21	-39	51
20	-3	7	-11	39
50	-27	55	-57	151
100	-15	277	-797	267
150	-3	147	-273	67
200	-75	235	-189	357
300	-153	157	-69	331
400	-593	181	-513	69
500	-863	55	-1037	961
600	-95	187	-1791	543
700	-1113	535	-2313	7
800	-105	25	-1007	1537
900	-207	693	-773	1873
1000	-1245	297	-1769	453

6. Define $p\#$ to be the product of the prime numbers less than or equal to p.

Form	Values of n or p for which the form is prime
$n! + 1$	1, 2, 3, 11, 27, 37, 41, 73, 77, 116, 154, 320, 340, 399, 427, 872, 1477, ...
$n! - 1$	3, 4, 6, 7, 12, 14, 30, 32, 33, 38, 94, 166, 324, 379, 469, 546, 974, 1963, 3507, 3610, ...
$p\# + 1$	2, 3, 5, 7, 11, 31, 379, 1019, 1021, 2657, 3229, 4547, 4787, 11549, 13649, 18523, 23801, 24029, ...
$p\# - 1$	3, 5, 11, 13, 41, 89, 317, 337, 991, 1873, 2053, 2377, 4093, 4297, 4583, 6569, 13033, 15877, ...

2.3.12 PRIME PERIOD LENGTHS

When an integer is divided by a prime p, and the result is represented as a decimal, the number of digits in the period is called $\lambda(p)$. For example, $1/7 = 0.142857\,142857\ldots$ so that $\lambda(7) = 6$, and $1/37 = 0.027\,027\ldots$ so that $\lambda(37) = 3$. The period $\lambda(p)$ always divides $p - 1$.

Prime	3	5	7	11	13	17	19	23	29	31	37
Period length	1	1	6	2	6	16	18	22	28	15	3

2.3.13 FACTORIZATION TABLE

The following is a list of the factors of numbers up to 1,000. When a number is prime, it is shown in a boldface.

	0	1	2	3	4	5	6	7	8	9
0_	$2 \cdot 5$	**1**	**2**	**3**	2^2	**5**	$2 \cdot 3$	**7**	2^3	3^2
1_	$2^2 \cdot 5$	**11**	$2^2 \cdot 3$	**13**	$2 \cdot 7$	$3 \cdot 5$	2^4	**17**	$2 \cdot 3^2$	**19**
2_	$2 \cdot 3 \cdot 5$	$3 \cdot 7$	$2 \cdot 11$	**23**	$2^3 \cdot 3$	5^2	$2 \cdot 13$	3^3	$2^2 \cdot 7$	**29**
3_	$2^3 \cdot 5$	**31**	2^5	$3 \cdot 11$	$2 \cdot 17$	$5 \cdot 7$	$2^2 \cdot 3^2$	**37**	$2 \cdot 19$	$3 \cdot 13$
4_	$2 \cdot 5^2$	**41**	$2 \cdot 3 \cdot 7$	**43**	$2^2 \cdot 11$	$3^2 \cdot 5$	$2 \cdot 23$	**47**	$2^4 \cdot 3$	7^2
5_	$2^2 \cdot 3 \cdot 5$	$3 \cdot 17$	$2^2 \cdot 13$	**53**	$2 \cdot 3^3$	$5 \cdot 11$	$2^3 \cdot 7$	$3 \cdot 19$	$2 \cdot 29$	**59**
6_	$2 \cdot 5 \cdot 7$	**61**	$2 \cdot 31$	$3^2 \cdot 7$	2^6	$5 \cdot 13$	$2 \cdot 3 \cdot 11$	**67**	$2^2 \cdot 17$	$3 \cdot 23$
7_	$2^4 \cdot 5$	**71**	$2^3 \cdot 3^2$	**73**	$2 \cdot 37$	$3 \cdot 5^2$	$2^2 \cdot 19$	$7 \cdot 11$	$2 \cdot 3 \cdot 13$	**79**
8_	$2 \cdot 3^2 \cdot 5$	3^4	$2 \cdot 41$	**83**	$2^2 \cdot 3 \cdot 7$	$5 \cdot 17$	$2 \cdot 43$	$3 \cdot 29$	$2^3 \cdot 11$	**89**
9_	$2 \cdot 3^2 \cdot 5$	$7 \cdot 13$	$2^2 \cdot 23$	$3 \cdot 31$	$2 \cdot 47$	$5 \cdot 19$	$2^5 \cdot 3$	**97**	$2 \cdot 7^2$	$3^2 \cdot 11$
10_	$2^2 \cdot 5^2$	**101**	$2 \cdot 3 \cdot 17$	**103**	$2^3 \cdot 13$	$3 \cdot 5 \cdot 7$	$2 \cdot 53$	**107**	$2^2 \cdot 3^3$	**109**
11_	$2 \cdot 5 \cdot 11$	$3 \cdot 37$	$2^4 \cdot 7$	**113**	$2 \cdot 3 \cdot 19$	$5 \cdot 23$	$2^2 \cdot 29$	$3^2 \cdot 13$	$2 \cdot 59$	$7 \cdot 17$
12_	$2^3 \cdot 3 \cdot 5$	11^2	$2 \cdot 61$	$3 \cdot 41$	$2^2 \cdot 31$	5^3	$2 \cdot 3^2 \cdot 7$	**127**	2^7	$3 \cdot 43$
13_	$2 \cdot 5 \cdot 13$	**131**	$2^2 \cdot 3 \cdot 11$	$7 \cdot 19$	$2 \cdot 67$	$3^3 \cdot 5$	$2^3 \cdot 17$	**137**	$2 \cdot 3 \cdot 23$	**139**
14_	$2^2 \cdot 5 \cdot 7$	$3 \cdot 47$	$2 \cdot 71$	$11 \cdot 13$	$2^4 \cdot 3^2$	$5 \cdot 29$	$2 \cdot 73$	$3 \cdot 7^2$	$2^2 \cdot 37$	**149**
15_	$2 \cdot 3 \cdot 5^2$	**151**	$2^3 \cdot 19$	$3^2 \cdot 17$	$2 \cdot 7 \cdot 11$	$5 \cdot 31$	$2^2 \cdot 3 \cdot 13$	**157**	$2 \cdot 79$	$3 \cdot 53$
16_	$2^5 \cdot 5$	$7 \cdot 23$	$2 \cdot 3^4$	**163**	$2^2 \cdot 41$	$3 \cdot 5 \cdot 11$	$2 \cdot 83$	**167**	$2^3 \cdot 3 \cdot 7$	13^2
17_	$2 \cdot 5 \cdot 17$	$3^2 \cdot 19$	$2^2 \cdot 43$	**173**	$2 \cdot 3 \cdot 29$	$5^2 \cdot 7$	$2^4 \cdot 11$	$3 \cdot 59$	$2 \cdot 89$	**179**
18_	$2^2 \cdot 3^2 \cdot 5$	**181**	$2 \cdot 7 \cdot 13$	$3 \cdot 61$	$2^3 \cdot 23$	$5 \cdot 37$	$2 \cdot 3 \cdot 31$	$11 \cdot 17$	$2^2 \cdot 47$	$3^3 \cdot 7$
19_	$2 \cdot 5 \cdot 19$	**191**	$2^6 \cdot 3$	**193**	$2 \cdot 97$	$3 \cdot 5 \cdot 13$	$2^2 \cdot 7^2$	**197**	$2 \cdot 3^2 \cdot 11$	**199**
20_	$2 \cdot 3 \cdot 5 \cdot 7$	$3 \cdot 67$	$2 \cdot 101$	$7 \cdot 29$	$2^2 \cdot 3 \cdot 17$	$5 \cdot 41$	$2 \cdot 103$	$3^2 \cdot 23$	$2^4 \cdot 13$	$11 \cdot 19$
21_	$2^2 \cdot 5 \cdot 11$	**211**	$2^2 \cdot 53$	$3 \cdot 71$	$2 \cdot 107$	$5 \cdot 43$	$2^3 \cdot 3^3$	$7 \cdot 31$	$2 \cdot 109$	$3 \cdot 73$
22_	$2 \cdot 5 \cdot 23$	$13 \cdot 17$	$2 \cdot 3 \cdot 37$	**223**	$2^5 \cdot 7$	$3^2 \cdot 5^2$	$2 \cdot 113$	**227**	$2^2 \cdot 3 \cdot 19$	**229**
23_	$2^4 \cdot 3 \cdot 5$	$3 \cdot 7 \cdot 11$	$2^3 \cdot 29$	**233**	$2 \cdot 3^2 \cdot 13$	$5 \cdot 47$	$2^2 \cdot 59$	$3 \cdot 79$	$2 \cdot 7 \cdot 17$	**239**
24_		**241**	$2 \cdot 11^2$	3^5	$2^2 \cdot 61$	$5 \cdot 7^2$	$2 \cdot 3 \cdot 41$	$13 \cdot 19$	$2^3 \cdot 31$	$3 \cdot 83$

	0	1	2	3	4	5	6	7	8	9
25_	$2 \cdot 5^3$	**251**	$2^2 \cdot 3^2 \cdot 7$	$11 \cdot 23$	$2 \cdot 127$	$3 \cdot 5 \cdot 17$	2^8	**257**	$2 \cdot 3 \cdot 43$	$7 \cdot 37$
26_	$2^2 \cdot 5 \cdot 13$	$3^2 \cdot 29$	$2 \cdot 131$	**263**	$2^3 \cdot 3 \cdot 11$	$5 \cdot 53$	$2 \cdot 7 \cdot 19$	$3 \cdot 89$	$2^2 \cdot 67$	**269**
27_	$2 \cdot 3^3 \cdot 5$	**271**	$2^4 \cdot 17$	$3 \cdot 7 \cdot 13$	$2 \cdot 137$	$5^2 \cdot 11$	$2^2 \cdot 3 \cdot 23$	**277**	$2 \cdot 139$	$3^2 \cdot 31$
28_	$2^3 \cdot 5 \cdot 7$	**281**	$2 \cdot 3 \cdot 47$	**283**	$2^2 \cdot 71$	$3 \cdot 5 \cdot 19$	$2 \cdot 11 \cdot 13$	$7 \cdot 41$	$2^5 \cdot 3^2$	17^2
29_	$2 \cdot 5 \cdot 29$	$3 \cdot 97$	$2^2 \cdot 73$	**293**	$2 \cdot 3 \cdot 7^2$	$5 \cdot 59$	$2^3 \cdot 37$	$3^3 \cdot 11$	$2 \cdot 149$	$13 \cdot 23$
30_	$2^2 \cdot 3 \cdot 5^2$	$7 \cdot 43$	$2 \cdot 151$	$3 \cdot 101$	$2^4 \cdot 19$	$5 \cdot 61$	$2 \cdot 3^2 \cdot 17$	**307**	$2^2 \cdot 7 \cdot 11$	$3 \cdot 103$
31_	$2 \cdot 5 \cdot 31$	**311**	$2^3 \cdot 3 \cdot 13$	**313**	$2 \cdot 157$	$3^2 \cdot 5 \cdot 7$	$2^2 \cdot 79$	**317**	$2 \cdot 3 \cdot 53$	$11 \cdot 29$
32_	$2^6 \cdot 5$	$3 \cdot 107$	$2 \cdot 7 \cdot 23$	$17 \cdot 19$	$2^2 \cdot 3^4$	$5^2 \cdot 13$	$2 \cdot 163$	$3 \cdot 109$	$2^3 \cdot 41$	$7 \cdot 47$
33_	$2 \cdot 3 \cdot 5 \cdot 11$	**331**	$2^2 \cdot 83$	$3^2 \cdot 37$	$2 \cdot 167$	$5 \cdot 67$	$2^4 \cdot 3 \cdot 7$	**337**	$2 \cdot 13^2$	$3 \cdot 113$
34_	$2^2 \cdot 5 \cdot 17$	$11 \cdot 31$	$2 \cdot 3^2 \cdot 19$	7^3	$2^3 \cdot 43$	$3 \cdot 5 \cdot 23$	$2 \cdot 173$	**347**	$2^2 \cdot 3 \cdot 29$	**349**
35_	$2 \cdot 5^2 \cdot 7$	$3^3 \cdot 13$	$2^5 \cdot 11$	**353**	$2 \cdot 3 \cdot 59$	$5 \cdot 71$	$2^2 \cdot 89$	$3 \cdot 7 \cdot 17$	$2 \cdot 179$	**359**
36_	$2^3 \cdot 3^2 \cdot 5$	19^2	$2 \cdot 181$	$3 \cdot 11^2$	$2^2 \cdot 7 \cdot 13$	$5 \cdot 73$	$2 \cdot 3 \cdot 61$	**367**	$2^4 \cdot 23$	$3^2 \cdot 41$
37_	$2 \cdot 5 \cdot 37$	$7 \cdot 53$	$2^2 \cdot 3 \cdot 31$	**373**	$2 \cdot 11 \cdot 17$	$3 \cdot 5^3$	$2^3 \cdot 47$	$13 \cdot 29$	$2 \cdot 3^3 \cdot 7$	**379**
38_	$2^2 \cdot 5 \cdot 19$	$3 \cdot 127$	$2 \cdot 191$	**383**	$2^7 \cdot 3$	$5 \cdot 7 \cdot 11$	$2 \cdot 193$	$3^2 \cdot 43$	$2^2 \cdot 97$	**389**
39_	$2 \cdot 3 \cdot 5 \cdot 13$	$17 \cdot 23$	$2^3 \cdot 7^2$	$3 \cdot 131$	$2 \cdot 197$	$5 \cdot 79$	$2^2 \cdot 3^2 \cdot 11$	**397**	$2 \cdot 199$	$3 \cdot 7 \cdot 19$
40_	$2^4 \cdot 5^2$	**401**	$2 \cdot 3 \cdot 67$	$13 \cdot 31$	$2^2 \cdot 101$	$3^4 \cdot 5$	$2 \cdot 7 \cdot 29$	$11 \cdot 37$	$2^3 \cdot 3 \cdot 17$	**409**
41_	$2 \cdot 5 \cdot 41$	$3 \cdot 137$	$2^2 \cdot 103$	$7 \cdot 59$	$2 \cdot 3^2 \cdot 23$	$5 \cdot 83$	$2^5 \cdot 13$	$3 \cdot 139$	$2 \cdot 11 \cdot 19$	**419**
42_	$2^2 \cdot 3 \cdot 5 \cdot 7$	**421**	$2 \cdot 211$	$3^2 \cdot 47$	$2^3 \cdot 53$	$5^2 \cdot 17$	$2 \cdot 3 \cdot 71$	$7 \cdot 61$	$2^2 \cdot 107$	$3 \cdot 11 \cdot 13$
43_	$2 \cdot 5 \cdot 43$	**431**	$2^4 \cdot 3^3$	**433**	$2 \cdot 7 \cdot 31$	$3 \cdot 5 \cdot 29$	$2^2 \cdot 109$	$19 \cdot 23$	$2 \cdot 3 \cdot 73$	**439**
44_	$2^3 \cdot 5 \cdot 11$	$3^2 \cdot 7^2$	$2 \cdot 13 \cdot 17$	**443**	$2^2 \cdot 3 \cdot 37$	$5 \cdot 89$	$2 \cdot 223$	$3 \cdot 149$	$2^6 \cdot 7$	**449**
45_	$2 \cdot 3^2 \cdot 5^2$	$11 \cdot 41$	$2^2 \cdot 113$	$3 \cdot 151$	$2 \cdot 227$	$5 \cdot 7 \cdot 13$	$2^3 \cdot 3 \cdot 19$	**457**	$2 \cdot 229$	$3^3 \cdot 17$
46_	$2^2 \cdot 5 \cdot 23$	**461**	$2 \cdot 3 \cdot 7 \cdot 11$	**463**	$2^4 \cdot 29$	$3 \cdot 5 \cdot 31$	$2 \cdot 233$	**467**	$2^2 \cdot 3^2 \cdot 13$	$7 \cdot 67$
47_	$2 \cdot 5 \cdot 47$	$3 \cdot 157$	$2^3 \cdot 59$	$11 \cdot 43$	$2 \cdot 3 \cdot 79$	$5^2 \cdot 19$	$2^2 \cdot 7 \cdot 17$	$3^2 \cdot 53$	$2 \cdot 239$	**479**
48_	$2^5 \cdot 3 \cdot 5$	$13 \cdot 37$	$2 \cdot 241$	$3 \cdot 7 \cdot 23$	$2^2 \cdot 11^2$	$5 \cdot 97$	$2 \cdot 3^5$	**487**	$2^3 \cdot 61$	$3 \cdot 163$
49_	$2 \cdot 5 \cdot 7^2$	**491**	$2^2 \cdot 3 \cdot 41$	$17 \cdot 29$	$2 \cdot 13 \cdot 19$	$3^2 \cdot 5 \cdot 11$	$2^4 \cdot 31$	$7 \cdot 71$	$2 \cdot 3 \cdot 83$	**499**

	0	1	2	3	4	5	6	7	8	9
50_	$2^2 \cdot 5^3$	$3 \cdot 167$	$2 \cdot 251$	**503**	$2^3 \cdot 3^2 \cdot 7$	$5 \cdot 101$	$2 \cdot 11 \cdot 23$	$3 \cdot 13^2$	$2^2 \cdot 127$	**509**
51_	$2 \cdot 3 \cdot 5 \cdot 17$	$7 \cdot 73$	2^9	$3^3 \cdot 19$	$2 \cdot 257$	$5 \cdot 103$	$2^2 \cdot 3 \cdot 43$	$11 \cdot 47$	$2 \cdot 7 \cdot 37$	$3 \cdot 173$
52_	$2^3 \cdot 5 \cdot 13$	**521**	$2 \cdot 3^2 \cdot 29$	**523**	$2^2 \cdot 131$	$3 \cdot 5^2 \cdot 7$	$2 \cdot 263$	$17 \cdot 31$	$2^4 \cdot 3 \cdot 11$	23^2
53_	$2 \cdot 5 \cdot 53$	$3^2 \cdot 59$	$2^2 \cdot 7 \cdot 19$	$13 \cdot 41$	$2 \cdot 3 \cdot 89$	$5 \cdot 107$	$2^3 \cdot 67$	$3 \cdot 179$	$2 \cdot 269$	$7^2 \cdot 11$
54_	$2^2 \cdot 3^3 \cdot 5$	**541**	$2 \cdot 271$	$3 \cdot 181$	$2^5 \cdot 17$	$5 \cdot 109$	$2 \cdot 3 \cdot 7 \cdot 13$	**547**	$2^2 \cdot 137$	$3^2 \cdot 61$
55_	$2 \cdot 5^2 \cdot 11$	$19 \cdot 29$	$2^3 \cdot 3 \cdot 23$	$7 \cdot 79$	$2 \cdot 277$	$3 \cdot 5 \cdot 37$	$2^2 \cdot 139$	**557**	$2 \cdot 3^2 \cdot 31$	$13 \cdot 43$
56_	$2^4 \cdot 5 \cdot 7$	$3 \cdot 11 \cdot 17$	$2 \cdot 281$	**563**	$2^2 \cdot 3 \cdot 47$	$5 \cdot 113$	$2 \cdot 283$	$3^4 \cdot 7$	$2^3 \cdot 71$	**569**
57_	$2 \cdot 3 \cdot 5 \cdot 19$	**571**	$2^2 \cdot 11 \cdot 13$	$3 \cdot 191$	$2 \cdot 7 \cdot 41$	$5^2 \cdot 23$	$2^6 \cdot 3^2$	**577**	$2 \cdot 17^2$	$3 \cdot 193$
58_	$2^2 \cdot 5 \cdot 29$	$7 \cdot 83$	$2 \cdot 3 \cdot 97$	$11 \cdot 53$	$2^3 \cdot 73$	$3^2 \cdot 5 \cdot 13$	$2 \cdot 293$	**587**	$2^2 \cdot 3 \cdot 7^2$	$19 \cdot 31$
59_	$2 \cdot 5 \cdot 59$	$3 \cdot 197$	$2^4 \cdot 37$	**593**	$2 \cdot 3^3 \cdot 11$	$5 \cdot 7 \cdot 17$	$2^2 \cdot 149$	$3 \cdot 199$	$2 \cdot 13 \cdot 23$	**599**
60_	$2^3 \cdot 3 \cdot 5^2$	**601**	$2 \cdot 7 \cdot 43$	$3^2 \cdot 67$	$2^2 \cdot 151$	$5 \cdot 11^2$	$2 \cdot 3 \cdot 101$	**607**	$2^5 \cdot 19$	$3 \cdot 7 \cdot 29$
61_	$2 \cdot 5 \cdot 61$	$13 \cdot 47$	$2^2 \cdot 3^2 \cdot 17$	**613**	$2 \cdot 307$	$3 \cdot 5 \cdot 41$	$2^3 \cdot 7 \cdot 11$	**617**	$2 \cdot 3 \cdot 103$	**619**
62_	$2^2 \cdot 5 \cdot 31$	$3^3 \cdot 23$	$2 \cdot 311$	$7 \cdot 89$	$2^4 \cdot 3 \cdot 13$	5^4	$2 \cdot 313$	$3 \cdot 11 \cdot 19$	$2^2 \cdot 157$	$17 \cdot 37$
63_	$2 \cdot 3^2 \cdot 5 \cdot 7$	**631**	$2^3 \cdot 79$	$3 \cdot 211$	$2 \cdot 317$	$5 \cdot 127$	$2^2 \cdot 3 \cdot 53$	$7^2 \cdot 13$	$2 \cdot 11 \cdot 29$	$3^2 \cdot 71$
64_	$2^7 \cdot 5$	**641**	$2 \cdot 3 \cdot 107$	**643**	$2^2 \cdot 7 \cdot 23$	$3 \cdot 5 \cdot 43$	$2 \cdot 17 \cdot 19$	**647**	$2^3 \cdot 3^4$	$11 \cdot 59$
65_	$2 \cdot 5^2 \cdot 13$	$3 \cdot 7 \cdot 31$	$2^2 \cdot 163$	**653**	$2 \cdot 3 \cdot 109$	$5 \cdot 131$	$2^4 \cdot 41$	$3^2 \cdot 73$	$2 \cdot 7 \cdot 47$	**659**
66_	$2^2 \cdot 3 \cdot 5 \cdot 11$	**661**	$2 \cdot 331$	$3 \cdot 13 \cdot 17$	$2^3 \cdot 83$	$5 \cdot 7 \cdot 19$	$2 \cdot 3^2 \cdot 37$	$23 \cdot 29$	$2^2 \cdot 167$	$3 \cdot 223$
67_	$2 \cdot 5 \cdot 67$	$11 \cdot 61$	$2^5 \cdot 3 \cdot 7$	**673**	$2 \cdot 337$	$3^3 \cdot 5^2$	$2^2 \cdot 13^2$	**677**	$2 \cdot 3 \cdot 113$	$7 \cdot 97$
68_	$2^3 \cdot 5 \cdot 17$	$3 \cdot 227$	$2 \cdot 11 \cdot 31$	**683**	$2^2 \cdot 3^2 \cdot 19$	$5 \cdot 137$	$2 \cdot 7^3$	$3 \cdot 229$	$2^4 \cdot 43$	$13 \cdot 53$
69_	$2 \cdot 3 \cdot 5 \cdot 23$	**691**	$2^2 \cdot 173$	$3^2 \cdot 7 \cdot 11$	$2 \cdot 347$	$5 \cdot 139$	$2^3 \cdot 3 \cdot 29$	$17 \cdot 41$	$2 \cdot 349$	$3 \cdot 233$
70_	$2^2 \cdot 5^2 \cdot 7$	**701**	$2 \cdot 3^3 \cdot 13$	$19 \cdot 37$	$2^6 \cdot 11$	$3 \cdot 5 \cdot 47$	$2 \cdot 353$	$7 \cdot 101$	$2^2 \cdot 3 \cdot 59$	**709**
71_	$2 \cdot 5 \cdot 71$	$3^2 \cdot 79$	$2^3 \cdot 89$	$23 \cdot 31$	$2 \cdot 3 \cdot 7 \cdot 17$	$5 \cdot 11 \cdot 13$	$2^2 \cdot 179$	$3 \cdot 239$	$2 \cdot 359$	**719**
72_	$2^4 \cdot 3^2 \cdot 5$	$7 \cdot 103$	$2 \cdot 19^2$	$3 \cdot 241$	$2^2 \cdot 181$	$5^2 \cdot 29$	$2 \cdot 3 \cdot 11^2$	**727**	$2^3 \cdot 7 \cdot 13$	3^6
73_	$2 \cdot 5 \cdot 73$	$17 \cdot 43$	$2^2 \cdot 3 \cdot 61$	**733**	$2 \cdot 367$	$3 \cdot 5 \cdot 7^2$	$2^5 \cdot 23$	$11 \cdot 67$	$2 \cdot 3^2 \cdot 41$	**739**
74_	$2^2 \cdot 5 \cdot 37$	$3 \cdot 13 \cdot 19$	$2 \cdot 7 \cdot 53$	**743**	$2^3 \cdot 3 \cdot 31$	$5 \cdot 149$	$2 \cdot 373$	$3^2 \cdot 83$	$2^2 \cdot 11 \cdot 17$	$7 \cdot 107$

	0	1	2	3	4	5	6	7	8	9
75_	$2\cdot3\cdot5^3$	**751**	$2^4\cdot47$	$3\cdot251$	$2\cdot13\cdot29$	$5\cdot151$	$2^2\cdot3^3\cdot7$	**757**	$2\cdot379$	$3\cdot11\cdot23$
76_	$2^3\cdot5\cdot19$	**761**	$2\cdot3\cdot127$	$7\cdot109$	$2^2\cdot191$	$3^2\cdot5\cdot17$	$2\cdot383$	$13\cdot59$	$2^8\cdot3$	**769**
77_	$2\cdot5\cdot7\cdot11$	$3\cdot257$	$2^2\cdot193$	**773**	$2\cdot3^2\cdot43$	$5^2\cdot31$	$2^3\cdot97$	$3\cdot7\cdot37$	$2\cdot389$	$19\cdot41$
78_	$2^2\cdot3\cdot5\cdot13$	$11\cdot71$	$2\cdot17\cdot23$	$3^3\cdot29$	$2^4\cdot7^2$	$5\cdot157$	$2\cdot3\cdot131$	**787**	$2^2\cdot197$	$3\cdot263$
79_	$2\cdot5\cdot79$	$7\cdot113$	$2^3\cdot3^2\cdot11$	$13\cdot61$	$2\cdot397$	$3\cdot5\cdot53$	$2^2\cdot199$	**797**	$2\cdot3\cdot7\cdot19$	$17\cdot47$
80_	$2^5\cdot5^2$	$3^2\cdot89$	$2\cdot401$	$11\cdot73$	$2^2\cdot3\cdot67$	$5\cdot7\cdot23$	$2\cdot13\cdot31$	$3\cdot269$	$2^3\cdot101$	**809**
81_	$2\cdot3^4\cdot5$	**811**	$2^2\cdot7\cdot29$	$3\cdot271$	$2\cdot11\cdot37$	$5\cdot163$	$2^4\cdot3\cdot17$	$19\cdot43$	$2\cdot409$	$3^2\cdot7\cdot13$
82_	$2^2\cdot5\cdot41$	**821**	$2\cdot3\cdot137$	**823**	$2^3\cdot103$	$3\cdot5^2\cdot11$	$2\cdot7\cdot59$	**827**	$2^2\cdot3^2\cdot23$	**829**
83_	$2\cdot5\cdot83$	$3\cdot277$	$2^6\cdot13$	$7^2\cdot17$	$2\cdot3\cdot139$	$5\cdot167$	$2^2\cdot11\cdot19$	$3^3\cdot31$	$2\cdot419$	**839**
84_	$2^3\cdot3\cdot5\cdot7$	29^2	$2\cdot421$	$3\cdot281$	$2^2\cdot211$	$5\cdot13^2$	$2\cdot3^2\cdot47$	$7\cdot11^2$	$2^4\cdot53$	$3\cdot283$
85_	$2\cdot5^2\cdot17$	$23\cdot37$	$2^2\cdot3\cdot71$	**853**	$2\cdot7\cdot61$	$3^2\cdot5\cdot19$	$2^3\cdot107$	**857**	$2\cdot3\cdot11\cdot13$	**859**
86_	$2^2\cdot5\cdot43$	$3\cdot7\cdot41$	$2\cdot431$	**863**	$2^5\cdot3^3$	$5\cdot173$	$2\cdot433$	$3\cdot17^2$	$2^2\cdot7\cdot31$	$11\cdot79$
87_	$2\cdot3\cdot5\cdot29$	$13\cdot67$	$2^3\cdot109$	$3^2\cdot97$	$2\cdot19\cdot23$	$5^3\cdot7$	$2^2\cdot3\cdot73$	**877**	$2\cdot439$	$3\cdot293$
88_	$2^4\cdot5\cdot11$	**881**	$2\cdot3^2\cdot7^2$	**883**	$2^2\cdot13\cdot17$	$3\cdot5\cdot59$	$2\cdot443$	**887**	$2^3\cdot3\cdot37$	$7\cdot127$
89_	$2\cdot5\cdot89$	$3^4\cdot11$	$2^2\cdot223$	$19\cdot47$	$2\cdot3\cdot149$	$5\cdot179$	$2^7\cdot7$	$3\cdot13\cdot23$	$2^4\cdot53$	$29\cdot31$
90_	$2^2\cdot3^2\cdot5^2$	$17\cdot53$	$2\cdot11\cdot41$	$3\cdot7\cdot43$	$2^3\cdot113$	$5\cdot181$	$2\cdot3\cdot151$	**907**	$2^2\cdot227$	$3^2\cdot101$
91_	$2\cdot5\cdot7\cdot13$	**911**	$2^4\cdot3\cdot19$	$11\cdot83$	$2\cdot457$	$3\cdot5\cdot61$	$2^2\cdot229$	$7\cdot131$	$2\cdot3^3\cdot17$	**919**
92_	$2^3\cdot5\cdot23$	$3\cdot307$	$2\cdot461$	$13\cdot71$	$2^2\cdot3\cdot7\cdot11$	$5^2\cdot37$	$2\cdot463$	$3^2\cdot103$	$2^5\cdot29$	**929**
93_	$2\cdot3\cdot5\cdot31$	$7^2\cdot19$	$2^2\cdot233$	$3\cdot311$	$2\cdot467$	$5\cdot11\cdot17$	$2^3\cdot3^2\cdot13$	**937**	$2\cdot7\cdot67$	$3\cdot313$
94_	$2^2\cdot5\cdot47$	**941**	$2\cdot3\cdot157$	$23\cdot41$	$2^4\cdot59$	$3^3\cdot5\cdot7$	$2\cdot11\cdot43$	**947**	$2^2\cdot3\cdot79$	$13\cdot73$
95_	$2\cdot5^2\cdot19$	$3\cdot317$	$2^3\cdot7\cdot17$	**953**	$2\cdot3^2\cdot53$	$5\cdot191$	$2^2\cdot239$	$3\cdot11\cdot29$	$2\cdot479$	$7\cdot137$
96_	$2^6\cdot3\cdot5$	31^2	$2\cdot13\cdot37$	$3^2\cdot107$	$2^2\cdot241$	$5\cdot193$	$2\cdot3\cdot7\cdot23$	**967**	$2^3\cdot11^2$	$3\cdot17\cdot19$
97_	$2\cdot5\cdot97$	**971**	$2^2\cdot3^5$	$7\cdot139$	$2\cdot487$	$3\cdot5^2\cdot13$	$2^4\cdot61$	**977**	$2\cdot3\cdot163$	$11\cdot89$
98_	$2^2\cdot5\cdot7^2$	$3^2\cdot109$	$2\cdot491$	**983**	$2^3\cdot3\cdot41$	$5\cdot197$	$2\cdot17\cdot29$	$3\cdot7\cdot47$	$2^2\cdot13\cdot19$	$23\cdot43$
99_	$2\cdot3^2\cdot5\cdot11$	**991**	$2^5\cdot31$	$3\cdot331$	$2\cdot7\cdot71$	$5\cdot199$	$2^2\cdot3\cdot83$	**997**	$2\cdot499$	$3^3\cdot37$

2.3.14   FACTORIZATION OF $2^m - 1$

$2^3 - 1 = 7$	$2^{19} - 1 = 524287$
$2^4 - 1 = 3 \times 5$	$2^{20} - 1 = 3 \times 5^2 \times 11 \times 31 \times 41$
$2^5 - 1 = 31$	$2^{21} - 1 = 7^2 \times 127 \times 337$
$2^6 - 1 = 3^2 \times 7$	$2^{22} - 1 = 3 \times 23 \times 89 \times 683$
$2^7 - 1 = 127$	$2^{23} - 1 = 47 \times 178481$
$2^8 - 1 = 3 \times 5 \times 17$	$2^{24} - 1 = 3^2 \times 5 \times 7 \times 13 \times 17 \times 241$
$2^9 - 1 = 7 \times 73$	$2^{25} - 1 = 31 \times 601 \times 1801$
$2^{10} - 1 = 3 \times 11 \times 31$	$2^{26} - 1 = 3 \times 2731 \times 8191$
$2^{11} - 1 = 23 \times 89$	$2^{27} - 1 = 7 \times 73 \times 262657$
$2^{12} - 1 = 3^2 \times 5 \times 7 \times 13$	$2^{28} - 1 = 3 \times 5 \times 29 \times 43 \times 113 \times 127$
$2^{13} - 1 = 8191$	$2^{29} - 1 = 233 \times 1103 \times 2089$
$2^{14} - 1 = 3 \times 43 \times 127$	$2^{30} - 1 = 3^2 \times 7 \times 11 \times 31 \times 151 \times 331$
$2^{15} - 1 = 7 \times 31 \times 151$	$2^{31} - 1 = 2147483647$
$2^{16} - 1 = 3 \times 5 \times 17 \times 257$	$2^{32} - 1 = 3 \times 5 \times 17 \times 257 \times 65537$
$2^{17} - 1 = 131071$	$2^{33} - 1 = 7 \times 23 \times 89 \times 599479$
$2^{18} - 1 = 3^3 \times 7 \times 19 \times 73$	$2^{34} - 1 = 3 \times 43691 \times 131071$

2.3.15   MAGIC SQUARES

A magic square is a square array of integers with the property that the sum of the integers in each row or column is the same. If $(c, n) = (d, n) = (e, n) = (f, n) = (cf - en, n) = 1$, then the array $A = (a_{ij})$ will be magic (and use the n^2 numbers 0, 1, ..., $n^2 - 1$) if $a_{ij} = k$ with

$$i \equiv ck + e \left\lfloor \frac{k}{n} \right\rfloor \quad (\text{mod } n) \qquad \text{and} \qquad j \equiv dk + f \left\lfloor \frac{k}{n} \right\rfloor \quad (\text{mod } n)$$

For example, with $c = 1, d = e = f = 2$, and $n = 3$, a magic square is

6	1	5
2	3	7
4	8	0

2.3.16   TOTIENT FUNCTION

Definitions

- $\phi(n)$ the totient function; is the number of integers not exceeding and relatively prime to n.

- $\sigma(n)$ is the sum of the divisors of n.

- $\tau(n)$ is the number of divisors of n.

Define $\sigma_k(n)$ to be the kth divisor function, the sum of the kth powers of the divisors of n. Then $\phi(n) = \sigma_0(n)$ and $\sigma(n) = \sigma_1(n)$.

A perfect number n satisfies $\sigma(n) = 2n$.

Example

The numbers less than 6 and relatively prime to 6 are $\{1, 5\}$. Hence $\phi(6) = 2$. The divisors of 6 are $\{1, 2, 3, 6\}$. There are $\tau(6) = 4$ divisors. The sum of these numbers is $\sigma(6) = 1 + 2 + 3 + 6 = 12$.

Properties

1. ϕ is a multiplicative function: if $(n, m) = 1$, then $\phi(nm) = \phi(m)\phi(n)$.

2. Gauss's theorem states: $n = \sum_{d|n} \phi(d)$.

3. When $n = \prod_i p_i^{\alpha_i}$.

$$\sigma_k(n) = \sum_{d|n} d^k = \prod_i \frac{p_i^{k(\alpha_i+1)} - 1}{p_i - 1}$$

4. Generating functions include

$$\sum_{n=0}^{\infty} \frac{\sigma_k(n)}{n^s} = \zeta(s)\zeta(s - k)$$

$$\sum_{n=0}^{\infty} \frac{\psi(n)}{n^s} = \frac{\zeta(s - 1)}{\zeta(s)}$$

5. The positive integer n is an even perfect number if, and only if, $n = 2^{m-1}(2^m - 1)$, where m is a positive integer such that $M_m = 2^m - 1$ is prime (M_m is called a Mersenne prime). The sequence of perfect numbers is $\{6, 28, 496, \dots\}$ (corresponding to $m = 2, 3, 5, \dots$).

Table of Values

n	$\phi(n)$	$\tau(n)$	$\sigma(n)$	n	$\phi(n)$	$\tau(n)$	$\sigma(n)$	n	$\phi(n)$	$\tau(n)$	$\sigma(n)$	n	$\phi(n)$	$\tau(n)$	$\sigma(n)$
1	0	1	1	46	22	4	72	91	72	4	112	136	64	8	270
2	1	2	3	47	46	2	48	92	44	6	168	137	136	2	138
3	2	2	4	48	16	10	124	93	60	4	128	138	44	8	288
4	2	3	7	49	42	3	57	94	46	4	144	139	138	2	140
5	4	2	6	50	20	6	93	95	72	4	120	140	48	12	336
6	2	4	12	51	32	4	72	96	32	12	252	141	92	4	192
7	6	2	8	52	24	6	98	97	96	2	98	142	70	4	216
8	4	4	15	53	52	2	54	98	42	6	171	143	120	4	168
9	6	3	13	54	18	8	120	99	60	6	156	144	48	15	403
10	4	4	18	55	40	4	72	100	40	9	217	145	112	4	180
11	10	2	12	56	24	8	120	101	100	2	102	146	72	4	222
12	4	6	28	57	36	4	80	102	32	8	216	147	84	6	228
13	12	2	14	58	28	4	90	103	102	2	104	148	72	6	266
14	6	4	24	59	58	2	60	104	48	8	210	149	148	2	150
15	8	4	24	60	16	12	168	105	48	8	192	150	40	12	372
16	8	5	31	61	60	2	62	106	52	4	162	151	150	2	152
17	16	2	18	62	30	4	96	107	106	2	108	152	72	8	300
18	6	6	39	63	36	6	104	108	36	12	280	153	96	6	234
19	18	2	20	64	32	7	127	109	108	2	110	154	60	8	288
20	8	6	42	65	48	4	84	110	40	8	216	155	120	4	192
21	12	4	32	66	20	8	144	111	72	4	152	156	48	12	392
22	10	4	36	67	66	2	68	112	48	10	248	157	156	2	158
23	22	2	24	68	32	6	126	113	112	2	114	158	78	4	240
24	8	8	60	69	44	4	96	114	36	8	240	159	104	4	216
25	20	3	31	70	24	8	144	115	88	4	144	160	64	12	378
26	12	4	42	71	70	2	72	116	56	6	210	161	132	4	192
27	18	4	40	72	24	12	195	117	72	6	182	162	54	10	363
28	12	6	56	73	72	2	74	118	58	4	180	163	162	2	164
29	28	2	30	74	36	4	114	119	96	4	144	164	80	6	294
30	8	8	72	75	40	6	124	120	32	16	360	165	80	8	288
31	30	2	32	76	36	6	140	121	110	3	133	166	82	4	252
32	16	6	63	77	60	4	96	122	60	4	186	167	166	2	168
33	20	4	48	78	24	8	168	123	80	4	168	168	48	16	480
34	16	4	54	79	78	2	80	124	60	6	224	169	156	3	183
35	24	4	48	80	32	10	186	125	100	4	156	170	64	8	324
36	12	9	91	81	54	5	121	126	36	12	312	171	108	6	260
37	36	2	38	82	40	4	126	127	126	2	128	172	84	6	308
38	18	4	60	83	82	2	84	128	64	8	255	173	172	2	174
39	24	4	56	84	24	12	224	129	84	4	176	174	56	8	360
40	16	8	90	85	64	4	108	130	48	8	252	175	120	6	248
41	40	2	42	86	42	4	132	131	130	2	132	176	80	10	372
42	12	8	96	87	56	4	120	132	40	12	336	177	116	4	240
43	42	2	44	88	40	8	180	133	108	4	160	178	88	4	270
44	20	6	84	89	88	2	90	134	66	4	204	179	178	2	180
45	24	6	78	90	24	12	234	135	72	8	240	180	48	18	546

n	φ(n)	τ(n)	σ(n)	n	φ(n)	τ(n)	σ(n)	n	φ(n)	τ(n)	σ(n)	n	φ(n)	τ(n)	σ(n)
181	180	2	182	226	112	4	342	271	270	2	272	316	156	6	560
182	72	8	336	227	226	2	228	272	128	10	558	317	316	2	318
183	120	4	248	228	72	12	560	273	144	8	448	318	104	8	648
184	88	8	360	229	228	2	230	274	136	4	414	319	280	4	360
185	144	4	228	230	88	8	432	275	200	6	372	320	128	14	762
186	60	8	384	231	120	8	384	276	88	12	672	321	212	4	432
187	160	4	216	232	112	8	450	277	276	2	278	322	132	8	576
188	92	6	336	233	232	2	234	278	138	4	420	323	288	4	360
189	108	8	320	234	72	12	546	279	180	6	416	324	108	15	847
190	72	8	360	235	184	4	288	280	96	16	720	325	240	6	434
191	190	2	192	236	116	6	420	281	280	2	282	326	162	4	492
192	64	14	508	237	156	4	320	282	92	8	576	327	216	4	440
193	192	2	194	238	96	8	432	283	282	2	284	328	160	8	630
194	96	4	294	239	238	2	240	284	140	6	504	329	276	4	384
195	96	8	336	240	64	20	744	285	144	8	480	330	80	16	864
196	84	9	399	241	240	2	242	286	120	8	504	331	330	2	332
197	196	2	198	242	110	6	399	287	240	4	336	332	164	6	588
198	60	12	468	243	162	6	364	288	96	18	819	333	216	6	494
199	198	2	200	244	120	6	434	289	272	3	307	334	166	4	504
200	80	12	465	245	168	6	342	290	112	8	540	335	264	4	408
201	132	4	272	246	80	8	504	291	192	4	392	336	96	20	992
202	100	4	306	247	216	4	280	292	144	6	518	337	336	2	338
203	168	4	240	248	120	8	480	293	292	2	294	338	156	6	549
204	64	12	504	249	164	4	336	294	84	12	684	339	224	4	456
205	160	4	252	250	100	8	468	295	232	4	360	340	128	12	756
206	102	4	312	251	250	2	252	296	144	8	570	341	300	4	384
207	132	6	312	252	72	18	728	297	180	8	480	342	108	12	780
208	96	10	434	253	220	4	288	298	148	4	450	343	294	4	400
209	180	4	240	254	126	4	384	299	264	4	336	344	168	8	660
210	48	16	576	255	128	8	432	300	80	18	868	345	176	8	576
211	210	2	212	256	128	9	511	301	252	4	352	346	172	4	522
212	104	6	378	257	256	2	258	302	150	4	456	347	346	2	348
213	140	4	288	258	84	8	528	303	200	4	408	348	112	12	840
214	106	4	324	259	216	4	304	304	144	10	620	349	348	2	350
215	168	4	264	260	96	12	588	305	240	4	372	350	120	12	744
216	72	16	600	261	168	6	390	306	96	12	702	351	216	8	560
217	180	4	256	262	130	4	396	307	306	2	308	352	160	12	756
218	108	4	330	263	262	2	264	308	120	12	672	353	352	2	354
219	144	4	296	264	80	16	720	309	204	4	416	354	116	8	720
220	80	12	504	265	208	4	324	310	120	8	576	355	280	4	432
221	192	4	252	266	108	8	480	311	310	2	312	356	176	6	630
222	72	8	456	267	176	4	360	312	96	16	840	357	192	8	576
223	222	2	224	268	132	6	476	313	312	2	314	358	178	4	540
224	96	12	504	269	268	2	270	314	156	4	474	359	358	2	360
225	120	9	403	270	72	16	720	315	144	12	624	360	96	24	1170

n	$\phi(n)$	$\tau(n)$	$\sigma(n)$	n	$\phi(n)$	$\tau(n)$	$\sigma(n)$	n	$\phi(n)$	$\tau(n)$	$\sigma(n)$	n	$\phi(n)$	$\tau(n)$	$\sigma(n)$
361	342	3	381	406	168	8	720	451	400	4	504	496	240	10	992
362	180	4	546	407	360	4	456	452	224	6	798	497	420	4	576
363	220	6	532	408	128	16	1080	453	300	4	608	498	164	8	1008
364	144	12	784	409	408	2	410	454	226	4	684	499	498	2	500
365	288	4	444	410	160	8	756	455	288	8	672	500	200	12	1092
366	120	8	744	411	272	4	552	456	144	16	1200	501	332	4	672
367	366	2	368	412	204	6	728	457	456	2	458	502	250	4	756
368	176	10	744	413	348	4	480	458	228	4	690	503	502	2	504
369	240	6	546	414	132	12	936	459	288	8	720	504	144	24	1560
370	144	8	684	415	328	4	504	460	176	12	1008	505	400	4	612
371	312	4	432	416	192	12	882	461	460	2	462	506	220	8	864
372	120	12	896	417	276	4	560	462	120	16	1152	507	312	6	732
373	372	2	374	418	180	8	720	463	462	2	464	508	252	6	896
374	160	8	648	419	418	2	420	464	224	10	930	509	508	2	510
375	200	8	624	420	96	24	1344	465	240	8	768	510	128	16	1296
376	184	8	720	421	420	2	422	466	232	4	702	511	432	4	592
377	336	4	420	422	210	4	636	467	466	2	468	512	256	10	1023
378	108	16	960	423	276	6	624	468	144	18	1274	513	324	8	800
379	378	2	380	424	208	8	810	469	396	4	544	514	256	8	774
380	144	12	840	425	320	6	558	470	184	8	864	515	408	4	624
381	252	4	512	426	140	8	864	471	312	4	632	516	168	12	1232
382	190	4	576	427	360	4	496	472	232	8	900	517	460	4	576
383	382	2	384	428	212	6	756	473	420	4	528	518	216	8	912
384	128	16	1020	429	240	8	672	474	156	8	960	519	344	4	696
385	240	8	576	430	168	8	792	475	360	6	620	520	192	16	1260
386	192	4	582	431	430	2	432	476	192	12	1008	521	520	2	522
387	252	6	572	432	144	20	1240	477	312	6	702	522	168	12	1170
388	192	6	686	433	432	2	434	478	238	4	720	523	522	2	524
389	388	2	390	434	180	8	768	479	478	2	480	524	260	6	924
390	96	16	1008	435	224	8	720	480	128	24	1512	525	240	12	992
391	352	4	432	436	216	6	770	481	432	4	532	526	262	4	792
392	168	12	855	437	396	4	480	482	240	4	726	527	480	4	576
393	260	4	528	438	144	8	888	483	264	8	768	528	160	20	1488
394	196	4	594	439	438	2	440	484	220	9	931	529	506	3	553
395	312	4	480	440	160	16	1080	485	384	4	588	530	208	8	972
396	120	18	1092	441	252	9	741	486	162	12	1092	531	348	6	780
397	396	2	398	442	192	8	756	487	486	2	488	532	216	12	1120
398	198	4	600	443	442	2	444	488	240	8	930	533	480	4	588
399	216	8	640	444	144	12	1064	489	324	4	656	534	176	8	1080
400	160	15	961	445	352	4	540	490	168	12	1026	535	424	4	648
401	400	2	402	446	222	4	672	491	490	2	492	536	264	8	1020
402	132	8	816	447	296	4	600	492	160	12	1176	537	356	4	720
403	360	4	448	448	192	14	1016	493	448	4	540	538	268	4	810
404	200	6	714	449	448	2	450	494	216	8	840	539	420	6	684
405	216	10	726	450	120	18	1209	495	240	12	936	540	144	24	1680

2.4   VECTOR ALGEBRA

2.4.1   NOTATION FOR VECTORS AND SCALARS

A *vector* is an ordered n-tuple of values. A vector is usually represented by a lower case, bold faced letter, such as $\mathbf{v}$. The individual components of a vector $\mathbf{v}$ are typically denoted by a lower case letter along with a subscript identifying the relative position of the component in the vector, such as $\mathbf{v} = [v_1, v_2, \ldots, v_n]$. In this case, the vector is said to be n-dimensional. If the n individual components of the vector are real numbers, then $\mathbf{v} \in \mathbb{R}^n$. Likewise, if the n components of $\mathbf{v}$ are complex, then $\mathbf{v} \in \mathbb{C}^n$.

Two vectors, $\mathbf{v}_1$ and $\mathbf{v}_2$, are said to be equal if they have exactly the same components. A negative vector, written as $-\mathbf{v}$, is one that acts in direction opposite to $\mathbf{v}$, but is of equal magnitude.

2.4.2   PHYSICAL VECTORS

Any quantity that is completely determined by its magnitude is called a *scalar*. For example, mass, density, and temperature are scalars. Any quantity that is completely determined by its magnitude and direction is called, in physics, a vector. We often use a three-dimensional vector to represent a physical vector. Examples of physical vectors include velocity, acceleration, and force. A physical vector is represented by a directed line segment, the length of which represents the magnitude of the vector. Two vectors are said to be *parallel* if they have exactly the same direction, i.e., the angle between the two vectors equals zero.

2.4.3   FUNDAMENTAL DEFINITIONS

1. A *row vector* is a vector whose components are aligned horizontally. A *column vector* has its components aligned vertically. The *transpose* operator, denoted by the superscript ^{T}, switches the orientation of a vector between horizontal and vertical.

EXAMPLE 2.4.1

$$\mathbf{v} = [1, 2, 3, 4], \quad \mathbf{v}^T = \begin{bmatrix} 1 \\ 2 \\ 3 \\ 4 \end{bmatrix}, \quad (\mathbf{v}^T)^T = [1, 2, 3, 4].$$

   row vector   *column vector*   *row vector*

Vectors are traditionally written with either rounded braces or with square brackets.

2. Two vectors, $\mathbf{v}_i$ and $\mathbf{v}_j$, are said to be *orthogonal* if $\mathbf{v}_i^T \cdot \mathbf{v}_j = 0$, where the operation "·" denotes an inner product.

3. A set of vectors $\{\mathbf{v}_1, \ldots, \mathbf{v}_n\}$ is said to be orthogonal if $\mathbf{v}_i^T \cdot \mathbf{v}_j = 0$ for all $i \neq j$.

4. A set of orthogonal vectors $\{\mathbf{v}_1, \ldots, \mathbf{v}_m\}$ is said to be *orthonormal* if, in addition to possessing the property of orthogonality, the set possesses the property that $\mathbf{v}_i^T \cdot \mathbf{v}_i = 1$ for all $1 \leq i \leq m$.

2.4.4   LAWS OF VECTOR ALGEBRA

1. The vector sum of $\mathbf{v}_1$ and $\mathbf{v}_2$, represented by $\mathbf{v}_1 + \mathbf{v}_2$, results in another vector of the same dimension, and is calculated by simply adding corresponding vector components, e.g., if $\mathbf{v}_1, \mathbf{v}_2 \in \mathbb{R}^n$, then $\mathbf{v}_1 + \mathbf{v}_2 = [v_{1_1} + v_{2_1}, \ldots, v_{1_n} + v_{2_n}]$.

2. The vector subtraction of $\mathbf{v}_2$ from $\mathbf{v}_1$, represented by $\mathbf{v}_1 - \mathbf{v}_2$, is equivalent to the addition of $\mathbf{v}_1$ and $-\mathbf{v}_2$.

3. If r is a scalar, then $r\mathbf{v}$ or $\mathbf{v}r$ represents a scaling of the vector $\mathbf{v}$ in the same direction as $\mathbf{v}$, since the multiplicative scalar is distributed to each component of $\mathbf{v}$.

4. If $0 \leq r < 1$, then the scalar multiplication $r\mathbf{v}$ shrinks the length of $\mathbf{v}$, multiplication by $r = 1$ leaves $\mathbf{v}$ unchanged, and, if $r > 1$, then $r\mathbf{v}$ stretches the length of $\mathbf{v}$. When $r < 0$, multiplication of $\mathbf{v}$ by r has the same effects on the magnitude, or length of $\mathbf{v}$, but results in a vector oriented in the direction opposite to $\mathbf{v}$.

EXAMPLE 2.4.2

$$4 \begin{bmatrix} 1 \\ 0 \\ 3 \end{bmatrix} = \begin{bmatrix} 4 \\ 0 \\ 12 \end{bmatrix}, \qquad -4 \begin{bmatrix} 1 \\ 0 \\ 3 \end{bmatrix} = \begin{bmatrix} -4 \\ 0 \\ -12 \end{bmatrix}.$$

5. If r and s are scalars, and $\mathbf{v}_1$, $\mathbf{v}_2$, and $\mathbf{v}_3$ are vectors, the following rules of algebra are valid:

$$\begin{aligned} \mathbf{v}_1 + \mathbf{v}_2 &= \mathbf{v}_2 + \mathbf{v}_1, \\ (r + s)\mathbf{v}_1 &= r\mathbf{v}_1 + s\mathbf{v}_1 = \mathbf{v}_1 r + \mathbf{v}_1 s = \mathbf{v}_1(r + s), \\ r(\mathbf{v}_1 + \mathbf{v}_2) &= r\mathbf{v}_1 + r\mathbf{v}_2, \quad \text{and} \\ \mathbf{v}_1 + (\mathbf{v}_2 + \mathbf{v}_3) &= (\mathbf{v}_1 + \mathbf{v}_2) + \mathbf{v}_3 = \mathbf{v}_1 + \mathbf{v}_2 + \mathbf{v}_3. \end{aligned} \tag{2.4.1}$$

2.4.5   VECTOR NORMS

1. A *norm* is the vector analog of absolute value for real scalars. Norms provide a distance measure for a vector space.

2. A vector norm applied to a vector $\mathbf{v}$ is denoted by a double bar notation $\|\mathbf{v}\|$.

3. An n-dimensional real number space $\mathbb{R}^n$ together with a norm defines a *metric space*.

4. The properties of a vector norm are

   - For any vector $\mathbf{x} \neq \mathbf{0}$, $\|\mathbf{x}\| > 0$,

   - $\|\gamma\mathbf{x}\| = |\gamma|\ \|\mathbf{x}\|$, and

   - $\|\mathbf{x} + \mathbf{y}\| \leq \|\mathbf{x}\| + \|\mathbf{y}\|$ (triangle inequality).

5. The three most commonly used vector norms are

   - The L_1 norm is defined as $\|\mathbf{v}\|_1 = |v_1| + \cdots + |v_n| = \sum_{i=1}^{n} |v_i|$.

   - The L_2 norm (Euclidean norm) is defined as

   $$\|\mathbf{v}\|_2 = (|v_1|^2 + |v_2|^2 + \cdots + |v_n|^2)^{1/2} = \left(\sum_{i=1}^{n} v_i^2 \right)^{1/2}. \tag{2.4.2}$$

   - The L_∞ norm is defined as $\|\mathbf{v}\|_\infty = \max_{1 \leq i \leq n} |v_i|$.

6. In the absence of any subscript, the norm $\|\cdot\|$ is usually assumed to be the L_2 norm.

7. A *unit vector* with respect to a particular norm $\|\cdot\|$ is a vector that satisfies the property that $\|\mathbf{v}\| = 1$, and is sometimes denoted by $\hat{\mathbf{v}}$.

2.4.6   DOT, SCALAR, OR INNER PRODUCT

1. The dot, scalar, or inner product of two vectors of the same dimension, represented by $\mathbf{v}_1 \cdot \mathbf{v}_2$ or $\mathbf{x}^{\mathrm{T}}\mathbf{y}$, has two common definitions, depending upon the context in which this product is encountered.

   (a) In vector calculus and physics, the dot or scalar product is defined by

   $$\mathbf{v}_1 \cdot \mathbf{v}_2 = \|\mathbf{v}_1\|_2 \|\mathbf{v}_2\|_2 \cos\theta, \tag{2.4.3}$$

   where θ represents the angle determined by $\mathbf{v}_1$ and $\mathbf{v}_2$ (see Figure 2.4.1).

   (b) In optimization, linear algebra, and computer science, the inner product of two vectors, $\mathbf{x}$ and $\mathbf{y}$, is equivalently defined as

   $$\mathbf{x}^{\mathrm{T}}\mathbf{y} = \sum_{i=1}^{n} x_i y_i = x_1 y_1 + \cdots + x_n y_n. \tag{2.4.4}$$

From the first definition, it is apparent that the inner product of two perpendicular, or orthogonal, vectors is zero, since the cosine of 90° is zero.

2. The inner product of two parallel vectors (with $\mathbf{v}_2 = r\mathbf{v}_1$) is given by $\mathbf{v}_1 \cdot \mathbf{v}_2 = r \|\mathbf{v}_1\|_2^2$. For example, when $r > 0$,

$$\mathbf{v}_1 \cdot \mathbf{v}_2 = \|\mathbf{v}_1\|_2 \|\mathbf{v}_2\|_2 \cos 0 = \|\mathbf{v}_1\|_2 \|\mathbf{v}_2\|_2 = r \|\mathbf{v}_1\|_2^2.$$

(2.4.5)

3. The dot, scalar, or inner product is distributive, e.g.,

$$(\mathbf{v}_1 + \mathbf{v}_2) \cdot \mathbf{v}_3 = \mathbf{v}_1 \cdot \mathbf{v}_3 + \mathbf{v}_2 \cdot \mathbf{v}_3.$$

(2.4.6)

4. For $\mathbf{a}, \mathbf{b}, \mathbf{c} \in \mathbb{R}^n$ with $n > 1$,

$$\mathbf{a}^T\mathbf{b} = \mathbf{a}^T\mathbf{c} \quad \nRightarrow \quad \mathbf{b} = \mathbf{c}.$$

(2.4.7)

However, it *is* valid to conclude that

$$\mathbf{a}^T\mathbf{b} = \mathbf{a}^T\mathbf{c} \quad \Rightarrow \quad \mathbf{a}^T(\mathbf{b} - \mathbf{c}) = 0,$$

(2.4.8)

and that the vector $\mathbf{a}$ is orthogonal to the vector $(\mathbf{b} - \mathbf{c})$.

FIGURE 2.4.1
Depiction of right-hand rule.

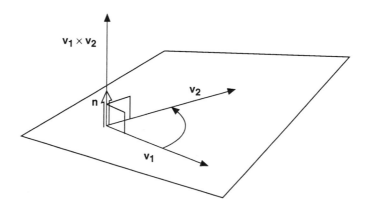

2.4.7 VECTOR OR CROSS PRODUCT

1. The vector or cross product of two nonzero three-dimensional vectors $\mathbf{v}_1$ and $\mathbf{v}_2$ is defined as

$$\mathbf{v}_1 \times \mathbf{v}_2 = \hat{\mathbf{n}} \|\mathbf{v}_1\|_2 \|\mathbf{v}_2\|_2 \sin\theta,$$

(2.4.9)

where $\hat{\mathbf{n}}$ is the unit *normal* vector perpendicular to both $\mathbf{v}_1$ and $\mathbf{v}_2$ in the direction adhering to the *right-hand rule* (see Figure 2.4.1) and θ is the angle between $\mathbf{v}_1$ and $\mathbf{v}_2$.

2. If $\mathbf{v}_1$ and $\mathbf{v}_2$ are parallel, then $\mathbf{v}_1 \times \mathbf{v}_2 = \mathbf{0}$.

3. The quantity $\|\mathbf{v}_1\|_2 \|\mathbf{v}_2\|_2 |\sin \theta|$ represents the area of the parallelogram determined by $\mathbf{v}_1$ and $\mathbf{v}_2$.

4. The following rules apply for vector products:

$$
\begin{aligned}
(\gamma \mathbf{v}_1) \times (\alpha \mathbf{v}_2) &= (\gamma \alpha) \mathbf{v}_1 \times \mathbf{v}_2, \\
\mathbf{v}_1 \times \mathbf{v}_2 &= -\mathbf{v}_2 \times \mathbf{v}_1, \\
\mathbf{v}_1 \times (\mathbf{v}_2 + \mathbf{v}_3) &= \mathbf{v}_1 \times \mathbf{v}_2 + \mathbf{v}_1 \times \mathbf{v}_3, \\
(\mathbf{v}_1 + \mathbf{v}_2) \times \mathbf{v}_3 &= \mathbf{v}_1 \times \mathbf{v}_3 + \mathbf{v}_2 \times \mathbf{v}_3, \\
\mathbf{v}_1 \times (\mathbf{v}_2 \times \mathbf{v}_3) &= \mathbf{v}_2(\mathbf{v}_3 \cdot \mathbf{v}_1) - \mathbf{v}_3(\mathbf{v}_1 \cdot \mathbf{v}_2), \\
(\mathbf{a} \times \mathbf{b}) \cdot (\mathbf{c} \times \mathbf{d}) &= (\mathbf{a} \cdot \mathbf{c})(\mathbf{b} \cdot \mathbf{d}) - (\mathbf{a} \cdot \mathbf{d})(\mathbf{b} \cdot \mathbf{c}), \\
(\mathbf{a} \times \mathbf{b}) \times (\mathbf{c} \times \mathbf{d}) &= [\mathbf{a} \cdot (\mathbf{b} \times \mathbf{d})]\mathbf{c} - [\mathbf{a} \cdot (\mathbf{b} \times \mathbf{c})]\mathbf{d} \\
&= [\mathbf{a} \cdot (\mathbf{c} \times \mathbf{d})]\mathbf{b} - [\mathbf{b} \cdot (\mathbf{c} \times \mathbf{d})]\mathbf{a}.
\end{aligned}
\tag{2.4.10}
$$

5. The pairwise cross products of the unit vectors $\hat{\mathbf{i}}$, $\hat{\mathbf{j}}$, and $\hat{\mathbf{k}}$, corresponding to the directions of $\mathbf{v} = v_1\hat{\mathbf{i}} + v_2\hat{\mathbf{j}} + v_3\hat{\mathbf{k}}$, are given by

$$
\begin{aligned}
\hat{\mathbf{i}} \times \hat{\mathbf{j}} &= -(\hat{\mathbf{j}} \times \hat{\mathbf{i}}) = \hat{\mathbf{k}}, \\
\hat{\mathbf{j}} \times \hat{\mathbf{k}} &= -(\hat{\mathbf{k}} \times \hat{\mathbf{j}}) = \hat{\mathbf{i}}, \\
\hat{\mathbf{k}} \times \hat{\mathbf{i}} &= -(\hat{\mathbf{i}} \times \hat{\mathbf{k}}) = \hat{\mathbf{j}}, \quad \text{and} \\
\hat{\mathbf{i}} \times \hat{\mathbf{i}} &= \hat{\mathbf{j}} \times \hat{\mathbf{j}} = \hat{\mathbf{k}} \times \hat{\mathbf{k}} = \mathbf{0}.
\end{aligned}
\tag{2.4.11}
$$

6. If $\mathbf{v}_1 = a_1\hat{\mathbf{i}} + a_2\hat{\mathbf{j}} + a_3\hat{\mathbf{k}}$ and $\mathbf{v}_2 = b_1\hat{\mathbf{i}} + b_2\hat{\mathbf{j}} + b_3\hat{\mathbf{k}}$, then

$$
\mathbf{v}_1 \times \mathbf{v}_2 = \begin{vmatrix} \hat{\mathbf{i}} & \hat{\mathbf{j}} & \hat{\mathbf{k}} \\ a_1 & a_2 & a_3 \\ b_1 & b_2 & b_3 \end{vmatrix},
$$

$$
= (a_2 b_3 - b_2 a_3)\hat{\mathbf{i}} + (a_3 b_1 - b_3 a_1)\hat{\mathbf{j}} + (a_1 b_2 - b_1 a_2)\hat{\mathbf{k}}.
\tag{2.4.12}
$$

2.4.8 SCALAR AND VECTOR TRIPLE PRODUCTS

1. The *scalar triple product* involving three three-dimensional vectors $\mathbf{a}$, $\mathbf{b}$, and $\mathbf{c}$, sometimes denoted by $[\mathbf{abc}]$ (not to be confused with a matrix containing three columns $\begin{bmatrix} \mathbf{a} & \mathbf{b} & \mathbf{c} \end{bmatrix}$), can be computed using the determinant

$$
\begin{aligned}
[\mathbf{abc}] = \mathbf{a} \cdot (\mathbf{b} \times \mathbf{c}) &= \mathbf{a} \cdot \left[\begin{vmatrix} b_2 & b_3 \\ c_2 & c_3 \end{vmatrix}\hat{\mathbf{i}} - \begin{vmatrix} b_1 & b_3 \\ c_1 & c_3 \end{vmatrix}\hat{\mathbf{j}} + \begin{vmatrix} b_1 & b_2 \\ c_1 & c_2 \end{vmatrix}\hat{\mathbf{k}} \right] \\
&= a_1 \begin{vmatrix} b_2 & b_3 \\ c_2 & c_3 \end{vmatrix} - a_2 \begin{vmatrix} b_1 & b_3 \\ c_1 & c_3 \end{vmatrix} + a_3 \begin{vmatrix} b_1 & b_2 \\ c_1 & c_2 \end{vmatrix} \\
&= \begin{vmatrix} a_1 & a_2 & a_3 \\ b_1 & b_2 & b_3 \\ c_1 & c_2 & c_3 \end{vmatrix} \\
&= \|a\| \ \|b\| \ \|c\| \cos \phi \sin \theta,
\end{aligned}
\tag{2.4.13}
$$

where θ is the angle between **b** and **c**, and ϕ is the angle between **a** and the normal to the plane defined by **b** and **c**.

2. The absolute value of the triple scalar product calculates the volume of the parallelipiped determined by the three vectors. The answer you get is therefore independent of the order in which the triple product is taken.

3. Given three noncoplanar reference vectors $\mathbf{v}_1$, $\mathbf{v}_2$, and $\mathbf{v}_3$, the *reciprocal system* is given by $\mathbf{v}_1^*$, $\mathbf{v}_2^*$, and $\mathbf{v}_3^*$, where

$$\mathbf{v}_1^* = \frac{\mathbf{v}_2 \times \mathbf{v}_3}{[\mathbf{v}_1 \mathbf{v}_2 \mathbf{v}_3]}, \qquad \mathbf{v}_2^* = \frac{\mathbf{v}_3 \times \mathbf{v}_1}{[\mathbf{v}_1 \mathbf{v}_2 \mathbf{v}_3]}, \qquad \mathbf{v}_3^* = \frac{\mathbf{v}_1 \times \mathbf{v}_2}{[\mathbf{v}_1 \mathbf{v}_2 \mathbf{v}_3]}. \tag{2.4.14}$$

Note that

$$1 = \|\mathbf{v}_1\| \, \left\|\mathbf{v}_1^*\right\| = \|\mathbf{v}_2\| \, \left\|\mathbf{v}_2^*\right\| = \|\mathbf{v}_3\| \, \left\|\mathbf{v}_3^*\right\|$$
$$\text{and } 0 = \|\mathbf{v}_1\| \, \left\|\mathbf{v}_2^*\right\| = \|\mathbf{v}_1\| \, \left\|\mathbf{v}_3^*\right\| = \|\mathbf{v}_2\| \, \left\|\mathbf{v}_1^*\right\|, \quad \text{etc.} \tag{2.4.15}$$

The system $\hat{\mathbf{i}}, \hat{\mathbf{j}}, \hat{\mathbf{k}}$ is its own reciprocal.

4. The *vector triple product* involving three three-dimensional vectors **a**, **b**, and **c**, given by $\mathbf{a} \times (\mathbf{b} \times \mathbf{c})$, results in a vector, perpendicular to **a**, lying in the plane of **b** and **c**, and is defined as

$$\mathbf{a} \times (\mathbf{b} \times \mathbf{c}) = (\mathbf{a} \cdot \mathbf{c})\mathbf{b} - (\mathbf{a} \cdot \mathbf{b})\mathbf{c},$$

$$= \begin{vmatrix} \hat{\mathbf{i}} & \hat{\mathbf{j}} & \hat{\mathbf{k}} \\ a_1 & a_2 & a_3 \\ \begin{vmatrix} b_2 & b_3 \\ c_2 & c_3 \end{vmatrix} & \begin{vmatrix} b_3 & b_1 \\ c_3 & c_1 \end{vmatrix} & \begin{vmatrix} b_1 & b_2 \\ c_1 & c_2 \end{vmatrix} \end{vmatrix}. \tag{2.4.16}$$

5. $(\mathbf{a} \times \mathbf{b}) \times (\mathbf{c} \times \mathbf{d}) = [\mathbf{acd}]\mathbf{b} - [\mathbf{bcd}]\mathbf{a} = [\mathbf{abd}]\mathbf{c} - [\mathbf{abc}]\mathbf{d}$

2.5 LINEAR AND MATRIX ALGEBRA

2.5.1 DEFINITIONS

1. An $m \times n$ *matrix* is a two-dimensional array of numbers consisting of m rows and n columns. By convention, a matrix is denoted by a capital letter emphasized with italics, as in A, B, D, or boldface, **A**, **B**, **D**, along with a subscript denoting the dimensions of the matrix, e.g., $\mathbf{A}_{2\times3}$. If **A** is a real $n \times m$ matrix, then we write $\mathbf{A} \in \mathbb{R}^{n \times m}$.

2. $\mathbf{A}_{m\times n}$ is called *rectangular* if $m \neq n$.

3. $\mathbf{A}_{m\times n}$ is called *square* if $m = n$.

4. A particular element or component of a matrix is denoted by the lower case letter of that which names the matrix, along with two subscripts corresponding to the row i and column j location of the component in the array, e.g.,

$$\mathbf{A}_{m \times n} \quad \text{has components } a_{ij};$$
$$\mathbf{B}_{m \times n} \quad \text{has components } b_{ij}.$$

For example, a_{23} is in the second row and third column of matrix $\mathbf{A}$.

5. Any component a_{ij} with $i = j$ is called a *diagonal* element.

6. Any component a_{ij} with $i \neq j$ is called an *off-diagonal* element.

7. Two matrices $\mathbf{A}$ and $\mathbf{B}$ are said to be equal if they have the same number of rows (m) and columns (n), and $a_{ij} = b_{ij}$ for all $1 \leq i \leq m$, $1 \leq j \leq n$.

8. An $m \times 1$ dimensional matrix is called a *column vector*. Similarly, a $1 \times n$ dimensional matrix is called a *row vector*.

9. A column (row) vector with all components equal to zero is called a *null* vector and is usually denoted by $\mathbf{0}$.

10. A column vector with all components equal to one is sometimes denoted by $\mathbf{e}$. The analogous row vector is denoted by $\mathbf{e}^T$.

11. The unit vectors of order n are usually $\{\mathbf{e}_1, \mathbf{e}_2, \ldots, \mathbf{e}_n\}$ where $\mathbf{e}_i$ is a $n \times 1$ vector of all zeros, except for the ith component, which is one.

12. The scalar $\mathbf{x}^T\mathbf{x} = \sum_{i=1}^{n} x_i^2$ is the sum of squares of all components of the vector $\mathbf{x}$.

13. The *weighted* sum of squares is defined by $\mathbf{x}^T\mathbf{D}_w\mathbf{x} = \sum_{i=1}^{n} w_i x_i^2$, when $\mathbf{x}$ has n components and the diagonal matrix $\mathbf{D}_w$ is of dimension $(n \times n)$.

14. If $\mathbf{Q}$ is a square matrix, then $\mathbf{x}^T\mathbf{Q}\mathbf{x}$ is called a *quadratic* form.

15. An $n \times n$ matrix $\mathbf{A}$ is called *non-singular*, or *regular*, if there exists an $n \times n$ matrix $\mathbf{B}$ such that $\mathbf{AB} = \mathbf{BA} = \mathbf{I}$. The unique matrix $\mathbf{B}$ is called the *inverse* of $\mathbf{A}$, and is denoted by $\mathbf{A}^{-1}$.

16. The scalar $\mathbf{x}^T\mathbf{y} = \sum_{i=1}^{n} x_i y_i$ is the sum of products of the components of $\mathbf{x}$ by those of $\mathbf{y}$.

17. The *weighted* sum of products is $\mathbf{x}^T\mathbf{D}_w\mathbf{y} = \sum_{i=1}^{n} w_i x_i y_i$, when $\mathbf{x}$ and $\mathbf{y}$ have n components, and the diagonal matrix $\mathbf{D}_w$ is $(n \times n)$.

18. The scalar $\mathbf{x}^T\mathbf{Q}\mathbf{y}$ is called a *bilinear* form, where $\mathbf{Q}$ is a matrix of any appropriate dimension.

19. The *transpose* of an $m \times n$ matrix $\mathbf{A}$, denoted by $\mathbf{A}^T$, is an $n \times m$ matrix with rows and columns interchanged, so that the (i, j) component of $\mathbf{A}$ is the (j, i) component of $\mathbf{A}^T$, and $(\mathbf{A}^T)_{ji} = \mathbf{A}_{ij}$.

20. The *Hermitian conjugate* of a matrix $\mathbf{A}$, denoted by $\mathbf{A}^H$, is obtained by transposing $\mathbf{A}$ and replacing each element by its complex conjugate. Hence, if $a_{kl} = u_{kl} + i v_{kl}$, then $(\mathbf{A}^H)_{kl} = u_{lk} - i v_{ik}$, with $i = \sqrt{-1}$.

21. If $\mathbf{Q}$ is a square matrix, then $\mathbf{x}^H\mathbf{Q}\mathbf{x}$ is called a *Hermitian* form.

2.5.2 TYPES OF MATRICES

1. The diagonal alignment of components in a matrix extending from the upper left to the lower right is called the *principal* or *main* diagonal.

2. A square matrix with all components off the principal diagonal equal to zero is called a *diagonal matrix*, typically denoted by the letter D with a subscript indicating the typical element in the principal diagonal.

EXAMPLE 2.5.1

$$D_a = \begin{bmatrix} a_{11} & 0 & 0 \\ 0 & a_{22} & 0 \\ 0 & 0 & a_{33} \end{bmatrix}, \qquad D_\lambda = \begin{bmatrix} \lambda_{11} & 0 & 0 \\ 0 & \lambda_{22} & 0 \\ 0 & 0 & \lambda_{33} \end{bmatrix}.$$

3. The *identity matrix*, denoted by $\mathbf{I}$, is the diagonal matrix with $a_{ij} = 1$ for all $i = j$, and $a_{ij} = 0$ for $i \neq j$. The $n \times n$ identity matrix is denoted I_n.

4. A matrix that has all main diagonal components equal to one and zeros everywhere else except a single nonzero component in location (i, j) is called an *elementary* matrix, denoted by $\mathbf{E}_{ij}$.

EXAMPLE 2.5.2

$$\mathbf{E}_{31} = \begin{bmatrix} 1 & 0 & 0 & 0 \\ 0 & 1 & 0 & 0 \\ -5 & 0 & 1 & 0 \\ 0 & 0 & 0 & 1 \end{bmatrix}.$$

An elementary matrix can also be expressed as $\mathbf{E} = \mathbf{I} - \alpha u v^{\mathrm{T}}$, where $\mathbf{I}$ is the identity matrix, α is a scalar, and u and v are vectors of the same dimension. In this context, the elementary matrix is referred to as a *rank one modification* of an identity matrix.

5. Other elementary matrices are those of the form $E_{ij} = \mathbf{e}_i \mathbf{e}_j^{\mathrm{T}}$. Note that, using these matrices, $A = \sum_i \sum_j a_{ij} E_{ij}$.

6. A matrix with all components above the principal diagonal equal to zero is called a *lower triangular matrix*.

EXAMPLE 2.5.3

$$L = \begin{bmatrix} a_{11} & 0 & 0 \\ a_{21} & a_{22} & 0 \\ a_{31} & a_{32} & a_{33} \end{bmatrix} \qquad \text{is lower triangular.}$$

7. The transpose of a lower triangular matrix is called an *upper triangular matrix.*

8. A matrix whose components are arranged in m rows and a single column is called a *column matrix*, or *column vector*, and is typically denoted using bold face, lower case letters, e.g., **a** and **b**.

9. A matrix whose components are arranged in n columns and a single row is called a *row matrix*, or *row vector*, and is typically denoted as a transposed column vector, e.g., $\mathbf{a}^T$ and $\mathbf{b}^T$.

10. A square matrix is called *symmetric* if $A = A^T$.

11. A square matrix is called *skew symmetric* if $A^T = -A$.

12. A square matrix $\mathbf{A}$ is called Hermitian if it equals its conjugate transpose, or $\mathbf{A} = \mathbf{A}^H$. All real symmetric matrices are Hermitian.

13. A square matrix $\mathbf{Q}$ with orthonormal columns is said to be *orthogonal*.[1] It follows directly that the rows of Q must also be orthonormal, so that $\mathbf{Q}\mathbf{Q}^T = \mathbf{Q}^T\mathbf{Q} = \mathbf{I}$, or $\mathbf{Q}^T = \mathbf{Q}^{-1}$.

14. A *principal submatrix* of a symmetric matrix $\mathbf{A}$ is formed by deleting rows and columns of $\mathbf{A}$ simultaneously, e.g., row 1 and column 1; row 9 and column 9, etc.

15. A *zero*, or *null, matrix* is one whose elements are all zero.

16. An $m \times n$ matrix $\mathbf{A}$ with orthonormal columns satisfies the property $\mathbf{A}^T\mathbf{A} = \mathbf{I}$, where $\mathbf{I}$ is an $n \times n$ identity matrix.

17. A square matrix, whose elements are constant along each diagonal, is called a *Toeplitz* matrix.

EXAMPLE 2.5.4

$$\mathbf{A} = \begin{bmatrix} a & d & e \\ b & a & d \\ c & b & a \end{bmatrix} \qquad and \qquad \mathbf{M} = \begin{bmatrix} 4 & 0 & 1 \\ -11 & 4 & 0 \\ 3 & -11 & 4 \end{bmatrix}$$

are Toeplitz matrices. Notice that Toeplitz matrices are symmetric about a diagonal extending from the upper right-hand corner element to the lower left-hand corner element. This type of symmetry is called *persymmetry.*

---

[1] Note the inconsistency in terminology that has persisted.

18. A *Vandermonde* matrix is a square matrix $\mathbf{V} \in \mathbb{R}^{(n+1) \times (n+1)}$ in which each column contains unit increasing powers of a single matrix value:

$$\mathbf{V} = \begin{bmatrix} 1 & 1 & \cdots & 1 \\ v_1 & v_2 & \cdots & v_{(n+1)} \\ v_1^2 & v_2^2 & \cdots & v_{(n+1)}^2 \\ \vdots & \vdots & & \vdots \\ v_1^n & v_2^n & \cdots & v_{(n+1)}^n \end{bmatrix}. \tag{2.5.1}$$

19. A square matrix $\mathbf{U}$ is said to be in *upper Hessenberg* form if $u_{ij} = 0$ whenever $i > j+1$. An upper Hessenberg matrix is essentially an upper triangular matrix with an extra nonzero element immediately below the main diagonal entry in each column of $\mathbf{U}$. For example,

$$\mathbf{U} = \begin{bmatrix} u_{11} & u_{12} & u_{13} & u_{14} \\ b_{21} & u_{22} & u_{23} & u_{24} \\ 0 & b_{32} & u_{33} & u_{34} \\ 0 & 0 & b_{43} & u_{44} \end{bmatrix} \quad \text{is upper Hessenberg.}$$

20. If the sum of the components of each column of a matrix $\mathbf{A} \in \mathbb{R}^{n \times n}$ equals one, then $\mathbf{A}$ is called a *Markov* matrix.

21. A *circulant* matrix is an $n \times n$ matrix of the form

$$\mathbf{C} = \begin{bmatrix} c_0 & c_1 & c_2 & \cdots & c_{n-2} & c_{n-1} \\ c_{n-1} & c_0 & c_1 & \cdots & c_{n-3} & c_{n-2} \\ c_{n-2} & c_{n-1} & c_0 & \cdots & c_{n-4} & c_{n-3} \\ \vdots & & & & & \vdots \\ c_1 & c_2 & c_3 & \cdots & c_{n-1} & c_0 \end{bmatrix}, \tag{2.5.2}$$

where the components c_{ij} are such that $(j - i) = k \mod n$ have the same value c_k. These components comprise the kth *stripe* of C.

22. A matrix A is called *graded across its rows* if $a_{ij} \leq a_{i,j+1}$, for all i, j; *graded up its columns* if $a_{ij} \leq a_{i+1,j}$; and *doubly graded* if both conditions apply.

2.5.3   CONFORMABILITY FOR ADDITION AND MULTIPLICATION

1. Two matrices $\mathbf{A}$ and $\mathbf{B}$ can be added (subtracted) if they are of the same dimension. The result is a matrix of the same dimension.

EXAMPLE 2.5.5

$$\mathbf{A}_{2 \times 3} + \mathbf{B}_{2 \times 3} = \begin{bmatrix} 3 & 2 & -1 \\ 4 & 0 & 9 \end{bmatrix} + \begin{bmatrix} 11 & -2 & 3 \\ 0 & 1 & 1 \end{bmatrix} = \begin{bmatrix} 14 & 0 & 2 \\ 4 & 1 & 10 \end{bmatrix}.$$

2. Multiplication of a matrix or a vector by a scalar is achieved by multiplying each component by that scalar. If $\mathbf{B} = \alpha\mathbf{A}$, then $b_{ij} = \alpha a_{ij}$ for all components.

3. The matrix multiplication $\mathbf{AB}$ is valid if the number of columns of $\mathbf{A}$ is equal to the number of rows of $\mathbf{B}$.

4. The multiplication of two matrices $\mathbf{A}_{m \times n}$ and $\mathbf{B}_{n \times q}$ results in a matrix $\mathbf{C}_{m \times q}$ whose components are defined as

$$c_{mq} = \sum_{k=1}^{n} a_{mk} b_{kq}. \tag{2.5.3}$$

Each c_{mq} is the result of the inner (dot) product of the mth row of A with the qth column of $\mathbf{B}$. This rule applies similarly for matrix multiplication involving more than two matrices, so that if $\mathbf{ABCD} = \mathbf{E}$, then

$$e_{ij} = \sum_{k} \sum_{l} \sum_{m} a_{ik} b_{kl} c_{lm} d_{mj}. \tag{2.5.4}$$

The second subscript for each matrix component must coincide with the first subscript of the next one.

EXAMPLE 2.5.6

$$\begin{bmatrix} 2 & -1 & 3 \\ -4 & 1 & 4 \end{bmatrix} \begin{bmatrix} 5 & -3 & -3 \\ 2 & 2 & -1 \\ -7 & 1 & 5 \end{bmatrix} = \begin{bmatrix} -13 & -5 & 10 \\ -46 & 18 & 31 \end{bmatrix}.$$

5. In general, matrix multiplication is not commutative: $\mathbf{AB} \neq \mathbf{BA}$.

6. Matrix multiplication is associative: $\mathbf{A(BC)} = \mathbf{(AB)C}$.

7. The distributive law of multiplication and addition holds: $\mathbf{C(A+B)} = \mathbf{CA + CB}$ and $\mathbf{(A+B)C} = \mathbf{AC + BC}$.

8. Both the transpose operator and the Hermitian operator reverse the order of matrix multiplication: $(\mathbf{ABC})^{\mathrm{T}} = \mathbf{C}^{\mathrm{T}}\mathbf{B}^{\mathrm{T}}\mathbf{A}^{\mathrm{T}}$ and $(\mathbf{ABC})^{\mathrm{H}} = \mathbf{C}^{\mathrm{H}}\mathbf{B}^{\mathrm{H}}\mathbf{A}^{\mathrm{H}}$.

9. Strassen algorithm: The matrix product $\begin{bmatrix} a_{11} & a_{12} \\ a_{21} & a_{22} \end{bmatrix} \begin{bmatrix} b_{11} & b_{12} \\ b_{21} & b_{22} \end{bmatrix} = \begin{bmatrix} c_{11} & c_{12} \\ c_{21} & c_{22} \end{bmatrix}$ can be computed in the following way:

$$m_1 = (a_{12} - a_{22})(b_{21} + b_{22}),$$
$$m_2 = (a_{11} + a_{22})(b_{11} + b_{22}),$$
$$m_3 = (a_{11} - a_{21})(b_{11} + b_{12}),$$
$$m_4 = (a_{11} + a_{12})b_{22},$$
$$m_5 = a_{11}(b_{12} - b_{22}),$$
$$m_6 = a_{22}(b_{21} - b_{11}),$$
$$m_7 = (a_{21} + a_{22})b_{11},$$

$$c_{11} = m_1 + m_2 - m_4 + m_6,$$
$$c_{12} = m_4 + m_5,$$
$$c_{21} = m_6 + m_7, \text{ and}$$
$$c_{22} = m_2 - m_3 + m_5 - m_7. \tag{2.5.5}$$

This computation uses 7 multiplications and 18 additions and subtractions. Using this formula recursively allows multiplication of two $n \times n$ matrices using $O(n^{\log_2 7}) = O(n^{2.807\cdots})$ scalar multiplications.

10. The order in which matrices are grouped together for multiplication can change the number of scalar multiplications required. The straightforward number of scalar multiplications required to multiply matrix $X_{a \times b}$ by matrix $Y_{b \times c}$ is abc, without using clever algorithms such as Strassen's. For example, consider the matrix product $P = A_{10 \times 100} B_{100 \times 5} C_{5 \times 50}$. The parenthesization $P = ((AB)C)$ requires $(10 \times 100 \times 5) + (10 \times 5 \times 50) = 7,500$ scalar multiplications. The parenthesization $P = (A(BC))$ requires $(10 \times 100 \times 50) + (100 \times 5 \times 50) = 75,000$ scalar multiplications.

2.5.4 DETERMINANTS AND PERMANENTS

1. The *determinant* of a square matrix $\mathbf{A}$, denoted by $|\mathbf{A}|$ or det $(\mathbf{A})$, is a scalar function of $\mathbf{A}$ defined as

$$\det(\mathbf{A}) = \sum_{\sigma} \text{sgn}(\sigma) a_{1,\sigma(1)} \, a_{2,\sigma(2)} \, \cdots a_{n,\sigma(n)} \qquad (2.5.6)$$

where the sum is taken over all permutations σ of $\{1, 2, \ldots, n\}$. The signum function $\text{sgn}(\sigma)$ is the number of successive transpositions required to change the permutation σ to the identity permutation. Note these properties of determinants: $|\mathbf{A}| \, |\mathbf{B}| = |\mathbf{AB}|$ and $|\mathbf{A}| = |\mathbf{A}^{\mathsf{T}}|$.

2. For a 2×2 matrix, $\begin{vmatrix} a_{11} & a_{12} \\ a_{21} & a_{22} \end{vmatrix} = a_{11}a_{22} - a_{12}a_{21}$.

For a 3×3 matrix,

$$\begin{vmatrix} a_{11} & a_{12} & a_{13} \\ a_{21} & a_{22} & a_{23} \\ a_{31} & a_{32} & a_{33} \end{vmatrix} = a_{11}a_{22}a_{33} + a_{12}a_{23}a_{31} + a_{13}a_{21}a_{32}$$
$$- a_{13}a_{22}a_{31} - a_{11}a_{23}a_{32} - a_{12}a_{21}a_{33}. \qquad (2.5.7)$$

In general, for $m = n$,

$$\begin{vmatrix} a_{11} & a_{12} & \cdots & a_{1n} \\ a_{21} & a_{22} & \cdots & a_{2n} \\ \vdots & \vdots & \vdots & \vdots \\ a_{n1} & a_{n2} & \cdots & a_{nn} \end{vmatrix} = \sum (-1)^{\delta} a_{1i_1} a_{2i_2} \cdots a_{ni_n} \qquad (2.5.8)$$

where the sum is over all permutations $i_1 \neq i_2 \neq \cdots \neq i_n$, and δ denotes the number of transpositions necessary to bring the sequence $(i_1, i_2, \ldots, i_n)$ back into the natural order $(1, 2, \ldots, n)$.

3. Interchanging two rows (or columns) of a matrix changes the sign of its determinant.

4. A determinant does not change its value if a linear combination of other rows (or columns) is added to or subtracted from any given row (or column).

5. Multiplying an entire row (or column) of $\mathbf{A}$ by a scalar γ causes the determinant to be multiplied by the same scalar γ.

6. For an $n \times n$ matrix $\mathbf{A}$, $|\gamma \mathbf{A}| = \gamma^n |\mathbf{A}|$.

7. If det $(\mathbf{A}) = 0$, then $\mathbf{A}$ is singular; if det $(\mathbf{A}) \neq 0$, then $\mathbf{A}$ is nonsingular or invertible. The determinant of the identity matrix is one.

8. det $(\mathbf{A}^{-1}) = 1/\det(\mathbf{A})$.

9. The size of the determinant of a square matrix $\mathbf{A}$ is *not* related to the condition number of $\mathbf{A}$.

10. When the edges of a parallelepiped P are defined by the rows (or columns) of $\mathbf{A}$, the absolute value of the determinant of $\mathbf{A}$ measures the volume of P. Thus, if any row (or column) of $\mathbf{A}$ is dependent upon another row (or column) of $\mathbf{A}$, the determinant of $\mathbf{A}$ equals zero.

11. The *cofactor* of a square matrix $\mathbf{A}$, $\mathrm{cof}_{ij}(\mathbf{A})$, is the determinant of a submatrix obtained by striking the ith row and the jth column of $\mathbf{A}$ and choosing a positive (negative) sign if $(i + j)$ is even (odd).

EXAMPLE 2.5.7

$$\mathrm{cof}_{23} \begin{bmatrix} 2 & 4 & 3 \\ 6 & 1 & 5 \\ -2 & 1 & 3 \end{bmatrix} = (-1)^{2+3} \begin{vmatrix} 2 & 4 \\ -2 & 1 \end{vmatrix} = -(2 + 8) = -10.$$

12. Let a_{ij} denote the components of $\mathbf{A}$ and a^{ij} those of $\mathbf{A}^{-1}$. Then,

$$a^{ij} = \mathrm{cof}_{ji}(\mathbf{A})/|\mathbf{A}|. \tag{2.5.9}$$

13. Partitioning of determinants: Let $\mathbf{A} = \begin{bmatrix} \mathbf{B} & \mathbf{C} \\ \mathbf{D} & \mathbf{E} \end{bmatrix}$. Assuming all inverses exist, then

$$|\mathbf{A}| = |\mathbf{E}| \; \left|\mathbf{B} - \mathbf{C}\mathbf{E}^{-1}\mathbf{D}\right| = |\mathbf{B}| \; \left|(\mathbf{E} - \mathbf{D}\mathbf{B}^{-1}\mathbf{C})\right|. \tag{2.5.10}$$

14. Laplace development: The determinant of $\mathbf{A}$ is a combination of row i (column j) and the cofactors of row i (column j), i.e.,

$$\begin{aligned} |\mathbf{A}| &= a_{i1}\mathrm{cof}_{i1}(\mathbf{A}) + a_{i2}\mathrm{cof}_{i2}(\mathbf{A}) + \cdots + a_{in}\mathrm{cof}_{in}(\mathbf{A}), \tag{2.5.11} \\ &= a_{1j}\mathrm{cof}_{1j}(\mathbf{A}) + a_{2j}\mathrm{cof}_{2j}(\mathbf{A}) + \cdots + a_{nj}\mathrm{cof}_{nj}(\mathbf{A}), \end{aligned}$$

for any row i or any column j.

15. Omitting the signum function in Equation (2.5.6) yields the definition of *permanent* of $\mathbf{A}$, given by per $\mathbf{A} = \sum_{\sigma} a_{1,\sigma(1)} \cdots a_{n,\sigma(n)}$. Properties of the permanent include:

    (a) If $\mathbf{A}$ is an $m \times n$ matrix and $\mathbf{B}$ is an $n \times m$ matrix, then

    $$|\mathrm{per}(\mathbf{AB})|^2 \leq \mathrm{per}(\mathbf{AA}^H)\,\mathrm{per}(\mathbf{B}^H\mathbf{B}). \tag{2.5.12}$$

(b) If $\mathbf{P}$ and $\mathbf{Q}$ are permutation matrices, then per $\mathbf{PAQ} = $ per $\mathbf{A}$.

(c) If $\mathbf{D}$ and $\mathbf{G}$ are diagonal matrices, then per $\mathbf{DAG} = $ per $\mathbf{D}$ per $\mathbf{A}$ per $\mathbf{G}$.

2.5.5 MATRIX NORMS

1. The mapping $g : \mathbb{R}^{m \times n} \Rightarrow \mathbb{R}$ is a *matrix norm* if g satisfies the same three properties as a vector norm:

   - $g(\mathbf{A}) \geq 0$ for $\mathbf{A} \neq \mathbf{0}$ and $g(\mathbf{A}) = 0$ if and only if $\mathbf{A} \equiv 0$, so that (in norm notation) $\|\mathbf{A}\| > 0$ for all nonzero $\mathbf{A}$.

   - For two matrices $\mathbf{A}, \mathbf{B} \in \mathbb{R}^{m \times n}$, $g(\mathbf{A} + \mathbf{B}) \leq g(\mathbf{A}) + g(\mathbf{B})$, so that $\|\mathbf{A} + \mathbf{B}\| \leq \|\mathbf{A}\| + \|\mathbf{B}\|$.

   - $g(r\mathbf{A}) = |r|g(\mathbf{A})$, where $r \in \mathbb{R}$, so that $\|\gamma\mathbf{A}\| = |\gamma|\ \|\mathbf{A}\|$.

2. The most common matrix norms are the L_p *matrix* norm and the *Frobenius* norm. The L_p *norm* of a matrix $\mathbf{A}$ is the number defined by

$$\|\mathbf{A}\|_p = \sup_{\mathbf{x} \neq \mathbf{0}} \frac{\|\mathbf{Ax}\|_p}{\|\mathbf{x}\|_p} \tag{2.5.13}$$

where $\|\cdot\|_p$ represents one of the L_p (vector) norms with $p = 1, 2,$ or ∞.

3. The matrix 1-norm of $\mathbf{A}_{m \times n}$ is defined as $\|\mathbf{A}\|_1 = \max_{1 \leq j \leq n} \sum_{i=1}^{m} |a_{ij}|$.

4. The matrix 2-norm of $\mathbf{A}$ is the square root of the greatest eigenvalue of $\mathbf{A}^T\mathbf{A}$, i.e., $\|\mathbf{A}\|_2^2 = \lambda_{\max}(\mathbf{A}^T\mathbf{A})$, which is the same as the largest singular value of $\mathbf{A}$, $\|\mathbf{A}\|_2 = \sigma_1(\mathbf{A})$. When $\mathbf{A}$ is symmetric, then $\|\mathbf{A}\| = \max |\lambda_j|$, where λ_j is the largest eigenvalue of $\mathbf{A}$.

5. The L_∞ norm is defined as $\|\mathbf{A}\|_\infty = \max_{1 \leq i \leq m} \sum_{j=1}^{n} |a_{ij}|$.

6. The following properties hold:

$$\frac{1}{\sqrt{m}}\ \|\mathbf{A}\|_1 \leq \|\mathbf{A}\|_2 \leq \sqrt{n}\ \|\mathbf{A}\|_1\ ,$$

$$\max_{i,j} |a_{ij}| \leq \|\mathbf{A}\|_2 \leq \sqrt{mn}\ \max_{i,j} |a_{ij}|,\ \text{and} \tag{2.5.14}$$

$$\frac{1}{\sqrt{n}}\ \|\mathbf{A}\|_\infty \leq \|\mathbf{A}\|_2 \leq \sqrt{m}\ \|\mathbf{A}\|_\infty\ .$$

7. The matrix p norms satisfy the additional property of *consistency*, defined as $\|\mathbf{AB}\|_p \leq \|\mathbf{A}\|_p \|\mathbf{B}\|_p$.

8. The *Frobenius* or *Hilbert-Schmidt norm* of a matrix $\mathbf{A}$ is a number defined by

$$\|\mathbf{A}\|_F = \sqrt{\sum_{i=1}^{m} \sum_{j=1}^{n} |a_{ij}|^2} \tag{2.5.15}$$

which satisfies $\|\mathbf{A}\|_F^2 = \text{trace}(\mathbf{A}^T\mathbf{A})$. Since $\mathbb{R}^{m \times n}$ is isomorphic to $\mathbb{R}^{mn}$, the Frobenius norm can be interpreted as the L_2 norm of an $nm \times 1$ column vector in which each column of $\mathbf{A}$ is appended to the next in succession. See Section 2.5.20.

9. The Frobenius norm is *compatible* with the vector 2 norm, i.e., $\|\mathbf{A}\mathbf{x}\|_F \le \|\mathbf{A}\|_F \|\mathbf{x}\|_2$. Additionally, the Frobenius norm satisfies the condition $\|\mathbf{A}\|_2 \le \|\mathbf{A}\|_F \le \sqrt{n} \|\mathbf{A}\|_2$.

2.5.6   SINGULARITY, RANK, AND INVERSES

1. An $n \times n$ matrix $\mathbf{A}$ is called *singular* if there exists a vector $\mathbf{x} \ne \mathbf{0}$ such that $\mathbf{A}\mathbf{x} = \mathbf{0}$ or $\mathbf{A}^T\mathbf{x} = \mathbf{0}$. (Note that $\mathbf{x} = \mathbf{0}$ means that all components of $\mathbf{x}$ are zero). If a matrix is not singular, it is called *nonsingular*.

2. $(\mathbf{A}\mathbf{B})^{-1} = \mathbf{B}^{-1}\mathbf{A}^{-1}$, provided all inverses exist.

3. $(\mathbf{A}^{-1})^T = (\mathbf{A}^T)^{-1}$.

4. $(\gamma\mathbf{A})^{-1} = (1/\gamma)\mathbf{A}^{-1}$.

5. If $\mathbf{D}_w$ is a diagonal matrix, then $\mathbf{D}_w^{-1} = \mathbf{D}_{1/w}$.

6. Partitioning: Let $\mathbf{A} = \begin{bmatrix} \mathbf{B} & \mathbf{C} \\ \mathbf{D} & \mathbf{E} \end{bmatrix}$. Assuming that all inverses exist, then $\mathbf{A}^{-1} = \begin{bmatrix} \mathbf{X} & \mathbf{Y} \\ \mathbf{Z} & \mathbf{U} \end{bmatrix}$, where

$$\mathbf{X} = (\mathbf{B} - \mathbf{C}\mathbf{E}^{-1})^{-1}, \qquad \mathbf{U} = (\mathbf{E} - \mathbf{D}\mathbf{B}^{-1}\mathbf{C})^{-1}, \qquad (2.5.16)$$

$$\mathbf{Y} = -\mathbf{B}^{-1}\mathbf{C}\mathbf{U}, \qquad \mathbf{Z} = -\mathbf{E}^{-1}\mathbf{D}\mathbf{X}. \qquad (2.5.17)$$

7. If $\mathbf{A}$ and $\mathbf{B}$ are both invertible, then

$$(\mathbf{A} + \mathbf{B})^{-1} = \mathbf{B}^{-1}\left(\mathbf{A}^{-1} + \mathbf{B}^{-1}\right)^{-1}\mathbf{A}^{-1} = \mathbf{A}^{-1}\left(\mathbf{A}^{-1} + \mathbf{B}^{-1}\right)^{-1}\mathbf{B}^{-1}.$$
$$(2.5.18)$$

8. The *row rank* of a matrix $\mathbf{A}$ is defined as the number of linearly independent rows of $\mathbf{A}$. Likewise, the *column rank* equals the number of linearly independent columns of $\mathbf{A}$.

9. For any matrix, the row rank equals the column rank.

10. If $\mathbf{A} \in \mathbb{R}^{n \times n}$ has rank of n, then $\mathbf{A}$ is said to have *full rank*.

11. A square matrix is invertible if, and only if, it has full rank.

12. Rank($\mathbf{A}\mathbf{B}$) $\le$ min $[\text{rank}(\mathbf{A}), \text{rank}(\mathbf{B})]$.

13. Rank($\mathbf{A}^T\mathbf{A}$) $= \text{rank}(\mathbf{A}\mathbf{A}^T) = \text{rank}(\mathbf{A})$.

2.5.7   SYSTEMS OF LINEAR EQUATIONS

1. Suppose that $\mathbf{A}$ is a matrix. Then $\mathbf{Ax} = \mathbf{b}$ is a system of linear equations. If $\mathbf{A}$ is square and nonsingular, there exists a unique solution $\mathbf{x} = \mathbf{A}^{-1}\mathbf{b}$.

2. For the linear system of equations involving n variables and m equations, written as $\mathbf{Ax} = \mathbf{c}$ or

$$
\begin{aligned}
a_{11}x_1 + a_{12}x_2 + \cdots + a_{1n}x_n &= c_1, \\
a_{21}x_1 + a_{22}x_2 + \cdots + a_{2n}x_n &= c_2, \\
&\vdots \\
a_{m1}x_1 + a_{m2}x_2 + \cdots + a_{mn}x_n &= c_m,
\end{aligned}
\tag{2.5.19}
$$

three possible outcomes exist for the simultaneous determination of a solution:

- No such solution exists and the system is called *inconsistent*.

- A unique solution exists, and the system is called *consistent*.

- Multiple solutions exist, the system has an infinite number of solutions, and the system is called *undetermined*.

3. For a system of linear equations $\mathbf{Ax} = \mathbf{b}$ (for which $\mathbf{A}$ is nonsingular), the sensitivity of the solution $\mathbf{x}$ to pertubations in $\mathbf{A}$ and $\mathbf{b}$ is given in terms of the *condition number* of $\mathbf{A}$ defined by

$$
\text{cond}(\mathbf{A}) = \left\| \mathbf{A}^{-1} \right\| \, \|\mathbf{A}\| .
\tag{2.5.20}
$$

where $\|\cdot\|$ is any of the p norms. In all cases, $\text{cond}(\mathbf{A}) \geq 1$. When $\text{cond}(\mathbf{A})$ is equal to one, $\mathbf{A}$ is said to be *perfectly conditioned*. Matrices with small condition numbers are called *well-conditioned*. If $\text{cond}(\mathbf{A})$ is large, then $\mathbf{A}$ is called *ill-conditioned*.

4. The size of the determinant of a square matrix $\mathbf{A}$ is *not* related to the condition number of $\mathbf{A}$.

5. When $\mathbf{A}$ is singular, the definition of condition number is modified slightly, incorporating the generalized, or pseudo inverse, of $\mathbf{A}$, and is defined by $\text{cond}(\mathbf{A}) = \left\| \mathbf{A}^+ \right\| \, \|\mathbf{A}\|$, where $\mathbf{A}^+$ represents the pseudo inverse of $\mathbf{A}$ (see Section 2.5.11).

6. Let $\mathbf{A} = (a_{ij})$ be an $n \times n$ matrix. Using the L_2 condition number, $\text{cond}\,\mathbf{A} = \max_j \left| \lambda_j(\mathbf{A}) \right| / \min_i |\lambda_i(\mathbf{A})|$:

Matrix $\mathbf{A}_{n \times n} = (a_{ij})$	Condition number
$a_{ij} = \sqrt{2/(n+1)} \sin(ij\pi/(n+1))$	cond $(\mathbf{A}) = 1$
$a_{ij} = n\delta_{ij} + 1$	cond $(\mathbf{A}) = 2$
$a_{ij} = (i+j)/p, \, n = p-1, \, p$ a prime	cond $(\mathbf{A}) = \sqrt{n+1}$
The circulant whose first row is $(1, 2, \ldots, n)$	cond $(\mathbf{A}) \sim n$
$a_{ij} = \begin{cases} i/j & \text{if } i \le j \\ j/i & \text{if } i > j \end{cases}$	cond $(\mathbf{A}) \sim cn^{1+\epsilon}$, $0 \le \epsilon \le 1$
$a_{ij} = \begin{cases} -2 & \text{if } i = j \\ 1 & \text{if } |i-j| = 1 \\ 0 & \text{if } |i-j| \ge 2 \end{cases}$	cond $(\mathbf{A}) \sim 4n^2/\pi^2$
$a_{ij} = 2\min(i, j) - 1$	cond $(\mathbf{A}) \sim 16n^2/\pi^2$
$a_{ij} = (i+j-1)^{-1}$ (Hilbert matrix)	log cond $(\mathbf{A}) \sim Kn$, $K \approx 3.5$

2.5.8   OTHER MATRIX TRANSFORMATIONS

1. A *Householder transformation*, or *Householder reflection*, is an $n \times n$ matrix $\mathbf{H}$ of the form $\mathbf{H} = \mathbf{I} - (2\mathbf{u}\mathbf{u}^{\mathrm{T}})/(\mathbf{u}^{\mathrm{T}}\mathbf{u})$, where the *Householder vector* $\mathbf{u} \in \mathbb{R}^n$ is nonzero.

2. A *Givens rotation* is defined as a rank two correction to the identity matrix given by

$$
\mathbf{G}(i, k, \theta) = \begin{bmatrix} 1 & \cdots & 0 & \cdots & 0 & \cdots & 0 \\ \vdots & \ddots & \vdots & & \vdots & & \vdots \\ 0 & \cdots & c & \cdots & s & \cdots & 0 \\ \vdots & & \vdots & \ddots & \vdots & & \vdots \\ 0 & \cdots & -s & \cdots & c & \cdots & 0 \\ \vdots & & \vdots & & \vdots & \ddots & \vdots \\ 0 & \cdots & 0 & \cdots & 0 & \cdots & 1 \end{bmatrix} \begin{matrix} \\ \\ i \\ \\ k \\ \\ \ \end{matrix}, \qquad (2.5.21)
$$

$$
\begin{matrix} & i & & k & \end{matrix}
$$

where $c = \cos\theta$ and $s = \sin\theta$ for some angle θ. Premultiplication by $\mathbf{G}(i, k, \theta)^{\mathrm{T}}$ induces a counterclockwise rotation of θ radians in the (i, k) plane. For $\mathbf{x} \in \mathbb{R}^n$ and $\mathbf{y} = \mathbf{G}(i, k, \theta)^{\mathrm{T}}\mathbf{x}$, the components of $\mathbf{y}$ are given by

$$
y_j = \begin{cases} cx_i - sx_k, & \text{for } j = i \\ sx_i + cx_k, & \text{for } j = k \\ x_j, & \text{for } j \ne i, k. \end{cases} \qquad (2.5.22)
$$

2.5.9   LINEAR SPACES AND LINEAR MAPPINGS

1. The *projection matrix*, **P**, onto a subspace S of the nonzero $m \times n$ matrix **A**, denoted by $\mathbf{P}_S$, is the unique $m \times m$ matrix possessing the three properties:

   (a) $\mathbf{P}_S = \mathbf{P}_S^\mathrm{T}$;

   (b) $\mathbf{P}_S^2 = \mathbf{P}_S$ (the projection matrix is *idempotent*);

   (c) The vector $\mathbf{b}_S$ lies in the subspace S if, and only if, $\mathbf{b}_S = \mathbf{P}_S \mathbf{v}$ for some m-dimensional vector **v**. In other words, $\mathbf{b}_S$ can be written as a linear combination of the columns of $\mathbf{P}_S$.

2. Let $R(\mathbf{A})$ and $N(\mathbf{A})$ denote, respectively, the range space and null space of an $m \times n$ matrix **A**. They are defined by

$$R(\mathbf{A}) = \left\{ \mathbf{y} \mid \mathbf{y} = \mathbf{Ax}; \text{ for some } \mathbf{x} \in \mathbb{R}^n \right\},$$

and

$$N(\mathbf{A}) = \left\{ \mathbf{x} \in \mathbb{R}^n \mid \mathbf{Ax} = \mathbf{0} \right\}.$$

3. When the $m \times n$ matrix **A** has rank n, the projection of **A** onto the subspaces of **A** is given by

$$\begin{aligned}
\mathbf{P}_{R(\mathbf{A})} &= \mathbf{A}(\mathbf{A}^\mathrm{T}\mathbf{A})^{-1}\mathbf{A}^\mathrm{T}, \\
\mathbf{P}_{R(\mathbf{A}^\mathrm{T})} &= I, \\
\mathbf{P}_{N(\mathbf{A}^\mathrm{T})} &= I - \mathbf{A}(\mathbf{A}^\mathrm{T}\mathbf{A})^{-1}\mathbf{A}^\mathrm{T}.
\end{aligned} \tag{2.5.23}$$

When **A** is of rank m, the projection of **A** onto the subspaces of **A** is given by

$$\begin{aligned}
\mathbf{P}_{R(\mathbf{A})} &= I, \\
\mathbf{P}_{R(\mathbf{A}^\mathrm{T})} &= \mathbf{A}^\mathrm{T}(\mathbf{A}\mathbf{A}^\mathrm{T})^{-1}\mathbf{A}, \\
\mathbf{P}_{N(\mathbf{A})} &= I - \mathbf{A}^\mathrm{T}(\mathbf{A}\mathbf{A}^\mathrm{T})^{-1}\mathbf{A}.
\end{aligned} \tag{2.5.24}$$

4. When **A** is not of full rank, the matrix $\mathbf{A}\tilde{\mathbf{A}}$ satisfies the requirements for a projection matrix. The matrix $\tilde{\mathbf{A}}$ is the coefficient matrix of the system of equations $\mathbf{x}_+ = \tilde{\mathbf{A}}\mathbf{b}$, generated by the *least squares* problem min $\|\mathbf{b} - \mathbf{Ax}\|_2^2$. Thus,

$$\begin{aligned}
\mathbf{P}_{R(\mathbf{A})} &= \mathbf{A}\tilde{\mathbf{A}}, \\
\mathbf{P}_{R(\mathbf{A}^\mathrm{T})} &= \tilde{\mathbf{A}}\mathbf{A}, \\
\mathbf{P}_{N(\mathbf{A})} &= I - \tilde{\mathbf{A}}\mathbf{A}, \\
\mathbf{P}_{N(\mathbf{A}^\mathrm{T})} &= I - \mathbf{A}\tilde{\mathbf{A}}.
\end{aligned} \tag{2.5.25}$$

5. A matrix $\mathbf{B} \in \mathbb{R}^{n \times n}$ is called *similar* to a matrix $\mathbf{A} \in \mathbb{R}^{n \times n}$ if $\mathbf{B} = \mathbf{T}^{-1}\mathbf{A}\mathbf{T}$ for some nonsingular matrix $\mathbf{T}$.

6. If $\mathbf{B}$ is similar to $\mathbf{A}$, then $\mathbf{B}$ has the same eigenvalues as $\mathbf{A}$.

7. If $\mathbf{B}$ is similar to $\mathbf{A}$ and if $\mathbf{x}$ is an eigenvector of $\mathbf{A}$, then $\mathbf{y} = \mathbf{T}^{-1}\mathbf{x}$ is an eigenvector of $\mathbf{B}$ corresponding to the same eigenvalue.

2.5.10 TRACES

1. The *trace* of an $n \times n$ matrix $\mathbf{A}$, usually denoted as tr $(\mathbf{A})$, is defined as the sum of the n diagonal components of $\mathbf{A}$.

2. The trace of an $n \times n$ matrix $\mathbf{A}$ equals the sum of the n eigenvalues of $\mathbf{A}$, i.e., $\operatorname{tr}\mathbf{A} = a_{11} + a_{22} + \cdots + a_{nn} = \lambda_1 + \lambda_2 + \cdots + \lambda_n$.

3. The trace of a 1×1 matrix, a scalar, is itself.

4. If $\mathbf{A} \in \mathbb{R}^{m \times k}$ and $\mathbf{B} \in \mathbb{R}^{k \times m}$, then $\operatorname{tr}(\mathbf{AB}) = \operatorname{tr}(\mathbf{BA})$.

5. If $\mathbf{A} \in \mathbb{R}^{m \times k}$, $\mathbf{B} \in \mathbb{R}^{k \times r}$, and $\mathbf{C} \in \mathbb{R}^{r \times m}$, then $\operatorname{tr}(\mathbf{ABC}) = \operatorname{tr}(\mathbf{BCA}) = \operatorname{tr}(\mathbf{CAB})$. For example, if $\mathbf{B} = \mathbf{b}$ is a column vector and $\mathbf{C} = \mathbf{c}^{\mathrm{T}}$ is a row vector, then $\operatorname{tr}(\mathbf{Abc}^{\mathrm{T}}) = \operatorname{tr}(\mathbf{bc}^{\mathrm{T}}\mathbf{A}) = \operatorname{tr}(\mathbf{c}^{\mathrm{T}}\mathbf{Ab})$.

6. $\operatorname{tr}(\mathbf{A} + \gamma\mathbf{B}) = \operatorname{tr}(\mathbf{A}) + \gamma \operatorname{tr}(\mathbf{B})$, where γ is a scalar.

7. $\operatorname{tr}(\mathbf{AB}) = (\operatorname{Vec}\mathbf{A}^{\mathrm{T}})^{\mathrm{T}} \operatorname{Vec}\mathbf{B}$ (see Section 2.5.20).

2.5.11 GENERALIZED INVERSES

1. Every matrix $\mathbf{A}$ (singular or nonsingular, rectangular or square) has a generalized inverse, or *pseudoinverse,* $\mathbf{A}^{+}$ defined by the *Moore–Penrose* conditions

$$
\begin{aligned}
\mathbf{AA}^{+}\mathbf{A} &= \mathbf{A}, \\
\mathbf{A}^{+}\mathbf{AA}^{+} &= \mathbf{A}^{+}, \\
(\mathbf{AA}^{+})^{\mathrm{T}} &= \mathbf{AA}^{+}, \\
(\mathbf{A}^{+}\mathbf{A})^{\mathrm{T}} &= \mathbf{A}^{+}\mathbf{A}.
\end{aligned}
\tag{2.5.26}
$$

2. Only if $\mathbf{A}$ is square and nonsingular, $\mathbf{A}^{+}$ will be unique and $\mathbf{A}^{+} = \mathbf{A}^{-1}$. Otherwise, there will exist infinitely many matrices $\mathbf{A}^{+}$ that will satisfy the defining relations.

3. If $\mathbf{A}$ is a rectangular $m \times n$ matrix of rank n, with $m > n$, then $\mathbf{A}^{+}$ is of order $n \times m$ and $\mathbf{A}^{+}\mathbf{A} = \mathbf{I} \in \mathbb{R}^{n \times n}$. In this case $\mathbf{A}^{+}$ is called a *left inverse,* and $\mathbf{AA}^{+} \neq \mathbf{I}$.

4. If $\mathbf{A}$ is a rectangular $m \times n$ matrix of rank m, with $m < n$, then $\mathbf{A}^{+}$ is of order $n \times m$ and $\mathbf{AA}^{+} = \mathbf{I} \in \mathbb{R}^{m \times m}$. In this case $\mathbf{A}^{+}$ is called a *right inverse,* and $\mathbf{A}^{+}\mathbf{A} \neq \mathbf{I}$.

5. For a square singular matrix $\mathbf{A}$, $\mathbf{AA}^{+} \neq \mathbf{I}$, and $\mathbf{A}^{+}\mathbf{A} \neq \mathbf{I}$.

6. The least squares problem is to find the $\mathbf{x}$ that minimizes $\|\mathbf{y} - \mathbf{Ax}\|$. The $\mathbf{x}$ of least norm is $\mathbf{x} = \mathbf{A}^+\mathbf{y}$.

7. A square matrix is called *idempotent* if $\mathbf{AA} = \mathbf{A}^2 = \mathbf{A}$.

8. $\mathbf{AA}^+$ and $\mathbf{A}^+\mathbf{A}$ are idempotent.

9. Let $\mathbf{A}$ be of rank r; and select r rows and r columns which form a basis of $\mathbf{A}$. Then, a pseudoinverse of $\mathbf{A}$ can be obtained as follows: invert the $r \times r$ matrix, place the inverse (without transposing) into the r rows corresponding to the column numbers and the r columns corresponding to the row numbers of the basis, and place zero into the remaining component positions. Thus, if $\mathbf{A}$ is of order 5×4 and rank 3, for example, and if rows 1, 2, 4 and columns 2, 3, 4 are selected as a basis, $\mathbf{A}^+$ of order 4×5 will contain the inverse components of the basis in rows 2, 3, 4 and column 1, 2, 4, and zeros elsewhere.

10. A pseudoinverse can also be computed for a general matrix $\mathbf{A}_{m \times n}$ using the singular value decomposition $\mathbf{A} = \mathbf{U\Sigma V}^T$, where $\mathbf{U}_{m \times m}$ and $\mathbf{V}_{n \times n}$ are orthogonal matrices. When $\mathbf{A}$ is of rank $r > 0$, $\Sigma_{m \times n}$ will have exactly r positive singular values (σ_i) along the main diagonal extending from the upper left-hand corner. The remaining components of Σ are zero. The pseudoinverse of $\mathbf{A}$ is then given by $\mathbf{A}^+ = (\mathbf{U\Sigma V}^T)^+ = (\mathbf{V}^T)^+\Sigma^+\mathbf{U}^+$, with $(\mathbf{V}^T)^+ = \mathbf{V}$ and $\mathbf{U}^+ = \mathbf{U}^T$ because of the orthogonality of $\mathbf{V}$ and $\mathbf{U}$. The components σ_i^+ of the pseudoinverse of Σ (rectangular, in this case) are given by

$$\sigma_i^+ = \begin{cases} 1/\sigma_i, & \text{if } \sigma_i \neq 0 ; \\ 0, & \text{if } \sigma_i = 0. \end{cases} \tag{2.5.27}$$

11. The pseudoinverse is ill-conditioned with respect to rank changing perturbations. For example

$$\left(\begin{bmatrix} 1 & -1 \\ 2 & -2 \end{bmatrix} + \epsilon \begin{bmatrix} 1 & 0 \\ 0 & 2 \end{bmatrix} \right)^+ = \frac{1}{\epsilon^2} \begin{bmatrix} -1 & \frac{1}{2} \\ -1 & \frac{1}{2} \end{bmatrix} + \frac{1}{\epsilon} \begin{bmatrix} 1 & 0 \\ 0 & \frac{1}{2} \end{bmatrix}.$$

2.5.12 EIGENSTRUCTURE

1. If $\mathbf{A}$ is a square $n \times n$ matrix, then the nth degree polynomial defined by $\det(\mathbf{A} - \lambda\mathbf{I}) = 0$ is called the *characteristic polynomial*, or *characteristic equation* of $\mathbf{A}$.

2. The n roots (not necessarily distinct) of the characteristic polynomial are called the *eigenvalues* (or characteristic roots) of $\mathbf{A}$. Therefore, the values, λ_i, $i = 1, \ldots, n$, are eigenvalues if, and only if, $|\mathbf{A} - \lambda_i\mathbf{I}| = 0$.

3. The characteristic polynomial $\det(\mathbf{A} - \lambda\mathbf{I}) = \sum_{i=0}^{n} r_i \lambda^i$ has the properties

$$r_n = (-1)^n$$

$$r_{n-1} = -r_n \operatorname{tr}(A)$$

$$r_{n-2} = -\frac{1}{2}\left[r_{n-1}\operatorname{tr}(A) + r_n\operatorname{tr}(A^2)\right]$$

$$r_{n-3} = -\frac{1}{3}\left[r_{n-2}\operatorname{tr}(A) + r_{n-1}\operatorname{tr}(A^2) + r_n\operatorname{tr}(A^3)\right]$$

$$\vdots$$

$$r_0 = -\frac{1}{n}\left[\sum_{j=1}^{n-1} r_{n-j}\operatorname{tr}(A^j)\right]$$

4. Each eigenvalue λ has a corresponding *eigenvector* $\mathbf{x}$ (different from $\mathbf{0}$) that solves the system $\mathbf{A}\mathbf{x} = \lambda\mathbf{x}$, or $(\mathbf{A} - \lambda\mathbf{I})\mathbf{x} = \mathbf{0}$.

5. If $\mathbf{x}$ solves $\mathbf{A}\mathbf{x} = \lambda\mathbf{x}$, then so does $\gamma\mathbf{x}$, where γ is an arbitrary scalar.

6. Cayley–Hamilton theorem: Any matrix $\mathbf{A}$ satisfies its own characteristic equation.

7. The eigenvalues of a triangular (or diagonal) matrix are the diagonal components of the matrix.

8. The eigenvalues of idempotent matrices are either zero or one.

9. If $\mathbf{A}$ is a real matrix with positive eigenvalues, then

$$\lambda_{\min}(\mathbf{A}\mathbf{A}^{\mathrm{T}}) \le [\lambda_{\min}(\mathbf{A})]^2 \le [\lambda_{\max}(\mathbf{A})]^2 \le \lambda_{\max}(\mathbf{A}\mathbf{A}^{\mathrm{T}}),$$

$$(2.5.28)$$

where $\lambda_{\min}$ denotes the smallest and $\lambda_{\max}$ the largest eigenvalue.

10. If all the eigenvalues of a real symmetric matrix are distinct, then their associated eigenvectors are also distinct (linearly independent).

11. Symmetric and Hermitian matrices have real eigenvalues.

12. For an $n \times n$ matrix $\mathbf{A}$ with eigenvalues $\lambda_1, \lambda_2, \dots, \lambda_n$, the product $\lambda_1\lambda_2\cdots\lambda_n = \det(\mathbf{A})$.

2.5.13 EIGENVALUE DIAGONALIZATION

1. If $\mathbf{A} \in \mathbb{R}^{n \times n}$ possesses n linearly independent eigenvectors $\mathbf{x}_1, \dots, \mathbf{x}_n$, then $\mathbf{A}$ can be diagonalized as $\mathbf{S}^{-1}\mathbf{A}\mathbf{S} = \Lambda = \operatorname{diag}(\lambda_1, \dots, \lambda_n)$, where the eigenvectors of $\mathbf{A}$ are chosen to comprise the columns of $\mathbf{S}$.

2. If $\mathbf{A} \in \mathbb{R}^{n \times n}$ can be diagonalized into $\mathbf{S}^{-1}\mathbf{A}\mathbf{S} = \Lambda$, then $\mathbf{A}^k = \mathbf{S}\Lambda^k\mathbf{S}^{-1}$, or $\Lambda^k = \mathbf{S}^{-1}\mathbf{A}^k\mathbf{S}$.

3. Spectral decomposition: Any real symmetric matrix $\mathbf{A} \in \mathbb{R}^{n \times n}$ can be diagonalized into the form $\mathbf{A} = \mathbf{U}\Lambda\mathbf{U}^{\mathrm{T}}$, where Λ is the diagonal matrix of ordered eigenvalues of $\mathbf{A}$ such that $\lambda_1 \ge \lambda_2 \ge \cdots \ge \lambda_n$, and the columns of $\mathbf{U}$ are the corresponding n *orthonormal* eigenvectors of $\mathbf{A}$.

4. The *spectral radius* of a real symmetric matrix $\mathbf{A}$, commonly denoted by $\rho(\mathbf{A})$, is defined as $\rho(\mathbf{A}) = \max_{1 \le i \le n} |\lambda_i(\mathbf{A})|$.

5. If $\mathbf{A} \in \mathbb{R}^{n \times n}$ and $\mathbf{B} \in \mathbb{R}^{n \times n}$ are diagonalizable, then they share a common eigenvector matrix $\mathbf{S}$ if and only if $\mathbf{AB} = \mathbf{BA}$. (Not every eigenvector of $\mathbf{A}$ need be an eigenvector for $\mathbf{B}$, e.g., $\mathbf{A} = \mathbf{I}$.)

6. Schur decomposition: If $\mathbf{A} \in \mathbb{C}^{n \times n}$, then a unitary matrix $\mathbf{Q} \in \mathbb{C}^{n \times n}$ exists such that $\mathbf{Q}^{H}\mathbf{AQ} = \mathbf{D} + \mathbf{N}$, where $\mathbf{D} = \text{diag}(\lambda_1, \ldots, \lambda_n)$ and $\mathbf{N} \in \mathbb{C}^{n \times n}$ is strictly upper triangular. The matrix $\mathbf{Q}$ can be chosen so that the eigenvalues λ_i appear in any order along the diagonal.

7. If $\mathbf{A} \in \mathbb{R}^{n \times n}$ and symmetric, then a real orthogonal matrix $\mathbf{Q}$ exists such that $\mathbf{Q}^{T}\mathbf{AQ} = \text{diag}(\lambda_1, \ldots, \lambda_n)$.

8. If $\mathbf{A} \in \mathbb{R}^{n \times n}$ possesses $s \le n$ linearly independent eigenvectors, it is similar to a matrix with s *Jordan blocks*

$$
\mathbf{J} = \mathbf{M}^{-1}\mathbf{AM} = \begin{bmatrix} \mathbf{J}_1 & & \mathbf{0} \\ & \ddots & \\ \mathbf{0} & & \mathbf{J}_s \end{bmatrix},
$$

where each Jordan block $\mathbf{J}_i$ is an upper triangular matrix with only a single eigenvalue λ_i and a single eigenvector:

$$
\mathbf{J}_i = \begin{bmatrix} \lambda_i & 1 & & \mathbf{0} \\ & \ddots & 1 & \\ & & \ddots & 1 \\ \mathbf{0} & & & \lambda_i \end{bmatrix} \tag{2.5.29}
$$

If $\mathbf{J}_i$ has $m > 1$, then λ_i repeats m times along the main diagonal, with $(m-1)$ 1's appearing above the diagonal entries, and all other components are equal to zero.

2.5.14   MATRIX EXPONENTIALS

1. Matrix exponentiation is defined as (the series always converges):

$$
e^{\mathbf{A}t} = \mathbf{I} + \mathbf{A}t + \frac{(\mathbf{A}t)^2}{2!} + \frac{(\mathbf{A}t)^3}{3!} + \cdots .
$$

2. Common properties of matrix exponentials are

(a) $\left(e^{\mathbf{A}s} \right) \left(e^{\mathbf{A}t} \right) = e^{\mathbf{A}(s+t)}$,

(b) $\left(e^{\mathbf{A}t} \right) \left(e^{-\mathbf{A}t} \right) = \mathbf{I}$,

(c) $\frac{d}{dt} e^{\mathbf{A}t} = \mathbf{A} e^{\mathbf{A}t}$, and

(d) when **A** and **B** are square matrices, the commutator of **A** and **B** is **C** = [**B, A**] = **BA** − **AB**. Then $e^{(\mathbf{A}+\mathbf{B})} = e^{\mathbf{A}}e^{\mathbf{B}}e^{\mathbf{C}/2}$ provided that [**C, A**] = [**C, B**] = **0** (i.e., each of **A** and **B** commute with their commutator).

3. For a matrix $\mathbf{A} \in \mathbb{R}^{n \times n}$, the determinant of $e^{\mathbf{A}t}$ is given by

$$\det\left(e^{\mathbf{A}t}\right) = e^{\lambda_1 t}e^{\lambda_2 t}\cdots e^{\lambda_n t} = e^{\text{trace}(\mathbf{A}t)}.$$

4. The diagonalization of $e^{\mathbf{A}t}$ is given by $e^{\mathbf{A}t} = \mathbf{S}e^{\mathbf{D}t}\mathbf{S}^{-1}$ where the columns of **S** consist of the eigenvectors of **A**, and the entries of the diagonal matrix **D** are the corresponding eigenvalues of **A**, that is, $\mathbf{A} = \mathbf{SDS}^{-1}$.

5. If **A** is skew-symmetric, then $e^{\mathbf{A}t}$ is an orthogonal matrix.

2.5.15 QUADRATIC FORMS

1. For a symmetric matrix **A**, the product $\mathbf{x}^T\mathbf{A}\mathbf{x}$ is called a *pure quadratic form*. It has the form

$$\mathbf{x}^T\mathbf{A}\mathbf{x} = \sum_{i=1}^{n}\sum_{j=1}^{n}a_{ij}x_ix_j = a_{11}x_1^2 + a_{12}x_1x_2 + a_{21}x_2x_1 + \cdots + a_{nn}x_n^2.$$

2. For **A** symmetric, the gradient of $\mathbf{x}^T\mathbf{A}\mathbf{x}/\mathbf{x}^T\mathbf{x}$ equals zero if, and only if, **x** is an eigenvector of **A**. Thus, the stationary values for this expression are the eigenvalues of **A**.

3. The ratio of two quadratic forms (**B** nonsingular) $u(\mathbf{x}) = (\mathbf{x}^T\mathbf{A}\mathbf{x})/(\mathbf{x}^T\mathbf{B}\mathbf{x})$ attains stationary values at the eigenvalues of $\mathbf{B}^{-1}\mathbf{A}$. In particular,

$$u_{\max} = \lambda_{\max}(\mathbf{B}^{-1}\mathbf{A}), \quad \text{and} \quad u_{\min} = \lambda_{\min}(\mathbf{B}^{-1}\mathbf{A}).$$

4. A matrix **A** is *positive definite* if $\mathbf{x}^T\mathbf{A}\mathbf{x} > 0$ for all $\mathbf{x} \neq \mathbf{0}$.

5. A matrix **A** is *positive semidefinite* if $\mathbf{x}^T\mathbf{A}\mathbf{x} \geq 0$ for all **x**.

6. For a real, symmetric matrix $\mathbf{A} \in \mathbb{R}^{n \times n}$, the following are necessary and sufficient conditions to establish the positive definiteness of **A**:

   (a) All eigenvalues, or characteristic roots, of **A** have $\lambda_i > 0$, for $i = 1, \ldots, n$, and

   (b) The upper-left submatrices of **A**, defined by

$$\mathbf{A}_1 = [a_{11}], \qquad \mathbf{A}_2 = \begin{bmatrix} a_{11} & a_{12} \\ a_{21} & a_{22} \end{bmatrix}, \qquad \ldots,$$

$$\mathbf{A}_n = \begin{bmatrix} a_{11} & a_{12} & \cdots & a_{1n} \\ a_{21} & a_{22} & \cdots & a_{2n} \\ \vdots & \vdots & & \vdots \\ a_{n1} & a_{n2} & \cdots & a_{nn} \end{bmatrix},$$

have $\det \mathbf{A}_k > 0$, for all $k = 1, \ldots, n$.

7. If $\mathbf{A}$ is positive definite, then all of the principal submatrices of $\mathbf{A}$ are also positive definite. Additionally, all diagonal entries of $\mathbf{A}$ are positive.

8. For a real, symmetric matrix $\mathbf{A} \in \mathbb{R}^{n \times n}$, the following are necessary and sufficient conditions to establish the positive semidefiniteness of $\mathbf{A}$:

   - All eigenvalues, or characteristic roots, of $\mathbf{A}$ have $\lambda_i \geq 0$, for $i = 1, \ldots, n$, and

   - The principal submatrices of $\mathbf{A}$ have $\det \mathbf{A}_k \geq 0$, for all $k = 1, \ldots, n$.

9. If $\mathbf{A}$ is positive definite, then all of the principal submatrices of $\mathbf{A}$ are also positive definite. Additionally, all diagonal entries of $\mathbf{A}$ are nonnegative.

10. If $\mathbf{x}^T$ denotes the radius vector (running coordinates $[x, y, z]$), and if a matrix $\mathbf{Q}$ is positive definite, then $(\mathbf{x}^T - \mathbf{x}_0^T)\mathbf{Q}^{-1}(\mathbf{x} - \mathbf{x}_0) = 1$ is the equation of an ellipsoid with its center at $[x_0, y_0, z_0] = \mathbf{x}_0^T$ and semiaxes equal to the square roots of the eigenvalues of $\mathbf{Q}$.

2.5.16   MATRIX FACTORIZATIONS

1. Singular value decomposition (SVD): Any $m \times n$ matrix $\mathbf{A}$ can be written as the product $\mathbf{A} = \mathbf{U}\boldsymbol{\Sigma}\mathbf{V}^T$, where $\mathbf{U}$ is an $m \times m$ orthogonal matrix, $\mathbf{V}$ is an $n \times n$ orthogonal matrix, and $\boldsymbol{\Sigma} = \mathrm{diag}(\sigma_1, \sigma_2, \ldots, \sigma_p)$, with $p = \min(m, n)$ and $\sigma_1 \geq \sigma_2 \geq \cdots \geq \sigma_p \geq 0$. The values σ_i, $i = 1, \ldots, p$, are called the *singular values* of $\mathbf{A}$.

2. When $\mathrm{rank}(\mathbf{A}) = r > 0$, $\mathbf{A}$ has exactly r positive singular values, and $\sigma_{r+1} = \cdots = \sigma_p = 0$.

3. When $\mathbf{A}$ is a symmetric $n \times n$ matrix, then $\sigma_1 = |\lambda_1|, \cdots, \sigma_n = |\lambda_n|$, where $\lambda_1, \lambda_2, \ldots, \lambda_n$ are the eigenvalues of $\mathbf{A}$.

4. When $\mathbf{A}$ is an $m \times n$ matrix, if $m \geq n$ then the singular values of $\mathbf{A}$ are the square roots of the eigenvalues of $\mathbf{A}^T\mathbf{A}$. Otherwise, they are the square roots of the eigenvalues of $\mathbf{A}\mathbf{A}^T$.

5. Any $m \times n$ matrix $\mathbf{A}$ can be factored as $\mathbf{PA} = \mathbf{LU}$, where $\mathbf{P}$ is a permutation matrix, $\mathbf{L}$ is lower triangular, and $\mathbf{U}$ is an $m \times n$ matrix in echelon form.

6. QR factorization: If all the columns of $\mathbf{A} \in \mathbb{R}^{m \times n}$ are linearly independent, then $\mathbf{A}$ can be factored as $\mathbf{A} = \mathbf{QR}$, where $\mathbf{Q} \in \mathbb{R}^{m \times n}$ has orthonormal columns and $\mathbf{R} \in \mathbb{R}^{n \times n}$ is upper triangular and nonsingular.

7. If $\mathbf{A} \in \mathbb{R}^{n \times n}$ is symmetric positive definite, then

$$\mathbf{A} = \mathbf{LDL}^T = \mathbf{LD}^{1/2}\mathbf{D}^{1/2}\mathbf{L}^T = \left(\mathbf{LD}^{1/2}\right)\left(\mathbf{LD}^{1/2}\right)^T = \mathbf{GG}^T$$

(2.5.30)

where $\mathbf{L}$ is a lower triangular matrix and $\mathbf{D}$ is a diagonal matrix. The factorization $\mathbf{A} = \mathbf{GG}^T$ is called the *Cholesky factorization*, and the matrix $\mathbf{G}$ is commonly referred to as the *Cholesky triangle*.

2.5.17 THEOREMS

1. *Frobenius–Perron theorem:* If $\mathbf{A} > \mathbf{0}$, then there exists a $\lambda_0 > 0$ and $\mathbf{x}_0 > \mathbf{0}$ such that

   (a) $\mathbf{A}\mathbf{x}_0 = \lambda_0\mathbf{x}_0$,

   (b) if λ is any other eigenvalue of $\mathbf{A}$, $\lambda \neq \lambda_0$, then $|\lambda| < \lambda_0$, and

   (c) λ_0 is an eigenvalue with geometric and algebraic multiplicity equal to one.

2. If $\mathbf{A} \geq \mathbf{0}$, and $\mathbf{A}^k > \mathbf{0}$ for some positive integer k, then the results of the Frobenius–Perron theorem apply to $\mathbf{A}$.

3. *Courant–Fischer minimax theorem:* If $\lambda_i(\mathbf{A})$ denotes the ith largest eigenvalue of a matrix $\mathbf{A} = \mathbf{A}^{\mathrm{T}} \in \mathbb{R}^{n \times n}$, then

$$\lambda_j(\mathbf{A}) = \max_{S_j} \min_{0 \neq \mathbf{x} \in S_j} \frac{\mathbf{x}^{\mathrm{T}}\mathbf{A}\mathbf{x}}{\mathbf{x}^{\mathrm{T}}\mathbf{x}} \qquad j = 1, \ldots, n$$

where $\mathbf{x} \in \mathbb{R}^n$ and S_j is a j-dimensional subspace.

4. *Cramer's rule:* The jth component of $\mathbf{x} = \mathbf{A}^{-1}\mathbf{b}$ is given by

$$x_j = \frac{\det \mathbf{B}_j}{\det \mathbf{A}}, \qquad \text{where} \qquad \mathbf{B}_j = \begin{bmatrix} a_{11} & a_{12} & b_1 & a_{1n} \\ \vdots & \vdots & \vdots & \vdots \\ a_{n1} & a_{n2} & b_n & a_{nn} \end{bmatrix}. \tag{2.5.31}$$

The vector $\mathbf{b} = (b_1, \ldots, b_n)^{\mathrm{T}}$ replaces the jth column of the matrix $\mathbf{A}$ to form the matrix $\mathbf{B}_j$.

5. *Sylvester's law of inertia:* For a symmetric matrix $\mathbf{A} \in \mathbb{R}^{n \times n}$, the congruence $\mathbf{A} \Rightarrow \mathbf{C}^{\mathrm{T}}\mathbf{A}\mathbf{C}$, for $\mathbf{C}$ nonsingular, has the same number of positive, negative, and zero eigenvalues.

6. *Raleigh's principle:* The quotient $R(\mathbf{x}) = \mathbf{x}^{\mathrm{T}}\mathbf{A}\mathbf{x}/\mathbf{x}^{\mathrm{T}}\mathbf{x}$ is minimized by the eigenvector $\mathbf{x} = \mathbf{x}_1$ corresponding to the smallest eigenvalue λ_1 of $\mathbf{A}$. The minimum of $R(x)$ is λ_1, that is,

$$\min R(\mathbf{x}) = \min \frac{\mathbf{x}^{\mathrm{T}}\mathbf{A}\mathbf{x}}{\mathbf{x}^{\mathrm{T}}\mathbf{x}} = R(\mathbf{x}_1) = \frac{\mathbf{x}_1^{\mathrm{T}}\mathbf{A}\mathbf{x}_1}{\mathbf{x}_1^{\mathrm{T}}\mathbf{x}_1} = \frac{\mathbf{x}_1^{\mathrm{T}}\lambda_1\mathbf{x}_1}{\mathbf{x}_1^{\mathrm{T}}\mathbf{x}_1} = \lambda_1.$$
$$\tag{2.5.32}$$

2.5.18 KRONECKER PRODUCTS OR TENSOR PRODUCTS

If the matrix $\mathbf{A} = (a_{ij})$ has size $m \times n$, and matrix $\mathbf{B} = (b_{ij})$ has size $r \times s$, then the Kronecker product of these matrices, denoted $\mathbf{A} \otimes \mathbf{B}$, is defined as the partitioned matrix

$$\mathbf{A} \otimes \mathbf{B} = \begin{bmatrix} a_{11}\mathbf{B} & a_{12}\mathbf{B} & \cdots & a_{1n}\mathbf{B} \\ a_{21}\mathbf{B} & a_{22}\mathbf{B} & \cdots & a_{2n}\mathbf{B} \\ \vdots & \vdots & & \vdots \\ a_{m1}\mathbf{B} & a_{m2}\mathbf{B} & \cdots & a_{mn}\mathbf{B} \end{bmatrix}. \tag{2.5.33}$$

Hence, the $\mathbf{A} \otimes \mathbf{B}$ matrix has size $mr \times ns$.

For example, if $\mathbf{A} = \begin{bmatrix} a_{11} & a_{12} \\ a_{21} & a_{22} \end{bmatrix}$ and $\mathbf{B} = \begin{bmatrix} b_{11} & b_{12} \\ b_{21} & b_{22} \end{bmatrix}$, then

$$
\mathbf{A} \otimes \mathbf{B} = \begin{bmatrix} a_{11}\mathbf{B} & a_{12}\mathbf{B} \\ a_{21}\mathbf{B} & a_{22}\mathbf{B} \end{bmatrix} = \left[\begin{array}{cc:cc} a_{11}b_{11} & a_{11}b_{12} & a_{12}b_{11} & a_{12}b_{12} \\ a_{11}b_{21} & a_{11}b_{22} & a_{12}b_{21} & a_{12}b_{22} \\ \hdashline a_{21}b_{11} & a_{21}b_{12} & a_{22}b_{11} & a_{22}b_{12} \\ a_{21}b_{21} & a_{21}b_{22} & a_{22}b_{21} & a_{22}b_{22} \end{array} \right].
$$

(2.5.34)

The Kronecker product has the following properties:

1. If $\mathbf{z}$ and $\mathbf{w}$ are vectors of appropriate dimensions, then
$\mathbf{Az} \otimes \mathbf{Bw} = (\mathbf{A} \otimes \mathbf{B})(\mathbf{z} \otimes \mathbf{w})$.

2. If α is a scalar, then $\mathbf{A} \otimes (\alpha\mathbf{B}) = \alpha(\mathbf{A} \otimes \mathbf{B})$.

3. The Kronecker product is distributive with respect to addition:

   • $(\mathbf{A} + \mathbf{B}) \otimes \mathbf{C} = \mathbf{A} \otimes \mathbf{C} + \mathbf{B} \otimes \mathbf{C}$, and

   • $\mathbf{A} \otimes (\mathbf{B} + \mathbf{C}) = \mathbf{A} \otimes \mathbf{B} + \mathbf{A} \otimes \mathbf{C}$.

4. The Kronecker product is associative: $\mathbf{A} \otimes (\mathbf{B} \otimes \mathbf{C}) = (\mathbf{A} \otimes \mathbf{B}) \otimes \mathbf{C}$.

5. $(\mathbf{A} \otimes \mathbf{B})^{\mathrm{T}} = \mathbf{A}^{\mathrm{T}} \otimes \mathbf{B}^{\mathrm{T}}$.

6. The mixed product rule: If the dimensions of the matrices are such that the expressions following exist, then $(\mathbf{A} \otimes \mathbf{B})(\mathbf{C} \otimes \mathbf{D}) = \mathbf{AC} \otimes \mathbf{BD}$.

7. If the inverses exist, then $(\mathbf{A} \otimes \mathbf{B})^{-1} = \mathbf{A}^{-1} \otimes \mathbf{B}^{-1}$.

8. If $\{\lambda_i\}$ and $\{\mathbf{x}_i\}$ are the eigenvalues and the corresponding eigenvectors for $\mathbf{A}$, and $\{\mu_j\}$ and $\{\mathbf{y}_j\}$ are the eigenvalues and the corresponding eigenvectors for $\mathbf{B}$, then $\mathbf{A} \otimes \mathbf{B}$ has eigenvalues $\{\lambda_i\mu_j\}$ with corresponding eigenvectors $\{\mathbf{x}_i \otimes \mathbf{y}_j\}$.

9. If matrix $\mathbf{A}$ has size $n \times n$ and $\mathbf{B}$ has size $m \times m$, then $\det(\mathbf{A}\otimes\mathbf{B}) = (\det \mathbf{A})^m (\det \mathbf{B})^n$.

10. If $f(z)$ is an analytic function and $\mathbf{A}$ has size $n \times n$, then

    • $f(\mathbf{I}_n \otimes \mathbf{A}) = \mathbf{I}_n \otimes f(\mathbf{A})$, and

    • $f(\mathbf{A} \otimes \mathbf{I}_n) = f(\mathbf{A}) \otimes \mathbf{I}_n$.

11. $\mathrm{tr}\,(\mathbf{A} \otimes \mathbf{B}) = (\,\mathrm{tr}\,\mathbf{A})(\,\mathrm{tr}\,\mathbf{B})$.

12. If $\mathbf{A}$, $\mathbf{B}$, $\mathbf{C}$, and $\mathbf{D}$ are matrices with $\mathbf{A}$ similar to $\mathbf{C}$ and $\mathbf{B}$ similar to $\mathbf{D}$, then $\mathbf{A} \otimes \mathbf{B}$ is similar to $\mathbf{C} \otimes \mathbf{D}$.

13. If $\mathbf{C}(t) = \mathbf{A}(t) \otimes \mathbf{B}(t)$, then $\frac{d\mathbf{C}}{dt} = \frac{d\mathbf{A}}{dt} \otimes \mathbf{B} + \mathbf{A} \otimes \frac{d\mathbf{B}}{dt}$.

2.5.19 KRONECKER SUMS

If the matrix $\mathbf{A} = (a_{ij})$ has size $n \times n$ and matrix $\mathbf{B} = (b_{ij})$ has size $m \times m$, then the Kronecker sum of these matrices, denoted $\mathbf{A} \oplus \mathbf{B}$, is defined[2] as $\mathbf{A} \oplus \mathbf{B} = \mathbf{A} \otimes \mathbf{I}_m + \mathbf{I}_n \otimes \mathbf{B}$.

The Kronecker sum has the following properties:

1. If $\mathbf{A}$ has eigenvalues $\{\lambda_i\}$ and $\mathbf{B}$ has eigenvalues $\{\mu_j\}$, then $\mathbf{A} \oplus \mathbf{B}$ has eigenvalues $\{\lambda_i + \mu_j\}$.

2. The matrix equation $\mathbf{AX} + \mathbf{XB} = \mathbf{C}$ may be equivalently written as $(\mathbf{B}^\mathsf{T} \oplus \mathbf{A})$ Vec $\mathbf{X} = $ Vec $\mathbf{C}$, where Vec is defined in Section 2.5.20.

3. $e^{\mathbf{A} \oplus \mathbf{B}} = e^\mathbf{A} \otimes e^\mathbf{B}$.

2.5.20 THE VECTOR OPERATION

The matrix $\mathbf{A}_{m \times n}$ can be represented as a collection of $m \times 1$ column vectors: $\mathbf{A} = \begin{bmatrix} \mathbf{a}_1 & \mathbf{a}_2 & \dots & \mathbf{a}_n \end{bmatrix}$. Define Vec $\mathbf{A}$ as the matrix of size $nm \times 1$ by

$$\text{Vec } \mathbf{A} = \begin{bmatrix} \mathbf{a}_1 \\ \mathbf{a}_2 \\ \vdots \\ \mathbf{a}_n \end{bmatrix}. \tag{2.5.35}$$

This operator has the following properties:

1. $\operatorname{tr}\mathbf{AB} = \left(\text{Vec } \mathbf{A}^\mathsf{T}\right)^\mathsf{T} \text{Vec } \mathbf{B}$.

2. The permutation matrix $\mathbf{U}$ that associates Vec $\mathbf{X}$ and Vec $\mathbf{X}^\mathsf{T}$ (that is, Vec $\mathbf{X}^\mathsf{T} = \mathbf{U}$ Vec $\mathbf{X}$) is given by:

$$\mathbf{U} = \begin{bmatrix} \text{Vec } \mathbf{E}_{11}^\mathsf{T} & \text{Vec } \mathbf{E}_{21}^\mathsf{T} & \dots & \text{Vec } \mathbf{E}_{n1}^\mathsf{T} \end{bmatrix} = \sum_{r,s} \mathbf{E}_{rs} \otimes \mathbf{E}_{rs}^\mathsf{T}. \tag{2.5.36}$$

3. $\text{Vec}(\mathbf{AYB}) = (\mathbf{B}^\mathsf{T} \otimes \mathbf{A}) \text{ Vec } \mathbf{Y}$.

4. If $\mathbf{A}$ and $\mathbf{B}$ are both of size $n \times n$, then
   (a) Vec $\mathbf{AB} = (\mathbf{I}_n \otimes \mathbf{A}) \text{ Vec } \mathbf{B}$.
   (b) Vec $\mathbf{AB} = (\mathbf{B}^\mathsf{T} \otimes \mathbf{A}) \text{ Vec } \mathbf{I}_n$.

---

[2]Note that $\mathbf{A} \oplus \mathbf{B}$ is also used to denote the $(m+n) \times (m+n)$ matrix $\begin{bmatrix} \mathbf{A} & 0 \\ 0 & \mathbf{B} \end{bmatrix}$.

2.6 ABSTRACT ALGEBRA

2.6.1 BASIC CONCEPTS

Definitions

1. A *binary operation on a set S* is a function $\star : S \times S \to S$.

2. An *algebraic structure* $(S, \star_1, \ldots, \star_n)$ consists of a nonempty set S with one or more binary operations $\star_i$ defined on S. If the operations are understood, then the binary operations need not be mentioned explicitly.

3. The *order* of an algebraic structure S is the number of elements in S, written $|S|$.

4. Properties that a binary operation $\star$ on an algebraic structure $(S, \star)$ may have are

   - *Associative*: $a \star (b \star c) = (a \star b) \star c$ for all $a, b, c \in S$.

   - *Identity*: there exists an element $e \in S$ (*identity element* of S) such that $e \star a = a \star e = a$ for all $a \in S$.

   - *Inverse*: $a^{-1} \in S$ is an *inverse* of a if $a \star a^{-1} = a^{-1} \star a = e$.

   - *Commutative* (or *abelian*): if $a \star b = b \star a$ for all $a, b \in S$.

5. A *semigroup* $(S, \star)$ consists of a nonempty set S and an associative binary operation $\star$ on S.

6. A *monoid* $(S, \star)$ consists of a nonempty set S with an identity element and an associative binary operation $\star$.

Examples of semigroups and monoids

1. The sets $\mathbb{N} = \{0, 1, 2, 3, \ldots\}$ (natural numbers), $\mathbb{Z} = \{0, \pm 1, \pm 2, \ldots\}$ (integers), $\mathbb{Q}$ (rational numbers), $\mathbb{R}$ (real numbers), and $\mathbb{C}$ (complex numbers) where $\star$ is either addition or multiplication are semigroups and monoids.

2. The set of positive integers under addition is a semigroup but not a monoid.

3. If A is any nonempty set, then the set of all functions $f : A \to A$ where $\star$ is the composition of functions is a semigroup and a monoid.

4. Given a set S, the set of all strings of elements of S, where $\star$ is concatenation of strings, is a monoid (the identity is λ, the empty string).

2.6.2 GROUPS

1. A *group* $(G, \star)$ consists of a set G with a binary operation $\star$ defined on G such that $\star$ satisfies the associative, identity, and inverse laws. *Note:* The operation $\star$ is often written as $+$ (an *additive group*) or as $\cdot$ or $\times$ (a *multiplicative* group). If $+$ is used, the identity is written 0 and the inverse of a is written $-a$. If multiplicative notation is used, $a \star b$ is often written ab and the identity is often written 1.

2. The *order* of $a \in G$ is the smallest positive integer n such that $a^n = 1$ where $a^n = a \cdot a \cdots a$ (n times) (or $a + a + \cdots + a = 0$ if G is written additively). If there is no such integer, the element has *infinite order*. In a finite group of order n, each element has some order k (depending on the particular element) and it must be that k divides n.

3. $(H, \star)$ is a subgroup of $(G, \star)$ if $H \subseteq G$ and $(H, \star)$ is a group (using the same binary operation used in $(G, \star)$).

4. The *cyclic subgroup* $\langle a \rangle$ generated by $a \in G$ is the subgroup $\{a^n \mid n \in \mathbb{Z}\} = \{\dots, a^{-2} = (a^{-1})^2, a^{-1}, a^0 = e, a, a^2, \dots\}$. The element a is a *generator* of $\langle a \rangle$. A group G is *cyclic* if there is $a \in G$ such that $G = \langle a \rangle$.

5. If H is a subgroup of a group G, then a *left [right] coset* of H in G is the set $aH = \{ah \mid h \in H\}$ $[Ha = \{ha \mid h \in H\}]$.

6. A *normal subgroup* of a group G is a subgroup H such that $aH = Ha$ for all $a \in G$.

7. A *simple group* is a group $G \neq \{e\}$ with only G and $\{e\}$ as normal subgroups.

8. If H is a normal subgroup of G, then the *quotient group* (or *factor group*) of G *modulo* H is the group $G/H = \{aH \mid a \in G\}$, with binary operation $aH \cdot bH = (ab)H$.

9. A finite group G is *solvable* if there is a sequence of subgroups $G_1 = G, G_2, \dots, G_{k-1}, G_k = \{e\}$ such that each G_{i+1} is a normal subgroup of G_i and G_i/G_{i+1} is abelian.

Facts about groups

1. The identity element is unique.

2. Each element has exactly one inverse.

3. Each of the equations $a \star x = b$ and $x \star a = b$ has exactly one solution, $x = a^{-1} \star b$ and $x = b \star a^{-1}$.

4. $(a^{-1})^{-1} = a$.

5. $(a \star b)^{-1} = b^{-1} \star a^{-1}$.

6. The *left [right] cancellation law* holds in all groups: If $a \star b = a \star c$ then $b = c$ [if $b \star a = c \star a$ then $b = c$].

7. *Lagrange's theorem*: If G is a finite group and H is a subgroup of G, then the order of H divides the order of G.

8. Every group of prime order is simple.

9. Every abelian group is solvable.

10. *Feit–Thompson theorem*: All groups of odd order are solvable. Hence, all finite non-Abelian simple groups have even order.

11. Finite simple groups are of the following types:

   - $\mathbb{Z}_p$ (p prime)

   - A group of Lie type

   - A_n ($n \geq 5$)

   - Sporadic groups (see table on page 151)

Examples of groups

1. $\mathbb{Z}, \mathbb{Q}, \mathbb{R}$, and $\mathbb{C}$, with $\star$ as addition of numbers, are additive groups.

2. For n a positive integer, $n\mathbb{Z} = \{nz \mid z \in \mathbb{Z}\}$ is an additive group.

3. $\mathbb{Q} - \{0\} = \mathbb{Q}^*, \mathbb{R} - \{0\} = \mathbb{R}^*, \mathbb{C} - \{0\} = \mathbb{C}^*$, with $\star$ as multiplication of numbers, are multiplicative groups.

4. $\mathbb{Z}_n = \mathbb{Z}/n\mathbb{Z} = \{0, 1, 2, \ldots, n - 1\}$ is a group where $\star$ is addition modulo n.

5. $\mathbb{Z}_n^* = \{k \mid k \in \mathbb{Z}_n, k$ has a multiplicative inverse (under multiplication modulo n) in $\mathbb{Z}_n\}$ is a group under multiplication modulo n. If p is prime, $\mathbb{Z}_p^*$ is cyclic. If p is prime and $a \in \mathbb{Z}_p^*$ has order (index) $p - 1$, then a is a *primitive root modulo* p. See the tables on pages 152 and 153 for primitive roots and power residues.

6. If $(G_1, \star_1), (G_2, \star_2), \ldots, (G_n, \star_n)$ are groups, the (*direct*) *product group* is $(G_1 \times G_2 \times \cdots \times G_n, \star) = \{(a_1, a_2, \ldots, a_n) \mid a_i \in G_i, i = 1, 2, \ldots, n\}$ where $\star$ is defined by $(a_1, a_2, \ldots, a_n) \star (b_1, b_2, \ldots, b_n) = (a_1 \star_1 b_1, a_2 \star_2 b_2, \ldots, a_n \star_n b_n)$.

7. All $m \times n$ matrices with real entries form a group under addition of matrices.

8. All $n \times n$ matrices with real entries and nonzero determinants form a group under matrix multiplication.

9. All 1–1, onto functions $f : S \to S$ (*permutations* of S), where S is any nonempty set, form a group under composition of functions. In particular, if $S = \{1, 2, 3, \ldots, n\}$, the group of permutations of S is called the *symmetric group S_n*. Each permutation can be written as a product of cycles. A *cycle* is a permutation $\sigma = (i_1 \ i_2 \ \cdots \ i_k)$, where $\sigma(i_1) = i_2, \sigma(i_2) = i_3, \ldots, \sigma(i_k) = i_1$. Each cycle of length greater than 1 can be written as a product of transpositions (cycles of length 2). A permutation is *even* (*odd*) if it can be written as the product of an even (odd) number of transpositions. (Every permutation is either even or odd.) The set of all even permutations in S_n is a subgroup A_n of S_n. The group A_n is called the *alternating group on n letters*.

10. Given a regular n-gon, the *dihedral group D_n* is the group of all symmetries of the n-gon, that is, the group generated by the set of all rotations around the center

of the n-gon through angles of $360k/n$ degrees (where $k = 0, 1, 2, \ldots, n-1$), together with all reflections in lines passing through a vertex and the center of the n-gon, using composition of functions. Alternately, $D_n = \{a^i b^j \mid i = 0, 1; \ j = 0, 1, \ldots, n-1; \ aba^{-1} = b^{-1}\}$.

11. The group T is of order 12 where $T = \{a^i b^j \mid i = 0, 1, \ldots, 5; \ j = 0, 1; \ b^2 = a^3, ba = a^{-1}b\}$.

12. The *quaternion group* Q_8 is the set $\{1, -1, i, -i, j, -j, k, -k\}$ where multiplication is defined by the following relationships:

$$i^2 = j^2 = k^2 = -1, \ ij = -ji = k, \ jk = -kj = i, \ ki = -ik = j$$

with 1 as the identity. These relations yield the following multiplication table:

$\times$	1	-1	i	$-i$	j	$-j$	k	$-k$
1	1	-1	i	$-i$	j	$-j$	k	$-k$
-1	-1	1	$-i$	i	$-j$	j	$-k$	k
i	i	$-i$	-1	1	k	$-k$	$-j$	j
$-i$	$-i$	i	1	-1	$-k$	k	j	$-j$
j	j	$-j$	$-k$	k	-1	1	i	$-i$
$-j$	$-j$	j	k	$-k$	1	-1	$-i$	i
k	k	$-k$	j	$-j$	$-i$	i	-1	1
$-k$	$-k$	k	$-j$	j	i	$-i$	1	-1

The quaternion group can also be defined as the following group of 8 matrices:

$$\begin{bmatrix} 1 & 0 \\ 0 & 1 \end{bmatrix}, \begin{bmatrix} -1 & 0 \\ 0 & -1 \end{bmatrix}, \begin{bmatrix} -i & 0 \\ 0 & i \end{bmatrix}, \begin{bmatrix} i & 0 \\ 0 & -i \end{bmatrix},$$

$$\begin{bmatrix} 0 & i \\ i & 0 \end{bmatrix}, \begin{bmatrix} 0 & -i \\ -i & 0 \end{bmatrix}, \begin{bmatrix} 0 & 1 \\ -1 & 0 \end{bmatrix}, \begin{bmatrix} 0 & -1 \\ 1 & 0 \end{bmatrix}$$

where $i^2 = -1$ and matrix multiplication is the group operation.

2.6.3 RINGS

Definitions

1. A *ring* $(R, +, \cdot)$ consists of a nonempty set R and two binary operations, $+$ and $\cdot$, such that $(R, +)$ is an abelian group, the operation $\cdot$ is associative, and the *left distributive law* $a(b + c) = (ab) + (ac)$ and the *right distributive law* $(a + b)c = (ac) + (bc)$ hold for all $a, b, c \in R$.

2. A subset S of a ring R is a *subring* of R if S is a ring using the same operations used in R.

3. A ring R is a *commutative* ring if the multiplication operation is commutative: $ab = ba$ for all $a, b \in R$.

4. A ring R is a *ring with unity* if there is an element 1 (called *unity*) such that $a1 = 1a = a$ for all $a \in R$.

5. A *unit* in a ring with unity is an element a with a multiplicative inverse a^{-1} ($aa^{-1} = a^{-1}a = 1$).

6. If $a \neq 0$, $b \neq 0$, and $ab = 0$, then a is a *left divisor of zero* and b is a *right divisor of zero*.

7. A subset I of a ring $(R, +, \cdot)$ is an *ideal* of R if $(I, +)$ is a subgroup of $(R, +)$ and I is closed under left and right multiplication by elements of R (if $x \in I$ and $r \in R$, then $rx \in I$ and $xr \in I$).

8. An ideal $I \subseteq R$ is

   - *Proper*: if $I \neq \{0\}$ and $I \neq R$

   - *Maximal*: if I is proper there is no proper ideal properly containing I

   - *Prime*: if $ab \in I$ implies that a or $b \in I$

   - *Principal*: if there is $a \in R$ such that I is the intersection of all ideals containing a.

9. If I is an ideal in a ring R, then a *coset* is a set $r + I = \{r + a \mid a \in I\}$.

10. If I is an ideal in a ring R, then the *quotient ring* is the ring $R/I = \{r+I \mid r \in R\}$, where $(r + I) + (s + I) = (r + s) + I$ and $(r + I)(s + I) = (rs) + I$.

11. An *integral domain* $(R, +, \cdot)$ consists of a nonempty set R and two binary operations, $+$ and $\cdot$, such that $(R, +, \cdot)$ is a commutative ring with unity, and the left [right] cancellation laws hold: if $ab = ac$ then $b = c$ [if $ba = ca$ then $b = c$] for all $a, b, c \in R$, where $a \neq 0$. (Equivalently, an integral domain is a commutative ring with unity that has no divisors of zero.)

12. If R is an integral domain, then a nonzero element $r \in R$ that is not a unit is *irreducible* if $r = ab$ implies that either a or b is a unit.

13. If R is an integral domain, a nonzero element $r \in R$ that is not a unit is a *prime* if, whenever $r \mid ab$, then either $r \mid a$ or $r \mid b$ ($x \mid y$ means that there is an element $z \in R$ such that $y = zx$.).

14. A *unique factorization domain* (UFD) is an integral domain such that every nonzero element that is not a unit can be written uniquely as the product of irreducible elements (except for factors that are units and except for the order in which the factor appears).

15. A *principal ideal domain* (PID) is an integral domain in which every ideal is a principal ideal.

16. A *division ring* is a ring in which every nonzero element has a multiplicative inverse (that is, every nonzero element is a unit). (Equivalently, a division ring is a ring in which the nonzero elements form a multiplicative group.) A noncommutative division ring is called a *skew field*.

Examples

1. $\mathbb{Z}$ (integers), $\mathbb{Q}$ (rational numbers), $\mathbb{R}$ (real numbers), and $\mathbb{C}$ (complex numbers) are rings, with ordinary addition and multiplication of numbers.

2. $\mathbb{Z}_n$ is a ring, with addition and multiplication modulo n.

3. If $\sqrt{n}$ is not an integer, then $\mathbb{Z}[\sqrt{n}] = \{a + b\sqrt{n} \mid a, b \in \mathbb{Z}\}$, where $(a + b\sqrt{n}) + (c + d\sqrt{n}) = (a + c) + (b + d)\sqrt{n}$ and $(a + b\sqrt{n})(c + d\sqrt{n}) = (ac + nbd) + (ad + bc)\sqrt{n}$ is a ring.

4. The set of *Gaussian integers* $\mathbb{Z}[i] = \{a + bi \mid a, b \in \mathbb{Z}\}$ is a ring, with the usual definitions of addition and multiplication of complex numbers.

5. The *polynomial ring* in one variable over a ring R is the ring $R[x] = \{a_n x^n + \cdots + a_1 x + a_0 \mid a_i \in R; \ i = 0, 1, \ldots, n; \ n \in \mathcal{N}\}$ (elements of $R[x]$ are added and multiplied using the usual rules for addition and multiplication of polynomials). The *degree* of a polynomial $a_n x^n + \cdots + a_1 x + a_0$ with $a_n \neq 0$ is n. A polynomial is *monic* if $a_n = 1$. A polynomial $f(x)$ is *irreducible over* R if $f(x)$ cannot be factored as a product of polynomials in $R[x]$ of degree less than the degree of $f(x)$. A monic irreducible polynomial $f(x)$ of degree k in $\mathbb{Z}_p[x]$ (p prime) is *primitive* if the order of x in $\mathbb{Z}_p[x]/(f(x))$ is $p^k - 1$, where $(f(x)) = \{f(x)g(x) \mid g(x) \in \mathbb{Z}_p[x]\}$ (the ideal generated by $f(x)$). For example, the polynomial $x^2 + 1$ is

- Irreducible in $\mathbb{R}[x]$ because $x^2 + 1$ has no real root

- Reducible in $\mathbb{C}[x]$ because $x^2 + 1 = (x - i)(x + i)$

- Reducible in $Z_2[x]$ because $x^2 + 1 = (x + 1)^2$

- Reducible in $Z_5[x]$ because $x^2 + 1 = (x + 2)(x + 3)$

6. The *division ring of quaternions* is the ring $(\{a + bi + cj + dk \mid a, b, c, d \in \mathbb{R}\}, +, \cdot)$, where operations are carried out using the rules for polynomial addition and multiplication and the defining relations for the quaternion group Q_8.

Facts

1. The set of all units of a ring is a group under the multiplication defined on the ring.

2. Every principal ideal domain is a unique factorization domain.

3. If R is a commutative ring with unity, then every maximal ideal is a prime ideal.

4. If R is a commutative ring with unity, then R is a field if and only if the only ideals of R are R and $\{0\}$.

5. If R is a commutative ring with unity and $I \neq R$ is an ideal, then R/I is an integral domain if and only if I is a prime ideal.

6. If R is a commutative ring with unity, then I is a maximal ideal if and only if R/I is a field.

7. If $f(x) \in F[x]$ (F a field) and the ideal $(f(x)) \neq \{0\}$, then the ideal $(f(x))$ is maximal if and only if $f(x)$ is irreducible over F.

2.6.4   FIELDS

Definitions

1. A *field* $(F, +, \cdot)$ consists of a commutative ring with unity such that each nonzero element of F has a multiplicative inverse (equivalently, a field is a commutative division ring).

2. The *characteristic* of a field is the smallest positive integer n such that $1 + 1 + \cdots + 1 = 0$ (n summands). If no such n exists, the field has characteristic 0 (or characteristic ∞).

3. Field K is an *extension field* of the field F if F is a subfield of K (i.e., $F \subseteq K$, and F is a field using the same operations used in K).

Examples

1. The sets $\mathbb{Q}$, $\mathbb{R}$, and $\mathbb{C}$ with ordinary addition and multiplication are fields.

2. $\mathbb{Z}_p$ (p a prime) is a field under addition and multiplication modulo p.

3. $F[x]/(f(x))$ is a field, provided that F is a field and $f(x)$ is a nonconstant polynomial irreducible in $F[x]$.

2.6.5   FINITE FIELDS

Facts

1. If p is prime, then the ring $\mathbb{Z}_p$ is a finite field.

2. If p is prime and n is a positive integer, then there is exactly one field (up to isomorphism) with p^n elements. This field is denoted $GF(p^n)$ or F_{p^n} and is called a *Galois field*. (See the tables beginnning on page 155.)

3. For F a finite field, there is a prime p and a positive integer n such that F has p^n elements. The prime number p is the characteristic of F. The field F is a *finite extension* of $\mathbb{Z}_p$, that is, F is a vector space over $\mathbb{Z}_p$.

4. If F is a finite field, then the set of nonzero elements of F under multiplication is a cyclic group. A generator of this group is a *primitive element*.

5. There are $\phi(p^n - 1)/n$ primitive polynomials of degree n ($n > 1$) over $GF(p)$, where ϕ is the Euler ϕ-function. (See table on page 154.)

6. There are $(\sum_{j|k} \mu(k/j) p^{nj})/k$ irreducible polynomials of degree k over $GF(p^n)$, where μ is the Möbius function.

7. If F is a finite field where $|F| = k$ and $p(x)$ is a polynomial of degree n irreducible over F, then the field $F[x]/(p(x))$ has order k^n. If α is a root of $p(x) \in F[x]$ of degree $n \geq 1$, then $F[x]/(p(x)) = \{c_{n-1}\alpha^{n-1} + \cdots + c_1\alpha + c_0 \mid c_i \in F \text{ for all } i\}$.

8. When q is a power of a prime, F_{q^n} can be viewed as a vector space of dimension n over F_q. A basis of F_{q^n} of the form $\{\alpha, \alpha^q, \alpha^{q^2}, \ldots, \alpha^{q^{n-1}}\}$ is called a *normal*

basis. If α is a primitive element of F_{q^n}, then the basis is said to be a *primitive normal basis.* Such an α satisfies a primitive normal polynomial of degree n over F_q.

Degree	Primitive normal polynomials		
n	$q = 2$	$q = 3$	$q = 5$
2	$x^2 + x + 1$	$x^2 + x + 2$	$x^2 + x + 2$
3	$x^3 + x^2 + 1$	$x^3 + 2x^2 + 1$	$x^3 + x^2 + 2$
4	$x^4 + x^3 + 1$	$x^4 + x^3 + 2$	$x^4 + x^3 + 4x + 2$
5	$x^5 + x^4 + x^2 + x + 1$	$x^5 + 2x^4 + 1$	$x^5 + 2x^4 + 3$
6	$x^6 + x^5 + 1$	$x^6 + x^5 + x^3 + 2$	$x^6 + x^5 + 2$
7	$x^7 + x^6 + 1$	$x^7 + x^6 + x^2 + 1$	$x^7 + x^6 + 2$

2.6.6 HOMOMORPHISMS AND ISOMORPHISMS

Definitions

1. A *group homomorphism* from group G_1 to group G_2 is a function $\varphi : G_1 \rightarrow G_2$ such that $\varphi(ab) = \varphi(a)\varphi(b)$ for all $a, b \in G_1$. *Note:* $a\varphi$ is often written instead of $\varphi(a)$.

2. A *character* of a group G is a group homomorphism $\chi : G \rightarrow \mathbb{C}^*$ (nonzero complex numbers under multiplication). (See table on page 149.)

3. A *ring homomorphism* from ring R_1 to ring R_2 is a function $\varphi : R_1 \rightarrow R_2$ such that $\varphi(a + b) = \varphi(a) + \varphi(b)$ and $\varphi(ab) = \varphi(a)\varphi(b)$ for all $a, b \in R_1$.

4. An *isomorphism* from group (ring) S_1 to group (ring) S_2 is a group (ring) homomorphism $\varphi : S_1 \rightarrow S_2$ that is 1-1 and onto S_2. If an isomorphism exists, then S_1 is said to be *isomorphic* to S_2. Write $S_1 \cong S_2$. (See the table on page 150 for numbers of nonisomorphic groups and the table on page 149 for examples of groups of orders less than 16.)

5. An *automorphism* of S is an isomorphism $\varphi : S \rightarrow S$.

6. The *kernel* of a group homomorphism $\varphi : G_1 \rightarrow G_2$ is $\varphi^{-1}(e) = \{g \in G_1 \mid \varphi(g) = e\}$. The *kernel* of a ring homomorphism $\varphi : R_1 \rightarrow R_2$ is $\varphi^{-1}(0) = \{r \in R_1 \mid \varphi(r) = 0\}$.

Facts

1. If $\varphi : G_1 \rightarrow G_2$ is a group homomorphism, then $\varphi(G_1)$ is a subgroup of G_2.

2. *Fundamental homomorphism theorem for groups:* If $\varphi : G_1 \rightarrow G_2$ is a group homomorphism with kernel K, then K is a normal subgroup of G_1 and $G_1/K \cong \varphi(G_1)$.

3. If G is a cyclic group of infinite order, then $G \cong (\mathbb{Z}, +)$.

4. If G is a cyclic group of order n, then $G \cong (\mathbb{Z}_n, +)$.

5. If p is prime, then there is only one group (up to isomorphism) of order p, the group $(\mathbb{Z}_p, +)$.

6. *Cayley's theorem*: If G is a finite group of order n, then G is isomorphic to some subgroup of the group of permutations on n objects.

7. $\mathbb{Z}_m \times \mathbb{Z}_n \cong \mathbb{Z}_{mn}$ if, and only if, m and n are relatively prime.

8. If $n = n_1 \cdot n_2 \cdot \ldots \cdot n_k$ where each n_i is a power of a different prime, then $\mathbb{Z}_n \cong \mathbb{Z}_{n_1} \times \mathbb{Z}_{n_2} \times \cdots \times \mathbb{Z}_{n_k}$.

9. *Fundamental theorem of finite abelian groups*: Every finite abelian group G (order ≥ 2) is isomorphic to a product of cyclic groups where each cyclic group has order a power of a prime, that is, there is a unique set $\{n_1, \ldots, n_k\}$ where each n_i is a power of some prime such that $G \cong \mathbb{Z}_{n_1} \times \mathbb{Z}_{n_2} \times \cdots \times \mathbb{Z}_{n_k}$.

10. *Fundamental theorem of finitely generated abelian groups*: If G is a finitely generated abelian group, then there is a unique integer $n \geq 0$ and a unique set $\{n_1, \ldots, n_k\}$ where each n_i is a power of some prime such that $G \cong \mathbb{Z}^n \times \mathbb{Z}_{n_1} \times \mathbb{Z}_{n_2} \times \cdots \times \mathbb{Z}_{n_k}$ (G is finitely generated if there are $a_1, a_2, \ldots, a_n \in G$ such that every element of G can be written as $a_{k_1}^{\epsilon_1} a_{k_2}^{\epsilon_2} \cdots a_{k_j}^{\epsilon_j}$ where $k_i \in \{1, \ldots, n\}$ (the k_i are not necessarily distinct) and $\epsilon_i \in \{1, -1\}$).

11. *Fundamental homomorphism theorem for rings*: If $\varphi : R_1 \rightarrow R_2$ is a ring homomorphism with kernel K, then K is an ideal in R_1 and $R_1/K \cong \varphi(R_1)$.

2.6.7   MATRIX CLASSES THAT ARE GROUPS

In the following examples, the group operation is ordinary matrix multiplication:

- $GL(n, \mathbb{C})$ all complex non-singular $n \times n$ matrices

- $GL(n, \mathbb{R})$ all real non-singular $n \times n$ matrices

- $O(n)$ all $n \times n$ matrices A with $AA^T = I$, also called the *orthogonal group*

- $SL(n, \mathbb{C})$ all complex $n \times n$ matrices of determinant 1, also called the *unimodular group* or the *special linear group*

- $SL(n, \mathbb{R})$ all real $n \times n$ matrices of determinant 1

- $SO(2)$ rotations of the plane: matrices of the form
$$A(\theta) = \begin{bmatrix} \cos \theta & -\sin \theta \\ \sin \theta & \cos \theta \end{bmatrix}$$

- $SO(n)$ rotations of n-dimensional space

- $SU(n)$ all $n \times n$ unitary matrices of determinant 1

- $U(n)$ all $n \times n$ unitary matrices with $UU^H = I$

2.6.8 PERMUTATION GROUPS

Name	Symbol	Order	Definition
Symmetric group	S_p	$p!$	All permutations on $\{1, 2, \ldots, p\}$
Alternating group	A_p	$p!/2$	All even permutations on $\{1, 2, \ldots, p\}$
Cyclic group	C_p	p	Generated by $(12 \cdots p)$
Dihedral group	D_p	$2p$	Generated by $(12 \cdots p)$ and $(1p)(2\,p-1)$
Identity group	E_p	1	$(1)(2) \cdots (p)$ is the only permutation

For example, with $p = 3$ elements

$$A_3 = \{(123), (231), (312)\},$$
$$C_3 = \{(123), (231), (312)\},$$
$$D_3 = \{(231), (213), (132), (321), (312), (123)\},$$
$$E_3 = \{(123)\} \text{ and}$$
$$S_3 = \{(231), (213), (132), (321), (312), (123)\}.$$

Creating new permutation groups

Let A have permutations $\{X_i\}$, order n, degree d, let B have permutations $\{Y_j\}$, order m, degree e, and let C (a function of A and B) have permutations $\{W_k\}$, order p, degree f.

Name	Definition	Permutation	Order	Degree
Sum	$C = A + B$	$W = X \cup Y$	$p = mn$	$f = d + e$
Product	$C = A \times B$	$W = X \times Y$	$p = mn$	$f = de$
Composition	$C = A[B]$	$W = X \times Y$	$p = mn^d$	$f = de$
Power	$C = B^A$	$W = Y^X$	$p = mn$	$f = e^d$

Polya theory

Define Inv (π) to be the number of invariant elements (i.e., mapped to themselves) of the permutation π. Define cyc (π) as the number of cycles in π.

1. *Burnside's Lemma*: Let G be a group of permutations of a set A, and let S be the equivalence relation on A induced by G. Then the number of equivalence classes in A is given by $\dfrac{1}{|G|} \sum_{\pi \in G} \text{Inv}(\pi)$.

2. *Special case of Polya's theorem*: Let R be an m element set of colors. Let G be a group of permutations $\{\pi_1, \pi_2, \ldots\}$ of the set A. Let $C(A, R)$ be the set of colorings of the elements of A using colors in R. Then the number of distinct colorings in $C(A, R)$ is given by

$$\frac{1}{|G|} \left[m^{\text{cyc}(\pi_1)} + m^{\text{cyc}(\pi_2)} + \ldots \right].$$

3. *Polya's theorem*: Let G be a group of permutations on a set A with cycle index $P_G(x_1, x_2, \ldots, x_k)$. Let $C(A, R)$ be the collection of all colorings of A using colors in R. If w is a weight assignment on R, then the pattern inventory of colorings in $C(A, R)$ is given by

$$P_G \left(\sum_{r \in R} w(r), \sum_{r \in R} w^2(r), \cdots \sum_{r \in R} w^k(r) \right).$$

For example, consider necklaces made of $2k$ beads. Allowing a necklace reversal results in the permutation group $G = \{\pi_1, \pi_2\}$ with $\pi_1 = (1)(2) \ldots (2k)$ and $\pi_2 = (1 \quad 2k)(2 \quad 2k-1)(3 \quad 2k-2) \ldots (k \quad k+1)$. Hence, cyc $(\pi_1) = 2k$, cyc $(\pi_2) = k$, and the cycle index is $P_G(x_1, x_2) = \left(x_1^{2k} + x_2^{k}\right)/2$. Using r colors, the number of distinct necklaces is $(r^{2k} + r^k)/2$.

For a 4 bead necklace ($k = 2$) using $r = 2$ colors (say b and g), the $(2^4 + 2^2)/2 = 10$ different necklaces are $\{bbbb\}$, $\{bbbg\}$, $\{bbgb\}$, $\{bbgg\}$, $\{bgbg\}$, $\{bggb\}$, $\{gbbg\}$, $\{bggg\}$, $\{gbgg\}$, and $\{gggg\}$. The pattern inventory of colorings, $P_G(\sum w, \sum w^2) = \left((b+g)^4 + (b^2+g^2)^2\right)/2 = b^4 + 2b^3g + 4b^2g^2 + 2bg^3 + g^4$, tells how many colorings of each type there are.

2.6.9 TABLES

Groups of Small Order

Order n	Distinct groups of order n
1	$\{e\}$
2	$\mathbb{Z}_2$
3	$\mathbb{Z}_3$
4	$\mathbb{Z}_2 \times \mathbb{Z}_2, \mathbb{Z}_4$
5	$\mathbb{Z}_5$
6	$\mathbb{Z}_6, D_3$
7	$\mathbb{Z}_7$
8	$\mathbb{Z}_2 \times \mathbb{Z}_2 \times \mathbb{Z}_2, \mathbb{Z}_2 \times \mathbb{Z}_4, \mathbb{Z}_8, Q_8, D_4$
9	$\mathbb{Z}_3 \times \mathbb{Z}_3, \mathbb{Z}_9$
10	$\mathbb{Z}_{10}, D_5$
11	$\mathbb{Z}_{11}$
12	$\mathbb{Z}_2 \times \mathbb{Z}_6, \mathbb{Z}_{12}, A_4, D_6, T$
13	$\mathbb{Z}_{13}$
14	$\mathbb{Z}_{14}, D_7$
15	$\mathbb{Z}_{15}$

Characters for Some Families of Groups

Group	Characters
$\mathbb{Z}_n$	For $m = 0, 1, \ldots, n-1$, $\chi_m : 1 \mapsto e^{2\pi i m/n}$
G finite Abelian	$G \cong \mathbb{Z}_{n_1} \times \mathbb{Z}_{n_2} \times \cdots \times \mathbb{Z}_{n_j}$ with each n_i a power of a prime. For $m_j = 0, 1, \ldots, n_j - 1$ and $g_j = (0, 0, \ldots, 0, 1, 0, \ldots, 0)\chi_{m_1,m_2,\ldots,m_n} : g_j \mapsto e^{2\pi i m_j/n_j}$
D_n dihedral	For $x = \pm 1$, $y = \begin{cases} \pm 1 & \text{if } n \text{ even} \\ 1 & \text{if } n \text{ odd} \end{cases}$ $\chi_{x,y} : a \mapsto x, b \mapsto y$. (See definition of D_n.)
Quaternions	For $x, y = \pm 1$ or $x, y = \pm i$, $\chi_{x,y} : \begin{bmatrix} 0 & 1 \\ -1 & 0 \end{bmatrix} \mapsto x, \chi_{x,y} : \begin{bmatrix} -i & 0 \\ 0 & i \end{bmatrix} \mapsto y$

Number of Nonisomorphic Groups

Order	No. groups	No. Abelian groups	Order	No. groups	No. Abelian groups
1	1	1	33	1	1
2	1	1	34	2	1
3	1	1	35	1	1
4	2	2	36	14	4
5	1	1	37	1	1
6	2	1	38	2	1
7	1	1	39	2	1
8	5	3	40	14	3
9	2	2	41	1	1
10	2	1	42	6	1
11	1	1	43	1	1
12	5	2	44	4	2
13	1	1	45	2	2
14	2	1	46	2	1
15	1	1	47	1	1
16	14	5	48	52	5
17	1	1	49	2	2
18	5	2	50	5	2
19	1	1	51	1	1
20	5	2	52	5	2
21	2	1	53	1	1
22	2	1	54	15	3
23	1	1	55	2	1
24	15	3	56	13	3
25	2	2	57	2	1
26	2	1	58	2	1
27	5	3	59	1	1
28	4	2	60	13	2
29	1	1	61	1	1
30	4	1	62	2	1
31	1	1	63	4	2
32	51	7	64	267	11

List of All Sporadic Simple Groups

Group	Order
M_{11}	$2^4 \cdot 3^2 \cdot 5 \cdot 11$
M_{12}	$2^6 \cdot 3^3 \cdot 5 \cdot 11$
M_{22}	$2^7 \cdot 3^2 \cdot 5 \cdot 7 \cdot 11$
M_{23}	$2^7 \cdot 3^2 \cdot 5 \cdot 7 \cdot 11 \cdot 23$
M_{24}	$2^{10} \cdot 3^3 \cdot 5 \cdot 7 \cdot 11 \cdot 23$
J_1	$2^3 \cdot 3 \cdot 5 \cdot 7 \cdot 11 \cdot 19$
J_2	$2^7 \cdot 3^3 \cdot 5^2 \cdot 7$
J_3	$2^7 \cdot 3^5 \cdot 5 \cdot 17 \cdot 19$
J_4	$2^{21} \cdot 3^3 \cdot 5 \cdot 7 \cdot 11^3 \cdot 23 \cdot 29 \cdot 31 \cdot 37 \cdot 43$
HS	$2^9 \cdot 3^2 \cdot 5^3 \cdot 7 \cdot 11$
Mc	$2^7 \cdot 3^6 \cdot 5^3 \cdot 11$
Suz	$2^{13} \cdot 3^7 \cdot 5^2 \cdot 7 \cdot 11 \cdot 13$
Ru	$2^{14} \cdot 3^3 \cdot 5^3 \cdot 7 \cdot 13 \cdot 29$
He	$2^{10} \cdot 3^3 \cdot 5^2 \cdot 7^3 \cdot 17$
Ly	$2^8 \cdot 3^7 \cdot 5^6 \cdot 7 \cdot 11 \cdot 31 \cdot 37 \cdot 67$
ON	$2^9 \cdot 3^4 \cdot 5 \cdot 7^3 \cdot 11 \cdot 19 \cdot 31$
$.1$	$2^{21} \cdot 3^9 \cdot 5^4 \cdot 7^2 \cdot 11 \cdot 13 \cdot 23$
$.2$	$2^{18} \cdot 3^6 \cdot 5^3 \cdot 7 \cdot 11 \cdot 23$
$.3$	$2^{10} \cdot 3^7 \cdot 5^3 \cdot 7 \cdot 11 \cdot 23$
$M(22)$	$2^{17} \cdot 3^9 \cdot 5^2 \cdot 7 \cdot 11 \cdot 13$
$M(23)$	$2^{18} \cdot 3^{13} \cdot 5^2 \cdot 7 \cdot 11 \cdot 13 \cdot 17 \cdot 23$
$M(24)'$	$2^{21} \cdot 3^{16} \cdot 5^2 \cdot 7^3 \cdot 11 \cdot 13 \cdot 23 \cdot 29$
F_5	$2^{15} \cdot 3^{10} \cdot 5^3 \cdot 7^2 \cdot 13 \cdot 19 \cdot 31$
F_3	$2^{14} \cdot 3^6 \cdot 5^6 \cdot 7 \cdot 11 \cdot 19$
F_2	$2^{41} \cdot 3^{13} \cdot 5^6 \cdot 7^2 \cdot 11 \cdot 13 \cdot 17 \cdot 19 \cdot 23 \cdot 31 \cdot 47$
F_1	$2^{46} \cdot 3^{20} \cdot 5^9 \cdot 7^6 \cdot 11^2 \cdot 13^3 \cdot 17 \cdot 19 \cdot 23 \cdot 29 \cdot 31 \cdot 41 \cdot 47 \cdot 59 \cdot 71$

Indices and Power Residues

For $\mathbb{Z}_n^*$ the following table lists the index (order) of a and the power residues $a, a^2, \ldots, a^{\text{index}(a)} = 1$ for each element a, where $(a, n) = 1$.

Group	Element	Index	Power residues	Group	Element	Index	Power residues
$\mathbb{Z}_2^*$	1	1	1	$\mathbb{Z}_{12}^*$	1	1	1
$\mathbb{Z}_3^*$	1	1	1		5	2	5,1
	2	2	2,1		7	2	7,1
$\mathbb{Z}_4^*$	1	1	1		11	2	11,1
	3	2	3,1	$\mathbb{Z}_{13}^*$	1	1	1
$\mathbb{Z}_5^*$	1	1	1		2	12	2,4,8,3,6,12, 11,9,5,10,7,1
	2	4	2,4,3,1				
	3	4	3,4,2,1		3	3	3,9,1
	4	2	4,1		4	6	4,3,12,9,10,1
$\mathbb{Z}_6^*$	1	1	1		5	4	5,12,8,1
	5	2	5,1		6	12	6,10,8,9,2,12, 7,3,5,4,11,1
$\mathbb{Z}_7^*$	1	1	1				
	2	3	2,4,1		7	12	7,10,5,9,11,12, 6,3,8,4,2,1
	3	6	3,2,6,4,5,1				
	4	3	4,2,1		8	4	8,12,5,1
	5	6	5,4,6,2,3,1		9	3	9,3,1
	6	2	6,1		10	6	10,9,12,3,4,1
$\mathbb{Z}_8^*$	1	1	1		11	12	11,4,5,3,7,12, 2,9,8,10,6,1
	3	2	3,1				
	5	2	5,1		12	2	12,1
	7	2	7,1	$\mathbb{Z}_{14}^*$	1	1	1
$\mathbb{Z}_9^*$	1	1	1		3	6	3,9,13,11,5,1
	2	6	2,4,8,7,5,1		5	6	5,11,13,9,3,1
	4	3	4,7,1		9	3	9,11,1
	5	6	5,7,8,4,2,1		11	3	11,9,1
	7	3	7,4,1		13	2	13,1
	8	2	8,1	$\mathbb{Z}_{15}^*$	1	1	1
$\mathbb{Z}_{10}^*$	1	1	1		2	4	2,4,8,1
	3	4	3,9,7,1		4	2	4,1
	7	4	7,9,3,1		7	4	7,4,13,1
	9	2	9,1		8	4	8,4,2,1
$\mathbb{Z}_{11}^*$	1	1	1		11	2	11,1
	2	10	2,4,8,5,10, 9,7,3,6,1		13	4	13,4,7,1
					14	2	14,1
	3	5	3,9,5,4,1	$\mathbb{Z}_{16}^*$	1	1	1
	4	5	4,5,9,3,1		3	4	3,9,11,1
	5	5	5,3,4,9,1		5	4	5,9,13,1
	6	10	6,3,7,9,10, 5,8,4,2,1		7	2	7,1
					9	2	9,1
	7	10	7,5,2,3,10, 4,6,9,8,1		11	4	11,9,3,1
					13	4	13,9,5,1
	8	10	8,9,6,4,10, 3,2,5,7,1		15	2	15,1
	9	5	9,4,3,5,1				
	10	2	10,1				

Power Residues in $\mathbb{Z}_p$

For prime $p < 40$, the following table lists the minimal primitive root a and the power residues of a. These can be used to find $a^m \pmod{p}$ for any $(a, p) = 1$. For example, to find $3^7 \pmod{11}$ $(a = 3, m = 7)$, look in row $p = 11$ until the power of a that is equal to 3 is found. In this case $2^8 \equiv 3 \pmod{11}$. This means that $3^7 \equiv (2^8)^7 \equiv 2^{56} \equiv (2^{10})^5 \cdot 2^6 \equiv 2^6 \equiv 9 \pmod{11}$.

p	a	Power residues									
3	2		0	1	2	3	4	5	6	7	8	9
		0	1	2	1							
5	2		0	1	2	3	4	5	6	7	8	9
		0	1	2	4	3	1					
7	3		0	1	2	3	4	5	6	7	8	9
		0	1	3	2	6	4	5	1			
11	2		0	1	2	3	4	5	6	7	8	9
		0	1	2	4	8	5	10	9	7	3	6
		1	1									
13	2		0	1	2	3	4	5	6	7	8	9
		0	1	2	4	8	3	6	12	11	9	5
		1	10	7	1							
17	3		0	1	2	3	4	5	6	7	8	9
		0	1	3	9	10	13	5	15	11	16	14
		1	8	7	4	12	2	6	1			
19	2		0	1	2	3	4	5	6	7	8	9
		0	1	2	4	8	16	13	7	14	9	18
		1	17	15	11	3	6	12	5	10	1	
23	5		0	1	2	3	4	5	6	7	8	9
		0	1	5	2	10	4	20	8	17	16	11
		1	9	22	18	21	13	19	3	15	6	7
		2	12	14	1							
29	2		0	1	2	3	4	5	6	7	8	9
		0	1	2	4	8	16	3	6	12	24	19
		1	9	18	7	14	28	27	25	21	13	26
		2	23	17	5	10	20	11	22	15	1	
31	3		0	1	2	3	4	5	6	7	8	9
		0	1	3	9	27	19	26	16	17	20	29
		1	25	13	8	24	10	30	28	22	4	12
		2	5	15	14	11	2	6	18	23	7	21
		3	1									
37	2		0	1	2	3	4	5	6	7	8	9
		0	1	2	4	8	16	32	27	17	34	31
		1	25	13	26	15	30	23	9	18	36	35
		2	33	29	21	5	10	20	3	6	12	24
		3	11	22	7	14	28	19	1			

Table of Primitive Monic Polynomials

		In the table below, the elements in each string are the coefficients of the polynomial after the highest power of x. (For example, 564 represents $x^3 + 5x^2 + 6x + 4$.)					
Field	Degree	Primitive polynomials					
F_2	1	0	1				
	2	11					
	3	011	101				
	4	0011	1001				
	5	00101	01001	01111	10111	11011	11101
	6	000101	011011	100001	100111	101101	110011
F_3	1	0	1				
	2	12	22				
	3	021	121	201	211		
	4	0012	0022	1002	1122	1222	2002
		2112	2212				
F_5	1	0	2	3			
	2	12	23	33	42		
	3	032	033	042	043	102	113
		143	203	213	222	223	242
		302	312	322	323	343	403
		412	442				
F_7	1	0	2	4			
	2	13	23	25	35	45	53
		55	63				
	3	032	052	062	112	124	152
		154	214	242	262	264	304
		314	322	334	352	354	362
		422	432	434	444	504	524
		532	534	542	552	564	604
		612	632	644	654	662	664

Small finite fields

In the following, the entries under α^i denote the coefficent of powers of α. For example, the last entry of the $p(x) = x^3 + x^2 + 1$ table is 1 1 0. That is: $\alpha^6 \equiv 1\alpha^2 + 1\alpha^1 + 0\alpha^0$ modulo $p(\alpha)$, where the coefficients are taken modulo 2.

$q = 8$	$x^3 + x + 1$
i	α^i
0	0 0 1
1	0 1 0
2	1 0 0
3	0 1 1
4	1 1 0
5	1 1 1
6	1 0 1

$q = 8$	$x^3 + x^2 + 1$
i	α^i
0	0 0 1
1	0 1 0
2	1 0 0
3	1 0 1
4	1 1 1
5	0 1 1
6	1 1 0

$q = 4$	$x^2 + x + 1$
i	α^i
0	0 1
1	1 0
2	1 1

$q = 16$	$x^4 + x + 1$		
i	α^i	7	1 0 1 1
0	0 0 0 1	8	0 1 0 1
1	0 0 1 0	9	1 0 1 0
2	0 1 0 0	10	0 1 1 1
3	1 0 0 0	11	1 1 1 0
4	0 0 1 1	12	1 1 1 1
5	0 1 1 0	13	1 1 0 1
6	1 1 0 0	14	1 0 0 1

$q = 16$	$x^4 + x^3 + 1$		
i	α^i	7	0 1 1 1
0	0 0 0 1	8	1 1 1 0
1	0 0 1 0	9	0 1 0 1
2	0 1 0 0	10	1 0 1 0
3	1 0 0 0	11	1 1 0 1
4	1 0 0 1	12	0 0 1 1
5	1 0 1 1	13	0 1 1 0
6	1 1 1 1	14	1 1 0 0

Addition and multiplication tables for F_2, F_3, F_4, and F_8

F_2 addition and multiplication:

+	0	1
0	0	1
1	1	0

·	0	1
0	0	0
1	0	1

F_3 addition and multiplication:

+	0	1	2
0	0	1	2
1	1	2	0
2	2	0	1

·	0	1	2
0	0	0	0
1	0	1	2
2	0	2	1

F_4 addition and multiplication (using $\beta = \alpha + 1$):

+	0	1	α	β
0	0	1	α	β
1	1	0	β	α
α	α	β	0	1
β	β	α	1	0

·	0	1	α	β
0	0	0	0	0
1	0	1	α	β
α	0	α	β	1
β	0	β	1	α

F_8 addition and multiplication (using strings of 0s and 1s to represent the polynomials: $0 = 000$, $1 = 001$, $\alpha = 010$, $\alpha + 1 = 011$, $\alpha^2 = 100$, $\alpha^2 + \alpha = 110$, $\alpha^2 + 1 = 101$, $\alpha^2 + \alpha + 1 = 111$):

+	000	001	010	011	100	101	110	111
000	000	001	010	011	100	101	110	111
001	001	000	011	010	101	100	111	110
010	010	011	000	001	110	111	100	101
011	011	010	001	000	111	110	101	100
100	100	101	110	111	000	001	010	011
101	101	100	111	110	001	000	011	010
110	110	111	100	101	010	011	000	001
111	111	110	101	100	011	010	001	000

·	000	001	010	011	100	101	110	111
000	000	000	000	000	000	000	000	000
001	000	001	010	011	100	101	110	111
010	000	010	100	110	011	001	111	101
011	000	011	110	101	111	100	001	010
100	000	100	011	111	110	010	101	001
101	000	101	001	100	010	111	011	110
110	000	110	111	001	101	011	010	100
111	000	111	101	010	001	110	100	011

Table of primitive roots

As noted on page 106, the number of integers not exceeding and relatively prime to a fixed integer n is represented by $\phi(n)$. These integers form a group; the group is cyclic if, and only if, $n = 1, 2, 4$ or n is of the form p^k or $2p^k$, where p is an odd prime. We refer to g as a primitive root of n if it generates that group, i.e., if $\{g, g^2, \ldots, g^{\phi(n)}\}$ are distinct modulo p. There are $\phi(\phi(n))$ primitive roots of n. If g is a primitive root of p and $g^{p-1} \not\equiv 1 \pmod{p^2}$, then g is a primitive root of p^k for all k. If $g^{p-1} \equiv 1 \pmod{p^2}$ then $g + p$ is a primitive root of p^k for all k.

If g is a primitive root of p^k, then either g or $g + p^k$, whichever is odd, is a primitive root of $2p^k$.

If g is a primitive root of n, then g^k is a primitive root of n if, and only if, k and $\phi(n)$ are relatively prime, and each primitive root of n is of this form, i.e., $(\phi(n), k) = 1$.

In the table below,

- g denotes the least primitive root of p

- G denotes the least negative primitive root of p

- ϵ denotes whether $10, -10$, or both, are primitive roots of p

p	$p-1$	g	G	ϵ	p	$p-1$	g	G	ϵ
3	2	2	-1	—	5	2^2	2	-2	—
7	$2 \cdot 3$	3	-2	10	11	$2 \cdot 5$	2	-3	—
13	$2^2 \cdot 3$	2	-2	—	17	2^4	3	-3	± 10
19	$2 \cdot 3^2$	2	-4	10	23	$2 \cdot 11$	5	-2	10
29	$2^2 \cdot 7$	2	-2	± 10	31	$2 \cdot 3 \cdot 5$	3	-7	-10

p	$p-1$	g	G	ϵ	p	$p-1$	g	G	ϵ
37	$2^2 \cdot 3^2$	2	-2	—	41	$2^3 \cdot 5$	6	-6	—
43	$2 \cdot 3 \cdot 7$	3	-9	-10	47	$2 \cdot 23$	5	-2	10
53	$2^2 \cdot 13$	2	-2	—	59	$2 \cdot 29$	2	-3	10
61	$2^2 \cdot 3 \cdot 5$	2	-2	± 10	67	$2 \cdot 3 \cdot 11$	2	-4	-10
71	$2 \cdot 5 \cdot 7$	7	-2	-10	73	$2^3 \cdot 3^2$	5	-5	—
79	$2 \cdot 3 \cdot 13$	3	-2	—	83	$2 \cdot 41$	2	-3	-10
89	$2^3 \cdot 11$	3	-3	—	97	$2^5 \cdot 3$	5	-5	± 10
101	$2^2 \cdot 5^2$	2	-2	—	103	$2 \cdot 3 \cdot 17$	5	-2	—
107	$2 \cdot 53$	2	-3	-10	109	$2^2 \cdot 3^3$	6	-6	± 10
113	$2^4 \cdot 7$	3	-3	± 10	127	$2 \cdot 3^2 \cdot 7$	3	-9	—
131	$2 \cdot 5 \cdot 13$	2	-3	10	137	$2^3 \cdot 17$	3	-3	—
139	$2 \cdot 3 \cdot 23$	2	-4	—	149	$2^2 \cdot 37$	2	-2	± 10
151	$2 \cdot 3 \cdot 5^2$	6	-5	-10	157	$2^2 \cdot 3 \cdot 13$	5	-5	—
163	$2 \cdot 3^4$	2	-4	-10	167	$2 \cdot 83$	5	-2	10
173	$2^2 \cdot 43$	2	-2	—	179	$2 \cdot 89$	2	-3	10
181	$2^2 \cdot 3^2 \cdot 5$	2	-2	± 10	191	$2 \cdot 5 \cdot 19$	19	-2	-10
193	$2^6 \cdot 3$	5	-5	± 10	197	$2^2 \cdot 7^2$	2	-2	—
199	$2 \cdot 3^2 \cdot 11$	3	-2	-10	211	$2 \cdot 3 \cdot 5 \cdot 7$	2	-4	—
223	$2 \cdot 3 \cdot 37$	3	-9	10	227	$2 \cdot 113$	2	-3	-10
229	$2^2 \cdot 3 \cdot 19$	6	-6	± 10	233	$2^3 \cdot 29$	3	-3	± 10
239	$2 \cdot 7 \cdot 17$	7	-2	—	241	$2^4 \cdot 3 \cdot 5$	7	-7	—
251	$2 \cdot 5^3$	6	-3	—	257	2^8	3	-3	± 10
263	$2 \cdot 131$	5	-2	10	269	$2^2 \cdot 67$	2	-2	± 10
271	$2 \cdot 3^3 \cdot 5$	6	-2	—	277	$2^2 \cdot 3 \cdot 23$	5	-5	—
281	$2^3 \cdot 5 \cdot 7$	3	-3	—	283	$2 \cdot 3 \cdot 47$	3	-6	-10
293	$2^2 \cdot 73$	2	-2	—	307	$2 \cdot 3^2 \cdot 17$	5	-7	-10
311	$2 \cdot 5 \cdot 31$	17	-2	-10	313	$2^3 \cdot 3 \cdot 13$	10	-10	± 10
317	$2^2 \cdot 79$	2	-2	—	331	$2 \cdot 3 \cdot 5 \cdot 11$	3	-5	—
337	$2^4 \cdot 3 \cdot 7$	10	-10	± 10	347	$2 \cdot 173$	2	-3	-10
349	$2^2 \cdot 3 \cdot 29$	2	-2	—	353	$2^5 \cdot 11$	3	-3	—
359	$2 \cdot 179$	7	-2	-10	367	$2 \cdot 3 \cdot 61$	6	-2	10
373	$2^2 \cdot 3 \cdot 31$	2	-2	—	379	$2 \cdot 3^3 \cdot 7$	2	-4	10
383	$2 \cdot 191$	5	-2	10	389	$2^2 \cdot 97$	2	-2	± 10
397	$2^2 \cdot 3^2 \cdot 11$	5	-5	—	401	$2^4 \cdot 5^2$	3	-3	—
409	$2^3 \cdot 3 \cdot 17$	21	-21	—	419	$2 \cdot 11 \cdot 19$	2	-3	10
421	$2^2 \cdot 3 \cdot 5 \cdot 7$	2	-2	—	431	$2 \cdot 5 \cdot 43$	7	-5	-10
433	$2^4 \cdot 3^3$	5	-5	± 10	439	$2 \cdot 3 \cdot 73$	15	-5	-10
443	$2 \cdot 13 \cdot 17$	2	-3	-10	449	$2^6 \cdot 7$	3	-3	—
457	$2^3 \cdot 3 \cdot 19$	13	-13	—	461	$2^2 \cdot 5 \cdot 23$	2	-2	± 10
463	$2 \cdot 3 \cdot 7 \cdot 11$	3	-2	—	467	$2 \cdot 233$	2	-3	-10
479	$2 \cdot 239$	13	-2	-10	487	$2 \cdot 3^5$	3	-2	10
491	$2 \cdot 5 \cdot 7^2$	2	-4	10	499	$2 \cdot 3 \cdot 83$	7	-5	10
503	$2 \cdot 251$	5	-2	10	509	$2^2 \cdot 127$	2	-2	± 10
521	$2^3 \cdot 5 \cdot 13$	3	-3	—	523	$2 \cdot 3^2 \cdot 29$	2	-4	-10

p	$p-1$	g	G	ϵ	p	$p-1$	g	G	ϵ
541	$2^2 \cdot 3^3 \cdot 5$	2	-2	± 10	547	$2 \cdot 3 \cdot 7 \cdot 13$	2	-4	—
557	$2^2 \cdot 139$	2	-2	—	563	$2 \cdot 281$	2	-3	-10
569	$2^3 \cdot 71$	3	-3	—	571	$2 \cdot 3 \cdot 5 \cdot 19$	3	-5	10
577	$2^6 \cdot 3^2$	5	-5	± 10	587	$2 \cdot 293$	2	-3	-10
593	$2^4 \cdot 37$	3	-3	± 10	599	$2 \cdot 13 \cdot 23$	7	-2	-10
601	$2^3 \cdot 3 \cdot 5^2$	7	-7	—	607	$2 \cdot 3 \cdot 101$	3	-2	—
613	$2^2 \cdot 3^2 \cdot 17$	2	-2	—	617	$2^3 \cdot 7 \cdot 11$	3	-3	—
619	$2 \cdot 3 \cdot 103$	2	-4	10	631	$2 \cdot 3^2 \cdot 5 \cdot 7$	3	-9	-10
641	$2^7 \cdot 5$	3	-3	—	643	$2 \cdot 3 \cdot 107$	11	-7	—
647	$2 \cdot 17 \cdot 19$	5	-2	10	653	$2^2 \cdot 163$	2	-2	—
659	$2 \cdot 7 \cdot 47$	2	-3	10	661	$2^2 \cdot 3 \cdot 5 \cdot 11$	2	-2	—
673	$2^5 \cdot 3 \cdot 7$	5	-5	—	677	$2^2 \cdot 13^2$	2	-2	—
683	$2 \cdot 11 \cdot 31$	5	-10	-10	691	$2 \cdot 3 \cdot 5 \cdot 23$	3	-6	—
701	$2^2 \cdot 5^2 \cdot 7$	2	-2	± 10	709	$2^2 \cdot 3 \cdot 59$	2	-2	± 10
719	$2 \cdot 359$	11	-2	-10	727	$2 \cdot 3 \cdot 11^2$	5	-7	10
733	$2^2 \cdot 3 \cdot 61$	6	-6	—	739	$2 \cdot 3^2 \cdot 41$	3	-6	—
743	$2 \cdot 7 \cdot 53$	5	-2	10	751	$2 \cdot 3 \cdot 5^3$	3	-2	—
757	$2^2 \cdot 3^3 \cdot 7$	2	-2	—	761	$2^3 \cdot 5 \cdot 19$	6	-6	—
769	$2^8 \cdot 3$	11	-11	—	773	$2^2 \cdot 193$	2	-2	—
787	$2 \cdot 3 \cdot 131$	2	-4	-10	797	$2^2 \cdot 199$	2	-2	—
809	$2^3 \cdot 101$	3	-3	—	811	$2 \cdot 3^4 \cdot 5$	3	-5	10
821	$2^2 \cdot 5 \cdot 41$	2	-2	± 10	823	$2 \cdot 3 \cdot 137$	3	-2	10
827	$2 \cdot 7 \cdot 59$	2	-3	-10	829	$2^2 \cdot 3^2 \cdot 23$	2	-2	—
839	$2 \cdot 419$	11	-2	-10	853	$2^2 \cdot 3 \cdot 71$	2	-2	—
857	$2^3 \cdot 107$	3	-3	± 10	859	$2 \cdot 3 \cdot 11 \cdot 13$	2	-4	—
863	$2 \cdot 431$	5	-2	10	877	$2^2 \cdot 3 \cdot 73$	2	-2	—
881	$2^4 \cdot 5 \cdot 11$	3	-3	—	883	$2 \cdot 3^2 \cdot 7^2$	2	-4	-10
887	$2 \cdot 443$	5	-2	10	907	$2 \cdot 3 \cdot 151$	2	-4	—
911	$2 \cdot 5 \cdot 7 \cdot 13$	17	-3	-10	919	$2 \cdot 3^3 \cdot 17$	7	-5	-10
929	$2^5 \cdot 29$	3	-3	—	937	$2^3 \cdot 3^2 \cdot 13$	5	-5	± 10
941	$2^2 \cdot 5 \cdot 47$	2	-2	± 10	947	$2 \cdot 11 \cdot 43$	2	-3	-10
953	$2^3 \cdot 7 \cdot 17$	3	-3	± 10	967	$2 \cdot 3 \cdot 7 \cdot 23$	5	-2	—
971	$2 \cdot 5 \cdot 97$	6	-3	10	977	$2^4 \cdot 61$	3	-3	± 10
983	$2 \cdot 491$	5	-2	10	991	$2 \cdot 3^2 \cdot 5 \cdot 11$	6	-2	-10
997	$2^2 \cdot 3 \cdot 83$	7	-7	—	1009	$2^4 \cdot 3^2 \cdot 7$	11	-11	—
1013	$2^2 \cdot 11 \cdot 23$	3	-3	—	1019	$2 \cdot 509$	2	-3	10
1021	$2^2 \cdot 3 \cdot 5 \cdot 17$	10	-10	± 10	1031	$2 \cdot 5 \cdot 103$	14	-2	—
1033	$2^3 \cdot 3 \cdot 43$	5	-5	± 10	1039	$2 \cdot 3 \cdot 173$	3	-2	-10
1049	$2^3 \cdot 131$	3	-3	—	1051	$2 \cdot 3 \cdot 5^2 \cdot 7$	7	-5	10
1061	$2^2 \cdot 5 \cdot 53$	2	-2	—	1063	$2 \cdot 3^2 \cdot 59$	3	-2	10
1069	$2^2 \cdot 3 \cdot 89$	6	-6	± 10	1087	$2 \cdot 3 \cdot 181$	3	-2	10
1091	$2 \cdot 5 \cdot 109$	2	-4	10	1093	$2^2 \cdot 3 \cdot 7 \cdot 13$	5	-5	—
1097	$2^3 \cdot 137$	3	-3	± 10	1103	$2 \cdot 19 \cdot 29$	5	-3	10

p	$p-1$	g	G	ϵ	p	$p-1$	g	G	ϵ
1109	$2^2 \cdot 277$	2	-2	± 10	1117	$2^2 \cdot 3^2 \cdot 31$	2	-2	—
1123	$2 \cdot 3 \cdot 11 \cdot 17$	2	-4	-10	1129	$2^3 \cdot 3 \cdot 47$	11	-11	—
1151	$2 \cdot 5^2 \cdot 23$	17	-2	-10	1153	$2^7 \cdot 3^2$	5	-5	± 10
1163	$2 \cdot 7 \cdot 83$	5	-3	-10	1171	$2 \cdot 3^2 \cdot 5 \cdot 13$	2	-4	10
1181	$2^2 \cdot 5 \cdot 59$	7	-7	± 10	1187	$2 \cdot 593$	2	-3	-10
1193	$2^3 \cdot 149$	3	-3	± 10	1201	$2^4 \cdot 3 \cdot 5^2$	11	-11	—
1213	$2^2 \cdot 3 \cdot 101$	2	-2	—	1217	$2^6 \cdot 19$	3	-3	± 10
1223	$2 \cdot 13 \cdot 47$	5	-2	10	1229	$2^2 \cdot 307$	2	-2	± 10
1231	$2 \cdot 3 \cdot 5 \cdot 41$	3	-2	—	1237	$2^2 \cdot 3 \cdot 103$	2	-2	—
1249	$2^5 \cdot 3 \cdot 13$	7	-7	—	1259	$2 \cdot 17 \cdot 37$	2	-3	10
1277	$2^2 \cdot 11 \cdot 29$	2	-2	—	1279	$2 \cdot 3^2 \cdot 71$	3	-2	-10
1283	$2 \cdot 641$	2	-3	-10	1289	$2^3 \cdot 7 \cdot 23$	6	-6	—
1291	$2 \cdot 3 \cdot 5 \cdot 43$	2	-4	10	1297	$2^4 \cdot 3^4$	10	-10	± 10
1301	$2^2 \cdot 5^2 \cdot 13$	2	-2	± 10	1303	$2 \cdot 3 \cdot 7 \cdot 31$	6	-2	10
1307	$2 \cdot 653$	2	-3	-10	1319	$2 \cdot 659$	13	-2	-10
1321	$2^3 \cdot 3 \cdot 5 \cdot 11$	13	-13	—	1327	$2 \cdot 3 \cdot 13 \cdot 17$	3	-9	10
1361	$2^4 \cdot 5 \cdot 17$	3	-3	—	1367	$2 \cdot 683$	5	-2	10
1373	$2^2 \cdot 7^3$	2	-2	—	1381	$2^2 \cdot 3 \cdot 5 \cdot 23$	2	-2	± 10
1399	$2 \cdot 3 \cdot 233$	13	-5	-10	1409	$2^7 \cdot 11$	3	-3	—
1423	$2 \cdot 3^2 \cdot 79$	3	-9	—	1427	$2 \cdot 23 \cdot 31$	2	-3	-10
1429	$2^2 \cdot 3 \cdot 7 \cdot 17$	6	-6	± 10	1433	$2^3 \cdot 179$	3	-3	± 10
1439	$2 \cdot 719$	7	-2	-10	1447	$2 \cdot 3 \cdot 241$	3	-2	10
1451	$2 \cdot 5^2 \cdot 29$	2	-3	—	1453	$2^2 \cdot 3 \cdot 11^2$	2	-2	—
1459	$2 \cdot 3^6$	3	-6	—	1471	$2 \cdot 3 \cdot 5 \cdot 7^2$	6	-5	-10
1481	$2^3 \cdot 5 \cdot 37$	3	-3	—	1483	$2 \cdot 3 \cdot 13 \cdot 19$	2	-4	—
1487	$2 \cdot 743$	5	-2	10	1489	$2^4 \cdot 3 \cdot 31$	14	-14	—
1493	$2^2 \cdot 373$	2	-2	—	1499	$2 \cdot 7 \cdot 107$	2	-3	—
1511	$2 \cdot 5 \cdot 151$	11	-2	-10	1523	$2 \cdot 761$	2	-3	-10
1531	$2 \cdot 3^2 \cdot 5 \cdot 17$	2	-4	10	1543	$2 \cdot 3 \cdot 257$	5	-2	10
1549	$2^2 \cdot 3^2 \cdot 43$	2	-2	± 10	1553	$2^4 \cdot 97$	3	-3	± 10
1559	$2 \cdot 19 \cdot 41$	19	-2	-10	1567	$2 \cdot 3^3 \cdot 29$	3	-2	10
1571	$2 \cdot 5 \cdot 157$	2	-3	10	1579	$2 \cdot 3 \cdot 263$	3	-5	10
1583	$2 \cdot 7 \cdot 113$	5	-2	10	1597	$2^2 \cdot 3 \cdot 7 \cdot 19$	11	-11	—
1601	$2^6 \cdot 5^2$	3	-3	—	1607	$2 \cdot 11 \cdot 73$	5	-2	10
1609	$2^3 \cdot 3 \cdot 67$	7	-7	—	1613	$2^2 \cdot 13 \cdot 31$	3	-3	—
1619	$2 \cdot 809$	2	-3	10	1621	$2^2 \cdot 3^4 \cdot 5$	2	-2	± 10
1627	$2 \cdot 3 \cdot 271$	3	-6	—	1637	$2^2 \cdot 409$	2	-2	—
1657	$2^3 \cdot 3^2 \cdot 23$	11	-11	—	1663	$2 \cdot 3 \cdot 277$	3	-2	10
1667	$2 \cdot 7^2 \cdot 17$	2	-3	-10	1669	$2^2 \cdot 3 \cdot 139$	2	-2	—
1693	$2^2 \cdot 3^2 \cdot 47$	2	-2	—	1697	$2^5 \cdot 53$	3	-3	± 10
1699	$2 \cdot 3 \cdot 283$	3	-6	—	1709	$2^2 \cdot 7 \cdot 61$	3	-3	± 10
1721	$2^3 \cdot 5 \cdot 43$	3	-3	—	1723	$2 \cdot 3 \cdot 7 \cdot 41$	3	-6	—
1733	$2^2 \cdot 433$	2	-2	—	1741	$2^2 \cdot 3 \cdot 5 \cdot 29$	2	-2	± 10

p	$p-1$	g	G	ϵ	p	$p-1$	g	G	ϵ
1747	$2 \cdot 3^2 \cdot 97$	2	-4	—	1753	$2^3 \cdot 3 \cdot 73$	7	-7	—
1759	$2 \cdot 3 \cdot 293$	6	-2	-10	1777	$2^4 \cdot 3 \cdot 37$	5	-5	± 10
1783	$2 \cdot 3^4 \cdot 11$	10	-2	10	1787	$2 \cdot 19 \cdot 47$	2	-3	-10
1789	$2^2 \cdot 3 \cdot 149$	6	-6	± 10	1801	$2^3 \cdot 3^2 \cdot 5^2$	11	-11	—
1811	$2 \cdot 5 \cdot 181$	6	-3	10	1823	$2 \cdot 911$	5	-2	10
1831	$2 \cdot 3 \cdot 5 \cdot 61$	3	-9	—	1847	$2 \cdot 13 \cdot 71$	5	-2	10
1861	$2^2 \cdot 3 \cdot 5 \cdot 31$	2	-2	± 10	1867	$2 \cdot 3 \cdot 311$	2	-4	-10
1871	$2 \cdot 5 \cdot 11 \cdot 17$	14	-2	-10	1873	$2^4 \cdot 3^2 \cdot 13$	10	-10	± 10
1877	$2^2 \cdot 7 \cdot 67$	2	-2	—	1879	$2 \cdot 3 \cdot 313$	6	-2	—
1889	$2^5 \cdot 59$	3	-3	—	1901	$2^2 \cdot 5^2 \cdot 19$	2	-2	—
1907	$2 \cdot 953$	2	-3	-10	1913	$2^3 \cdot 239$	3	-3	± 10
1931	$2 \cdot 5 \cdot 193$	2	-3	—	1933	$2^2 \cdot 3 \cdot 7 \cdot 23$	5	-5	—
1949	$2^2 \cdot 487$	2	-2	± 10	1951	$2 \cdot 3 \cdot 5^2 \cdot 13$	3	-2	—
1973	$2^2 \cdot 17 \cdot 29$	2	-2	—	1979	$2 \cdot 23 \cdot 43$	2	-3	10
1987	$2 \cdot 3 \cdot 331$	2	-4	—	1993	$2^3 \cdot 3 \cdot 83$	5	-5	—
1997	$2^2 \cdot 499$	2	-2	—	1999	$2 \cdot 3^3 \cdot 37$	3	-5	-10
2003	$2 \cdot 7 \cdot 11 \cdot 13$	5	-3	-10	2011	$2 \cdot 3 \cdot 5 \cdot 67$	3	-5	—
2017	$2^5 \cdot 3^2 \cdot 7$	5	-5	± 10	2027	$2 \cdot 1013$	2	-3	-10
2029	$2^2 \cdot 3 \cdot 13^2$	2	-2	± 10	2039	$2 \cdot 1019$	7	-2	-10
2053	$2^2 \cdot 3^3 \cdot 19$	2	-2	—	2063	$2 \cdot 1031$	5	-2	10
2069	$2^2 \cdot 11 \cdot 47$	2	-2	± 10	2081	$2^5 \cdot 5 \cdot 13$	3	-3	—
2083	$2 \cdot 3 \cdot 347$	2	-4	-10	2087	$2 \cdot 7 \cdot 149$	5	-2	—
2089	$2^3 \cdot 3^2 \cdot 29$	7	-7	—	2099	$2 \cdot 1049$	2	-3	10
2111	$2 \cdot 5 \cdot 211$	7	-2	-10	2113	$2^6 \cdot 3 \cdot 11$	5	-5	± 10
2129	$2^4 \cdot 7 \cdot 19$	3	-3	—	2131	$2 \cdot 3 \cdot 5 \cdot 71$	2	-4	—
2137	$2^3 \cdot 3 \cdot 89$	10	-10	± 10	2141	$2^2 \cdot 5 \cdot 107$	2	-2	± 10
2143	$2 \cdot 3^2 \cdot 7 \cdot 17$	3	-9	10	2153	$2^3 \cdot 269$	3	-3	± 10
2161	$2^4 \cdot 3^3 \cdot 5$	23	-23	—	2179	$2 \cdot 3^2 \cdot 11^2$	7	-5	10
2203	$2 \cdot 3 \cdot 367$	5	-7	-10	2207	$2 \cdot 1103$	5	-2	10
2213	$2^2 \cdot 7 \cdot 79$	2	-2	—	2221	$2^2 \cdot 3 \cdot 5 \cdot 37$	2	-2	± 10
2237	$2^2 \cdot 13 \cdot 43$	2	-2	—	2239	$2 \cdot 3 \cdot 373$	3	-2	-10
2243	$2 \cdot 19 \cdot 59$	2	-3	-10	2251	$2 \cdot 3^2 \cdot 5^3$	7	-5	10
2267	$2 \cdot 11 \cdot 103$	2	-3	-10	2269	$2^2 \cdot 3^4 \cdot 7$	2	-2	± 10
2273	$2^5 \cdot 71$	3	-3	± 10	2281	$2^3 \cdot 3 \cdot 5 \cdot 19$	7	-7	—
2287	$2 \cdot 3^2 \cdot 127$	19	-7	—	2293	$2^2 \cdot 3 \cdot 191$	2	-2	—

Chapter 3

Discrete Mathematics

0-8493-2479-3/96/$0.00+$.50
© 1996 CRC Press, Inc.

3.1   SET THEORY

3.1.1   PROPOSITIONAL CALCULUS

Propositional calculus is the study of statements: how they are combined and how to determine their truth. Statements (or propositions) are combined by means of *connectives* such as *and* ($\wedge$) *or* ($\vee$), *not* ($\neg$, or sometimes $\sim$), *implies* ($\rightarrow$), and *if and only if* ($\leftrightarrow$). Propositions are assigned letters $\{p, q, r, \dots\}$. For example, if p is the statement "$x = 3$", and q the statement "$y = 4$," then $p \vee \neg q$ would be interpreted as "$x = 3$ or $y \neq 4$." To determine the truth of a statement, *truth tables* are used. Using T (for true) and F (for false), the truth tables for these connectives are as follows:

p	q	$p \wedge q$	$p \vee q$	$p \rightarrow q$	$p \leftrightarrow q$		p	$\neg p$
T	T	T	T	T	T		T	F
T	F	F	T	F	F		F	T
F	T	F	T	T	F			
F	F	F	F	T	T			

The proposition $p \rightarrow q$ can be read "*If p then q*" or, less often, "*q if p*." The table shows that "$p \vee q$" is an *inclusive or* because it is true even when p and q are both true. Thus, the statement "I'm watching TV or I'm doing homework" is a true statement if the narrator happens to be both watching TV and doing homework. Note that $p \rightarrow q$ is false only when p is true and q is false. Thus, *a false statement implies any statement* and *a true statement is implied by any statement*.

3.1.2   TAUTOLOGIES

A statement such as $(p \rightarrow (q \wedge r)) \vee \neg p$ is a compound statement composed of the atomic propositions p, q, and r. The letters P, Q, and R are used to designate compound statements. A *tautology* is a compound statement which always is true, regardless of the truth values of the atomic statements used to define it. For example, a simple tautology is $(\neg \neg p) \leftrightarrow p$. Tautologies are logical truths. Some examples are as follows:

Law of the excluded middle	$p \vee \neg p$,
De Morgan's laws	$\neg(p \vee q) \leftrightarrow (\neg p \wedge \neg q)$,
	$\neg(p \wedge q) \leftrightarrow (\neg p \vee \neg q)$,
Modus ponens	$(p \wedge (p \rightarrow q)) \rightarrow q$,
Contrapositive law	$(p \rightarrow q) \leftrightarrow (\neg q \rightarrow \neg p)$,
Reductio ad absurdum	$(\neg p \rightarrow p) \rightarrow p$,
Elimination of cases	$((p \vee q) \wedge \neg p) \rightarrow q$,
Transitivity of implication	$((p \rightarrow q) \wedge (q \rightarrow r)) \rightarrow (p \rightarrow r)$,
Proof by cases	$((p \rightarrow q) \wedge (\neg p \rightarrow q)) \rightarrow q$,
Idempotent laws	$p \wedge p \leftrightarrow p; \ p \vee p \leftrightarrow p$,
Commutative laws	$(p \wedge q) \leftrightarrow (q \wedge p); \ (p \vee q) \leftrightarrow (q \vee p)$,
Associative laws	$(p \wedge (q \wedge r)) \leftrightarrow ((p \wedge q) \wedge r)$, and
	$(p \vee (q \vee r)) \leftrightarrow ((p \vee q) \vee r)$.

3.1.3   TRUTH TABLES AS FUNCTIONS

If we assign the value 1 to T, and 0 to F, then the truth table for $p \wedge q$ is simply the value pq. This can be done with all the connectives as follows:

Connective	Arithmetic function
$p \wedge q$	pq
$p \vee q$	$p + q - pq$
$p \rightarrow q$	$1 - p + pq$
$p \leftrightarrow q$	$1 - p - q + 2pq$
$\neg p$	$1 - p$

These formulas may be used to verify tautologies, because, from this point of view, a tautology is a function whose value is identically 1. In using them, it is useful to remember that $pp = p^2 = p$, since $p = 0$ or $p = 1$.

3.1.4   RULES OF INFERENCE

A *rule of inference* in propositional calculus is a method of arriving at a valid (true) *conclusion*, given certain statements, assumed to be true, which are called the *hypotheses*. For example, suppose that P and Q are compound statements. Then if P and $P \rightarrow Q$ are true, then Q must necessarily be true. This follows from the *modus ponens* tautology in the above list of tautologies. We write this rule of inference $P, P \rightarrow Q \Rightarrow Q$. It is also classically written

$$\frac{\begin{array}{c} P \\ P \rightarrow Q \end{array}}{Q}.$$

Some examples of rules of inferences follow, all derived from the above list of tautologies:

Modus ponens	$P, P \to Q \Rightarrow Q$
Contrapositive	$P \to Q \Rightarrow \neg Q \to \neg P$
Modus tollens	$P \to Q, \neg Q \Rightarrow \neg P$
Transitivity	$P \to Q, Q \to R \Rightarrow P \to R$
Elimination of cases	$P \vee Q, \neg P \Rightarrow Q$
"And" usage	$P \wedge Q \Rightarrow P, P \wedge Q \Rightarrow Q$

3.1.5 DEDUCTIONS

A *deduction* from hypotheses is a list of statements, each one of which is either one of the hypotheses, a tautology, or follows from previous statements in the list by a valid rule of inference. It follows that if the hypotheses are true, then the conclusion must be true. Suppose for example, that we are given *hypotheses* $\neg q \to p$, $q \to \neg r$, r; it is required to deduce the *conclusion p*. A deduction showing this, with reasons for each step is as follows:

	Statement	Reason
1.	$q \to \neg r$	Hypothesis
2.	r	Hypothesis
3.	$\neg q$	Modus tollens (1,2)
4.	$\neg q \to p$	Hypothesis
5.	p	Modus ponens (3,4)

3.1.6 SETS

A set is a collection of objects. Some examples of sets are

- The population of Cleveland on January 1, 1995

- The real numbers between 0 and 1 inclusive

- The prime numbers 2, 3, 5, 7, 11, . . .

- The numbers 1, 2, 3, and 4

- All of the formulas in this book

3.1.7 SET OPERATIONS AND RELATIONS

If x is an object in a set A, then we write $x \in A$ (read "x is in A.") If x is not in A, we write $x \notin A$. When considering sets, a set U, called the universe, is chosen, from which all elements are taken. The *null set* or *empty set* $\emptyset$ is the set containing no elements. Thus, $x \notin \emptyset$ for all $x \in U$. Some relations on sets are as follows:

Relation	Read as	Definition
$A \subseteq B$	A is contained in B	Any element of A is also an element of B
$A = B$	A equals B	$(A \subseteq B) \wedge (B \subseteq A)$

Some basic operations on sets are as follows:

Operation	Read as	Definition
$A \cup B$	A union B	The elements in A or in B
$A \cap B$	A intersection B	The elements in both A and B
$A - B$	A minus B	The elements in A which are not in B
A' or $\overline{A}$	Complement of A	The elements in U which are not in A
$\mathbf{P}(A)$ or 2^A	Power set of A	The collection of all subsets of A

3.1.8   VENN DIAGRAMS

The operations and relations on sets can be illustrated by *Venn diagrams*. The diagrams below shows a few possibilities.

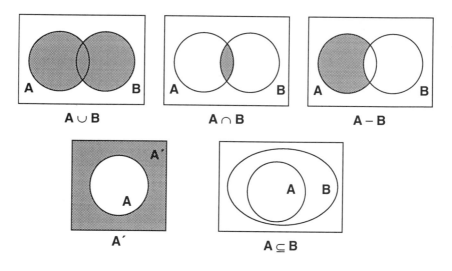

3.1.9   PARADOXES AND THEOREMS OF SET THEORY

Russell's paradox

In about 1900, Bertrand Russell presented a paradox, paraphrased as follows: since the elements of sets can be arbitrary, sets can contain sets. Therefore, a set can possibly be a member of itself. (For example, the set of all sets would be a member of itself. Another example is the collection of all sets that can be described in fewer than 50 words.) Now let A be the set of all sets which are *not* members of themselves. Then if A is a member of itself, it is not a member of itself. And if A is not a member of itself, then by definition, A is a member of itself. This paradox leads to a much more careful evaluation of how sets can be defined.

Infinite sets and the continuum hypothesis

Georg Cantor showed how infinite sets can be counted, much as finite sets. He used the symbol $\aleph_0$ (*read* aleph null) for the number of integers and introduced larger infinite numbers such as $\aleph_1$, $\aleph_2$, and so on. Cantor introduced a consistent arithmetic on infinite cardinals and a way of comparing infinite cardinals. A few of his results were as follows:

$$\aleph_0 + \aleph_0 = \aleph_0, \qquad (\aleph_0)^2 = \aleph_0, \qquad 2^{\aleph_0} = \aleph_0^{\aleph_0} > \aleph_0.$$

Cantor showed that $\mathbf{c} = 2^{\aleph_0} > \aleph_0$, where $\mathbf{c}$ is the cardinality of real numbers. The *continuum hypothesis* asked whether or not $\mathbf{c} = \aleph_1$, the first infinite cardinal greater than $\aleph_0$. In 1963, Paul J. Cohen showed that this result is independent of the other axioms of set theory. In his words, ". . . the truth or falsity of the continuum hypothesis . . . cannot be determined by set theory as we know it today."

3.1.10   PREDICATE CALCULUS

Unlike propositional calculus, which may be considered the skeleton of logical discourse, predicate calculus is the language in which most mathematical reasoning takes place. It uses the symbols of propositional calculus, with the exception of the propositional variables $p, q, \ldots$. Predicate calculus uses the *universal quantifier* $\forall$, the *existential quantifier* $\exists$, predicates $P(x)$, $Q(x, y)$, $\ldots$, *variables* $x, y, \ldots$, and assumes a *universe U* from which the variables are taken. The quantifiers are illustrated in the following table.

Symbol	Read as	Usage	Interpretation
$\exists$	There exists an	$\exists x (x > 10)$	There is an x such that $x > 10$
$\forall$	For all	$\forall x (x^2 + 1 \neq 0)$	For all $x, x^2 + 1 \neq 0$

Predicates are variable statements which may be true or false, depending on the values of its variable. In the above table, "$x > 10$" is a predicate in the one variable x as is "$x^2 + 1 \neq 0$." Without a given universe, we have no way of deciding whether a statement is true or false. Thus $\forall x (x^2 + 1 \neq 0)$ is true if the universe U is the real numbers, but false if U is the complex numbers. A useful rule for manipulating quantifiers is

$$\neg \forall x P(x) \leftrightarrow \exists x \neg P(x).$$

For example, it is not true that all people are mortal if, and only if, there is a person who is immortal. Here the universe U is the set of people, and $P(x)$ is the predicate "x is mortal." This works with more than one quantifier. Thus,

$$\neg \forall x \exists y P(x, y) \leftrightarrow \exists x \forall y \neg P(x, y).$$

For example, if it is not true that every person loves someone, then it follows that there is a person who loves no one.

Fermat's last theorem, stated in terms of the predicate calculus (U = the positive integers), is

$$\forall n \forall a \forall b \forall c [(n > 2) \rightarrow (a^n + b^n \neq c^n)]$$

It was proven in 1995; its proof is extremely complicated. One does not expect a simple deduction, as in the propositional calculus. In 1931, Gödel proved the *Gödel Incompleteness Theorem*. This states that, in any logical system complex enough to contain arithmetic, it will always be possible to find a true result which is not formally provable using predicate logic. This result was especially startling because the notion of truth and provability had been often identified with each other.

3.2   COMBINATORICS

3.2.1   SAMPLE SELECTION

There are four ways in which a sample of r elements can be obtained from a set of m distinguishable objects.

Order counts?	Repetitions allowed?	The sample is called an	Number of ways to choose the sample
No	No	r-combination	$C(m, r)$
Yes	No	r-permutation	$P(m, r)$
No	Yes	r-combination with replacement	$C^R(m, r)$
Yes	Yes	r-permutation with replacement	$P^R(m, r)$

where

$$C(m, r) = \binom{m}{r} = \frac{m!}{r!\,(m - r)!},$$

$$P(m, r) = (m)_r = m^{\underline{r}} = \frac{m!}{(m - r)!},$$

$$C^R(m, r) = C(m + r - 1, r) = \frac{(m + r - 1)!}{r!\,(m - 1)!}, \text{ and}$$ (3.2.1)

$$P^R(m, r) = m^r.$$

For example, choosing a 2-element sample from the set $\{a, b\}$:

r-combination	$C(2, 2) = 1$	ab
r-permutation	$P(2, 2) = 2$	ab and ba
r-combination with replacement	$C^R(2, 2) = 3$	aa, ab, and bb
r-permutation with replacement	$P^R(2, 2) = 4$	aa, ab, ba, and bb

3.2.2 BALLS INTO CELLS

There are eight different ways in which n balls can be placed into k cells:

Distinguish the balls?	Distinguish the cells?	Can cells be empty?	Number of ways to place n balls into k cells
Yes	Yes	Yes	k^n
Yes	Yes	No	$k! \left\{ {n \atop k} \right\}$
No	Yes	Yes	$C(k+n-1, n) = \binom{k+n-1}{n}$
No	Yes	No	$C(n-1, k-1) = \binom{n-1}{k-1}$
Yes	No	Yes	$\left\{ {n \atop 1} \right\} + \left\{ {n \atop 2} \right\} + \cdots + \left\{ {n \atop k} \right\}$
Yes	No	No	$\left\{ {n \atop k} \right\}$
No	No	Yes	$p_1(n) + p_2(n) + \cdots + p_k(n)$
No	No	No	$p_k(n)$

where $\left\{ {n \atop k} \right\}$ is the Stirling cycle number (see page 174) and $p_k(n)$ is the number of partitions of the number n into exactly k integer pieces (see page 173).

Given n distinguishable balls and k distinguishable cells, the number of ways in which we can place n_1 balls into cell 1, n_2 balls into cell 2, ..., n_k balls into cell k, is given by the multinomial coefficient $\binom{n}{n_1, n_2, \ldots, n_k}$ (see page 171).

3.2.3 BINOMIAL COEFFICIENTS

The binomial coefficient $\binom{n}{m}$ is the number of ways of choosing m objects from a collection of n distinct objects without regard to order:

1. $$\binom{n}{m} = \frac{n!}{m!(n-m)!} = \frac{n(n-1)\cdots(n-m+1)}{m!} = \binom{n}{n-m}.$$

2. $$\binom{n}{0} = \binom{n}{n} = 1 \text{ and } \binom{n}{1} = n.$$

3. $$\binom{2n}{n} = \frac{2^n(2n-1)!!}{n!} = \frac{2^n(2n-1)(2n-3)\cdots 3 \cdot 1}{n!}.$$

4. Example: For the 5 element set $\{a, b, c, d, e\}$ there are $\binom{5}{3} = \frac{5!}{3!2!} = 10$ subsets containing exactly three elements. They are

$$(a, b, c), \quad (a, b, d), \quad (a, b, e), \quad (a, c, d), \quad (a, c, e),$$
$$(a, d, e), \quad (b, c, d), \quad (b, c, e), \quad (b, d, e), \text{ and } (c, d, e).$$

5. The recurrence relation: $\binom{n+1}{m} = \binom{n}{m} + \binom{n}{m-1}$.

6. Two generating functions for binomial coefficients are $\sum_{m=0}^{n} \binom{n}{m} x^m = (1+x)^n$ for $n = 1, 2, \ldots$, and $\sum_{n=m}^{\infty} \binom{n}{m} x^{n-m} = (1-x)^{-m-1}$.

7. The Vandermonde convolution is $\begin{pmatrix} x+y \\ n \end{pmatrix} = \sum_{k=0}^{n} \begin{pmatrix} x \\ k \end{pmatrix} \begin{pmatrix} y \\ n-k \end{pmatrix}$.

8. The Gaussian binomial coefficient $\begin{bmatrix} n \\ r \end{bmatrix}_q$ is defined to be

$$\begin{bmatrix} n \\ r \end{bmatrix}_q = \begin{cases} \dfrac{q^n-1}{q-1} \dfrac{q^{n-1}-1}{q^2-1} \cdots \dfrac{q^{n+1-r}-1}{q^r-1} & \text{if } 0 < r \le n \\ 1 & \text{if } r = 0 \\ 0 & \text{if } r < 0 \text{ or } r > n \end{cases}$$

where q is a real number. Note that

$$\begin{bmatrix} n \\ r \end{bmatrix}_q = \begin{bmatrix} n \\ n-r \end{bmatrix}_q \qquad \text{and} \qquad \lim_{q \to 1} \begin{bmatrix} n \\ r \end{bmatrix}_q = \begin{pmatrix} n \\ r \end{pmatrix}. \qquad (3.2.2)$$

Note also that, treated as polynomials, they are reciprocal.

$$\begin{bmatrix} n \\ r \end{bmatrix}_{q \to q^{-1}} = q^{m(m-n)} \begin{bmatrix} n \\ r \end{bmatrix}_q. \qquad (3.2.3)$$

Pascal's triangle

The binomial coefficients $\binom{n}{k}$ can be arranged in a triangle

$$1$$
$$1\ 2\ 1$$
$$1\ 3\ 3\ 1$$
$$1\ 4\ 6\ 4\ 1$$
$$1\ 5\ 10\ 10\ 5\ 1$$
$$1\ 6\ 15\ 20\ 15\ 6\ 1$$

in which each number is the sum of the two numbers above it.

The binomial coefficients satisfy

$$\binom{n}{m} + \binom{n}{m+1} = \binom{n+1}{m+1},$$

$$\binom{n}{m} = \binom{n}{n-m},$$

$$\binom{n}{0} + \binom{n}{1} + \cdots + \binom{n}{n} = 2^n,$$

$$\binom{n}{0} - \binom{n}{1} + \cdots + (-1)^n \binom{n}{n} = 0,$$

$$\binom{n}{n} + \binom{n+1}{n} + \binom{n+2}{n} + \cdots + \binom{n+m}{n} = \binom{n+m+1}{n+1},$$

$$\binom{n}{0} + \binom{n}{2} + \binom{n}{4} + \cdots = 2^{n-1},$$

$$\binom{n}{1} + \binom{n}{3} + \binom{n}{5} + \cdots = 2^{n-1},$$

$$\binom{n}{0}^2 + \binom{n}{1}^2 + \cdots + \binom{n}{n}^2 = \binom{2n}{n},$$

$$\binom{m}{0}\binom{n}{p} + \binom{m}{1}\binom{n}{p-1} + \cdots + \binom{m}{p}\binom{n}{0} = \binom{m+n}{p},$$

$$1\binom{n}{1} + 2\binom{n}{2} + \cdots + n\binom{n}{n} = n2^{n-1}, \text{ and}$$

$$1\binom{n}{1} - 2\binom{n}{2} + \cdots + (-1)^{n+1} n\binom{n}{n} = 0.$$

3.2.4 MULTINOMIAL COEFFICIENTS

The multinomial coefficient $\binom{n}{n_1, n_2, \ldots, n_k}$ (also written $C(n; n_1, n_2, \ldots, n_k)$) is the number of ways of choosing n_1 objects, then n_2 objects, ... , then n_k objects from a collection of n distinct objects without regard to order. This requires that $\sum_{j=1}^{k} n_j = n$. The multinomial symbol is numerically evaluated as

$$\binom{n}{n_1, n_2, \ldots, n_k} = \frac{n!}{n_1! n_2! \cdots n_k!}. \tag{3.2.4}$$

For example, the number of ways to choose 2 objects, then 1 object, then 1 object from the set $\{a, b, c, d\}$ is $\binom{4}{2,1,1} = 12$; they are as follows (vertical bars show the ordered selections):

$$
\begin{array}{llll}
| \, ab \mid c \mid d \, |, & | \, ab \mid d \mid c \, |, & | \, ac \mid b \mid d \, |, & | \, ac \mid d \mid b \, |, \\
| \, ad \mid b \mid c \, |, & | \, ad \mid c \mid b \, |, & | \, bc \mid a \mid d \, |, & | \, bc \mid d \mid a \, |, \\
| \, bd \mid a \mid c \, |, & | \, bd \mid c \mid a \, |, & | \, cd \mid a \mid b \, |, & | \, cd \mid b \mid a \, |.
\end{array}
$$

3.2.5 ARRANGEMENTS AND DERANGEMENTS

The number of ways to arrange n distinct objects in a row is $n!$; this is the number of permutations of n objects. For example, for the three objects $\{a, b, c\}$, the number of arrangements is $3! = 6$. These permutations are $\{abc, bac, cab, acb, bca, \text{and } cba\}$.

The number of ways to arrange n objects (assuming that there are k types of objects and n_i copies of each object of type i) is the multinomial coefficient $\binom{n}{n_1, n_2, \ldots, n_k}$. For example, for the set $\{a, a, b, c\}$ the parameters are $n = 4, k = 3, n_1 = 2, n_2 = 1$, and $n_3 = 1$. Hence, there are $\binom{4}{2,1,1} = \frac{4!}{2!\,1!\,1!} = 12$ arrangements; they are

$$aabc, \quad aacb, \quad abac, \quad abca, \quad acab, \quad acba,$$
$$baac, \quad baca, \quad bcaa, \quad caab, \quad caba, \quad cbaa.$$

A derangement is a permutation of objects, in which object i is not in the ith location. For example, all of the derangements of $\{1, 2, 3, 4\}$ are

$$2143, \quad 2341, \quad 2413,$$
$$3142, \quad 3412, \quad 3421,$$
$$4123, \quad 4312, \quad 4321.$$

The number of derangements of n elements, D_n, satisfies the recursion relation, $D_n = (n-1)(D_{n-1} + D_{n-2})$, with the initial values $D_1 = 0$ and $D_2 = 1$. Hence,

$$D_n = n! \left(1 - \frac{1}{1!} + \frac{1}{2!} - \frac{1}{3!} + \cdots + (-1)^n \frac{1}{n!}\right).$$

The numbers D_n are also called *subfactorials* or *rencontres numbers*. For large values of n, $D_n/n! \sim e^{-1} \approx 0.37$. Hence more than one of every three permutations is a derangement.

n	1	2	3	4	5	6	7	8	9	10
D_n	0	1	2	9	44	265	1854	14833	133496	1334961

3.2.6 CATALAN NUMBERS

The Catalan number is $C_n = \dfrac{1}{n-1}\dbinom{2n-2}{n-2}$. Given the product $A_1 A_2 \ldots A_n$, the number of ways to pair up terms keeping the original order is C_n. For example, with $n = 4$, there are the $C_4 = 5$ ways to group the terms; they are $(A_1 A_2)(A_3 A_4)$, $((A_1 A_2)A_3)A_4$, $(A_1(A_2 A_3))A_4$, $A_1((A_2 A_3)A_4)$, and $A_1(A_2(A_3 A_4))$.

n	1	2	3	4	5	6	7	8	9	10
C_n	1	1	2	5	14	42	132	429	1430	4862

3.2.7 PARTITIONS

A partition of a number n is a representation of n as the sum of any number of positive integral parts (for example: $5 = 4 + 1 = 3 + 2 = 3 + 1 + 1 = 2 + 2 + 1 = 2 + 1 + 1 + 1 = 1 + 1 + 1 + 1 + 1$). The number of partitions of n is denoted $p(n)$ (for example, $p(5) = 7$). The number of partitions of n into at most m parts is equal to the number of partitions of n into parts which do not exceed m; this is denoted $p_m(n)$ (for example, $p_3(5) = 5$ and $p_2(5) = 3$).

The generating functions for $p(n)$ and $p_m(n)$ are

$$1 + \sum_{n=1}^{\infty} p(n)x^n = \frac{1}{(1-x)(1-x^2)(1-x^3)\cdots}, \text{ and}$$

(3.2.5)

$$1 + \sum_{n=1}^{\infty} \sum_{m=1}^{n} p_m(n)x^n t^m = \frac{1}{(1-tx)(1-tx^2)(1-tx^3)\cdots}.$$

(3.2.6)

n	1	2	3	4	5	6	7	8	9	10
$p(n)$	1	2	3	5	7	11	15	22	30	42
n	11	12	13	14	15	16	17	18	19	20
$p(n)$	56	77	101	135	176	231	297	385	490	627
n	21	22	23	24	25	26	27	28	29	30
$p(n)$	792	1002	1255	1575	1958	2436	3010	3718	4565	5604
n	31	32	33	34	35	40	45	50		
$p(n)$	6842	8349	10143	12310	14883	37338	89134	204226		

3.2.8 STIRLING NUMBERS

The number $(-1)^{n-m} \left[{n \atop m} \right]$ is the number of permutations of n symbols which have exactly m cycles. The term $\left[{n \atop m} \right]$ is called a Stirling number (or a Stirling number of the first kind). It can be numerically evaluated as

$$\left[{n \atop m} \right] = \sum_{k=0}^{n-m} (-1)^k \binom{n-1+k}{n-m+k} \binom{2n-m}{n-m-k} \left\{ {n-m-k \atop k} \right\}$$

where $\left\{ {n-m-k \atop k} \right\}$ is a Stirling cycle number.

- Example: For the 4 element set $\{a, b, c, d\}$, there are $\begin{bmatrix} 4 \\ 2 \end{bmatrix} = 11$ permutations containing exactly 2 cycles. They are

$$\begin{pmatrix} 1\,2\,3\,4 \\ 2\,3\,1\,4 \end{pmatrix} = (123)(4), \quad \begin{pmatrix} 1\,2\,3\,4 \\ 3\,1\,2\,4 \end{pmatrix} = (132)(4), \quad \begin{pmatrix} 1\,2\,3\,4 \\ 3\,2\,4\,1 \end{pmatrix} = (134)(2),$$

$$\begin{pmatrix} 1\,2\,3\,4 \\ 4\,2\,1\,3 \end{pmatrix} = (143)(2), \quad \begin{pmatrix} 1\,2\,3\,4 \\ 2\,4\,3\,1 \end{pmatrix} = (124)(3), \quad \begin{pmatrix} 1\,2\,3\,4 \\ 4\,1\,3\,2 \end{pmatrix} = (142)(3),$$

$$\begin{pmatrix} 1\,2\,3\,4 \\ 1\,3\,4\,2 \end{pmatrix} = (234)(1), \quad \begin{pmatrix} 1\,2\,3\,4 \\ 1\,4\,2\,3 \end{pmatrix} = (243)(1), \quad \begin{pmatrix} 1\,2\,3\,4 \\ 2\,1\,4\,3 \end{pmatrix} = (12)(34),$$

$$\begin{pmatrix} 1\,2\,3\,4 \\ 3\,4\,1\,2 \end{pmatrix} = (13)(24), \quad \begin{pmatrix} 1\,2\,3\,4 \\ 4\,3\,2\,1 \end{pmatrix} = (14)(23).$$

- There is the recurrence relation: $\begin{bmatrix} n+1 \\ m \end{bmatrix} = \begin{bmatrix} n \\ m-1 \end{bmatrix} - n \begin{bmatrix} n \\ m \end{bmatrix}$.

- The factorial polynomial is defined as $x^{(n)} = x(1-x)\ldots(x-n+1)$ with $x^{(0)} = 1$ by definition. If $n > 0$, then

$$x^{(n)} = \begin{bmatrix} n \\ 1 \end{bmatrix} x + \begin{bmatrix} n \\ 2 \end{bmatrix} x^2 + \cdots + \begin{bmatrix} n \\ n \end{bmatrix} x^n.$$

For example: $x^{(3)} = x(x-1)(x-2) = 2x - 3x^2 + x^3 = \begin{bmatrix} 3 \\ 1 \end{bmatrix} x + \begin{bmatrix} 3 \\ 2 \end{bmatrix} x^2 + \begin{bmatrix} 3 \\ 3 \end{bmatrix} x^3$.

- Stirling numbers satisfy $\sum_{n=m}^{\infty} \begin{bmatrix} n \\ m \end{bmatrix} \frac{x^n}{n!} = \frac{(\log(1+x))^m}{m!}$ for $|x| < 1$.

3.2.9   STIRLING CYCLE NUMBERS

The Stirling cycle number, $\left\{ \begin{matrix} n \\ m \end{matrix} \right\}$, is the number of ways to partition n into m blocks (this is also called a Stirling number of the second kind). (Equivalently, it is the number of ways that n distinguishable balls can be placed into m indistinguishable cells, with no cell empty.) This Stirling number can be numerically evaluated as

$$\left\{ \begin{matrix} n \\ m \end{matrix} \right\} = \frac{1}{k!} \sum_{i=0}^{k} (-1)^{k-i} \binom{k}{i} i^n.$$

For example, placing the 4 distinguishable balls $\{a, b, c, d\}$ into 2 indistinguishable cells, so that no cell is empty can be done in $\left\{ \begin{matrix} 4 \\ 2 \end{matrix} \right\} = 7$ ways. These are (vertical bars delineate the cells)

$$| ab | cd |, \quad | ad | bc |, \quad | ac | bd |, \quad | a | bcd |,$$
$$| b | acd |, \quad | c | abd |, \quad | d | abc |.$$

- Ordinary powers can be expanded in terms of factorial polynomials. If $n > 0$, then

$$x^n = \left\{ {n \atop 1} \right\} x^{(1)} + \left\{ {n \atop 2} \right\} x^{(2)} + \cdots + \left\{ {n \atop n} \right\} x^{(n)}.$$

For example, $x^3 = \left\{ {3 \atop 1} \right\} x^{(1)} + \left\{ {3 \atop 2} \right\} x^{(2)} + \left\{ {3 \atop 3} \right\} x^{(3)}$.

3.2.10 BELL NUMBERS

The nth Bell number, B_n, denotes the number of partitions of a set with n elements. Computationally, the Bell numbers may be written in terms of the Stirling cycle numbers, $B_n = \sum_{m=1}^{n} \left\{ {n \atop m} \right\}$.

For example, there are $B_4 = 15$ different ways to partition the 4 element set $\{a, b, c, d\}$:

$\{a\}, \{c\}, \{b, d\},$ $\{a\}, \{d\}, \{b, c\},$ $\{b\}, \{c\}, \{a, d\},$ $\{b\}, \{d\}, \{a, c\},$ $\{c\}, \{d\}, \{a, b\},$
$\{a, b, c, d\},$ $\{a, b\}, \{c, d\},$ $\{a, c\}, \{b, d\},$ $\{a, d\}, \{b, c\},$ $\{a\}, \{b\}, \{c\}, \{d\},$
$\{a\}, \{b, c, d\},$ $\{b\}, \{a, c, d\},$ $\{c\}, \{a, b, d\},$ $\{d\}, \{a, b, c\},$ $\{a\}, \{b\}, \{c, d\}.$

n	1	2	3	4	5	6	7	8	9	10
B_n	1	2	5	15	52	203	877	4140	21147	115975

- A generating function for Bell numbers is $\sum_{n=0}^{\infty} B_n x^n = \exp(e^x - 1) - 1$. This results in *Dobinski's formula* for the nth Bell number, $B_n = e^{-1} \sum_{m=0}^{\infty} m^n / m!$.
- For large values of n, $B_n \sim n^{-1/2} [\lambda(n)]^{n+1/2} e^{\lambda(n)-n-1}$ where $\lambda(n)$ is defined by the relation: $\lambda(n) \log \lambda(n) = n$.

3.2.11 TABLES

Permutations $P(n, m)$

This table contains the number of permutations of n distinct things taken m at a time, given by

$$P(n, m) = \frac{n!}{(n - m)!} = n(n - 1) \cdots (n - m + 1).$$

n	$m = 0$	1	2	3	4	5	6	7	8
0	1								
1	1	1							
2	1	2	2						
3	1	3	6	6					
4	1	4	12	24	24				
5	1	5	20	60	120	120			
6	1	6	30	120	360	720	720		
7	1	7	42	210	840	2520	5040	5040	
8	1	8	56	336	1680	6720	20160	40320	40320
9	1	9	72	504	3024	15120	60480	181440	362880
10	1	10	90	720	5040	30240	151200	604800	1814400
11	1	11	110	990	7920	55440	332640	1663200	6652800
12	1	12	132	1320	11880	95040	665280	3991680	19958400
13	1	13	156	1716	17160	154440	1235520	8648640	51891840
14	1	14	182	2184	24024	240240	2162160	17297280	121080960
15	1	15	210	2730	32760	360360	3603600	32432400	259459200

n	$m = 9$	10	11	12	13
11	19958400	39916800	39916800		
12	79833600	239500800	479001600	479001600	
13	259459200	1037836800	3113510400	6227020800	6227020800
14	726485760	3632428800	14529715200	43589145600	87178291200
15	1816214400	10897286400	54486432000	217945728000	653837184000

Combinations $C(n, m) = \binom{n}{m}$

This table contains the number of combinations of n distinct things taken m at a time, given by

$$C(n, m) = \binom{n}{m} = \frac{n!}{m!(n-m)!}.$$

n	$m = 0$	1	2	3	4	5	6	7
1	1	1						
2	1	2	1					
3	1	3	3	1				
4	1	4	6	4	1			
5	1	5	10	10	5	1		
6	1	6	15	20	15	6	1	
7	1	7	21	35	35	21	7	1
8	1	8	28	56	70	56	28	8
9	1	9	36	84	126	126	84	36
10	1	10	45	120	210	252	210	120
11	1	11	55	165	330	462	462	330
12	1	12	66	220	495	792	924	792
13	1	13	78	286	715	1287	1716	1716
14	1	14	91	364	1001	2002	3003	3432
15	1	15	105	455	1365	3003	5005	6435
16	1	16	120	560	1820	4368	8008	11440
17	1	17	136	680	2380	6188	12376	19448
18	1	18	153	816	3060	8568	18564	31824
19	1	19	171	969	3876	11628	27132	50388
20	1	20	190	1140	4845	15504	38760	77520
21	1	21	210	1330	5985	20349	54264	116280
22	1	22	231	1540	7315	26334	74613	170544
23	1	23	253	1771	8855	33649	100947	245157
24	1	24	276	2024	10626	42504	134596	346104
25	1	25	300	2300	12650	53130	177100	480700
26	1	26	325	2600	14950	65780	230230	657800
27	1	27	351	2925	17550	80730	296010	888030
28	1	28	378	3276	20475	98280	376740	1184040
29	1	29	406	3654	23751	118755	475020	1560780
30	1	30	435	4060	27405	142506	593775	2035800

Combinations $C(n, m) = \binom{n}{m}$

This table contains the number of combinations of n distinct things taken m at a time, given by

$$C(n, m) = \binom{n}{m} = \frac{n!}{m!(n-m)!}.$$

n	$m = 0$	1	2	3	4	5	6	7
31	1	31	465	4495	31465	169911	736281	2629575
32	1	32	496	4960	35960	201376	906192	3365856
33	1	33	528	5456	40920	237336	1107568	4272048
34	1	34	561	5984	46376	278256	1344904	5379616
35	1	35	595	6545	52360	324632	1623160	6724520
36	1	36	630	7140	58905	376992	1947792	8347680
37	1	37	666	7770	66045	435897	2324784	10295472
38	1	38	703	8436	73815	501942	2760681	12620256
39	1	39	741	9139	82251	575757	3262623	15380937
40	1	40	780	9880	91390	658008	3838380	18643560
41	1	41	820	10660	101270	749398	4496388	22481940
42	1	42	861	11480	111930	850668	5245786	26978328
43	1	43	903	12341	123410	962598	6096454	32224114
44	1	44	946	13244	135751	1086008	7059052	38320568
45	1	45	990	14190	148995	1221759	8145060	45379620
46	1	46	1035	15180	163185	1370754	9366819	53524680
47	1	47	1081	16215	178365	1533939	10737573	62891499
48	1	48	1128	17296	194580	1712304	12271512	73629072
49	1	49	1176	18424	211876	1906884	13983816	85900584
50	1	50	1225	19600	230300	2118760	15890700	99884400

n	m = 8	9	10	11	12
8	1				
9	9	1			
10	45	10	1		
11	165	55	11	1	
12	495	220	66	12	1
13	1287	715	286	78	13
14	3003	2002	1001	364	91
15	6435	5005	3003	1365	455
16	12870	11440	8008	4368	1820
17	24310	24310	19448	12376	6188
18	43758	48620	43758	31824	18564
19	75582	92378	92378	75582	50388
20	125970	167960	184756	167960	125970
21	203490	293930	352716	352716	293930
22	319770	497420	646646	705432	646646
23	490314	817190	1144066	1352078	1352078
24	735471	1307504	1961256	2496144	2704156
25	1081575	2042975	3268760	4457400	5200300
26	1562275	3124550	5311735	7726160	9657700
27	2220075	4686825	8436285	13037895	17383860
28	3108105	6906900	13123110	21474180	30421755
29	4292145	10015005	20030010	34597290	51895935
30	5852925	14307150	30045015	54627300	86493225
31	7888725	20160075	44352165	84672315	141120525
32	10518300	28048800	64512240	129024480	225792840
33	13884156	38567100	92561040	193536720	354817320
34	18156204	52451256	131128140	286097760	548354040
35	23535820	70607460	183579396	417225900	834451800
36	30260340	94143280	254186856	600805296	1251677700
37	38608020	124403620	348330136	854992152	1852482996
38	48903492	163011640	472733756	1203322288	2707475148
39	61523748	211915132	635745396	1676056044	3910797436
40	76904685	273438880	847660528	2311801440	5586853480
41	95548245	350343565	1121099408	3159461968	7898654920
42	118030185	445891810	1471442973	4280561376	11058116888
43	145008513	563921995	1917334783	5752004349	15338678264
44	177232627	708930508	2481256778	7669339132	21090682613
45	215553195	886163135	3190187286	10150595910	28760021745
46	260932815	1101716330	4076350421	13340783196	38910617655
47	314457495	1362649145	5178066751	17417133617	52251400851
48	377348994	1677106640	6540715896	22595200368	69668534468
49	450978066	2054455634	8217822536	29135916264	92263734836
50	536878650	2505433700	10272278170	37353738800	121399651100

n	m = 13	14	15	16	17
13	1				
14	14	1			
15	105	15	1		
16	560	120	16	1	
17	2380	680	136	17	1
18	8568	3060	816	153	18
19	27132	11628	3876	969	171
20	77520	38760	15504	4845	1140
21	203490	116280	54264	20349	5985
22	497420	319770	170544	74613	26334
23	1144066	817190	490314	245157	100947
24	2496144	1961256	1307504	735471	346104
25	5200300	4457400	3268760	2042975	1081575
26	10400600	9657700	7726160	5311735	3124550
27	20058300	20058300	17383860	13037895	8436285
28	37442160	40116600	37442160	30421755	21474180
29	67863915	77558760	77558760	67863915	51895935
30	119759850	145422675	155117520	145422675	119759850
31	206253075	265182525	300540195	300540195	265182525
32	347373600	471435600	565722720	601080390	565722720
33	573166440	818809200	1037158320	1166803110	1166803110
34	927983760	1391975640	1855967520	2203961430	2333606220
35	1476337800	2319959400	3247943160	4059928950	4537567650
36	2310789600	3796297200	5567902560	7307872110	8597496600
37	3562467300	6107086800	9364199760	12875774670	15905368710
38	5414950296	9669554100	15471286560	22239974430	28781143380
39	8122425444	15084504396	25140840660	37711260990	51021117810
40	12033222880	23206929840	40225345056	62852101650	88732378800
41	17620076360	35240152720	63432274896	103077446706	151584480450
42	25518731280	52860229080	98672427616	166509721602	254661927156
43	36576848168	78378960360	151532656696	265182149218	421171648758
44	51915526432	114955808528	229911617056	416714805914	686353797976
45	73006209045	166871334960	344867425584	646626422970	1103068603890
46	101766230790	239877544005	511738760544	991493848554	1749695026860
47	140676848445	341643774795	751616304549	1503232609098	2741188875414
48	192928249296	482320623240	1093260079344	2254848913647	4244421484512
49	262596783764	675248872536	1575580702584	3348108992991	6499270398159
50	354860518600	937845656300	2250829575120	4923689695575	9847379391150

Fractional binomial coefficients $\binom{a}{k}$						
a	$k = 0$	1	2	3	4	5
1/9	1	1/9	−4/81	68/2187	−442/19683	3094/177147
1/8	1	1/8	−7/128	35/1024	−805/32768	4991/262144
1/7	1	1/7	−3/49	13/343	−65/2401	351/16807
1/6	1	1/6	−5/72	55/1296	−935/31104	4301/186624
1/5	1	1/5	−2/25	6/125	−21/625	399/15625
2/9	1	2/9	−7/81	112/2187	−700/19683	4760/177147
1/4	1	1/4	−3/32	7/128	−77/2048	231/8192
2/7	1	2/7	−5/49	20/343	−95/2401	494/16807
1/3	1	1/3	−1/9	5/81	−10/243	22/729
3/8	1	3/8	−15/128	65/1024	−1365/32768	7917/262144
2/5	1	2/5	−3/25	8/125	−26/625	468/15625
3/7	1	3/7	−6/49	22/343	−99/2401	495/16807
4/9	1	4/9	−10/81	140/2187	−805/19683	5152/177147
1/2	1	1/2	−1/8	1/16	−5/128	7/256
5/9	1	5/9	−10/81	130/2187	−715/19683	4433/177147
4/7	1	4/7	−6/49	20/343	−85/2401	408/16807
3/5	1	3/5	−3/25	7/125	−21/625	357/15625
5/8	1	5/8	−15/128	55/1024	−1045/32768	5643/262144
2/3	1	2/3	−1/9	4/81	−7/243	14/729
5/7	1	5/7	−5/49	15/343	−60/2401	276/16807
3/4	1	3/4	−3/32	5/128	−45/2048	117/8192
7/9	1	7/9	−7/81	77/2187	−385/19683	2233/177147
4/5	1	4/5	−2/25	4/125	−11/625	176/15625
5/6	1	5/6	−5/72	35/1296	−455/31104	1729/186624
6/7	1	6/7	−3/49	8/343	−30/2401	132/16807
7/8	1	7/8	−7/128	21/1024	−357/32768	1785/262144
8/9	1	8/9	−4/81	40/2187	−190/19683	1064/177147

Stirling numbers $\left[{n \atop m} \right]$							
n	$m = 1$	2	3	4	5	6	7
1	1						
2	−1	1					
3	2	−3	1				
4	−6	11	−6	1			
5	24	−50	35	−10	1		
6	−120	274	−225	85	−15	1	
7	720	−1764	1624	−735	175	−21	1
8	−5040	13068	−13132	6769	−1960	322	−28
9	40320	−109584	118124	−67284	22449	−4536	546
10	−362880	1026576	−1172700	723680	−269325	63273	−9450

Stirling cycle numbers $\left\{ {n \atop m} \right\}$						
n	$m = 1$	2	3	4	5	6	7
1	1						
2	1	1					
3	1	3	1				
4	1	7	6	1			
5	1	15	25	10	1		
6	1	31	90	65	15	1	
7	1	63	301	350	140	21	1
8	1	127	966	1701	1050	266	28
9	1	255	3025	7770	6951	2646	462
10	1	511	9330	34105	42525	22827	5880
11	1	1023	28501	145750	246730	179487	63987
12	1	2047	86526	611501	1379400	1323652	627396
13	1	4095	261625	2532530	7508501	9321312	5715424
14	1	8191	788970	10391745	40075035	63436373	49329280
15	1	16383	2375101	42355950	210766920	420693273	408741333

3.3 GRAPHS

3.3.1 NOTATION

Notation for graphs

E edge set V vertex set
G graph ϕ incidence mapping

Invariants

$|G|$ order $\text{gir}(G)$ girth
$\text{Aut}(G)$ automorphism group $\text{rad}(G)$ radius
$c(G)$ circumference $P_G(x)$ chromatic polynomial
$d(u, v)$ distance between two vertices $Z(G)$ center
$\deg x$ degree of a vertex $\alpha(G)$ independence number
$\text{diam}(G)$ diameter $\delta(G)$ minimum degree
$e(G)$ size $\Delta(G)$ maximum degree
$\text{ecc}(x)$ eccentricity $\gamma(G)$ genus

$\kappa(G)$	vertex connectivity	$\theta(G)$	thickness
$\lambda(G)$	edge connectivity	$\chi(G)$	chromatic number
$v(G)$	crossing number	$\chi'(G)$	chromatic index
$\bar{v}(G)$	rectilinear crossing number	$\Upsilon(G)$	arboricity
$\omega(G)$	clique number		

Examples

C_n	cycle	M_n	Möbius ladder
$\bar{K}_n$	empty graph	O_n	odd graph
K_n	complete graph	P_n	path
$K_{m,n}$	complete bipartite graph	Q_n	cube
		$T_{n,k}$	Turán graph
$K_{1,n-1}$	star	W_n	wheel
$K_n^{(m)}$	Kneser graphs		

3.3.2 BASIC DEFINITIONS

There are two standard definitions of graphs, a general definition and a more common simplification. Except where otherwise indicated, this book uses the simplified definition, according to which a *graph* is an ordered pair (V, E) consisting of an arbitrary set V and a set E of 2-element subsets of V. Each element of V is called a *vertex* (plural *vertices*). Each element of E is called an *edge*.

According to the general definition, a *graph* is an ordered triple $G = (V, E, \phi)$ consisting of arbitrary sets V and E and an *incidence mapping* ϕ that assigns to each element $e \in E$ a nonempty set $\phi(e) \subseteq V$ of cardinality at most two. Again, the elements of V are called *vertices* and the elements of E are called *edges*. A *loop* is an edge e for which $|\phi(e)| = 1$. A graph has *multiple edges* if edges $e \neq e'$ exist for which $\phi(e) = \phi(e')$.

A (general) graph is called *simple* if it has neither loops nor multiple edges. Because each edge in a simple graph can be identified with the two-element set $\phi(e) \subseteq V$, the simplified definition of graph given above is just an alternative definition of a simple graph.

The word *multigraph* is used to discuss general graphs with multiple edges but no loops. Occasionally the word *pseudograph* is used to emphasize that the graphs under discussion may have both loops and multiple edges. Every graph $G = (V, E)$ considered here is *finite*, i.e., both V and E are finite sets.

Specialized graph terms include the following:

acyclic: A graph is *acyclic* if it has no cycles.

adjacency: Two distinct vertices v and w in a graph are *adjacent* if the pair $\{v, w\}$ is an edge. Two distinct edges are *adjacent* if their intersection is nonempty, i.e., if there is a vertex incident with both of them.

adjacency matrix: For an ordering $v_1, v_2, \ldots, v_n$ of the vertices of a graph $G = (V, E)$ of order $|G| = n$, there is a corresponding $n \times n$ *adjacency matrix* $A = (a_{ij})$ defined as follows:

$$a_{ij} = \begin{cases} 1 & \text{if } \{v_i, v_j\} \in E; \\ 0 & \text{otherwise.} \end{cases}$$

arboricity: The *arboricity* $\Upsilon(G)$ of a graph G is the minimum number of edge-disjoint spanning forests into which G can be partitioned.

automorphism: An *automorphism* of a graph is a permutation of its vertices that is an isomorphism.

automorphism group: The composition of two automorphisms is again an automorphism; with this binary operation, the automorphisms of a graph G form a group $\mathrm{Aut}(G)$ called the *automorphism group* of G.

ball: The *ball* of radius k about a vertex u in a graph is the set

$$B(u, k) = \{v \in V \mid d(u, v) \le k\}.$$

See also *sphere* and *neighborhood*.

block: A *block* is a graph with no cut vertex. A *block* of a graph is a maximal subgraph that is a block.

boundary operator: The *boundary operator* for a graph is the linear mapping from 1-chains (elements of the edge space) to 0-chains (elements of the vertex space) that sends each edge to the indicator mapping the set of two vertices incident with it. See also *vertex space* and *edge space*.

bridge: A *bridge* is an edge in a connected graph whose removal would disconnect the graph.

cactus: A *cactus* is a connected graph, each of whose blocks is a cycle.

cage: An (r, n)-*cage* is a graph of minimal order among r-regular graphs with girth n. A $(3, n)$-cage is also called an n-cage.

center: The *center* $Z(G)$ of a graph $G = (V, E)$ consists of all vertices whose eccentricity equals the radius of G:

$$Z(G) = \{v \in V(G) \mid \mathrm{ecc}(v) = \mathrm{rad}(G)\}.$$

Each vertex in the center of G is called a *central vertex*.

characteristic polynomial: All adjacency matrices of a graph G have the same characteristic polynomial, which is called the *characteristic polynomial* of G.

chromatic index: The *chromatic index* $\chi'(G)$ is the least k for which there exists a proper k-coloring of the edges of G; in other words, it is the least number of matchings into which the edge set can be decomposed.

chromatic number: The *chromatic number* $\chi(G)$ of a graph G is the least k for which there exists a proper k-coloring of the vertices of G; in other words, it is the least k for which G is k-partite. See also *multipartite*.

chromatic polynomial: For a graph G of order $|G| = n$ with exactly k connected components, the *chromatic polynomial* of G is the unique polynomial $P_G(x)$ for which $P_G(m)$ is the number of proper colorings of G with m colors for each positive integer m.

circuit: A *circuit* in a graph is a trail whose first and last vertices are identical.

circulant graph: A graph G is a *circulant graph* if its adjacency matrix is a circulant matrix; that is, the rows are circular shifts of one another.

circumference: The circumference of a graph is the length of its longest cycle.

clique: A *clique* is a set S of vertices for which the induced subgraph $G[S]$ is complete.

clique number: The *clique number* $\omega(G)$ of a graph G is the largest cardinality of a clique in G.

coboundary operator: The *coboundary operator* for a graph is the linear mapping from 0-chains (elements of the vertex space) to 1-chains (elements of the edge space) that sends each vertex to the indicator mapping of the set of edges incident with it.

cocycle vector: A cut vector is sometimes called a *cocycle vector*.

coloring: A partition of the vertex set of a graph is called a *coloring*, and the blocks of the partition are called *color classes*. A coloring with k color classes is called a *k-coloring*. A coloring is *proper* if no two adjacent vertices belong to the same color class. See also *chromatic number* and *chromatic polynomial*.

complement: The *complement* $\overline{G}$ of a graph $G = (V, E)$ has vertex set V and edge set $\binom{V}{2} \setminus E$; that is, its edges are exactly the pairs of vertices that are not edges of G.

complete graph: A graph is *complete* if every pair of distinct vertices is an edge; K_n denotes a complete graph with n vertices.

component: A *component* of a graph is a maximal connected subgraph.

connectedness: A graph is said to be *connected* if each pair of vertices is joined by a walk; otherwise, the graph is *disconnected*. A graph is *k-connected* if it has order at least $k+1$ and each pair of vertices is joined by k pairwise internally disjoint paths.

connectivity: The *connectivity* $\kappa(G)$ of G is the largest k for which G is k-connected.

contraction: To *contract* an edge $\{v, w\}$ of a graph G is to construct a new graph G' from G by removing the edge $\{v, w\}$ and identifying the vertices v and w. A graph G is *contractible* to a graph H if H can be obtained from G via the contraction of one or more edges of G.

cover: A set $S \subseteq V$ is a *vertex cover* if every edge of G is incident with some vertex in S. A set $T \subseteq E$ is an *edge cover* of a graph $G = (V, E)$ if each vertex of G is incident to at least one edge in T.

crosscap number: The *crosscap number* $\tilde{\gamma}(G)$ of a graph G is the least g for which G has an embedding in a nonorientable surface obtained from the sphere by adding g crosscaps. See also *genus*.

crossing: A *crossing* is a point lying in images of two edges of a drawing of a graph on a surface.

crossing number: The *crossing number* $v(G)$ of a graph G is the minimum number of crossings among all drawings of G in the plane. The *rectilinear crossing number* $\overline{v}(G)$ of a graph G is the minimum number of crossings among all drawings of G in the plane for which the image of each edge is a straight line segment.

cubic: A graph is a *cubic* graph if it is regular of degree 3.

cut: For each partition $V = V_1 \uplus V_2$ of the vertex set of a graph $G = (V, E)$ into two disjoint blocks, the set of all edges joining a vertex in V_1 to a vertex in V_2 is called a *cut*.

cut space: The *cut space* of a graph G is the subspace of the edge space of G spanned by the cut vectors.

cut vector: The *cut vector* corresponding to a cut C of a graph $G = (V, E)$ is the mapping $v \colon E \to GF(2)$ in the edge space of G

$$v(e) = \begin{cases} 1, & e \in C, \\ 0, & \text{otherwise.} \end{cases}$$

cut vertex: A cut vertex of a connected graph is a vertex whose removal, along with all edges incident with it, leaves a disconnected graph.

cycle: A *cycle* is a circuit, each pair of whose vertices other than the first and the last are distinct.

cycle space: The *cycle space* of a graph G is the subspace of the edge space of G consisting of all 1-chains with boundary 0. An indicator mapping of a set of edges with which each vertex is incident an even number of times is called a *cycle vector*. The cycle space is the span of the cycle vectors.

degree: The *degree* $\deg x$ of a vertex x in a graph is the number of vertices adjacent to it. The maximum and minimum degrees of vertices in a graph G are denoted $\Delta(G)$ and $\delta(G)$, respectively.

degree sequence: A sequence $(d_1, \ldots, d_n)$ is a degree sequence of a graph if there is some ordering $v_1, \ldots, v_n$ of the vertices for which d_i is the degree of v_i for each i.

diameter: The *diameter* of G is the maximum distance between two vertices of G; thus it is also the maximum eccentricity of a vertex in G.

distance: The *distance* $d(u, v)$ between vertices u and v in a graph G is the minimum among the lengths of u, v-paths in G, or ∞ if there is no u, v-path.

drawing: A *drawing* of a graph G in a surface S consists of a one-to-one mapping from the vertices of G to points of S and a one-to-one mapping from the edges of G to open arcs in X so that (i) no image of an edge contains an image of some vertex, (ii) the image of each edge $\{v, w\}$ joins the images of v and w, (iii) the images of adjacent edges are disjoint, (iv) the images of two distinct edges never have more than one point in common, and (v) no point of the surface lies on the images of more than two edges.

eccentricity: The *eccentricity* $\text{ecc}(x)$ of a vertex x in a graph G is the maximum distance from x to a vertex of G.

edge connectivity: The *edge connectivity* of G, denoted $\lambda(G)$, is the minimum number of edges whose removal results in a disconnected graph.

edge space: The *edge space* of a graph $G = (V, E)$, is the vector space of all mappings from E to the two-element field $GF(2)$. Elements of the edge space are called 1-*chains*.

embedding: An *embedding* of a graph G in a topological space X consists of an assignment of the vertices of G to distinct points of X and an assignment of the edges of G to disjoint open arcs in X so that no arc representing an edge contains some point representing a vertex and so that each arc representing an edge joins the points representing the vertices incident with the edge. See also *drawing*.

end vertex: A vertex of degree 1 in a graph is called an *end vertex*.

Eulerian circuits and trails: A trail or circuit that includes every edge of a graph is said to be *Eulerian*, and a graph is *Eulerian* if it has an Eulerian circuit.

even: A graph is *even* if the degree of every vertex is even.

factor: A *factor* of a graph G is a spanning subgraph of G. A factor in which every vertex has the same degree k is called a *k-factor*. If $G_1, G_2, \ldots, G_k$ ($k \geq 2$) are edge-disjoint factors of the graph G, and if $\bigcup_{i=1}^{k} E(G_i) = E(G)$, then G is said to be *factored* into $G_1, G_2, \ldots, G_k$ and we write $G = G_1 \oplus G_2 \oplus \cdots \oplus G_k$.

forest: A *forest* is an acyclic simple graph; see also *tree*.

genus: The *genus* $\gamma(G)$ (plural form *genera*) of a graph G is the least g for which G has an embedding in an orientable surface of genus g. See also *crosscap number*.

girth: The *girth* gir(G) of a graph G is the minimum length of a cycle in G, or ∞ if G is acyclic.

Hamiltonian cycles and paths: A path or cycle through all the vertices of a graph is said to be *Hamiltonian*. A graph is *Hamiltonian* if it has a Hamiltonian cycle.

homeomorphic graphs: Two graphs are *homeomorphic* to one another if there is a third graph of which each is a subdivision.

identification of vertices: To *identify* vertices v and w of a graph G is to construct a new graph G' from G by removing the vertices v and w and all the edges of G incident with them and introducing a new vertex u and new edges joining u to each vertex that was adjacent to v or to w in G. See also *contraction*.

incidence: A vertex v and an edge e are *incident* with one another if $v \in e$.

incidence matrix: For an ordering $v_1, v_2, \ldots, v_n$ of the vertices and an ordering $e_1, e_2, \ldots, e_m$ of the edges of a graph $G = (V, E)$ with order $|G| = n$ and size $e(G) = m$, there is a corresponding $n \times m$ *incidence matrix* $B = (b_{ij})$ defined as follows:

$$b_{ij} = \begin{cases} 1, & \text{if } v_i \text{ and } e_j \text{ are incident,} \\ 0, & \text{otherwise.} \end{cases}$$

independence number: The *independence number* $\alpha(G)$ of a graph $G = (V, E)$ is the largest cardinality of an independent subset of V.

independent set: A set $S \subseteq V$ is said to be *independent* if the induced subgraph $G[S]$ is empty. See also *matching*.

internally disjoint paths: Two paths in a graph with the same initial vertex v and terminal vertex w are *internally disjoint* if they have no internal vertex in common.

isolated vertex: A vertex is *isolated* if it is adjacent to no other vertex.

isomorphism: An *isomorphism* between graphs $G = (V_G, E_G)$ and $H = (V_H, E_H)$ is a bijective mapping $\psi: V_G \rightarrow V_H$ for which $\{x, y\} \in E_G$ if and only if $\{\psi(x), \psi(y)\} \in E_H$. If there is an isomorphism between G and H, then G and H are said to be *isomorphic* to one another; this is denoted as $G \cong H$. Figure 3.3.1 contains three graphs that are isomorphic.

FIGURE 3.3.1

Three graphs that are isomorphic.

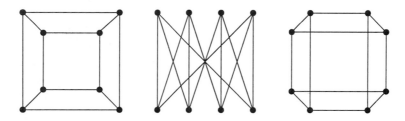

labeled graph: Graph theorists sometimes speak loosely of *labeled graphs* of order n and *unlabeled graphs* of order n to distinguish between graphs with a fixed vertex set of cardinality n and the family of isomorphism classes of such graphs. Thus, one may refer to *labeled graphs* to indicate an intention to distinguish between any two graphs that are *distinct* (i.e., have different vertex sets and/or or different edge sets). One may refer to *unlabeled graphs* to indicate the intention to view any two distinct but isomorphic graphs as the 'same' graph, and to distinguish only between nonisomorphic graphs.

matching: A *matching* in a graph is a set of edges, no two having a vertex in common. A *maximal matching* is a matching that is not a proper subset of any other matching. A *maximum matching* is a matching of greatest cardinality. For a matching M, an M-*alternating* path is a path whose every other edge belongs to M, and an M-*augmenting* path is an M-alternating path whose first and last edges do not belong to M. A matching *saturates* a vertex if the vertex belongs to some edge of the matching.

monotone graph property: A property $\mathcal{P}$ that a graph may or may not enjoy is said to be *monotone* if, whenever H is a graph enjoying $\mathcal{P}$, every supergraph G of H with $|G| = |H|$ also enjoys $\mathcal{P}$.

multipartite graph: A graph is k-*partite* if its vertex set can be partitioned into k disjoint sets called *color classes* in such a way that every edge joins vertices in two different color classes (see also *coloring*). A two-partite graph is called *bipartite*.

neighbor: Adjacent vertices v and w in a graph are said to be *neighbors* of one another.

neighborhood: The sphere $S(x, 1)$ is called the *neighborhood* of x, and the ball $B(x, 1)$ is called the *closed neighborhood* of x.

order: The *order* $|G|$ of a graph $G = (V, E)$ is the number of vertices in G; in other words, $|G| = |V|$.

path: A *path* is a walk whose vertices are distinct.

perfect graph: A graph is *perfect* if $\chi(H) = \omega(H)$ for all induced subgraphs H of G.

planarity: A graph is *planar* if it has a proper embedding in the plane.

radius: The *radius* rad(G) of a graph G is the minimum vertex eccentricity in G.

regularity: A graph is k-*regular* if each of its vertices has degree k. A graph is *strongly regular* with parameters (k, λ, μ) if (i) it is k-regular, (ii) every pair of adjacent vertices has exactly λ common neighbors, and (iii) every pair of nonadjacent vertices has exactly μ common neighbors. A graph $G = (V, E)$ of order $|G| \ge 3$ is called *highly regular* if there exists an $n \times n$ matrix $C = (c_{ij})$, where $2 \le n < |G|$, called a *collapsed adjacency matrix*, so that, for each vertex v of G, there is a partition of V into n subsets $V_1 = \{v\}$, $V_2, \ldots, V_n$ so that every vertex $y \in V_j$ is adjacent to exactly c_{ij} vertices in V_i. Every highly regular graph is also regular.

rooted graph: A *rooted graph* is an ordered pair (G, v) consisting of a graph G and a distinguished vertex v of G called the *root*.

self-complementary: A graph is *self-complementary* if it is isomorphic to its complement.

similarity: Two vertices u and v of a graph G are *similar* (in symbols $u \sim v$) if there is an automorphism α of G for which $\alpha(u) = v$. Similarly, two edges (u, v) and (a, b) in the graph G are *similar* if an automorphism α of G exists for which $\{\alpha(u), \alpha(v)\} = \{a, b\}$.

size: The *size* $e(G)$ of a graph $G = (V, E)$ is the number of edges of G, that is, $e(G) = |E|$.

spectrum: The *spectrum* of a graph G is the spectrum of its characteristic polynomial, i.e., the nondecreasing sequence of $|G|$ eigenvalues of the characteristic polynomial of G.

sphere: The *sphere* of radius k about a vertex u is the set

$$S(u, k) = \{v \in V \mid d(u, v) = k\}.$$

See also *ball* and *neighborhood*.

subdivision: To *subdivide* an edge $\{v, w\}$ of a graph G is to construct a new graph G' from G by removing the edge $\{v, w\}$ and introducing new vertices x_i and new edges $\{v, x_1\}$, $\{x_k, w\}$ and $\{x_i, x_{i+1}\}$ for $1 \le i < k$. A *subdivision* of a graph is a graph obtained by subdividing one or more edges of the graph.

subgraph: A graph $H = (V_H, E_H)$ is a *subgraph* of a graph $G = (V_G, E_G)$ (in symbols, $H \preceq G$), if $V_H \subseteq V_G$ and $E_H \subseteq E_G$. In that case, G is a *supergraph* of H (in symbols, $G \succeq H$). If $V_H = V_G$, then H is called a *spanning subgraph* of G. For each set $S \subseteq V_G$, the subgraph $G[S]$ of G *induced* by S is the unique subgraph of G with vertex set S for which every edge of G incident with two vertices in S is also an edge of $G[S]$.

symmetry: A graph is *vertex symmetric* if every pair of vertices is similar. A graph is *edge symmetric* if every pair of edges is similar. A graph is *symmetric* if it is both vertex and edge symmetric.

2-switch: For vertices v, w, x, y in a graph G for which $\{v, w\}$ and $\{x, y\}$ are edges, but $\{v, y\}$ and $\{x, w\}$ are not edges, the construction of a new graph G' from G via the removal of edges $\{v, w\}$ and $\{x, y\}$ together with the insertion of the edges $\{v, y\}$ and $\{x, w\}$ is called a *2-switch*.

thickness: The *thickness* $\theta(G)$ of a graph G is the least k for which G is a union of k planar graphs.

trail: A *trail* in a graph is a walk whose edges are distinct.

tree: A *tree* is a connected forest, i.e., a connected acyclic graph. A spanning subgraph of a graph G that is a tree is called a *spanning tree* of G.

triangle: A 3-cycle is called a triangle.

trivial graph: A *trivial* graph is a graph with exactly one vertex and no edges.

unicyclic graph: A unicyclic graph is a connected graph that contains exactly one cycle.

vertex space: The *vertex space* of a graph G is the vector space of all mappings from V to the two-element field $GF(2)$. The elements of the vertex space are called 0-*chains*.

walk: A *walk* in a graph is an alternating sequence $v_0, e_1, v_1, \ldots, e_k, v_k$ of vertices v_i and edges e_i for which e_i is incident with v_{i-1} and with v_i for each i. Such a walk is said to have *length* k and to *join* v_0 and v_k. The vertices v_0 and v_k are called the *initial vertex* and *terminal vertex* of the walk; the remaining vertices are called *internal vertices* of the walk.

3.3.3 CONSTRUCTIONS

Operations on graphs

For graphs $G_1 = (V_1, E_1)$ and $G_2 = (V_2, E_2)$, there are several binary operations that yield a new graph from G_1 and G_2. The following table gives the names of those operations and the orders and sizes of the resulting graphs.

Operation producing G		Order $\lvert G \rvert$	Size $e(G)$
Composition	$G_1[G_2]$	$\lvert G_1 \rvert \cdot \lvert G_2 \rvert$	$\lvert G_1 \rvert e(G_2) + \lvert G_2 \rvert^2 e(G_1)$
Conjunction	$G_1 \wedge G_2$	$\lvert G_1 \rvert \cdot \lvert G_2 \rvert$	
Edge sum[a]	$G_1 \oplus G_2$	$\lvert G_1 \rvert = \lvert G_2 \rvert$	$e(G_1) + e(G_2)$
Join	$G_1 + G_2$	$\lvert G_1 \rvert + \lvert G_2 \rvert$	$e(G_1) + e(G_2) + \lvert G_1 \rvert \cdot \lvert G_2 \rvert$
Product	$G_1 \times G_2$	$\lvert G_1 \rvert \cdot \lvert G_2 \rvert$	$\lvert G_1 \rvert e(G_2) + \lvert G_2 \rvert e(G_1)$
Union	$G_1 \cup G_2$	$\lvert G_1 \rvert + \lvert G_2 \rvert$	$e(G_1) + e(G_2)$

[a] When applicable.

composition: For graphs $G_1 = (V_1, E_1)$ and $G_2 = (V_2, E_2)$, the *composition* $G = G_1[G_2]$ is the graph with vertex set $V_1 \times V_2$ whose edges are the pairs $\{(u, v), (u, w)\}$ with $u \in V_1$ and $\{v, w\} \in E_2$ and the pairs $\{(t, u), (v, w)\}$ for which $\{t, v\} \in E_1$ and $\{u, w\} \in E_2$.

conjunction: The conjunction $G_1 \wedge G_2$ of two graphs $G_1 = (V_1, E_1)$ and $G_2 = (V_2, E_2)$ is the graph $G_3 = (V_3, E_3)$ for which $V_3 = V_1 \times V_2$ and for which vertices $\mathbf{e}_1 = (u_1, u_2)$ and $\mathbf{e}_2 = (v_1, v_2)$ in V_3 are adjacent in G_3 if, and only if, u_1 is adjacent to v_1 in G_1 and u_2 is adjacent to v_2 in G_2.

edge difference: For graphs $G_1 = (V, E_1)$ and $G_2 = (V, E_2)$ with the same vertex set V, the *edge difference* $G_1 - G_2$ is the graph with vertex set V and edge set $E_1 \setminus E_2$.

edge sum: For graphs $G_1 = (V, E_1)$ and $G_2 = (V, E_2)$ with the same vertex set V, the *edge sum* of G_1 and G_2 is the graph $G_1 \oplus G_2$ with vertex set V and edge set $E_1 \cup E_2$. Sometimes the edge sum is denoted $G_1 \cup G_2$.

join: For graphs $G_1 = (V_1, E_1)$ and $G_2 = (V_2, E_2)$ with $V_1 \cap V_2 = \emptyset$, the *join* $G_1 + G_2 = G_2 + G_1$ is the graph obtained from the union of G_1 and G_2 by adding edges joining each vertex in V_1 to each vertex in V_2.

power: For a graph $G = (V, E)$, the kth *power* G^k is the graph with the same vertex set V whose the edges are the pairs $\{u, v\}$ for which $d(u, v) \leq k$ in G. The *square* of G is G^2.

product: For graphs $G_1 = (V_1, E_1)$ and $G_2 = (V_2, E_2)$, the *product* $G_1 \times G_2$ has vertex set $V_1 \times V_2$; its edges are all of the pairs $\{(u, v), (u, w)\}$ for which $u \in V_1$ and $\{v, w\} \in E_2$ and all of the pairs $\{(t, v), (u, v)\}$ for which $\{t, u\} \in E_1$ and $v \in V_2$.

union: For graphs $G_1 = (V_1, E_1)$ and $G_2 = (V_2, E_2)$ with $V_1 \cap V_2 = \emptyset$, the *union* of G_1 and G_2 is the graph $G_1 \cup G_2 = (V_1 \cup V_2, E_1 \cup E_2)$. The union is sometimes called the *disjoint union* to distinguish it from the *edge sum*.

Graphs described by one parameter

complete graph, K_n: A complete graph of order n is a graph isomorphic to the graph K_n with vertex set $\{1, 2, \ldots, n\}$ whose every pair of vertices is an edge. The graph K_n has size $\binom{n}{2}$ and is Hamiltonian. If G is a graph g of order n, then $K_n = G \oplus \overline{G}$.

cube, Q_n: An *n-cube* is a graph isomorphic to the graph Q_n whose vertices are the 2^n binary n-vectors and whose edges are the pairs of vectors that differ in exactly one place. It is an n-regular bipartite graph of order 2^n and size $n2^{n-1}$ An equivalent recursive definition, $Q_1 = K_2$ and $Q_n = Q_{n-1} \times K_2$.

cycle, C_n: A *cycle* of order n is a graph isomorphic to the graph C_n with vertex set $\{0, 1, \ldots, n - 1\}$ whose edges are the pairs $\{v_i, v_{i+1}\}$ with $0 \leq i < n$ and arithmetic modulo n. The cycle C_n has size n and is Hamiltonian.

The graph C_n is a special case of a circulant graph. The graph C_3 is called a *triangle*, the graph C_4 is called a *square*.

empty graph: A graph is *empty* if it has no edges; $\overline{K}_n$ denotes an empty graph of order n.

Kneser graphs, $K_n^{(m)}$: For $n \geq 2m$, the *Kneser graph* $K_n^{(m)}$ is the complement of the intersection graph of the m-subsets of a n-set. The *odd graph* O_m is the Kneser graph $K_{2m+1}^{(m)}$. The *Petersen graph* is the odd graph $O_2 = K_5^{(2)}$

ladder: A *ladder* is a graph of the form $P_n \times P_2$. The *Möbius ladder* M_n is the graph obtained from the ladder $P_n \times P_2$ by joining the opposite end vertices of the two copies of P_n.

path, P_n: A *path* of order n is a graph isomorphic to the graph P_n whose vertex set is $\{1, \ldots, n\}$ and whose edges are the pairs $\{v_i, v_{i+1}\}$ with $1 \leq i < n$. A path of order n has size $n - 1$ and is a tree.

star, S_n: A *star* of order n is a graph isomorphic to the graph $S_n = K_{1,n-1}$. It has a vertex cover consisting of a single vertex, its size is $n - 1$, and it is a complete bipartite graph and a tree.

wheel, W_n: The wheel W_n of order $n \geq 4$ consists of a cycle of order $n - 1$ and an additional vertex adjacent to every vertex in the cycle. Equivalently, $W_n = C_{n-1} + K_1$. This graph has size $2(n - 1)$.

Graphs described by two parameters

complete bipartite graph, $K_{n,m}$: The complete bipartite graph $K_{n,m}$ is the graph $\overline{K}_n +$

$\overline{K}_m$. Its vertex set can be partitioned into two color classes of cardinalities n and m, respectively, so that each vertex in one color class is adjacent to every vertex in the other color class. The graph $K_{n,m}$ has order $n + m$ and size nm.

planar mesh: A graph of the form $P_n \times P_m$ is called a *planar mesh*.

prism: A graph of the form $C_m \times P_n$ is called a *prism*.

Toeplitz graph, TN(w, s): The Toeplitz graph TN(w, s) is defined in terms of its adjacency matrix $A = (a_{ij})$, for which

$$a_{ij} = \begin{cases} 1, & \text{if } |i - j| = 1 \pmod{w}, \\ 0, & \text{otherwise.} \end{cases}$$

The Toeplitz graph is of order $ws + 2$, size $(s + 1)(w - s + 2)/2$, and girth 3 or 4; it is $(s + 1)$-regular and Hamiltonian. Moreover, TN$(1, s) = K_{s+2}$ and TN$(w, 1) = C_{w+2}$.

toroidal mesh: A graph of the form $C_m \times C_n$ with $m \geq 2$ and $n \geq 2$ is called a *toroidal mesh*.

Turán graph, $T_{n,k}$: The *Turán graph* $T_{n,k}$ is the complete k-partite graph in which the cardinalities of any two color classes differ by, at most, one. It has $n - k\lfloor n/k \rfloor$ color classes of cardinality $\lfloor n/k \rfloor + 1$ and $k - n + k \lfloor n/k \rfloor$ color classes of cardinality $\lfloor n/k \rfloor$. Note that $\omega(T_{n,k}) = k$.

Graphs described by three or more parameters

Cayley graph: For a group Γ and a set X of generators of Γ, the *Cayley graph* of the pair (Γ, X) is the graph with vertex set Γ in which $\{\alpha, \beta\}$ is an edge if either $\alpha^{-1}\beta \in X$ or $\beta^{-1}\alpha \in X$.

complete multipartite graph, $K_{n_1, n_2, \dots, n_k}$: The *complete k-partite graph* $K_{n_1, n_2, \dots, n_k}$ is the graph $\overline{K}_{n_1} + \cdots + \overline{K}_{n_k}$. It is a a k-partite graph with color classes V_i of cardinalities $|V_i| = n_i$ for which every pair of vertices in two distinct color classes is an edge. The graph $K_{n_1, n_2, \dots, n_k}$ has order $\sum_{i=1}^{k} n_k$ and size $\prod_{1 \leq i < j \leq k} n_i n_j$.

double loop graph, DLG(n; a, b): The double loop graph DLG(n; a, b) (with a and b between 1 and $(n - 1)/2$), consists of n vertices with every vertex i connected by an edge to the vertices $i \pm a$ and $i \pm b$ (modulo n). The name comes from the following fact: If $\gcd(a, b, n) = 1$, then DLG(n; a, b) is Hamiltonian and, additionally, DLG(n; a, b) can be decomposed into two Hamiltonian cycles. These graphs are also known as circulant graphs.

intersection graph: For a family $F = \{S_1, \dots, S_n\}$ of subsets of a set S, the *intersection graph* of F is the graph with vertex set F in which $\{S_i, S_j\}$ is an edge if and only if $S_i \cap S_j \neq \emptyset$. Each graph G is an intersection graph of some family of subsets of a set of cardinality at most $\lfloor |G|^2/4 \rfloor$.

interval graph: An interval graph is an intersection graph of a family of intervals on the real line.

Small examples

The small graphs can be described in terms of the operations on page 190. Let $\mathcal{G}_{n,m}$ denote the family of isomorphism classes of graphs of order n and size m. Then

FIGURE 3.3.2
Examples of graphs with 6 vertices.

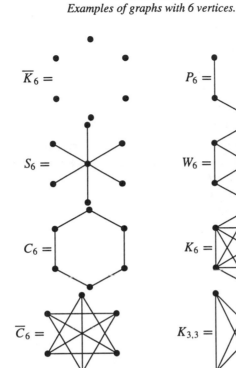
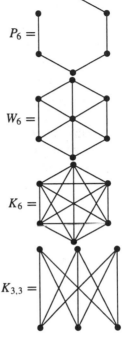

$\mathcal{G}_{1,0} = \{K_1\},$

$\mathcal{G}_{2,0} = \{\overline{K}_2\},$

$\mathcal{G}_{2,1} = \{K_2\},$

$\mathcal{G}_{3,0} = \{\overline{K}_3\},$

$\mathcal{G}_{3,1} = \{K_2 \cup K_1\},$

$\mathcal{G}_{3,2} = \{P_3\},$

$\mathcal{G}_{3,2} = \{K_3\},$

$\mathcal{G}_{4,0} = \{\overline{K}_4\},$

$\mathcal{G}_{4,1} = \{P_2 \cup \overline{K}_2\},$

$\mathcal{G}_{4,2} = \{P_3 \cup \overline{K}_1, P_2 \cup P_2\},$

$\mathcal{G}_{4,3} = \{P_4, K_3 \cup \overline{K}_1, K_{1,3}\},$

$\mathcal{G}_{4,4} = \{C_4, (K_2 \cup K_1) + K_1\},$

$\mathcal{G}_{4,5} = \{K_4 - e\},$ and

$\mathcal{G}_{4,6} = \{K_4\}.$

3.3.4 FUNDAMENTAL RESULTS

Walks and connectivity

1. Every x, y walk includes all the edges of some x, y path.

2. Some path in G has length $\delta(G)$.

3. Connectivity is a monotone graph property. If more edges are added to a

connected graph, the new graph is itself connected.

4. A graph is disconnected if, and only if, it is the sum of two graphs.

5. The sets S for which $G[S]$ is a component partition of the vertex set V.

6. Every vertex of a graph lies in at least one block.

7. For every graph G, $0 \le \kappa(G) \le |G| - 1$.

8. For all integers a, b, c with $0 < a \le b \le c$, a graph G exists with $\kappa(G) = a$, $\lambda(G) = b$, and $\delta(G) = c$.

9. For any graph G, $\kappa(G) \le \lambda(G) \le \delta(G)$

10. *Menger's theorem*: Suppose that G is a connected graph of order greater than k. Then G is k-connected if, and only if, it is impossible to disconnect G by removing fewer than k vertices, and G is k-edge connected if, and only if, it is impossible to disconnect G by removing fewer than k edges.

11. If G is a connected graph with a bridge, then $\lambda(G) = 1$. If G has order n and is r-regular with $r \ge n/2$, then $\lambda(G) = r$.

Trees

1. A graph is a tree if, and only if, it is acyclic and has size $|G| - 1$.

2. A graph is a tree if, and only if, it is connected and has size $|G| - 1$.

3. A graph is a tree if, and only if, each of its edges is a bridge.

4. A graph is a tree if, and only if, each vertex of degree greater than 1 is a cut vertex.

5. A graph is a tree if, and only if, each pair of its vertices is joined by exactly one path.

6. Every tree of order greater than 1 has at least two end vertices.

7. The center of a tree consists of one vertex or two adjacent vertices.

8. For each graph G, every tree with at most $\delta(G)$ edges is a subgraph of G.

9. Every connected graph has a spanning tree.

10. *Kirchhoff matrix-tree theorem*: Let G be a connected graph and let A be an adjacency matrix for G. Obtain a matrix M from $-A$ by replacing each term a_{ii} on the main diagonal with deg v_i. Then all cofactors of M have the same value, which is the number of spanning trees of G.

11. *Nash–Williams arboricity theorem*: For a graph G and for each $n \le |G|$, define $e_n(G) = \max\{e(H) : H \preceq G, \text{ and } |H| = n\}$. Then

$$\Upsilon(G) = \max_n \left\lceil \frac{e_n}{n-1} \right\rceil.$$

Circuits and cycles

1. *Euler's theorem*: A multigraph is Eulerian if and only if it is connected and even.

2. If G is Hamiltonian, and if G' is obtained from G by removing a nonempty set S of vertices, then the number of components of G' is at most $|S|$.

3. *Ore's theorem*: If G is a graph for which $\deg v + \deg w \geq |G|$ whenever v and w are nonadjacent vertices, then G is Hamiltonian.

4. *Dirac's theorem*: If G is a graph of order $|G| \geq 3$ and $\deg v \geq |G|/2$ for each vertex v, then G is Hamiltonian.

5. (Erdös–Chvátal) If $\alpha(G) \leq \kappa(G)$, then G is Hamiltonian.

6. Every 4-connected planar graph is Hamiltonian.

Cliques and independent sets

1. A set $S \subseteq V$ is a vertex cover if, and only if, $V \setminus S$ is an independent set.

2. *Turán's theorem*: If $|G| = n$ and $\omega(G) \leq k$, then $e(G) \leq e(T_{n,k})$.

3. *Ramsey's theorem*: For all positive integers k and l, there is a least integer $R(k, l)$ for which every graph of order at least $R(k, l)$ has either a clique of cardinality k or an independent set of cardinality l. For $k \geq 2$ and $l \geq 2$, $R(k, l) \leq R(k, l - 1) + R(k - 1, l)$. The following table gives the values of $R(k, l)$ for $k \leq 3$ and $l \leq 7$.

	$l = 1$	2	3	4	5	6	7
$k = 1$	1	1	1	1	1	1	1
2	1	2	3	4	5	6	7
3	1	3	6	9	14	18	23

Colorings and partitions

1. Every graph G is k-partite for some k; in particular, G is $|G|$-partite.

2. Every graph G has a bipartite subgraph H for which $e(H) \geq e(G)/2$.

3. $P_G(x) = P_{G-e}(x) - P_{G\backslash e}(x)$.

4. *Brooks's theorem*: If G is a connected graph that is neither a complete graph nor a cycle of odd length, then $\chi(G) \leq \Delta(G)$.

5. For all positive integers g and c, a graph G exists with $\chi(G) \geq c$ and $\mathrm{gir}(G) \geq g$.

6. *Nordhaus–Gaddum bounds*: For every graph G,

$$2\sqrt{|G|} \leq \chi(G) + \chi(\bar{G}) \leq |G| + 1, \quad \text{and}$$

$$|G| \leq \chi(G)\chi(\bar{G}) \leq \left(\frac{|G| + 1}{2} \right)^2.$$

7. *Szekeres–Wilf theorem*: For every graph $G = (V, E)$,

$$\chi(G) \leq 1 + \max_{S \subseteq V} \delta(G[S]).$$

8. (König) If G is bipartite, then $\chi'(G) = \Delta(G)$.

9. *Vizing's theorem*: For every graph G, $\Delta(G) \leq \chi'(G) \leq \Delta(G) + 1$.

10. The following table gives the chromatic numbers and chromatic polynomials of various graphs:

G	$\chi(G)$	$P_G(x)$
K_n	n	$x(x-1)\cdots(x-n+1)$
$\overline{K}_n$	1	x^n
T_n	2	$x(x-1)^{n-1}$
P_n	2	$x(x-1)^{n-1}$
C_4	2	$x(x-1)(x^2-3x+3)$

11. (Appel-Haken) *Four-color theorem*: $\chi(G) \leq 4$ for every planar graph G.

12. For each graph G of order $|G| = n$ and size $e(G) = m$ with exactly k components, the chromatic polynomial is of the form

$$P_G(x) = \sum_{i=0}^{n-k} (-1)^i a_i x^{n-i},$$

with $a_0 = 1$, $a_1 = m$ and every a_i positive.

13. Not every polynomial is a chromatic polynomial. For example $P(x) = x^4 - 4x^3 + 3x^2$ is not a chromatic polynomial.

14. Sometimes a class of chromatic polynomials can only come from a specific class of graphs. For example:

   (a) If $P_G(x) = x^n$, then $G = \overline{K}_n$.

   (b) If $P_G(x) = (x)_n$, then $G = K_n$.

   (c) If $P_G(x) = x(x-1)\cdots(x-r+2)(x-r+1)^2(x-r)^{n-r-1}$ for a graph of order $n \geq r+1$, then G can be obtained from a r-tree T of order n by deleting an edge contained in exactly $r-1$ triangles of T.

Distance

1. A metric space (X, d) is the metric space associated with a connected graph with vertex set X if, and only if, it satisfies two conditions: (i) $d(u, v)$ is a nonnegative integer for all $u, v \in X$, and (ii) whenever $d(u, v) \geq 2$, some element of X lies between u and v. The edges of the graph are the pairs $\{u, v\} \subseteq X$ for which $d(u, v) = 1$. (In an arbitrary metric space (X, d), a point $v \in X$ is said to lie *between* distinct points $u \in X$ and $w \in X$ if it satisfies the *triangle equality* $d(u, w) = d(u, v) + d(v, w)$.)

2. If $G = (V, E)$ is connected, then distance is always finite, and d is a metric on V. Note that $\deg(x) = |S(x, 1)|$.

3. *Moore bound*: For every connected graph G,

$$|G| \leq 1 + \Delta(G) \sum_{i=1}^{\text{diam}(G)} (\Delta(G) - 1)^i.$$

A graph for which the Moore bound holds exactly is called a *Moore graph* with parameters $(|G|, \Delta(G), \text{diam}(G))$. Every Moore graph is regular. If G is a Moore graph with parameters (n, r, d), then $(n, r, d) = (n, n-1, 1)$ (in which case G is complete) or $(n, r, d) = (2m+1, 2, m)$ (in which case G is a $(2m+1)$-cycle), $(n, r, d) \in \{(10, 3, 2), (50, 7, 2), (3250, 57, 2)\}$.

Drawings, embeddings, planarity, and thickness

1. Every graph has an embedding in $\mathbb{R}^3$ for which the arcs representing edges are all straight line segments. Such an embedding can be constructed by using distinct points on the curve $\{(t, t^2, t^3) : 0 \le t \le 1$ as representatives for the vertices.

2. For $n \ge 2$,
$$\gamma(Q_n) = (n-4)2^{n-3} + 1, \quad \text{and}$$
$$\tilde{\gamma}(Q_n) = (n-4)2^{n-2} + 2.$$

3. For $r, s \ge 2$,
$$\gamma(K_{r,s}) = \left\lceil \frac{(r-2)(s-2)}{4} \right\rceil, \quad \text{and}$$
$$\tilde{\gamma}(K_{r,s}) = \left\lceil \frac{(r-2)(s-2)}{2} \right\rceil.$$

4. For $n \ge 3$,
$$\gamma(K_n) = \left\lceil \frac{(n-3)(n-4)}{12} \right\rceil, \quad \text{and}$$
$$\tilde{\gamma}(K_n) = \left\lceil \frac{(n-3)(n-4)}{6} \right\rceil.$$

5. *Heawood map coloring theorem*: The greatest chromatic number among graphs of genus n is
$$\max\{\chi(G) \mid \gamma(G) = n\} = \left\lceil \frac{7 + \sqrt{1 + 48n}}{2} \right\rceil.$$

6. *Kuratowski's theorem*: A graph is planar if and only if it has no subgraph homeomorphic to K_5 or $K_{3,3}$.

7. A graph is planar if and only if it does not have a subgraph contractible to K_5 or $K_{3,3}$.

8. The graph K_n is nonplanar if and only if $n \ge 5$.

9. Every planar graph can be embedded in the plane so that every edge is a straight line segment; this is a Fary embedding.

10. The four-color theorem states that any planar graph is four colorable.

11. For every graph G of order $|G| \ge 3$, $\theta(G) \ge \left\lceil \frac{e(G)}{3|G| - 6} \right\rceil$.

12. The complete graphs K_9 and K_{10} have thickness 3; for $n \notin \{9, 10\}$,

$$\theta(K_n) = \left\lfloor \frac{n + 7}{6} \right\rfloor.$$

13. The n-cube has thickness $\theta(Q_n) = \lfloor n/4 \rfloor + 1$.

14. For every planar graph G, $\nu(G) = \overline{\nu}(G)$. That equality does not hold for all graphs: $\nu(K_8) = 18$, and $\overline{\nu}(K_8) = 19$.

Vertex degrees

1. *Handshaking lemma*: For every graph G, $\sum_{v \in V} \deg v = 2e(G)$.

2. Every 2-switch preserves the degree sequence.

3. If G and H have the same degree sequence, then H can be obtained from G via a sequence of 2-switches.

4. (Havel–Hakimi) A sequence $\{d_1, d_2, \ldots, d_n\}$ of nonnegative integers with $d_1 \geq d_2 \geq \cdots \geq d_n$ (with $n \geq 2$ and $d_1 \geq 1$) is a degree sequence if and only if the sequence $\{d_2 - 1, d_3 - 1, \ldots, d_{d_1+1} - 1, d_{d_1+2}, \ldots, d_n\}$ is a degree sequence.

Algebraic methods

1. The bipartite graphs $K_{n,n}$ are circulant graphs.

2. For a graph G with exactly k connected components, the cycle space has dimension $e(G) - |G| + k$, and the cut space has dimension $|G| - k$.

3. In the kth power $A^k = (a_{ij}^k)$ of the adjacency matrix, each entry a_{ij}^k is the number of v_i, v_j walks of length k.

4. The incidence matrix of a graph G is totally unimodular if, and only if, G is bipartite.

5. Every odd graph is vertex-transitive.

6. The smallest graph that is vertex symmetric, but is not edge symmetric, is the prism $K_3 \times K_2$. The smallest graph that is edge symmetric, but is not vertex symmetric, is $S_2 = P_3 = K_{1,2}$.

7. The spectrum of a disconnected graph is the union of the spectra of its components.

8. The sum of the eigenvalues in the spectrum of a graph is zero.

9. The number of distinct eigenvalues in the spectrum of a graph is greater than the diameter of the graph.

10. The largest eigenvalue in the spectrum of a graph G is, at most, $\Delta(G)$, with equality if, and only if, G is regular.

11. (Wilf) If G is a connected graph and its largest eigenvalue is λ, then $\chi(G) \leq 1 + \lambda$. Moreover, equality holds if, and only if, G is a complete graph or a cycle of odd length.

12. (Hoffman) If G is a connected graph of order n with spectrum $\lambda_1 \geq \cdots \geq \lambda_n$, then $\chi(G) \geq 1 - \lambda_1/\lambda_n$.

13. *Integrality condition*: If G is a strongly regular graph with parameters (k, λ, μ), then the quantities

$$\frac{1}{2}\left(|G| - 1 \pm \frac{(|G| - 1)(\mu - \lambda) - 2k}{\sqrt{(\mu - \lambda)^2 + 4(k - \mu)}}\right)$$

are nonnegative integers.

14. The following table gives the automorphism groups of various graphs:

G	$\mathrm{Aut}(G)$
C_n	D_n
$\overline{K}_n$	S_n
K_n	S_n
$K_{1,n}$	$E_1 + S_n$
P_n	C_n

15. A graph and its complement have the same group; $\mathrm{Aut}(G) = \mathrm{Aut}(\overline{G})$.

16. *Frucht's theorem*: Every finite group is the automorphism group of some graph.

17. If G and G' are edge isomorphic, then G and G' are not required to be isomorphic. For example, the graphs C_3 and S_3 are edge isomorphic, but not isomorphic.

18. If the graph G has order n, then the order of its automorphism group $|\mathrm{Aut}(G)|$ is a divisor of $n!$. The order of the automorphism group equals $n!$ if and only if $G \simeq K_n$ or $G \simeq \overline{K}_n$.

Matchings

1. A matching M is a maximum matching if, and only if, there is no M-augmenting path.

2. *Hall's theorem*: A bipartite graph G with bipartition (B_1, B_2) has a matching that saturates every vertex in B_1 if, and only if, $|S(A, 1)| \geq |A|$ for every $A \subseteq B_1$.

3. *König's theorem*: In a bipartite graph, the cardinality of a maximum matching equals the cardinality of a minimum vertex cover.

Enumeration

1. The number of labeled graphs of order n is $2^{\binom{n}{2}}$.

2. The number of labeled graphs of order n and size m is $\binom{\binom{n}{2}}{m}$.

3. The number of different ways in which a graph G of order n can be labeled is $n!/|\mathrm{Aut}(G)|$.

4. *Cayley's formula*: The number of labeled trees of order n is n^{n-2}.

5. The number of labeled trees of order n with exactly t end vertices is $\frac{n!}{t!}\left\{{n-2 \atop n-t}\right\}$ for $2 \leq t \leq n - 1$.

Order	Graphs	Digraphs	Trees (t_n)	Rooted trees (T_n)
1	1	1	1	1
2	2	3	1	1
3	4	16	1	2
4	11	218	2	4
5	34	9608	3	9
6	156	1540944	6	20
7	1044	882033440	11	48
8	12346	1793359192848	23	115
9	274668		47	286
10	12005168		106	719

Define the generating functions $T(x) = \sum_{n=0}^{\infty} T_n x^n$ and $t(x) = \sum_{n=0}^{\infty} t_n x^n$. Then $T(x) = x \exp\left(\sum_{r=1}^{\infty} \frac{1}{r} T(x^r)\right)$, and $t(x) = T(x) - \frac{1}{2}\left[T^2(x) - T\left(x^2\right)\right]$.

The following table lists the number of isomorphism classes of graphs of order n and size m.

m	$n = 1$	2	3	4	5	6	7	8	9
0	1	1	1	1	1	1	1	1	1
1		1	1	1	1	1	1	1	1
2			1	2	2	2	2	2	1
3			1	3	4	5	5	5	5
4				2	6	9	10	11	11
5				1	6	15	21	24	25
6				1	6	21	41	56	63
7					4	24	65	115	148
8					2	24	97	221	345
9					1	21	131	402	771
10					1	15	148	663	1637
11						9	148	980	3252
12						5	131	1312	5995
13						2	97	1557	10120
14						1	65	1646	15615
15						1	41	1557	21933
16							21	1312	27987
17							10	980	32403
18							5	663	34040

The following table gives the number of labeled graphs of order n having various properties:

n	1	2	3	4	5	6	7	8
All	1	2	8	64	1 024	2^{15}	2^{21}	2^{28}
Connected	1	1	4	38	728	26 704	1 866 256	251 548 592
Even	1	1	2	8	64	1 024	2^{15}	2^{21}
Trees	1	1	3	16	125	1 296	16 807	262 144

The following table gives the numbers of isomorphism classes of graphs of order n exhibiting various properties:

n	1	2	3	4	5	6	7	8
All	1	2	4	11	34	156	1 044	12 346
Connected	1	1	2	6	21	112	853	11 117
Even	1	1	2	3	7	16	54	243
Eulerian	1	0	1	1	4	8	37	184
Blocks	0	1	1	3	10	56	468	7 123
Trees	1	1	1	2	3	6	11	23
Rooted trees	1	1	2	4	9	20	48	115

3.3.5 TREE DIAGRAMS

Let $T_{n,m}$ denote the mth isomorphism class of trees of order n. Figure 3.3.3 depicts trees of order at most 7. Figure 3.3.4 depicts trees of order 8.

3.4 PARTIALLY ORDERED SETS

Consider a set S and a relation on it. Given any two elements x and y in S, we can determine whether or not x is "related" to y; if it is, "$x \preceq y$". The relation "$\preceq$" will be a *partial order* on S if it satisfies the following three conditions:

reflexive	$s \preceq s$ for every $s \in S$,
antisymmetric	$s \preceq t$ and $t \preceq s$ imply $s = t$, and
transitive	$s \preceq t$ and $t \preceq u$ imply $s \preceq u$.

If $\preceq$ is a partial order on S, then the pair $(S, \preceq)$ is called a *partially ordered set* or a *poset*. Given the partial order $\preceq$ on the set S, define the relation $\prec$ by

$$x \prec y \qquad \text{if and only if} \qquad x \preceq y \text{ and } x \neq y.$$

We say that the element t *covers* the element s if $s \prec t$ and there is no element u with $s \prec u \prec t$. A Hasse diagram of the poset $(S, \preceq)$ is a figure consisting of the elements of S with a line segment directed generally upward from s to t whenever t covers s.

FIGURE 3.3.3

Trees with 7 or fewer vertices.

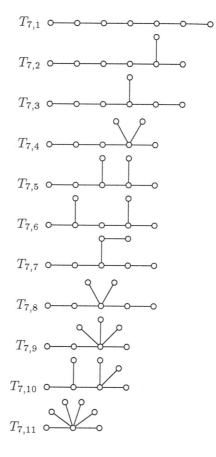

FIGURE 3.3.4

Trees with 8 vertices.

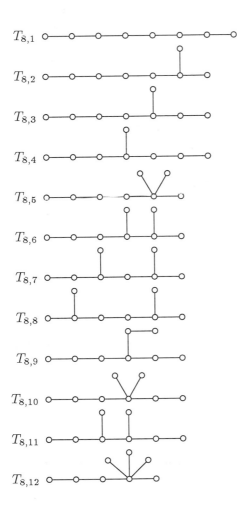

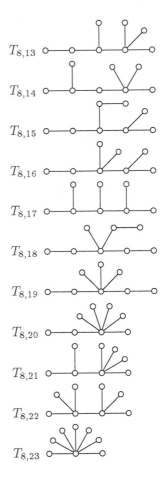

FIGURE 3.4.5

Left: Hasse diagram for integers up to 12 with $x \preceq y$ meaning "the number x divides the number y." Right: Hasse diagram for $\{a, b, c\}$ with $x \preceq y$ meaning "the set x is a subset of the set y."

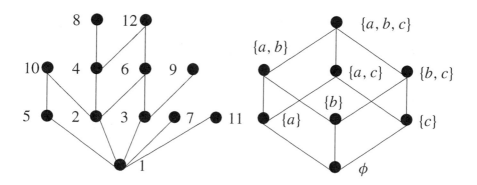

Two elements x and y in a poset $(S, \preceq)$ are said to be *comparable* if either $x \preceq y$ or $y \preceq x$. If every pair of elements in a poset is comparable, then $(S, \preceq)$ is a *chain*. An *antichain* is a poset in which no two elements are comparable (i.e., it is not true that $x \preceq y$ or $y \preceq x$ for all x and y in the antichain). A maximal chain is a chain that is not properly contained in another chain (and similarly for a maximal antichain). For example:

1. Let S be the set of natural numbers up to 12 and let "$x \preceq y$" mean "the number x divides the number y." Then $(S, \preceq)$ is a poset with the Hasse diagram shown in Figure 3.4.5 (left). Observe that the elements 2 and 4 are comparable, but elements 2 and 5 are not comparable.

2. Let S be the set of all subsets of the set $\{a, b, c\}$ and let "$x \preceq y$" mean "the set x is contained in the set y." Then $(S, \preceq)$ is a poset with the Hasse diagram shown in Figure 3.4.5 (right).

3.5   COMBINATORIAL DESIGN THEORY

Combinatorial design theory is the study of families of subsets with various prescribed regularity properties. An *incidence structure* is an ordered pair $(X, \mathcal{B})$:

- $X = x_1, \ldots, x_v$ is a set of *points*.
- $\mathcal{B} = B_1, \ldots, B_b$ is a set of *blocks* or *lines*; each $B_j \subseteq X$.
- The *replication number* r_i of x_i is the number of blocks that contain x_i.
- The size of B_j is k_j.

Counting the number of pairs (x, B) with $x \in B$ yields $\sum_{i=1}^{v} r_i = \sum_{j=1}^{b} k_j$. The *incidence matrix* of an incidence structure is the $v \times b$ matrix $A = (a_{ij})$ with $a_{ij} = 1$ if $x_i \in B_j$ and 0 otherwise.

3.5.1   *t*-DESIGNS

The incidence structure $(X, \mathcal{B})$ is called a t-(v, k, λ) *design* if

1. For all j, $k_j = k$ and $1 < k < v$, and
2. Any subset of t points lies on exactly λ blocks.

A 1-design is equivalent to a $v \times b$ 0-1 matrix with constant row and column sums. Every t-(v, k, λ) design is also a ℓ-(v, k, λ_ℓ) design ($1 \le \ell \le t$), where

$$\lambda_\ell = \lambda \binom{v - \ell}{t - \ell} \Big/ \binom{k - \ell}{t - \ell}. \tag{3.5.1}$$

A necessary condition for the existence of a t-(v, k, λ) design is that λ_ℓ must be an integer for all ℓ, $1 \le \ell \le t$. Another necessary condition is the generalized Fisher's inequality when $t = 2s$: $b \ge \binom{v}{s}$.

Related designs

A t-(v, k, λ) design also implies the existence of the following designs:

Complementary design
   Let $\mathcal{B}_C = \{X \backslash B \mid B \in \mathcal{B}\}$. Then the incidence structure $(X, \mathcal{B}_C)$ is a t-$(v, v - k, \lambda \binom{v-t}{k} / \binom{v-t}{k-t})$ design (provided $v \ge k + t$).

Derived design
   Fix $x \in X$ and let $\mathcal{B}_D = \{B \backslash \{x\} \mid B \in \mathcal{B} \text{ with } x \in B\}$. Then the incidence structure $(X \backslash \{x\}, \mathcal{B}_D)$ is a $(t - 1)$-$(v - 1, k - 1, \lambda)$ design.

Residual design
   Fix $x \in X$ and let $\mathcal{B}_R = \{B \mid B \in \mathcal{B} \text{ with } x \notin B\}$. Then the incidence structure $(X \backslash \{x\}, \mathcal{B}_R)$ is a $(t - 1)$-$(v - 1, k - 1, \lambda \binom{v-t}{k-t+1} / \binom{v-t}{k-t})$ design.

The Mathieu 5-design

The following are the 132 blocks of a 5-$(12,6,1)$ design. The blocks are the supports of the weight-6 codewords in the ternary Golay code (page 220). Similarly, the supports of the 759 weight-8 codewords in the binary Golay code form the blocks of a 5-$(24,8,1)$ design.

0	1	2	3	4	11		0	2	5	7	8	10		1	3	4	7	8	11
0	1	2	3	5	10		0	2	5	7	9	11		1	3	5	6	7	10
0	1	2	3	6	8		0	2	6	7	8	9		1	3	5	6	8	11
0	1	2	3	7	9		0	2	6	8	10	11		1	3	5	8	9	10

0	1	2	4	5	9	0	3	4	5	6	10	1	3	6	7	8	9
0	1	2	4	6	10	0	3	4	5	9	11	1	3	7	9	10	11
0	1	2	4	7	8	0	3	4	6	8	11	1	4	5	6	7	8
0	1	2	5	6	7	0	3	4	7	8	9	1	4	5	6	9	10
0	1	2	5	8	11	0	3	4	7	10	11	1	4	5	8	9	11
0	1	2	6	9	11	0	3	5	6	7	8	1	4	6	7	10	11
0	1	2	7	10	11	0	3	5	7	9	10	1	4	7	8	9	10
0	1	2	8	9	10	0	3	5	8	10	11	1	5	6	7	9	11
0	1	3	4	5	8	0	3	6	7	9	11	1	5	7	8	10	11
0	1	3	4	6	7	0	3	6	8	9	10	1	6	8	9	10	11
0	1	3	4	9	10	0	4	5	6	7	9	2	3	4	5	8	11
0	1	3	5	6	9	0	4	5	7	8	11	2	3	4	5	9	10
0	1	3	5	7	11	0	4	5	8	9	10	2	3	4	6	7	8
0	1	3	6	10	11	0	4	6	7	8	10	2	3	4	6	10	11
0	1	3	7	8	10	0	4	6	9	10	11	2	3	4	7	9	11
0	1	3	8	9	11	0	5	6	7	10	11	2	3	5	6	7	9
0	1	4	5	6	11	0	5	6	8	9	11	2	3	5	6	8	10
0	1	4	5	7	10	0	7	8	9	10	11	2	3	5	7	10	11
0	1	4	6	8	9	1	2	3	4	5	6	2	3	6	8	9	11
0	1	4	7	9	11	1	2	3	4	7	10	2	3	7	8	9	10
0	1	4	8	10	11	1	2	3	4	8	9	2	4	5	6	7	10
0	1	5	6	8	10	1	2	3	5	7	8	2	4	5	6	9	11
0	1	5	7	8	9	1	2	3	5	9	11	2	4	5	7	8	9
0	1	5	9	10	11	1	2	3	6	7	11	2	4	6	8	9	10
0	1	6	7	8	11	1	2	3	6	9	10	2	4	7	8	10	11
0	1	6	7	9	10	1	2	3	8	10	11	2	5	6	7	8	11
0	2	3	4	5	7	1	2	4	5	7	11	2	5	8	9	10	11
0	2	3	4	6	9	1	2	4	5	8	10	2	6	7	9	10	11
0	2	3	4	8	10	1	2	4	6	7	9	3	4	5	6	7	11
0	2	3	5	6	11	1	2	4	6	8	11	3	4	5	6	8	9
0	2	3	5	8	9	1	2	4	9	10	11	3	4	5	7	8	10
0	2	3	6	7	10	1	2	5	6	8	9	3	4	6	7	9	10
0	2	3	7	8	11	1	2	5	6	10	11	3	4	8	9	10	11
0	2	3	9	10	11	1	2	5	7	9	10	3	5	6	9	10	11
0	2	4	5	6	8	1	2	6	7	8	10	3	5	7	8	9	11
0	2	4	5	10	11	1	2	7	8	9	11	3	6	7	8	10	11
0	2	4	6	7	11	1	3	4	5	7	9	4	5	6	8	10	11
0	2	4	7	9	10	1	3	4	5	10	11	4	5	7	9	10	11
0	2	4	8	9	11	1	3	4	6	8	10	4	6	7	8	9	11
0	2	5	6	9	10	1	3	4	6	9	11	5	6	7	8	9	10

3.5.2   BALANCED INCOMPLETE BLOCK DESIGNS (BIBDS)

Balanced incomplete block designs (BIBDs) are *t*-designs with $t = 2$, so that every pair of points is on the same number of blocks. The relevant parameters are $v, b, r, k,$ and λ with

$$vr = bk \qquad \text{and} \qquad v(v - 1)\lambda = bk(k - 1). \qquad (3.5.2)$$

If A is the $v \times b$ incidence matrix, then $AA^{\mathrm{T}} = (r - \lambda)I_v + \lambda J_v$, where I_n is the $n \times n$ identity matrix and J_n is the $n \times n$ matrix of all ones.

Symmetric designs

Fisher's inequality states that $b \geq v$. If $b = v$ (equivalently, $r = k$), then the BIBD is called a *symmetric design*, denoted as a (v, k, λ)-design. The incidence matrix for a symmetric design satisfies

$$J_v A = k J_v = A J_v \quad \text{and} \quad A^{\mathrm{T}} A = (k - \lambda)I_v + \lambda J_v, \tag{3.5.3}$$

that is, any two blocks intersect in λ points. The dualness of symmetric designs can be summarized by the following:

v points	$\leftrightarrow$	v blocks,
k blocks on a point	$\leftrightarrow$	k points in a block, and
Any two points on λ blocks	$\leftrightarrow$	Any two blocks share λ points.

Some necessary conditions for symmetric designs are

1. If v is even, then $k - \lambda$ is a square integer.
2. *Bruck–Ryser–Chowla theorem*: If v is odd, then the following equation has integer solutions (not all zero):

$$x^2 = (k - \lambda)y^2 + (-1)^{(v-1)/2}\lambda z^2.$$

Existence table for BIBDs

Some of the most fruitful construction methods for BIBD are dealt with in separate sections, difference sets (page 208), finite geometry (page 209), Steiner triple systems (page 211), and Hadamard matrices (page 211). The table below gives all parameters for which BIBDs exists with $k \leq v/2$ and $b \leq 30$.

v	b	r	k	λ	v	b	r	k	λ	v	b	r	k	λ
6	10	5	3	2	10	18	9	5	4	15	30	14	7	6
6	20	10	3	4	10	30	9	3	2	16	16	6	6	2
6	30	15	3	6	10	30	12	4	4	16	20	5	4	1
7	7	3	3	1	11	11	5	5	2	16	24	9	6	3
7	14	6	3	2	11	22	10	5	4	16	30	15	8	7
7	21	9	3	3	12	22	11	6	5	19	19	9	9	4
7	28	12	3	4	13	13	4	4	1	21	21	5	5	1
8	14	7	4	3	13	26	6	3	1	21	30	10	7	3
8	28	14	4	6	13	26	8	4	2	23	23	11	11	5
9	12	4	3	1	13	26	12	6	5	25	25	9	9	3
9	18	8	4	3	14	26	13	7	6	25	30	6	5	1
9	24	8	3	2	15	15	7	7	3	27	27	13	13	6
10	15	6	4	2										

3.5.3   DIFFERENCE SETS

Let G be a finite group of order v (see page 139). A subset D of size k is a (v, k, λ)-*difference set* in G if every nonidentity element of G can be written λ times as a "difference" $d_1 d_2^{-1}$ with d_1 and d_2 in D. If G is the cyclic group $\mathcal{Z}_v$, then the difference set is a *cyclic difference set*. The *order* of a difference set is $n = k - \lambda$. For example, $\{1, 2, 4\}$ is a $(7, 3, 1)$ cyclic difference set of order 2.

A (v, k, λ)-difference set implies the existence of a (v, k, λ)-design. The points are the elements of G and the blocks are the translates of D: all sets $Dg = \{dg : d \in D\}$ for $g \in G$. Note that each translate Dg is itself a difference set. Here are the 7 blocks for a $(7, 3, 1)$-design based on $D = \{1, 2, 4\}$:

$$1\,2\,4 \quad 2\,3\,5 \quad 3\,4\,6 \quad 4\,5\,0 \quad 5\,6\,1 \quad 6\,0\,2 \quad 0\,1\,3$$

Example: A $(16, 6, 2)$-difference set in $G = \mathcal{Z}_2 \oplus \mathcal{Z}_2 \oplus \mathcal{Z}_2 \oplus \mathcal{Z}_2$ is

$$0000 \quad 0001 \quad 0010 \quad 0100 \quad 1000 \quad 1111$$

Example: A $(21, 5, 1)$-difference set in $G = \langle a, b : a^3 = b^7 = 1, a^{-1}ba = a^4 \rangle$ is $\{a, a^2, b, b^2, b^4\}$.

Some families of cyclic difference sets

Paley: Let v be a prime congruent to 3 modulo 4. Then the nonzero squares in $\mathcal{Z}_v$ form a $(v, (v-1)/2, (v-3)/4)$-difference set. Example: $(v, k, \lambda) = (11, 5, 2)$.

Stanton–Sprott: Let $v = p(p+2)$, where p and $p+2$ are both primes. Then there is a $(v, (v-1)/2, (v-3)/4)$-difference set. Example: $(v, k, \lambda) = (35, 17, 8)$.

Biquadratic Residues (I): If $v = 4a^2 + 1$ is a prime with a odd, then the nonzero fourth powers modulo v form a $(v, (v-1)/4, (v-5)/16)$-difference set. Example: $(v, k, \lambda) = (37, 9, 2)$.

Biquadratic Residues (II): If $v = 4a^2 + 9$ is a prime with a odd, then zero and the fourth powers modulo v form a $(v, (v+3)/4, (v+3)/16)$-difference set. Example: $(v, k, \lambda) = (13, 4, 1)$.

Singer: If q is a prime power, then there exists a $((q^m - 1)/(q-1), (q^{m-1} - 1)/(q-1), (q^{m-2} - 1)/(q-1))$-difference set for all $m \geq 3$.

Existence table of cyclic difference sets

This table gives all cyclic difference sets for $k \leq v/2$ and $v \leq 50$ up to equivalence by translation and multiplication by a number relatively prime to v.

v	k	λ	n	Difference set
7	3	1	2	1 2 4
11	5	2	3	1 3 4 5 9
13	4	1	3	0 1 3 9
15	7	3	4	0 1 2 4 5 8 10
19	9	4	5	1 4 5 6 7 9 11 16 17
21	5	1	4	3 6 7 12 14
23	11	5	6	1 2 3 4 6 8 9 12 13 16 18
31	6	1	5	1 5 11 24 25 27
31	15	7	8	1 2 3 4 6 8 12 15 16 17 23 24 27 29 30
				1 2 4 5 7 8 9 10 14 16 18 19 20 25 28
35	17	8	9	0 1 3 4 7 9 11 12 13 14 16 17 21 27 28 29 33
37	9	2	7	1 7 9 10 12 16 26 33 34
40	13	4	9	1 2 3 5 6 9 14 15 18 20 25 27 35
43	21	10	11	1 2 3 4 5 8 11 12 16 19 20 21 22 27 32 33 35 37 39 41 42
				1 4 6 9 10 11 13 14 15 16 17 21 23 24 25 31 35 36 38 40 41
47	23	11	12	1 2 3 4 6 7 8 9 12 14 16 17 18 21 24 25 27 28 32 34 36 37 42

3.5.4 FINITE GEOMETRY

Affine planes

A finite *affine plane* is a finite set of points that satisfy the axioms:

- Any two points are on exactly one line.

- *(Parallel postulate)* Given a point P and a line L not containing P, there is exactly one line through P that does not intersect L.

- There are four points, no three of which are collinear.

These axioms are sufficient to show that a finite affine plane is a BIBD (see page 206) with

$$v = n^2 \qquad b = n^2 + n \qquad r = n + 1 \qquad k = n \qquad \lambda = 1$$

(n is the *order* of the plane). The lines of an affine plane can be divided into $n + 1$ parallel classes each containing n lines. A sufficient condition for affine planes to exist is for n to be a prime power.

Below are two views of the affine plane of order 2 showing the parallel classes.

Below is the affine plane of order 3 showing the parallel classes.

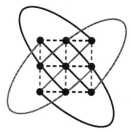

Projective planes

A finite *projective plane* is a finite set of points that satisfy the axioms:

1. Any two points are on exactly one line.
2. Any two lines intersect in exactly one point.
3. There are four points, no three of which are collinear.

These axioms are sufficient to show that a finite affine plane is a symmetric design (see page 207) with

$$v = n^2 + n + 1 \qquad k = n + 1 \qquad \lambda = 1$$

(*n* is the *order* of the plane). A sufficient condition for affine planes to exist is for *n* to be a prime power.

A projective plane of order *n* can be constructed from an affine plane of order *n* by adding a *line at infinity*. A line of *n* + 1 new points is added to the affine plane. For each parallel class, one distinct new point is added to each line. The construction works in reverse: removing any one line from a projective plane of order *n* and its points leaves an affine plane of order *n*. Below is the projective plane of order 2. The center circle functions as a line at infinity; removing it produces the affine plane of order 2.

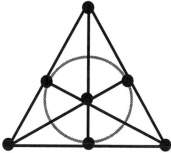

3.5.5   STEINER TRIPLE SYSTEMS

A *Steiner triple system* (STS) is a 2-(v,3,1) design. In particular, STSs are BIBDs (see page 206). STSs exist if, and only if, $v \equiv 1$ or 3 (mod 6). The number of blocks in an STS is $b = v(v - 1)/6$.

Some families of Steiner triple systems

$v = 2^m - 1$: Take as points all nonzero vectors over $\mathbb{Z}_2$ of length m. A block consists of any set of three distinct vectors $\{x, y, z\}$ such that $x + y + z = 0$.

$v = 3^m$: Take as points all vectors over $\mathbb{Z}_3$ of length m. A block consists of any set of three distinct vectors $\{x, y, z\}$ such that $x + y + z = 0$.

Resolvable Steiner triple systems

An STS is *resolvable* if the blocks can be divided into parallel classes such that each point occurs in exactly one block per class. A resolvable STS exists if and only if $v \equiv 3 \pmod 6$. For example, the affine plane of order 3 is a resolvable STS with $v = 9$ (see page 209).

A resolvable STS with $v = 15$ ($b = 35$) is known as the Kirkman schoolgirl problem and dates from 1850. Here is an example. Each column of 5 triples is a parallel class:

```
a b i    a c j    a d k    a e l    a f m    a g n    a h o
c d f    d e g    e f h    f g b    g h c    h b d    b c e
g j o    h k i    b l j    c m k    d n l    e o m    f i n
e k n    f l o    g m i    h n j    b o k    c i l    d j m
h l m    b m n    c n o    d o i    e i j    f j k    g k l.
```

3.5.6   HADAMARD MATRICES

A *Hadamard matrix* of order n is an $n \times n$ matrix H with entries ± 1 such that $H H^{\mathsf{T}} = nI_n$. In order for a Hadamard matrix to exist, n must be 1, 2, or a multiple of 4. It is conjectured that these values are also sufficient. If H_1 and H_2 are Hadamard matrices, then so is the Kronecker product $H_1 \otimes H_2$.

Some Hadamard matrices

We use "$-$" to denote -1.

$$
n = 2 \qquad n = 4 \qquad\qquad\qquad n = 8
$$

$$
\begin{bmatrix} 1 & 1 \\ 1 & - \end{bmatrix}
\quad
\begin{bmatrix} 1 & 1 & 1 & 1 \\ 1 & - & 1 & - \\ 1 & 1 & - & - \\ 1 & - & - & 1 \end{bmatrix}
\quad
\begin{bmatrix}
1 & 1 & 1 & 1 & 1 & 1 & 1 & 1 \\
1 & - & 1 & - & 1 & - & 1 & - \\
1 & 1 & - & - & 1 & 1 & - & - \\
1 & - & - & 1 & 1 & - & - & 1 \\
1 & 1 & 1 & 1 & - & - & - & - \\
1 & - & 1 & - & - & 1 & - & 1 \\
1 & 1 & - & - & - & - & 1 & 1 \\
1 & - & - & 1 & - & 1 & 1 & -
\end{bmatrix}
$$

$$n = 12$$

$$\begin{bmatrix}
1 & 1 & 1 & 1 & - & - & 1 & - & - & 1 & - & - \\
1 & 1 & 1 & - & 1 & - & - & 1 & - & - & 1 & - \\
1 & 1 & 1 & - & - & 1 & - & - & 1 & - & - & 1 \\
- & 1 & 1 & 1 & 1 & 1 & - & 1 & 1 & 1 & - & - \\
1 & - & 1 & 1 & 1 & 1 & 1 & - & 1 & - & 1 & - \\
1 & 1 & - & 1 & 1 & 1 & 1 & 1 & - & - & - & 1 \\
- & 1 & 1 & 1 & - & - & 1 & 1 & 1 & - & 1 & 1 \\
1 & - & 1 & - & 1 & - & 1 & 1 & 1 & 1 & - & 1 \\
1 & 1 & - & - & - & 1 & 1 & 1 & 1 & 1 & 1 & - \\
- & 1 & 1 & - & 1 & 1 & 1 & - & - & 1 & 1 & 1 \\
1 & - & 1 & 1 & - & 1 & - & 1 & - & 1 & 1 & 1 \\
1 & 1 & - & 1 & 1 & - & - & - & - & 1 & 1 & 1
\end{bmatrix}$$

$$n = 16$$

$$\begin{bmatrix}
1 & 1 & 1 & 1 & 1 & 1 & 1 & 1 & 1 & 1 & 1 & 1 & 1 & 1 & 1 & 1 \\
1 & - & 1 & - & 1 & - & 1 & - & 1 & - & 1 & - & 1 & - & 1 & - \\
1 & 1 & - & - & 1 & 1 & - & - & 1 & 1 & - & - & 1 & 1 & - & - \\
1 & - & - & 1 & 1 & - & - & 1 & 1 & - & - & 1 & 1 & - & - & 1 \\
1 & 1 & 1 & 1 & - & - & - & - & 1 & 1 & 1 & 1 & - & - & - & - \\
1 & - & 1 & - & - & 1 & - & 1 & 1 & - & 1 & - & - & 1 & - & 1 \\
1 & 1 & - & - & - & - & 1 & 1 & 1 & 1 & - & - & - & - & 1 & 1 \\
1 & - & - & 1 & - & 1 & 1 & - & 1 & - & - & 1 & - & 1 & 1 & - \\
1 & 1 & 1 & 1 & 1 & 1 & 1 & 1 & - & - & - & - & - & - & - & - \\
1 & - & 1 & - & 1 & - & 1 & - & - & 1 & - & 1 & - & 1 & - & 1 \\
1 & 1 & - & - & 1 & 1 & - & - & - & - & 1 & 1 & - & - & 1 & 1 \\
1 & - & - & 1 & 1 & - & - & 1 & - & 1 & 1 & - & - & 1 & 1 & - \\
1 & 1 & 1 & 1 & - & - & - & - & - & - & - & - & 1 & 1 & 1 & 1 \\
1 & - & 1 & - & - & 1 & - & 1 & - & 1 & - & 1 & 1 & - & 1 & - \\
1 & 1 & - & - & - & - & 1 & 1 & - & - & 1 & 1 & 1 & 1 & - & - \\
1 & - & - & 1 & - & 1 & 1 & - & - & 1 & 1 & - & 1 & - & - & 1
\end{bmatrix}$$

Designs and Hadamard matrices

Without loss of generality, a Hadamard matrix can be assumed to have a first row and column consisting of all $+1$s.

BIBDs: Delete the first row and column. The points of the design are the remaining column indices. Each row produces a block of the design, namely those indices where the entry is $+1$. The resulting design is an $(n-1, (n-1)/2, (n-5)/4)$ symmetric design (see page 211).

3-Designs: The points are the indices of the columns. Each row, except the first row, yields two blocks, one block for those indices where the entries are $+1$ and one block for those indices where the entries are -1. The resulting design is a 3-$(n, n/2, (n-5)/4)$ design.

3.5.7 LATIN SQUARES

A *Latin square* of size n is an $n \times n$ array $S = [s_{ij}]$ of n symbols such that every symbol appears exactly once in each row and column. Two Latin squares S and T are *orthogonal* if every pair of symbols occurs exactly once as a pair (s_{ij}, t_{ij}). Let $M(n)$ be the maximum size of a set of mutually orthogonal Latin squares (MOLS).

- $M(n) \le n - 1$.
- $M(n) = n - 1$ if n is a prime power.
- $M(n_1 n_2) \ge \min(M(n_1), M(n_2))$.
- $M(6) = 1$ (i.e., there are no two MOLS of size 6).
- $M(n) \ge 2$ for all $n \ge 3$ except $n = 6$.

The existence of $n - 1$ MOLS of size n is equivalent to the existence of an affine plane of order n (see page 209).

Examples of mutually orthogonal Latin squares

These are complete sets of MOLS for $n = 3$, 4, and 5.

$n = 3$

0	1	2
1	2	0
2	0	1

0	1	2
2	0	1
1	2	0

$n = 4$

0	1	2	3
1	0	3	2
2	3	0	1
3	2	1	0

0	1	2	3
2	3	0	1
3	2	1	0
1	0	3	2

0	1	2	3
3	2	1	0
1	0	3	2
2	3	0	1

$n = 5$

0	1	2	3	4
1	2	3	4	0
2	3	4	0	1
3	4	0	1	2
4	0	1	2	3

0	1	2	3	4
2	3	4	0	1
4	0	1	2	3
1	2	3	4	0
3	4	0	1	2

0	1	2	3	4
3	4	0	1	2
1	2	3	4	0
4	0	1	2	3
2	3	4	0	1

0	1	2	3	4
4	0	1	2	3
3	4	0	1	2
2	3	4	0	1
1	2	3	4	0

These are two superimposed MOLS for $n = 7$, 8, 9, and 10.

$n = 7$

00	11	22	33	44	55	66
16	20	31	42	53	64	05
25	36	40	51	62	03	14
34	45	56	60	01	12	23
43	54	65	06	10	21	32
52	63	04	15	26	30	41
61	02	13	24	35	46	50

$n = 8$

00	11	22	33	44	55	66	77
12	03	30	21	56	47	74	65
24	35	06	17	60	71	42	53
33	22	11	00	77	66	55	44
46	57	64	75	02	13	20	31
57	46	75	64	13	02	31	20
65	74	47	56	21	30	03	12
71	60	53	42	35	24	17	06

$$n = 9$$

00	11	22	33	44	55	66	77	88
12	20	01	45	53	34	78	86	67
21	02	10	54	35	43	87	68	76
36	47	58	60	71	82	03	14	25
48	56	37	72	80	61	15	23	04
57	38	46	81	62	70	24	05	13
63	74	85	06	17	28	30	41	52
75	83	64	18	26	07	42	50	31
84	65	73	27	08	16	51	32	40

$$n = 10$$

00	67	58	49	91	83	75	12	24	36
76	11	07	68	59	92	84	23	35	40
85	70	22	17	08	69	93	34	46	51
94	86	71	33	27	18	09	45	59	62
19	95	80	72	44	37	28	56	61	03
38	29	96	81	73	55	47	60	02	14
57	48	39	90	82	74	66	01	13	25
21	32	43	54	65	06	10	77	88	99
42	53	64	05	16	20	31	89	97	78
63	04	15	26	30	41	52	98	79	87

3.5.8   ROOM SQUARES

A *Room square* of side n is an $n \times n$ array with entries either empty or consisting of an unordered pair of symbols from a symbol set of size $n + 1$ with the requirements:

1. Each symbol appears exactly once in each row and column.

2. Every unordered pair occurs exactly once in the array.

Room squares exist if and only if n is odd and $n \geq 7$.

A Room square yields a construction of a round-robin tournament between $n + 1$ opponents:

1. Rows of the square represent rounds in the tournament.

2. Columns in the square represent locales.

3. Each pair represents one competition.

Then each team plays exactly once in each round, at each locale, and against each opponent.

For example, this is a Room square of side 7:

01			26		57	34
45	02			37		61
72	56	03			41	
	13	67	04			52
63		24	71	05		
	74		35	12	06	
		15		46	23	07

3.6 INCLUSION/EXCLUSION

Let $\{a_1, a_2, \ldots, a_r\}$ be properties that the elements of a set may or may not have. If the set has N objects, then the number of objects having exactly m properties (with $m \leq r$), e_m, is given by

$$e_m = s_m - \binom{m+1}{1} s_{m+1} + \binom{m+2}{2} s_{m+2} - \binom{m+3}{3} s_{m+3}$$
$$\cdots + (-1)^p \binom{m+p}{p} s_{m+p} \cdots + (-1)^{r-m} \binom{m+(r-m)}{(r-m)} s_r.$$

Here $s_t = \sum N(a_{i_1} a_{i_2} \cdots a_{i_t})$. When $m = 0$, this is the usual inclusion/exclusion rule:

$$e_0 = s_0 - s_1 + s_2 - \cdots + (-1)^r s_r,$$
$$= N - \sum_i N(a_i) + \sum_{\substack{i,j \\ i \neq j}} N(a_i a_j) - \sum_{\substack{i,j,k \\ i \neq j \\ i \neq k \\ j \neq k}} N(a_i a_j a_k) + \cdots + (-1)^r N(a_1 a_2 \ldots a_r).$$

3.7 COMMUNICATION THEORY

3.7.1 INFORMATION THEORY

Definitions

Let $\mathbf{p}_X$ be a probability distribution on the discrete random variable X with $\mathrm{Prob}(X = x) = p_x$. The *entropy* of the distribution is

$$H(\mathbf{p}_X) = -\sum_x p_x \log_2 p_x. \tag{3.7.1}$$

When X takes only two values,

$$H(\mathbf{p}_X) = H(p) = -p \log_2 p - (1-p) \log_2(1-p). \tag{3.7.2}$$

The units for entropy are *bits*. The range of $H(p)$ is from 0 to 1 with a maximum at $p = 0.5$. The maximum of $H(\mathbf{p}_X)$ is $\log_2 n$ and is obtained when X is a uniform random variable taking n values. Entropy measures how much information is gained from learning the value of X. Below is a plot of p versus $H(p)$.

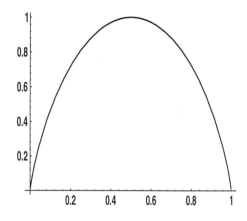

Given two discrete random variables X and Y, $\mathbf{p}_{X \times Y}$ is the joint distribution of X and Y. The *mutual information* of X and Y is defined by

$$I(X, Y) = H(\mathbf{p}_X) + H(\mathbf{p}_Y) - H(\mathbf{p}_{X \times Y}). \tag{3.7.3}$$

Note that $I(X, Y) \geq 0$ and that $I(X, Y) = 0$ if, and only if, X and Y are independent. Mutual information gives the amount of information that learning a value of X says about the value of Y (and vice versa).

Channel capacity

The *transition probabilities* are defined by $t_{x,y} = \text{Prob}(Y = y \mid X = x)$. The distribution $\mathbf{p}_X$ determines $\mathbf{p}_Y$ by $p_y = \sum t_{x,y} p_x$. The matrix $T = (t_{x,y})$ is the *transition matrix*. The matrix T defines a *channel* given by a transition diagram (input is X, output is Y). For example (here X and Y only take two values),

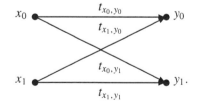

The *capacity* of the channel is defined as

$$C = \max_{\mathbf{p}_X} I(X, Y). \tag{3.7.4}$$

A channel is *symmetric* if each row is a permutation of the first row, and the transition matrix is a symmetric matrix. The capacity of a symmetric channel is $C = \log_2 n - H(\mathbf{p})$, where $\mathbf{p}$ is the first row. The capacity of a symmetric channel is achieved with equally likely inputs. The channel below on the left is symmetric; both channels achieve capacity with equally likely inputs.

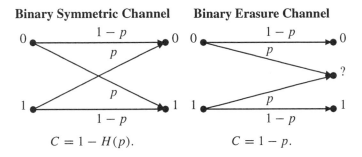

Binary Symmetric Channel   **Binary Erasure Channel**

$$C = 1 - H(p).$$ $$C = 1 - p.$$

Shannon's theorem

Let both X and Y be discrete random variables with values in an alphabet A. A *code* is a set of n-tuples (*codewords*) with entries from A that is in one-to-one correspondence with M messages. The *rate* R of the code is defined as $\frac{1}{n} \log_2 M$. Assume that the codeword is sent via a channel with transition matrix T by sending each vector element independently. Define

$$e = \max_{\text{all codewords}} \text{Prob(codeword incorrectly decoded)}. \qquad (3.7.5)$$

Then *Shannon's coding theorem* states:

- If $R < C$, then there is a sequence of codes with $n \to \infty$ such that $e \to 0$.

- If $R \geq C$, then e is always bounded away from 0.

3.7.2 BLOCK CODING

Definitions

A *code* C over an alphabet A is a set of vectors of a fixed length n with entries from A. Let A be the finite field GF(q) (see Section 3.7.3). If C is a vector space over A, then C is a *linear code*; the *dimension* k of a linear code is its dimension as a vector space.

The *Hamming distance* $d_H(\mathbf{u}, \mathbf{v})$ between two vectors, $\mathbf{u}$ and $\mathbf{v}$, is the number of places in which they differ. For a vector $\mathbf{u}$ over GF(q), define the *weight,* $\text{wt}(\mathbf{u})$, as the number of nonzero components. Then $d_H(\mathbf{u}, \mathbf{v}) = \text{wt}(\mathbf{u} - \mathbf{v})$. The minimum Hamming distance between two distinct vectors in a code C is called the *minimum distance d*. A code can detect e errors if $e < d$. A code can correct t errors if $2t + 1 < d$.

Coding diagram for linear codes

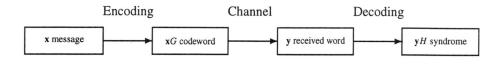

1. A *message* **x** consists of k information symbols.
2. The message is encoded as $\mathbf{x}G \in C$, where G is a $k \times n$ matrix called the generating matrix.
3. After transmission over a channel, a (possibly corrupted) vector **y** is received.
4. There exists a *parity check matrix* H such that $\mathbf{c} \in C$ if and only if $\mathbf{c}H = \mathbf{0}$. Thus the *syndrome* $\mathbf{z} = \mathbf{y}H$ can be used to try to decode **y**.
5. If G has the form $[I \; A]$, where I is the $k \times k$ identity matrix, then $H = \begin{bmatrix} -A \\ I \end{bmatrix}$.

Cyclic codes

A linear code C of length n is *cyclic* if $(a_0, a_1, \ldots, a_{n-1}) \in C$ implies $(a_{n-1}, a_0, \ldots, a_{n-2}) \in C$. To each codeword $(a_0, a_1, \ldots, a_{n-1}) \in C$ is associated the polynomial $a(x) = \sum_{i=0}^{n-1} a_i x^i$. Every cyclic code has a *generating polynomial* $g(x)$ such that $a(x)$ corresponds to a codeword if, and only if, $a(x) \equiv d(x)g(x) \pmod{x^n - 1}$ for some $d(x)$. The *roots* of a cyclic code are roots of $g(x)$ under some extension field $\mathrm{GF}(q')$ with primitive element α.

   BCH Bound: If a cyclic code C has roots $\alpha^i, \alpha^{i+1}, \ldots, \alpha^{i+d-2}$, then the minimum distance of C is at least d.

   Binary BCH codes (BCH stands for Bose, Ray-Chaudhuri, and Hocquenghem): Fix m, define $n = 2^m - 1$, and let α be a primitive element in $\mathrm{GF}(2^m)$. Define $f_i(x)$ as the minimum binary polynomial of α^i. Then

$$g(x) = \mathrm{LCM}\,(f_1(x) \cdots f_{2e}(x)) \tag{3.7.6}$$

defines a generating polynomial for a binary BCH code of length n and minimum distance at least $\delta = 2e + 1$ (δ is called the *designed distance*). The code dimension is at least $n - me$.

Table of binary BCH codes

n	k	d
7	4	3
15	11	3
	7	5
	5	7
31	26	3
	21	5
	16	7
	11	11
	6	15
63	57	3
	51	5

n	k	d
63	45	7
	39	9
	36	11
	30	13
	24	15
	18	21
	16	23
	10	27
	7	31
127	120	3
	113	5
	106	7
	99	9

n	k	d
127	92	11
	85	13
	78	15
	71	19
	64	21
	57	23
	50	27
	43	31
	36	31
	29	≥ 43
	22	47
	15	55
	8	63

Dual code: Given a code C, the dual code is $C^\perp = \{\mathbf{a} \mid \mathbf{a} \cdot \mathbf{x} = 0 \text{ for all } \mathbf{x} \in C\}$. The code $C^\perp$ is an $(n, n - k)$ linear code over F_q. A code is *self-dual* if $C = C^\perp$.

MDS codes: A linear code that meets the Singleton bound, $n + 1 = k + d$, is called *MDS* (for *maximum distance separable*). The generating matrix of an MDS code has any k columns linearly independent.

Reed–Solomon codes: Let α be a primitive element for GF(q) and $n = q - 1$. The generating polynomial $g(x) = (x - \alpha)(x - \alpha^2) \cdots (x - \alpha^{d-1})$ defines a cyclic MDS code with distance d and dimension $k = n - d + 1$.

Hexacode: The hexacode is a $(6, 3, 4)$ self-dual MDS code over GF(4). Let the finite field of four elements be $\{0, 1, a, b\}$ with $b = a^2 = a + 1$. The code is generated by the vectors $(1, 0, 0, 1, a, b)$, $(0, 1, 0, 1, a, b)$, and $(0, 0, 1, 1, 1, 1)$. The 64 codewords are

```
000000  1001ba  a00a1b  b00ba1   0101ab  110011  a10bb0  b10a0a
0a0ab1  1a0b0b  aa00aa  ba0110   0b0b1a  1b0aa0  ab0101  bb00bb
001111  1010ab  a01b0a  b01ab0   0110ba  111100  a11aa1  b11b1b
0a1ba0  1a1a1a  aa11bb  ba1001   0b1a0b  1b1bb1  ab1010  bb11aa
00aaaa  10ab10  a0a0b1  b0a10b   01ab01  11aabb  a1a11a  b1a0a0
0aa01b  1aa1a1  aaaa00  baabba   0ba1b0  1ba00a  ababab  bbaa11
00bbbb  10ba01  a0b1a0  b0b01a   01ba10  11bbaa  a1b00b  b1b1b1
0ab10a  1ab0b0  aabb11  babaab   0bb0a1  1bb11b  abbaba  bbbb00 .
```

Perfect codes: A linear code is *perfect* if it satisfies the Hamming bound, $q^{n-k} = \sum_{i=0}^{e} \binom{n}{i}(q - 1)^i$. The binary Hamming codes and Golay codes are perfect.

Binary Hamming codes: Have the parameters $\{n = 2^m - 1, k = 2^m - 1 - m, d = 3\}$. The parity check matrix is the $2^m - 1 \times m$ matrix whose rows are all of the binary m-tuples in a fixed order. The generating and parity check matrices for the

$(7, 4)$ Hamming code are

$$G = \begin{bmatrix} 1 & 0 & 0 & 0 & 1 & 1 & 0 \\ 0 & 1 & 0 & 0 & 1 & 0 & 1 \\ 0 & 0 & 1 & 0 & 0 & 1 & 1 \\ 0 & 0 & 0 & 1 & 1 & 1 & 1 \end{bmatrix}, \qquad H = \begin{bmatrix} 1 & 1 & 0 \\ 1 & 0 & 1 \\ 0 & 1 & 1 \\ 1 & 1 & 1 \\ 1 & 0 & 0 \\ 0 & 1 & 0 \\ 0 & 0 & 1 \end{bmatrix}. \tag{3.7.7}$$

Binary Golay code: This has the parameters $\{n = 24, k = 12, d = 8\}$. The generating matrix is

$$G = \begin{bmatrix} 1\,0\,0\,0\,0\,0\,0\,0\,0\,0\,0\,0 & 0\,1\,1\,1\,1\,1\,1\,1\,1\,1\,1\,1 \\ 0\,1\,0\,0\,0\,0\,0\,0\,0\,0\,0\,0 & 1\,1\,1\,0\,1\,1\,1\,0\,0\,0\,1\,0 \\ 0\,0\,1\,0\,0\,0\,0\,0\,0\,0\,0\,0 & 1\,1\,0\,1\,1\,1\,0\,0\,0\,1\,0\,1 \\ 0\,0\,0\,1\,0\,0\,0\,0\,0\,0\,0\,0 & 1\,0\,1\,1\,1\,0\,0\,0\,1\,0\,1\,1 \\ 0\,0\,0\,0\,1\,0\,0\,0\,0\,0\,0\,0 & 1\,1\,1\,1\,0\,0\,0\,1\,0\,1\,1\,0 \\ 0\,0\,0\,0\,0\,1\,0\,0\,0\,0\,0\,0 & 1\,1\,1\,0\,0\,0\,1\,0\,1\,1\,0\,1 \\ 0\,0\,0\,0\,0\,0\,1\,0\,0\,0\,0\,0 & 1\,1\,0\,0\,0\,1\,0\,1\,1\,0\,1\,1 \\ 0\,0\,0\,0\,0\,0\,0\,1\,0\,0\,0\,0 & 1\,0\,0\,0\,1\,0\,1\,1\,0\,1\,1\,1 \\ 0\,0\,0\,0\,0\,0\,0\,0\,1\,0\,0\,0 & 1\,0\,0\,1\,0\,1\,1\,0\,1\,1\,1\,0 \\ 0\,0\,0\,0\,0\,0\,0\,0\,0\,1\,0\,0 & 1\,0\,1\,0\,1\,1\,0\,1\,1\,1\,0\,0 \\ 0\,0\,0\,0\,0\,0\,0\,0\,0\,0\,1\,0 & 1\,1\,0\,1\,1\,0\,1\,1\,1\,0\,0\,0 \\ 0\,0\,0\,0\,0\,0\,0\,0\,0\,0\,0\,1 & 1\,0\,1\,1\,0\,1\,1\,1\,0\,0\,0\,1 \end{bmatrix}. \tag{3.7.8}$$

Ternary Golay code: This has the parameters $\{n = 12, k = 6, d = 6\}$. The generating matrix is

$$G = \begin{bmatrix} 1\,0\,0\,0\,0\,0 & 0\,1\,1\,1\,1\,1 \\ 0\,1\,0\,0\,0\,0 & 1\,0\,1\,2\,2\,1 \\ 0\,0\,1\,0\,0\,0 & 1\,1\,0\,1\,2\,2 \\ 0\,0\,0\,1\,0\,0 & 1\,2\,1\,0\,1\,2 \\ 0\,0\,0\,0\,1\,0 & 1\,2\,2\,1\,0\,1 \\ 0\,0\,0\,0\,0\,1 & 1\,1\,2\,2\,1\,0 \end{bmatrix}. \tag{3.7.9}$$

Bounds

Bounds for block codes investigate the trade-offs between the length n, the number of codewords M, the minimum distance d, and the alphabet size q. The number of errors that can be corrected is e with $2e + 1 \leq d$. If the code is linear, then the bounds concern the dimension k with $M = q^k$.

1. Hamming or sphere-packing bound: $M \leq q^n \big/ \sum_{i=0}^{e} \binom{n}{i}(q - 1)^i$.

2. Plotkin bound: Suppose that $d > n(q - 1)/q$. Then $M \leq \frac{qd}{qd - n(q-1)}$.

3. Singleton bound: For any code, $M \leq q^{n-d+1}$; if the code is linear, then $k + d \leq n + 1$.

4. Varsharmov–Gilbert bound: There is a block code with minimum distance at least d and $M \geq q^n \big/ \sum_{i=0}^{d-1} \binom{n}{i}(q - 1)^i$.

Table of best binary codes

$A(n, d)$ is the number of codewords[1] in the largest binary code of length n and minimum distance d. Note that $A(n - 1, d - 1) = A(n, d)$ if d is odd and $A(n, 2) = 2^{n-1}$ (given, e.g., by even weight words).

n	$d = 4$	$d = 6$	$d = 8$	$d = 10$
6	4	2	1	1
7	8	2	1	1
8	16	2	2	1
9	20	4	2	1
10	40	6	2	2
11	72–79	12	2	2
12	144–158	24	4	2
13	256	32	4	2
14	512	64	8	2
15	1024	128	16	4
16	2048	256	32	4
17	2720–3276	256–340	36–37	6
18	5248–6552	512–680	64–74	10
19	10496–13104	1024–1288	128–144	20
20	20480–26208	2048–2372	256–279	40
21	36864–43690	2560–4096	512	42–48
22	73728–87380	4096–6942	1024	68–88
23	147456–173784	8192–13774	2048	64–150
24	294912–344636	16384–24106	4096	128-280

3.7.3 FINITE FIELDS

Pertinent definitions for finite fields can be found in Section 2.6.5.

Irreducible and primitive polynomials

Let $N_q(n)$ be the number of monic irreducible polynomials over GF(q). Then

$$q^n = \sum_{d|n} d N_q(d) \quad \text{and} \quad N_q(n) = \frac{1}{n} \sum_{d|n} \mu\left(\frac{n}{d}\right) q^d,$$

(3.7.10)

where $\mu()$ is the number theoretic Möbius function (see Section 2.3.8).

Table of binary irreducible polynomials

The table lists the nonzero coefficients of the polynomial, e.g., 2 1 0 corresponds to $x^2 + x^1 + x^0 = x^2 + x + 1$. The *exponent* of an irreducible polynomial is the smallest

---

[1] Data from *Sphere Packing, Lattices and Groups* by J.H. Conway and N.J.A. Sloane, 2nd ed., Springer-Verlag, New York, 1993.

L such that $f(x)$ divides $x^L - 1$. A P after the exponent indicates that the polynomial is primitive.

$f(x)$	Exponent	$f(x)$	Exponent
2 1 0	3 P	7 6 5 3 2 1 0	127 P
3 1 0	7 P	7 6 5 4 0	127 P
3 2 0	7 P	7 6 5 4 2 1 0	127 P
4 1 0	15 P	7 6 5 4 3 2 0	127 P
4 2 0	15 P	8 4 3 1 0	51
4 3 2 1 0	5	8 4 3 2 0	255 P
5 2 0	31 P	8 5 3 1 0	255 P
5 3 0	31 P	8 5 3 2 0	255 P
5 3 2 1 0	31 P	8 5 4 3 0	17
5 4 2 1 0	31 P	8 5 4 3 2 1 0	85
5 4 3 1 0	31 P	8 6 3 2 0	255 P
5 4 3 2 0	31 P	8 6 4 3 2 1 0	255 P
6 1 0	63 P	8 6 5 1 0	255 P
6 3 0	9	8 6 5 2 0	255 P
6 4 2 1 0	21	8 6 5 3 0	255 P
6 4 3 1 0	63 P	8 6 5 4 0	255 P
6 5 0	63 P	8 6 5 4 2 1 0	85
6 5 2 1 0	63 P	8 6 5 4 3 1 0	85
6 5 3 2 0	63 P	8 7 2 1 0	255 P
6 5 4 1 0	63	8 7 3 1 0	85
6 5 4 2 0	21 P	8 7 3 2 0	255 P
7 1 0	127 P	8 7 4 3 2 1 0	51
7 3 0	127 P	8 7 5 1 0	85
7 3 2 1 0	127 P	8 7 5 3 0	255 P
7 4 0	127 P	8 7 5 4 0	51
7 4 3 2 0	127 P	8 7 5 4 3 2 0	85
7 5 2 1 0	127 P	8 7 6 1 0	255 P
7 5 3 1 0	127 P	8 7 6 3 2 1 0	255 P
7 5 4 3 0	127 P	8 7 6 4 2 1 0	17
7 5 4 3 2 1 0	127 P	8 7 6 4 3 2 0	85
7 6 0	127 P	8 7 6 5 2 1 0	255 P
7 6 3 1 0	127 P	8 7 6 5 4 1 0	51
7 6 4 1 0	127 P	8 7 6 5 4 2 0	255 P
7 6 4 2 0	127 P	8 7 6 5 4 3 0	85
7 6 5 2 0	127 P		

Table of binary primitive polynomials[2]

Listed below are primitive polynomials, with the least number of nonzero terms, of degree from 1 to 64. Only the nonzero terms are listed, e.g., 2 1 0 corresponds to $x^2 + x + 1$.

[2]Taken in part from "Primitive Polynomials (Mod 2)", E.J. Watson, *Math. Comp.*, **16**, 368–369, 1962.

$f(x)$	$f(x)$	$f(x)$	$f(x)$
1 0	17 3 0	33 6 4 1 0	49 6 5 4 0
2 1 0	18 5 2 1 0	34 7 6 5 2 1 0	50 4 3 2 0
3 1 0	19 5 2 1 0	35 2 0	51 6 3 1 0
4 1 0	20 3 0	36 6 5 4 2 1 0	52 3 0
5 2 0	21 2 0	37 5 4 3 2 1 0	53 6 2 1 0
6 1 0	22 1 0	38 6 5 1 0	54 6 5 4 3 2 0
7 1 0	23 5 0	39 4 0	55 6 2 1 0
8 4 3 2 0	24 4 3 1 0	40 5 4 3 0	56 7 4 2 0
9 4 0	25 3 0	41 3 0	57 5 3 2 0
10 3 0	26 6 2 1 0	42 5 4 3 2 1 0	58 6 5 1 0
11 2 0	27 5 2 1 0	43 6 4 3 0	59 6 5 4 3 1 0
12 6 4 1 0	28 3 0	44 6 5 2 0	60 1 0
13 4 3 1 0	29 2 0	45 4 3 1 0	61 5 2 1 0
14 5 3 1 0	30 6 4 1 0	46 8 5 3 2 1 0	62 6 5 3 0
15 1 0	31 3 0	47 5 0	63 1 0
16 5 3 2 0	32 7 5 3 2 1 0	48 7 5 4 2 1 0	64 4 3 1 0

3.7.4 BINARY SEQUENCES

Barker sequences

A *Barker sequence* is a sequence $(s_1, \ldots, s_N)$ with $s_j = \pm 1$ such that $\sum_{j=1}^{N-i} s_j s_{j+i} = \pm 1$ or 0, for $i = 1, \ldots, N-1$. The following table lists all known Barker sequences (up to reversal, multiplication by -1, and multiplying alternate values by -1).

Length	Barker sequence											
2	+1	+1										
3	+1	+1	−1									
4	+1	+1	+1	−1								
4	+1	+1	−1	+1								
5	+1	+1	+1	−1	+1							
7	+1	+1	+1	−1	−1	+1	−1					
11	+1	+1	+1	−1	−1	−1	+1	−1	−1	+1	−1	
13	+1	+1	+1	+1	+1	−1	−1	+1	+1	−1	+1	−1	+1

Periodic sequences

Let $\mathbf{s} = (s_0, s_1, \ldots, s_{N-1})$ be a periodic sequence with period N. A (left) shift of $\mathbf{s}$ is the sequence $(s_1, \ldots, s_{N-1}, s_0)$. For τ relatively prime to N, the *decimation* of $\mathbf{s}$ is the sequence $(s_0, s_\tau, s_{2\tau}, \ldots)$, which also has period N. The *periodic autocorrelation* is defined as the vector $(a_0, \ldots, a_{N-1})$, with

$$a_i = \sum_{j=0}^{N-1} s_j s_{j+i}, \qquad \text{subscripts taken modulo } N. \tag{3.7.11}$$

An autocorrelation is *two-valued* if all values are equal except possibly for the 0th term.

The *m*-sequences

A binary *m-sequence* of length $N = 2^r - 1$ is the sequence of period N

$$(s_0, s_1, \ldots, s_{N-1}), \qquad s_i = \mathrm{Tr}(\alpha^i),$$

where α is a primitive element of $\mathrm{GF}(2^r)$ and Tr is the trace function from $\mathrm{GF}(2^r)$ to $\mathrm{GF}(2)$.

- All *m*-sequences of a given length are equivalent under decimation.
- Binary *m*-sequences have a two-valued autocorrelation (with the identification that $0 \leftrightarrow +1$ and $1 \leftrightarrow -1$).
- All *m*-sequences possess the *span property*: all binary *r*-tuples occur in the sequence except the all-zeros *r*-tuple.

A binary sequence of length $2^n - 1$ with a two-valued autocorrelation is equivalent to the existence of a cyclic difference set with parameters $(2^n - 1, 2^{n-1} - 1, 2^{n-2} - 1)$.

Shift registers

Below are examples of the two types of shift registers used to generate binary *m*-sequences. The generating polynomial in each case is $x^4 + x + 1$, the initial register loading is 1 0 0 0, and the generated sequence is $\{0, 0, 0, 1, 0, 0, 1, 1, 0, 1, 0, 1, 1, 1, 1, \ldots\}$.

Additive shift register   **Multiplicative shift register**

Table of binary sequences with two-valued autocorrelation

The following table lists all binary sequences with two-valued periodic autocorrelation of length $2^n - 1$ for $n = 3$ to 8 (up to shifts, decimations, and complementation). The table indicates the positions of 0; the remaining values are 1. An *S* indicates that that sequence has the span property.

n	Positions of 0
3 S	1 2 4
4 S	0 1 2 4 5 8 10
5 S	1 2 3 4 6 8 12 15 16 17 23 24 27 29 30
5	1 2 4 5 7 8 9 10 14 16 18 19 20 25 28
6 S	0 1 2 3 4 6 7 8 9 12 13 14 16 18 19 24 26 27 28 32 33 35 36 38 41 45 48 49 52 54 56
6	0 1 2 3 4 5 6 8 9 10 12 16 17 18 20 23 24 27 29 32 33 34 36 40 43 45 46 48 53 54 58
7 S	1 2 4 8 9 11 13 15 16 17 18 19 21 22 25 26 30 31 32 34 35 36 37 38 41 42 44 47 49 50 52 60 61 62 64 68 69 70 71 72 73 74 76 79 81 82 84 87 88 94 98 99 100 103 104 107 113 115 117 120 121 122 124
7	1 2 3 4 5 6 7 8 10 12 14 16 19 20 23 24 25 27 28 32 33 38 40 46 47 48 50 51 54 56 57 61 63 64 65 66 67 73 75 76 77 80 87 89 92 94 95 96 97 100 101 102 107 108 111 112 114 117 119 122 123 125 126
7	1 2 3 4 6 7 8 9 12 14 15 16 17 18 24 27 28 29 30 31 32 34 36 39 47 48 51 54 56 58 60 61 62 64 65 67 68 71 72 77 78 79 83 87 89 94 96 97 99 102 103 105 107 108 112 113 115 116 117 120 121 122 124
7	1 2 3 4 6 7 8 9 12 13 14 16 17 18 19 24 25 26 27 28 31 32 34 35 36 38 47 48 50 51 52 54 56 61 62 64 65 67 68 70 72 73 76 77 79 81 87 89 94 96 97 100 102 103 104 107 108 112 115 117 121 122 124
7	1 2 3 4 5 6 8 9 10 12 15 16 17 18 19 20 24 25 27 29 30 32 33 34 36 38 39 40 48 50 51 54 55 58 59 60 64 65 66 68 71 72 73 76 77 78 80 83 89 91 93 96 99 100 102 105 108 109 110 113 116 118 120
7	1 2 3 4 5 6 8 10 11 12 16 19 20 21 22 24 25 27 29 32 33 37 38 39 40 41 42 44 48 49 50 51 54 58 63 64 65 66 69 73 74 76 77 78 80 82 83 84 88 89 95 96 98 100 102 105 108 111 116 119 123 125 126
8 S	0 1 2 3 4 6 7 8 12 13 14 16 17 19 23 24 25 26 27 28 31 32 34 35 37 38 41 45 46 48 49 50 51 52 54 56 59 62 64 67 68 70 73 74 75 76 82 85 90 92 96 98 99 100 102 103 104 105 108 111 112 113 118 119 123 124 127 128 129 131 134 136 137 139 140 141 143 145 146 148 150 152 153 157 161 164 165 170 177 179 180 183 184 187 189 191 192 193 196 197 198 199 200 204 206 208 210 216 217 219 221 222 223 224 226 227 236 237 238 239 241 246 247 248 251 253 254
8	0 1 2 4 7 8 9 11 14 16 17 18 19 21 22 23 25 27 28 29 32 33 34 35 36 38 42 43 44 46 49 50 51 54 56 58 61 64 66 68 69 70 71 72 76 79 81 84 85 86 87 88 89 92 93 95 97 98 99 100 101 102 108 112 113 116 117 119 122 125 128 131 132 133 136 137 138 139 140 141 142 144 145 149 152 153 158 162 163 167 168 170 171 172 174 175 176 177 178 184 186 187 190 193 194 196 197 198 200 202 204 209 211 213 215 216 221 224 226 232 233 234 235 238 244 245 250
8	0 1 2 3 4 6 8 12 13 15 16 17 24 25 26 27 29 30 31 32 34 35 39 47 48 50 51 52 54 57 58 59 60 61 62 64 67 68 70 71 78 79 85 91 94 96 99 100 102 103 104 107 108 109 114 116 118 119 120 121 122 124 127 128 129 134 135 136 140 141 142 143 145 147 151 153 156 157 158 161 163 167 170 173 177 179 181 182 187 188 191 192 195 198 199 200 201 203 204 206 208 209 211 214 216 217 218 221 223 225 227 228 229 232 233 236 238 239 240 241 242 244 247 248 251 253 254
8	0 1 2 3 4 6 7 8 11 12 14 15 16 17 21 22 23 24 25 28 29 30 32 34 35 37 41 42 44 46 47 48 50 51 56 58 60 64 68 69 70 71 73 74 81 82 84 85 88 91 92 94 96 97 100 102 107 109 111 112 113 116 119 120 121 123 127 128 129 131 133 135 136 138 139 140 142 145 146 148 151 153 162 163 164 168 170 173 176 181 182 183 184 187 188 189 191 192 193 194 195 197 200 203 204 209 214 218 219 221 222 223 224 225 226 229 232 237 238 239 240 242 246 247 251 253 254

3.7.5   MORSE CODE

International version of Morse code is

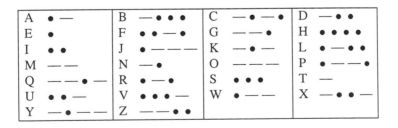

3.7.6   SOURCE CODING FOR ENGLISH TEXT

English text has, on average, 4.08 bits/character.

Letter	Probability	Huffman code	Alphabetical code
Space	0.1859	000	00
A	0.0642	0100	0100
B	0.0127	011111	010100
C	0.0218	11111	010101
D	0.0317	01011	01011
E	0.1031	101	0110
F	0.0208	001100	011100
G	0.0152	011101	011101
H	0.0467	1110	01111
I	0.0575	1000	1000
J	0.0008	0111001110	1001000
K	0.0049	01110010	1001001
L	0.0321	01010	100101
M	0.0198	001101	10011
N	0.0574	1001	1010
O	0.0632	0110	1011
P	0.0152	011110	110000
Q	0.0008	0111001101	110001
R	0.0484	1101	11001
S	0.0514	0010	1101
T	0.0796	0010	1110
U	0.0228	11110	111100
V	0.0083	0111000	111101
W	0.0175	001110	111110
X	0.0013	0111001100	1111110
Y	0.0164	001111	11111110
Z	0.0005	0111001111	11111111
Cost	4.0799	4.1195	4.1978

3.7.7 GRAY CODE

A Gray code is a sequence ordering such that a small change in the sequence number results in a small change in the sequence. For example, the 16 4-bit strings {0000, 0001, . . . , 1111} can be ordered so that adjacent bit strings differ in only 1 bit:

Sequence number	Bit string	Sequence number	Bit string
0	0000	8	1100
1	0001	9	1101
2	0011	10	1111
3	0010	11	1110
4	0110	12	1010
5	0111	13	1011
6	0101	14	1001
7	0100	15	1000

As another example, the subsets of $\{a, b, c\}$ can be ordered so that adjacent subsets differ by only the insertion or deletion of a single element:

$$\phi, \quad \{a\}, \quad \{a, b\}, \quad \{b\}, \quad \{b, c\}, \quad \{a, b, c\}, \quad \{a, c\}, \quad \{c\}.$$

3.8 COSTAS ARRAYS

An $n \times n$ Costas array is an array of zeros and ones whose autocorrelation function is n at the origin and no more than 1 anywhere else. There are B_n basic Costas arrays; there are C_n arrays when rotations and flips are allowed. Each array can be interpreted as a permutation.

n	1	2	3	4	5	6	7	8	9	10	11	12
B_n	1	1	1	2	6	17	13	17	30	60	555	990
C_n	1	2	4	12	40	116	200	444	760	2160	4368	7852

n	13	14	15	16	17	18	19	20
B_n	1616	2168	2467	2648	2294	1892	1283	810
C_n	12828	17252	19612	21104	18276	15096	10240	6464

B_n:

C_4:

3.9   DIFFERENCE EQUATIONS

3.9.1   THE CALCULUS OF FINITE DIFFERENCES

1. $\Delta(f(x)) = f(x + h) - f(x)$ (forward difference).
2. $\Delta^2(f(x)) = f(x + 2h) - 2f(x + h) + f(x)$.
3. $\Delta^n(f(x)) = \Delta\left(\Delta^{n-1}(f(x))\right) = \sum_{k=0}^{n}(-1)^k \binom{n}{k} f(x + (n - k)h)$.
4. $\Delta(cf(x)) = c\Delta(f(x))$.
5. $\Delta(f(x) + g(x)) = \Delta(f(x)) + \Delta(g(x))$.
6. $\Delta(f(x)g(x)) = g(x)\Delta(f(x)) + f(x)\Delta(g(x))$.
7. $\Delta\left(\dfrac{f(x)}{g(x)}\right) = \dfrac{g(x)\Delta(f(x)) - f(x)\Delta(g(x))}{g(x)g(x+h)}$,
   provided that $g(x)g(x + h) \neq 0$.
8. $\Delta^n(x^n) = n\,!h^n$, $n = 0, 1, \dots$.

3.9.2   EXISTENCE AND UNIQUENESS

A *difference equation of order k* has the form

$$x_{n+k} = f(x_n, x_{n+1}, \dots, x_{n+(k-1)}, n) \tag{3.9.1}$$

where f is a given function and k is a positive integer. A *solution* to Equation (3.9.1) is a sequence of numbers $\{x_n\}_{n=0}^{\infty}$ which satisfies the equation. Any constant solution of Equation (3.9.1) is called an *equilibrium solution*.

A *linear* difference equation of order k has the form

$$a_n^{(k)}x_{n+k} + a_n^{(k-1)}x_{n+(k-1)} + \cdots + a_n^{(1)}x_{n-1} + a_n^{(0)}x_n = g_n, \tag{3.9.2}$$

where k is a positive integer and the coefficients $a_n^{(0)}, \dots, a_n^{(k)}$ along with g_n are given sequences. If the sequence g_n is identically zero, then Equation (3.9.2) is called *homogeneous*; otherwise, it is called *nonhomogeneous*. If the coefficients $a^{(0)}, \dots, a^{(k)}$ are constants, Equation (3.9.2) is a difference equation with constant coefficients; otherwise it is a difference equation with variable coefficients.

THEOREM 3.9.1   *(Existence and uniqueness)*

Consider the initial value problem (IVP)

$$x_{n+k} + b_n^{(k-1)}x_{n+(k-1)} + \cdots + b_n^{(1)}x_{n+1} + b_n^{(0)}x_n = f_n, \tag{3.9.3}$$

$$x_i = \alpha_i, \qquad i = 0, 1, \dots, k - 1, \tag{3.9.4}$$

for $n = 0, 1, \ldots$, *where* $b_n^{(i)}$ *and* f_n *are given sequences with* $b_n^{(0)} \neq 0$ *for all* n *and the* $\{\alpha_i\}$ *are given initial conditions. Then the above equations have exactly one solution.*

3.9.3 LINEAR INDEPENDENCE: GENERAL SOLUTION

The sequences $x_n^{(1)}, x_n^{(2)}, \ldots, x_n^{(k)}$ are *linearly dependent* if constants $c_1, c_2, \ldots, c_k$ (not all of them zero) exist such that

$$\sum_{i=1}^{k} c_i x_n^{(i)} = 0 \quad \text{for } n = 0, 1, \ldots. \tag{3.9.5}$$

Otherwise the sequences $x_n^{(1)}, x_n^{(2)}, \ldots, x_n^{(k)}$ are *linearly independent*.

The *Casoratian* of the k sequences $x_n^{(1)}, x_n^{(2)}, \ldots, x_n^{(k)}$ is the $k \times k$ determinant

$$C\left(x_n^{(1)}, x_n^{(2)}, \ldots, x_n^{(k)}\right) = \begin{vmatrix} x_n^{(1)} & x_n^{(2)} & \cdots & x_n^{(k)} \\ x_{n+1}^{(1)} & x_{n+1}^{(2)} & \cdots & x_{n+1}^{(k)} \\ \cdots\cdots\cdots\cdots\cdots\cdots\cdots \\ x_{n+k-1}^{(1)} & x_{n+k-1}^{(2)} & \cdots & x_{n+k-1}^{(k)} \end{vmatrix}. \tag{3.9.6}$$

THEOREM 3.9.2

The solutions $x_n^{(1)}, x_n^{(2)}, \ldots, x_n^{(k)}$ *of the linear homogeneous difference equation,*

$$x_{n+k} + b_n^{(k-1)} x_{n+(k-1)} + \cdots + b_n^{(1)} x_{n+1} + b_n^{(0)} x_n = 0, \quad n = 0, 1, \ldots, \tag{3.9.7}$$

are linearly independent if, and only if, their Casoratian is different from zero for $n = 0$.

The set $\left\{x_n^{(1)}, x_n^{(2)}, \ldots, x_n^{(k)}\right\}$ is a *fundamental system* of solutions for Equation (3.9.7) if, and only if, the sequences $x_n^{(1)}, x_n^{(2)}, \ldots, x_n^{(k)}$ are linearly independent solutions of the homogeneous difference equation (3.9.7).

THEOREM 3.9.3

Consider the nonhomogeneous linear difference equation

$$x_{n+k} + b_n^{(k-1)} x_{n+(k-1)} + \cdots + b_n^{(1)} x_{n+1} + b_n^{(0)} x_n = d_n, \quad n = 0, 1, \ldots \tag{3.9.8}$$

where $b_n^{(i)}$ *and* d_n *are given sequences. Let* $x_n^{(h)}$ *be the general solution of the corresponding homogeneous equation*

$$x_{n+k} + b_n^{(k-1)} x_{n+(k-1)} + \cdots + b_n^{(1)} x_{n+1} + b_n^{(0)} x_n = 0, \quad n = 0, 1, \ldots,$$

and let $x_n^{(p)}$ *be a particular solution of Equation (3.9.8). Then* $x_n^{(p)} + x_n^{(h)}$ *is the general solution of Equation (3.9.8).*

THEOREM 3.9.4   *(Superposition principle)*

Let $x_n^{(1)}$ and $x_n^{(2)}$ be solutions of the nonhomogeneous linear difference equations

$$x_{n+k} + b_n^{(k-1)} x_{n+(k-1)} + \cdots + b_n^{(1)} x_{n+1} + b_n^{(0)} x_n = \alpha_n, \quad n = 0, 1, \dots,$$

and

$$x_{n+k} + b_n^{(k-1)} x_{n+(k-1)} + \cdots + b_n^{(1)} x_{n+1} + b_n^{(0)} x_n = \beta_n, \quad n = 0, 1, \dots,$$

respectively, where $b_n^{(i)}$ and $\{\alpha_n\}$ and $\{\beta_n\}$ are given sequences. Then $x_n^{(1)} + x_n^{(2)}$ is a solution of the equation

$$x_{n+k} + b_n^{(k-1)} x_{n+(k-1)} + \cdots + b_n^{(1)} x_{n+1} + b_n^{(0)} x_n = \alpha_n + \beta_n, \quad n = 0, 1, \dots.$$

3.9.4   HOMOGENEOUS EQUATIONS WITH CONSTANT COEFFICIENTS

The results given below for second-order linear difference equations extend naturally to higher order equations.

Consider the second-order linear homogeneous difference equation,

$$\alpha_2 x_{n+2} + \alpha_1 x_{n+1} + \alpha_0 x_n = 0, \tag{3.9.9}$$

where the $\{\alpha_i\}$ are real constant coefficients with $\alpha_2 \alpha_0 \neq 0$. The *characteristic equation* corresponding to Equation (3.9.9) is defined as the quadratic equation

$$\alpha_2 \lambda^2 + \alpha_1 \lambda + \alpha_0 = 0. \tag{3.9.10}$$

The solutions λ_1, λ_2 of the characteristic equation are the *eigenvalues* or the *characteristic roots* of Equation (3.9.9).

THEOREM 3.9.5

Let λ_1 and λ_2 be the eigenvalues of Equation (3.9.9). Then the general solution of Equation (3.9.9) is given as described below with arbitrary constants c_1 and c_2.

Case 1: $\lambda_1 \neq \lambda_2$ with $\lambda_1, \lambda_2 \in \mathbb{R}$ *(real and distinct roots).*
    The general solution is given by $x_n = c_1 \lambda_1^n + c_2 \lambda_2^n$.
Case 2: $\lambda_1 = \lambda_2 \in \mathbb{R}$ *(real and equal roots).*
    The general solution is given by $x_n = c_1 \lambda_1^n + c_2 n \lambda_1^n$.
Case 3: $\lambda_1 = \overline{\lambda_2}$ *(complex conjugate roots).*
    Suppose that $\lambda_1 = r e^{i\phi}$. The general solution is given by

$$x_n = c_1 r^n \cos(n\phi) + c_2 r^n \sin(n\phi).$$

Example: The unique solution of the initial value problem

$$F_{n+2} = F_{n+1} + F_n, \qquad n = 0, 1, \dots,$$
$$F_0 = 0, \qquad F_1 = 1,$$

is the Fibonacci sequence. Using Theorem 3.9.5 one can show that

$$F_n = \frac{1}{\sqrt{5}} \left[\left(\frac{1+\sqrt{5}}{2} \right)^n - \left(\frac{1-\sqrt{5}}{2} \right)^n \right], \qquad n = 0, 1, \dots.$$

3.9.5 NONHOMOGENEOUS EQUATIONS WITH CONSTANT COEFFICIENTS

THEOREM 3.9.6 *(Variation of parameters)*

Consider the difference equation, $x_{n+2} + \alpha_n x_{n+1} + \beta_n x_n = \gamma_n$, where α_n, β_n, and γ_n are given sequences with $\beta_n \neq 0$. Let $x_n^{(1)}$ and $x_n^{(2)}$ be two linearly independent solutions of the homogeneous equation corresponding to this equation. A particular solution is given by $x_n^{(p)} = x_n^{(1)} v_n^{(1)} + x_n^{(2)} v_n^{(2)}$ where the sequences $v_n^{(1)}$ and $v_n^{(2)}$ satisfy the following system of equations:

$$x_{n+1}^{(1)} \left(v_{n+1}^{(1)} - v_n^{(1)} \right) + x_{n+1}^{(2)} \left(v_{n+1}^{(2)} - v_n^{(2)} \right) = 0, \quad \text{and}$$

$$x_{n+2}^{(1)} \left(v_{n+1}^{(1)} - v_n^{(1)} \right) + x_{n+2}^{(2)} \left(v_{n+1}^{(2)} - v_n^{(2)} \right) = \gamma_n. \qquad (3.9.11)$$

3.9.6 GENERATING FUNCTIONS AND Z TRANSFORMS

Generating functions can be used to solve initial value problems of difference equations in the same way that Laplace transforms are used to solve initial value problems of differential equations.

The *generating function* of the sequence $\{x_n\}$, denoted by $G[x_n]$, is defined by the infinite series

$$G[x_n] = \sum_{n=0}^{\infty} x_n s^n \qquad (3.9.12)$$

provided that the series converges for $|s| < r$, for some positive number r. The following are useful properties of the generating function:

1. *Linearity:* $G\{c_1 x_n + c_2 y_n\} = c_1 G\{x_n\} + c_2 G\{y_n\}$.

2. *Translation invariance:* $G\left[x_{n+k}\right] = \frac{1}{s^k} \left(G[x_n] - \sum_{n=0}^{k-1} x_n s^n \right)$.

3. *Uniqueness:* $G[x_n] = G[y_n] \Leftrightarrow x_n = y_n \quad \text{for} \quad n = 0, 1, \dots,$

x_n	$G[x_n]$
1	$\dfrac{1}{1-s}$
a^n	$\dfrac{1}{1-as}$
na^n	$\dfrac{as}{(1-as)^2}$
$n^p a^n$	$\left(s\dfrac{d}{ds}\right)^p \dfrac{1}{1-as}$
n	$\dfrac{s}{(1-s)^2}$
$n+1$	$\dfrac{1}{(1-s)^2}$
n^p	$\left(s\dfrac{d}{ds}\right)^p \dfrac{1}{1-s}$
$\sin(\beta n)$	$\dfrac{s\sin\beta}{1-2s\cos\beta+s^2}$
$\cos(\beta n)$	$\dfrac{1-s\cos\beta}{1-2s\cos\beta+s^2}$
$a^n\sin(\beta n)$	$\dfrac{as\sin\beta}{1-2as\cos\beta+a^2s^2}$
$a^n\cos(\beta n)$	$\dfrac{1-as\cos\beta}{1-2as\cos\beta+a^2s^2}$
x_{n+1}	$\dfrac{1}{s}(G[x_n]-x_0)$
x_{n+2}	$\dfrac{1}{s^2}(G[x_n]-x_0-sx_1)$
x_{n+k}	$\dfrac{1}{s^k}\left(G[x_n]-\sum_{n=0}^{k-1}x_n s^n\right)$

The *Z-transform* of a sequence $\{x_n\}$ is denoted by $\mathcal{Z}[x_n]$ and is defined by the infinite series,

$$\mathcal{Z}[x_n] = \sum_{n=0}^{\infty} \frac{x_n}{z^n}, \qquad (3.9.13)$$

provided that the series converges for $|z| > r$, for some positive number r.

Comparing the definitions for the generating function and the Z-tranform one can see that they are connected because Equation (3.9.13) can be obtained from Equation (3.9.12) by setting $s = z^{-1}$.

3.9.7 CLOSED FORM SOLUTIONS FOR SPECIAL EQUATIONS

In general, it is difficult to find a closed form solution for a difference equation which is not linear of order one or linear of any order with constant coefficients. A few special difference equations which possess closed form solutions are presented below.

THEOREM 3.9.7

The general solution of the first-order linear difference equation with variable coefficients,

$$x_{n+1} - \alpha_n x_n = \beta_n, \qquad n = 0, 1, \dots, \tag{3.9.14}$$

is given by

$$x_n = \left(\prod_{k=0}^{n-1} \alpha_k \right) x_0 + \sum_{m=0}^{n-2} \left(\prod_{k=m+1}^{n-1} \alpha_k \right) \beta_m + \beta_{n-1}, \qquad n = 0, 1, \dots, \tag{3.9.15}$$

where x_0 is an arbitrary constant.

Riccati equation

Consider the nonlinear first order equation,

$$x_{n+1} = \frac{\alpha_n x_n + \beta_n}{\gamma_n x_n + \delta_n}, \qquad n = 0, 1, \dots, \tag{3.9.16}$$

where $\alpha_n, \beta_n, \gamma_n, \delta_n$ are given sequences of real numbers with

$$\gamma_n \neq 0 \quad \text{and} \quad \begin{vmatrix} \alpha_n & \beta_n \\ \gamma_n & \delta_n \end{vmatrix} \neq 0, \qquad n = 0, 1, \dots. \tag{3.9.17}$$

The following statements are true:

1. The change of variables,

$$\frac{u_{n+1}}{u_n} = \gamma_n x_n + \delta_n, \qquad n = 0, 1, \dots, \tag{3.9.18}$$

$$u_0 = 1,$$

    reduces Equation (3.9.16) to the linear second order equation,

$$u_{n+2} = A_n u_n + B_n, \qquad n = 0, 1, \dots, \tag{3.9.19}$$

$$u_0 = 1,$$

$$u_1 = \gamma_0 x_0 + \delta_0,$$

    where $A_n = \delta_{n+1} + \alpha_n \dfrac{\gamma_{n+1}}{\gamma_n}$, and $B_n = (\beta_n \gamma_n - \alpha_n \delta_n) \dfrac{\gamma_{n+1}}{\gamma_n}$.

2. Let $\left\{x_n^{(p)}\right\}$ be a particular solution of Equation (3.9.16). The change of variables,

$$v_n = \frac{1}{x_n - x_n^{(p)}}, \qquad n = 0, 1, \ldots, \tag{3.9.20}$$

reduces Equation (3.9.16) to the linear first-order equation,

$$v_{n+1} + C_n v_n + D_n = 0, \qquad n = 0, 1, \ldots, \tag{3.9.21}$$

where $C_n = \dfrac{\left(\gamma_n x_n^{(p)} + \delta_n\right)^2}{\beta_n \gamma_n - \alpha_n \delta_n}$, and $D_n = \dfrac{\gamma_n \left(\gamma_n x_n^{(p)} + \delta_n\right)}{\beta_n \gamma_n - \alpha_n \delta_n}$.

3. Let $x_n^{(1)}$ and $x_n^{(2)}$ be two particular solutions of Equation (3.9.16) with $x_n^{(1)} \neq x_n^{(2)}$ for $n = 0, 1, \ldots$. Then the change of variables,

$$w_n = \frac{1}{x_n - x_n^{(1)}} + \frac{1}{x_n^{(1)} - x_n^{(2)}}, \qquad n = 0, 1, \ldots, \tag{3.9.22}$$

reduces Equation (3.9.16) to the linear homogeneous first-order equation,

$$w_{n+1} + E_n w_n = 0, \qquad n = 0, 1, \ldots, \tag{3.9.23}$$

where $E_n = \dfrac{\left(\gamma_n x_n^{(1)} + \delta_n\right)^2}{\beta_n \gamma_n - \alpha_n \delta_n}$.

Logistic equation

Consider the initial value problem

$$x_{n+1} = r x_n \left(1 - \frac{x_n}{k}\right), \qquad n = 0, 1, \ldots,$$
$$x_0 = \alpha, \quad \text{with} \quad \alpha \in [0, k], \tag{3.9.24}$$

where r and k are positive numbers with $r \leq 4$. The following are true:

1. When $r = k = 4$, Equation (3.9.24) reduces to

$$x_{n+1} = 4x_n - x_n^2. \tag{3.9.25}$$

By setting $\alpha = 4\sin^2(\theta)$ with $\theta \in [0, \frac{\pi}{2}]$, then Equation (3.9.25) has the closed form solution

$$x_{n+1} = 4\sin^2(2^{n+1}\theta), \qquad n = 0, 1, \ldots,$$
$$x_0 = 4\sin^2(\theta), \quad \text{with} \quad \theta \in \left[0, \frac{\pi}{2}\right]. \tag{3.9.26}$$

2. When $r = 4$ and $k = 1$, Equation (3.9.24) reduces to

$$x_{n+1} = 4x_n - 4x_n^2. \tag{3.9.27}$$

By setting $\alpha = \sin^2(\theta)$ with $\theta \in \left[0, \frac{\pi}{2}\right]$, then Equation (3.9.27) has the closed form solution

$$x_{n+1} = \sin^2(2^{n+1}\theta), \qquad n = 0, 1, \ldots,$$

$$x_0 = \sin^2(\theta), \quad \text{with} \quad \theta \in \left[0, \frac{\pi}{2}\right].$$

3.10   DISCRETE DYNAMICAL SYSTEMS AND CHAOS

Let the distance between successive bifurcations of a process be d_k. The limiting ratio, $\delta = \lim_{k\to\infty} d_k/d_{k+1}$, Feigenbaum's constant, is constant in many situations; $\delta \approx 4.6692016091029$.

3.10.1   CHAOTIC ONE-DIMENSIONAL MAPS

1. Logistic map: $x_{n+1} = 4x_n(1 - x_n)$.
   Solution is $x_n = \dfrac{1}{2} - \dfrac{1}{2} \cos[2^n \cos^{-1}(1 - 2x_0)]$.

2. Tent map: $x_{n+1} = 1 - 2\left|x_n - \frac{1}{2}\right|$.
   Solution is $x_n = \dfrac{1}{\pi} \cos^{-1}[\cos(2^n \pi x_0)]$.

3. Baker transformation: $x_{n+1} = 2x_n \pmod 1$.
   Solution is $x_n = \dfrac{1}{\pi} \cot^{-1}[\cot(2^n \pi x_0)]$.

3.10.2   LOGISTIC MAP

Consider $u_{n+1} = f(u_n) = au_n(1 - u_n)$. The fixed points satisfy $u = f(u) = au(1 - u)$; they are $u = 0$ and $u = (a - 1)/a$.

- If $a = 0$ then $u_n = 0$.
- If $0 < a \leq 1$ then $u_n \to 0$.
- If $1 < a < 3$ then $u_n \to (a - 1)/a$.
- If $3 < a < 3.449490\ldots$ then u_n oscillates between the two roots of $u = f(f(u))$ which are not roots of $u = f(u)$, that is, $u_{\pm} = (a+1\pm\sqrt{a^2 - 2a - 3})/2a$.

The location of the final state is summarized by the following diagram.

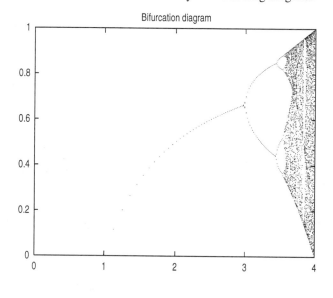

3.10.3   JULIA SETS AND THE MANDELBROT SET

For the function $f(x) = x^2 + c$ consider the iterates of all complex points z, $z_{n+1} = f(z_n)$ with $z_0 = z$. For each z, either the iterates remain bounded (z is in the *prisoner set*) or they escape to infinity (z is in the *escape set*). The Julia set J_c is the common boundary between these two sets. Using lighter colors to indicate a "faster" escape to infinity, Figure 3.10.6 shows two Julia sets. One of these Julia sets is connected, the other is disconnected. The Mandelbrot set, M, is the set of those complex values c for which J_c is a connected set (see Figure 3.10.7). Alternately, the *Mandelbrot* set consists of all points c for which the discrete dynamical system, $z_{n+1} = z_n^2 + c$ with $z_0 = 0$, converges.

The boundary of the Mandelbrot set is a *fractal*. There is no universally agreed upon definition of "fractal". One definition is that it is a set whose fractal dimension differs from its topological dimension.

3.11   OPERATIONS RESEARCH

3.11.1   LINEAR PROGRAMMING

Linear programming (LP) is a technique for modeling problems with linear objective functions and linear constraints. The standard form for an LP model with n decision

FIGURE 3.10.6
Connected Julia set for $c = -0.5i$ (left). Disconnected Julia set for $c = -\frac{3}{4}(1 + i)$ (right).

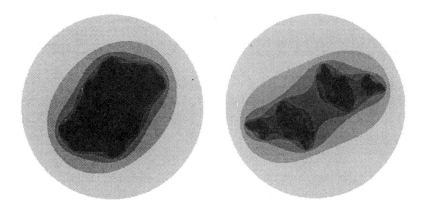

FIGURE 3.10.7
The Mandelbrot set. The leftmost point has the coordinates $(-2, 0)$.

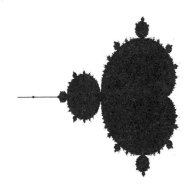

variables and m resource constraints is

$$\text{Minimize} \quad \sum_{j=1}^{n} c_j x_j \quad \text{(objective function)},$$

$$\text{Subject to} \quad \begin{cases} x_j \geq 0 \quad \text{for } j = 1, \cdots, n, \\ \sum_{j=1}^{n} a_{ij} x_j = b_i \quad \text{for } i = 1, \cdots, m \quad \text{(constraint functions)}, \end{cases} \quad (3.11.1)$$

where x_j is the amount of decision variable j used, c_j is decision $j's$ per unit contribution to the objective, a_{ij} is decision $j's$ per unit usage of resource i, and b_i is the total amount of resource i available. Let $\mathbf{x}$ represent the $(n \times 1)$ vector $(x_1, x_2, \cdots, x_n)^{\text{T}}$, $\mathbf{c}$ the $(1 \times n)$ vector $(c_1, c_2, \cdots, c_n)$, $\mathbf{b}$ the $(m \times 1)$ vector $(b_1, b_2, \cdots, b_m)^{\text{T}}$, A the $(m \times n)$ matrix (a_{ij}), and $\mathbf{A}_{.j}$ the $(n \times 1)$ column of A associated with x_j.

The standard model, written in matrix notation, is "minimize $\mathbf{cx}$ subject to $A\mathbf{x} \geq \mathbf{b}$ and $\mathbf{x} \geq \mathbf{0}$." A vector $\mathbf{x}$ is called *feasible* if, and only if, $A\mathbf{x} = \mathbf{b}$ and $\mathbf{x} \geq \mathbf{0}$.

Modeling in LP

LP is an appropriate modeling technique if the following four assumptions are satisfied by the situation:

1. All data coefficients are known with certainty.
2. There is a single objective.
3. The problem relationships are linear functions of the decisions.
4. The decisions can take on continuous values.

Branches of optimization such as stochastic programming, multiobjective programming, nonlinear programming, and integer programming have developed in operations research to allow a richer variety of models and solution techniques for situations where the assumptions required for LP are inappropriate.

- Product mix problem:
  Consider a company that has three products to sell. Each product requires four operations and the per unit data are given in the following table:

Product	Drilling	Assembly	Finishing	Packing	Profit
A	2	3	1	2	45
B	3	6	2	4	90
C	2	1	4	1	55
Hours available	480	960	540	320	

Let x_A, x_B, and x_C represent the number of units of A, B, and C manufactured daily. A model to maximize profit subject to the labor restrictions is

$$\text{Maximize} \quad 45x_A + 90x_B + 55x_C \qquad \text{(total profit)},$$

$$\text{Subject to:} \begin{cases} 2x_A + 3x_B + 2x_C \leq 480 & \text{(drilling hours)}, \\ 3x_A + 6x_B + 1x_C \leq 960 & \text{(assembly hours)}, \\ 1x_A + 2x_B + 4x_C \leq 540 & \text{(finishing hours)}, \\ 2x_A + 4x_B + 1x_C \leq 320 & \text{(packing hours)}, \\ x_A \geq 0, \quad x_B \geq 0, \quad x_C \geq 0. \end{cases} \qquad (3.11.2)$$

- Maximum flow through a network:
  Consider the directed network in Figure 3.11.8. Node S denotes the source node and node T denotes the terminal node. On each arc shipping material up to the arc capacity C_{ij} is permitted. Material is neither created nor destroyed at nodes other than S and T. The goal is to maximize the amount of material that can be shipped through the network from S to T. Letting x_{ij} represent the amount of material shipped from node i to node j, a model that determines the maximum flow is shown below.

FIGURE 3.11.8
Directed network modeling a flow problem.

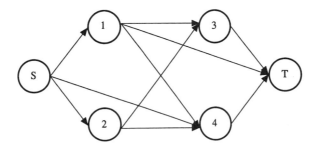

Maximize $x_{1T} + x_{3T} + x_{4T}$,

Subject to
$$
\begin{cases}
x_{S1} = x_{13} + x_{14} + x_{1T} & \text{(node 1 conservation),} \\
x_{S2} = x_{23} + x_{24} & \text{(node 2 conservation),} \\
x_{13} + x_{23} = x_{3T} & \text{(node 3 conservation),} \\
x_{S4} + x_{24} + x_{14} = x_{4T} & \text{(node 4 conservation),} \\
0 \le x_{ij} \le C_{ij} & \text{for all } (i, j) \text{ pairs   (arc capacity).}
\end{cases}
$$
(3.11.3)

Transformation to standard form

Any LP model can be transformed to standard form using the operations in the following table:

Original model	Standard form
maximize objective	minimize objective
multiply c_j by -1 (for example: $c_j = -c_j$)	
$\le$ constraint	$=$ constraint
add slack variable(s) to $\displaystyle\sum_{j=1}^{n} a_{ij}x_j \le b_i$	
(for example: $\displaystyle\sum_{j=1}^{n} a_{ij}x_j + S_i = b_i$.)	
$\ge$ constraint	$=$ constraint
subtract surplus variable(s) from $\displaystyle\sum_{j=1}^{n} a_{ij}x_j \ge b_i$	
(for example: $\displaystyle\sum_{j=1}^{n} a_{ij}x_j - U_i = b_i$)	
$=$ constraint	$=$ constraint
no change required	

LP requires that the slack and surplus variables be nonnegative, therefore, decisions are feasible to the new constraint if, and only if, they are feasible to the original constraint. All slack and surplus variables have $c_j = 0$.

Solving LP models: simplex method

Assume that there is at least one feasible $\mathbf{x}$ vector, and that A has rank m. Geometrically, because all constraints are linear, the set of feasible $\mathbf{x}$ forms a convex polyhedral set (bounded or unbounded) that must have at least one extreme point. The motivation for the simplex method for solving LP models is the following:

> For any LP model with a bounded optimal solution, an optimal solution exists at an extreme point of the feasible set.

Given a feasible solution $\mathbf{x}$, let $\mathbf{x}^B$ be the components of $\mathbf{x}$ with $x_j > 0$ and $\mathbf{x}^N$ be the components with $x_j = 0$. Associated with $\mathbf{x}^B$, define B as the columns of A associated with each x_j in $\mathbf{x}^B$. For example, if x_2, x_4, and S_1 are positive in $\mathbf{x}$, then $x^B = (x_2, x_4, S_1)$, and B is the matrix with columns $A_{.2}, A_{.4}, A_{.S_1}$. Define N as the remaining columns of A, i.e., those associated with $\mathbf{x}^N$. A *basic feasible solution* (BFS) is a feasible solution where the columns of B are linearly independent. The following theorem relates a BFS with extreme points:

> A feasible solution $\mathbf{x}$ is at an extreme point of the feasible region if, and only if, $\mathbf{x}$ is a BFS.

The following simplex method finds an optimal solution to the LP by finding the optimal partition of $\mathbf{x}$ into $\mathbf{x}^B$ and $\mathbf{x}^N$:

1. Find an initial basic feasible solution. Define $\mathbf{x}^B$, $\mathbf{x}^N$, B, N, $\mathbf{c}^B$, and $\mathbf{c}^N$ as above.

2. Compute the vector $\mathbf{c}' = (\mathbf{c}^N - \mathbf{c}^B B^{-1} N)$. If $c'_j \geq 0$ for all j, then stop; the solution $\mathbf{x}^B = B^{-1}\mathbf{b}$ is optimal with objective value $\mathbf{c}^B B^{-1}\mathbf{b}$. Otherwise, select the variable x_j in $\mathbf{x}^N$ with the most negative c'_j value, and go to step 3.

3. Compute $\mathbf{A}'_{.j} = B^{-1}\mathbf{A}_{.j}$. If $A'_{ij} \leq 0$ for all j, then stop; the problem is unbounded and the objective can decrease to $-\infty$. Otherwise, compute $\mathbf{b}' = B^{-1}\mathbf{b}$ and find $\min\limits_{i | a'_{ij} > 0} \dfrac{b'_i}{a'_{ij}}$. Assume the minimum ratio occurs in row r. Insert x_j into the rth position of $\mathbf{x}^B$, take the variable that was in this position, and move it to $\mathbf{x}^N$. Update B, N, $\mathbf{c}^B$, and $\mathbf{c}^N$ accordingly. Return to step 2.

Ties in the selections in steps 2 and 3 can be broken arbitrarily. The unboundedness signal suggests that the model is missing constraints or that there has been a data entry or computational error, because, in real problems, the profit or cost cannot be unbounded. For maximization problems, only step 2 changes. The solution is optimal when $c'_j \leq 0$ for all j, then choose the variable with the maximum c'_j value to move into $\mathbf{x}^B$. Effective methods for updating B^{-1} in each iteration of step 3 exist to ease the computational burden.

To find an initial basic feasible solution define a variable A_i and add this variable to the left hand side of constraint i transforming to $\sum_{j=1}^{n} a_{ij} + A_i = b_i$. The new constraint is equivalent to the original constraint if, and only if, $A_i = 0$. Also, because A_i appears only in constraint i and there are m A_i variables, the columns corresponding to the A_i variables are a rank m linearly independent set. We now solve a "new" LP model with the adjusted constraints and the new objective "minimize $\sum_{i=1}^{m} A_i$." If the optimal solution to this new model is 0, the solution is a basic feasible solution to the original problem. Otherwise, no basic feasible solution exists for the original problem.

Solving LP models: interior point method

An alternative method to searching extreme points is to cut through the middle of the polyhedron and go directly towards the optimal solution. Extreme points, however, provide an efficient method of determining movement directions (step 1 of simplex method) and movement distances (step 2 of simplex method). There were no effective methods on the interior of the feasible set until Karmarkar's method was developed in 1984. The method assumes that the model has the following form:

$$\text{Minimize} \quad \sum_{j=1}^{n} c_j x_j,$$

$$\text{Subject to} \quad \begin{cases} \sum_{j=1}^{n} a_{ij} x_j = 0 & \text{for } i = 1, \cdots, m, \\ \sum_{j=1}^{n} x_j = 1, \\ x_j \geq 0, & \text{for } j = 1, \cdots, n. \end{cases} \quad (3.11.4)$$

Also, assume that the optimal objective value is 0 and that the $x_j = 1/n$ for $j = 1, \cdots, n$ is feasible. Any model can be transformed so that these assumptions hold.

The following *centering transformation*, relative to the kth estimate of solution vector $\mathbf{x}^k$, takes any feasible solution vector $\mathbf{x}$ and transforms it to $\mathbf{y}$ such that the $\mathbf{x}^k$ is transformed to the center of the feasible simplex: $\mathbf{y}_j = \dfrac{x_j/x_j^k}{\sum_{r=1}^{n}(x_r/x_r^k)}$. Let $\text{Diag}(x^k)$ represent an $n \times n$ matrix with off-diagonal entries equal to 0 and the diagonal entry in row j equal to x_j^k. The formal algorithm is as follows:

1. Initialize $x_j^0 = 1/n$ and set the iteration count $k = 0$.

2. If $\sum_{j=1}^{n} x_j^k c_j$ is sufficiently close to 0, then stop. $\mathbf{x}^k$ is optimal. Otherwise go to step 3.

3. Move from the center of the transformed space in an improving direction using

$$\mathbf{y}^{k+1} = \left[\frac{1}{n}, \frac{1}{n}, \cdots, \frac{1}{n} \right]^{\text{T}} - \frac{\theta(I - P^T(PP^T)^{-1}P)[\text{Diag}(\mathbf{x}^k)]\mathbf{c}^{\text{T}}}{\|C_p\|\sqrt{n(n-1)}},$$

where $\|C_p\|$ is the length of the vector $(I - P^T(PP^T)^{-1}P)[\text{Diag}(\mathbf{x}^k)]\mathbf{c}^T$, P is an $(m+1) \times n$ matrix whose first m rows are $A[\text{Diag}(\mathbf{x}^k)]$ and whose last row is a vector of $1's$, and θ is a parameter that must be between 0 and 1. Go to step 4.

4. Find the new point $\mathbf{x}^{k+1}$ in the original space by applying the inverse transformation of the centering transformation to $\mathbf{y}^{k+1}$. Set $k = k + 1$ and return to step 2.

The method is guaranteed to converge to the optimal solution when $\theta = \frac{1}{4}$ is used.

3.11.2 DUALITY AND COMPLEMENTARY SLACKNESS

Define y_i as the *dual variable (shadow price)* representing the purchase price for a unit of resource i. The *dual problem* to the primal model (maximize objective, all $\leq$ constraints) is

$$\text{Minimize} \sum_{i=1}^{m} b_i y_i,$$

$$\text{Subject to} \begin{cases} \sum_{i=1}^{m} a_{ij} y_i \geq c_j & \text{for } j = 1, \ldots, n, \\[2mm] y_i \geq 0, & \text{for } i = 1, \ldots, m. \end{cases} \qquad (3.11.5)$$

The objective minimizes the amount of money spent to obtain the resources. The constraints ensure that the marginal cost of the resources is greater than or equal to the marginal profit for each product.

The following results link the dual model (minimization) with its primal model (maximization).

- Weak duality theorem: Assume that $\mathbf{x}$ and $\mathbf{y}$ are feasible solutions to the respective primal and dual problems. Then

$$\sum_{j=1}^{n} c_j x_j \leq \sum_{i=1}^{m} b_i y_i.$$

- Strong duality theorem: Assume that the primal has a finite optimal solution $\mathbf{x}^*$. Then the dual has a finite optimal solution $\mathbf{y}^*$, and

$$\sum_{j=1}^{n} c_j x_j^* = \sum_{i=1}^{m} b_i y_i^*.$$

- Complementary slackness theorem: Assume that x and y are feasible solutions to the respective primal and dual problems. Then, x is optimal for the primal and y is optimal for the dual if and only if:

$$y_i \cdot \left(b_i - \sum_{j=1}^{n} a_{ij} x_j \right) = 0, \qquad \text{for } i = 1, \cdots, m,$$

$$\text{and } x_j \cdot \left(\sum_{i=1}^{m} a_{ij} y_i - c_j \right) = 0, \qquad \text{for } j = 1, \cdots, n. \qquad (3.11.6)$$

3.11.3 LINEAR INTEGER PROGRAMMING

Linear integer programming models result from restricting the decisions in linear programming models to be integer valued. The standard form is

$$\text{Minimize} \quad \sum_{j=1}^{n} c_j x_j \quad \text{(objective function)},$$

Subject to
$$
\begin{cases}
x_j \geq 0, & \text{and integer for } j = 1, \ldots, n, \\
\sum_{j=1}^{n} a_{ij} x_j = b_i & \text{for } i = 1, \ldots, m \quad \text{(constraint functions)}.
\end{cases}
\qquad (3.11.7)
$$

As long as the variable values are bounded, then the general model can be transformed into a model where all variable values are restricted to either 0 or 1. Therefore, algorithms that can solve 0–1 integer programming models are sufficient for most applications.

3.11.4 BRANCH AND BOUND

Branch and bound implicitly enumerates all feasible integer solutions to find the optimal solution. The main idea is to break the feasible set into subsets (branching) and then evaluate the best solution in each subset or determine that the subset cannot contain the optimal solution (bounding). When a subset is evaluated, it is said to be "fathomed". The following algorithm performs the branching by partitioning on variables with fractional values and uses a linear programming relaxation to generate a bound on the best solution in a subset:

1. Assume that a feasible integer solution, denoted "the incumbent", is known whose objective function value is z (initially, z may be set to infinity if no feasible solution is known). Set p, the subset counter equal to 1. Set the original model as the first problem in the subset list.

2. If $p = 0$, then stop. The incumbent solution is the optimal solution. Otherwise go to step 3.

3. Solve the LP relaxation of problem p in the subset list (allow all integer valued variables to take on continuous values). Denote the LP objective value by v. If $v \geq z$ or the LP is infeasible, then set $p = p - 1$ (fathom by bound or infeasibility), and return to step 2. If the LP solution is integer valued, then update the incumbent to the LP solution, set $z = \min(z, v)$ and $p = p - 1$, and return to step 2. Otherwise, go to step 4.

4. Take any variable x_j with fractional value in the LP solution. Replace problem p with two problems created by individually adding the constraints $x_j \leq \lfloor x_j \rfloor$ and $x_j \geq \lceil x_j \rceil$ to problem p. Add these two problems to the bottom of the subset list, set $p = p + 1$, and go to step 2.

3.11.5   NETWORK FLOW METHODS

A network consists of N, the set of nodes, and A, the set of arcs. Each arc (i, j) defines a connection from node i to node j. Depending on the application, arc (i, j) may have an associated cost and upper and lower capacity on flow.

Decision problems on networks can often be modeled using linear programming models, and these models usually have the property that solutions from the simplex method are integer valued (the total unimodularity property). Because of the underlying graphical structure, more efficient algorithms are also available. We present the augmenting path algorithm for the maximum flow problem and the Hungarian method for the assignment problem.

Maximum flow

Let x_{ij} represent the flow on arc (i, j), c_{ij} the flow capacity of (i, j), S be the source node, and T be the terminal node. The maximum flow problem is to ship as much flow from S to T without violating the capacity on any arc, and all flow sent into node i must leave i (for $i \neq S, T$). The following algorithm solves the problem by continually adding flow-carrying paths until no path can be found:

1. Initialize $x_{ij} = 0$ for all (i, j).

2. Find a flow-augmenting path from S to T using the following labeling method. Start by labeling S with a^*. From any labeled node i, label node j with the label i if j is unlabeled and $x_{ij} < c_{ij}$ ("forward labeling arc"). From any labeled node i, label node j with the label i if j is unlabeled and $x_{ji} > 0$ ("backward labeling arc"). Perform labeling until no additional nodes can be labeled. If T cannot be labeled, then stop. The current x_{ij} values are optimal. Otherwise, go to step 3.

3. There is a path from S to T where flow is increased on the forward labeling arcs, decreased on the backward labeling arcs, and gets more flow from S to T. Let F be the minimum of $c_{ij} - x_{ij}$ over all forward labeling arcs and of x_{ij} over all backward labeling arcs. Set $x_{ij} = x_{ij} + F$ for the forward arcs and $x_{ij} = x_{ij} - F$ for the backward arcs. Return to step 2.

The algorithm terminates with a set of arcs with $x_{ij} = c_{ij}$ and if these are deleted, then S and T are in two disconnected pieces of the network. The algorithm finds the maximum flow by finding the minimum capacity set of arcs that disconnects S and T (minimum capacity cutset).

3.11.6   ASSIGNMENT PROBLEM

Consider a set J of jobs and a set I of employees. Each employee can do 1 job, and each job must be done by 1 employee. If job j is assigned to employee i, then the cost to the company is c_{ij}. The problem is to assign employees to jobs to minimize the overall cost.

This problem can be formulated as an optimization problem on a bipartite graph where the jobs are one part and the employees are the other. Let m be the cardinality of J and I (they must be equal cardinality sets or there is no feasible solution), and let C be the $m \times m$ matrix of costs c_{ij}. The following algorithm solves for the optimal assignment.

1. Find $l_i = \min_j c_{ij}$ for each row i. Let $c_{ij} = c_{ij} - l_i$. Find $n_j = \min_i c_{ij}$ for each column j. Let $c_{ij} = c_{ij} - n_j$.

2. Construct a graph with nodes for S, T, and each element of the sets J and I. Construct an arc from S to each node in I, and set its capacity to 1. Construct an arc from each node in J to T, and set its capacity to 1. If $c_{ij} = 0$, then construct an arc from $i \in I$ to $j \in J$, and set its capacity to 2. Solve a maximum flow problem on the constructed graph. If m units of flow can go through the network, then stop. The maximum flow solution on the arcs between I and J represents the optimal assignment. Otherwise, go to step 3.

3. Update C using the following rules based on the labels in the solution to the maximum flow problem: Let L_I and L_J be the set of elements of I and J respectively with labels when the maximum flow algorithm terminates. Let $\delta = \min_{i \in L_I, j \in (J - L_J)} c_{ij}$; note that $\delta > 0$. For $i \in L_I$ and $j \in (J - L_J)$, set $c_{ij} = c_{ij} - \delta$. For $i \in (I - L_I)$ and $j \in L_J$, set $c_{ij} = c_{ij} + \delta$. Leave all other c_{ij} values unchanged. Return to step 2.

In step 3, the algorithm creates new arcs, eliminates some unused arcs, and leaves unchanged arcs with $x_{ij} = 1$. When returning to step 2, you can solve the next maximum flow problem by adding and deleting the appropriate arcs and starting with the flows and labels of the preceding execution of the maximum flow algorithm.

3.11.7 DYNAMIC PROGRAMMING

Dynamic programming is a technique for determining a sequence of optimal decisions for a system or process that operates over time and requires successive dependent decisions. The following five properties are required for using dynamic programming:

1. The system can be characterized by a set of parameters called *state variables*.

2. At each decision point or *stage* of the process, there is a choice of actions.

3. Given the current state and the decision, it is possible to specify how the state evolves before the next decision.

4. Only the current state matters, not the path by which the system arrived at the state (termed "time separability").

5. An objective function depends on the state and the decisions made.

The separability requirement is necessary to formulate a functional form for the decision problem. Let $f_t^*(i)$ denote the optimal objective value to take the system from stage t to the end of the process, given that the process is now in state i, $A_t(i)$ is the set of decisions possible at stage t and state i, a_j is a particular action in $A_t(i)$, $\Delta_{it}(a_j)$ is the change from state i between stage t and stage $t+1$ based on the action taken, and $c_{it}(a_j)$ is the immediate impact on the objective of taking action a_j at stage t and state i.

The *principle of optimality* states as follows:

> An optimal sequence of decisions has the property that, whatever the initial state and initial decision are, the remaining decisions must be an optimal policy based on the state resulting from the initial information.

Using the principle, Bellman's equations are

$$f_t^*(i) = \min_{a_j \in A_t(i)} \{c_{it}(a_j) + f_{t+1}^*[\Delta_{it}(a_j)]\}, \qquad \text{for all } i.$$

3.11.8   SHORTEST PATH PROBLEM

Consider a network (N, A) where N is the set of nodes, A the set of arcs, and d_{ij} represents the "distance" of traveling on arc (i, j) (if no arc exists between i and j, $d_{ij} = \infty$). For any two nodes R and S, the shortest path problem is to find the shortest distance route through the network from R to S. Let the state space be N and a stage representing travel along one arc. $f^*(i)$ is the optimal distance from node i to S. The resultant recursive equations to solve are

$$f^*(i) = \min_{j \in N} \left[d_{ij} + f^*(j) \right], \qquad \text{for all } i.$$

Dijkstra's algorithm can be used successively to approximate the solution to the equations when $d_{ij} > 0$ for all (i, j).

1. Set $f^*(S) = 0$ and $f^*(i) = d_{iS}$ for all $i \in N$. Let P be the set of permanently labeled nodes. $P = \{S\}$. Let $T = N - P$ be the set of temporarily labeled nodes.

2. Find $i \in T$ with $f^*(i) = \min_{j \in T} f^*(j)$. Set $T = T - i$ and $P = P + i$. If $T = \emptyset$ (the empty set), then stop; $f^*(R)$ is the optimal path length. Otherwise, go to step 3.

3. Set $f^*(j) = \min[f^*(j), f^*(i) + d_{ij}]$ for all $j \in T$. Return to step 2.

References

1. B. Bollobás, *Graph Theory*, Springer–Verlag, Berlin, 1979.

2. J. O'Rourke and J.E. Goodman, *Handbook of Discrete and Computational Geometry*, CRC Press, Boca Raton, FL, to appear.

3. C. J. Colbourn and J.H. Dinitz, *Handbook of Combinatorial Designs*, CRC Press, Boca Raton, FL, 1996.

4. J. Gross, *Handbook of Graph Theory*, CRC Press, Boca Raton, FL, to appear.

5. F. Harary, *Graph Theory*, Addison–Wesley, Reading, MA, 1972.

6. F.J. MacWilliams and N.J.A. Sloane, *The Theory of Error-Correcting Codes*, North–Holland, Amsterdam, 1977.

Chapter 4

Geometry

0-8493-2479-3/96/$0.00+$.50
© 1996 CRC Press, Inc.

4.1   COORDINATE SYSTEMS IN THE PLANE

Convention

When we talk about "the point with coordinates (x, y)" or "the curve with equation $y = f(x)$", we always mean Cartesian coordinates. If a formula involves other coordinates, this fact will be stated explicitly.

4.1.1   SUBSTITUTIONS AND TRANSFORMATIONS

Formulas for changes in coordinate systems can lead to confusion because (for example) moving the coordinate axes *up* has the same effect on equations as moving objects *down* while the axes stay fixed. (To read the next paragraph, you can move your eyes down or slide the page up.)

   To avoid confusion, we will carefully distinguish between transformations of the plane and substitutions, as explained below. Similar considerations will apply to transformations and substitutions in three dimensions (Section 4.9).

Substitutions

A *substitution*, or *change of coordinates*, relates the coordinates of a point in one coordinate system to those of *the same point in a different coordinate system*. Usually one coordinate system has the superscript $'$ and the other does not, and we write

$$\begin{cases} x = F_x(x', y'), \\ y = F_y(x', y'), \end{cases} \qquad \text{or} \qquad (x, y) = F(x', y') \qquad (4.1.1)$$

(where subscripts are not derivatives). This means: given the equation of an object in the unprimed coordinate system, one obtains the equation of the *same* object in the primed coordinate system by substituting $F_x(x', y')$ for x and $F_y(x', y')$ for y in the equation. For instance, suppose the primed coordinate system is obtained from the unprimed system by moving the axes up a distance d. Then $x = x'$ and $y = y' + d$. The circle with equation $x^2 + y^2 = 1$ in the unprimed system has equation $x'^2 + (y' + d)^2 = 1$ in the primed system. Thus, transforming an implicit equation in (x, y) into one in (x', y') is immediate.

   The point $P = (a, b)$ in the unprimed system, with equation $x = a$, $y = b$, has equation $F_x(x', y') = a$, $F_y(x', y') = b$ in the new system. To get the primed coordinates explicitly, one must solve for x' and y' (in the example just given we have

$x' = a$, $y' + d = b$, which yields $x' = a$, $y' = b - d$). Therefore, if possible, we give the *inverse equations*

$$\begin{cases} x' = G_{x'}(x, y), \\ y' = G_{y'}(x, y) \end{cases} \qquad \text{or} \qquad (x', y') = G(x, y),$$

which are equivalent to Equation (4.1.1) if $G(F(x, y)) = (x, y)$ and $F(G(x, y)) = (x, y)$. Then to go from the unprimed to the unprimed system, one merely inserts the known values of x and y into these equations. This is also the best strategy when dealing with a curve expressed parametrically, that is, $x = x(t)$, $y = y(t)$.

Transformations

A *transformation* associates with each point (x, y) *a different point in the same coordinate system*; we denote this by

$$(x, y) \mapsto F(x, y), \tag{4.1.2}$$

where F is a map from the plane to itself (a two-component function of two variables). For example, translating down by a distance d is accomplished by $(x, y) \mapsto (x, y-d)$ (see Section 4.2). Thus, the action of the transformation on a point whose coordinates are known (or on a curve expressed parametrically) can be immediately computed.

   If, on the other hand, we have an object (say a curve) defined *implicitly* by the equation $C(x, y) = 0$, finding the equation of the transformed object requires using the *inverse transformation*

$$(x, y) \mapsto G(x, y)$$

defined by $G(F(x, y)) = (x, y)$ and $F(G(x, y)) = (x, y)$. The equation of the transformed object is $C(G(x, y)) = 0$. For instance, if C is the circle with equation $x^2 + y^2 = 1$ and we are translating down by a distance d, the inverse transformation is $(x, y) \mapsto (x, y + d)$ (translating up), and the equation of the translated circle is $x^2 + (y + d)^2 = 1$. Compare the example following Equation (4.1.1).

Using transformations to perform changes of coordinates

Usually, we will not give formulas of the form (4.1.1) for changes between two coordinate systems of the same type, because they can be immediately derived from the corresponding formulas (4.1.2) for transformations, which are given in Section 4.2. We give two examples for clarity.

   Let the two Cartesian coordinate systems (x, y) and (x', y') be related as follows: They have the same origin, and the positive x'-axis is obtained from the positive x-axis by a (counterclockwise) rotation through an angle θ (Figure 4.1.1). If a point has coordinates (x, y) in the unprimed system, its coordinates (x', y') in the primed system are the same as the coordinates in the unprimed system of a point that undergoes the *inverse rotation*, that is, a rotation by an angle $\alpha = -\theta$. According to Equation (4.2.1) (page 257), this transformation acts as follows:

$$(x, y) \mapsto \begin{bmatrix} \cos\theta & \sin\theta \\ -\sin\theta & \cos\theta \end{bmatrix} (x, y) = (x\cos\theta + y\sin\theta, \ -x\sin\theta + y\cos\theta). \tag{4.1.3}$$

FIGURE 4.1.1
Change of coordinates by a rotation.

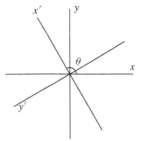

Therefore the right-hand side of Equation (4.1.3) is (x', y'), and the desired substitution is

$$x' = x \cos \theta + y \sin \theta,$$
$$y' = -x \sin \theta + y \cos \theta.$$

Switching the roles of the primed and unprimed systems we get the equivalent substitution

$$x = x' \cos \theta - y' \sin \theta,$$
$$y = x' \sin \theta + y' \cos \theta$$

(because the x-axis is obtained from the x'-axis by a rotation through an angle $-\theta$).

Similarly, let the two Cartesian coordinate systems (x, y) and (x', y') differ by a translation: x is parallel to x' and y to y', and the origin of the second system coincides with the point (x_0, y_0) of the first system. The coordinates (x, y) and (x', y') of a point are related by

$$
\begin{aligned}
x &= x' + x_0, & x' &= x - x_0, \\
y &= y' + y_0, & y' &= y - y_0.
\end{aligned}
\tag{4.1.4}
$$

4.1.2 CARTESIAN COORDINATES IN THE PLANE

In *Cartesian coordinates* (or *rectangular coordinates*), the "address" of a point P is given by two real numbers indicating the positions of the perpendicular projections from the point to two fixed, perpendicular, graduated lines, called the *axes*. If one coordinate is denoted x and the other y, the axes are called the *x-axis* and the *y-axis*, and we write $P = (x, y)$. Usually the x-axis is horizontal, with x increasing to the right, and the y-axis is vertical, with y increasing vertically up. The point $x = 0$, $y = 0$, where the axes intersect, is the *origin*. See Figure 4.1.2.

4.1.3 POLAR COORDINATES IN THE PLANE

In *polar coordinates* a point P is also characterized by two numbers: the distance $r \geq 0$ to a fixed *pole* or *origin* O, and the angle θ that the ray OP makes with a fixed

FIGURE 4.1.2

In Cartesian coordinates, $P_1 = (4, 3)$, $P_2 = (-1.3, 2.5)$, $P_3 = (-1.5, -1.5)$, $P_4 = (3.5, -1)$, and $P_5 = (4.5, 0)$. The axes divide the plane into four quadrants. P_1 is in the first quadrant, P_2 in the second, P_3 in the third, and P_4 in the fourth. P_5 is on the positive x-axis.

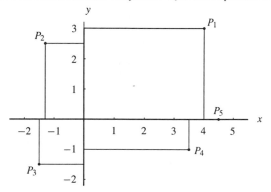

ray originating at O, which is generally drawn pointing to the right (this is called the *initial ray*). The angle θ is defined only up to a multiple of 360° or 2π radians. In addition, it is sometimes convenient to relax the condition $r > 0$ and allow r to be a signed distance, so (r, θ) and $(-r, \theta + 180°)$ represent the same point (Figure 4.1.3).

FIGURE 4.1.3

Among the possible sets of polar coordinates for P are $(10, 30°)$, $(10, 390°)$ and $(10, -330°)$. Among the sets of polar coordinates for Q are $(2.5, 210°)$ and $(-2.5, 30°)$.

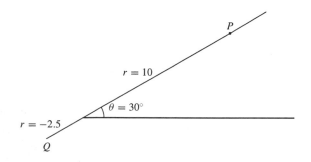

Relations between Cartesian and polar coordinates

Consider a system of polar coordinates and a system of Cartesian coordinates with the same origin. Assume that the initial ray of the polar coordinate system coincides with the positive x-axis, and that the ray $\theta = 90°$ coincides with the positive y-axis. Then the polar coordinates (r, θ) and the Cartesian coordinates (x, y) of the same point are related as follows:

$$\begin{cases} x = r\cos\theta, \\ y = r\sin\theta, \end{cases} \qquad \begin{cases} r = \sqrt{x^2 + y^2}, \\ \theta = \tan^{-1}\dfrac{y}{x}, \end{cases} \qquad \begin{cases} \sin\theta = \dfrac{y}{\sqrt{x^2 + y^2}}, \\ \cos\theta = \dfrac{x}{\sqrt{x^2 + y^2}}. \end{cases}$$

4.1.4   HOMOGENEOUS COORDINATES IN THE PLANE

A triple of real numbers $(x : y : t)$, with $t \neq 0$, is a set of *homogeneous coordinates* for the point P with Cartesian coordinates $(x/t, \ y/t)$. Thus the same point has many sets of homogeneous coordinates: $(x : y : t)$ and $(x' : y' : t')$ represent the same point if and only if there is some real number α such that $x' = \alpha x$, $y' = \alpha y$, $z' = \alpha z$.

When we think of the same triple of numbers as the Cartesian coordinates of a point in three-dimensional space (page 296), we write it as (x, y, t) instead of $(x : y : t)$. The connection between the point in space with Cartesian coordinates (x, y, t) and the point in the plane with homogeneous coordinates $(x : y : t)$ becomes apparent when we consider the plane $t = 1$ in space, with Cartesian coordinates given by the first two coordinates x, y of space (Figure 4.1.4). The point (x, y, t) in space can be connected to the origin by a line L that intersects the plane $t = 1$ in the point with Cartesian coordinates $(x/t, \ y/t)$ or homogeneous coordinates $(x : y : t)$.

FIGURE 4.1.4
The point P with spatial coordinates (x, y, t) projects to the point Q with spatial coordinates $(x/t, \ y/t, \ 1)$. The plane Cartesian coordinates of Q are $(x/t, \ y/t)$, and $(x : y : t)$ is one set of homogeneous coordinates for Q. Any point on the line L (except for the origin O) would also project to P'.

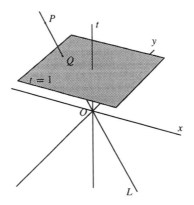

Projective coordinates are useful for several reasons. One the most important is that they allow one to unify all symmetries of the plane (as well as other transformations) under a single umbrella. All of these transformations can be regarded as linear maps in the space of triples $(x : y : t)$, and so can be expressed in terms of matrix multiplications (see page 258).

If we consider triples $(x : y : t)$ such that at least one of x, y, t is nonzero, we can name not only the points in the plane but also points "at infinity". Thus, $(x : y : 0)$ represents the point at infinity in the direction of the line whose slope is y/x.

4.1.5   OBLIQUE COORDINATES IN THE PLANE

The following generalization of Cartesian coordinates is sometimes useful. Consider two *axes* (graduated lines), intersecting at the *origin* but not necessarily perpendicularly. Let the angle between them be ω. In this system of *oblique coordinates*, a point P is given by two real numbers indicating the positions of the projections from the point to each axis, in the direction of the other axis (see Figure 4.1.5). The first axis (x-axis) is generally drawn horizontally. The case $\omega = 90°$ yields a Cartesian coordinate system.

FIGURE 4.1.5
In oblique coordinates, $P_1 = (4, 3)$, $P_2 = (-1.3, 2.5)$, $P_3 = (-1.5, -1.5)$, $P_4 = (3.5, -1)$, and $P_5 = (4.5, 0)$. Compare to Figure 4.1.2.

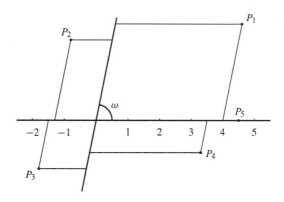

Relations between two oblique coordinate systems

Let the two oblique coordinate systems (x, y) and (x', y'), with angles ω and ω', share the same origin, and suppose the x'-axis makes an angle θ with the x-axis. The coordinates (x, y) and (x', y') of a point in the two systems are related by

$$x = \frac{x' \sin(\omega - \theta) + y' \sin(\omega - \omega' - \theta)}{\sin \omega},$$

$$y = \frac{x' \sin \theta + y' \sin(\omega' + \theta)}{\sin \omega}.$$

This formula also covers passing from a Cartesian system to an oblique system and vice versa, by taking $\omega = 90°$ or $\omega' = 90°$.

The relation between two oblique coordinate systems that differ by a translation is the same as for Cartesian systems. See Equation (4.1.4).

4.2 PLANE SYMMETRIES OR ISOMETRIES

A transformation of the plane (invertible map of the plane to itself) that preserves distances is called an *isometry* of the plane. Every isometry of the plane is of one of the following types:

- The *identity* (which leaves every point fixed)

- A *translation* by a vector **v**

- A *rotation* through an angle α around a point P

- A *reflection* in a line L

- A *glide-reflection* in a line L with displacement d

Although the identity is a particular case of a translation and a rotation, and reflections are particular cases of glide-reflections, it is more intuitive to consider each case separately.

4.2.1 FORMULAS FOR SYMMETRIES: CARTESIAN COORDINATES

In the formulas below, a multiplication between a matrix and a pair of coordinates should be carried out regarding the pair as a column vector (or a matrix with two rows and one column). Thus $\begin{bmatrix} a & b \\ c & d \end{bmatrix}(x, y) = (ax + by, \ cx + dy)$.

Translation by (x_0, y_0):

$$(x, y) \mapsto (x + x_0, \ y + y_0).$$

Rotation through α (counterclockwise) around the origin:

$$(x, y) \mapsto \begin{bmatrix} \cos \alpha & -\sin \alpha \\ \sin \alpha & \cos \alpha \end{bmatrix}(x, y). \qquad (4.2.1)$$

Rotation through α (counterclockwise) around an arbitrary point (x_0, y_0):

$$(x, y) \mapsto (x_0, y_0) + \begin{bmatrix} \cos \alpha & -\sin \alpha \\ \sin \alpha & \cos \alpha \end{bmatrix}(x - x_0, \ y - y_0).$$

Reflection:

$$
\begin{array}{ll}
\text{in the } x\text{-axis:} & (x, y) \mapsto (x, -y), \\
\text{in the } y\text{-axis:} & (x, y) \mapsto (-x, y), \\
\text{in the diagonal } x = y: & (x, y) \mapsto (y, x).
\end{array}
$$

Reflection in a line with equation $ax + by + c = 0$:

$$(x, y) \mapsto \frac{1}{a^2 + b^2}\left(\begin{bmatrix} b^2 - a^2 & -2ab \\ -2ab & a^2 - b^2 \end{bmatrix}(x, y) - (2ac, 2bc) \right).$$

Reflection in a line going through (x_0, y_0) and making an angle α with the x-axis:

$$(x, y) \mapsto (x_0, y_0) + \begin{bmatrix} \cos 2\alpha & \sin 2\alpha \\ \sin 2\alpha & -\cos 2\alpha \end{bmatrix} (x - x_0, \, y - y_0).$$

Glide-reflection in a line L with displacement d: Apply first a reflection in L, then a translation by a vector of length d in the direction of L, that is, by the vector

$$\frac{1}{a^2 + b^2}(\pm ad, \mp bd)$$

if L has equation $ax + by + c = 0$.

4.2.2   FORMULAS FOR SYMMETRIES: HOMOGENEOUS COORDINATES

All isometries of the plane can be expressed in homogeneous coordinates in terms of multiplication by a matrix. This fact is useful in implementing these transformations on a computer. It also means that the successive application of transformations reduces to matrix multiplication. The corresponding matrices are as follows:

Translation by (x_0, y_0):

$$T_{(x_0, y_0)} = \begin{bmatrix} 1 & 0 & x_0 \\ 0 & 1 & y_0 \\ 0 & 0 & 1 \end{bmatrix}.$$

Rotation through α around the origin:

$$R_\alpha = \begin{bmatrix} \cos \alpha & -\sin \alpha & 0 \\ \sin \alpha & \cos \alpha & 0 \\ 0 & 0 & 1 \end{bmatrix}.$$

Reflection in a line going through the origin and making an angle α with the x-axis:

$$M_\alpha = \begin{bmatrix} \cos 2\alpha & \sin 2\alpha & 0 \\ \sin 2\alpha & -\cos 2\alpha & 0 \\ 0 & 0 & 1 \end{bmatrix}.$$

From this one can deduce all other transformations. For example, to find the matrix for a rotation through α around an arbitrary point $P = (x_0, y_0)$, we apply a translation by $-(x_0, y_0)$ to move P to the origin, a rotation through α around the origin, and then a translation by (x_0, y_0):

$$T_{(x_0, y_0)} R_\alpha T_{-(x_0, y_0)} = \begin{bmatrix} \cos \alpha & -\sin \alpha & x_0 - x_0 \cos \alpha + y_0 \sin \alpha \\ \sin \alpha & \cos \alpha & y_0 - y_0 \cos \alpha - x_0 \sin \alpha \\ 0 & 0 & 1 \end{bmatrix}$$

(notice the order of the multiplication).

4.2.3 FORMULAS FOR SYMMETRIES: POLAR COORDINATES

Rotation around the origin through an angle α:

$$(r, \theta) \mapsto (r, \theta + \alpha).$$

Reflection in a line through the origin and making an angle α with the positive x-axis:

$$(r, \theta) \mapsto (r, 2\alpha - \theta).$$

4.2.4 CRYSTALLOGRAPHIC GROUPS

A group of symmetries of the plane that is doubly infinite is a *wallpaper group*, or *crystallographic group*. There are 17 types of such groups, corresponding to 17 essentially distinct ways to tile the plane in a doubly periodical pattern. (There are also 230 three-dimensional crystallographic groups.)

The simplest crystallographic group involves translations only (page 261, top left). The others involve, in addition to translations, one or more of the other types of symmetries (rotations, reflections, glide-reflections). The *Conway notation* for crystallographic groups is based on the types of nontranslational symmetries occurring in the "simplest description" of the group: * indicates a reflection (mirror symmetry), $^\times$ a glide-reflection, and a number n indicates a rotational symmetry of order n (rotation by $360°/n$). In addition, if a number n comes after the *, the center of the corresponding rotation lies on mirror lines, so that the symmetry there is actually dihedral of order $2n$.

Thus the group ** in the table below (page 261, middle left) has two inequivalent lines of mirror symmetry; the group 333 (page 263, top left) has three inequivalent centers of order-3 rotation; the group 22* (page 261, bottom right) has two inequivalent centers of order-2 rotation as well as mirror lines; and *632 (page 263, bottom) has points of dihedral symmetry of order $12(= 2 \times 6)$, 6, and 4.

The following table gives the groups in the Conway notation and in the notation traditional in crystallography. It also gives the quotient space of the plane by the action of the group. The entry "4,4,2 turnover" means the surface of a triangular puff pastry with corner angles $45°(= 180°/4)$, $45°$ and $90°$. The entry "4,4,2 turnover slit along 2,4" means the same surface, slit along the edge joining a $45°$ vertex to the $90°$ vertex. Open edges are silvered (mirror lines); such edges occur exactly for those groups whose Conway notation includes a *.

The last column of the table gives the dimension of the space of inequivalent groups of the given type (equivalent groups are those that can be obtained from one another by proportional scaling or rigid motion). For instance, there is a group of type $°$ for every shape parallelogram, and there are two degrees of freedom for the choice of such a shape (say the ratio and angle between sides). Thus, the $°$ group of page 261 (top left) is based on a square fundamental domain, while for the $°$ group of page 263 (top left) a fundamental parallelogram would have the shape of two juxtaposed equilateral triangles. These two groups are inequivalent, although they are of the same type.

Look on page	Conway	Cryst	Quotient space	Dim
261 top left; 263 top left	°	p1	Torus	2
261 top right	××	pg	Klein bottle	1
261 middle left	**	pm	Cylinder	1
261 middle right	×*	cm	Möbius strip	1
261 bottom left	22×	pgg	Nonorientable football	1
261 bottom right	22*	pmg	Open pillowcase	1
262 top left	2222	p2	Closed pillowcase	2
262 top right	2*22	cmm	4,4,2 turnover, slit along 4,4	1
262 middle left	*2222	pmm	Square	1
262 middle right	442	p4	4,4,2 turnover	0
262 bottom left	4*2	p4g	4,4,2 turnover, slit along 4,2	0
262 bottom right	*442	p4m	4,4,2 triangle	0
263 top right	333	p3	3,3,3 turnover	0
263 middle left	*333	p3m1	3,3,3 triangle	0
263 middle right	3*3	p31m	6,3,2 turnover, slit along 3,2	0
263 bottom left	632	p6	6,3,2 turnover	0
263 bottom right	*632	p6m	6,3,2 triangle	0

The figures on pages 261–263 show wallpaper patterns based on each of the 17 types of crystallographic groups (two patterns are shown for the °, or translations-only, type). Thin lines bound *unit cells*, or *fundamental domains*. When solid, they represent lines of mirror symmetry, and are fully determined. When dashed, they represent arbitrary boundaries, which can be shifted so as to give different fundamental domains. One can even make these lines into curves, provided the symmetry is respected. Dots at the intersections of thin lines represent centers of rotational symmetry.

Some of the relationships between the types are made obvious by the patterns. For instance, on the first row of page 261, we see that the group on the right, of type ××, contains the one on the left, of type °, with index two. However, there are more relationships than can be indicated in a single set of pictures. For instance, there is a group of type ×× hiding in any group of type 3*3.

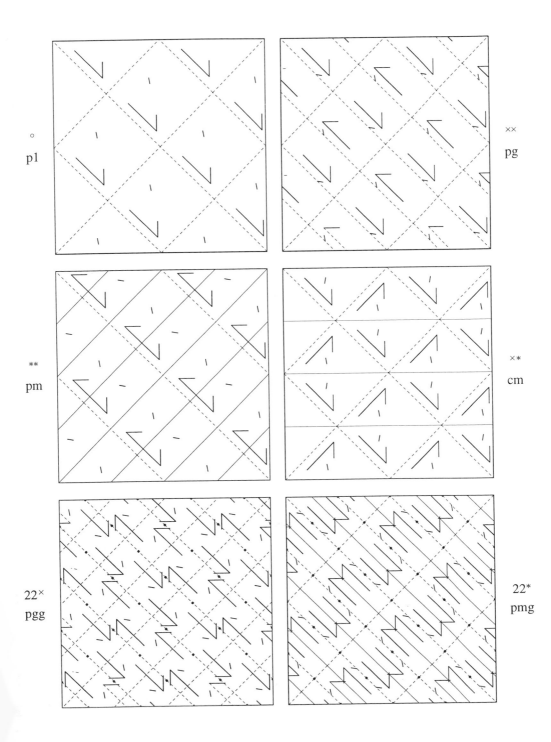

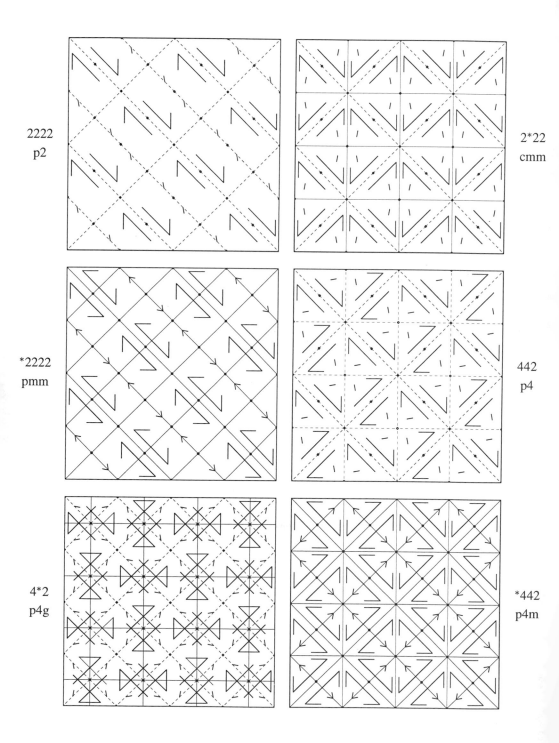

2222
p2

2*22
cmm

*2222
pmm

442
p4

4*2
p4g

*442
p4m

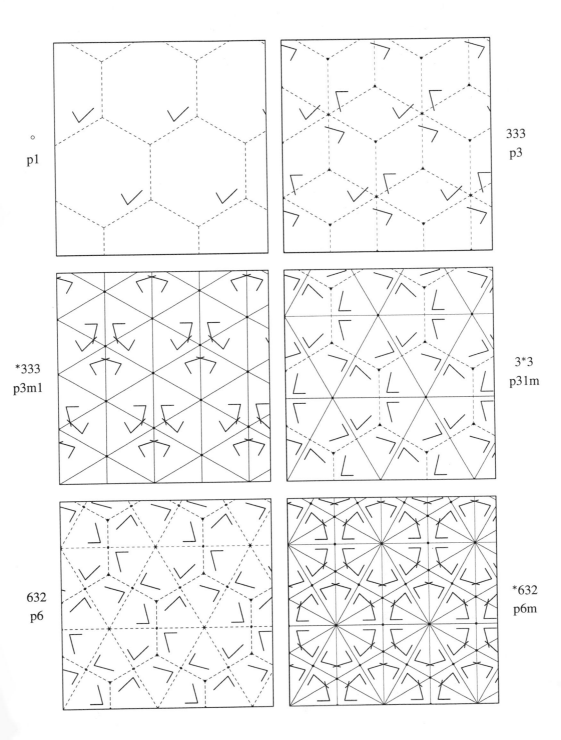

p1

333
p3

*333
p3m1

3*3
p31m

632
p6

*632
p6m

4.2.5 CLASSIFYING THE CRYSTALLOGRAPHIC GROUPS

To classify an image representing a crystallographic group, answer the following sequence of questions starting with: "What is the minimal rotational invariance?".

- None
  Is there a reflection?
    - No.
      Is there a glide-reflection?
        * No: p1 (page 261)
        * Yes: pg (page 261)
    - Yes.
      Is there a glide-reflection in an axis that is not a reflection axis?
        * No: pm (page 261)
        * Yes: cm (page 261)

- 2-fold (180° rotation)
  Is there a reflection?
    - No.
      Is there a glide-reflection?
        * No: p2 (page 262)
        * Yes: pgg (page 261)
    - Yes.
      Are there reflections in two directions?
        * No: pmg (page 261)
        * Yes: Are all rotation centers on reflection axes?
          · No: cmm   (page 262)
          · Yes: pmm   (page 262)

- 3-fold (120° rotation)
  Is there a reflection?
    - No: p3 (page 263)
    - Yes.
      Are all centers of threefold reflections on reflection axes?
        * No: p31m (page 263)
        * Yes: p3m1 (page 263)

- 4-fold (90° rotation)
  Is there a reflection?
    - No: p4 (page 262)
    - Yes.
      Are there four reflection axes?
        * No: p4g (page 262)
        * Yes: p4m (page 262)

- 6-fold (60° rotation)
  Is there a reflection?
    - No: p6 (page 263)
    - Yes: p6m (page 263)

4.3   OTHER TRANSFORMATIONS OF THE PLANE

4.3.1   SIMILARITIES

A transformation of the plane that preserves shapes is called a *similarity*. Every similarity of the plane is obtained by composing a *proportional scaling transformation* (also known as a *homothety*) with an isometry. A proportional scaling transformation centered at the origin has the form

$$(x, y) \mapsto (ax, ay),$$

where $a \neq 0$ is the scaling factor (a real number). The corresponding matrix in *homogeneous coordinates* is

$$H_a = \begin{bmatrix} a & 0 & 0 \\ 0 & a & 0 \\ 0 & 0 & 1 \end{bmatrix}.$$

In *polar coordinates*, the transformation is $(r, \theta) \mapsto (ar, \theta)$.

4.3.2   AFFINE TRANSFORMATIONS

A transformation that preserves lines and parallelism (maps parallel lines to parallel lines) is an *affine transformation*. There are two important particular cases of such transformations:

A *nonproportional scaling transformation* centered at the origin has the form $(x, y) \mapsto (ax, by)$, where $a, b \neq 0$ are the scaling factors (real numbers). The corresponding matrix in *homogeneous coordinates* is

$$H_{a,b} = \begin{bmatrix} a & 0 & 0 \\ 0 & b & 0 \\ 0 & 0 & 1 \end{bmatrix}.$$

A *shear* preserving horizontal lines has the form $(x, y) \mapsto (x + ry, y)$, where r is the shearing factor (see Figure 4.3.6). The corresponding matrix in *homogeneous coordinates* is

$$S_r = \begin{bmatrix} 1 & r & 0 \\ 0 & 1 & 0 \\ 0 & 0 & 1 \end{bmatrix}.$$

Every affine transformation is obtained by composing a scaling transformation with an isometry, or a shear with a homothety and an isometry.

FIGURE 4.3.6

A shear with factor $r = \frac{1}{2}$.

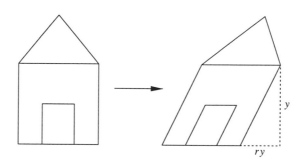

4.3.3 PROJECTIVE TRANSFORMATIONS

A transformation that maps lines to lines (but does not necessarily preserve parallelism) is a *projective transformation*. Any plane projective transformation can be expressed by an invertible 3×3 matrix in homogeneous coordinates; conversely, any invertible 3×3 matrix defines a projective transformation of the plane. Projective transformations (if not affine) are not defined on all of the plane but only on the complement of a line (the missing line is "mapped to infinity").

A common example of a projective transformation is given by a *perspective transformation* (Figure 4.3.7). Strictly speaking this gives a transformation from one plane to another, but, if we identify the two planes by (for example) fixing a Cartesian system in each, we get a projective transformation from the plane to itself.

FIGURE 4.3.7

A perspective transformation with center O, mapping the plane P to the plane Q. The transformation is not defined on the line L, where P intersects the plane parallel to Q and going through O.

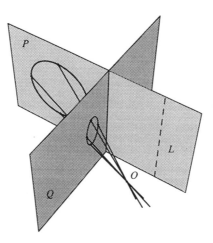

4.4 LINES

The (Cartesian) equation of a *straight line* is linear in the coordinates x and y:

$$ax + by + c = 0. \tag{4.4.1}$$

The *slope* of this line is $-a/b$, the *intersection with the x-axis* (or *x-intercept*) is $x = -c/a$, and the *intersection with the y-axis* (or *y*-intercept) is $y = -c/b$. If $a = 0$, the line is parallel to the x-axis, and if $b = 0$, then the line is parallel to the y-axis.

(In an *oblique coordinate system*, everything in the preceding paragraph remains true, except for the value of the slope.)

When $a^2 + b^2 = 1$ and $c \leq 0$ in the equation $ax + by + c = 0$, the equation is said to be in *normal form*. In this case c is the *distance of the line to the origin*, and $\omega = \sin^{-1} a = \cos^{-1} b$ is the angle that the perpendicular dropped to the line from the origin makes with the positive x-axis (Figure 4.4.8).

FIGURE 4.4.8
The normal form of the line L is $x \cos \omega + y \sin \omega = p$.

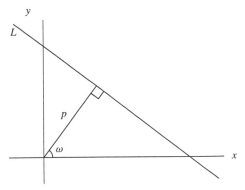

To reduce an arbitrary equation $ax + by + c = 0$ to normal form, divide by $\pm\sqrt{a^2 + b^2}$, where the sign of the radical is chosen opposite the sign of c when $c \neq 0$ and the same as the sign of b when $c = 0$.

Lines with prescribed properties

- Line of slope m intersecting the x-axis at $x = x_0$: $y = m(x + x_0)$.

- Line of slope m intersecting the y-axis at $y = y_0$: $y = mx + y_0$.

- Line intersecting the x-axis at $x = x_0$ and the y-axis at $y = y_0$:

$$\frac{x}{x_0} + \frac{y}{y_0} = 1.$$

(This formula remains true in *oblique coordinates*.)

- Line of slope m passing though (x_0, y_0): $y - y_0 = m(x - x_0)$.
- Line passing through points (x_0, y_0) and (x_1, y_1):

$$\frac{y - y_1}{x - x_1} = \frac{y_0 - y_1}{x_0 - x_1} \qquad \text{or} \qquad \begin{vmatrix} x & y & 1 \\ x_0 & y_0 & 1 \\ x_1 & y_1 & 1 \end{vmatrix} = 0. \qquad (4.4.2)$$

(These formulas remain true in *oblique coordinates*.)

- *Slope* of line going through points (x_0, y_0) and (x_1, y_1): $\dfrac{y_1 - y_0}{x_1 - x_0}$.
- Line passing through points with *polar coordinates* (r_0, θ_0) and (r_1, θ_1):

$$r(r_0 \sin(\theta - \theta_0) - r_1 \sin(\theta - \theta_1)) = r_0 r_1 \sin(\theta_1 - \theta_0). \qquad (4.4.3)$$

4.4.1   DISTANCES

The *distance* between two points in the plane is the *length of the line segment* joining the two points. If the points have *Cartesian coordinates* (x_0, y_0) and (x_1, y_1), this distance is

$$\sqrt{(x_1 - x_0)^2 + (y_1 - y_0)^2}. \qquad (4.4.4)$$

If the points have *polar coordinates* (r_0, θ_0) and (r_1, θ_1), this distance is

$$\sqrt{r_0^2 + r_1^2 - 2r_0 r_1 \cos(\theta_0 - \theta_1)}. \qquad (4.4.5)$$

If the points have *oblique coordinates* (x_0, y_0) and (x_1, y_1), this distance is

$$\sqrt{(x_1 - x_0)^2 + (y_1 - y_0)^2 + 2(x_1 - x_0)(y_1 - y_0) \cos \omega}, \qquad (4.4.6)$$

where ω is the angle between the axes (Figure 4.1.5).

The point $k\%$ of the way from $P_0 = (x_0, y_0)$ to $P_1 = (x_1, y_1)$ is

$$\left(\frac{kx_1 + (100 - k)x_2}{100}, \frac{ky_1 + (100 - k)y_2}{100} \right). \qquad (4.4.7)$$

(The same formula also works in oblique coordinates.) This point divides the segment $P_0 P_1$ in the ratio $k : (100 - k)$. As a particular case, the *midpoint* of $P_0 P_1$ is given by $\left(\frac{1}{2}(x_1 + x_2), \frac{1}{2}(y_1 + y_2) \right)$.

The *distance* from the point (x_0, y_0) to the line $ax + by + c = 0$ is

$$\left| \frac{ax_0 + by_0 + c}{\sqrt{a^2 + b^2}} \right|.$$

4.4.2 ANGLES

The *angle* between two lines $a_0 x + b_0 y + c_0 = 0$ and $a_1 x + b_1 y + c_1 = 0$ is

$$\tan^{-1} \frac{b_1}{a_1} - \tan^{-1} \frac{b_0}{a_0} = \tan^{-1} \frac{a_0 b_1 - a_1 b_0}{a_0 a_1 + b_0 b_1}. \tag{4.4.8}$$

In particular, the two lines are *parallel* when $a_0 b_1 = a_1 b_0$, and *perpendicular* when $a_0 a_1 = -b_0 b_1$.

The *angle* between two lines of slopes m_0 and m_1 is $\tan^{-1}((m_1 - m_0)/(1 + m_0 m_1))$. In particular, the two lines are *parallel* when $m_0 = m_1$ and *perpendicular* when $m_0 m_1 = -1$.

4.4.3 CONCURRENCE AND COLLINEARITY

Three lines $a_0 x + b_0 y + c_0 = 0$, $a_1 x + b_1 y + c_1 = 0$, and $a_2 x + b_2 y + c_2 = 0$ are *concurrent* if and only if

$$\begin{vmatrix} a_0 & b_0 & c_0 \\ a_1 & b_1 & c_1 \\ a_2 & b_2 & c_2 \end{vmatrix} = 0.$$

(This remains true in *oblique coordinates*.)

Three points (x_0, y_0), (x_1, y_1) and (x_2, y_2) are *collinear* if and only if

$$\begin{vmatrix} x_0 & y_0 & 1 \\ x_1 & y_1 & 1 \\ x_2 & y_2 & 1 \end{vmatrix} = 0.$$

(This remains true in *oblique coordinates*.)

Three points with polar coordinates (r_0, θ_0), (r_1, θ_1) and (r_2, θ_2) are collinear if and only if

$$r_1 r_2 \sin(\theta_2 - \theta_1) + r_0 r_1 \sin(\theta_1 - \theta_0) + r_2 r_0 \sin(\theta_0 - \theta_2) = 0.$$

4.5 POLYGONS

Given $k \geq 3$ points $A_1, \ldots, A_k$ in the plane, in a certain order, we obtain a *k-sided polygon* or *k-gon* by connecting each point to the next, and the last to the first, with a line segment. The points A_i are the *vertices* and the segments $A_i A_{i+1}$ are the *sides* or *edges* of the polygon. When $k = 3$ we have a *triangle*, when $k = 4$ we have a *quadrangle* or *quadrilateral*, and so on (see page 276). Here we will assume that all polygons are *simple*: this means that no consecutive edges are on the same line and no two edges intersect (except that consecutive edges intersect at the common vertex) (see Figure 4.5.9).

FIGURE 4.5.9

Two simple quadrilaterals (left and middle) and one that is not simple (right). We will treat only simple polygons.

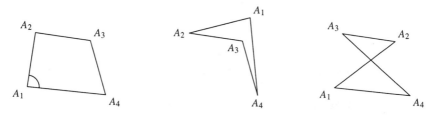

When we refer to the *angle* at a vertex A_k we have in mind the interior angle (as marked in the leftmost polygon in Figure 4.5.9). We denote this angle by the same symbol as the vertex. The complement of A_k is the *exterior angle* at that vertex; geometrically, it is the angle between one side and the extension of the adjacent side. *In any k-gon, the sum of the angles equals* $2(k-2)$ *right angles, or* $2(k-2) \times 90°$; for example, the sum of the angles of a triangle is $180°$.

The *area* of a polygon whose vertices A_i have coordinates (x_i, y_i), for $1 \le i \le k$, is the absolute value of

$$\text{area} = \tfrac{1}{2}(x_1 y_2 - x_2 y_1) + \cdots + \tfrac{1}{2}(x_{k-1} y_k - x_k y_{k-1}) + \tfrac{1}{2}(x_k y_1 - x_1 y_k),$$

$$= \frac{1}{2} \sum_{i=1}^{k} (x_i y_{i+1} - x_{i+1} y_i), \tag{4.5.1}$$

where in the summation we take $x_{k+1} = x_1$ and $y_{k+1} = y_1$. In particular, for a triangle we have

$$\text{area} = \tfrac{1}{2}(x_1 y_2 - x_2 y_1 + x_2 y_3 - x_3 y_2 + x_3 y_1 - x_1 y_3) = \frac{1}{2} \begin{vmatrix} x_1 & y_1 & 1 \\ x_2 & y_2 & 1 \\ x_3 & y_3 & 1 \end{vmatrix}.$$

In *oblique coordinates* with angle ω between the axes, the area is as given above, multiplied by $\sin \omega$.

If the vertices have *polar coordinates* (r_i, θ_i), for $1 \le i \le k$, the area is the absolute value of

$$\text{area} = \frac{1}{2} \sum_{i=1}^{k} r_i r_{i+1} \sin(\theta_{i+1} - \theta_i), \tag{4.5.2}$$

where we take $r_{k+1} = r_1$ and $\theta_{k+1} = \theta_1$.

Formulas for specific polygons in terms of side lengths, angles, etc., are given below.

4.5.1 TRIANGLES

Because the angles of a triangle add up to 180°, at least two of them must be acute (less than 90°). In an *acute triangle* all angles are acute. A *right triangle* has one right angle, and an *obtuse triangle* has one obtuse angle.

The *altitude* corresponding to a side is the perpendicular dropped to the line containing that side from the opposite vertex. The *bisector* of a vertex is the line that divides the angle at that vertex into two equal parts. The *median* is the segment joining a vertex to the midpoint of the opposite side. See Figure 4.5.10.

FIGURE 4.5.10

Notations for an arbitrary triangle of sides a, b, c and vertices A, B, C. The altitude corresponding to C is h_c, the median is m_c, the bisector is t_c. The radius of the circumscribed circle is R, that of the inscribed circle is r.

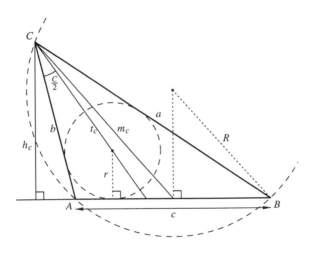

Every triangle also has an *inscribed circle* tangent to its sides and interior to the triangle (in other words, any three nonconcurrent lines determine a circle). The center of this circle is the point of intersection of the bisectors. We denote the radius of the inscribed circle by r.

Every triangle has a *circumscribed circle* going through its vertices; in other words, any three noncollinear points determine a circle. The point of intersection of the medians is the center of mass of the triangle (considered as an area in the plane). We denote the radius of the circumscribed circle by R.

Introduce the following notations for an *arbitrary triangle* of vertices A, B, C and sides a, b, c (see Figure 4.5.10). Let h_c, t_c, and m_c be the lengths of the altitude, bisector and median originating in vertex C, let r and R be as usual the radii of the inscribed and circumscribed circles, and let s be the semi-perimeter: $s = \frac{1}{2}(a+b+c)$.

Then

$$c^2 = a^2 + b^2 - 2ab \cos C \quad \textit{(law of cosines)},$$

$$a = b \cos C + c \cos B,$$

$$\frac{a}{\sin A} = \frac{b}{\sin B} = \frac{c}{\sin C} \quad \textit{(law of sines)},$$

$$\text{area} = \tfrac{1}{2} h_c c = \tfrac{1}{2} ab \sin C = \frac{c^2 \sin A \sin B}{2 \sin C} = rs = \frac{abc}{4R},$$

$$= \sqrt{s(s-a)(s-b)(s-c)} \quad \textit{(Heron)},$$

$$r = c \sin(\tfrac{1}{2}A) \sin(\tfrac{1}{2}B) \sec(\tfrac{1}{2}C) = \frac{ab \sin C}{2s} = (s-c) \tan(\tfrac{1}{2}C),$$

$$= \left(\frac{1}{h_a} + \frac{1}{h_b} + \frac{1}{h_c} \right)^{-1},$$

$$R = \frac{c}{2 \sin C} = \frac{abc}{4 \, \text{area}},$$

$$h_c = a \sin B = b \sin A = \frac{2 \, \text{area}}{c},$$

$$t_c = \frac{2ab}{a+b} \cos \tfrac{1}{2}C = \sqrt{ab\left(1 - \frac{c^2}{(a+b)^2}\right)}, \quad \text{and}$$

$$m_c = \sqrt{\tfrac{1}{2}a^2 + \tfrac{1}{2}b^2 - \tfrac{1}{4}c^2}.$$

A triangle is *equilateral* if all of its sides have the same length, or, equivalently, if all of its angles are the same (and equal to 60°). It is *isosceles* if two sides are the same, or, equivalently, if two angles are the same. Otherwise it is *scalene*.

For an *equilateral triangle* of side a we have

$$\text{area} = \tfrac{1}{4}a^2\sqrt{3}, \quad r = \tfrac{1}{6}a\sqrt{3}, \quad R = \tfrac{1}{3}a\sqrt{3}, \quad h = \tfrac{1}{2}a\sqrt{3},$$

where h is any altitude. The altitude, the bisector, and the median for each vertex coincide.

For an *isosceles triangle*, the altitude for the unequal side is also the corresponding bisector and median, but this is not true for the other two altitudes. Many formulas for an isosceles triangle of sides a, a, c can be immediately derived from those for a right triangle of legs $a, \tfrac{1}{2}c$ (see Figure 4.5.11, left).

For a *right triangle*, the *hypotenuse* is the longest side opposite the right angle; the *legs* are the two shorter sides adjacent to the right angle. The altitude for each leg equals the other leg. In Figure 4.5.11 (right), h denotes the altitude for the hypotenuse, while m and n denote the segments into which this altitude divides the hypotenuse.

The following formulas apply for a right triangle:

$$A + B = 90°, \qquad\qquad c^2 = a^2 + b^2 \quad \textit{(Pythagoras)},$$

$$r = \frac{ab}{a+b+c}, \qquad\qquad R = \tfrac{1}{2}c,$$

$$a = c \sin A = c \cos B, \qquad b = c \sin B = c \cos A,$$

$$mc = b^2, \qquad\qquad\qquad nc = a^2,$$

$$\text{area} = \tfrac{1}{2}ab, \qquad\qquad\quad hc = ab.$$

FIGURE 4.5.11
Left: an isosceles triangle can be divided into two congruent right triangles. Right: notations for a right triangle.

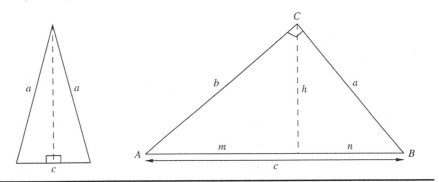

FIGURE 4.5.12
Left: Ceva's theorem. Right: Menelaus's theorem.

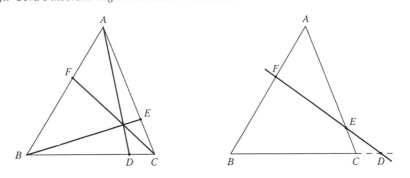

The hypotenuse is a diameter of the circumscribed circle. The median joining the midpoint of the hypotenuse (the center of the circumscribed circle) to the right angle makes angles $2A$ and $2B$ with the hypotenuse.

Additional facts about triangles:

1. In any triangle, the longest side is opposite the largest angle, and the shortest side is opposite the smallest angle. This follows from the law of sines.

2. *Ceva's theorem* (see Figure 4.5.12, left): In a triangle ABC, let D, E, and F be points on the lines BC, CA, and AB, respectively. Then the lines AD, BE, and CF are concurrent if, and only if, the signed distances BD, CE, ... satisfy

$$BD \cdot CE \cdot AF = DC \cdot EA \cdot FB.$$

This is so in three important particular cases: when the three lines are the medians, when they are the bisectors, and when they are the altitudes.

3. *Menelaus's theorem* (see Figure 4.5.12, right): In a triangle ABC, let D, E, and F be points on the lines BC, CA, and AB, respectively. Then D, E, and F are collinear if, and only if, the signed distances BD, CE, ... satisfy

$$BD \cdot CE \cdot AF = -DC \cdot EA \cdot FB.$$

4. Each side of a triangle is less than the sum of the other two. For any three lengths such that each is less than the sum of the other two, there is a triangle with these side lengths.

4.5.2 QUADRILATERALS

The following formulas give the area of a *general quadrilateral* (see Figure 4.5.13, left, for the notation).

$$\text{area} = \tfrac{1}{2}pq \sin\theta = \tfrac{1}{4}(b^2 + d^2 - a^2 - c^2)\tan\theta$$

$$= \tfrac{1}{4}\sqrt{4p^2q^2 - (b^2 + d^2 - a^2 - c^2)^2}$$

$$= \sqrt{(s-a)(s-b)(s-c)(s-d) - abcd\cos\tfrac{1}{2}(A+C)}. \qquad (4.5.3)$$

FIGURE 4.5.13

Left: notation for a general quadrilateral; in addition $s = \tfrac{1}{2}(a + b + c + d)$. *Right: a parallelogram.*

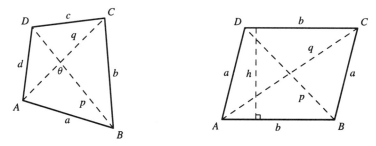

Often, however, it is easiest to compute the area by dividing the quadrilateral into triangles. One can also divide the quadrilateral into triangles to compute one side given the other sides and angles, etc.

More formulas can be given for *special cases* of quadrilaterals. In a *parallelogram*, opposite sides are parallel and the diagonals intersect in the middle (Figure 4.5.13, right). It follows that opposite sides have the same length and that two consecutive angles add up to 180°. In the notation of the figure, we have

$$A = C, \quad B = D, \qquad\qquad A + B = 180°,$$

$$h = a\sin A = a\sin B, \qquad\qquad \text{area} = bh,$$

$$p = \sqrt{a^2 + b^2 - 2ab\cos A}, \qquad q = \sqrt{a^2 + b^2 - 2ab\cos B}.$$

(All this follows from the triangle formulas applied to the triangles ABD and ABC.)

Two particular cases of parallelograms are

1. The *rectangle* ▭, where all angles equal 90°. The diagonals of a rectangle have the same length. The general formulas for parallelograms reduce to

$$h = a, \quad \text{area} = ab, \quad \text{and} \quad p = q = \sqrt{a^2 + b^2},$$

2. The *rhombus* or *diamond* $\diamond$, where adjacent sides have the same length ($a = b$). The diagonals of a rhombus are perpendicular. In addition to the general formulas for parallelograms, we have area $= \frac{1}{2}pq$ and $p^2 + q^2 = 4a^2$.

The *square* or regular quadrilateral is both a rectangle and a rhombus. See page 276.
    A quadrilateral is a *trapezoid* if two sides are parallel. In the notation of the figure on the right we have

$$A + D = B + C = 180°, \quad \text{area} = \frac{1}{2}(AB + CD)h.$$

    The diagonals of a quadrilateral with consecutive sides a, b, c, d are perpendicular if and only if $a^2 + c^2 = b^2 + d^2$.
    A quadrilateral is *cyclic* if it can be inscribed in a circle, that is, if its four vertices belong to a single, circumscribed, circle. This is possible if and only if the sum of opposite angles is 180°. If R is the radius of the circumscribed circle, we have (in the notation of Figure 4.5.13, left)

$$\text{area} = \sqrt{(s-a)(s-b)(s-c)(s-d)} = \frac{1}{2}(ac + bd)\sin\theta,$$

$$= \frac{\sqrt{(ac+bd)(ad+bc)(ab+cd)}}{4R} \quad \text{(Brahmagupta)},$$

$$p = \sqrt{\frac{(ac+bd)(ab+cd)}{(ad+bc)}},$$

$$R = \frac{1}{4}\sqrt{\frac{(ac+bd)(ad+bc)(ab+cd)}{(s-a)(s-b)(s-c)(s-d)}},$$

$$\sin\theta = \frac{2\,\text{area}}{ac+bd},$$

$$pq = ac + bd \quad \text{(Ptolemy)}.$$

    A quadrilateral is *circumscribable* if it has an inscribed circle (that is, a circle tangent to all four sides). Its area is rs, where r is the radius of the inscribed circle and s is as above.
    For a quadrilateral that is both cyclic and circumscribable, we have the following additional equalities, where m is the distance between the centers of the inscribed and circumscribed circles:

$$a + c = b + d,$$

$$R = \frac{1}{4}\sqrt{\frac{(ac+bd)(ad+bc)(ab+cd)}{abcd}},$$

$$\text{area} = \sqrt{abcd} = rs,$$

$$\frac{1}{r^2} = \frac{1}{(R-m)^2} + \frac{1}{(R+m)^2}.$$

4.5.3   REGULAR POLYGONS

A polygon is *regular* if all its sides are equal and all its angles are equal. Either condition implies the other in the case of a triangle, but not in general. (A rhombus has equal sides but not necessarily equal angles, and a rectangle has equal angles but not necessarily equal sides.)

For a k-sided regular polygon of side a, let θ be the angle at any vertex, and r and R the radii of the inscribed and circumscribed circles (r is called the *apothem*). As usual, let $s = \frac{1}{2}ka$ be the half-perimeter. Then

$$\theta = \left(\frac{k-2}{k}\right)180°,$$

$$a = 2r \tan \frac{180°}{k} = 2R \sin \frac{180°}{k},$$

$$\text{area} = \tfrac{1}{4}ks^2 \cot \frac{180°}{k} = kr^2 \tan \frac{180°}{k}$$

$$= \tfrac{1}{2}kR^2 \sin \frac{360°}{k},$$

$$r = \tfrac{1}{2}s \cot \frac{180°}{k},$$

$$R = \tfrac{1}{2}s \csc \frac{180°}{k}.$$

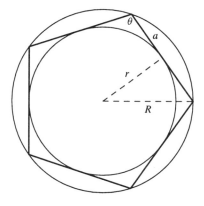

Name	k	Area	r	R
Equilateral triangle	3	$0.43301\,a^2$	$0.28868\,a$	$0.57735\,a$
Square	4	a^2	$0.50000\,a$	$0.70711\,a$
Regular pentagon	5	$1.72048\,a^2$	$0.68819\,a$	$0.85065\,a$
Regular hexagon	6	$2.59808\,a^2$	$0.86603\,a$	a
Regular heptagon	7	$3.63391\,a^2$	$1.03826\,a$	$1.15238\,a$
Regular octagon	8	$4.82843\,a^2$	$1.20711\,a$	$1.30656\,a$
Regular nonagon	9	$6.18182\,a^2$	$1.37374\,a$	$1.46190\,a$
Regular decagon	10	$7.69421\,a^2$	$1.53884\,a$	$1.61803\,a$
Regular undecagon	11	$9.36564\,a^2$	$1.70284\,a$	$1.77473\,a$
Regular dodecagon	12	$11.19625\,a^2$	$1.86603\,a$	$1.93185\,a$

If a_k denotes the side of a k-sided regular polygon inscribed in a circle of radius R, we have

$$a_{2k} = \sqrt{2R^2 - R\sqrt{4R^2 - a_k^2}}.$$

If A_k denotes the side of a k-sided regular polygon circumscribed about the same circle,

$$A_{2k} = \frac{2RA_k}{2R + \sqrt{4R^2 + A_k^2}}.$$

In particular,

$$A_{2k} = \frac{a_k A_k}{a_k + A_k}, \qquad a_{2k} = \sqrt{\frac{a_k A_{2k}}{2}}.$$

The areas s_k, s_{2k}, S_k and S_{2k} of the same polygons satisfy

$$s_{2k} = \sqrt{s_k S_k}, \qquad S_{2k} = \frac{2 s_{2k} S_k}{s_{2k} + S_k}.$$

4.6 CIRCLES

The set of points whose distance to a fixed point (the *center*) is a fixed positive number (the *radius*) is a *circle*. A circle of radius r and center (x_0, y_0) is described by the equation

$$(x - x_0)^2 + (y - y_0)^2 = r^2,$$

or

$$x^2 + y^2 - 2xx_0 - 2yy_0 + x_0^2 + y_0^2 - r^2 = 0.$$

Conversely, an equation of the form

$$x^2 + y^2 + 2dx + 2ey + f = 0$$

defines a circle if $d^2 + e^2 > f$; the center is $(-d, -e)$ and the radius is $\sqrt{d^2 + e^2 - f}$.

Three points not on the same line determine a unique circle. If the points have coordinates (x_1, y_1), (x_2, y_2) and (x_3, y_3), then the equation of the circle is

$$\begin{vmatrix} x^2 + y^2 & x & y & 1 \\ x_1^2 + y_1^2 & x_1 & y_1 & 1 \\ x_2^2 + y_2^2 & x_2 & y_2 & 1 \\ x_3^2 + y_3^2 & x_3 & y_3 & 1 \end{vmatrix} = 0.$$

A *chord* of a circle is a line segment between two points (Figure 4.6.14). A *diameter* is a chord that goes through the center, or the length of such a chord (therefore the diameter is twice the radius). Given two points $P_1 = (x_1, y_1)$ and $P_2 = (x_2, y_2)$, there is a unique circle whose diameter is $P_1 P_2$; its equation is

$$(x - x_1)(x - x_2) + (y - y_1)(y - y_2) = 0.$$

The *length* or *circumference* of a circle of radius r is $2\pi r$, and the *area* is πr^2. The length of the *arc of circle* subtended by an angle θ, shown as s in Figure 4.6.14, is $r\theta$. Other relations between the radius, the arc length, the chord, and the areas of the corresponding *sector* and *segment* are, in the notation of Figure 4.6.14,

$$d = R \cos \tfrac{1}{2}\theta = \tfrac{1}{2}c \cot \tfrac{1}{2}\theta = \tfrac{1}{2}\sqrt{4R^2 - c^2},$$

$$c = 2R \sin \tfrac{1}{2}\theta = 2d \tan \tfrac{1}{2}\theta = 2\sqrt{R^2 - d^2} = \sqrt{4h(2R - h)},$$

$$\theta = \frac{s}{R} = 2\cos^{-1}\frac{d}{R} = 2\tan^{-1}\frac{c}{2d} = 2\sin^{-1}\frac{c}{2R},$$

$$\text{area of sector} = \tfrac{1}{2}Rs = \tfrac{1}{2}R^2\theta,$$

$$\text{area of segment} = \tfrac{1}{2}R^2(\theta - \sin\theta) = \tfrac{1}{2}(Rs - cd) = R^2 \cos^{-1}\frac{d}{R} - d\sqrt{R^2 - d^2},$$

$$= R^2 \cos^{-1}\frac{R - h}{R} - (R - h)\sqrt{2Rh - h^2}.$$

FIGURE 4.6.14
The arc of a circle subtended by the angle θ is s; the chord is c; the sector is the whole slice of the pie; the segment is the cap bounded by the arc and the chord (that is, the slice minus the triangle).

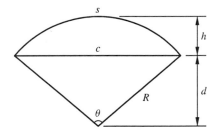

Other properties of circles:

1. If the central angle AOB equals θ, the angle ACB, where C is any point on the circle, equals $\tfrac{1}{2}\theta$ or $180° - \tfrac{1}{2}\theta$ (Figure 4.6.15, left). Conversely, given a segment AB, the set of points that "see" AB under a fixed angle is an arc of a circle (Figure 4.6.15, right). In particular, the set of points that see AB under a right angle is a circle with diameter AB.

2. Let P_1, P_2, P_3, P_4 be points in the plane, and let d_{ij}, for $1 \le i, j \le 4$, be the distance between P_i and P_j. A necessary and sufficient condition for all of the points to lie on the same circle (or line) is that one of the following equalities be satisfied:

$$\pm d_{12}d_{34} \pm d_{13}d_{24} \pm d_{14}d_{23} = 0.$$

This is equivalent to Ptolemy's formula for cyclic quadrilaterals (page 275).

3. In *oblique coordinates* with angle ω, a circle of center (x_0, y_0) and radius r is described by the equation

$$(x - x_0)^2 + (y - y_0)^2 + 2(x - x_0)(y - y_0) \cos\omega = r^2.$$

FIGURE 4.6.15

Left: the angle ACB equals $\frac{1}{2}\theta$ for any C in the long arc AB; ADB equals $180° - \frac{1}{2}\theta$ for any D in the short arc AB. Right: the locus of points, from which the segment AB subtends a fixed angle θ, is an arc of the circle.

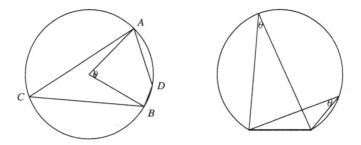

4. In *polar coordinates*, the equation for a circle centered at the pole and having radius a is $r = a$. The equation for a circle of radius a passing through the pole and with center at the point $(r, \theta) = (a, \theta_0)$ is $r = 2a\cos(\theta - \theta_0)$. The equation for a circle of radius a and with center at the point $(r, \theta) = (r_0, \theta_0)$ is

$$r^2 - 2r_0 r \cos(\theta - \theta_0) + r_0^2 - a^2 = 0.$$

5. If a line intersects a circle of center O at points A and B, the segments OA and OB make equal angles with the line. In particular, a tangent line is perpendicular to the radius that goes through the point of tangency.

6. Fix a circle and a point P in the plane, and consider a line through P that intersects the circle at A and B (with $A = B$ for a tangent). Then the product of the distances $PA \cdot PB$ is the same for all such lines. It is called the *power* of P with respect to the circle.

4.7 CONICS

A *conic* (or *conic section*) is a plane curve that can be obtained by intersecting a right circular cone (page 312) with a plane that does not go through the vertex of the cone. There are three possibilities, depending on the relative positions of the cone and the plane (Figure 4.7.16). If no line of the cone is parallel to the plane, then the intersection is a closed curve, called an *ellipse*. If one line of the cone is parallel to the plane, the intersection is an open curve whose two ends are asymptotically parallel; this is called a *parabola*. Finally, there may be two lines in the cone parallel to the plane; the curve in this case has two open segments, and is called a *hyperbola*.

FIGURE 4.7.16

A section of a cone by a plane can yield an ellipse (left), a parabola (middle) or a hyperbola (right).

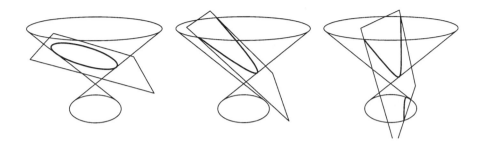

4.7.1   ALTERNATIVE CHARACTERIZATION

Assume given a point F in the plane, a line d not going through F, and a positive real number e. The set of points P such that the distance PF is e times the distance from P to d (measured along a perpendicular) is a conic. We call F the *focus*, d the *directrix*, and e the *eccentricity* of the conic. If $e < 1$ we have an ellipse, if $e = 1$ a parabola, and if $e > 1$ a hyperbola (Figure 4.7.17). This construction gives all conics except the circle, which is a particular case of the ellipse according to the earlier definition (we can recover it by taking the limit $e \to 0$).

FIGURE 4.7.17

Definition of conics by means of the ratio (eccentricity) between the distance to a point and the distance to a line. On the left, $e = .7$; in the middle, $e = 1$; on the right, $e = 2$.

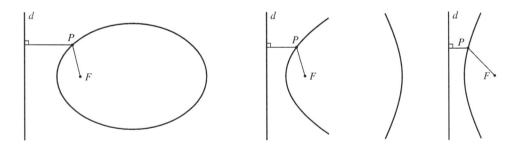

For any conic, a line perpendicular to d and passing through F is an axis of symmetry. The ellipse and the hyperbola have an additional axis of symmetry, perpendicular to the first, so that there is an alternate focus and directrix, F' and d', obtained as the reflection of F and d with respect to this axis. (By contrast, the focus and directrix are uniquely defined for a parabola.)

The simplest analytic form for the ellipse and hyperbola is obtained when the two symmetry axes coincide with the coordinate axes. The ellipse in Figure 4.7.18

has equation

$$\frac{x^2}{a^2} + \frac{y^2}{b^2} = 1,$$ (4.7.1)

with $b < a$. The x-axis is the *major axis*, and the y-axis is the *minor axis*. These names are also applied to the segments, determined on the axes by the ellipse, and to the lengths of these segments: $2a$ for the major axis and $2b$ for the minor. The *vertices* are the intersections of the major axis with the ellipse and have coordinates $(a, 0)$ and $(-a, 0)$. The distance from the center to either *focus* is $\sqrt{a^2 - b^2}$, and the sum of the distances from a point in the ellipse to the foci is $2a$. The *latera recta* (in the singular, *latus rectum*) are the chords perpendicular to the major axis and going through the foci; their length is $2b^2/a$. The *eccentricity* is $\sqrt{a^2 - b^2}/a$. All ellipses of the same eccentricity are similar; in other words, the shape of an ellipse depends only on the ratio b/a. The distance from the center to either *directrix* is $a^2/\sqrt{a^2 - b^2}$.

FIGURE 4.7.18
Ellipse with major semiaxis a and minor semiaxis b. Here b/a = 0.6.

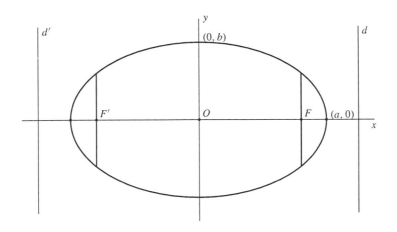

The hyperbola in Figure 4.7.19 has equation

$$\frac{x^2}{a^2} - \frac{y^2}{b^2} = 1.$$ (4.7.2)

The x-axis is the *transverse axis*, and the y-axis is the *conjugate axis*. The *vertices* are the intersections of the transverse axis with the ellipse and have coordinates $(a, 0)$ and $(-a, 0)$. The segment thus determined, or its length $2a$, is also called the transverse axis, while the length $2b$ is also called the conjugate axis. The distance from the center to either *focus* is $\sqrt{a^2 + b^2}$, and the difference between the distances from a point in the hyperbola to the foci is $2a$. The *latera recta* are the chords perpendicular to the transverse axis and going through the foci; their length is $2b^2/a$. The *eccentricity* is $\sqrt{a^2 + b^2}/a$. The distance from the center to either *directrix* is $a^2/\sqrt{a^2 + b^2}$. The

FIGURE 4.7.19

Hyperbola with transverse semiaxis a and conjugate semiaxis b. Here b/a = 0.4.

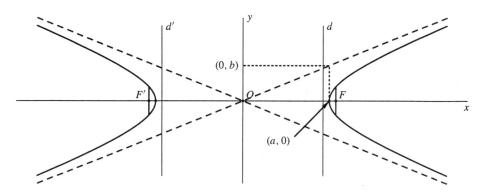

legs of the hyperbola approach the *asymptotes*, lines of slope $\pm b/a$ that cross at the center.

All hyperbolas of the same eccentricity are similar; in other words, the shape of a hyperbola depends only on the ratio b/a. Unlike the case of the ellipse (where the major axis, containing the foci, is always longer than the minor axis), the two axes of a hyperbola can have arbitrary lengths. When they have the same length, so that $a = b$, the asymptotes are perpendicular, and $e = \sqrt{2}$, the hyperbola is called *rectangular*.

The simplest analytic form for the parabola is obtained when the axis of symmetry coincides with one coordinate axis, and the *vertex* (the intersection of the axis with the curve) is at the origin. The equation of the parabola on the right is

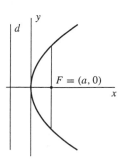

$$y^2 = 4ax, \tag{4.7.3}$$

where a is the distance from the vertex to the focus, or, which is the same, from the vertex to the directrix. The *latus rectum* is the chord perpendicular to the axis and going through the focus; its length is $4a$. All parabolas are similar: they can be made to look identical by scaling, translation, and rotation.

4.7.2   THE GENERAL QUADRATIC EQUATION

The analytic equation for a conic in arbitrary position is the following:

$$Ax^2 + By^2 + Cxy + Dx + Ey + F = 0, \tag{4.7.4}$$

where at least one of A, B, C is nonzero. To reduce this to one of the forms given previously, perform the following steps (note that the decisions are based on the most recent values of the coefficients, taken after all the transformations so far):

1. If $C \neq 0$, simultaneously perform the substitutions $x \mapsto qx+y$ and $y \mapsto qy-x$, where

$$q = \sqrt{\left(\frac{B-A}{C}\right)^2 + 1} + \frac{B-A}{C}. \qquad (4.7.5)$$

Now $C = 0$. (This step corresponds to rotating and scaling about the origin.)

2. If $B = 0$, interchange x and y. Now $B \neq 0$.

3. If $E \neq 0$, perform the substitution $y \mapsto y - \frac{1}{2}(E/B)$. (This corresponds to translating in the y direction.) Now $E = 0$.

4. If $A = 0$:

   (a) If $D \neq 0$, perform the substitution $x \mapsto x - (F/D)$ (translation in the x direction), and divide the equation by B to get Equation (4.7.3). The conic is a *parabola*.

   (b) If $D = 0$, the equation gives a *degenerate conic*. If $F = 0$, we have the line $y = 0$ with multiplicity two. If $F < 0$, we have two parallel lines $y = \pm\sqrt{F/B}$. If $F > 0$ we have two imaginary lines; the equation has no solution within the real numbers.

5. If $A \neq 0$:

   (a) If $D \neq 0$, perform the substitution $x \mapsto x - \frac{1}{2}(D/A)$. Now $D = 0$. (This corresponds to translating in the x direction.)

   (b) If $F \neq 0$, divide the equation by F to get a form with $F = 1$.

      i. If A and B have opposite signs, the conic is a *hyperbola*; to get to Equation (4.7.2), interchange x and y, if necessary, so that A is positive; then make $a = 1/\sqrt{A}$ and $b = 1/\sqrt{B}$.

      ii. If A and B are both positive, the conic is an *ellipse*; to get to Equation (4.7.1), interchange x and y, if necessary, so that $A \leq B$, then make $a = 1/\sqrt{A}$ and $b = 1/\sqrt{B}$. The *circle* is the particular case $a = b$.

      iii. If A and B are both negative, we have an *imaginary ellipse*; the equation has no solution in real numbers.

   (c) If $F = 0$, the equation again represents a *degenerate conic*: when A and B have different signs, we have a pair of lines $y = \pm\sqrt{-B/A}x$, and, when they have the same sign, we get a point (the origin).

We work out an example for clarity. Suppose the original equation is

$$4x^2 + y^2 - 4xy + 3x - 4y + 1 = 0. \qquad (4.7.6)$$

In step 1 we apply the substitutions $x \mapsto 2x + y$ and $y \mapsto 2y - x$. This gives $25x^2 + 10x - 5y + 1 = 0$. Next we interchange x and y (step 2) and get $25y^2 + 10y - 5x + 1 = 0$. Replacing y by $y - \frac{1}{5}$ in step 3, we get $25y^2 - 5x = 0$. Finally, in step 4a we divide the equation by 25, thus giving it the form of Equation (4.7.3) with $a = \frac{1}{20}$. We have reduced the conic to a parabola with vertex at the origin and focus at

$(\frac{1}{20}, 0)$. To locate the features of the original curve, we work our way back along the chain of substitutions (recall the convention about substitutions and transformations from Section 4.1.1):

Substitution	$y \mapsto y - \frac{1}{5}$	$\begin{matrix} x \mapsto y \\ y \mapsto x \end{matrix}$	$\begin{matrix} x \mapsto 2x+y \\ y \mapsto 2y-x \end{matrix}$
Vertex $(0,0)$	$(0, -\frac{1}{5})$	$(-\frac{1}{5}, 0)$	$(-\frac{2}{5}, -\frac{1}{5})$
Focus $(\frac{1}{20}, 0)$	$(\frac{1}{20}, -\frac{1}{5})$	$(-\frac{1}{5}, \frac{1}{20})$	$(-\frac{7}{20}, \frac{6}{20})$

We conclude that the original curve, Equation (4.7.6), is a parabola with vertex $(-\frac{2}{5}, -\frac{1}{5})$ and focus $(-\frac{7}{20}, \frac{6}{20})$.

If one just wants to know the type of the conic defined by Equation (4.7.4), an alternative analysis consists in forming the quantities

$$\Delta = \begin{vmatrix} A & \frac{1}{2}C & \frac{1}{2}D \\ \frac{1}{2}C & B & \frac{1}{2}E \\ \frac{1}{2}D & \frac{1}{2}E & F \end{vmatrix}, \quad J = \begin{vmatrix} A & \frac{1}{2}C \\ \frac{1}{2}C & B \end{vmatrix}, \quad I = A + B,$$

$$K = \begin{vmatrix} A & \frac{1}{2}D \\ \frac{1}{2}D & F \end{vmatrix} + \begin{vmatrix} B & \frac{1}{2}E \\ \frac{1}{2}E & F \end{vmatrix}, \tag{4.7.7}$$

and finding the appropriate case in the following table, where an entry in parentheses indicates that the equation has no solution in real numbers:

Δ	J	Δ/I	K	Type of conic
$\neq 0$	< 0			Hyperbola
$\neq 0$	0			Parabola
$\neq 0$	> 0	< 0		Ellipse
$\neq 0$	> 0	> 0		(Imaginary ellipse)
0	< 0			Intersecting lines
0	> 0			Point
0	0		< 0	Distinct parallel lines
0	0		> 0	(Imaginary parallel lines)
0	0		0	Coincident lines

For the central conics (the ellipse, the point, and the hyperbola), the center (x_0, y_0) is the solution of the system of equations

$$2Ax + Cy + D = 0,$$
$$Cx + 2By + E = 0,$$

and the axes have slope q and $-1/q$, where q is given by Equation (4.7.5).

4.7.3 ADDITIONAL PROPERTIES OF ELLIPSES

Let C be the ellipse with equation $x^2/a^2 + y^2/b^2 = 1$, with $a > b$, and let F, $F' = (\pm\sqrt{a^2 - b^2}, 0)$ be its foci (see Figure 4.7.18).

1. A *parametric representation* for C is given by $(a \cos\theta, b \sin\theta)$. The *area* of the shaded sector on the right is $\frac{1}{2}ab\theta = \frac{1}{2}ab \cos^{-1}(x/a)$. The *length* of the arc from $(a, 0)$ to the point $(a \cos\theta, b \sin\theta)$ is given by the elliptic integral

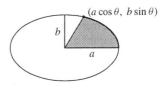

$(a \cos\theta, b \sin\theta)$

$$a \int_0^\theta \sqrt{1 - e^2 \cos^2\phi}\, d\phi = a\, E(\pi/2 - \theta\, e),$$

where e is the eccentricity. (See page 523 for elliptic integrals.) Setting $\theta = 2\pi$ results in

$$\text{area } C = \pi ab, \qquad \text{perimeter } C = 4a\, E(0, e).$$

2. A *rational parametric representation* for C is given by $\left(a\,\dfrac{1 - t^2}{1 + t^2}, \dfrac{2bt}{1 + t^2}\right)$.

3. The *polar equation* for C in the usual polar coordinate system is

$$r = \frac{ab}{\sqrt{a^2 \sin^2\theta + b^2 \cos^2\theta}}.$$

With respect to a coordinate system with origin at a focus, the equation is

$$r = \frac{l}{1 \pm e \cos\theta},$$

where $l = b^2/a$ is half the latus rectum. (Use the $+$ sign for the focus with positive x-coordinate and the $-$ sign for the focus with negative x-coordinate.)

4. Let P be any point of C. The *sum of the distances* PF and PF' is constant and equal to $2a$.

5. Let P be any point of C. Then the rays PF and PF' make the same angle with the tangent to C at P. Thus any light ray originating at F and reflected in the ellipse will also go through F'.

6. Let T be any line tangent to C. The product of the distances from F and F' to T is constant and equals b^2.

7. *Lahire's theorem*: Let D and D' be fixed lines in the plane, and consider a third moving line on which three points P, P' and P'' are marked. If we constrain P to lie in D and P' to lie in D', then P'' describes an ellipse.

4.7.4   ADDITIONAL PROPERTIES OF HYPERBOLAS

Let C be the hyperbola with equation $x^2/a^2 - y^2/b^2 = 1$, and let

$$F, F' = (\pm\sqrt{a^2 + b^2}, 0)$$

be its foci (see Figure 4.7.19). The *conjugate hyperbola* of C is the hyperbola C' with equation $-x^2/a^2 + y^2/b^2 = 1$. It has the same asymptotes as C, the same axes (transverse and conjugate axes being interchanged), and its eccentricity e' is related to that of C by $e'^{-2} + e^{-2} = 1$.

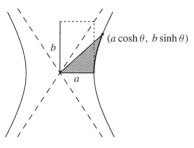

1. A *parametric representation* for C is given by $(a\sec\theta, b\tan\theta)$. A different parametric representation, which gives one branch only, is $(a\cosh\theta, b\sinh\theta)$. The *area* of the shaded sector on the right is

$$\tfrac{1}{2}ab\theta = \tfrac{1}{2}ab\cosh^{-1}(x/a)$$
$$= \tfrac{1}{2}ab\log\frac{x + \sqrt{x^2 - a^2}}{a}.$$

The *length* of the arc from $(a, 0)$ to the point $(a\cosh\theta, b\sinh\theta)$ is given by the elliptic integral

$$a\int_0^\theta \sqrt{e^2\cosh^2\phi - 1}\,d\phi = -bi\,E\!\left(\theta i, \frac{ea}{b}\right) = a\int_1^x \sqrt{\frac{e^2\xi^2 - a^2}{\xi^2 - a^2}}\,d\xi,$$

where e is the eccentricity, $i = \sqrt{-1}$, and $x = a\cosh\theta$.

2. A *rational parametric representation* for C is given by

$$\left(a\,\frac{1 + t^2}{1 - t^2}, \frac{2bt}{1 - t^2}\right).$$

3. The *polar equation* for C in the usual polar coordinate system is

$$r = \frac{ab}{\sqrt{a^2\sin^2\theta - b^2\cos^2\theta}}.$$

With respect to a system with origin at a focus, the equation is

$$r = \frac{l}{1 \pm e\cos\theta},$$

where $l = b^2/a$ is half the latus rectum. (Use the $-$ sign for the focus with positive x-coordinate and the $+$ sign for the focus with negative x-coordinate.)

4. Let P be any point of C. The unsigned *difference between the distances* PF and PF' is constant and equal to $2a$.

5. Let P be any point of C. Then the rays PF and PF' make the same angle with the tangent to C at P. Thus any light ray originating at F and reflected in the hyperbola will appear to emanate from F'.

6. Let T be any line tangent to C. The product of the distances from F and F' to T is constant and equals b^2.

7. Let P be any point of C. The area of the parallelogram formed by the asymptotes and the parallels to the asymptotes going through P is constant and equals $\frac{1}{2}ab$.

8. Let L be any line in the plane. If L intersects C at P and P' and intersects the asymptotes at Q and Q', the distances PQ and $P'Q'$ are the same. If L is tangent to C we have $P = P'$, so that the point of tangency bisects the segment QQ'.

4.7.5 ADDITIONAL PROPERTIES OF PARABOLAS

Let C be the parabola with equation $y^2 = 4ax$, and let $F = (a, 0)$ be its focus.

1. Let $P = (x, y)$ and $P' = (x', y')$ be points on C. The area bounded by the chord PP' and the corresponding arc of the parabola is

$$\frac{|y' - y|^3}{24a}.$$

It equals four-thirds of the area of the triangle PQP', where Q is the point on C whose tangent is parallel to the chord PP' (formula due to *Archimedes*).

2. The *length* of the arc from $(0, 0)$ to the point (x, y) is

$$\frac{y}{4}\sqrt{4 + \frac{y^2}{a^2}} + a\sinh^{-1}\left(\frac{y}{2a}\right) = \frac{y}{4}\sqrt{4 + \frac{y^2}{a^2}} + a\log\frac{y + \sqrt{y^2 + 4a^2}}{2a}.$$

3. The *polar equation* for C in the usual polar coordinate system is

$$r = \frac{4a\cos\theta}{\sin^2\theta}.$$

With respect to a coordinate system with origin at F, the equation is

$$r = \frac{l}{1 - \cos\theta},$$

where $l = 2a$ is half the latus rectum.

4. Let P be any point of C. Then the ray PF and the horizontal line through P make the same angle with the tangent to C at P. Thus light rays parallel to the axis and reflected in the parabola converge onto F (principle of the *parabolic reflector*).

4.8 SPECIAL PLANE CURVES

4.8.1   ALGEBRAIC CURVES

Curves that can be given in implicit form as $f(x, y) = 0$, where f is a polynomial, are called *algebraic*. The degree of f is called the degree or *order* of the curve. Thus, conics (page 279) are algebraic curves of degree two. Curves of degree three already have a great variety of shapes, and only a few common ones will be given here.

The simplest case is the curve whose graph is of a polynomial of degree three: $y = ax^3 + bx^2 + cx + d$, with $a \neq 0$. This curve is a (general) *cubic parabola* (Figure 4.8.20), symmetric with respect to the point B where $x = -b/3a$.

FIGURE 4.8.20
The general cubic parabola for $a > 0$. For $a < 0$, reflect in a horizontal line.

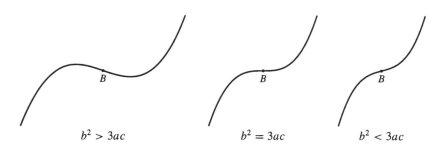

$b^2 > 3ac$ $\qquad\qquad\qquad$ $b^2 = 3ac$ $\qquad\qquad\qquad$ $b^2 < 3ac$

The equation of a *semicubic parabola* (Figure 4.8.21, left) is $y^2 = kx^3$; by proportional scaling one can take $k = 1$. This curve should not be confused with the *cissoid of Diocles* (Figure 4.8.21, middle), whose equation is $(a - x)y^2 = x^3$ with $a \neq 0$.

The latter is asymptotic to the line $x = a$, whereas the semicubic parabola has no asymptotes. The cissoid's points are characterized by the equality $OP = AB$ in Figure 4.8.21, right. One can take $a = 1$ by proportional scaling.

More generally, any curve of degree three with equation $(x - x_0)y^2 = f(x)$, where f is a polynomial, is symmetric with respect to the x-axis and asymptotic to the line $x = x_0$. In addition to the cissoid, the following particular cases are important:

1. The *witch of Agnesi* has equation $xy^2 = a^2(a - x)$, with $a \neq 0$, and is characterized by the geometric property shown in Figure 4.8.21, right. The same property provides the parametric representation $x = a \cos^2 \theta$, $y = a \tan \theta$. Once more, proportional scaling reduces to the case $a = 1$.

2. The *folium of Descartes* (Figure 4.8.22, left) is described by equation $(x - a)y^2 = -x^2(\frac{1}{3}x + a)$, with $a \neq 0$ (reducible to $a = 1$ by proportional scaling). By rotating 135° (right) we get the alternative and more familiar equation $x^3 + y^3 = cxy$, where $c = \frac{1}{3}\sqrt{2}a$. The folium of Descartes is a *rational curve*, this is, it

FIGURE 4.8.21
The semicubic parabola, the cissoid of Diocles, and the witch of Agnesi.

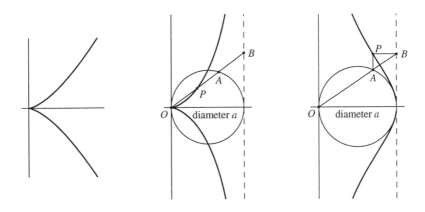

is parametrically represented by rational functions. In the tilted position, the equation is $x = ct/(1 + t^3)$, $y = ct^2/(1 + t^3)$ (so that $t = y/x$).

3. The *strophoid's* equation is $(x - a)y^2 = -x^2(x + a)$, with $a \neq 0$ (reducible to $a = 1$ by proportional scaling). It satisfies the property $AP = AP' = OA$ in Figure 4.8.22, right; this means that POP' is a right angle. The strophoid's polar representation is $r = -a \cos 2\theta \sec \theta$, and the rational parametric representation is $x = a(t^2 - 1)/(t^2 + 1)$, $y = at(t^2 - 1)/(t^2 + 1)$ (so that $t = y/x$).

FIGURE 4.8.22
The folium of Descartes in two positions, and the strophoid.

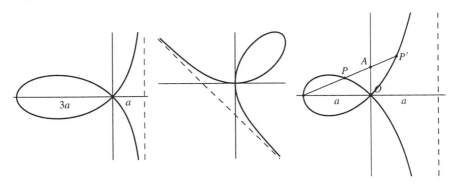

Among the important curves of degree four are the following:

1. A *Cassini's oval* is characterized by the following condition: Given two *foci* F and F', a distance $2a$ apart, a point P belongs to the curve if the product of the distances PF and PF' is a constant k^2. If the foci are on the x-axis and equidistant from the origin, the curve's equation is $(x^2 + y^2 + a^2)^2 - 4a^2x^2 = k^4$. Changes in a correspond to rescaling, while the value of k/a controls the shape:

the curve has one smooth segment and one with a self-intersection, or two segments depending on whether k is greater than, equal to, or smaller than a (Figure 4.8.23). The case $k = a$ is also known as the *lemniscate* (of Jakob Bernoulli); the equation reduces to $(x^2 + y^2)^2 = a^2(x^2 - y^2)$, and upon a 45° rotation to $(x^2 + y^2)^2 = 2a^2xy$. Each Cassini oval is the section of a torus of revolution by a plane parallel to the axis of revolution.

FIGURE 4.8.23

Cassini's ovals for $k = 0.5a$, $0.9a$, a, $1.1a$ and $1.5a$ (from the inside to the outside). The foci (dots) are at $x = a$ and $x = -a$. The black curve, $k = a$, is also called Bernoulli's lemniscate.

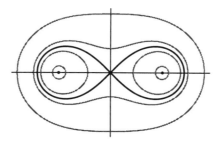

2. A *conchoid of Nichomedes* is the set of points such that the signed distance AP in Figure 4.8.24, left, equals a fixed real number k (the line L and the origin O being fixed). If L is the line $x = a$, the conchoid's polar equation is $r = a \sec\theta + k$. Once more, a is a scaling parameter, and the value of k/a controls the shape: when $k > -a$ the curve is smooth, when $k = -a$ there is a cusp, and when $k < -a$ there is a self-intersection. The curves for k and $-k$ can also be considered two leaves of the same conchoid, with Cartesian equation $(x - a)^2(x^2 + y^2) = k^2 x^2$.

FIGURE 4.8.24

Defining property of the conchoid of Nichomedes (left), and curves for $k = \pm 0.5a$, $k = \pm a$, and $k = \pm 1.5a$ (right).

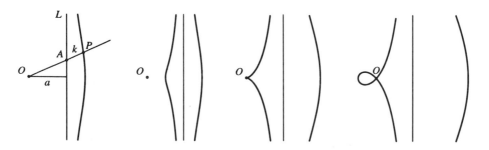

3. A *limaçon of Pascal* is the set of points such that the distance AP in Figure 4.8.25, left, equals a fixed positive number k measured on either side (the circle C and

the origin O being fixed). If C has diameter a and center at $(0, \frac{1}{2}a)$, the limaçon's polar equation is $r = a \cos\theta + k$, and its Cartesian equation is

$$(x^2 + y^2 - ax)^2 = k^2(x^2 + y^2).$$

The value of k/a controls the shape, and there are two particularly interesting cases. For $k = a$, we get a *cardioid* (see also page 293). For $a = \frac{1}{2}k$, we get a curve that can be used to *trisect* an arbitrary angle α. If we draw a line L through the center of the circle C making an angle α with the positive x-axis, and if we call P the intersection of L with the limaçon $a = 2k$, the line from O to P makes an angle with L equal to $\frac{1}{3}\alpha$.

FIGURE 4.8.25
Defining property of the limaçon of Pascal (left), and curves for $k = 1.5a$, $k = a$, and $k = 0.5a$ (right). The middle curve is the cardioid; the one on the right a trisectrix.

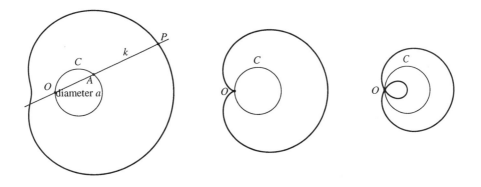

Hypocycloids and epicycloids with rational ratios (see next section) are also algebraic curves, generally of higher degree.

4.8.2 ROULETTES (SPIROGRAPH CURVES)

Suppose given a fixed curve C and a moving curve M, which rolls on C without slipping. The curve drawn by a point P kept fixed with respect to M is called a *roulette*, of which P is the *pole*.

The most important examples of roulettes arise when M is a circle and C is a straight line or a circle, but an interesting additional example is provided by the *catenary* $y = a\cosh(x/a)$, which arises by rolling the parabola $y = x^2/(4a)$ on the x-axis with pole the focus of the parabola (that is, $P = (0, a)$ in the initial position). The catenary is the shape taken under the action of gravity by a chain or string of uniform density whose ends are held in the air.

A circle rolling on a straight line gives a *trochoid*, with the *cycloid* as a special case when the pole P lies on the circle (Figure 4.8.26). If the moving circle M has radius a and the distance from the pole P to the center of M is k, the trochoid's parametric equation is

$$x = a\phi - k\sin\phi, \qquad y = a - k\cos\phi.$$

FIGURE 4.8.26
Cycloid (top) and trochoids with $k = 0.5a$ and $k = 1.5a$, where k is the distance PQ from the center of the rolling circle to the pole.

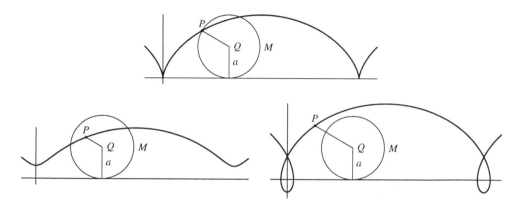

The cycloid, therefore, has the parametric equation

$$x = a(\phi - \sin\phi), \; y = a(1 - \cos\phi).$$

One can eliminate ϕ to get x as a (multivalued) function of y, which takes the following form for the cycloid:

$$x = \cos^{-1}\frac{a - y}{a} \pm \sqrt{2ay - y^2}.$$

The length of one arch of the cycloid is $8a$, and the area under the arch is $3\pi a^2$.

A trochoid is also called a *curtate cycloid* when $k < a$ (that is, when P is inside the circle) and a *prolate cycloid* when $k > a$.

A circle rolling on another circle and exterior to it gives an *epitrochoid*. If a is the radius of the fixed circle, b that of the rolling circle, and k is the distance from P to the center of the rolling circle, the parametric equation of the epitrochoid is

$$x = (a + b)\cos\theta - k\cos((1 + b/a)\theta), \qquad y = (a + b)\sin\theta - k\sin((1 + b/a)\theta).$$

These equations assume that, at the start, everything is aligned along the positive x-axis, as in Figure 4.8.27, left. Usually one considers the case when a/b is a rational number, say $a/b = p/q$ where p and q are relatively prime. Then the rolling circle returns to its original position after rotating q times around the fixed circle, and the epitrochoid is a closed curve—in fact, an algebraic curve. One also usually takes $k = b$, so that P lies on the rolling circle; the curve in this case is called an *epicycloid*. The middle diagram in Figure 4.8.27 shows the case $b = k = \frac{1}{2}a$, called the *nephroid*; this curve is the cross section of the caustic of a spherical mirror. The diagram on the

FIGURE 4.8.27
*Left: initial configuration for epicycloid (black) and configuration at parameter value θ (gray).
Middle: epicycloid with b = ½a (nephroid). Right: epicycloid with b = a (cardioid).*

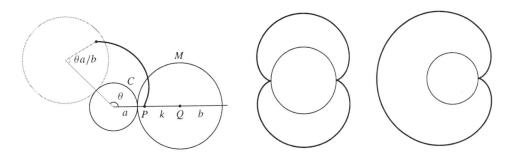

right shows the case $b = k = a$, which gives the cardioid (compare to Figure 4.8.25, middle).

Hypotrochoids and *hypocycloids* are defined in the same way as epitrochoids and epicycloids, but the rolling circle is inside the fixed one. The parametric equation of the hypotrochoid is

$$x = (a - b)\cos\theta + k\cos((a/b - 1)\theta), \qquad y = (a - b)\sin\theta - k\sin((a/b - 1)\theta),$$

where the letters have the same meaning as for the epitrochoid. Usually one takes a/b rational and $k = b$. There are several interesting particular cases:

- $b = k = a$ gives a point.

- $b = k = \frac{1}{2}a$ gives a diameter of the circle C.

- $b = k = \frac{1}{3}a$ gives the *deltoid* (Figure 4.8.28, left), whose algebraic equation is

$$(x^2 + y^2)^2 - 8ax^3 + 24axy^2 + 18a^2(x^2 + y^2) - 27a^4 = 0.$$

- $b = k = \frac{1}{4}a$ gives the *astroid* (Figure 4.8.28, right), an algebraic curve of degree six whose equation can be reduced to $x^{2/3} + y^{2/3} = a^{2/3}$. The figure illustrates another property of the astroid: its tangent intersects the coordinate axes at points that are always the same distance a apart. Otherwise said, the astroid is the envelope of a moving segment of fixed length whose endpoints are constrained to lie on the two coordinate axes.

4.8.3 SPIRALS

A number of interesting curves have polar equation $r = f(\theta)$, where f is a monotonic function (always increasing or decreasing). This property leads to a spiral shape. The *logarithmic spiral* or *Bernoulli spiral* (Figure 4.8.29, left) is self-similar: by rotation the curve can be made to match any scaled copy of itself. Its equation is $r = ke^{a\theta}$; the angle between the radius from the origin and the tangent to the curve is constant and

FIGURE 4.8.28
The hypocycloids with a = 3b (deltoid) and a = 4b (astroid).

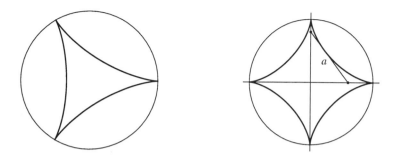

FIGURE 4.8.29
The Bernoulli or logarithmic spiral (left), the Archimedes or linear spiral (middle), and the Cornu spiral (right).

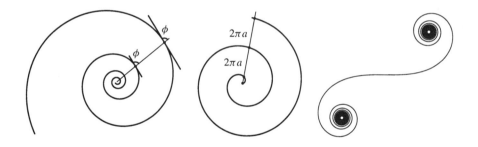

equal to $\phi = \cot^{-1} a$. A curve parametrized by arc length and such that the curvature is proportional to the parameter at each point is a Bernoulli spiral.

In the *Archimedean spiral* or *linear spiral* (Figure 4.8.29, middle), the spacing between intersections along a ray from the origin is constant. The equation of this spiral is $r = a\theta$; by scaling one can take $a = 1$. It has an inner endpoint, in contrast with the logarithmic spiral, which spirals down to the origin without reaching it. The *Cornu spiral* or *clothoid* (Figure 4.8.29, right), important in optics and engineering, has the following parametric representation in Cartesian coordinates:

$$ X = aC(t) = a \int_0^t \cos(\tfrac{1}{2}\pi s^2)\,ds, \qquad y = aS(t) = a \int_0^t \sin(\tfrac{1}{2}\pi s^2)\,ds. $$

(C and S are the so-called Fresnel integrals; see page 498). A curve parametrized by arclength and such that the curvature is inversely proportional to the parameter at each point is a Cornu spiral (compare the Bernoulli spiral).

4.8.4 THE PEANO CURVE AND FRACTAL CURVES

There are curves (in the sense of continuous maps from the real line to the plane) that completely cover a two-dimensional region of the plane. We give a construction of such a *Peano curve*, adapted from David Hilbert's example. The construction is inductive and is based on replacement rules. We consider building blocks of six shapes: 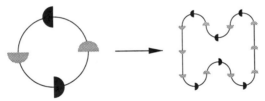 , the length of the straight segments being twice the radius of the curved ones. A sequence of these patterns, end-to-end, represents a curve, if we disregard the gray and black half-disks. The replacement rules are the following:

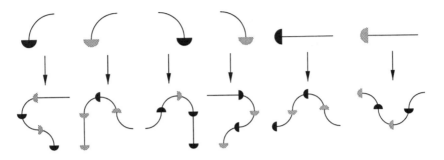

The rules are applied taking into account the way each piece is turned. Here we apply the replacement rules to a particular initial pattern:

(We scale the result so it has the same size as the original.) Applying the process repeatedly gives, in the limit, the Peano curve. Here are the first five steps:

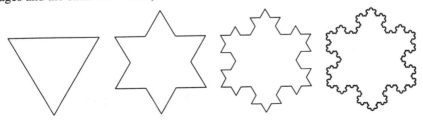

The same idea of replacement rules leads to many interesting fractal, and often self-similar, curves. For example, the substitution ⎯⎯ → ⎯⋀⎯ leads to the *Koch snowflake* when applied to an initial equilateral triangle, like this (the first three stages and the sixth are shown):

4.8.5   CLASSICAL CONSTRUCTIONS

The ancient Greeks used straightedges and compasses to find the solutions to numerical problems. For example, they found square roots by constructing the geometric mean of two segments. Three famous problems that have been proved intractable by this method are

- The trisection of an arbitrary angle

- The squaring of the circle (the construction of a square whose area is equal to that of a given circle)

- The doubling of the cube (the construction of a cube with double the volume of a given cube)

A regular n-gon inscribed in the unit circle can be constructed by straightedge and compass alone if, and only if, n has the form $n = 2^{\ell} p_1 p_2 \ldots p_k$, where ℓ is a nonnegative integer and $\{p_i\}$ are distinct Fermat primes (primes of the form $2^{2^m} + 1$). The only known Fermat primes are for $m = 1, 2, 3, 4$. Thus, regular n-gons can be constructed for $n = 3, 4, 5, 6, 8, 10, 12, 15, 16, 17, 20, 24, \ldots, 257, \ldots$.

4.9   COORDINATE SYSTEMS IN SPACE

Conventions

When we talk about "the point with coordinates (x, y, z)" or "the surface with equation $f(x, y, z)$", we always mean Cartesian coordinates. If a formula involves another type of coordinates, this fact will be stated explicitly. Note that Section 4.1.1 has information on substitutions and transformations relevant to the three-dimensional case.

4.9.1   CARTESIAN COORDINATES IN SPACE

In *Cartesian coordinates* (or *rectangular coordinates*), a point P is referred to by three real numbers, indicating the positions of the perpendicular projections from the point to three fixed, perpendicular, graduated lines, called the *axes*. If the coordinates are denoted x, y, z, in that order, the axes are called the *x-axis*, etc., and we write $P = (x, y, z)$. Often the x-axis is imagined to be horizontal and pointing roughly toward the viewer (out of the page), the y-axis also horizontal and pointing more or less to the right, and the z-axis vertical, pointing up. The system is called *right-handed* if it can be rotated so the three axes are in this position. Figure 4.9.30 shows a right-handed system. The point $x = 0$, $y = 0$, $z = 0$ is the *origin*, where the three axes intersect.

FIGURE 4.9.30
In Cartesian coordinates, $P = (4.2, 3.4, 2.2)$.

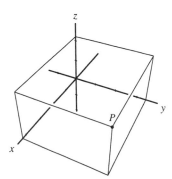

4.9.2   CYLINDRICAL COORDINATES IN SPACE

To define *cylindrical coordinates*, we take an axis (usually called the *z-axis*) and a perpendicular plane, on which we choose a ray (the *initial ray*) originating at the intersection of the plane and the axis (the *origin*). The coordinates of a point P are the polar coordinates (r, θ) of the projection of P on the plane, and the coordinate z of the projection of P on the axis (Figure 4.9.31). See Section 4.1.3 for remarks on the values of r and θ.

FIGURE 4.9.31
Among the possible sets (r, θ, z) of cylindrical coordinates for P are $(10, 30°, 5)$ and $(10, 390°, 5)$.

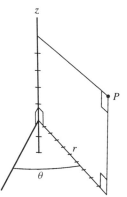

4.9.3   SPHERICAL COORDINATES IN SPACE

To define *spherical coordinates*, we take an axis (the *polar axis*) and a perpendicular plane (the *equatorial plane*), on which we choose a ray (the *initial ray*) originating at the intersection of the plane and the axis (the *origin O*). The coordinates of a point P are the distance ρ from P to the origin, the angle ϕ (*zenith*) between the line OP

and the positive polar axis, and the angle θ (*azimuth*) between the initial ray and the projection of OP to the equatorial plane. See Figure 4.9.32. As in the case of polar and cylindrical coordinates, θ is only defined up to multiples of $360°$, and likewise ϕ. Usually ϕ is assigned a value between 0 and $180°$, but values of ϕ between $180°$ and $360°$ can also be used; the triples (ρ, ϕ, θ) and $(\rho,\ 360° - \phi,\ 180° + \theta)$ represent the same point. Similarly, one can extend ρ to negative values; the triples (ρ, ϕ, θ) and $(-\rho,\ 180° - \phi,\ 180° + \theta)$ represent the same point.

FIGURE 4.9.32

A set of spherical coordinates for P is $(\rho, \theta, \phi) = (10, 60°, 30°)$.

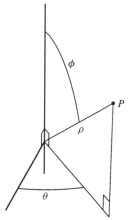

FIGURE 4.9.33

Standard relations between Cartesian, cylindrical, and spherical coordinate systems. The origin is the same for all three. The positive z-axes of the Cartesian and cylindrical systems coincide with the positive polar axis of the spherical system. The initial rays of the cylindrical and spherical systems coincide with the positive x-axis of the Cartesian system, and the rays $\theta = 90°$ coincide with the positive y-axis.

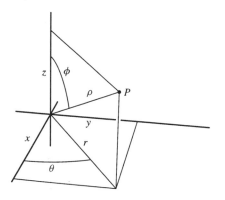

4.9.4 RELATIONS BETWEEN CARTESIAN, CYLINDRICAL, AND SPHERICAL COORDINATES

Consider a Cartesian, a cylindrical, and a spherical coordinate system, related as shown in Figure 4.9.33. The Cartesian coordinates (x, y, z), the cylindrical coordinates (r, θ, z), and the spherical coordinates (ρ, ϕ, θ) of a point are related as follows:

cart $\leftrightarrow$ cyl
$$\begin{cases} x = r\cos\theta, \\ y = r\sin\theta, \end{cases} \qquad \begin{cases} r = \sqrt{x^2 + y^2}, \\ \theta = \tan^{-1}\dfrac{y}{x}, \end{cases} \qquad \begin{cases} \sin\theta = \dfrac{y}{\sqrt{x^2 + y^2}}, \\ \cos\theta = \dfrac{x}{\sqrt{x^2 + y^2}}. \end{cases}$$

cyl $\leftrightarrow$ sph
$$\begin{cases} r = \rho\sin\phi, \\ z = \rho\cos\phi, \end{cases} \qquad \begin{cases} \rho = \sqrt{r^2 + z^2}, \\ \phi = \tan^{-1}\dfrac{r}{z}, \end{cases} \qquad \begin{cases} \sin\phi = \dfrac{r}{\sqrt{r^2 + z^2}}, \\ \cos\phi = \dfrac{z}{\sqrt{r^2 + z^2}}. \end{cases}$$

cart $\leftrightarrow$ sph
$$\begin{cases} x = \rho\cos\theta\sin\phi, \\ y = \rho\sin\theta\sin\phi, \\ z = \rho\cos\phi, \end{cases} \qquad \begin{cases} \rho = \sqrt{x^2 + y^2 + z^2}, \\ \theta = \tan^{-1}\dfrac{y}{x}, \\ \phi = \tan^{-1}\dfrac{\sqrt{x^2 + y^2}}{z}, \\ \quad = \cos^{-1}\dfrac{z}{\sqrt{x^2 + y^2 + z^2}}. \end{cases}$$

4.9.5 HOMOGENEOUS COORDINATES IN SPACE

A quadruple of real numbers $(x : y : z : t)$, with $t \neq 0$, is a set of *homogeneous coordinates* for the point P with Cartesian coordinates $(x/t, y/t, z/t)$. Thus the same point has many sets of homogeneous coordinates: $(x : y : z : t)$ and $(x' : y' : z' : t')$ represent the same point if, and only if, there is some real number α such that $x' = \alpha x$, $y' = \alpha y$, $z' = \alpha z$, $t' = \alpha t$. If P has Cartesian coordinates (x_0, y_0, z_0), one set of homogeneous coordinates for P is $(x_0, y_0, z_0, 1)$.

Section 4.1.4 has more information on the relationship between Cartesian and homogeneous coordinates. Section 4.10.2 has formulas for space transformations in homogeneous coordinates.

4.10 SPACE SYMMETRIES OR ISOMETRIES

A transformation of space (invertible map of space to itself) that preserves distances is called an *isometry* of space. Every isometry of space is a composition of transformations of the following types:

- The *identity* (which leaves every point fixed)
- A *translation* by a vector **v**
- A *rotation* through an angle α around a line L
- A *screw motion* through an angle α around a line L, with displacement d
- A *reflection* in a line P
- A *glide-reflection* in a line P with displacement vector **v**

The identity is a particular case of a translation and of a rotation; rotations are particular cases of screw motions; reflections are particular cases of glide-reflections. However, as in the plane case, it is more intuitive to consider each case separately.

4.10.1 FORMULAS FOR SYMMETRIES: CARTESIAN COORDINATES

In the formulas below, multiplication between a matrix and a triple of coordinates should be carried out regarding the triple as a column vector (or a matrix with three rows and one column).

Translation by (x_0, y_0, z_0):

$$(x, y, z) \mapsto (x + x_0, \ y + y_0, \ z + z_0).$$

Rotation through α (counterclockwise) around the line through the origin with direction cosines a, b, c (see page 304): $(x, y, z) \mapsto M(x, y, z)$, where M is the matrix,

$$\begin{bmatrix} a^2(1 - \cos\alpha) + \cos\alpha & ab(1 - \cos\alpha) - c\sin\alpha & ac(1 - \cos\alpha) + b\sin\alpha \\ ab(1 - \cos\alpha) + c\sin\alpha & b^2(1 - \cos\alpha) + \cos\alpha & bc(1 - \cos\alpha) - a\sin\alpha \\ ac(1 - \cos\alpha) - b\sin\alpha & bc(1 - \cos\alpha) + a\sin\alpha & c^2(1 - \cos\alpha) + \cos\alpha \end{bmatrix}$$

$$(4.10.1)$$

Rotation through α (counterclockwise) around the line with direction cosines a, b, c through an arbitrary point (x_0, y_0, z_0):

$$(x, y, z) \mapsto (x_0, y_0, z_0) + M(x - x_0, \ y - y_0, \ z - z_0),$$

where M is given by Equation (4.10.1).

Arbitrary rotations and Euler angles: Any rotation of space fixing the origin can be decomposed as a rotation by ϕ about the z-axis, followed by a rotation by θ about the y-axis, followed by a rotation by ψ about the z-axis. The numbers ϕ, θ and ψ are called the *Euler angles* of the composite rotation, which acts as: $(x, y, z) \mapsto M(x, y, z)$, where M is the matrix given by

$$\begin{bmatrix} \cos\phi\cos\theta\cos\psi - \sin\phi\sin\psi & -\sin\phi\cos\theta\cos\psi - \cos\phi\sin\psi & \sin\theta\cos\psi \\ \sin\phi\cos\psi + \cos\phi\cos\theta\sin\psi & -\sin\phi\cos\theta\sin\psi + \cos\phi\cos\psi & \sin\theta\sin\psi \\ -\cos\phi\sin\theta & \sin\theta\sin\phi & \cos\theta \end{bmatrix}.$$

$$(4.10.2)$$

(An alternative decomposition, more natural if we think of the coordinate system as a rigid trihedron that rotates in space, is the following: a rotation by ψ about the z-axis, followed by a rotation by θ about the *rotated* y-axis, followed by a rotation by ϕ about the *rotated* z-axis. Note that the order is reversed.)

Provided that θ is not a multiple of 180°, the decomposition of a rotation in this form is unique (apart from the ambiguity arising from the possibility of adding a multiple of 360° to any angle). Figure 4.10.34 shows how the Euler angles can be read off geometrically.

FIGURE 4.10.34

The coordinate rays Ox, Oy, Oz, together with their images $O\xi$, $O\eta$, $O\zeta$ under a rotation, fix the Euler angles associated with that rotation, as follows: $\theta = zO\zeta$, $\psi = xOr = yOs$, and $\phi = sO\eta$. (Here the ray Or is the projection of $O\zeta$ to the xy-plane. The ray Os is determined by the intersection of the xy- and $\xi\eta$-planes.)

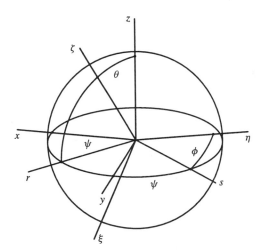

Warning: Some references define Euler angles differently; the most common variation is that the second rotation is taken about the x-axis instead of about the y-axis.

Screw motion with angle α and displacement d around the line with direction cosines a, b, c through an arbitrary point (x_0, y_0, z_0):

$$(x, y, z) \mapsto (x_0 + ad, y_0 + bd, z_0 + cd) + M(x - x_0, y - y_0, z - z_0),$$

where M is given by (4.10.1).

Reflection

in the xy-plane:	$(x, y, z) \mapsto (x, y, -z).$	
in the xz-plane:	$(x, y, z) \mapsto (x, -y, z).$	(4.10.3)
in the yz-plane:	$(x, y, z) \mapsto (-x, y, z).$	

Reflection in a plane with equation $ax + by + cz + d = 0$:

$$(x, y, z) \mapsto \frac{1}{a^2 + b^2 + c^2}(M(x_0, y_0, z_0) - (2ad, 2bd, 2cd)),$$

where M is the matrix

$$M = \begin{bmatrix} -a^2 + b^2 + c^2 & -2ab & -2ac \\ -2ab & a^2 - b^2 + c^2 & -2bc \\ -2ac & -2bc & a^2 + b^2 - c^2 \end{bmatrix}. \quad (4.10.4)$$

Reflection in a plane going through (x_0, y_0, z_0) and whose normal has direction cosines a, b, c:

$$(x, y, z) \mapsto (x_0 + y_0 + z_0) + M(x - x_0, y - y_0, z - z_0),$$

where M is as in (4.10.4).

Glide-reflection in a plane P with displacement vector $\mathbf{v}$: Apply first a reflection in P, then a translation by the vector $\mathbf{v}$.

4.10.2   FORMULAS FOR SYMMETRIES: HOMOGENEOUS COORDINATES

All isometries of space can be expressed in homogeneous coordinates in terms of multiplication by a matrix. As in the case of plane isometries (Section 4.2.2), this means that the successive application of transformations reduces to matrix multiplication. (In the formulas below, $\begin{bmatrix} M & 0 \\ 0 & 1 \end{bmatrix}$ is the 4×4 projective matrix obtained from the 3×3 matrix M by adding a row and a column as stated.)

Translation by (x_0, y_0, z_0): $\qquad \begin{bmatrix} 1 & 0 & 0 & x_0 \\ 0 & 1 & 0 & y_0 \\ 0 & 0 & 1 & z_0 \\ 0 & 0 & 0 & 1 \end{bmatrix}.$

Rotation through the origin: $\qquad \begin{bmatrix} M & 0 \\ 0 & 1 \end{bmatrix},$

where M is given in (4.10.1) or (4.10.2), as the case may be.

Reflection in a plane through the origin: $\qquad \begin{bmatrix} M & 0 \\ 0 & 1 \end{bmatrix},$

where M is given in (4.10.4).

From this one can deduce all other transformations, as in the case of plane transformations (see page 255).

4.11 OTHER TRANSFORMATIONS OF SPACE

4.11.1 SIMILARITIES

A transformation of space that preserves shapes is called a *similarity*. Every similarity of the plane is obtained by composing a *proportional scaling transformation* (also known as a *homothety*) with an isometry. A proportional scaling transformation centered at the origin has the form

$$(x, y, z) \mapsto (ax, ay, az),$$

where $a \neq 0$ is the scaling factor (a real number). The corresponding matrix in *homogeneous coordinates* is

$$H_a = \begin{bmatrix} a & 0 & 0 & 0 \\ 0 & a & 0 & 0 \\ 0 & 0 & a & 0 \\ 0 & 0 & 0 & 1 \end{bmatrix}.$$

In *cylindrical coordinates*, the transformation is $(r, \theta, z) \mapsto (ar, \theta, az)$. In *spherical coordinates*, it is $(r, \phi, \theta) \mapsto (ar, \phi, \theta)$.

4.11.2 AFFINE TRANSFORMATIONS

A transformation that preserves lines and parallelism (maps parallel lines to parallel lines) is an *affine transformation*. There are two important particular cases of such transformations:

1. A *nonproportional scaling transformation* centered at the origin has the form $(x, y, z) \mapsto (ax, by, cz)$, where $a, b, c \neq 0$ are the scaling factors (real numbers). The corresponding matrix in *homogeneous coordinates* is

$$H_{a,b,c} = \begin{bmatrix} a & 0 & 0 & 0 \\ 0 & b & 0 & 0 \\ 0 & 0 & c & 0 \\ 0 & 0 & 0 & 1 \end{bmatrix}.$$

2. A *shear* in the x-direction and preserving horizontal planes has the form $(x, y, z) \mapsto (x + rz, y, z)$, where r is the shearing factor. The corresponding matrix in *homogeneous coordinates* is

$$S_r = \begin{bmatrix} 1 & 0 & r & 0 \\ 0 & 1 & 0 & 0 \\ 0 & 0 & 1 & 0 \\ 0 & 0 & 0 & 1 \end{bmatrix}.$$

Every affine transformation is obtained by composing a scaling transformation with an isometry, or one or two shears with a homothety and an isometry.

4.11.3 PROJECTIVE TRANSFORMATIONS

A transformation that maps lines to lines (but does not necessarily preserve parallelism) is a *projective transformation*. Any spatial projective transformation can be expressed by an invertible 4×4 matrix in homogeneous coordinates; conversely, any invertible 4×4 matrix defines a projective transformation of space. Projective transformations (if not affine) are not defined on all of space, but only on the complement of a plane (the missing plane is "mapped to infinity").

The following particular case is often useful, especially in computer graphics, in *projecting a scene* from space to the plane. Suppose an observer is at the point $E = (x_0, y_0, z_0)$ of space, looking toward the origin $O = (0, 0, 0)$. Let P, the *screen*, be the plane through O and perpendicular to the ray EO. Place a rectangular coordinate system $\xi\eta$ on P with origin at O so that the positive η-axis lies in the half-plane determined by E and the positive z-axis of space (that is, the z-axis is pointing "up" as seen from E). Then consider the transformation that associates with a point $X = (x, y, z)$ the triple (ξ, η, ζ), where (ξ, η) are the coordinates of the point, where the line EX intersects P (the *screen coordinates* of X as seen from E), and ζ is the inverse of the signed distance from X to E along the line EO (this distance is the *depth* of X as seen from E). This is a projective transformation, given by the matrix

$$\begin{bmatrix} -r^2 y_0 & r^2 x_0 & 0 & 0 \\ -r x_0 z_0 & -r y_0 z_0 & r\rho^2 & 0 \\ 0 & 0 & 0 & r\rho \\ -\rho x_0 & -\rho y_0 & -\rho z_0 & r^2\rho \end{bmatrix}$$

with $\rho = \sqrt{x_0^2 + y_0^2}$ and $r = \sqrt{x_0^2 + y_0^2 + z_0^2}$.

4.12 DIRECTION ANGLES AND DIRECTION COSINES

Given a vector (a, b, c) in three-dimensional space, the *direction cosines* of this vector are

$$\begin{aligned} \cos\alpha &= \frac{a}{\sqrt{a^2 + b^2 + c^2}}, \\ \cos\beta &= \frac{b}{\sqrt{a^2 + b^2 + c^2}}, \\ \cos\gamma &= \frac{c}{\sqrt{a^2 + b^2 + c^2}}. \end{aligned} \qquad (4.12.1)$$

Here the *direction angles* α, β, γ are the angles that the vector makes with the positive x-, y- and z-axes, respectively. In formulas, usually the direction cosines appear, rather than the direction angles. We have

$$\cos^2\alpha + \cos^2\beta + \cos^2\gamma = 1.$$

4.13 PLANES

The (Cartesian) equation of a *plane* is linear in the coordinates x, y, and z:

$$ax + by + cz + d = 0. \tag{4.13.1}$$

The *normal direction* to this plane is (a, b, c). The *intersection* of this plane with the x-axis, or *x-intercept*, is $x = -d/a$, the *y-intercept* is $y = -d/b$, and the *z-intercept* is $z = -d/c$. The plane is vertical (perpendicular to the xy-plane) if $c = 0$. It is perpendicular to the x-axis if $b = c = 0$, and likewise for the other coordinates.

When $a^2 + b^2 + c^2 = 1$ and $d \leq 0$ in the equation $ax + by + cz + d = 0$, the equation is said to be in *normal form*. In this case d is the *distance of the plane to the origin*, and (a, b, c) are the *direction cosines* of the normal.

To reduce an arbitrary equation $ax + by + cz + d = 0$ to normal form, divide by $\pm\sqrt{a^2 + b^2 + c^2}$, where the sign of the radical is chosen opposite the sign of d when $d \neq 0$, the same as the sign of c when $d = 0$ and $c \neq 0$, and the same as the sign of b otherwise.

Planes with prescribed properties

- Plane through (x_0, y_0, z_0) and perpendicular to the direction (a, b, c):

$$a(x - x_0) + b(y - y_0) + c(z - z_0) = 0. \tag{4.13.2}$$

- Plane through (x_0, y_0, z_0) and parallel to the directions (a_1, b_1, c_1) and (a_2, b_2, c_2):

$$\begin{vmatrix} x - x_0 & y - y_0 & z - z_0 \\ a_1 & b_1 & c_1 \\ a_2 & b_2 & c_2 \end{vmatrix} = 0. \tag{4.13.3}$$

- Plane through (x_0, y_0, z_0) and (x_1, y_1, z_1) and parallel to the direction (a, b, c):

$$\begin{vmatrix} x - x_0 & y - y_0 & z - z_0 \\ x_1 - x_0 & y_1 - y_0 & z_1 - z_0 \\ a & b & c \end{vmatrix} = 0. \tag{4.13.4}$$

- Plane going through (x_0, y_0, z_0), (x_1, y_1, z_1) and (x_2, y_2, z_2):

$$\begin{vmatrix} x & y & z & 1 \\ x_0 & y_0 & z_0 & 1 \\ x_1 & y_1 & z_1 & 1 \\ x_2 & y_2 & z_2 & 1 \end{vmatrix} = 0 \quad \text{or} \quad \begin{vmatrix} x - x_0 & y - y_0 & z - z_0 \\ x_1 - x_0 & y_1 - y_0 & z_1 - z_0 \\ x_2 - x_0 & y_2 - y_0 & z_2 - z_0 \end{vmatrix} = 0.$$

$$\tag{4.13.5}$$

(The last three formulas remain true in *oblique coordinates*.)

- The *distance* from the point (x_0, y_0, z_0) to the plane $ax + by + cz + d = 0$ is

$$\left| \frac{ax_0 + by_0 + cz_0 + d}{\sqrt{a^2 + b^2 + c^2}} \right|. \tag{4.13.6}$$

- The *angle* between two planes $a_0x+b_0y+c_0z+d_0 = 0$ and $a_1x+b_1y+c_1z+d_1 = 0$ is

$$\cos^{-1}\frac{a_0a_1 + b_0b_1 + c_0c_1}{\sqrt{a_0^2 + b_0^2 + c_0^2}\sqrt{a_1^2 + b_1^2 + c_1^2}}. \tag{4.13.7}$$

In particular, the two planes are *parallel* when $a_0 : b_0 : c_0 = a_1 : b_1 : c_1$, and *perpendicular* when $a_0a_1 + b_0b_1 + c_0c_1 = 0$.

Concurrence and coplanarity

Four planes $a_0x + b_0y + c_0 = 0$, $a_1x + b_1y + c_1 = 0$, $a_2x + b_2y + c_2 = 0$ and $a_3x + b_3y + c_3 = 0$ are *concurrent* if and only if

$$\begin{vmatrix} 1 & a_0 & b_0 & c_0 \\ 1 & a_1 & b_1 & c_1 \\ 1 & a_2 & b_2 & c_2 \\ 1 & a_3 & b_3 & c_3 \end{vmatrix} = 0.$$

Four points (x_0, y_0, z_0), (x_1, y_1, z_1), (x_2, y_2, z_2) and (x_3, y_3, z_3) are *coplanar* if and only if

$$\begin{vmatrix} x_0 & y_0 & z_0 & 1 \\ x_1 & y_1 & z_1 & 1 \\ x_2 & y_2 & z_2 & 1 \\ x_3 & y_3 & z_3 & 1 \end{vmatrix} = 0.$$

(Both of these assertions remain true in *oblique coordinates*.)

4.14   LINES

Two planes that are not parallel or coincident intersect in a *straight line*, such that one can express a line by a pair of linear equations

$$\left.\begin{cases} ax + by + cz + d = 0 \\ a'x + b'y + c'z + d' = 0 \end{cases}\right\}$$

such that $bc' - cb'$, $ca' - ac'$, and $ab' - ba'$ are not all zero. The line thus defined is parallel to the vector $(bc' - cb', ca' - ac', ab' - ba')$. The *direction cosines* of the line are those of this vector. See Equation (4.12.1). (The direction cosines of a line are only defined up to a simultaneous change in sign, because the opposite vector still gives the same line.)

The following particular cases are important:

- Line through (x_0, y_0, z_0) parallel to the vector (a, b, c):

$$\frac{x - x_0}{a} = \frac{y - y_0}{b} = \frac{z - z_0}{c}.$$

- Line through (x_0, y_0, z_0) and (x_1, y_1, z_1):

$$\frac{x - x_0}{x_1 - x_0} = \frac{y - y_0}{y_1 - y_0} = \frac{z - z_0}{z_1 - z_0}.$$

This line is parallel to the vector $(x_1 - x_0, y_1 - y_0, z_1 - z_0)$.

Distances

- The *distance* between two points in space is the *length of the line segment* joining them. The distance between the points (x_0, y_0, z_0) and (x_1, y_1, z_1) is

$$\sqrt{(x_1 - x_0)^2 + (y_1 - y_0)^2 + (z_1 - z_0)^2}.$$

- The point $k\%$ of the way from $P_0 = (x_0, y_0, z_0)$ to $P_1 = (x_1, y_1, z_1)$ is

$$\left(\frac{kx_1 + (100 - k)x_2}{100}, \frac{ky_1 + (100 - k)y_2}{100}, \frac{kz_1 + (100 - k)z_2}{100} \right).$$

(The same formula also applies in oblique coordinates.) This point divides the segment $P_0 P_1$ in the ratio $k : (100 - k)$. As a particular case, the *midpoint* of $P_0 P_1$ is given by

$$\left(\frac{x_1 + x_2}{2}, \frac{y_1 + y_2}{2}, \frac{z_1 + z_2}{2} \right).$$

- The *distance* between the point (x_0, y_0, z_0) and the line through (x_1, y_1, z_1) in direction (a, b, c):

$$\sqrt{\frac{\begin{vmatrix} y_0 - y_1 & z_0 - z_1 \\ b & c \end{vmatrix}^2 + \begin{vmatrix} z_0 - z_1 & x_0 - x_1 \\ c & a \end{vmatrix}^2 + \begin{vmatrix} x_0 - x_1 & y_0 - y_1 \\ a & b \end{vmatrix}^2}{a^2 + b^2 + c^2}}$$

- The *distance* between the line through (x_0, y_0, z_0) in direction (a_0, b_0, c_0) and the line through (x_1, y_1, z_1) in direction (a_1, b_1, c_1):

$$\left| \frac{\begin{vmatrix} x_1 - x_0 & y_1 - y_0 & z_1 - z_0 \\ a_0 & b_0 & c_0 \\ a_1 & b_1 & c_1 \end{vmatrix}}{\sqrt{\begin{vmatrix} b_0 & c_0 \\ b_1 & c_1 \end{vmatrix}^2 + \begin{vmatrix} c_0 & a_0 \\ c_1 & a_1 \end{vmatrix}^2 + \begin{vmatrix} a_0 & b_0 \\ a_1 & b_1 \end{vmatrix}^2}} \right|. \tag{4.14.1}$$

Angles

Angle between lines with directions (x_0, y_0, z_0) and (x_1, y_1, z_1):

$$\cos^{-1} \frac{a_0 a_1 + b_0 b_1 + c_0 c_1}{\sqrt{a_0^2 + b_0^2 + c_0^2} \sqrt{a_1^2 + b_1^2 + c_1^2}}.$$

In particular, the two lines are *parallel* when $a_0 : b_0 : c_0 = a_1 : b_1 : c_1$, and *perpendicular* when $a_0a_1 + b_0b_1 + c_0c_1 = 0$.

Angle between lines with direction angles $\alpha_0, \beta_0, \gamma_0$ and $\alpha_1, \beta_1, \gamma_1$:

$$\cos^{-1}(\cos \alpha_0 \cos \alpha_1 + \cos \beta_0 \cos \beta_1 + \cos \gamma_0 \cos \gamma_1).$$

Concurrence, coplanarity, parallelism

Two lines specified by point and direction are *coplanar* if, and only if, the determinant in the numerator of Equation (4.14.1) is zero. In this case they are *concurrent* (if the denominator is nonzero) or *parallel* (if the denominator is zero).

Three lines with directions (a_0, b_0, c_0), (a_1, b_1, c_1) and (a_2, b_2, c_2) are *parallel to a common plane* if and only if

$$\begin{vmatrix} a_0 & b_0 & c_0 \\ a_1 & b_1 & c_1 \\ a_2 & b_2 & c_2 \end{vmatrix} = 0.$$

4.15   POLYHEDRA

For any polyhedron topologically equivalent to a sphere—in particular, for any *convex polyhedron*—the *Euler formula* holds:

$$v - e + f = 2,$$

where v is the number of vertices, e is the number of edges, and f is the number of faces.

Many common polyhedra are particular cases of cylinders (Section 4.16) or cones (Section 4.17). A cylinder with a polygonal base (the base is also called a directrix) is called a *prism*. A cone with a polygonal base is called a *pyramid*. A frustum of a cone with a polygonal base is called a *truncated pyramid*. Formulas (4.16.1), (4.17.1), and (4.17.2) give the volumes of a general prism, pyramid, and trucated pyramid.

A prism whose base is a parallelogram is a *parallelepiped*. The *volume* of a parallelepiped with one vertex at the origin and adjacent vertices at (x_1, y_1, z_1), (x_2, y_2, z_2), and (x_3, y_3, z_3) is given by

$$\begin{vmatrix} x_1 & y_1 & z_1 \\ x_2 & y_2 & z_2 \\ x_3 & y_3 & z_3 \end{vmatrix}.$$

The *rectangular parallelepiped* is a particular case: all of its faces are rectangles. If the side lengths are a, b, c, the *volume* is abc, the *total area* is $2(ab + ac + bc)$, and each *diagonal* has length $\sqrt{a^2 + b^2 + c^2}$. When $a = b = c$ we get the *cube*. See Section 4.15.1.

A pyramid whose base is a triangle is a *tetrahedron*. The *volume* of a tetrahedon with one vertex at the origin and the other vertices at (x_1, y_1, z_1), (x_2, y_2, z_2), and (x_3, y_3, z_3) is given by

$$\frac{1}{6} \begin{vmatrix} x_1 & y_1 & z_1 \\ x_2 & y_2 & z_2 \\ x_3 & y_3 & z_3 \end{vmatrix}.$$

In a tetrahedron with vertices P_0, P_1, P_2, P_3, let d_{ij} be the distance (edge length) from P_i to P_j. Form the determinants

$$\Delta = \begin{vmatrix} 0 & 1 & 1 & 1 & 1 \\ 1 & 0 & d_{01}^2 & d_{02}^2 & d_{03}^2 \\ 1 & d_{01}^2 & 0 & d_{12}^2 & d_{13}^2 \\ 1 & d_{02}^2 & d_{12}^2 & 0 & d_{23}^2 \\ 1 & d_{03}^2 & d_{13}^2 & d_{23}^2 & 0 \end{vmatrix} \quad \text{and} \quad \Gamma = \begin{vmatrix} 0 & d_{01}^2 & d_{02}^2 & d_{03}^2 \\ d_{01}^2 & 0 & d_{12}^2 & d_{13}^2 \\ d_{02}^2 & d_{12}^2 & 0 & d_{23}^2 \\ d_{03}^2 & d_{13}^2 & d_{23}^2 & 0 \end{vmatrix}.$$

Then the *volume* of the tetrahedron is $\sqrt{|\Delta|/288}$, and the radius of the *circumscribed sphere* is $\frac{1}{2}\sqrt{|\Gamma/2\Delta|}$.

4.15.1 REGULAR POLYHEDRA

Figure 4.15.35 shows the five regular polyhedra, or *Platonic solids*. In the following tables and formulas, a is the length of an edge, θ the dihedral angle at each edge, R the radius of the circumscribed sphere, r the radius of the inscribed sphere, V the volume, S the total surface area, v the total number of vertices, e the total number of edges, f the total number of faces, p the number of edges in a face (3 for equilateral triangles, 4 for squares, 5 for regular pentagons), and q the number of edges meeting at a vertex.

$$\theta = 2\sin^{-1}\frac{\cos(180°/q)}{\sin(180°/p)}, \qquad \frac{R}{r} = \tan\frac{180°}{p}\tan\frac{180°}{q},$$

$$\frac{R}{a} = \frac{\frac{1}{2}\sin(180°/q)}{\sin(180°/p)\cos\frac{1}{2}\theta}, \qquad \frac{S}{a^2} = \frac{fp}{4}\cot\frac{180°}{p}, \quad \text{and}$$

$$\frac{r}{a} = a\cot\frac{180°}{p}\tan\frac{\theta}{2}, \qquad V = \frac{1}{3}rS.$$

Name	v	e	f	p	q	$\sin\theta$	θ
Regular tetrahedron	4	6	4	3	3	$2\sqrt{2}/3$	$70°31'44''$
Cube	8	12	6	4	3	1	$90°$
Regular octahedron	6	12	8	3	4	$2\sqrt{2}/3$	$109°28'16''$
Regular dodecahedron	20	30	12	5	3	$2/\sqrt{5}$	$116°33'54''$
Regular icosahedron	12	30	20	3	5	$2/3$	$138°11'23''$

FIGURE 4.15.35

*The Platonic solids. Top: the tetrahedron (self-dual). Middle: the cube and the octahedron
(dual to one another). Bottom: the dodecahedron and the icosahedron (dual to one another).*

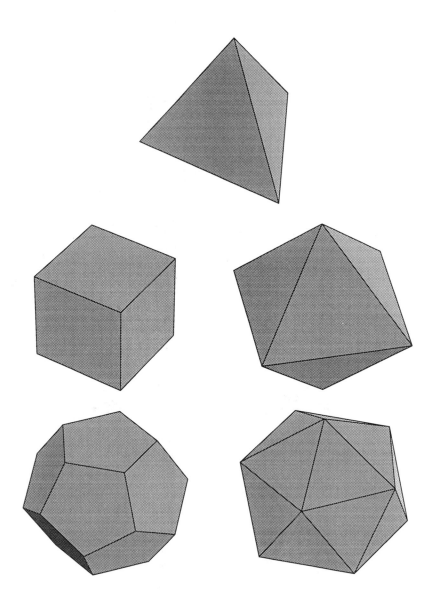

Name	R/a		r/a	
Tetrahedron	$\sqrt{6}/4$	0.612372	$\sqrt{6}/12$	0.204124
Cube	$\sqrt{3}/2$	0.866025	$\frac{1}{2}$	0.5
Octahedron	$\sqrt{2}/2$	0.707107	$\sqrt{6}/6$	0.408248
Dodecahedron	$\frac{1}{4}(\sqrt{15}+\sqrt{3})$	1.401259	$\frac{1}{20}\sqrt{250+110\sqrt{5}}$	1.113516
Icosahedron	$\frac{1}{4}\sqrt{10+2\sqrt{5}}$	0.951057	$\frac{1}{12}\sqrt{42+18\sqrt{5}}$	0.755761

Name	S/a^2		V/a^3	
Tetrahedron	$\sqrt{3}$	1.73205	$\sqrt{2}/12$	0.117851
Cube	6	6.	1	1.
Octahedron	$2\sqrt{3}$	3.46410	$\sqrt{2}/3$	0.471405
Dodecahedron	$3\sqrt{25+10\sqrt{5}}$	20.64573	$\frac{1}{4}\sqrt{15+7\sqrt{5}}$	7.663119
Icosahedron	$5\sqrt{3}$	8.66025	$\frac{5}{12}(3+\sqrt{5})$	2.181695

4.16 CYLINDERS

Given a line L and a curve C in a plane P, the *cylinder* with *generator L* and *directrix C* is the surface obtained by moving L parallel to itself, so that a point of L is always on C. If L is parallel to the z-axis, the surface's implicit equation does not involve the variable z. Conversely, any implicit equation that does not involve one of the variables (or that can be brought to that form by a change of coordinates) represents a cylinder.

If C is a simple closed curve, we also apply the word *cylinder* to the solid enclosed by the surface generated in this way (Figure 4.16.36, left). The *volume*

FIGURE 4.16.36
Left: an oblique cylinder with generator L and directrix C. Right: a right circular cylinder.

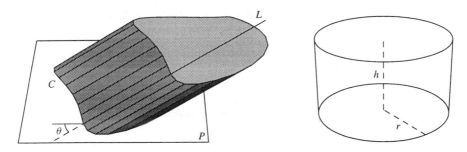

contained between P and a plane P' parallel to P is

$$V = Ah = Al \sin\theta, \qquad (4.16.1)$$

where A is the area in the plane P enclosed by C, h is the distance between P and P' (measured perpendicularly), l is the length of the segment of L contained between P and P', and θ is the angle that L makes with P. When $\theta = 90°$ we have a *right cylinder*, and $h = l$. For a right cylinder, the *lateral area* between P and P' is hs, where s is the length (circumference) of C.

The most important particular case is the *right circular cylinder* (often simply called a *cylinder*). If r is the radius of the base and h is the altitude (Figure 4.16.36, right), the *lateral area* is $2\pi rh$, the *total area* is $2\pi r(r + h)$, and the *volume* is $\pi r^2 h$. The *implicit equation* of this surface can be written $x^2 + y^2 = r^2$; see also Section 4.20.

4.17 CONES

Given a curve C in a plane P and a point O not in P, the *cone* with *vertex* O and *directrix* C is the surface obtained as the union of all lines that join O with points of C. If O is the origin and the surface is given implicity by an algebraic equation, that equation is homogeneous (all terms have the same total degree in the variables). Conversely, any homogeneous implicit equation (or one that can be made homogeneous by a change of coordinates) represents a cone.

If C is a simple closed curve, we also apply the word *cone* to the solid enclosed by the surface generated in this way (Figure 4.17.37, top). The *volume* contained between P and the vertex O is

$$V = \tfrac{1}{3}Ah, \qquad (4.17.1)$$

where A is the area in the plane P enclosed by C and h is the distance from O and P (measured perpendicularly).

The solid contained between P and a plane P' parallel to P (on the same side of the vertex) is called a *frustum*. Its volume is

$$V = \tfrac{1}{3}h(A + A' + \sqrt{AA'}), \qquad (4.17.2)$$

where A and A' are the areas enclosed by the sections of the cone by P and P' (often called the *bases* of the frustum).

The most important particular case of a cone is the *right circular cone* (often simply called a *cone*). If r is the radius of the base, h is the altitude, and l is the length between the vertex and a point on the base circle (Figure 4.17.37, bottom left), the

FIGURE 4.17.37

Top: a cone with vertex O and directrix C. Bottom left: a right circular cone. Bottom right: A frustum of the latter.

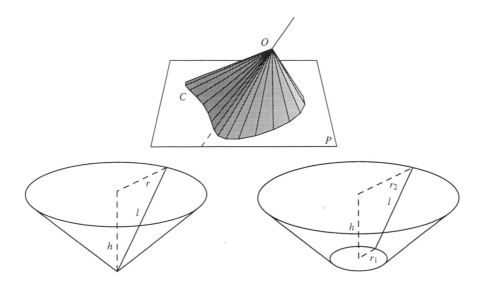

following relationships apply:

$$l = \sqrt{r^2 + h^2},$$

$$\text{Lateral area} = \pi r l = \pi r \sqrt{r^2 + h^2},$$

$$\text{Total area} = \pi r(l + r) = \pi r(r + \sqrt{r^2 + h^2}), \text{ and}$$

$$\text{Volume} = \tfrac{1}{3}\pi r^2 h.$$

The *implicit equation* of this surface can be written $x^2 + y^2 = z^2$; see also Section 4.20. For a *frustum* of a right circular cone (Figure 4.17.37, bottom right),

$$l = \sqrt{(r_1 - r_2)^2 + h^2},$$

$$\text{Lateral area} = \pi(r_1 + r_2)l,$$

$$\text{Total area} = \pi(r_1^2 + r_2^2 + (r_1 + r_2)l), \text{ and}$$

$$\text{Volume} = \tfrac{1}{3}\pi h(r_1^2 + r_2^2 + r_1 r_2).$$

4.18 SPHERES

The set of points in space whose distance to a fixed point (the *center*) is a fixed positive number (the *radius*) is a *sphere*. A circle of radius r and center (x_0, y_0, z_0) is defined by the equation

$$(x - x_0)^2 + (y - y_0)^2 + (z - z_0)^2 = r^2,$$

or

$$x^2 + y^2 + z^2 - 2xx_0 - 2yy_0 - 2zz_0 + x_0^2 + y_0^2 + z_0^2 - r^2 = 0.$$

Conversely, an equation of the form

$$x^2 + y^2 + z^2 + 2dx + 2ey + 2fz + g = 0$$

defines a sphere if $d^2 + e^2 + f^2 > g$; the center is $(-d, -e, -f)$ and the radius is $\sqrt{d^2 + e^2 + f^2 - g}$.

Four points not on the same line determine a unique sphere. If the points have coordinates (x_1, y_1, z_1), (x_2, y_2, z_2), (x_3, y_3, z_3) and (x_4, x_4, z_4), the equation of the sphere is

$$\begin{vmatrix} x^2 + y^2 + z^2 & x & y & z & 1 \\ x_1^2 + y_1^2 + z_1^2 & x_1 & y_1 & z_1 & 1 \\ x_2^2 + y_2^2 + z_2^2 & x_2 & y_2 & z_2 & 1 \\ x_3^2 + y_3^2 + z_3^2 & x_3 & y_3 & z_3 & 1 \\ x_4^2 + y_4^2 + z_4^2 & x_4 & y_4 & z_4 & 1 \end{vmatrix} = 0.$$

Given two points $P_1 = (x_1, y_1, z_1)$ and $P_2 = (x_2, y_2, z_2)$, there is a unique sphere whose diameter is $P_1 P_2$; its equation is

$$(x - x_1)(x - x_2) + (y - y_1)(y - y_2) + (z - z_1)(z - z_2) = 0.$$

The *area* of a sphere of radius r is $4\pi r^2$, and the *volume* is $\frac{4}{3}\pi r^3$.

The *area of a spherical polygon* (that is, of a polygon on the sphere whose sides are arcs of great circles) is

$$S = \left(\sum_{i=1}^{n} \theta_i - (n-2)\pi\right) r^2, \tag{4.18.1}$$

where r is the radius of the sphere, n is the number of vertices, and θ_i are the internal angles of the polygons in radians. In particular, the sum of the angles of a spherical triangle is always greater than $\pi = 180°$, and the excess is proportional to the area.

Spherical cap

Let the radius be r (Figure 4.18.38, left). The *area* of the curved region is $2\pi rh = \pi p^2$. The *volume* of the cap is $\frac{1}{3}\pi h^2(3r - h) = \frac{1}{6}\pi h(3a^2 + h^2)$.

Spherical zone (of two bases)

Let the radius be r (Figure 4.18.38, middle). The *area* of the curved region is $2\pi rh$. The *volume* of the zone is $\frac{1}{6}\pi h(3a^2 + 3b^2 + h^2)$.

FIGURE 4.18.38
Left: a spherical cap. Middle: a spherical zone (of two bases). Right: a spherical segment.

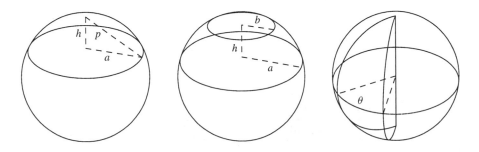

Spherical segment and lune

Let the radius be r (Figure 4.18.38, right). The *area* of the curved region (lune) is $2r^2\theta$, the angle being measured in radians. The *volume* of the segment is $\frac{2}{3}r^3\theta$.

Spheres in arbitrary dimensions

If the volume of an n-dimensional sphere of radius r is $V_n(r)$ and its surface area is $S_n(r)$, then

$$V_n(r) = \frac{2\pi r^2}{n} V_{n-2} = \frac{2\pi^{n/2} r^n}{n \Gamma\left(\frac{n}{2}\right)},$$

$$S_n(r) = \frac{n}{r} V_n = \frac{d}{dr}[V_n(r)].$$

(4.18.2)

Hence, $V_2 = \pi r^2$, $V_3 = \frac{4}{3}\pi r^3, \ldots, S_2 = 2\pi r$, $S_3 = 4\pi r^2, \ldots$.

4.19 SURFACES OF REVOLUTION: THE TORUS

A *surface of revolution* is formed by the rotation of a planar curve C about an axis in the plane of the curve and not cutting the curve. The *Pappus–Guldinus theorem* says that:

- The *area of the surface of revolution* on a curve C is equal to the product of the length of C and the length of the path traced by the centroid of C (which is 2π the distance from this centroid to the axis of revolution).

- The *volume bounded by the surface of revolution* on a simple closed curve C is equal to the product of the area bounded by C and the length of the path traced by the centroid of the area bounded by C.

When C is a circle, the surface obtained is a *circular torus* or *torus of revolution* (Figure 4.19.39). Let r be the radius of the revolving circle and let R be the distance from its center to the axis of rotation. The *area* of the torus is $4\pi^2 Rr$, and its *volume* is $2\pi^2 Rr^2$.

FIGURE 4.19.39
A torus of revolution.

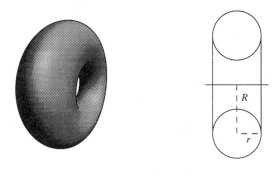

4.20   QUADRICS

A surface defined by an algebraic equation of degree two is called a *quadric*. Spheres, circular cylinders, and circular cones are quadrics. By means of a rigid motion, any quadric can be transformed into a quadric having one of the following equations (where $a, b, c \neq 0$):

1. Real ellipsoid: $x^2/a^2 + y^2/b^2 + z^2/c^2 = 1.$
2. Imaginary ellipsoid: $x^2/a^2 + y^2/b^2 + z^2/c^2 = -1.$
3. Hyperboloid of one sheet: $x^2/a^2 + y^2/b^2 - z^2/c^2 = 1.$
4. Hyperboloid of two sheets: $x^2/a^2 + y^2/b^2 - z^2/c^2 = -1.$
5. Real quadric cone: $x^2/a^2 + y^2/b^2 - z^2/c^2 = 0.$
6. Imaginary quadric cone: $x^2/a^2 + y^2/b^2 + z^2/c^2 = 0.$
7. Elliptic paraboloid: $x^2/a^2 + y^2/b^2 + 2z = 0.$
8. Hyperbolic paraboloid: $x^2/a^2 - y^2/b^2 + 2z = 0.$
9. Real elliptic cylinder: $x^2/a^2 + y^2/b^2 = 1.$
10. Imaginary elliptic cylinder: $x^2/a^2 + y^2/b^2 = -1.$
11. Hyperbolic cylinder: $x^2/a^2 - y^2/b^2 = 1.$
12. Real intersecting planes: $x^2/a^2 - y^2/b^2 = 0.$
13. Imaginary intersecting planes: $x^2/a^2 + y^2/b^2 = 0.$
14. Parabolic cylinder: $x^2 + 2y = 0.$
15. Real parallel planes: $x^2 = 1.$
16. Imaginary parallel planes: $x^2 = -1.$
17. Coincident planes: $x^2 = 0.$

Surfaces with Equations 9–17 are cylinders over the plane curves of the same equation (Section 4.16). Equations 2, 6, 10, and 16 have no real solutions, so that they

FIGURE 4.20.40

The five nondegenerate real quadrics. Top: ellipsoid. Middle left: hyperboloid of one sheet. Middle right: hyperboloid of two sheets. Bottom left: elliptic paraboloid. Bottom right: hyperbolic paraboloid.

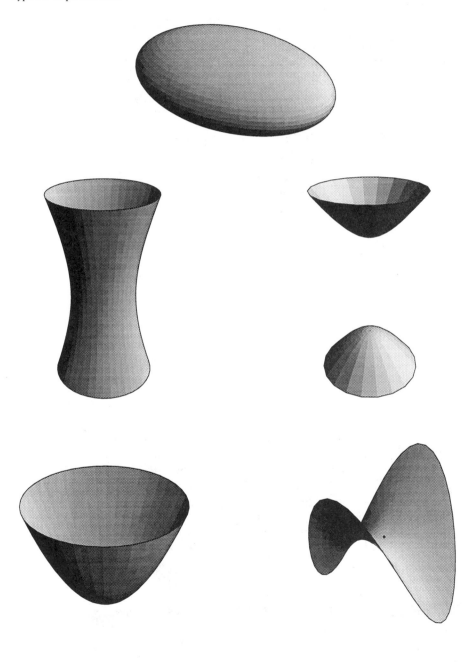

do not describe surfaces in real three-dimensional space. A surface with Equation 5 can be regarded as a cone (Section 4.17) over a conic C (any ellipse, parabola or hyperbola can be taken as the directrix; there is a two-parameter family of essentially distinct cones over it, determined by the position of the vertex with respect to C). The surfaces with Equations 1, 3, 4, 7, and 8 are shown in Figure 4.20.40.

The surfaces with Equations 1–6 are *central quadrics*; in the form given, the center is at the origin. The quantities a, b, c are the *semiaxes*.

The *volume of the ellipsoid* with semiaxes a, b, c is $\frac{4}{3}\pi abc$. When two of the semiaxes are the same, we can also write the *area of the ellipsoid* in closed form. Suppose $b = c$, so the ellipsoid $x^2/a^2 + (y^2 + z^2)/b^2 = 1$ is the surface of revolution obtained by rotating the ellipse $x^2/a^2 + y^2/b^2 = 1$ around the x-axis. Its area is

$$2\pi b^2 + \frac{2\pi a^2 b}{\sqrt{a^2 - b^2}}\sin^{-1}\frac{\sqrt{a^2 - b^2}}{a} = 2\pi b^2 + \frac{\pi a^2 b}{\sqrt{b^2 - a^2}}\log\frac{b + \sqrt{b^2 - a^2}}{b - \sqrt{b^2 - a^2}}.$$

The two quantities are equal, but only one avoids complex numbers, depending on whether $a > b$ or $a < b$. When $a > b$, we have a *prolate spheroid*, that is, an ellipse rotated around its major axis; when $a < b$ we have an *oblate spheroid*, which is an ellipse rotated around its minor axis.

Given a general quadratic equation in three variables,

$$ax^2 + by^2 + cz^2 + 2fyz + 2gzx + 2hxy + 2px + 2qy + 2rz + d = 0,$$

$$(4.20.1)$$

one can determine the type of conic by consulting the table:

ρ_3	ρ_4	Δ	k signs	K signs	Type of quadric
3	4	< 0			Real ellipsoid
3	4	> 0	Same		Imaginary ellipsoid
3	4	> 0	Opp		Hyperboloid of one sheet
3	4	< 0	Opp		Hyperboloid of two sheets
3	3		Opp		Real quadric cone
3	3		Same		Imaginary quadric cone
2	4	< 0	Same		Elliptic paraboloid
2	4	> 0	Opp		Hyperbolic paraboloid
2	3		Same	Opp	Real elliptic cylinder
2	3		Same	Same	Imaginary elliptic cylinder
2	3		Opp		Hyperbolic cylinder
2	2		Opp		Real intersecting planes
2	2		Same		Imaginary intersecting planes
1	3				Parabolic cylinder
1	2			Opp	Real parallel planes
1	2			Same	Imaginary parallel planes
1	1				Coincident planes

The columns have the following meaning. Let

$$e = \begin{bmatrix} a & h & g \\ h & b & f \\ g & f & c \end{bmatrix} \quad \text{and} \quad E = \begin{bmatrix} a & h & g & p \\ h & b & f & q \\ g & f & c & r \\ p & q & r & d \end{bmatrix}.$$

Let ρ_3 and ρ_4 be the ranks of e and E, and let Δ be the determinant of E. The column "k signs" refers to the nonzero eigenvalues of e, that is, the roots of

$$\begin{vmatrix} a-x & h & g \\ h & b-x & f \\ g & f & c-x \end{vmatrix} = 0;$$

if all nonzero eigenvalues have the same sign, choose "same", otherwise "opposite". Similarly, "K signs" refers to the sign of the nonzero eigenvalues of E.

4.21   KNOTS UP TO EIGHT CROSSINGS

n	3	4	5	6	7	8	9	10	11
Number of knots with n crossings	1	1	2	3	7	21	49	165	552

Image by Charlie Gunn and David Broman. Copyright The Geometry Center, University of Minnesota. With permission.

4.22 DIFFERENTIAL GEOMETRY

4.22.1 CURVES

Definitions

A *regular parametric representation of class* C^k, $k \geq 1$, is a vector valued function $\mathbf{f} : I \to \mathbb{R}^n$, where $I \subset \mathbb{R}$ is an interval that satisfies (i) $\mathbf{f}$ is of class C^k, and (ii) $\mathbf{f}'(t) \neq 0$, for all $t \in I$.

In terms of a standard basis of $\mathbb{R}^3$, we write $\mathbf{x} = \mathbf{f}(t) = (f_1(t), f_2(t), f_3(t))$, where the real valued functions f_i, $i = 1, 2, 3$ are the *component functions* of $\mathbf{f}$.

An *allowable change of parameter of class* C^k is any C^k function $\phi : J \to I$, where J is an interval and $\phi(J) \subset I$, that satisfies $\phi'(\tau) \neq 0$, for all $\tau \in J$.

A C^k regular parametric representation $\mathbf{f}$ is *equivalent* to a C^k regular parametric representation $\mathbf{g}$ if and only if an allowable change of parameter ϕ exists so that $\phi(I_g) = I_f$, and $\mathbf{g}(\tau) = \mathbf{f}(\phi(\tau))$, for all $\tau \in I_g$.

A *regular curve C of class* C^k is an equivalence class of C^k regular parametric representation under the equivalence relation on the set of regular parametric representations defined in Section 4.22.1.

The *arc length* of any regular curve C defined by the regular parametric representation $\mathbf{f}$, with $I_f = [a, b]$, is defined by

$$L = \int_a^b |\mathbf{f}'(u)| \, du. \tag{4.22.1}$$

An *arc length parameter* along C is defined by

$$s = \alpha(t) = \pm \int_c^t |\mathbf{f}'(u)| \, du. \tag{4.22.2}$$

The choice of sign is arbitrary and c is any number in I_f.

A *natural representation of class* C^k of the regular curve defined by the regular parametric representation $\mathbf{f}$ is defined by $\mathbf{g}(s) = \mathbf{f}(\alpha^{-1}(s))$, for all $s \in [0, L]$.

A *property* of a regular curve C is any property of a regular parametric representation that defines C as invariant under any allowable change of parameter.

Let $\mathbf{g}$ be a natural representation of a regular curve C. The following quantities may be defined at each point $\mathbf{x} = \mathbf{g}(s)$ of C:

Unit tangent vector	$\mathbf{t}(s) = \dot{\mathbf{g}}(s)$ with $\left(\dot{\mathbf{g}}(s) = \frac{d\mathbf{g}}{ds}\right)$
Curvature vector	$\mathbf{k}(s) = \dot{\mathbf{t}}(s)$
Principal normal unit vector	$\mathbf{n}(s) = \pm\mathbf{k}(s)/|\mathbf{k}(s)|$, for $\mathbf{k}(s) \neq 0$ defined to be continuous along C
Unit binormal vector	$\mathbf{b}(s) = \mathbf{t}(s) \times \mathbf{n}(s)$
Moving trihedron	$\{\mathbf{t}(s), \mathbf{n}(s), \mathbf{b}(s)\}$
Curvature	$\kappa(s) = \mathbf{n}(s) \cdot \mathbf{k}(s)$

Radius of curvature	$\rho(s) = 1/|\kappa(s)|$, when $\kappa(s) \neq 0$
Torsion	$\tau(s) = -\mathbf{n}(s) \cdot \dot{\mathbf{b}}(s)$
Tangent line	$\mathbf{y} = \lambda\mathbf{t}(s) + \mathbf{x}$
Normal plane	$(\mathbf{y} - \mathbf{x}) \cdot \mathbf{t}(s) = 0$
Principal normal line	$\mathbf{y} = \lambda\mathbf{n}(s) + \mathbf{x}$
Rectifying plane	$(\mathbf{y} - \mathbf{x}) \cdot \mathbf{n}(s) = 0$
Binormal line	$\mathbf{y} = \lambda\mathbf{b}(s) + \mathbf{x}$
Osculating plane	$(\mathbf{y} - \mathbf{x}) \cdot \mathbf{b}(s) = 0$
	$(\mathbf{y} - \mathbf{c}) \cdot (\mathbf{y} - \mathbf{c}) = r^2$, where
Osculating sphere	$\mathbf{c} = \mathbf{x} + \rho(s)\mathbf{n}(s) - (\dot{\kappa}(s)/(\kappa^2(s)\tau(s)))\mathbf{b}(s)$,
	and $r^2 = \rho^2(s) + \kappa^2(s)/(\kappa^4(s)\tau^2(s))$

Results

The arc length L and the arc length parameter s of any regular parametric representation $\mathbf{f}$ are *invariant* under any allowable change of parameter. Thus, L is a property of the regular curve C defined by $\mathbf{f}$.

The arc length parameter satisfies $\frac{ds}{dt} = \alpha'(t) = \pm |\mathbf{f}'(t)|$, which implies that $|\mathbf{f}'(s)| = 1$, if and only if t is an arc length parameter. Thus, arc length parameters are uniquely determined up to the transformation $s \to \tilde{s} = \pm s + s_0$, where s_0 is any constant.

The curvature, torsion, tangent line, normal plane, principal normal line, rectifying plane, binormal line, and osculating plane are properties of the regular curve C defined by any regular parametric representation $\mathbf{f}$.

If $\mathbf{x} = \mathbf{f}(t)$ is any regular representation of a regular curve C, the following results hold at point $\mathbf{f}(t)$ of C:

$$|\kappa| = \frac{|\mathbf{x}'' \times \mathbf{x}'|}{|\mathbf{x}'|^3}, \qquad \tau = \frac{\mathbf{x}' \cdot (\mathbf{x}'' \times \mathbf{x}''')}{|\mathbf{x}' \times \mathbf{x}''|^2}. \tag{4.22.3}$$

The vectors of the moving trihedron satisfy the *Serret–Frenet equations*

$$\dot{\mathbf{t}} = \kappa\mathbf{n}, \quad \dot{\mathbf{n}} = -\kappa\mathbf{t} + \tau\mathbf{b}, \quad \dot{\mathbf{b}} = -\tau\mathbf{n}. \tag{4.22.4}$$

For any plane curve represented parametrically by $\mathbf{x} = \mathbf{f}(t) = (t, f(t), 0)$,

$$|\kappa| = \frac{\left|\frac{d^2x}{dt^2}\right|}{\left(1 + \left(\frac{dx}{dt}\right)^2\right)^{3/2}}. \tag{4.22.5}$$

Expressions for the curvature vector and curvature of a *plane curve* corresponding to different representations are given in the following table:

Representation	$x = f(t), y = g(t)$	$y = f(x)$	$r = f(\theta)$	
Curvature vector $\mathbf{k}$	$\dfrac{(\dot{x}\ddot{y} - \dot{y}\ddot{x})}{(\dot{x}^2 + \dot{y}^2)^2}(-\dot{y}, \dot{x})$	$\dfrac{y''}{(1 + y'^2)^2}(-y', 1)$	$\dfrac{(r^2 + 2r'^2 - rr'')}{(r^2 + r'^2)^2}$	$(-\dot{r}\sin\theta - r\cos\theta, \dot{r}\cos\theta - r\sin\theta)$
Curvature $|\kappa| = \rho^{-1}$	$\dfrac{|\dot{x}\ddot{y} - \dot{y}\ddot{x}|}{(\dot{x}^2 + \dot{y}^2)^{3/2}}$	$\dfrac{|y''|}{(1 + y'^2)^{3/2}}$	$\dfrac{r^2 + 2r'^2 - rr''}{(r^2 + r'^2)^{3/2}}$	

The equation of the *osculating circle* of a plane curve is given by

$$(\mathbf{y} - \mathbf{c}) \cdot (\mathbf{y} - \mathbf{c}) = \rho^2,$$

where $\mathbf{c} = \mathbf{x} + \rho^2 \mathbf{k}$ is the *center of curvature*.

THEOREM 4.22.1   *(Fundamental existence and uniqueness theorem)*

Let $\kappa(s)$ and $\tau(s)$ be any continuous functions defined for all $s \in [a, b]$. Then there exists, up to a congruence, a unique space curve C for which κ is the curvature function, τ is the torsion function, and s an arc length parameter along C.

Example

A regular parametric representation of the *circular helix* is given by $\mathbf{x} = \mathbf{f}(t) = (a \cos t, a \sin t, bt)$, for all $t \in \mathbb{R}$, where $a > 0$ and $b \neq 0$ are constant. By successive differentiation,

$$\mathbf{x}' = (-a \sin t, \quad a \cos t, b),$$
$$\mathbf{x}'' = (-a \cos t, -a \sin t, 0),$$
$$\mathbf{x}''' = (\quad a \sin t, -a \cos t, 0),$$

so that $\frac{ds}{dt} = |\mathbf{x}'| = \sqrt{a^2 + b^2}$. Hence,

- *Arc length parameter:* $s = \alpha(t) = t(a^2 + b^2)^{\frac{1}{2}}$
- *Unit tangent vector:* $\mathbf{t} = \frac{\mathbf{x}'}{|\mathbf{x}'|} = (a^2 + b^2)^{-\frac{1}{2}}(-a \sin t, a \cos t, b)$
- *Curvature vector:* $\mathbf{k} = \frac{d\mathbf{t}}{ds} = \frac{dt}{ds}\frac{d\mathbf{t}}{dt} = (a^2 + b^2)^{-1}(-a \cos t, -a \sin t, 0)$
- *Curvature:* $\kappa = |\mathbf{k}| = a(a^2 + b^2)^{-1}$
- *Principal normal unit vector:* $\mathbf{n} = \mathbf{k}/|\mathbf{k}| = (-\cos t, -\sin t, 0)$
- *Unit binormal vector:*

$$\mathbf{b} = \mathbf{t} \times \mathbf{n} = (a^2 + b^2)^{-\frac{1}{2}}(b \sin t, b \cos t, a)$$
$$\dot{\mathbf{b}} = \frac{dt}{ds}\frac{d\mathbf{b}}{dt} = b(a^2 + b^2)^{-1}(\cos t, \sin t, 0)$$

- *Torsion:* $\tau = -\mathbf{n} \cdot \dot{\mathbf{b}} = b(a^2 + b^2)^{-1}$

The values of $|\kappa|$ and τ can be verified using the formulae in (4.22.3). The sign of (the invariant) τ determines whether the helix is right handed, $\tau > 0$, or left handed, $\tau < 0$.

4.22.2 SURFACES

Definitions

A *coordinate patch of class* C^k, $k \geq 1$ on a surface $S \subset \mathbb{R}^3$ is a vector valued function $f : U \to S$, where $U \subset \mathbb{R}^2$ is an open set, that satisfies (i) **f** is class C^k on U, (ii) $\frac{\partial \mathbf{f}}{\partial u}(u, v) \times \frac{\partial \mathbf{f}}{\partial v}(u, v) \neq 0$, for all $(u, v) \in U$, and (iii) **f** is one-to-one and bi-continuous on U.

In terms of a standard basis of $\mathbb{R}^3$ we write $\mathbf{x} = \mathbf{f}(u, v) = (f_1(u, v), f_2(u, v), f_3(u, v))$, where the real valued functions $\{f_1, f_2, f_3\}$ are the *component functions* of **f**. The notation $\mathbf{x}_1 = \mathbf{x}_u = \frac{\partial \mathbf{f}}{\partial u}$, $\mathbf{x}_2 = \mathbf{x}_v = \frac{\partial \mathbf{f}}{\partial v}$, $u^1 = u$, $u^2 = v$, is frequently used.

A *Monge patch* is a coordinate patch where **f** has the form $\mathbf{f}(u, v) = (u, v, f(u, v))$, where f is a real valued function of class C^k.

The *u-parameter curves* $v = v_0$ on S are the images of the lines $v = v_0$ in U. They are parametrically represented by $\mathbf{x} = \mathbf{f}(u, v_0)$. The *v-parameter curves* $u = u_0$ are defined similarly.

An *allowable parametric transformation* of class C^k is a one-to-one function $\phi : U \to V$, where $U, V \subset \mathbb{R}^2$ are open, that satisfies

$$\det \begin{bmatrix} \frac{\partial \phi^1}{\partial u}(u, v) & \frac{\partial \phi^1}{\partial v}(u, v) \\ \frac{\partial \phi^2}{\partial u}(u, v) & \frac{\partial \phi^2}{\partial v}(u, v) \end{bmatrix} \neq 0,$$

for all $(u, v) \in U$, where the real valued functions, ϕ^1 and ϕ^2, defined by $\boldsymbol{\phi}(u, v) = [\phi^1(u, v), \phi^2(u, v)]$, are the component functions of $\boldsymbol{\phi}$. One may also write the parametric transformation as $\tilde{u}^1 = \phi^1(u^1, u^2)$, $\tilde{u}^2 = \phi^2(u^1, u^2)$.

A *local property* of surface S is any property of a coordinate patch that is invariant under any allowable parametric transformation.

Let **f** define a coordinate patch on a surface S. The following quantities may be defined at each point $\mathbf{x} = \mathbf{f}(u, v)$ on the patch:

Normal vector	$\mathcal{N} = \mathbf{x}_u \times \mathbf{x}_v$
Unit normal vector	$\mathbf{N} = \dfrac{\mathbf{x}_u \times \mathbf{x}_v}{|\mathbf{x}_u \times \mathbf{x}_v|}$
Normal line	$\mathbf{y} = \lambda \mathcal{N} + \mathbf{x}$
Tangent plane	$(\mathbf{y} - \mathbf{x}) \cdot \mathcal{N} = 0$, or $\mathbf{y} = \mathbf{x} + \lambda \mathbf{x}_u + \mu \mathbf{x}_v$
Fundamental differential	$d\mathbf{x} = \mathbf{x}_\alpha \, du^\alpha = \mathbf{x}_u \, du + \mathbf{x}_v \, dv$ (a repeated upper and lower index signifies a summation over the range $\alpha = 1, 2$)
First fundamental form	$I = d\mathbf{x} \cdot d\mathbf{x} = g_{\alpha\beta}(u, v) \, du^\alpha \, du^\beta$ $= E(u, v) \, du^2 + 2F(u, v) \, du \, dv + G(u, v) \, dv^2$
First fundamental metric coefficients	$\begin{cases} E(u, v) = g_{11}(u, v) = \mathbf{x}_1 \cdot \mathbf{x}_1 \\ F(u, v) = g_{12}(u, v) = \mathbf{x}_1 \cdot \mathbf{x}_2 \\ G(u, v) = g_{22}(u, v) = \mathbf{x}_2 \cdot \mathbf{x}_2 \end{cases}$
Second fundamental form	$II = -d\mathbf{x} \cdot d\mathbf{N} = b_{\alpha\beta}(u, v) \, du^\alpha \, du^\beta$ $= e(u, v) \, du^2 + 2f(u, v) \, du \, dv + g(u, v) \, dv^2$

Second fundamental metric coefficients	$\begin{cases} e(u, v) = b_{11}(u, v) = \mathbf{x}_{11} \cdot \mathbf{N} \\ f(u, v) = b_{12}(u, v) = \mathbf{x}_{12} \cdot \mathbf{N} \\ g(u, v) = b_{22}(u, v) = \mathbf{x}_{22} \cdot \mathbf{N} \end{cases}$
Normal curvature vector of curve C on S through x	$\mathbf{k}_n = (\mathbf{k} \cdot \mathbf{N})\mathbf{N}$
Normal curvature in the du : dv direction	$\kappa_n = \mathbf{k} \cdot \mathbf{N} = II/I$
Dupin's indicatrix	$ex_1^2 + 2fx_1x_2 + gx_2^2 = \pm 1$
Elliptic point	$eg - f^2 > 0$
Hyperbolic point	$eg - f^2 < 0,$
Parabolic point	$eg - f^2 = 0$ not all of $e, f, g = 0$
Planar point	$e = f = g = 0$
Umbilical point	κ_n = constant for all directions $du : dv$
Principal directions	The perpendicular directions $du : dv$ in which κ_n attains its extreme values
Principal curvatures	The extreme values κ_1 and κ_2 of κ_n
Line of curvature	A curve on S whose tangent line at each point coincides with an asymptotic direction
Asymptotic direction	A direction $du : dv$ for which $\kappa_n = 0$
Asymptotic line	A curve on S whose tangent line at each point coincides with a principal direction
Gaussian curvature	$K = \kappa_1 \kappa_2 = \dfrac{eg - f^2}{EG - F^2}$
Mean curvature	$H = \dfrac{\kappa_1 + \kappa_2}{2} = \dfrac{gE + eG - 2fF}{2(EG - F^2)}$
Geodesic curvature vector of a curve C on S through x	$\mathbf{k}_g = \mathbf{k} - (\mathbf{k} \cdot \mathbf{N})\mathbf{N} = [\ddot{u}^\alpha + \Gamma^\alpha_{\beta\gamma} \dot{u}^\beta \dot{u}^\gamma]\mathbf{x}_\alpha$ where $\Gamma^\alpha_{\beta\gamma}$ denote the Christoffel symbols of the second kind for the metric $g_{\alpha\beta}$, defined in Section 5.10
Geodesic on S	A curve on S which satisfies $\mathbf{k}_g = 0$ at each point

Results

The tangent plane, normal line, first fundamental form, second fundamental form and all derived quantities thereof are local properties of any surface S.

The transformation laws for the first and second fundamental metric coefficients and any allowable parametric transformation are given respectively by

$$\tilde{g}_{\alpha\beta} = g_{\gamma\delta} \frac{\partial u^\gamma}{\partial \tilde{u}^\alpha} \frac{\partial u^\delta}{\partial \tilde{u}^\beta}, \quad \text{and} \quad \tilde{b}_{\alpha\beta} = b_{\gamma\delta} \frac{\partial u^\gamma}{\partial \tilde{u}^\alpha} \frac{\partial u^\delta}{\partial \tilde{u}^\beta}.$$

Thus $g_{\alpha\beta}$ and $b_{\alpha\beta}$ are the components of type $(0, 2)$ tensors.

$I \geq 0$ for all directions $du : dv$; $I = 0$ if and only if $du = dv = 0$.

The angle θ between two tangent lines to S at $\mathbf{x} = \mathbf{f}(u, v)$ defined by the directions $du : dv$ and $\delta u : \delta v$, is given by

$$\cos\theta = \frac{g_{\alpha\beta}\, du^{\alpha}\delta u^{\beta}}{(g_{\alpha\beta}\, du^{\alpha}\, du^{\beta})^{\frac{1}{2}}(g_{\alpha\beta}\delta u^{\alpha}\delta u^{\beta})^{\frac{1}{2}}}.$$

The angle between the u-parameter curves and the v-parameter curves is given by $\cos\theta = F(u, v)/(E(u, v)G(u, v))^{\frac{1}{2}}$. The u-parameter curves and v-parameter curves are orthogonal if and only if $F(u, v) = 0$.

The arc length of a curve C on S, defined by $\mathbf{x} = \mathbf{f}(u^1(t), u^2(t))$, $a \le t \le b$, is given by

$$L = \int_a^b \sqrt{g_{\alpha\beta}(u^1(t), u^2(t))\dot{u}^{\alpha}\dot{u}^{\beta}}\, dt,$$

$$= \int_a^b \sqrt{E(u(t), v(t))\dot{u}^2 + 2F(u(t), v(t))\dot{u}\dot{v} + G(u(t), v(t))\dot{v}^2}\, dt.$$

The area of $S = \mathbf{f}(U)$ is given by

$$A = \iint_U \sqrt{\det(g_{\alpha\beta}(u^1, u^2))}\, du^1\, du^2,$$

$$= \iint_U \sqrt{E(u, v)G(u, v) - F^2(u, v)}\, du\, dv.$$

The principal curvatures are the roots of the *characteristic equation*, $\det(b_{\alpha\beta} - \lambda g_{\alpha\beta}) = 0$, which may be written as $\lambda^2 - b_{\alpha\beta}g^{\alpha\beta}\lambda + b/g = 0$, where $g^{\alpha\beta}$ is the inverse of $g_{\alpha\beta}$, $b = \det(b_{\alpha\beta})$, and $g = \det(g_{\alpha\beta})$. The expanded form of the characteristic equation is

$$(EG - F^2)\lambda^2 - (eG - 2fF + gE)\lambda + eg - f^2 = 0. \qquad (4.22.6)$$

The principal directions $du : dv$ are obtained by solving the homogeneous equation,

$$b_{1\alpha}g_{2\beta}\, du^{\alpha}\, du^{\beta} - b_{2\alpha}g_{1\beta}\, du^{\alpha}\, du^{\beta} = 0,$$

or

$$(eF - fE)\, du^2 + (eG - gE)\, du\, dv + (fG - gF)\, dv^2 = 0.$$

Rodrigues formula: $du : dv$ is a principal direction with principal curvature κ if, and only if, $d\mathbf{N} + \kappa\, d\mathbf{x} = 0$.

A point $\mathbf{x} = \mathbf{f}(u, v)$ on S is an umbilical point if and only if there exists a constant k such that $b_{\alpha\beta}(u, v) = kg_{\alpha\beta}(u, v)$.

The principal directions at $\mathbf{x}$ are orthogonal if $\mathbf{x}$ is not an umbilical point.

The u- and v-parameter curves at any nonumbilical point $\mathbf{x}$ are tangent to the principal directions if and only if $f(u, v) = F(u, v) = 0$. If $\mathbf{f}$ defines a coordinate patch without umbilical points, the u- and v-parameter curves are lines of curvature if and only if $f = F = 0$.

If $f = F = 0$ on a coordinate patch, the principal curvatures are given by $\kappa_1 = e/E$, $\kappa_2 = g/G$. It follows that the Gaussian and mean curvatures have the forms

$$K = \frac{eg}{EG}, \quad \text{and} \quad H = \frac{1}{2}\left(\frac{e}{E} + \frac{g}{G}\right). \tag{4.22.7}$$

The *Gauss equation*: $\mathbf{x}_{\alpha\beta} = \Gamma^\gamma_{\alpha\beta}\mathbf{x}_\gamma + b_{\alpha\beta}\mathbf{N}$.

The *Weingarten equation*: $\mathbf{N}_\alpha = -b_{\alpha\beta}g^{\beta\gamma}\mathbf{x}_\gamma$.

The *Gauss–Mainardi–Codazzi equations*: $b_{\alpha\beta}b_{\gamma\delta} - b_{\alpha\gamma}b_{\beta\delta} = R_{\delta\alpha\beta\gamma}$, $b_{\alpha\beta,\gamma} - b_{\alpha\gamma,\beta} + \Gamma^\delta_{\alpha\beta}b_{\delta\gamma} - \Gamma^\delta_{\alpha\gamma}b_{\delta\beta} = 0$, where $R_{\delta\alpha\beta\gamma}$ denotes the Riemann curvature tensor defined in Section 5.10.

THEOREM 4.22.2   *(Gauss's theorema egregium)*

The Gaussian curvature K depends only on the components of the first fundamental metric $g_{\alpha\beta}$ and their derivatives.

THEOREM 4.22.3   *(Fundamental theorem of surface theory)*

If $g_{\alpha\beta}$ and $b_{\alpha\beta}$ are sufficiently differentiable functions of u and v which satisfy the Gauss–Mainardi–Codazzi equations, $\det(g_{\alpha\beta}) > 0$, $g_{11} > 0$, and $g_{22} > 0$, then a surface exists with $I = g_{\alpha\beta}\,du^\alpha\,du^\beta$ and $II = b_{\alpha\beta}\,du^\alpha\,du^\beta$ as its first and second fundamental forms. This surface is unique up to a congruence.

Examples

A Monge patch for a paraboloid of revolution is given by $\mathbf{x} = \mathbf{f}(u, v) = (u, v, u^2 + v^2)$, for all $(u, v) \in U = \mathbb{R}^2$. By successive differentiation one obtains $\mathbf{x}_u = (1, 0, 2u)$, $\mathbf{x}_v = (0, 1, 2v)$, $\mathbf{x}_{uu} = (0, 0, 2)$, $\mathbf{x}_{uv} = (0, 0, 0)$, and $\mathbf{x}_{vv} = (0, 0, 2)$.

- *Unit normal vector*: $\mathbf{N} = (1 + 4u^2 + 4v^2)^{-\frac{1}{2}}(-2u, -2v, 1)$.

- *First fundamental coefficients*: $E(u, v) = g_{11}(u, v) = 1 + 4u^2$, $F(u, v) = g_{12}(u, v) = 4uv$, $G(u, v) = g_{22}(u, v) = 1 + 4v^2$.

- *First fundamental form*: $I = (1 + 4u^2)\,du^2 + 8uv\,du\,dv + (1 + 4v^2)\,dv^2$. Since $F(u, v) = 0 \Rightarrow u = 0$ or $v = 0$, it follows that the u-parameter curve $v = 0$, is orthogonal to any v-parameter curve, and the v-parameter curve $u = 0$ is orthogonal to any u-parameter curve. Otherwise the u- and v-parameter curves are *not* orthogonal.

- *Second fundamental coefficients*: $e(u, v) = b_{11}(u, v) = 2(1 + 4u^2 + 4v^2)^{-\frac{1}{2}}$, $f(u, v) = b_{12}(u, v) = 0$, $g(u, v) = b_{22}(u, v) = 2(1 + 4u^2 + 4v^2)^{-\frac{1}{2}}$.

- *Second fundamental form*: $II = 2(1 + 4u^2 + 4v^2)^{-\frac{1}{2}}(du^2 + dv^2)$.

- *Classification of points*: $e(u, v)g(u, v) = 4(1 + 4u^2 + 4v^2) > 0$ implies that all points on S are elliptic points. The point $(0, 0, 0)$ is the only umbilical point.

- *Equation for the principal directions*: $uv\,du^2 + (v^2 - u^2)\,du\,dv + uv\,dv^2 = 0$ factors to read $(u\,du + v\,dv)(v\,du - u\,dv) = 0$.

- *Lines of curvature*: Integrate the differential equations, $u\,dv + v\,dv = 0$, and $v\,du - v\,du = 0$, to obtain, respectively, the equations of the lines of curvature, $u^2 + v^2 = r^2$, and $u/v = \cot\theta$, where r and θ are constant.

- *Characteristic equation*: $(1 + 4u^2 + 4v^2)\lambda^2 - 4(1 + 2u^2 + 2v^2)\,(1 + 4u^2 + 4v^2)^{-\frac{1}{2}}\lambda + 4(1 + 4u^2 + 4v^2)^{-1} = 0$.

- *Principal curvatures*: $\kappa_1 = 2(1 + 4u^2 + 4v^2)^{-\frac{1}{2}}$, $\kappa_2 = 2(1 + 4u^2 + 4v^2)^{-\frac{3}{2}}$. The paraboloid of revolution may also be represented by $\mathbf{x} = \hat{\mathbf{f}}(r, \theta) = (r\cos\theta, r\sin\theta, r^2)$. In this representation the r- and θ-parameter curves are lines of curvature.

- *Gaussian curvature*: $K = 4(1 + 4u^2 + 4v^2)^{-2}$.

- *Mean curvature*: $H = 2(1 + 2u^2 + 2v^2)(1 + 4u^2 + 4v^2)^{-\frac{3}{2}}$.

4.23 ANGLE CONVERSION

Degrees	Radians
1°	0.0174533
2°	0.0349066
3°	0.0523599
4°	0.0698132
5°	0.0872665
6°	0.1047198
7°	0.1221730
8°	0.1396263
9°	0.1570796
10°	0.1745329

Minutes	Radians
1'	0.00029089
2'	0.00058178
3'	0.00087266
4'	0.00116355
5'	0.00145444
6'	0.00174533
7'	0.00203622
8'	0.00232711
9'	0.00261799
10'	0.00290888

Seconds	Radians
1"	0.0000048481
2"	0.0000096963
3"	0.0000145444
4"	0.0000193925
5"	0.0000242407
6"	0.0000290888
7"	0.0000339370
8"	0.0000387851
9"	0.0000436332
10"	0.0000484814

Radians	Deg.	Min.	Sec.	Degrees
0.001	0°	3'	26.3"	0.0573
0.002	0°	6'	52.5"	0.1146
0.003	0°	10'	18.8"	0.1719
0.004	0°	13'	45.1"	0.2292
0.005	0°	17'	11.3"	0.2865
0.006	0°	20'	37.6"	0.3438
0.007	0°	24'	3.9"	0.4011
0.008	0°	27'	30.1"	0.4584
0.009	0°	30'	56.4"	0.5157
0.01	0°	34'	22.6"	0.5730
0.02	1°	8'	45.3"	1.1459
0.03	1°	43'	7.9"	1.7189
0.04	2°	17'	30.6"	2.2918
0.05	2°	51'	53.2"	2.8648
0.06	3°	26'	15.9"	3.4377
0.07	4°	0'	38.5"	4.0107
0.08	4°	35'	1.2"	4.5837
0.09	5°	9'	23.8"	5.1566
0.1	5°	43'	46.5"	5.7296
0.2	11°	27'	33.0"	11.4592
0.3	17°	11'	19.4"	17.1887
0.4	22°	55'	5.9"	22.9183
0.5	28°	38'	52.4"	28.6479
0.6	34°	22'	38.9"	34.3775
0.7	40°	6'	25.4"	40.1070
0.8	45°	50'	11.8"	45.8366
0.9	51°	33'	58.3"	51.5662
1	57°	17'	44.8"	57.2958
2	114°	35'	29.6"	114.5916
3	171°	53'	14.4"	171.8873
4	229°	10'	59.2"	229.1831
5	286°	28'	44.0"	286.4789
6	343°	46'	28.8"	343.7747
7	401°	4'	13.6"	401.0705
8	458°	21'	58.4"	458.3662
9	515°	39'	43.3"	515.6620
10	572°	57'	28.1"	572.9578

References

1. C. Livingston, *Knot Theory*, The Mathematical Association of America, Washington, D.C., 1993.

2. D. J. Struik, *Lectures in Classical Differential Geometry*, 2nd ed., Dover, New York, 1988.

3. A. Gray, *Modern Differential Geometry of Curves and Surfaces,* CRC Press, Boca Raton, FL, 1993.

Chapter  5

Continuous Mathematics

0-8493-2479-3/96/$0.00+$.50
© 1996 CRC Press, Inc.

5.1   DIFFERENTIAL CALCULUS

Limits

If $\lim_{x \to a} f(x) = A$ and $\lim_{x \to a} g(x) = B$ then

- $\lim_{x \to a} (f(x) \pm g(x)) = A \pm B$

- $\lim_{x \to a} f(x)g(x) = AB$

- $\lim_{x \to a} \dfrac{f(x)}{g(x)} = \dfrac{A}{B}$ (if $B \neq 0$)

- $\lim_{x \to a} [f(x)]^{g(x)} = A^B$ (if $A > 0$)

- $\lim_{x \to a} h(f(x)) = h(A)$
  (if h continuous)

- if $f(x) \leq g(x)$, then $A \leq B$

- if $A = B$ and $f(x) \leq h(x) \leq g(x)$, then $\lim_{x \to a} h(x) = A$

Examples:

- $\lim_{x \to \infty} \left(1 + \dfrac{t}{x}\right)^x = e^t$

- $\lim_{x \to \infty} x^{1/x} = 1$

- $\lim_{x \to \infty} \dfrac{(\log x)^p}{x^q} = 0$ (if $q > 0$)

- $\lim_{x \to 0} x^p |\log x|^q = 0$ (if $p > 0$)

- $\lim_{x \to 0} \dfrac{\sin ax}{x} = a$

- $\lim_{x \to 0} \dfrac{a^x - 1}{x} = \log a$

- $\lim_{x \to 0} \dfrac{\log(1 + x)}{x} = 1$

Derivatives

The derivative of the function $f(x)$, written $f'(x)$, is defined as

$$f'(x) = \lim_{\Delta x \to 0} \frac{f(x + \Delta x) - f(x)}{\Delta x} \tag{5.1.1}$$

if the limit exists. If $y = f(x)$, then $\frac{dy}{dx} = f'(x)$. The nth derivative is

$$y^{(n)} = \frac{dy^{(n-1)}}{dx} = \frac{d}{dx}\left(\frac{d^{n-1}y}{dx^{n-1}}\right) = \frac{d^n y}{dx^n} = f^{(n)}(x)$$

Sometimes the fourth (or fifth) derivative is written $y^{(iv)}$ (or $y^{(v)}$).

The partial derivative of $f(x, y)$ with respect to x, $f_x(x, y)$ or $\frac{\partial f}{\partial x}$, is defined as

$$f_x(x, y) = \lim_{\Delta x \to 0} \frac{f(x + \Delta x, y) - f(x, y)}{\Delta x}. \tag{5.1.2}$$

Derivatives of common functions

$f(x)$	$f'(x)$	$f(x)$	$f'(x)$	$f(x)$	$f'(x)$
$\sin x$	$\cos x$	$\sinh x$	$\cosh x$	x^a	ax^{a-1}
$\cos x$	$-\sin x$	$\cosh x$	$\sinh x$	$\frac{1}{x^a}$	$-\frac{a}{x^{a+1}}$
$\tan x$	$\sec^2 x$	$\tanh x$	$\text{sech}^2 x$	$\sqrt{x}$	$\frac{1}{2\sqrt{x}}$
$\csc x$	$-\csc x \cot x$	$\text{csch}\, x$	$-\text{csch}\, x \coth x$	$\log |x|$	$1/x$
$\sec x$	$\sec x \tan x$	$\text{sech}\, x$	$-\text{sech}\, x \tanh x$	a^x	$a^x \log a$
$\cot x$	$-\csc^2 x$	$\coth x$	$-\text{csch}^2 x$	e^x	e^x
$\sin^{-1} x$	$\frac{1}{\sqrt{1-x^2}}$	$\sinh^{-1} x$	$\frac{1}{\sqrt{x^2+1}}$		
$\cos^{-1} x$	$-\frac{1}{\sqrt{1-x^2}}$	$\cosh^{-1} x$	$\frac{1}{\sqrt{x^2-1}}$		
$\tan^{-1} x$	$\frac{1}{1+x^2}$	$\tanh^{-1} x$	$\frac{1}{1-x^2}$		
$\csc^{-1} x$	$-\frac{1}{x\sqrt{x^2-1}}$	$\text{csch}^{-1} x$	$\mp\frac{1}{x\sqrt{1+x^2}}$ †		
$\sec^{-1} x$	$\frac{1}{x\sqrt{x^2-1}}$	$\text{sech}^{-1} x$	$\mp\frac{1}{x\sqrt{1-x^2}}$ †		
$\cot^{-1} x$	$-\frac{1}{1+x^2}$	$\coth^{-1} x$	$\frac{1}{1-x^2}$		

† Use the $-$ sign when $x > 0$, use the $+$ sign when $x < 0$.

Derivative formulae

Let u, v, w be functions of x, and let a, c, and n be constants.

- $\dfrac{d}{dx}(a) = 0$

- $\dfrac{d}{dx}(x) = 1$

- $\dfrac{d}{dx}(au) = a\dfrac{du}{dx}$

- $\dfrac{d}{dx}(u + v) = \dfrac{du}{dx} + \dfrac{dv}{dx}$

- $\dfrac{d}{dx}(uv) = v\dfrac{du}{dx} + u\dfrac{dv}{dx}$

- $\dfrac{d}{dx}(uvw) = uv\dfrac{dw}{dx} + uw\dfrac{dv}{dx} + vw\dfrac{du}{dx}$

- $\dfrac{d}{dx}\left(\dfrac{u}{v}\right) = \dfrac{1}{v}\dfrac{du}{dx} - \dfrac{u}{v^2}\dfrac{dv}{dx} = \dfrac{v(du/dx) - u(dv/dx)}{v^2}$

- $\dfrac{d}{dx}(u^n) = nu^{n-1}\dfrac{du}{dx}$

- $\dfrac{d}{dx}(\sqrt{u}) = \dfrac{1}{2\sqrt{u}}\dfrac{du}{dx}$

- $\dfrac{d}{dx}\left(\dfrac{1}{u}\right) = -\dfrac{1}{u^2}\dfrac{du}{dx}$

- $\dfrac{d}{dx}\left(\dfrac{1}{u^n}\right) = -\dfrac{n}{u^{n+1}}\dfrac{du}{dx}$

- $\dfrac{d}{dx}\left(\dfrac{u^n}{v^m}\right) = \dfrac{u^{n-1}}{v^{m+1}}\left(nv\dfrac{du}{dx} - mu\dfrac{dv}{dx}\right)$

- $\dfrac{d}{dx}(u^n v^m) = u^{n-1}v^{m-1}\left(nv\dfrac{du}{dx} + mu\dfrac{dv}{dx}\right)$

- $\dfrac{d}{dx}(f(u)) = \dfrac{df}{du}(u)\cdot\dfrac{du}{dx}$

- $\dfrac{d^2}{dx^2}(f(u)) = \dfrac{df}{du}(u)\cdot\dfrac{d^2u}{dx^2} + \dfrac{d^2f}{du^2}(u)\cdot\left(\dfrac{du}{dx}\right)^2$

- $\dfrac{d^n}{dx^n}(uv) = \binom{n}{0}v\dfrac{d^nu}{dx^n} + \binom{n}{1}\dfrac{dv}{dx}\dfrac{d^{n-1}u}{dx^{n-1}} + \cdots + \binom{n}{n}\dfrac{d^nv}{dx^n}u$

- $\dfrac{d}{dx}\displaystyle\int_c^x f(t)\,dt = f(x)$

- $\dfrac{d}{dx}\displaystyle\int_x^c f(t)\,dt = -f(x)$

- $\dfrac{dx}{dy} = \left(\dfrac{dy}{dx}\right)^{-1}$ and $\dfrac{d^2x}{dy^2} = -\dfrac{d^2y}{dx^2}\Big/\left(\dfrac{dy}{dx}\right)^3$

- If $F(x, y) = 0$, then $\dfrac{dy}{dx} = -\dfrac{F_x}{F_y}$ and

  $\dfrac{d^2y}{dx^2} = -\dfrac{(F_{xx}F_y^2 - 2F_{xy}F_xF_y + F_{yy}F_x^2)}{F_y^3}$

- Leibniz's rule gives the derivative of an integral:

  $$\frac{d}{dx}\left(\int_{f(x)}^{g(x)} h(x, t)\,dt\right) = g'(x)h(x, g(x)) - f'(x)h(x, f(x)) + \int_{f(x)}^{g(x)} \frac{\partial h}{\partial x}(x, t)\,dt.$$

- If $x = x(t)$ and $y = y(t)$ then (the dots denote differentiation with respect to t):

  $$\frac{dy}{dx} = \frac{\dot{y}(t)}{\dot{x}(t)}, \qquad \frac{d^2y}{dx^2} = \frac{\dot{x}\ddot{y} - \ddot{x}\dot{y}}{(\dot{x})^2}$$

Derivative theorems

- *Fundamental theorem of calculus*:
  Suppose f is continuous on $[a, b]$.

  - If G is defined as $G(x) = \displaystyle\int_a^x f(t)\, dt$ for all x in $[a, b]$, then G is an antiderivative of f on $[a, b]$.

  - If F is any antiderivative of f, then $\displaystyle\int_a^b f(t)\, dt = F(b) - F(a)$. (Recall that $\int_a^b f(x)\, dx$ is defined as a limit of Riemann sums.)

- *Intermediate value theorem*:
  If $f(x)$ is continuous on $[a, b]$ and if $f(a) \neq f(b)$, then f takes on every value between $f(a)$ and $f(b)$ in the interval (a, b).

- *Rolle's theorem*:
  If $f(x)$ is continuous on $[a, b]$ and differentiable on (a, b), and if $f(a) = f(b)$, then $f'(c) = 0$ for at least one number c in (a, b).

- *Mean value theorem*:
  If $f(x)$ is continuous on $[a, b]$ and differentiable on (a, b), then a number c exists in (a, b) such that $f(b) - f(a) = (b - a) f'(c)$.

The chain rule

If $x = x(t)$, $y = y(t)$, and $z = z(x, y)$, then

$$\frac{dz}{dt} = \frac{\partial z}{\partial x}\frac{dx}{dt} + \frac{\partial z}{\partial y}\frac{dy}{dt}, \text{ and}$$

$$\frac{d^2z}{dt^2} = \frac{\partial z}{\partial x}\frac{d^2x}{dt^2} + \frac{dx}{dt}\left(\frac{\partial^2 z}{\partial x^2}\frac{dx}{dt} + \frac{\partial^2 z}{\partial x \partial y}\frac{dy}{dt}\right)$$

$$+ \frac{\partial z}{\partial y}\frac{d^2y}{dt^2} + \frac{dy}{dt}\left(\frac{\partial^2 z}{\partial y^2}\frac{dy}{dt} + \frac{\partial^2 z}{\partial x \partial y}\frac{dx}{dt}\right).$$

If $x = x(u, v)$, $y = y(u, v)$, and $z = z(x, y)$, then

$$\frac{\partial z}{\partial u} = \frac{\partial z}{\partial x}\frac{\partial x}{\partial u} + \frac{\partial z}{\partial y}\frac{\partial y}{\partial u} \quad \text{and} \quad \frac{\partial z}{\partial v} = \frac{\partial z}{\partial x}\frac{\partial x}{\partial v} + \frac{\partial z}{\partial y}\frac{\partial y}{\partial v}.$$

If $u = u(x, y)$, $v = v(x, y)$, and $f = f(x, y)$, then the partial derivative of f with respect to u, holding v constant, written $\left(\frac{\partial f}{\partial u}\right)_v$, can be expressed as

$$\left(\frac{\partial f}{\partial u}\right)_v = \left(\frac{\partial f}{\partial x}\right)_y \left(\frac{\partial x}{\partial u}\right)_v + \left(\frac{\partial f}{\partial y}\right)_x \left(\frac{\partial y}{\partial u}\right)_v. \tag{5.1.3}$$

If x, y, and z all depend on one another (say, through $f(x, y, z) = 0$), then the partial derivative of x with respect to y, holding z constant, written $\left(\frac{\partial x}{\partial y}\right)_z$, is

$$\left(\frac{\partial x}{\partial y}\right)_z = \left[\left(\frac{\partial y}{\partial x}\right)_z\right]^{-1} = -\frac{(\partial f/\partial y)_{x,z}}{(\partial f/\partial x)_{y,z}},$$

$$\left(\frac{\partial x}{\partial y}\right)_z \left(\frac{\partial y}{\partial z}\right)_x \left(\frac{\partial z}{\partial x}\right)_y = -1.$$

(5.1.4)

l'Hôpital's rule

If $f(x)$ and $g(x)$ are continuous in the neighborhood of point a, and if $f(x)$ and $g(x)$ both tend to 0 or ∞ as $x \to a$, then

$$\lim_{x \to a} \frac{f(x)}{g(x)} = \lim_{x \to a} \frac{f'(x)}{g'(x)}$$

(5.1.5)

if the right hand side exists. For example

$$\lim_{x \to 0} \frac{x - \sin x}{x^3} = \lim_{x \to 0} \frac{1 - \cos x}{3x^2} = \lim_{x \to 0} \frac{\sin x}{6x} = \lim_{x \to 0} \frac{\cos x}{6} = \frac{1}{6},$$

and

$$\lim_{x \to \infty} \frac{x^n}{e^x} = \lim_{x \to \infty} \frac{nx^{n-1}}{e^x} = \lim_{x \to \infty} \frac{n(n-1)x^{n-2}}{e^x} = \cdots = \lim_{x \to \infty} \frac{n!}{e^x} = 0.$$

5.1.1 MAXIMA AND MINIMA OF FUNCTIONS

- If a function $f(x)$ has a local extremum at a number c, then either $f'(c) = 0$ or $f'(c)$ does not exist.

- If $f'(c) = 0$, $f(x)$ is differentiable on an open interval containing c, and
  - if $f''(c) < 0$, then f has a local maximum at c;
  - if $f''(c) > 0$, then f has a local minimum at c.

Lagrange multipliers

To extremize the function $f(x_1, x_2, \ldots, x_n) = f(\mathbf{x})$ subject to the $n - 1$ side constraints $\mathbf{g}(\mathbf{x}) = 0$, introduce an $(n - 1)$-dimensional vector of Lagrange multipliers $\boldsymbol{\lambda}$ and define $F(\mathbf{x}, \boldsymbol{\lambda}) = f(\mathbf{x}) + \boldsymbol{\lambda}^T \mathbf{g}(\mathbf{x})$. Then extremize F with respect to all of its arguments:

$$\frac{\partial F}{\partial x_i} = \frac{\partial f}{\partial x_i} + \boldsymbol{\lambda}^T \frac{\partial \mathbf{g}}{\partial x_i} = 0, \quad \text{and} \quad \frac{\partial F}{\partial \lambda_j} = g_j = 0.$$

For the simplest case, extremizing $f(x, y)$ subject to $g(x, y) = 0$,

$$f_x + \lambda g_x = 0, \quad f_y + \lambda g_y = 0, \quad \text{and} \quad g = 0.$$

For example, finding the points on the unit circle, $g(x, y) = (x-1)^2+(y-2)^2-1 = 0$, that are closest and furthest from the origin, the distance squared is $f(x, y) = x^2+y^2$, can be determined by solving the three (nonlinear) algebraic equations:

$$2x + 2\lambda(x - 1) = 0, \qquad 2y + 2\lambda(y - 2) = 0, \qquad (x - 1)^2 + (y - 2)^2 = 0.$$

The solutions are $x = 1 + 1\sqrt{5}$, $y = 2 + 2/\sqrt{5}$, $\lambda = -1 - \sqrt{5}$ (furthest), and $x = 1 - 1\sqrt{5}$, $y = 2 - 2/\sqrt{5}$, $\lambda = \sqrt{5} - 1$ (closest).

5.1.2   VECTOR CALCULUS

In rectilinear coordinates, $\nabla = \left(\frac{\partial}{\partial x}, \frac{\partial}{\partial y}, \frac{\partial}{\partial z}\right) = \mathbf{i}\frac{\partial}{\partial x} + \mathbf{j}\frac{\partial}{\partial y} + \mathbf{k}\frac{\partial}{\partial z}$. If u and v are scalars and $\mathbf{F}$ and $\mathbf{G}$ are vectors, then

$$\nabla(u + v) = \nabla u + \nabla v,$$
$$\nabla(uv) = u\nabla v + v\nabla u,$$
$$\nabla(\mathbf{F} + \mathbf{G}) = \nabla\mathbf{F} + \nabla\mathbf{G},$$
$$\nabla(\mathbf{F} \cdot \mathbf{G}) = (\mathbf{F} \cdot \nabla)\mathbf{G} + (\mathbf{G} \cdot \nabla)\mathbf{F} + \mathbf{F} \times (\nabla \times \mathbf{G}) + \mathbf{G} \times (\nabla \times \mathbf{F}),$$
$$\nabla \cdot (u\mathbf{F}) = u(\nabla \cdot \mathbf{F}) + \mathbf{F} \cdot \nabla u,$$
$$\nabla \cdot (\mathbf{F} \times \mathbf{G}) = \mathbf{G} \cdot (\nabla \times \mathbf{F}) - \mathbf{F} \cdot (\nabla \times \mathbf{G}),$$
$$\nabla \times (u\mathbf{F}) = u(\nabla \times \mathbf{F}) + (\nabla u) \times \mathbf{F},$$
$$\nabla \times (\mathbf{F} \times \mathbf{G}) = \mathbf{F}(\nabla \cdot \mathbf{G}) - \mathbf{G}(\nabla \cdot \mathbf{F}) + (\mathbf{G} \cdot \nabla)\mathbf{F} - (\mathbf{F} \cdot \nabla)\mathbf{G},$$
$$\mathbf{F} \cdot \frac{d\mathbf{F}}{dt} = |\mathbf{F}| \frac{d|\mathbf{F}|}{dt},$$
$$\nabla \times (\nabla \times \mathbf{F}) = \nabla(\nabla \cdot \mathbf{F}) - \nabla^2\mathbf{F},$$
$$\nabla \times (\nabla u) = \mathbf{0},$$
$$\nabla \cdot (\nabla \times \mathbf{F}) = 0, \quad \text{and}$$
$$\nabla^2(uv) = u\nabla^2 v + 2(\nabla u) \cdot (\nabla v) + v\nabla^2 u.$$

A vector field $\mathbf{F}$ is *irrotational* if $\nabla \times \mathbf{F} = 0$. A vector field $\mathbf{F}$ is *solenoidal* if $\nabla \cdot \mathbf{F} = 0$.

If $r = |\mathbf{r}|$, $\mathbf{a}$ is a constant vector, and n is an integer, then

Φ	$\nabla\Phi$	$\nabla^2\Phi$
$\mathbf{a} \cdot \mathbf{r}$	$\mathbf{a}$	0
r^n	$nr^{n-2}\mathbf{r}$	$n(n + 1)r^{n-2}$
$\log r$	$\mathbf{r}/r^2$	$1/r^2$

$\mathbf{F}$	$\nabla \cdot \mathbf{F}$	$\nabla \times \mathbf{F}$	$(\mathbf{G} \cdot \nabla)\mathbf{F}$
$\mathbf{r}$	3	0	$\mathbf{G}$
$\mathbf{a} \times \mathbf{r}$	0	$2\mathbf{a}$	$\mathbf{a} \times \mathbf{G}$
$\mathbf{a}r^n$	$nr^{n-2}(\mathbf{r} \cdot \mathbf{a})$	$nr^{n-2}(\mathbf{r} \times \mathbf{a})$	$nr^{n-2}(\mathbf{r} \cdot \mathbf{G})\mathbf{a}$
$\mathbf{r}r^n$	$(n + 3)r^n$	0	$r^n\mathbf{G} + nr^{n-2}(\mathbf{r} \cdot \mathbf{G})\mathbf{r}$
$\mathbf{a}\log r$	$\mathbf{r} \cdot \mathbf{a}/r^2$	$\mathbf{r} \times \mathbf{a}/r^2$	$(\mathbf{G} \cdot \mathbf{r})\mathbf{a}/r^2$

$\mathbf{F}$	$\nabla^2\mathbf{F}$	$\nabla\nabla\cdot\mathbf{F}$
$\mathbf{r}$	0	0
$\mathbf{a}\times\mathbf{r}$	0	0
$\mathbf{a}r^n$	$n(n+1)r^{n-2}\mathbf{a}$	$nr^{n-2}\mathbf{a}+n(n-2)r^{n-4}(\mathbf{r}\cdot\mathbf{a})\mathbf{r}$
$\mathbf{r}r^n$	$n(n+3)r^{n-2}\mathbf{r}$	$n(n+3)r^{n-2}\mathbf{r}$
$\mathbf{a}\log r$	$\mathbf{a}/r^2$	$[r^2\mathbf{a}-2(\mathbf{r}\cdot\mathbf{a})\mathbf{r}]/r^4$

$$\frac{d}{dt}(\mathbf{F}+\mathbf{G})=\frac{d\mathbf{F}}{dt}+\frac{d\mathbf{G}}{dt},$$

$$\frac{d}{dt}(\mathbf{F}\cdot\mathbf{G})=\mathbf{F}\cdot\frac{d\mathbf{G}}{dt}+\frac{d\mathbf{F}}{dt}\cdot\mathbf{G},$$

$$\frac{d}{dt}(\mathbf{F}\times\mathbf{G})=\mathbf{F}\times\frac{d\mathbf{G}}{dt}+\frac{d\mathbf{F}}{dt}\times\mathbf{G},$$

$$\frac{d}{dt}[\mathbf{V}_1\mathbf{V}_2\mathbf{V}_3]=\left[\left(\frac{d\mathbf{V}_1}{dt}\right)\mathbf{V}_2\mathbf{V}_3\right]+\left[\mathbf{V}_1\left(\frac{d\mathbf{V}_2}{dt}\right)\mathbf{V}_3\right]+\left[\mathbf{V}_1\mathbf{V}_2\left(\frac{d\mathbf{V}_3}{dt}\right)\right],$$

$$\frac{d}{dt}(\mathbf{V}_1\times\mathbf{V}_2\times\mathbf{V}_3)=\left(\frac{d\mathbf{V}_1}{dt}\right)\times(\mathbf{V}_2\times\mathbf{V}_3)+\mathbf{V}_1\times\left(\left(\frac{d\mathbf{V}_2}{dt}\right)\times\mathbf{V}_3\right),$$

$$+\mathbf{V}_1\times\left(\mathbf{V}_2\times\left(\frac{d\mathbf{V}_3}{dt}\right)\right),$$

where $[\mathbf{V}_1\mathbf{V}_2\mathbf{V}_3]=\mathbf{V}_1\cdot(\mathbf{V}_2\times\mathbf{V}_3)$ is the scalar triple product.

5.1.3 MATRIX AND VECTOR DERIVATIVES

Definitions

1. The derivative of the row vector $\mathbf{y}$ with respect to the scalar x is

$$\frac{\partial\mathbf{y}}{\partial x}=\begin{bmatrix}\dfrac{\partial y_1}{\partial x} & \dfrac{\partial y_2}{\partial x} & \cdots & \dfrac{\partial y_m}{\partial x}\end{bmatrix}.$$

2. The derivative of a scalar y with respect to the vector $\mathbf{x}$ is

$$\frac{\partial y}{\partial\mathbf{x}}=\begin{bmatrix}\dfrac{\partial y}{\partial x_1}\\[4pt]\dfrac{\partial y}{\partial x_2}\\[4pt]\vdots\\[4pt]\dfrac{\partial y}{\partial x_n}\end{bmatrix}.$$

3. Let $\mathbf{x}$ be a $n\times 1$ vector and let $\mathbf{y}$ be a $m\times 1$ vector. The derivative of $\mathbf{y}$ with respect to $\mathbf{x}$ is the matrix

$$\frac{\partial\mathbf{y}}{\partial\mathbf{x}}=\begin{bmatrix}\dfrac{\partial y_1}{\partial x_1} & \dfrac{\partial y_2}{\partial x_1} & \cdots & \dfrac{\partial y_m}{\partial x_1}\\[6pt]\dfrac{\partial y_1}{\partial x_2} & \dfrac{\partial y_2}{\partial x_2} & \cdots & \dfrac{\partial y_m}{\partial x_2}\\[6pt]\vdots & \vdots & \ddots & \vdots\\[6pt]\dfrac{\partial y_1}{\partial x_n} & \dfrac{\partial y_2}{\partial x_n} & \cdots & \dfrac{\partial y_m}{\partial x_n}\end{bmatrix}.$$

In multivariate analysis, if $\mathbf{x}$ and $\mathbf{y}$ have the same length, then the absolute value of the determinant of $\frac{\partial \mathbf{y}}{\partial \mathbf{x}}$ is called the Jacobian of the transformation determined by $\mathbf{y} = \mathbf{y}(\mathbf{x})$.

4. The derivative of the matrix $A(t) = (a_{ij}(t))$, with respect to the scalar t, is the matrix $\frac{dA(t)}{dt} = \left(\frac{da_{ij}(t)}{dt} \right)$.

5. If $X = (x_{ij})$ is a $n \times m$ matrix and if y is a scalar function of X given by $y = f(X)$, then the derivative of y with respect to X is

$$
\frac{\partial y}{\partial X} =
\begin{bmatrix}
\frac{\partial y}{\partial x_{11}} & \frac{\partial y}{\partial x_{12}} & \cdots & \frac{\partial y}{\partial x_{1n}} \\
\frac{\partial y}{\partial x_{21}} & \frac{\partial y}{\partial x_{22}} & \cdots & \frac{\partial y}{\partial x_{2n}} \\
\vdots & \vdots & \ddots & \vdots \\
\frac{\partial y}{\partial x_{m1}} & \frac{\partial y}{\partial x_{m2}} & \cdots & \frac{\partial y}{\partial x_{mn}}
\end{bmatrix}
= \sum_{ij} E_{ij} \frac{\partial y}{\partial x_{ij}}.
$$

6. If $Y = (y_{ij})$ is a $p \times q$ matrix and X is a $m \times n$ matrix, then the derivative of Y with respect to X is

$$
\frac{\partial Y}{\partial X} =
\begin{bmatrix}
\frac{\partial Y}{\partial x_{11}} & \frac{\partial Y}{\partial x_{12}} & \cdots & \frac{\partial Y}{\partial x_{1n}} \\
\frac{\partial Y}{\partial x_{21}} & \frac{\partial Y}{\partial x_{22}} & \cdots & \frac{\partial Y}{\partial x_{2n}} \\
\vdots & \vdots & \ddots & \vdots \\
\frac{\partial Y}{\partial x_{m1}} & \frac{\partial Y}{\partial x_{m2}} & \cdots & \frac{\partial Y}{\partial x_{mn}}
\end{bmatrix}
= \sum_{rs} E_{rs} \otimes \frac{\partial Y}{\partial x_{rs}}.
$$

Properties

y (scalar or a vector)	$\frac{\partial y}{\partial \mathbf{X}}$
$A\mathbf{x}$	A^{T}
$\mathbf{x}^{\mathrm{T}} A$	A
$\mathbf{x}^{\mathrm{T}} \mathbf{x}$	$2\mathbf{x}$
$\mathbf{x}^{\mathrm{T}} A \mathbf{x}$	$A\mathbf{x} + A^{\mathrm{T}}\mathbf{x}$

(row 1.)

2. If the matrices A and B can be multiplied, then $\frac{d(AB)}{dt} = \frac{dA}{dt} B + A \frac{dB}{dt}$.

3. If $C = A \otimes B$, then $\frac{dC}{dt} = \frac{dA}{dt} \otimes B + A \otimes \frac{dB}{dt}$.

4. If $\mathbf{z} = \mathbf{y}(\mathbf{x})$, then $\frac{\partial \mathbf{z}}{\partial \mathbf{y}} = \frac{\partial \mathbf{y}}{\partial \mathbf{x}} \frac{\partial \mathbf{z}}{\partial \mathbf{y}}$.

5. If $y = \operatorname{tr} X$, then $\frac{\partial y}{\partial X} = I_n$.

6. The derivative of the determinant of a matrix can be written:

- If Y_{ij} is the cofactor of element y_{ij} in $|Y|$, then $\frac{\partial |Y|}{\partial x_{rs}} = \sum_i \sum_j Y_{ij} \frac{\partial y_{ij}}{\partial x_{rs}}$.

- If all of the components (x_{ij}) of X are independent, then $\frac{\partial |X|}{\partial X} = |X| \, (X^{-1})^{\mathrm{T}}$.

- If X is a symmetric matrix, then $\frac{\partial |X|}{\partial X} = 2X - \sum_i x_{ii}$.

7. $\frac{\partial (AXB)}{\partial x_{rs}} = A E_{rs} B$ where E_{rs} is an elementary matrix of the same size as X.

8. If $Y = A X^{\mathrm{T}} B$, then $\frac{\partial y_{ij}}{\partial X} = B E_{ij}^{\mathrm{T}} A$.

9. If $Y = AX^{-1}B$, then

   - $\frac{\partial Y}{\partial x_{rs}} = -AX^{-1}E_{rs}X^{-1}B$.

   - $\frac{\partial y_{ij}}{\partial X} = -(X^{-1})^{\mathrm{T}}A^{\mathrm{T}}E_{ij}B^{\mathrm{T}}(X^{-1})^{\mathrm{T}}$.

10. If $Y = X^{\mathrm{T}}AX$, then

    - $\frac{\partial Y}{\partial x_{rs}} = E_{rs}^{\mathrm{T}}AX + X^{\mathrm{T}}AE_{rs}$.

    - $\frac{\partial y_{ij}}{\partial X} = AXE_{ij}^{\mathrm{T}} + A^{\mathrm{T}}XE_{ij}$.

11. Derivatives of powers of matrices are obtained as follows:

    - If $Y = X^r$, then $\frac{\partial Y}{\partial x_{rs}} = \sum_{k=0}^{r-1} X^k E_{rs} X^{n-k-1}$.

    - If $Y = X^{-r}$, then $\frac{\partial Y}{\partial x_{rs}} = -X^{-r}\left(\sum_{k=0}^{r-1} X^k E_{rs} X^{n-k-1}\right)X^{-r}$.

12. If $\mathbf{y} = \operatorname{Vec} Y$ and $\mathbf{x} = \operatorname{Vec} X$, then

    - If $Y = AX$, then $\frac{\partial \mathbf{y}}{\partial \mathbf{x}} = I \otimes A^{\mathrm{T}}$.

    - If $Y = XA$, then $\frac{\partial \mathbf{y}}{\partial \mathbf{x}} = A \otimes I$.

    - If $Y = AX^{-1}B$, then $\frac{\partial \mathbf{y}}{\partial \mathbf{x}} = -(X^{-1}B) \otimes (X^{-1})^{\mathrm{T}}A^{\mathrm{T}}$.

13. Derivative formulae:

    - $\frac{\partial \log |X|}{\partial X} = (X^{-1})^{\mathrm{T}}$.

    - $\frac{\partial \operatorname{tr}(AX)}{\partial X} = A^{\mathrm{T}}$.

    - $\frac{\partial \operatorname{tr}(X^{\mathrm{T}}A)}{\partial X} = A$.

    - $\frac{\partial \operatorname{tr}(X^{\mathrm{T}}AXB)}{\partial X} = AXB + A^{\mathrm{T}}XB^{\mathrm{T}}$.

    - If X and Y are matrices, then $\left(\frac{\partial Y}{\partial X}\right)^{\mathrm{T}} = \frac{\partial Y^{\mathrm{T}}}{\partial X^{\mathrm{T}}}$.

    - If X, Y, and Z are matrices of size $m \times n$, $n \times v$, and $p \times q$, then $\frac{\partial(XY)}{\partial Z} = \frac{\partial X}{\partial Z}(I_q \otimes Y) + (I_p \otimes X)\frac{\partial Y}{\partial Z}$.

5.2 DIFFERENTIAL FORMS

For the vector $\mathbf{a} = (a_1, \ldots, a_k, \ldots, a_n)$, define dx_k to be the function that assigns to the vector $\mathbf{a}$ its kth coordinate (that is, $dx_k(\mathbf{a}) = a_k$). Geometrically, $dx_k(\mathbf{a})$ is the length, with appropriate sign, of the projection of $\mathbf{a}$ on the kth coordinate axis. When $\{F_i\}$ are functions, the linear combination of the functions $\{dx_k\}$

$$\omega_{\mathbf{x}} = F_1(\mathbf{x})\,dx_1 + F_2(\mathbf{x})\,dx_2 + \cdots + F_n(\mathbf{x})\,dx_n \tag{5.2.1}$$

produces a new function $\omega_{\mathbf{x}}$. This function acts on vectors $\mathbf{a}$ as

$$\omega_{\mathbf{x}}(\mathbf{a}) = F_1(\mathbf{x})\,dx_1(\mathbf{a}) + F_2(\mathbf{x})\,dx_2(\mathbf{a}) + \cdots + F_n(\mathbf{x})\,dx_n(\mathbf{a}).$$

Such a function is a "differential 1-form" or a "1-form". For example:

1. If $\mathbf{a} = (-2, 0, 4)$ then $dx_1(\mathbf{a}) = -2$, $dx_2(\mathbf{a}) = 0$, and $dx_3(\mathbf{a}) = 4$.
2. If in $\mathbb{R}^2$, $\omega_{\mathbf{x}} = \omega_{(x,y)} = x^2\,dx + y^2\,dy$, then $\omega_{(x,y)}(a, b) = ax^2 + by^2$ and $\omega_{(1,-3)}(a, b) = a + 9b$.
3. If $f(\mathbf{x})$ is a differentiable function, then $\nabla_{\mathbf{x}} f$, the differential of f at $\mathbf{x}$, is a 1-form. Note that $\nabla_{\mathbf{x}} f$ acting on $\mathbf{a} = (a_1, a_2, a_3)$ is

$$\begin{aligned}
\nabla_{\mathbf{x}} f(\mathbf{a}) &= \frac{\partial f}{\partial x_1}(\mathbf{x})\,dx_1(\mathbf{a}) + \frac{\partial f}{\partial x_2}(\mathbf{x})\,dx_2(\mathbf{a}) + \frac{\partial f}{\partial x_3}(\mathbf{x})\,dx_3(\mathbf{a}), \\
&= \frac{\partial f}{\partial x_1}(\mathbf{x})a_1 + \frac{\partial f}{\partial x_2}(\mathbf{x})a_2 + \frac{\partial f}{\partial x_3}(\mathbf{x})a_3.
\end{aligned}$$

Products of 1-forms

The basic 1-forms in $\mathbb{R}^3$ are dx_1, dx_2, and dx_3. The wedge product $dx_1 \wedge dx_2$ is defined so that it is a function of ordered pairs in $\mathbb{R}^2$. Geometrically, $dx_1 \wedge dx_2(\mathbf{a}, \mathbf{b})$ will be the area of the parallelogram spanned by the projections of $\mathbf{a}$ and $\mathbf{b}$ into the (x_1, x_2)-plane. The sign of the area is determined so that if the projections of $\mathbf{a}$ and $\mathbf{b}$ have the same orientation as the positive x_1 and x_2 axes, then the area is positive; it is negative when these orientations are opposite. Thus, if $\mathbf{a} = (a_1, a_2, a_3)$ and $\mathbf{b} = (b_1, b_2, b_3)$, then

$$dx_1 \wedge dx_2(\mathbf{a}, \mathbf{b}) = \det \begin{bmatrix} a_1 & b_1 \\ a_2 & b_2 \end{bmatrix} = a_1 b_2 - a_2 b_1,$$

and the determinant automatically gives the correct sign. This generalizes to

$$dx_i \wedge dx_j(\mathbf{a}, \mathbf{b}) = \det \begin{bmatrix} dx_i(\mathbf{a}) & dx_i(\mathbf{b}) \\ dx_j(\mathbf{a}) & dx_j(\mathbf{b}) \end{bmatrix} = \det \begin{bmatrix} a_i & b_i \\ a_j & b_j \end{bmatrix}. \qquad (5.2.2)$$

- If ω and μ are 1-forms, and f and g are real-valued functions, then $f\omega + g\mu$ is a 1-form.
- If ω, ν, and μ are 1-forms, then $(f\omega + g\nu) \wedge \mu = f\,\omega \wedge \mu + g\,\nu \wedge \mu$.
- $dx_i \wedge dx_j = -dx_j \wedge dx_i$
- $dx_i \wedge dx_i = 0$
- $dx_i \wedge dx_j(\mathbf{b}, \mathbf{a}) = -dx_i \wedge dx_j(\mathbf{a}, \mathbf{b})$

Differential 2-forms

In $\mathbb{R}^3$, the most general linear combination of the functions $dx_i \wedge dx_j$ has the form $c_1\, dx_2 \wedge dx_3 + c_2\, dx_3 \wedge dx_1 + c_3\, dx_1 \wedge dx_2$. If $\mathbf{F} = (F_1, F_2, F_3)$ is a vector field, then the function of ordered pairs,

$$\tau_{\mathbf{X}}(\mathbf{a}, \mathbf{b}) = F_1(\mathbf{x})\, dx_2 \wedge dx_3 + F_2(\mathbf{x})\, dx_3 \wedge dx_1 + F_3(\mathbf{x})\, dx_1 \wedge dx_2 \qquad (5.2.3)$$

is a "differential 2-form" or "2-form".

1. For the specific 2-form $\tau_{\mathbf{X}} = 2\, dx_2 \wedge dx_3 + dx_3 \wedge dx_1 + 5\, dx_1 \wedge dx_2$, if $\mathbf{a} = (1, 2, 3)$ and $\mathbf{b} = (0, 1, 1)$, then

$$\tau_{\mathbf{X}}(\mathbf{a}, \mathbf{b}) = 2 \det \begin{bmatrix} 2 & 1 \\ 3 & 1 \end{bmatrix} + \det \begin{bmatrix} 3 & 1 \\ 1 & 0 \end{bmatrix} + 5 \det \begin{bmatrix} 1 & 0 \\ 2 & 1 \end{bmatrix}$$

$$= 2 \cdot (-1) + 1 \cdot (-1) + 5 \cdot (1) = 2$$

independent of $\mathbf{x}$. Note that $\mathbf{a} \times \mathbf{b} = \det \begin{bmatrix} \mathbf{i} & \mathbf{j} & \mathbf{k} \\ 1 & 2 & 3 \\ 0 & 1 & 1 \end{bmatrix} = (-1, -1, 1)$, and so $\tau_{\mathbf{X}}(\mathbf{a}, \mathbf{b}) = (2, 1, 5) \cdot (\mathbf{a} \times \mathbf{b})$.

2. When changing from Cartesian coordinates to polar coordinates, the element of area dA can be written

$$\begin{aligned} dA &= dx \wedge dy \\ &= (-r \sin \theta\, d\theta + \cos \theta\, dr) \wedge (r \cos \theta\, d\theta + \sin \theta\, dr) \\ &= -r^2 \sin \theta \cos \theta\, d\theta \wedge d\theta + \sin \theta \cos \theta\, dr \wedge dr \\ &\quad - r \sin^2 \theta\, d\theta \wedge dr + r \cos^2 \theta\, dr \wedge d\theta \\ &= r\, dr \wedge d\theta \end{aligned}$$

The 2-forms in $\mathbb{R}^n$

Every 2-form can be written in terms of a set of "basic 2-forms". For example, in $\mathbb{R}^2$ there is only one basic 2-form (which may be taken to be $dx_1 \wedge dx_2$) and in $\mathbb{R}^3$ there are 3 basic 2-forms (possibly the set $\{dx_1 \wedge dx_2, dx_2 \wedge dx_3, dx_3 \wedge dx_1\}$). The exterior product of any two 1-forms (in, say, $\mathbb{R}^n$) is found by multiplying the 1-forms as if there were ordinary polynomials in the variables $dx_1, \ldots, dx_n$, and then simplifying using the rules for $dx_i \wedge dx_j$.

For example, denoting the basic 1-forms in $\mathbb{R}^3$ as dx, dy, and dz then

$$\begin{aligned} (x\, dx + y^2\, dy) \wedge (dx + x\, dy) &= x\, dx \wedge dx + y^2\, dy \wedge dx, \\ &\quad + x^2\, dx \wedge dy + xy^2\, dy \wedge dy, \\ &= 0 - y^2\, dx \wedge dy + x^2\, dx \wedge dy + 0, \\ &= (x^2 - y^2)\, dx \wedge dy. \end{aligned}$$

Higher dimensional forms

The meaning of the basic 3-form $dx_1 \wedge dx_2 \wedge dx_3$ is that of a signed volume function. Thus, if $\mathbf{a} = (a_1, a_2, a_3)$, $\mathbf{b} = (b_1, b_2, b_3)$, and $\mathbf{c} = (c_1, c_2, c_3)$ then

$$dx_1 \wedge dx_2 \wedge dx_3(\mathbf{a}, \mathbf{b}, \mathbf{c}) = \det \begin{bmatrix} a_1 & b_1 & c_1 \\ a_2 & b_2 & c_2 \\ a_3 & b_3 & c_3 \end{bmatrix}$$

which is a 3-dimensional oriented volume of the parallelepiped defined by the vectors $\mathbf{a}$, $\mathbf{b}$, and $\mathbf{c}$.

For an ordered p-tuple of vectors in $\mathbb{R}^n$ $(\mathbf{a}_1, \mathbf{a}_2, \ldots, \mathbf{a}_p)$, where $p \geq 1$

$$dx_{k_1} \wedge dx_{k_2} \wedge \cdots \wedge dx_{k_p}(\mathbf{a}_1, \ldots \mathbf{a}_p) = \det(dx_{k_i}(\mathbf{a}_j))_{\substack{i=1,\ldots,p \\ j=1,\ldots,p}}. \qquad (5.2.4)$$

This equation defines the basic p-forms in $\mathbb{R}^n$, of which the general p-forms are linear combinations. Properties include:

1. The interchange of adjacent factors in a basic p-form changes the sign of the form.

2. A basic p-form with a repeated factor is zero.

3. The general p-form can be written $\omega^p = \sum_{i_1 < \cdots < i_p} f_{i_1,\ldots,i_p} dx_{i_1} \wedge \cdots \wedge dx_{i_k}$, where $1 \leq i_k \leq n$ for $k = 1, \ldots, p$. This sum has $\binom{n}{p}$ distinct nonzero terms in it.

4. If $p > n$, then ω^p is identically zero.

5. If ω^p is a p-form in $\mathbb{R}^n$ and ω^q is a q-form in $\mathbb{R}^n$, then $\omega^p \wedge \omega^q = (-1)^{pq} \omega^q \wedge \omega^p$.

The exterior derivative

The exterior differentiation operator is denoted by d. When d is applied to a scalar function $f(\mathbf{x})$, the result is the 1-form that is equivalent to the usual "total differential" $df = \frac{\partial f}{\partial x_1} dx_1 + \cdots + \frac{\partial f}{\partial x_n} dx_n$. For the 1-form $\omega^1 = f_1 dx + \cdots + f_n dx_n$ the exterior derivative is $d\omega^1 = (df_1) \wedge dx_1 + \cdots + (df_n) \wedge dx_n$. This generalizes to higher dimensional forms.

1. If $f(x_1, x_2) = x_1^2 + x_2^3$, then $df = d(x_1^2 + x_2^3) = 2x_1 dx_1 + 3x_2^2 dx_2$.

2. If $\omega^1_{(x_1,x_2)} = x_1 x_2 dx_1 + (x_1^2 + x_2^2) dx_2$, then $d\omega^1$ is given by

$$\begin{aligned} d\omega^1 &= d(x_1 x_2 dx_1 + (x_1^2 + x_2^2) dx_2) \\ &= (x_2 dx_1 + x_1 dx_2) \wedge dx_1 + (2x_1 dx_1 + 2x_2 dx_2) \wedge dx_2 \\ &= x_1 dx_1 \wedge dx_2. \end{aligned}$$

Properties of the exterior derivative

1. If $f_1(x_1, x_2)$ and $f_2(x_1, x_2)$ are differentiable functions, then

$$df_1 \wedge df_2 = \frac{\partial(f_1, f_2)}{\partial(x_1, x_2)} dx_1 \wedge dx_2.$$

2. If ω^p and ω^q represent a p-form and a q-form, then

$$d(\omega^p \wedge \omega^q) = (d\omega^p) \wedge \omega^q + (-1)^{pq} \omega^p \wedge (d\omega^q).$$

3. If ω^p is a p-form with at least two derivatives, then $d(d\omega^p) = 0$.

   - The relation $d(d\omega^0) = 0$ is equivalent to curl(grad $\mathbf{F}$) = 0.
   - The relation $d(d\omega^1) = 0$ is equivalent to div(curl f) = 0.

5.3   INTEGRATION

5.3.1   DEFINITIONS

The following definitions apply to the expression $I = \int_a^b f(x)\,dx$:

- The *integrand*   is $f(x)$.
- The *upper limit*   is b.
- The *lower limit*   is a.
- I is "the integral of $f(x)$ from a to b".

It is conventional to indicate the indefinite integral of a function represented by a lowercase letter by the corresponding uppercase letter. For example, $F(x) = \int_a^x f(t)\,dt$ and $G(x) = \int_a^x g(t)\,dt$. Note that all functions that differ from $F(x)$ by a constant are also indefinite integrals of $f(x)$.

- $\int f(x)\,dx$ indefinite integral of $f(x)$ (also written $\int^x f(t)\,dt$)

- $\int_a^b f(x)\,dx$ definite integral of $f(x)$, defined as

$$\lim_{n \to \infty} \left(\frac{b-a}{n} \sum_{k=1}^{n} f\left[a + \frac{k}{n}(b-a)\right] \right)$$

- $\oint_C f(x)\,dx$ definite integral of $f(x)$, taken along the contour C

- $\int_a^\infty f(x)\,dx$ defined as $\displaystyle\lim_{R \to \infty} \int_a^R f(x)\,dx$

- $\int_{-\infty}^{\infty} f(x)\,dx$ defined as the limit of $\int_{-S}^{R} f(x)\,dx$ as R and S independently go to ∞
- $\int f$ shorthand for $\int f(x)\,dx$
- *Improper integral*   integral for which the region of integration is not bounded, or the integrand is not bounded
- *Cauchy principal value*

  - The Cauchy principal value of the integral $\int_{a}^{b} f(x)\,dx$, denoted $f_{a}^{b}\, f(x)\,dx$, is defined as $\lim\limits_{\epsilon \to 0+} \left(\int_{a}^{c-\epsilon} f(x)\,dx + \int_{c+\epsilon}^{b} f(x)\,dx \right)$, assuming that f is singular only at c.
  - The Cauchy principal value of the integral $\int_{-\infty}^{\infty} f(x)\,dx$ is defined as the limit of $\int_{-R}^{R} f(x)\,dx$ as $R \to \infty$.

- If, at the complex point $z = a$, $f(z)$ is either analytic or has an isolated singularity, then the residue of $f(z)$ at $z = a$ is given by the complex integral $\mathrm{Res}_f(a) = \frac{1}{2\pi i} \oint_C f(\xi)\,d\xi$.

5.3.2   PROPERTIES OF INTEGRATION

Indefinite integrals have the properties:

1. $\int [af(x) + bg(x)]\,dx = a \int f(x)\,dx + b \int g(x)\,dx$ (linearity).
2. $\int f(x)g(x)\,dx = F(x)g(x) - \int F(x)g'(x)\,dx$ (integration by parts).
3. $\int f(g(x))g'(x)\,dx = F(g(x))$ (substitution).
4. $\int f(ax + b)\,dx = \frac{1}{a} F(ax + b)$.
5. If $f(x)$ is an odd function, then $F(x)$ is an even function.
6. If $f(x)$ is an even function and $F(0) = 0$, then $F(x)$ is an odd function.
7. If $f(x)$ has a finite number of discontinuities, then the integral $\int f(x)\,dx$ is the sum of the integrals over those subintervals where $f(x)$ is continuous (provided they exist).
8. *Fundamental theorem of integral calculus* If $f(x)$ is single-valued, bounded, and integrable on $[a, b]$, and there exists a function $F(x)$ such that $F'(x) = f(x)$ for $a \le x \le b$ then

$$\int_{a}^{x} f(x)\,dx = F(x) \Big|_{a}^{x} = F(x) - F(a)$$

for $a \le x \le b$.

Definite integrals have the properties:

1. $\int_{a}^{a} f(x)\,dx = 0$.

2. $\int_a^b f(x)\,dx = -\int_b^a f(x)\,dx.$

3. $\int_a^b f(x)\,dx + \int_b^c f(x)\,dx = \int_a^c f(x)\,dx$ (additivity).

4. $\int_a^b [cf(x) + dg(x)]\,dx = c\int_a^b f(x)\,dx + d\int_a^b g(x)\,dx$ (linearity).

5.3.3 INEQUALITIES

1. *Schwarz' inequality:*

$$\int_a^b |fg| \leq \sqrt{\left(\int_a^b f^2\right)\left(\int_a^b g^2\right)}.$$

2. *Minkowski's inequality:*

$$\left(\int_a^b |f+g|^p\right)^{1/p} \leq \left(\int_a^b |f|^p\right)^{1/p} + \left(\int_a^b |g|^p\right)^{1/p} \quad \text{when } p \geq 1.$$

3. *Hölder's inequality:*

$$\int_a^b |fg| \leq \left[\int_a^b |f|^p\right]^{1/p}\left[\int_a^b |g|^q\right]^{1/q} \quad \text{when } \frac{1}{p} + \frac{1}{q} = 1,\ p > 1,\ \text{and } q > 1.$$

4. $\left|\int_a^b f(x)\,dx\right| \leq \int_a^b |f(x)|\,dx \leq \left(\max\limits_{x\in[a,b]} |f(x)|\right)(b-a)$ assuming $a \leq b$.

5. If $f(x) \leq g(x)$ on the interval $[a,b]$, then $\int_a^b f(x)\,dx \leq \int_a^b g(x)\,dx$.

5.3.4 CONVERGENCE TESTS

1. If $\int_a^b |f(x)|\,dx$ is convergent, then $\int_a^b f(x)\,dx$ is convergent.

2. If $0 \leq f(x) \leq g(x)$ and $\int_a^b g(x)\,dx$ is convergent,
   then $\int_a^b f(x)\,dx$ is convergent.

3. If $0 \leq g(x) \leq f(x)$ and $\int_a^b g(x)\,dx$ is divergent,
   then $\int_a^b f(x)\,dx$ is divergent.

The following integrals may be used, for example, with the above tests:

- $\displaystyle\int_2^\infty \frac{dx}{x(\log x)^p}$ and $\displaystyle\int_1^\infty \frac{dx}{x^p}$ are convergent when $p > 1$, and divergent when $p \leq 1$.

- $\displaystyle\int_0^1 \frac{dx}{x^p}$ is convergent when $p < 1$, and divergent when $p \geq 1$.

5.3.5 SUBSTITUTION

Substitution can be used to change integrals to simpler forms. When the transform $t = g(x)$ is chosen, the integral $I = \int f(t)\,dt$ becomes $I = \int f(g(x))\,dt = \int f(g(x))g'(x)\,dx$. Several precautions must be observed when using substitutions:

- Be sure to make the substitution in the dx term, as well as everywhere else in the integral.

- Be sure that the function substituted is one-to-one and continuous. If this is not the case, then the integral must be restricted in such a way as to make it true.

- With definite integrals, the limits should also be expressed in terms of the new dependent variables. With indefinite integrals, it is necessary to perform the reverse substitution to obtain the answer in terms of the original independent variable. This may also be done for definite integrals, but it is usually easier to change the limits.

Example

Consider the integral

$$I = \int \frac{x^4}{\sqrt{a^2 - x^2}}\,dx$$

Here we choose to make the substitution $x = |a|\sin\theta$. From this we find $dx = |a|\cos\theta\,d\theta$ and

$$\sqrt{a^2 - x^2} = \sqrt{a^2 - a^2\sin^2\theta} = |a|\sqrt{1 - \sin^2\theta} = |a|\,|\cos\theta|$$

Note the absolute value signs. It is very important to interpret the square root radical consistently as the positive square root. Thus $\sqrt{x^2} = |x|$. Failure to observe this is a common cause of errors in integration.

Note that the substitution used above is not a one-to-one function, that is, it does not have a unique inverse. Thus the range of θ must be restricted in such a way as to make the function one-to-one. In this case we can solve for θ to obtain

$$\theta = \sin^{-1}\frac{x}{|a|}$$

This will be unique if we restrict the inverse sine to the principal values $-\frac{\pi}{2} \le \theta \le \frac{\pi}{2}$.

Thus, the integral becomes (with $dx = |a|\cos\theta\,d\theta$)

$$I = \int \frac{a^4\sin^4\theta}{|a|\,|\cos\theta|}\,|a|\cos\theta\,d\theta.$$

Now, however, in the range of values chosen for θ, we find that $\cos\theta$ is always positive. Thus, we may remove the absolute value signs from $\cos\theta$ in the denominator. Then the $\cos\theta$ terms cancel and the integral becomes

$$I = a^4 \int \sin^4\theta\,d\theta.$$

By application of the integration formula on page 378 this is integrated to obtain

$$I = -\frac{a^4}{4} \sin^3 \theta \cos \theta - \frac{3a^4}{8} \sin \theta \cos \theta + \frac{3a^4}{8} \theta + C. \qquad (5.3.1)$$

To obtain an evaluation of I as a function of x, we must transform variables from θ to x. We have

$$\cos \theta = \pm\sqrt{1 - \sin^2 \theta} = \pm\sqrt{1 - \frac{x^2}{a^2}} = \pm\frac{\sqrt{a^2 - x^2}}{|a|}.$$

Because of the previously recorded fact that $\cos \theta$ is positive for our range of θ, we may omit the $\pm$ sign. Using $\sin \theta = x/|a|$ and $\cos \theta = \sqrt{a^2 - x^2}/|a|$ we can evaluate Equation (5.3.1) to obtain the final result,

$$I = \int \frac{x^4}{\sqrt{a^2 - x^2}} = -\frac{x^3}{4}\sqrt{a^2 - x^2} - \frac{3a^2 x}{8}\sqrt{a^2 - x^2} + \frac{3a^4}{8}\sin^{-1}\frac{x}{|a|} + C.$$

Useful transformations

The following transformations may make evaluation of an integral easier:

1. $\int f\left(x, \sqrt{x^2 + a^2}\right) dx = a \int f(a \tan u, a \sec u) \sec^2 u \, du$

   when $u = \tan^{-1}\frac{x}{a}$ and $a > 0$.

2. $\int f\left(x, \sqrt{x^2 - a^2}\right) dx = a \int f(a \sec u, a \tan u) \sec u \tan u \, du$

   when $u = \sec^{-1}\frac{x}{a}$ and $a > 0$.

3. $\int f\left(x, \sqrt{a^2 - x^2}\right) dx = a \int f(a \sin u, a \cos u) \cos u \, du$

   when $u = \sin^{-1}\frac{x}{a}$ and $a > 0$.

4. $\int f(\sin x) \, dx = 2 \int f\left(\frac{2z}{1+z^2}\right) \frac{dz}{1+z^2}$ when $z = \tan \frac{x}{2}$.

5. $\int f(\cos x) \, dx = 2 \int f\left(\frac{1-z^2}{1+z^2}\right) \frac{dz}{1+z^2}$ when $z = \tan \frac{x}{2}$.

6. $\int f(\cos x) \, dx = -\int f(v)\frac{dv}{\sqrt{1-v^2}}$ when $v = \cos x$.

7. $\int f(\sin x) \, dx = \int f(u)\frac{du}{\sqrt{1-u^2}}$ when $u = \sin x$.

8. $\int f(\sin x, \cos x) \, dx = \int f\left(u, \sqrt{1-u^2}\right) \frac{du}{\sqrt{1-u^2}}$ when $u = \sin x$.

9. $\int f(\sin x, \cos x) \, dx = 2 \int f\left(\frac{2z}{1+z^2}, \frac{1-z^2}{1+z^2}\right) \frac{dz}{1+z^2}$ when $z = \tan \frac{x}{2}$.

10. $\int_{-\infty}^{\infty} F(u) \, du = \int_{-\infty}^{\infty} F(x) \, dx$ when $u = x - \sum\limits_{j=1}^{n} \frac{a_j}{x - c_j}$ where $\{a_i\}$ is any

    sequence of positive constants and the $\{c_j\}$ are any real constants whatsoever.

Several transformations of the integral $\int_0^{\infty} f(x) \, dx$, with an infinite integration range, to an integral with a finite integration range, are shown:

$t(x)$	$x(t)$	$\frac{dx}{dt}$	Finite interval integral
e^{-x}	$-\log t$	$-\frac{1}{t}$	$\int_0^1 \frac{f(-\log t)}{t}\, dt$
$\frac{x}{1+x}$	$\frac{t}{1-t}$	$\frac{1}{(1-t)^2}$	$\int_0^1 f\left(\frac{t}{1-t}\right) \frac{dt}{(1-t)^2}$
$\tanh x$	$\frac{1}{2}\log\frac{1+t}{1-t}$	$\frac{1}{1-t^2}$	$\int_0^1 f\left(\frac{1}{2}\log\frac{1+t}{1-t}\right)\frac{dt}{1-t^2}$

5.3.6   PARTIAL FRACTION DECOMPOSITION

Every integral of the form $\int R(x)\, dx$, where R is a rational function, can be evaluated (in principle) in terms of elementary functions. The technique is to factor the denominator of R and create a partial fraction decomposition. Then each resulting subintegral is elementary.

Example

Consider the integral $I = \displaystyle\int \frac{2x^3 - 10x^2 + 13x - 4}{x^2 - 5x + 6}\, dx$. This can be written as

$$I = \int \left(2x + \frac{x-4}{x^2 - 5x + 6}\right) dx = \int \left(2x + \frac{2}{x-2} - \frac{1}{x-3}\right) dx$$

which can be readily integrated $I = x^2 + 2\ln(x-2) - \ln(x-3)$.

5.3.7   INTEGRATION BY PARTS

In one dimension, the integration by parts formula is

$$\int u\, dv = uv - \int v\, du \qquad \text{for indefinite integrals,} \qquad (5.3.2)$$

$$\int_a^b u\, dv = uv \,\Big|_a^b - \int_a^b v\, du \qquad \text{for definite integrals.} \qquad (5.3.3)$$

When evaluating a given integral by this method, u and v must be chosen so that the form $\int u\, dv$ becomes identical to the given integral. This is usually accomplished by specifying u and dv and deriving du and v. Then the integration by parts formula will produce a boundary term and another integral to be evaluated. If u and v were well chosen, then this second integral may be easier to evaluate.

Example

Consider the integral

$$I = \int x \sin x\, dx.$$

Two obvious choices for the integration by parts formula are $\{u = x, dv = \sin x\, dx\}$ and $\{u = \sin x, dv = x\, dx\}$. We will try each of them in turn.

- Using $\{u = x, dv = \sin x \, dx\}$, we compute $du = dx$ and $v = \int dv = \int \sin x \, dx = -\cos x$. Hence, we can represent I in the alternative form as

$$I = \int x \sin x \, dx = \int u \, dv = uv - \int v \, du = -x \cos x + \int \cos x \, dx.$$

In this representation of I, we must evaluate the last integral. Because we know $\int \cos x \, dx = \sin x$ the final result is $I = \sin x - x \cos x$.

- Using $\{u = \sin x, dv = x \, dx\}$ we compute $du = \cos x \, dx$ and $v = \int dv = \int x \, dx = x^2/2$. Hence, we can represent I in the alternative form as

$$I = \int x \sin x \, dx = \int u \, dv = uv - \int v \, du = \frac{x^2}{2} \cos x - \int \frac{x^2}{2} \cos x \, dx.$$

In this case, we have actually made the problem "worse" since the remaining integral appearing in I is "harder" than the one we started with.

Example

Consider the integral

$$I = \int e^x \sin x \, dx.$$

We choose to use the integration by parts formula with $u = e^x$ and $dv = \sin x \, dx$. From these we compute $du = e^x \, dx$ and $v = \int dv = \int \sin x \, dx = -\cos x$. Hence, we can represent I in the alternative form as

$$I = \int e^x \sin x \, dx = \int u \, dv = uv - \int v \, du = -e^x \cos x + \int e^x \cos x \, dx$$

If we write this as

$$I = -e^x \cos x + J \qquad \text{with} \qquad J = \int e^x \cos x \, dx, \tag{5.3.4}$$

then we can apply integration by parts to J using $\{u = e^x, dv = \cos x \, dx\}$. From these we compute $du = e^x \, dx$ and $v = \int dv = \int \cos x \, dx = \sin x$. Hence, we can represent J in the alternative form as

$$J = \int e^x \cos x \, dx = \int u \, dv = uv - \int v \, du = e^x \sin x - \int e^x \sin x \, dx$$

If we write this as

$$J = e^x \sin x - I, \tag{5.3.5}$$

then we can solve the linear equations (5.3.4) and (5.3.5) simultaneously to determine both I and J. We find

$$I = \int e^x \sin x \, dx = \frac{1}{2} \left(e^x \sin x - e^x \cos x \right), \quad \text{and}$$

$$J = \int e^x \cos x \, dx = \frac{1}{2} \left(e^x \sin x + e^x \cos x \right).$$

Extended integration by parts rule

The following rule is obtained by $n+1$ successive applications of integration by parts. Let

$$g_1(x) = \int g(x)\,dx, \qquad g_2(x) = \int g_1(x)\,dx,$$

$$g_3(x) = \int g_2(x)\,dx, \qquad \ldots, \qquad g_m(x) = \int g_{m-1}(x)\,dx. \qquad (5.3.6)$$

Then

$$\int f(x)g(x)\,dx = f(x)g_1(x) - f'(x)g_2(x) + f''(x)g_3(x) - \ldots$$

$$+ (-1)^n f^{(n)}(x)g_{n+1}(x) + (-1)^{n+1} \int f^{(n+1)}(x)g_{n+1}(x)\,dx. \qquad (5.3.7)$$

5.3.8   SPECIAL FUNCTIONS DEFINED BY INTEGRALS

Not all integrals of elementary functions (sines, cosines, rational functions, and others) can be evaluated in terms of elementary functions. For example, the integral $\int e^{-x^2}\,dx$ is represented by the special function "erf(x)" (see page 498). Other useful functions include dilogarithms (see page 506) and elliptic integrals (see page 522).

The dilogarithm function is defined by $\mathrm{Li}_2(x) = -\int_0^x \ln(1-x)/x\,dx$. All integrals of the form $\int^x P(x, \sqrt{R}) \log Q(x, \sqrt{R})\,dx$, where P and Q are rational functions and $R = A^2 + Bx + Cx^2$, can be evaluated in terms of elementary functions and dilogarithms.

All integrals of the form $\int_x R(x, \sqrt{T(x)})\,dx$, where R is a rational function of its arguments and $T(x)$ is a third or fourth order polynomial, can be integrated in terms of elementary functions and elliptic functions.

5.3.9   VARIATIONAL PRINCIPLES

If J depends on a function $g(x)$ and its derivatives through an integral of the form $J[g] = \int F(g, g', \ldots)\,dx$, then J will be stationary to small perturbations if F satisfies the corresponding Euler–Lagrange equation.

Function	Euler–Lagrange equation
$\int_R F\left(x, y, y'\right) dx$	$\frac{\partial F}{\partial y} - \frac{d}{dx}\left(\frac{\partial F}{\partial y'}\right) = 0$
$\int_R F\left(x, y, y', \dots, y^{(n)}\right) dx$	$\frac{\partial F}{\partial y} - \frac{d}{dx}\left(\frac{\partial F}{\partial y'}\right) + \frac{d^2}{dx^2}\left(\frac{\partial F}{\partial y''}\right) - \dots + (-1)^n \frac{d^n}{dx^n}\left(\frac{\partial F}{\partial y^{(n)}}\right) = 0$
$\iint_R \left[a\left(\frac{\partial u}{\partial x}\right)^2 + b\left(\frac{\partial u}{\partial x}\right)^2 + cu^2 + 2fu\right] dx\, dy,$	$\frac{\partial}{\partial x}\left(a\frac{\partial u}{\partial x}\right) + \frac{\partial}{\partial y}\left(b\frac{\partial u}{\partial y}\right) - cu = f$
$\iint_R F(x, y, u, u_x, u_y, u_{xx}, u_{xy}, u_{yy})\, dx\, dy$	$\frac{\partial F}{\partial u} - \frac{\partial}{\partial x}\left(\frac{\partial F}{\partial u_x}\right) - \frac{\partial}{\partial y}\left(\frac{\partial F}{\partial u_y}\right) + \frac{\partial^2}{\partial x^2}\left(\frac{\partial F}{\partial u_{xx}}\right) + \frac{\partial^2}{\partial x\partial y}\left(\frac{\partial F}{\partial u_{xy}}\right) + \frac{\partial^2}{\partial y^2}\left(\frac{\partial F}{\partial u_{yy}}\right) = 0$

5.3.10 LINE AND SURFACE INTEGRALS

A line integral is a definite integral whose path of integration is along a specified curve; it can be evaluated by reducing it to ordinary integrals. If $f(x, y)$ is continuous on C, and the integration contour C is parameterized by $(\phi(t), \psi(t))$ as t varies from a to b, then

$$\int_C f(x, y)\, dx = \int_a^b f\left(\phi(t), \psi(t)\right) \phi'(t)\, dt, \tag{5.3.8}$$

$$\int_C f(x, y)\, dy = \int_a^b f\left(\phi(t), \psi(t)\right) \psi'(t)\, dt. \tag{5.3.9}$$

In a simply connected domain, the line integral $I = \int_C X\, dx + Y\, dy + Z\, dz$ is independent of the path C (beginning and ending at the same place) if, and only if, $\mathbf{u} = (X, Y, Z)$ is a gradient vector, $\mathbf{u} = \operatorname{grad} F$ (that is, $F_x = X$, $F_y = Y$, and $F_z = Z$).

Green's theorem: Let D be a domain of the xy plane, and let C be a piecewise smooth, simple closed curve in D whose interior R is also in D. Let $P(x, y)$ and $Q(x, y)$ be functions defined in D with continuous first partial derivatives in D. Then

$$\oint_C (P\, dx + Q\, dy) = \iint_R \left(\frac{\partial Q}{\partial x} - \frac{\partial P}{\partial y}\right) dx\, dy. \tag{5.3.10}$$

The above theorem may be written in the two alternative forms (using $\mathbf{u} = P(x, y)\mathbf{i} + Q(x, y)\mathbf{j}$ and $\mathbf{v} = Q(x, y)\mathbf{i} - P(x, y)\mathbf{j}$),

$$\oint_C \mathbf{u}_T\, ds = \iint_R \operatorname{curl} \mathbf{u}\, dx\, dy \quad \text{and} \quad \oint_C \mathbf{v}_n\, ds = \iint_R \operatorname{div} \mathbf{v}\, dx\, dy. \tag{5.3.11}$$

The first equation above is a simplification of Stokes's theorem, the second equation is the divergence theorem.

Stokes's theorem: Let S be a piecewise smooth oriented surface in space, whose boundary $\mathcal{C}$ is a piecewise smooth simple closed curve, directed in accordance with the given orientation of S. Let $\mathbf{u} = L\mathbf{i} + M\mathbf{j} + N\mathbf{k}$ be a vector field with continuous and differentiable components in a domain D of space including S. Then, $\int_{\mathcal{C}} u_T\, ds = \iint_S (\text{curl } \mathbf{u}) \cdot \mathbf{n}\, d\sigma$, where $\mathbf{n}$ is the chosen unit normal vector on S, that is

$$\int_{\mathcal{C}} L\, dx + M\, dy + N\, dz = \iint_S \left(\frac{\partial N}{\partial y} - \frac{\partial M}{\partial z} \right) dy\, dz$$

$$+ \left(\frac{\partial L}{\partial z} - \frac{\partial N}{\partial x} \right) dz\, dx + \left(\frac{\partial M}{\partial x} - \frac{\partial L}{\partial y} \right) dx\, dy. \quad (5.3.12)$$

Divergence theorem: Let $\mathbf{v} = L\mathbf{i} + M\mathbf{j} + N\mathbf{k}$ be a vector field in a domain D of space. Let L, M, and N be continuous with continuous derivatives in D. Let S be a piecewise smooth surface in D that forms the complete boundary of a bounded closed region R in D. Let $\mathbf{n}$ be the outer normal of S with respect to R. Then $\iint_S v_n\, d\sigma = \iiint_R \text{div } \mathbf{v}\, dx\, dy\, dz$, that is

$$\iint_S L\, dy\, dz + M\, dz\, dx + N\, dx\, dy$$

$$= \iiint_R \left(\frac{\partial L}{\partial x} + \frac{\partial M}{\partial y} + \frac{\partial N}{\partial z} \right) dx\, dy\, dz. \quad (5.3.13)$$

If D is a three-dimensional domain with boundary B, let dV represent the volume element of D, let dS represent the surface element of B, and let $d\mathbf{S} = \mathbf{n}\, dS$, where $\mathbf{n}$ is the outer normal vector of the surface B. Then Gauss's formulae are

$$\iiint_D \nabla \cdot \mathbf{A}\, dV = \iint_B d\mathbf{S} \cdot \mathbf{A} = \iint_B (\mathbf{n} \cdot \mathbf{A})\, dS, \quad (5.3.14)$$

$$\iiint_D \nabla \times \mathbf{A}\, dV = \iint_B d\mathbf{S} \times \mathbf{A} = \iint_B (\mathbf{n} \times \mathbf{A})\, dS, \quad \text{and}$$
$$\quad (5.3.15)$$

$$\iiint_D \nabla \phi\, dV = \iint_B \phi\, d\mathbf{S}, \quad (5.3.16)$$

where ϕ is an arbitrary scalar and $\mathbf{A}$ is an arbitrary vector.

Green's theorems also relate a volume integral to a surface integral: Let V be a volume with surface S, which we assume is simple and closed. Define n as the outward normal to S. Let ϕ and ψ be scalar functions which, together with $\nabla^2 \phi$ and $\nabla^2 \psi$, are defined in V and on S. Then

1. Green's first theorem states that

$$\int_S \phi \frac{\partial \psi}{\partial n}\, dS = \int_V \left(\phi \nabla^2 \psi + \nabla \phi \cdot \nabla \psi \right) dV. \quad (5.3.17)$$

2. Green's second theorem states that

$$\int_S \left(\phi \frac{\partial \psi}{\partial n} - \psi \frac{\partial \phi}{\partial n} \right) dS = \int_V \left(\phi \nabla^2 \psi - \psi \nabla^2 \phi \right) dV.$$

(5.3.18)

5.3.11 CONTOUR INTEGRALS

If $f(z)$ is analytic in the region inside of the simple closed curve C (with proper orientation), then

1. The Cauchy–Goursat integral theorem is $\oint_C f(\xi) \, d\xi = 0$.
2. Cauchy's integral formula is

$$f(z) = \frac{1}{2\pi i} \oint_C \frac{f(\xi)}{\xi - z} \, d\xi \quad \text{and} \quad f'(z) = \frac{1}{2\pi i} \oint_C \frac{f(\xi)}{(\xi - z)^2} \, d\xi.$$

In general, $f^{(n)}(z) = \frac{n!}{2\pi i} \oint_C \frac{f(\xi)}{(\xi-z)^{n+1}} \, d\xi$.

The *residue theorem*: For every simple closed contour C enclosing at most a finite number of (necessarily isolated) singularities $\{z_1, z_2, \ldots, z_n\}$ of a single-valued function $f(z)$ continuous on C,

$$\frac{1}{2\pi i} \oint_C f(\xi) \, d\xi = \sum_{k=1}^{n} \text{Res}_f(z_k)$$

5.3.12 CONTINUITY OF INTEGRAL ANTIDERIVATIVES

Consider the following different evaluations of an integral

$$F(x) = \int f(x) \, dx = \int \frac{3}{5 - 4\cos x} \, dx = \begin{cases} 2\tan^{-1}(3\tan(x/2)) \\ 2\tan^{-1}(3\sin x/(\cos x + 1)) \\ -\tan^{-1}(-3\sin x/(5\cos x - 4)) \\ 2\tan^{-1}\left(3\tan\frac{x}{2}\right) + 2\pi \left\lfloor \frac{x}{2\pi} + \frac{1}{2} \right\rfloor \end{cases}$$

where $\lfloor \cdot \rfloor$ denotes the floor function. These evaluations are all "correct" because differentiating any of them results in the original integrand. However, if we expect that $\int_0^{4\pi} f(x) \, dx = F(4\pi) - F(0)$ is correct, then only the last evaluation is correct. This is true because the other evaluations of $F(x)$ are discontinuous when x is a multiple of π.

In general, if $\hat{F}(x) = \int^x f(x) \, dx$ is a discontinuous evaluation (with $\hat{F}(x)$ discontinuous at the single point $x = b$), then a continuous evaluation on a finite interval is given by $\int_a^c f(x) \, dx = F(c) - F(a)$, where

$$F(x) = \hat{F}(x) - \hat{F}(a) + H(x - b) \left[\lim_{x \to b-} \hat{F}(x) - \lim_{x \to b+} \hat{F}(x) \right]$$

and where $H(\cdot)$ is the Heaviside function. For functions with an infinite number of discontinuities, note that $\sum_{n=1}^{\infty} H(x - pn - q) = \left\lfloor \frac{x - q}{p} \right\rfloor$.

Applications of integration

- Using Green's theorems, the area bounded by the simple, closed, positively oriented contour $\mathcal{C}$ is

$$\text{area} = \oint_{\mathcal{C}} x\,dy = -\oint_{\mathcal{C}} y\,dx. \tag{5.3.19}$$

- Arc length:

  1. $s = \displaystyle\int_{x_1}^{x_2} \sqrt{1 + y'^2}\,dx$ for $y = f(x)$.

  2. $s = \displaystyle\int_{t_1}^{t_2} \sqrt{\dot{\phi}^2 + \dot{\psi}^2}\,dt$ for $x = \phi(t)$, $y = \psi(t)$.

  3. $s = \displaystyle\int_{\theta_1}^{\theta_2} \sqrt{r^2 + \left(\frac{dr}{d\phi}\right)^2}\,d\theta = \int_{r_1}^{r_2} \sqrt{1 + r^2 \left(\frac{dr}{d\phi}\right)^2}\,dr$ for $r = f(\theta)$.

- Surface area for surfaces of revolution:

  1. $A = 2\pi \displaystyle\int_{x_1}^{x_2} f(x)\sqrt{1 + (f'(x))^2}\,dx$ when $y = f(x)$ is rotated about the x-axis.

  2. $A = 2\pi \displaystyle\int_{y_1}^{y_2} x\sqrt{1 + (f'(x))^2}\,dy$ when $y = f(x)$ is rotated about the y-axis.

  3. $A = 2\pi \displaystyle\int_{t_1}^{t_2} \psi\sqrt{\dot{\phi}^2 + \dot{\psi}^2}\,dt$ for $x = \phi(t)$, $y = \psi(t)$ rotated about the x-axis.

  4. $A = 2\pi \displaystyle\int_{t_1}^{t_2} \phi\sqrt{\dot{\phi}^2 + \dot{\psi}^2}\,dt$ for $x = \phi(t)$, $y = \psi(t)$ rotated about the y-axis.

  5. $A = 2\pi \displaystyle\int_{\phi_1}^{\phi_2} r\sin\phi\sqrt{r^2 + \left(\frac{dr}{d\phi}\right)^2}\,d\phi$ for $r = r(\phi)$ rotated about the x-axis.

  6. $A = 2\pi \displaystyle\int_{\phi_1}^{\phi_2} r\cos\phi\sqrt{r^2 + \left(\frac{dr}{d\phi}\right)^2}\,d\phi$ for $r = r(\phi)$ rotated about the y-axis.

- Volumes of revolution:

  1. $V = \pi \displaystyle\int_{x_1}^{x_2} f^2(x)\,dx$ for $y = f(x)$ rotated about the x-axis.

  2. $V = \pi \displaystyle\int_{x_1}^{x_2} x^2 f'(x)\,dx$ for $y = f(x)$ rotated about the y-axis.

  3. $V = \pi \displaystyle\int_{y_1}^{y_2} g^2(y)\,dy$ for $x = g(y)$ rotated about the y-axis.

4. $V = \pi \int_{t_1}^{t_2} \psi^2 \dot{\phi} \, dt$ for $x = \phi(t)$, $y = \psi(t)$ rotated about the x-axis.

5. $V = \pi \int_{t_1}^{t_2} \phi^2 \dot{\psi} \, dt$ for $x = \phi(t)$, $y = \psi(t)$ rotated about the y-axis.

6. $V = \pi \int_{\phi_1}^{\phi_2} \sin^2 \phi \left(\frac{dr}{d\phi} \cos \phi - r \sin \phi \right) d\phi$ for $r = f(\phi)$ rotated about the x-axis.

7. $V = \pi \int_{\phi_1}^{\phi_2} \cos^2 \phi \left(\frac{dr}{d\phi} \sin \phi - r \cos \phi \right) d\phi$ for $r = f(\phi)$ rotated about the y-axis.

- The area enclosed by the curve defined by the equation $x^{b/c} + y^{b/c} = a^{b/c}$, where $a > 0$, c is an odd integer and b is an even integer, is given by $A = \dfrac{2ca^2}{b} \dfrac{\left[\Gamma \left(\frac{c}{b} \right) \right]^2}{\Gamma \left(\frac{2c}{b} \right)}$.

- The integral $I = \iiint_R x^{h-1} y^{m-1} z^{n-1} \, dV$, where R is the region of space bounded by the coordinate planes and that portion of the surface $\left(\frac{x}{a} \right)^p + \left(\frac{y}{b} \right)^q + \left(\frac{z}{c} \right)^k = 1$, in the first octant, and where $\{h, m, n, p, q, k, a, b, c\}$ are all positive real numbers, is given by

$$\int_0^a x^{h-1} \, dx \int_0^{b[1-(\frac{x}{a})^p]^{\frac{1}{q}}} y^{m-1} \, dy \int_0^{c[1-(\frac{x}{a})^p-(\frac{y}{b})^q]^{\frac{1}{k}}} z^{n-1} \, dz$$

$$= \frac{a^h b^m c^n}{pqk} \frac{\Gamma \left(\frac{h}{p} \right) \Gamma \left(\frac{m}{q} \right) \Gamma \left(\frac{n}{k} \right)}{\Gamma \left(\frac{h}{p} + \frac{m}{q} + \frac{n}{k} + 1 \right)}.$$

5.3.13 ASYMPTOTIC INTEGRAL EVALUATION

Laplace's method: If $f'(x_0) = 0$, $f''(x_0) < 0$, and $\lambda \to \infty$, then

$$I_{x_0,\epsilon}(\lambda) \equiv \int_{x_0-\epsilon}^{x_0+\epsilon} g(x) e^{\lambda f(x)} \, dx \sim g(x_0) e^{\lambda f(x_0)} \left[\sqrt{\frac{2\pi}{\lambda |f''(x_0)|}} \right] + \dots \tag{5.3.20}$$

Hence, if points of local maximum $\{x_i\}$ satisfy $f'(x_i) = 0$ and $f''(x_i) < 0$, then $\int_{-\infty}^{\infty} g(x) e^{\lambda f(x)} \, dx \sim \sum_i I_{x_i,\epsilon}(\lambda)$.

Method of stationary phase: If $f(x_0) \neq 0$, $f'(x_0) = 0$, $f''(x_0) \neq 0$, $g(x_0) \neq 0$, and $\lambda \to \infty$, then

$$J_{x_0,\epsilon}(\lambda) = \int_{x_0-\epsilon}^{x_0+\epsilon} g(x) e^{i\lambda f(x)} \, dx$$

$$\sim g(x_0) \sqrt{\frac{2\pi}{\lambda |f''(x_0)|}} \left[i\lambda f(x_0) - \frac{i\pi}{4} \operatorname{sgn} f''(x_0) \right] + \dots \tag{5.3.21}$$

5.3.14   MOMENTS OF INERTIA FOR VARIOUS BODIES

Body	Axis	Moment of inertia
Uniform thin rod	Normal to the length, at one end	$m\frac{l^2}{3}$
Uniform thin rod	Normal to the length, at the center	$m\frac{l^2}{12}$
Thin rectangular sheet, sides a and b	Through the center parallel to b	$m\frac{a^2}{12}$
Thin rectangular sheet, sides a and b	Through the center perpendicular to the sheet	$m\frac{a^2+b^2}{12}$
Thin circular sheet of radius r	Normal to the plate through the center	$m\frac{r^2}{2}$
Thin circular sheet of radius r	Along any diameter	$m\frac{r^2}{4}$
Thin circular ring, radii r_1 and r_2	Through center normal to plane of ring	$m\frac{r_1^2+r_2^2}{2}$
Thin circular ring, radii r_1 and r_2	Along any diameter	$m\frac{r_1^2+r_2^2}{4}$
Rectangular parallelopiped, edges a, b, and c	Through center perpendicular to face ab (parallel to edge c)	$m\frac{a^2+b^2}{12}$
Sphere, radius r	Any diameter	$m\frac{2}{5}r^2$
Spherical shell, external radius r_1, internal radius r_2	Any diameter	$m\frac{2}{5}\frac{r_1^5-r_2^5}{r_1^3-r_2^3}$
Spherical shell, very thin, mean radius r	Any diameter	$m\frac{2}{3}r^3$
Right circular cylinder of radius r, length l	Longitudinal axis of the slide	$m\frac{r^2}{2}$
Right circular cylinder of radius r, length l	Transverse diameter	$m\left(\frac{r^2}{4}+\frac{l^2}{12}\right)$
Hollow circular cylinder, radii r_1 and r_2, length l	Longitudinal axis of the figure	$m\frac{r_1^2+r_2^2}{2}$
Thin cylindrical shell, length l, mean radius r	Longitudinal axis of the figure	mr^2
Hollow circular cylinder, radii r_1 and r_2, length l	Transverse diameter	$m\left(\frac{r_1^2+r_2^2}{4}+\frac{l^2}{12}\right)$
Hollow circular cylinder, very thin, length l, mean radius r	Transverse diameter	$m\left(\frac{r^2}{2}+\frac{l^2}{12}\right)$
Elliptic cylinder, length l, transverse semiaxes a and b	Longitudinal axis	$m\left(\frac{a^2+b^2}{4}\right)$
Right cone, altitude h, radius of base r	Axis of the figure	$m\frac{3}{10}r^2$
Spheroid of revolution, equatorial radius r	Polar axis	$m\frac{2}{5}r^2$
Ellipsoid, axes $2a$, $2b$, $2c$	Axis $2a$	$m\frac{b^2+c^2}{5}$

5.3.15   TABLE OF SEMI-INTEGRALS

f	$\dfrac{d^{-1/2} f}{dx^{-1/2}}$
0	0
C, a constant	$2C\sqrt{\frac{x}{\pi}}$
$x^{-1/2}$	$\sqrt{\pi}$
x	$\dfrac{4x^{2/3}}{3\sqrt{\pi}}$
$x^n,\ n = 0, 1, 2, \ldots$	$\dfrac{(n!)^2 (4x)^{n+1/2}}{(2n+1)!\sqrt{\pi}}$
$x^p,\ p > -1$	$\dfrac{\Gamma(p+1)}{\Gamma(p+\frac{3}{2})} x^{p+1/2}$
$\sqrt{1+x}$	$\sqrt{\frac{x}{\pi}} + \dfrac{(1+x)\tan^{-1}\left(\sqrt{x}\right)}{\sqrt{\pi}}$
$\dfrac{1}{\sqrt{1+x}}$	$\dfrac{2}{\sqrt{\pi}} \tan^{-1}\left(\sqrt{x}\right)$
$\dfrac{1}{1+x}$	$\dfrac{2\sinh^{-1}\left(\sqrt{x}\right)}{\sqrt{\pi(1+x)}}$
e^x	$e^x \operatorname{erf}\left(\sqrt{x}\right)$
$e^x \operatorname{erf}\left(\sqrt{x}\right)$	$e^x - 1$
$\sin\left(\sqrt{x}\right)$	$\sqrt{\pi x}\, J_1\left(\sqrt{x}\right)$
$\cos\left(\sqrt{x}\right)$	$\sqrt{\pi x}\, H_{-1}\left(\sqrt{x}\right)$
$\sinh\left(\sqrt{x}\right)$	$\sqrt{\pi x}\, I_1\left(\sqrt{x}\right)$
$\cosh\left(\sqrt{x}\right)$	$\sqrt{\pi x}\, L_{-1}\left(\sqrt{x}\right)$
$\dfrac{\sin\left(\sqrt{x}\right)}{\sqrt{x}}$	$\sqrt{\pi}\, H_0\left(\sqrt{x}\right)$
$\dfrac{\cos\left(\sqrt{x}\right)}{\sqrt{x}}$	$\sqrt{\pi}\, J_0\left(\sqrt{x}\right)$
$\log x$	$2\sqrt{\frac{x}{\pi}}\left[\log(4x) - 2\right]$
$\dfrac{\log x}{\sqrt{x}}$	$\sqrt{\pi}\,\log\left(\frac{x}{4}\right)$

5.3.16   TABLES OF INTEGRALS

Many extensive compilations of integrals tables exist. No matter how extensive the integral table, it is fairly uncommon to find the exact integral desired. Usually some form of transformation will have to be made. The simplest type of transformation is substitution. Simple forms of substitutions, such as $y = ax$ are employed, almost unconsciously, by experienced users of integral tables. Finding the right substitution is largely a matter of intuition and experience.

We adopt the following conventions in our integral tables:

- A constant of integration must be included with all indefinite integrals.

- All angles are measured in radians, and inverse trigonometric and hyperbolic functions represent principal values.

- Logarithmic expressions are to base $e = 2.71828\ldots$, unless otherwise specified, and are to be evaluated for the absolute value of the arguments involved therein.

- When inverse trigonometric functions occur in the integrals, be sure that any replacements made for them are strictly in accordance with the rules for such functions. This causes little difficulty when the argument of the inverse trigonometric function is positive, because all angles involved are in the first quadrant. However, if the argument is negative, special care must be used. Thus, if $u > 0$ then

$$\sin^{-1} u = \cos^{-1} \sqrt{1 - u^2} = \csc^{-1} \frac{1}{u} = \ldots.$$

However, if $u < 0$, then

$$\sin^{-1} u = -\cos^{-1} \sqrt{1 - u^2} = -\pi - \csc^{-1} \frac{1}{u} = \ldots.$$

The following sections contain tables of indefinite and definite integrals.

5.4 TABLE OF INDEFINITE INTEGRALS

All integrals listed below that do not have stars next to their numbers have been verified by computer. Note that the natural logarithm function is denoted as $\log x$.

5.4.1 ELEMENTARY FORMS

1. $\displaystyle\int a\, dx = ax.$

2. * $\displaystyle\int a\, f(x)\, dx = a \int f(x)\, dx.$

3. * $\displaystyle\int \phi(y(x))\, dx = \int \frac{\phi(y)}{y'}\, dy,$ where $y' = \frac{dy}{dx}.$

4. * $\displaystyle\int (u + v)\, dx = \int u\, dx + \int v\, dx,$ where u and v are any functions of $x.$

5. * $\displaystyle\int u\, dv = u \int dv - \int v\, du = uv - \int v\, du.$

6. * $\displaystyle\int u \frac{dv}{dx}\, dx = uv - \int v \frac{du}{dx}\, dx.$

7. $\displaystyle\int x^n\, dx = \frac{x^{n+1}}{n+1},$ except when $n = -1.$

8. $\displaystyle\int \frac{dx}{x} = \log x.$

9. $* \int \dfrac{f'(x)}{f(x)}\, dx = \log f(x), \ (df(x) = f'(x)\, dx).$

10. $* \int \dfrac{f'(x)}{2\sqrt{f(x)}}\, dx = \sqrt{f(x)}, \ (df(x) = f'(x)\, dx).$

11. $\int e^x \, dx = e^x.$

12. $\int e^{ax} \, dx = \dfrac{e^{ax}}{a}.$

13. $\int b^{ax} \, dx = \dfrac{b^{ax}}{a \log b}, \ \ b > 0.$

14. $\int \log x \, dx = x \log x - x.$

15. $\int a^x \, dx = \dfrac{a^x}{\log a}, \ \ a > 0.$

16. $\int \dfrac{dx}{a^2 + x^2} = \dfrac{1}{a} \tan^{-1} \dfrac{x}{a}.$

17. $\int \dfrac{dx}{a^2 - x^2} = \begin{cases} \dfrac{1}{a} \tanh^{-1} \dfrac{x}{a}, \\ \quad \text{or} \\ \dfrac{1}{2a} \log \dfrac{a+x}{a-x}, \end{cases} \ a^2 > x^2.$

18. $\int \dfrac{dx}{x^2 - a^2} = \begin{cases} -\dfrac{1}{a} \coth^{-1} \dfrac{x}{a}, \\ \quad \text{or} \\ \dfrac{1}{2a} \log \dfrac{x-a}{x+a}, \end{cases} \ x^2 > a^2.$

19. $\int \dfrac{dx}{\sqrt{a^2 - x^2}} = \begin{cases} \sin^{-1} \dfrac{x}{|a|}, \\ \quad \text{or} \\ -\cos^{-1} \dfrac{x}{|a|}, \end{cases} \ a^2 > x^2.$

20. $\int \dfrac{dx}{\sqrt{x^2 \pm a^2}} = \log\left(x + \sqrt{x^2 \pm a^2}\right).$

21. $\int \dfrac{dx}{x\sqrt{x^2 - a^2}} = \dfrac{1}{|a|} \sec^{-1} \dfrac{x}{a}.$

22. $\int \dfrac{dx}{x\sqrt{a^2 \pm x^2}} = -\dfrac{1}{a} \log\left(\dfrac{a + \sqrt{a^2 \pm x^2}}{x}\right).$

5.4.2   FORMS CONTAINING $a + bx$

23. $\int (a + bx)^n \, dx = \dfrac{(a + bx)^{n+1}}{(n + 1)b}, \ \ n \neq -1.$

24. $\int x(a + bx)^n \, dx = \dfrac{1}{b^2(n + 2)} (a + bx)^{n+2} - \dfrac{a}{b^2(n + 1)} (a + bx)^{n+1}, \ \ n \neq -1, \ n \neq -2.$

25. $\int x^2 (a + bx)^n \, dx = \dfrac{1}{b^3} \left[\dfrac{(a + bx)^{n+3}}{n + 3} - 2a \dfrac{(a + bx)^{n+2}}{n + 2} + a^2 \dfrac{(a + bx)^{n+1}}{n + 1} \right], \ \ n \neq -1,$
$n \neq -2, \ n \neq -3.$

26. $\displaystyle\int x^m (a + bx)^n \, dx =$

$$\begin{cases} \dfrac{x^{m+1}(a + bx)^n}{m + n + 1} + \dfrac{an}{m + n + 1}\displaystyle\int x^m (a + bx)^{n-1} \, dx, \\[2mm] \text{or} \\[2mm] \dfrac{1}{a(n + 1)}\left[-x^{m+1}(a + bx)^{n+1} + (m + n + 2)\displaystyle\int x^m (a + bx)^{n+1} \, dx \right], \\[2mm] \text{or} \\[2mm] \dfrac{1}{b(m + n + 1)}\left[x^m (a + bx)^{n+1} - ma\displaystyle\int x^{m-1}(a + bx)^n \, dx \right]. \end{cases}$$

27. $\displaystyle\int \frac{dx}{a + bx} = \frac{1}{b}\log |(a + bx)|.$

28. $\displaystyle\int \frac{dx}{(a + bx)^2} = -\frac{1}{b(a + bx)}.$

29. $\displaystyle\int \frac{dx}{(a + bx)^3} = -\frac{1}{2b(a + bx)^2}.$

30. $\displaystyle\int \frac{x}{a + bx}\, dx = \begin{cases} \dfrac{1}{b^2}\left[a + bx - a\log(a + bx) \right], \\[2mm] \text{or} \\[2mm] \dfrac{x}{b} - \dfrac{a}{b^2}\log(a + bx). \end{cases}$

31. $\displaystyle\int \frac{x}{(a + bx)^2}\, dx = \frac{1}{b^2}\left[\log(a + bx) + \frac{a}{a + bx} \right].$

32. $\displaystyle\int \frac{x}{(a + bx)^n}\, dx = \frac{1}{b^2}\left[\frac{-1}{(n - 2)(a + bx)^{n-2}} + \frac{a}{(n - 1)(a + bx)^{n-1}} \right], \quad n \neq 1,\ n \neq 2.$

33. $\displaystyle\int \frac{x^2}{a + bx}\, dx = \frac{1}{b^3}\left(\frac{1}{2}(a + bx)^2 - 2a(a + bx) + a^2\log(a + bx) \right).$

34. $\displaystyle\int \frac{x^2}{(a + bx)^2}\, dx = \frac{1}{b^3}\left(a + bx - 2a\log(a + bx) - \frac{a^2}{a + bx} \right).$

35. $\displaystyle\int \frac{x^2}{(a + bx)^3}\, dx = \frac{1}{b^3}\left(\log(a + bx) + \frac{2a}{a + bx} - \frac{a^2}{2(a + bx)^2} \right).$

36. $\displaystyle\int \frac{x^2}{(a + bx)^n}\, dx = \frac{1}{b^3}\left[\frac{-1}{(n - 3)(a + bx)^{n-3}} + \frac{2a}{(n - 2)(a + bx)^{n-2}} \right.$
$$\left. - \frac{a^2}{(n - 1)(a + bx)^{n-1}} \right], \quad n \neq 1,\ n \neq 2,\ n \neq 3.$$

37. $\displaystyle\int \frac{dx}{x(a + bx)} = -\frac{1}{a}\log \frac{a + bx}{x}.$

38. $\displaystyle\int \frac{dx}{x(a + bx)^2} = \frac{1}{a(a + bx)} - \frac{1}{a^2}\log \frac{a + bx}{x}.$

39. $\displaystyle\int \frac{dx}{x(a + bx)^3} = \frac{1}{a^3}\left[\frac{1}{2}\left(\frac{2a + bx}{a + bx} \right)^2 - \log \frac{a + bx}{x} \right].$

40. $\displaystyle\int \frac{dx}{x^2(a + bx)} = -\frac{1}{ax} + \frac{b}{a^2}\log \frac{a + bx}{x}.$

41. $\displaystyle\int \frac{dx}{x^3(a + bx)} = \frac{2bx - a}{2a^2x^2} + \frac{b^2}{a^3}\log \frac{x}{a + bx}.$

42. $\displaystyle\int \frac{dx}{x^2(a + bx)^2} = -\frac{a + 2bx}{a^2x(a + bx)} + \frac{2b}{a^3}\log \frac{a + bx}{x}.$

5.4.3 FORMS CONTAINING $c^2 \pm x^2$ AND $x^2 - c^2$

43. $\displaystyle\int \frac{dx}{c^2 + x^2} = \frac{1}{c} \tan^{-1} \frac{x}{c}.$

44. $\displaystyle\int \frac{dx}{c^2 - x^2} = \frac{1}{2c} \log \frac{c + x}{c - x}, \quad c^2 > x^2.$

45. $\displaystyle\int \frac{dx}{x^2 - c^2} = \frac{1}{2c} \log \frac{x - c}{x + c}, \quad x^2 > c^2.$

46. $\displaystyle\int \frac{x}{c^2 \pm x^2} \, dx = \pm\frac{1}{2} \log (c^2 \pm x^2).$

47. $\displaystyle\int \frac{x}{(c^2 \pm x^2)^{n+1}} \, dx = \mp \frac{1}{2n(c^2 \pm x^2)^n}.$

48. $\displaystyle\int \frac{dx}{(c^2 \pm x^2)^n} = \frac{1}{2c^2(n-1)} \left[\frac{x}{(c^2 \pm x^2)^{n-1}} + (2n - 3) \int \frac{dx}{(c^2 \pm x^2)^{n-1}} \right].$

49. $\displaystyle\int \frac{dx}{(x^2 - c^2)^n} = \frac{1}{2c^2(n-1)} \left[-\frac{x}{(x^2 - c^2)^{n-1}} - (2n - 3) \int \frac{dx}{(x^2 - c^2)^{n-1}} \right].$

50. $\displaystyle\int \frac{x}{x^2 - c^2} \, dx = \frac{1}{2} \log (x^2 - c^2).$

51. $\displaystyle\int \frac{x}{(x^2 - c^2)^{n+1}} \, dx = -\frac{1}{2n(x^2 - c^2)^n}.$

5.4.4 FORMS CONTAINING $a + bx$ AND $c + dx$

$u = a + bx, \quad v = c + dx, \quad$ and $k = ad - bc. \quad$ (If $k = 0$, then $v = (c/a)u$.)

52. $\displaystyle\int \frac{dx}{uv} = \frac{1}{k} \log \left(\frac{v}{u} \right).$

53. $\displaystyle\int \frac{x}{uv} \, dx = \frac{1}{k} \left(\frac{a}{b} \log u - \frac{c}{d} \log v \right).$

54. $\displaystyle\int \frac{dx}{u^2 v} = \frac{1}{k} \left(\frac{1}{u} + \frac{d}{k} \log \frac{v}{u} \right).$

55. $\displaystyle\int \frac{x}{u^2 v} \, dx = -\frac{a}{bku} - \frac{c}{k^2} \log \frac{v}{u}.$

56. $\displaystyle\int \frac{x^2}{u^2 v} \, dx = \frac{a^2}{b^2 ku} + \frac{1}{k^2} \left(\frac{c^2}{d} \log v + \frac{a(k - bc)}{b^2} \log u \right).$

57. $\displaystyle\int \frac{dx}{u^n v^m} = \frac{1}{k(m-1)} \left[\frac{-1}{u^{n-1} v^{m-1}} - b(m + n - 2) \int \frac{dx}{u^n v^{m-1}} \right].$

58. $\displaystyle\int \frac{u}{v} \, dx = \frac{bx}{d} + \frac{k}{d^2} \log v.$

59. $\displaystyle\int \frac{u^m}{v^n} \, dx = \begin{cases} -\dfrac{1}{k(n-1)} \left[\dfrac{u^{m+1}}{v^{n-1}} + b(n - m - 2) \displaystyle\int \dfrac{u^m}{v^{n-1}} \, dx \right], \\[4pt] \text{or} \\[4pt] -\dfrac{1}{d(n - m - 1)} \left[\dfrac{u^m}{v^{n-1}} + mk \displaystyle\int \dfrac{u^{m-1}}{v^n} \, dx \right], \\[4pt] \text{or} \\[4pt] -\dfrac{1}{d(n-1)} \left[\dfrac{u^m}{v^{n-1}} - mb \displaystyle\int \dfrac{u^{m-1}}{v^{n-1}} \, dx \right]. \end{cases}$

5.4.5   FORMS CONTAINING $a + bx^n$

60. $\displaystyle\int \frac{dx}{a + bx^2} = \frac{1}{\sqrt{ab}}\tan^{-1}\frac{x\sqrt{ab}}{a}, \quad ab > 0.$

61. $\displaystyle\int \frac{dx}{a + bx^2} = \begin{cases} \dfrac{1}{2\sqrt{-ab}}\log\dfrac{a + x\sqrt{-ab}}{a - x\sqrt{-ab}}, & ab < 0, \\[2ex] \text{or} \\[1ex] \dfrac{1}{\sqrt{-ab}}\tanh^{-1}\dfrac{x\sqrt{-ab}}{a}, & ab < 0. \end{cases}$

62. $\displaystyle\int \frac{dx}{a^2 + b^2 x^2}\,dx = \frac{1}{ab}\tan^{-1}\frac{bx}{a}.$

63. $\displaystyle\int \frac{x}{a + bx^2}\,dx = \frac{1}{2b}\log(a + bx^2).$

64. $\displaystyle\int \frac{x^2}{a + bx^2}\,dx = \frac{x}{b} - \frac{a}{b}\int \frac{dx}{a + bx^2}.$

65. $\displaystyle\int \frac{dx}{(a + bx^2)^2} = \frac{x}{2a(a + bx^2)} + \frac{1}{2a}\int \frac{dx}{a + bx^2}.$

66. $\displaystyle\int \frac{dx}{a^2 - b^2 x^2} = \frac{1}{2ab}\log\frac{a + bx}{a - bx}.$

67. $\displaystyle\int \frac{dx}{(a + bx^2)^{m+1}} =$
$\begin{cases} \dfrac{1}{2ma}\dfrac{x}{(a + bx^2)^m} + \dfrac{2m - 1}{2ma}\displaystyle\int \dfrac{dx}{(a + bx^2)^m}, \\[2ex] \text{or} \\[1ex] \dfrac{(2m)!}{(m!)^2}\left[\dfrac{x}{2a}\displaystyle\sum_{r=1}^{m}\dfrac{r!(r - 1)!}{(4a)^{m-r}(2r)!(a + bx^2)^r} + \dfrac{1}{(4a)^m}\displaystyle\int \dfrac{dx}{a + bx^2}\right]. \end{cases}$

68. $\displaystyle\int \frac{x\,dx}{(a + bx^2)^{m+1}} = -\frac{1}{2bm(a + bx^2)^m}.$

69. $\displaystyle\int \frac{x^2\,dx}{(a + bx^2)^{m+1}} = -\frac{x}{2mb(a + bx^2)^m} + \frac{1}{2mb}\int \frac{dx}{(a + bx^2)^m}.$

70. $\displaystyle\int \frac{dx}{x(a + bx^2)} = \frac{1}{2a}\log\frac{x^2}{a + bx^2}.$

71. $\displaystyle\int \frac{dx}{x^2(a + bx^2)} = -\frac{1}{ax} - \frac{b}{a}\int \frac{dx}{a + bx^2}.$

72. $\displaystyle\int \frac{dx}{x\left(a + bx^2\right)^{m+1}} = \begin{cases} \dfrac{1}{2am(a + bx^2)^m} + \dfrac{1}{a}\displaystyle\int \dfrac{dx}{x\left(a + bx^2\right)^m}, \\[2ex] \text{or} \\[1ex] \dfrac{1}{2a^{m+1}}\left[\displaystyle\sum_{r=1}^{m}\dfrac{a^r}{r(a + bx^2)^r} + \log\dfrac{x^2}{a + bx^2}\right]. \end{cases}$

73. $\displaystyle\int \frac{dx}{x^2\left(a + bx^2\right)^{m+1}} = \frac{1}{a}\int \frac{dx}{x^2(a + bx^2)^m} - \frac{b}{a}\int \frac{dx}{(a + bx^2)^{m+1}}.$

74. $\displaystyle\int \frac{dx}{a + bx^3} = \frac{k}{3a}\left[\frac{1}{2}\log\frac{(k + x)^3}{a + bx^3} + \sqrt{3}\tan^{-1}\frac{2x - k}{k\sqrt{3}}\right], \quad k = \sqrt[3]{\frac{a}{b}}.$

75. $\displaystyle\int \frac{x\,dx}{a + bx^3} = \frac{1}{3bk}\left[\frac{1}{2}\log\frac{a + bx^3}{(k + x)^3} + \sqrt{3}\tan^{-1}\frac{2x - k}{k\sqrt{3}}\right], \quad k = \sqrt[3]{\frac{a}{b}}.$

76. $\displaystyle\int \frac{x^2\,dx}{a+bx^3} = \frac{1}{3b}\log a+bx^3.$

77. $*\displaystyle\int \frac{dx}{a+bx^4} =$

$$\begin{cases} \dfrac{k}{2a}\left[\dfrac{1}{2}\log\dfrac{x^2+2kx+2k^2}{x^2-2kx+2k^2} + \tan^{-1}\dfrac{2kx}{2k^2-x^2}\right], & ab>0,\ k=\left(\dfrac{a}{4b}\right)^{1/4}, \\[4pt] \text{or} \\[4pt] \dfrac{k}{2a}\left[\dfrac{1}{2}\log\dfrac{x+k}{x-k} + \tan^{-1}\dfrac{x}{k}\right], & ab<0,\ k=\left(-\dfrac{a}{b}\right)^{1/4}. \end{cases}$$

78. $\displaystyle\int \frac{x}{a+bx^4}\,dx = \frac{1}{2bk}\tan^{-1}\frac{x^2}{k},\ \ ab>0,\ k=\sqrt{\frac{a}{b}}.$

79. $\displaystyle\int \frac{x}{a+bx^4}\,dx = \frac{1}{4bk}\log\frac{x^2-k}{x^2+k},\ \ ab<0,\ k=\sqrt{-\frac{a}{b}}.$

80. $\displaystyle\int \frac{x^2}{a+bx^4}\,dx = \frac{1}{4bk}\left[\frac{1}{2}\log\frac{x^2-2kx+2k^2}{x^2+2kx+2k^2} + \tan^{-1}\frac{2kx}{2k^2-x^2}\right],$

$ab>0,\ k=\left(\frac{a}{4b}\right)^{1/4}.$

81. $\displaystyle\int \frac{x^2\,dx}{a+bx^4} = \frac{1}{4bk}\left[\log\frac{x-k}{x+k} + 2\tan^{-1}\frac{x}{k}\right],\ \ ab<0,\ k=\sqrt[4]{-\frac{a}{b}}.$

82. $\displaystyle\int \frac{x^3\,dx}{a+bx^4} = \frac{1}{4b}\log\left(a+bx^4\right).$

83. $\displaystyle\int \frac{dx}{x(a+bx^n)} = \frac{1}{an}\log\frac{x^n}{a+bx^n}.$

84. $\displaystyle\int \frac{dx}{(a+bx^n)^{m+1}} = \frac{1}{a}\int \frac{dx}{(a+bx^n)^m} - \frac{b}{a}\int \frac{x^n\,dx}{(a+bx^n)^{m+1}}.$

85. $\displaystyle\int \frac{x^m\,dx}{(a+bx^n)^{p+1}} = \frac{1}{b}\int \frac{x^{m-n}\,dx}{(a+bx^n)^p} - \frac{a}{b}\int \frac{x^{m-n}\,dx}{(a+bx^n)^{p+1}}.$

86. $\displaystyle\int \frac{dx}{x^m(a+bx^n)^{p+1}} = \frac{1}{a}\int \frac{dx}{x^m(a+bx^n)^p} - \frac{b}{a}\int \frac{dx}{x^{m-n}(a+bx^n)^{p+1}}.$

87. $\displaystyle\int x^m(a+bx^n)^p\,dx =$

$$\begin{cases} \dfrac{1}{b(np+m+1)}\left[x^{m-n+1}(a+bx^n)^{p+1} - a(m-n+1)\int x^{m-n}(a+bx^n)^p\,dx\right], \\[4pt] \text{or} \\[4pt] \dfrac{1}{np+m+1}\left[x^{m+1}(a+bx^n)^p + anp\int x^m(a+bx^n)^{p-1}\,dx\right], \\[4pt] \text{or} \\[4pt] \dfrac{1}{a(m+1)}\left[x^{m+1}(a+bx^n)^{p+1} - b(m+1+np+n)\int x^{m+n}(a+bx^n)^p\,dx\right], \\[4pt] \text{or} \\[4pt] \dfrac{1}{an(p+1)}\left[-x^{m+1}(a+bx^n)^{p+1} + (m+1+np+n)\int x^m(a+bx^n)^{p+1}\,dx\right]. \end{cases}$$

5.4.6   FORMS CONTAINING $c^3 \pm x^3$

88. $\displaystyle\int \frac{dx}{c^3\pm x^3} = \pm\frac{1}{6c^2}\log\left(\frac{(c\pm x)^3}{c^3\pm x^3}\right) + \frac{1}{c^2\sqrt{3}}\tan^{-1}\frac{2x\mp c}{c\sqrt{3}}.$

89. $\int \dfrac{dx}{(c^3 \pm x^3)^2} = \dfrac{x}{3c^3(c^3 \pm x^3)} + \dfrac{2}{3c^3} \int \dfrac{dx}{c^3 \pm x^3}$.

90. $\int \dfrac{dx}{(c^3 \pm x^3)^{n+1}} = \dfrac{1}{3nc^3} \left[\dfrac{x}{(c^3 \pm x^3)^n} + (3n - 1) \int \dfrac{dx}{(c^3 \pm x^3)^n} \right]$.

91. $\int \dfrac{x\, dx}{c^3 \pm x^3} = \dfrac{1}{6c} \log \dfrac{c^3 \pm x^3}{(c \pm x)^3} \pm \dfrac{1}{c\sqrt{3}} \tan^{-1} \dfrac{2x \mp c}{c\sqrt{3}}$.

92. $\int \dfrac{x\, dx}{(c^3 \pm x^3)^2} = \dfrac{x^2}{3c^3(c^3 \pm x^3)} + \dfrac{1}{3c^3} \int \dfrac{x\, dx}{c^3 \pm x^3}$.

93. $\int \dfrac{x\, dx}{(c^3 \pm x^3)^{n+1}} = \dfrac{1}{3nc^3} \left[\dfrac{x^2}{(c^3 \pm x^3)^n} + (3n - 2) \int \dfrac{x\, dx}{(c^3 \pm x^3)^n} \right]$.

94. $\int \dfrac{x^2\, dx}{c^3 \pm x^3} = \pm \dfrac{1}{3} \log (c^3 \pm x^3)$.

95. $\int \dfrac{x^2\, dx}{(c^3 \pm x^3)^{n+1}} = \mp \dfrac{1}{3n(c^3 \pm x^3)^n}$.

96. $\int \dfrac{dx}{x(c^3 \pm x^3)} = \dfrac{1}{3c^3} \log \dfrac{x^3}{c^3 \pm x^3}$.

97. $\int \dfrac{dx}{x(c^3 \pm x^3)^2} = \dfrac{1}{3c^3(c^3 \pm x^3)} + \dfrac{1}{3c^6} \log \dfrac{x^3}{c^3 \pm x^3}$.

98. $\int \dfrac{dx}{x(c^3 \pm x^3)^{n+1}} = \dfrac{1}{3nc^3(c^3 \pm x^3)^n} + \dfrac{1}{c^3} \int \dfrac{dx}{x(c^3 \pm x^3)^n}$.

99. $\int \dfrac{dx}{x^2(c^3 \pm x^3)} = -\dfrac{1}{c^3 x} \mp \dfrac{1}{c^3} \int \dfrac{x\, dx}{(c^3 \pm x^3)}$.

100. $\int \dfrac{dx}{x^2(c^3 \pm x^3)^{n+1}} = \dfrac{1}{c^3} \int \dfrac{dx}{x^2(c^3 \pm x^3)^n} \mp \dfrac{1}{c^3} \int \dfrac{x\, dx}{(c^3 \pm x^3)^{n+1}}$.

5.4.7   FORMS CONTAINING $c^4 \pm x^4$

101. $\int \dfrac{dx}{c^4 + x^4} = \dfrac{1}{2c^3\sqrt{2}} \left[\dfrac{1}{2} \log \left(\dfrac{x^2 + cx\sqrt{2} + c^2}{x^2 - cx\sqrt{2} + c^2} \right) + \tan^{-1} \dfrac{cx\sqrt{2}}{c^2 - x^2} \right]$.

102. $\int \dfrac{dx}{c^4 - x^4} = \dfrac{1}{2c^3} \left[\dfrac{1}{2} \log \dfrac{c + x}{c - x} + \tan^{-1} \dfrac{x}{c} \right]$.

103. $\int \dfrac{x\, dx}{c^4 + x^4} = \dfrac{1}{2c^2} \tan^{-1} \dfrac{x^2}{c^2}$.

104. $\int \dfrac{x\, dx}{c^4 - x^4} = \dfrac{1}{4c^2} \log \dfrac{c^2 + x^2}{c^2 - x^2}$.

105. $\int \dfrac{x^2\, dx}{c^4 + x^4} = \dfrac{1}{2c\sqrt{2}} \left[\dfrac{1}{2} \log \left(\dfrac{x^2 - cx\sqrt{2} + c^2}{x^2 + cx\sqrt{2} + c^2} \right) + \tan^{-1} \dfrac{cx\sqrt{2}}{c^2 - x^2} \right]$.

106. $\int \dfrac{x^2\, dx}{c^4 - x^4} = \dfrac{1}{2c} \left[\dfrac{1}{2} \log \dfrac{c + x}{c - x} - \tan^{-1} \dfrac{x}{c} \right]$.

107. $\int \dfrac{x^3\, dx}{c^4 \pm x^4} = \pm \dfrac{1}{4} \log (c^4 \pm x^4)$.

5.4.8   FORMS CONTAINING $a + bx + cx^2$

$$X = a + bx + cx^2 \quad \text{and} \quad q = 4ac - b^2.$$

If $q = 0$, then $X = c\left(x + \frac{b}{2c}\right)^2$ and other formulae should be used.

108. $\displaystyle \int \frac{dx}{X} = \begin{cases} \dfrac{2}{\sqrt{q}} \tan^{-1} \dfrac{2cx+b}{\sqrt{q}}, & q > 0, \\ \text{or} \\ \dfrac{-2}{\sqrt{-q}} \tanh^{-1} \dfrac{2cx+b}{\sqrt{-q}}, & q < 0, \\ \text{or} \\ \dfrac{1}{\sqrt{-q}} \log \dfrac{2cx+b-\sqrt{-q}}{2cx+b+\sqrt{-q}}, & q < 0. \end{cases}$

109. $\displaystyle \int \frac{dx}{X^2} = \frac{2cx+b}{qX} + \frac{2c}{q}\int \frac{dx}{X}.$

110. $\displaystyle \int \frac{dx}{X^3} = \frac{2cx+b}{q}\left(\frac{1}{2X^2} + \frac{3c}{qX}\right) + \frac{6c^2}{q^2}\int \frac{dx}{X}.$

111. $\displaystyle \int \frac{dx}{X^{n+1}} = \begin{cases} \dfrac{2cx+b}{nq\,X^n} + \dfrac{2(2n-1)c}{qn}\int \dfrac{dx}{X^n}, \\ \text{or} \\ \dfrac{(2n)!}{(n!)^2}\left(\dfrac{c}{q}\right)^n\left[\dfrac{2cx+b}{q}\sum_{r=1}^{n}\left(\dfrac{q}{cX}\right)^r\left(\dfrac{(r-1)!r!}{(2r)!}\right) + \int \dfrac{dx}{X}\right]. \end{cases}$

112. $\displaystyle \int \frac{x\,dx}{X} = \frac{1}{2c}\log X - \frac{b}{2c}\int \frac{dx}{X}.$

113. $\displaystyle \int \frac{x\,dx}{X^2} = -\frac{bx+2a}{qX} - \frac{b}{q}\int \frac{dx}{X}.$

114. $\displaystyle \int \frac{x\,dx}{X^{n+1}} = -\frac{2a+bx}{nq\,X^n} - \frac{b(2n-1)}{nq}\int \frac{dx}{X^n}.$

115. $\displaystyle \int \frac{x^2\,dx}{X} = \frac{x}{c} - \frac{b}{2c^2}\log X + \frac{b^2-2ac}{2c^2}\int \frac{dx}{X}.$

116. $\displaystyle \int \frac{x^2\,dx}{X^2} = \frac{(b^2-2ac)x+ab}{cqX} + \frac{2a}{q}\int \frac{dx}{X}.$

117. $\displaystyle \int \frac{x^m\,dx}{X^{n+1}} = -\frac{x^{m-1}}{(2n-m+1)cX^n} - \frac{n-m+1}{2n-m+1}\frac{b}{c}\int \frac{x^{m-1}}{X^{n+1}}\,dx$
$$+ \frac{m-1}{2n-m+1}\frac{a}{c}\int \frac{x^{m-2}}{X^{n+1}}\,dx.$$

118. $\displaystyle \int \frac{dx}{xX} = \frac{1}{2a}\log \frac{x^2}{X} - \frac{b}{2a}\int \frac{dx}{X}.$

119. $\displaystyle \int \frac{dx}{x^2X} = \frac{b}{2a^2}\log \frac{X}{x^2} - \frac{1}{ax} + \left(\frac{b^2}{2a^2} - \frac{c}{a}\right)\int \frac{dx}{X}.$

120. $\displaystyle \int \frac{dx}{xX^n} = \frac{1}{2a(n-1)X^{n-1}} - \frac{b}{2a}\int \frac{dx}{X^n} + \frac{1}{a}\int \frac{dx}{xX^{n-1}}.$

121. $\displaystyle \int \frac{dx}{x^m X^{n+1}} = -\frac{1}{(m-1)ax^{m-1}X^n} - \frac{n+m-1}{m-1}\frac{b}{a}\int \frac{dx}{x^{m-1}X^{n+1}}$
$$-\frac{2n+m-1}{m-1}\frac{c}{a}\int \frac{dx}{x^{m-2}X^{n+1}}.$$

5.4.9   FORMS CONTAINING $\sqrt{a+bx}$

122. $\displaystyle \int \sqrt{a+bx}\,dx = \frac{2}{3b}\sqrt{(a+bx)^3}.$

123. $\displaystyle \int x\sqrt{a+bx}\,dx = -\frac{2(2a-3bx)}{15b^2}\sqrt{(a+bx)^3}.$

124. $\displaystyle \int x^2\sqrt{a+bx}\,dx = \frac{2(8a^2-12abx+15b^2x^2)}{105b^3}\sqrt{(a+bx)^3}.$

125. $\displaystyle \int x^m\sqrt{a+bx}\,dx =$

$$\begin{cases} \dfrac{2}{b(2m+3)}\left[x^m\sqrt{(a+bx)^3} - ma\int x^{m-1}\sqrt{a+bx}\,dx\right], \\ \quad\text{or} \\ \dfrac{2}{b^{m+1}}\sqrt{a+bx}\displaystyle\sum_{r=0}^{m}\frac{m!(-a)^{m-r}}{r!(m-r)!(2r+3)}(a+bx)^{r+1}. \end{cases}$$

126. $\displaystyle \int \frac{\sqrt{a+bx}}{x}\,dx = 2\sqrt{a+bx} + a\int \frac{dx}{x\sqrt{a+bx}}.$

127. $\displaystyle \int \frac{\sqrt{a+bx}}{x^m}\,dx = -\frac{1}{(m-1)a}\left[\frac{\sqrt{(a+bx)^3}}{x^{m-1}} + \frac{(2m-5)b}{2}\int \frac{\sqrt{a+bx}}{x^{m-1}}\,dx\right].$

128. $\displaystyle \int \frac{dx}{\sqrt{a+bx}} = \frac{2\sqrt{a+bx}}{b}.$

129. $\displaystyle \int \frac{x\,dx}{\sqrt{a+bx}} = -\frac{2(2a-bx)}{3b^2}\sqrt{a+bx}.$

130. $\displaystyle \int \frac{x^2\,dx}{\sqrt{a+bx}} = \frac{2(8a^2-4abx+3b^2x^2)}{15b^3}\sqrt{a+bx}.$

131. $\displaystyle \int \frac{x^m\,dx}{\sqrt{a+bx}} = \begin{cases} \dfrac{2}{(2m+1)b}\left[x^m\sqrt{a+bx} - ma\int \frac{x^{m-1}}{\sqrt{a+bx}}\,dx\right], \\ \quad\text{or} \\ \dfrac{2(-a)^m\sqrt{a+bx}}{b^{m+1}}\displaystyle\sum_{r=0}^{m}\frac{(-1)^r m!(a+bx)^r}{(2r+1)r!(m-r)!a^r}. \end{cases}$

132. $\displaystyle \int \frac{dx}{x\sqrt{a+bx}} = \begin{cases} \dfrac{2}{\sqrt{-a}}\tan^{-1}\sqrt{\dfrac{a+bx}{-a}}, & a < 0, \\ \quad\text{or} \\ \dfrac{1}{\sqrt{a}}\log\left(\dfrac{\sqrt{a+bx}-\sqrt{a}}{\sqrt{a+bx}+\sqrt{a}}\right), & a > 0. \end{cases}$

133. $\displaystyle \int \frac{dx}{x^2\sqrt{a+bx}} = -\frac{\sqrt{a+bx}}{ax} - \frac{b}{2a}\int \frac{dx}{x\sqrt{a+bx}}.$

134. $\displaystyle \int \frac{dx}{x^n \sqrt{a + bx}} =$

$$\begin{cases} -\dfrac{\sqrt{a + bx}}{(n - 1)ax^{n-1}} - \dfrac{(2n - 3)b}{(2n - 2)a} \displaystyle\int \dfrac{dx}{x^{n-1}\sqrt{a + bx}}, \\ \text{or} \\ \dfrac{(2n - 2)!}{[(n - 1)!]^2} \left[-\dfrac{\sqrt{a + bx}}{a} \displaystyle\sum_{r=1}^{n-1} \dfrac{r!(r - 1)!}{x^r (2r)!} \left(-\dfrac{b}{4a} \right)^{n-r-1} + \left(-\dfrac{b}{4a} \right)^{n-1} \displaystyle\int \dfrac{dx}{x\sqrt{a + bx}} \right]. \end{cases}$$

135. $\displaystyle \int (a + bx)^{\pm n/2} \, dx = \frac{2(a + bx)^{(2 \pm n)/2}}{b(2 \pm n)}.$

136. $\displaystyle \int x(a + bx)^{\pm n/2} \, dx = \frac{2}{b^2} \left[\frac{(a + bx)^{(4 \pm n)/2}}{4 \pm n} - \frac{a(a + bx)^{(2 \pm n)/2}}{2 \pm n} \right].$

137. $\displaystyle \int \frac{dx}{x(a + bx)^{n/2}} = \frac{1}{a} \int \frac{dx}{x(a + bx)^{(n-2)/2}} - \frac{b}{a} \int \frac{dx}{(a + bx)^{n/2}}.$

138. $\displaystyle \int \frac{(a + bx)^{n/2}}{x} \, dx = b \int (a + bx)^{(n-2)/2} \, dx + a \int \frac{(a + bx)^{(n-2)/2}}{x} \, dx.$

5.4.10   FORMS CONTAINING $\sqrt{a + bx}$ AND $\sqrt{c + dx}$

$$u = a + bx, \qquad v = c + dx, \qquad k = ad - bc.$$

If $k = 0$, then $v = \frac{c}{a}u$, and other formulae should be used.

139. $\displaystyle \int \frac{dx}{\sqrt{uv}} = \begin{cases} \dfrac{2}{\sqrt{bd}} \tanh^{-1} \dfrac{\sqrt{bduv}}{bv}, & bd > 0, \; k < 0, \\[2mm] \dfrac{2}{\sqrt{bd}} \tanh^{-1} \dfrac{\sqrt{bduv}}{du}, & bd > 0, \; k > 0, \\[2mm] \dfrac{1}{\sqrt{bd}} \log \dfrac{(bv + \sqrt{bduv})^2}{v}, & bd > 0, \\[2mm] \dfrac{2}{\sqrt{-bd}} \tan^{-1} \dfrac{\sqrt{-bduv}}{bv}, & bd < 0, \\[2mm] -\dfrac{1}{\sqrt{-bd}} \sin^{-1} \left(\dfrac{2bdx + ad + bc}{|k|} \right), & bd < 0. \end{cases}$

140. $\displaystyle \int \sqrt{uv} \, dx = \frac{k + 2bv}{4bd} \sqrt{uv} - \frac{k^2}{8bd} \int \frac{dx}{\sqrt{uv}}.$

141. $\displaystyle \int \frac{dx}{v\sqrt{u}} = \begin{cases} \dfrac{1}{\sqrt{kd}} \log \dfrac{d\sqrt{u} - \sqrt{kd}}{d\sqrt{u} + \sqrt{kd}}, & kd > 0, \\[2mm] \text{or} \\[2mm] \dfrac{1}{\sqrt{kd}} \log \dfrac{\left(d\sqrt{u} - \sqrt{kd}\right)^2}{v}, & kd > 0, \\[2mm] \text{or} \\[2mm] \dfrac{2}{\sqrt{-kd}} \tan^{-1} \dfrac{d\sqrt{u}}{\sqrt{-kd}}, & kd < 0. \end{cases}$

142. $\displaystyle \int \frac{x \, dx}{\sqrt{uv}} = \frac{\sqrt{uv}}{bd} - \frac{ad + bc}{2bd} \int \frac{dx}{\sqrt{uv}}.$

143. $\displaystyle \int \frac{dx}{v\sqrt{uv}} = -\frac{2\sqrt{uv}}{kv}.$

144. $\displaystyle\int \frac{v\,dx}{\sqrt{uv}} = \frac{\sqrt{uv}}{b} - \frac{k}{2b}\int \frac{dx}{\sqrt{uv}}.$

145. $\displaystyle\int \sqrt{\frac{v}{u}}\,dx = \frac{v}{|v|}\int \frac{v\,dx}{\sqrt{uv}}.$

146. $\displaystyle\int v^m \sqrt{u}\,dx = \frac{1}{(2m+3)d}\left(2v^{m+1}\sqrt{u} + k\int \frac{v^m\,dx}{\sqrt{u}}\right).$

147. $\displaystyle\int \frac{dx}{v^m \sqrt{u}} = -\frac{1}{(m-1)k}\left(\frac{\sqrt{u}}{v^{m-1}} + \left(m-\frac{3}{2}\right)b\int \frac{dx}{v^{m-1}\sqrt{u}}\right).$

148. $\displaystyle\int \frac{v^m}{\sqrt{u}}\,dx = \begin{cases} \dfrac{2}{b(2m+1)}\left(v^m\sqrt{u} - mk\displaystyle\int \dfrac{v^{m-1}}{\sqrt{u}}\,dx\right), \\ \text{or} \\ \dfrac{2(m!)^2\sqrt{u}}{b(2m+1)!}\displaystyle\sum_{r=0}^{m}\left(-\dfrac{4k}{b}\right)^{m-r}\dfrac{(2r)!}{(r!)^2}v^r. \end{cases}$

5.4.11   FORMS CONTAINING $\sqrt{x^2 \pm a^2}$

149. $\displaystyle\int \sqrt{x^2 \pm a^2}\,dx = \frac{1}{2}\left[x\sqrt{x^2 \pm a^2} \pm a^2 \log x + \sqrt{x^2 \pm a^2}\right].$

150. $\displaystyle\int \frac{dx}{\sqrt{x^2 \pm a^2}} = \log x + \sqrt{x^2 \pm a^2}.$

151. $\displaystyle\int \frac{dx}{x\sqrt{x^2 - a^2}} = \frac{1}{|a|}\sec^{-1}\frac{x}{a}.$

152. $\displaystyle\int \frac{dx}{x\sqrt{x^2 + a^2}} = -\frac{1}{a}\log\left(\frac{a + \sqrt{x^2 + a^2}}{x}\right).$

153. $\displaystyle\int \frac{\sqrt{x^2 + a^2}}{x}\,dx = \sqrt{x^2 + a^2} - a\log\left(\frac{a + \sqrt{x^2 + a^2}}{x}\right).$

154. $\displaystyle\int \frac{\sqrt{x^2 - a^2}}{x}\,dx = \sqrt{x^2 - a^2} - |a|\sec^{-1}\frac{x}{a}.$

155. $\displaystyle\int \frac{x}{\sqrt{x^2 \pm a^2}}\,dx = \sqrt{x^2 \pm a^2}.$

156. $\displaystyle\int x\sqrt{x^2 \pm a^2}\,dx = \frac{1}{3}\sqrt{(x^2 \pm a^2)^3}.$

157. $\displaystyle\int \sqrt{(x^2 \pm a^2)^3}\,dx = \frac{1}{4}\left[x\sqrt{(x^2 \pm a^2)^3} \pm \frac{3a^2 x}{2}\sqrt{x^2 \pm a^2}\right.$
$$\left. + \frac{3a^4}{2}\log\left(x + \sqrt{x^2 \pm a^2}\right)\right].$$

158. $\displaystyle\int \frac{dx}{\sqrt{(x^2 \pm a^2)^3}} = \frac{\pm x}{a^2\sqrt{x^2 \pm a^2}}.$

159. $\displaystyle\int \frac{x}{\sqrt{(x^2 \pm a^2)^3}}\,dx = \frac{-1}{\sqrt{x^2 \pm a^2}}.$

160. $\displaystyle\int x\sqrt{(x^2 \pm a^2)^3}\,dx = \frac{1}{5}\sqrt{(x^2 \pm a^2)^5}.$

161. $\displaystyle\int x^2\sqrt{x^2 \pm a^2}\,dx = \frac{x}{4}\sqrt{(x^2 \pm a^2)^3} \mp \frac{a^2}{8}x\sqrt{x^2 \pm a^2} - \frac{a^4}{8}\log x + \sqrt{x^2 \pm a^2}.$

162. $\int x^3 \sqrt{x^2 + a^2}\, dx = \frac{1}{15}(3x^2 - 2a^2)\sqrt{(x^2 + a^2)^3}.$

163. $\int x^3 \sqrt{x^2 - a^2}\, dx = \frac{1}{5}\sqrt{(x^2 - a^2)^5} + \frac{a^2}{3}\sqrt{(x^2 - a^2)^3}.$

164. $\int \frac{x^2}{\sqrt{x^2 \pm a^2}}\, dx = \frac{x}{2}\sqrt{x^2 \pm a^2} \mp \frac{a^2}{2}\log x + \sqrt{x^2 \pm a^2}.$

165. $\int \frac{x^3}{\sqrt{x^2 \pm a^2}}\, dx = \frac{1}{3}\sqrt{(x^2 \pm a^2)^3} \mp a^2\sqrt{x^2 \pm a^2}.$

166. $\int \frac{dx}{x^2\sqrt{x^2 \pm a^2}}\, dx = \mp \frac{\sqrt{x^2 \pm a^2}}{a^2 x}.$

167. $\int \frac{dx}{x^3\sqrt{x^2 + a^2}}\, dx = -\frac{\sqrt{x^2 + a^2}}{2a^2 x^2} + \frac{1}{2a^3}\log \frac{a + \sqrt{x^2 + a^2}}{x}.$

168. $\int \frac{dx}{x^3\sqrt{x^2 - a^2}}\, dx = \frac{\sqrt{x^2 - a^2}}{2a^2 x^2} + \frac{1}{2|a|^3}\sec^{-1}\frac{x}{a}.$

169. $\int x^2 \sqrt{(x^2 \pm a^2)^3}\, dx = \frac{x}{6}\sqrt{(x^2 \pm a^2)^5} \mp \frac{a^2 x}{24}\sqrt{(x^2 \pm a^2)^3} - \frac{a^4 x}{16}\sqrt{x^2 \pm a^2}$
$$\mp \frac{a^6}{16}\log\left(x + \sqrt{x^2 \pm a^2}\right).$$

170. $\int x^3 \sqrt{(x^2 \pm a^2)^3}\, dx = \frac{1}{7}\sqrt{(x^2 \pm a^2)^7} \mp \frac{a^2}{5}\sqrt{(x^2 \pm a^2)^5}.$

171. $\int \frac{\sqrt{x^2 \pm a^2}}{x^2}\, dx = -\frac{\sqrt{x^2 \pm a^2}}{x} + \log\left(x + \sqrt{x^2 \pm a^2}\right).$

172. $\int \frac{\sqrt{x^2 + a^2}}{x^3}\, dx = -\frac{\sqrt{x^2 + a^2}}{2x^2} - \frac{1}{2a}\log \frac{a + \sqrt{x^2 + a^2}}{x}.$

173. $\int \frac{\sqrt{x^2 - a^2}}{x^3}\, dx = -\frac{\sqrt{x^2 - a^2}}{2x^2} + \frac{1}{2|a|}\sec^{-1}\frac{x}{a}.$

174. $\int \frac{\sqrt{x^2 \pm a^2}}{x^4}\, dx = \mp \frac{\sqrt{(x^2 \pm a^2)^3}}{3a^2 x^3}.$

175. $\int \frac{x^2\, dx}{\sqrt{(x^2 \pm a^2)^3}} = -\frac{x}{\sqrt{x^2 \pm a^2}} + \log\left(x + \sqrt{x^2 \pm a^2}\right).$

176. $\int \frac{x^3\, dx}{\sqrt{(x^2 \pm a^2)^3}} = \sqrt{x^2 \pm a^2} \pm \frac{a^2}{\sqrt{x^2 \pm a^2}}.$

177. $\int \frac{dx}{x\sqrt{(x^2 + a^2)^3}} = \frac{1}{a^2\sqrt{x^2 + a^2}} - \frac{1}{a^3}\log \frac{a + \sqrt{x^2 + a^2}}{x}.$

178. $\int \frac{dx}{x\sqrt{(x^2 - a^2)^3}} = -\frac{1}{a^2\sqrt{x^2 - a^2}} - \frac{1}{|a^3|}\sec^{-1}\frac{x}{a}.$

179. $\int \frac{dx}{x^2\sqrt{(x^2 \pm a^2)^3}} = -\frac{1}{a^4}\left[\frac{\sqrt{x^2 \pm a^2}}{x} + \frac{x}{\sqrt{x^2 \pm a^2}}\right].$

180. $\int \frac{dx}{x^3\sqrt{(x^2 + a^2)^3}} = -\frac{1}{2a^2 x^2\sqrt{x^2 + a^2}} - \frac{3}{2a^4\sqrt{x^2 + a^2}} + \frac{3}{2a^5}\log \frac{a + \sqrt{x^2 + a^2}}{x}.$

181. $\int \frac{dx}{x^3\sqrt{(x^2 - a^2)^3}} = \frac{1}{2a^2 x^2\sqrt{x^2 - a^2}} - \frac{3}{2a^4\sqrt{x^2 - a^2}} - \frac{3}{2|a^5|}\sec^{-1}\frac{x}{a}.$

182. $\displaystyle\int \frac{x^m \, dx}{\sqrt{x^2 \pm a^2}} = \frac{1}{m}x^{m-1}\sqrt{x^2 \pm a^2} \mp \frac{m-1}{m}a^2 \int \frac{x^{m-2}}{\sqrt{x^2 \pm a^2}} \, dx.$

183. $\displaystyle\int \frac{x^{2m} \, dx}{\sqrt{x^2 \pm a^2}} = \frac{(2m)!}{2^{2m}(m!)^2}\left[\sqrt{x^2 \pm a^2}\sum_{r=1}^{m}\frac{r!(r-1)!}{(2r)!}(\mp a^2)^{m-r}(2x)^{2r-1}\right.$

$$\left. + (\mp a^2)^m \log\left(x + \sqrt{x^2 \pm a^2}\right)\right].$$

184. $\displaystyle\int \frac{x^{2m+1} \, dx}{\sqrt{x^2 \pm a^2}} = \sqrt{x^2 \pm a^2}\sum_{r=0}^{m}\frac{(2r)!(m!)^2}{(2m+1)!(r!)^2}(\mp 4a^2)^{m-r}x^{2r}.$

185. $\displaystyle\int \frac{dx}{x^m\sqrt{x^2 \pm a^2}} = \mp\frac{\sqrt{x^2 \pm a^2}}{(m-1)a^2 x^{m-1}} \mp \frac{(m-2)}{(m-1)a^2}\int \frac{dx}{x^{m-2}\sqrt{x^2 \pm a^2}}.$

186. $\displaystyle\int \frac{dx}{x^{2m}\sqrt{x^2 \pm a^2}} = \sqrt{x^2 \pm a^2}\sum_{r=0}^{m-1}\frac{(m-1)!m!(2r)!2^{2m-2r-1}}{(r!)^2(2m)!(\mp a^2)^{m-r}x^{2r+1}}.$

187. $\displaystyle\int \frac{dx}{x^{2m+1}\sqrt{x^2 + a^2}} = \frac{(2m)!}{(m!)^2}\left[\frac{\sqrt{x^2 + a^2}}{a^2}\sum_{r=1}^{m}(-1)^{m-r+1}\frac{r!(r-1)!}{2(2r)!(4a^2)^{m-r}x^{2r}}\right.$

$$\left. + \frac{(-1)^{m+1}}{2^{2m}a^{2m+1}}\log\frac{\sqrt{x^2 + a^2} + a}{x}\right].$$

188. $\displaystyle\int \frac{dx}{x^{2m+1}\sqrt{x^2 - a^2}} = \frac{(2m)!}{(m!)^2}\left[\frac{\sqrt{x^2 - a^2}}{a^2}\sum_{r=1}^{m}\frac{r!(r-1)!}{2(2r)!(4a^2)^{m-r}x^{2r}}\right.$

$$\left. + \frac{1}{2^{2m}\,|a|^{2m+1}}\sec^{-1}\frac{x}{a}\right].$$

189. $\displaystyle\int \frac{dx}{(x-a)\sqrt{x^2 - a^2}} = -\frac{\sqrt{x^2 - a^2}}{a(x-a)}.$

190. $\displaystyle\int \frac{dx}{(x+a)\sqrt{x^2 - a^2}} = \frac{\sqrt{x^2 - a^2}}{a(x+a)}.$

5.4.12   FORMS CONTAINING $\sqrt{a^2 - x^2}$

191. $\displaystyle\int \sqrt{a^2 - x^2}\, dx = \frac{1}{2}\left(x\sqrt{a^2 - x^2} + a^2\sin^{-1}\frac{x}{|a|}\right).$

192. $\displaystyle\int \frac{dx}{\sqrt{a^2 - x^2}} = \sin^{-1}\frac{x}{|a|} = -\cos^{-1}\frac{x}{|a|}.$

193. $\displaystyle\int \frac{dx}{x\sqrt{a^2 - x^2}} = -\frac{1}{a}\log\left(\frac{a + \sqrt{a^2 - x^2}}{x}\right).$

194. $\displaystyle\int \frac{\sqrt{a^2 - x^2}}{x}\, dx = \sqrt{a^2 - x^2} - a\log\left(\frac{a + \sqrt{a^2 - x^2}}{x}\right).$

195. $\displaystyle\int \frac{x}{\sqrt{a^2 - x^2}}\, dx = -\sqrt{a^2 - x^2}.$

196. $\displaystyle\int x\sqrt{a^2 - x^2}\, dx = -\frac{1}{3}\sqrt{(a^2 - x^2)^3}.$

197. $\displaystyle\int \sqrt{(a^2 - x^2)^3}\, dx = \frac{1}{4}\left(x\sqrt{(a^2 - x^2)^3} + \frac{3a^2 x}{2}\sqrt{a^2 - x^2} + \frac{3a^4}{2}\sin^{-1}\frac{x}{|a|}\right).$

198. $\displaystyle\int \frac{dx}{\sqrt{(a^2 - x^2)^3}} = \frac{x}{a^2\sqrt{a^2 - x^2}}.$

199. $\int \dfrac{x}{\sqrt{(a^2 - x^2)^3}}\, dx = \dfrac{1}{\sqrt{a^2 - x^2}}.$

200. $\int x\sqrt{(a^2 - x^2)^3}\, dx = -\dfrac{1}{5}\sqrt{(a^2 - x^2)^5}.$

201. $\int x^2\sqrt{a^2 - x^2}\, dx = -\dfrac{x}{4}\sqrt{(a^2 - x^2)^3} + \dfrac{a^2}{8}\left(x\sqrt{a^2 - x^2} + a^2 \sin^{-1}\dfrac{x}{|a|}\right).$

202. $\int x^3\sqrt{a^2 - x^2}\, dx = \left(-\dfrac{1}{5}x^2 - \dfrac{2}{15}a^2\right)\sqrt{(a^2 - x^2)^3}.$

203. $\int x^2\sqrt{(a^2 - x^2)^3}\, dx = -\dfrac{1}{6}x\sqrt{(a^2 - x^2)^5} + \dfrac{a^2 x}{24}\sqrt{(a^2 - x^2)^3}$
$$+ \dfrac{a^4 x}{16}\sqrt{a^2 - x^2} + \dfrac{a^6}{16}\sin^{-1}\dfrac{x}{|a|}.$$

204. $\int x^3\sqrt{(a^2 - x^2)^3}\, dx = \dfrac{1}{7}\sqrt{(a^2 - x^2)^7} - \dfrac{a^2}{5}\sqrt{(a^2 - x^2)^5}.$

205. $\int \dfrac{x^2}{\sqrt{a^2 - x^2}}\, dx = -\dfrac{x}{2}\sqrt{a^2 - x^2} + \dfrac{a^2}{2}\sin^{-1}\dfrac{x}{|a|}.$

206. $\int \dfrac{dx}{x^2\sqrt{a^2 - x^2}} = -\dfrac{\sqrt{a^2 - x^2}}{a^2 x}.$

207. $\int \dfrac{\sqrt{a^2 - x^2}}{x^2}\, dx = -\dfrac{\sqrt{a^2 - x^2}}{x} - \sin^{-1}\dfrac{x}{|a|}.$

208. $\int \dfrac{\sqrt{a^2 - x^2}}{x^3} = -\dfrac{\sqrt{a^2 - x^2}}{2x^2} + \dfrac{1}{2a}\log\dfrac{a + \sqrt{a^2 - x^2}}{x}.$

209. $\int \dfrac{\sqrt{a^2 - x^2}}{x^4}\, dx = -\dfrac{\sqrt{(a^2 - x^2)^3}}{3a^2 x^3}.$

210. $\int \dfrac{x^2\, dx}{\sqrt{(a^2 - x^2)^3}} = \dfrac{x}{\sqrt{a^2 - x^2}} - \sin^{-1}\dfrac{x}{|a|}.$

211. $\int \dfrac{x^3\, dx}{\sqrt{a^2 - x^2}} = -\dfrac{2}{3}\sqrt{(a^2 - x^2)^3} - x^2\sqrt{a^2 - x^2}.$

212. $\int \dfrac{x^3\, dx}{\sqrt{(a^2 - x^2)^3}} = 2\sqrt{a^2 - x^2} + \dfrac{x^2}{\sqrt{a^2 - x^2}} = \dfrac{a^2}{\sqrt{a^2 - x^2}} + \sqrt{a^2 - x^2}.$

213. $\int \dfrac{dx}{x^3\sqrt{a^2 - x^2}} = -\dfrac{\sqrt{a^2 - x^2}}{2a^2 x^2} - \dfrac{1}{2a^3}\log\dfrac{a + \sqrt{a^2 - x^2}}{x}.$

214. $\int \dfrac{dx}{x\sqrt{(a^2 - x^2)^3}} = \dfrac{1}{a^2\sqrt{a^2 - x^2}} - \dfrac{1}{a^3}\log\dfrac{a + \sqrt{a^2 - x^2}}{x}.$

215. $\int \dfrac{dx}{x^2\sqrt{(a^2 - x^2)^3}} = \dfrac{1}{a^4}\left(-\dfrac{\sqrt{a^2 - x^2}}{x} + \dfrac{x}{\sqrt{a^2 - x^2}}\right).$

216. $\int \dfrac{dx}{x^3\sqrt{(a^2 - x^2)^3}} = -\dfrac{1}{2a^2 x^2\sqrt{a^2 - x^2}} + \dfrac{3}{2a^4\sqrt{a^2 - x^2}} - \dfrac{3}{2a^5}\log\dfrac{a + \sqrt{a^2 - x^2}}{x}.$

217. $\int \dfrac{x^m}{\sqrt{a^2 - x^2}}\, dx = -\dfrac{x^{m-1}\sqrt{a^2 - x^2}}{m} + \dfrac{(m - 1)a^2}{m}\int \dfrac{x^{m-2}}{\sqrt{a^2 - x^2}}\, dx.$

218. $\int \dfrac{x^{2m}}{\sqrt{a^2 - x^2}}\, dx = \dfrac{(2m)!}{(m!)^2}\left[-\sqrt{a^2 - x^2}\displaystyle\sum_{r=1}^{m}\dfrac{r!(r - 1)!}{2^{2m-2r+1}(2r)!}a^{2m-2r}x^{2r-1}\right.$
$$\left.+ \dfrac{a^{2m}}{2^{2m}}\sin^{-1}\dfrac{x}{|a|}\right].$$

219. $\int \dfrac{x^{2m+1}}{\sqrt{a^2 - x^2}} \, dx = -\sqrt{a^2 - x^2} \displaystyle\sum_{r=0}^{m} \dfrac{(2r)!(m!)^2}{(2m+1)!(r!)^2} (4a^2)^{m-r} x^{2r}.$

220. $\int \dfrac{dx}{x^m \sqrt{a^2 - x^2}} = -\dfrac{\sqrt{a^2 - x^2}}{(m-1)a^2 x^{m-1}} + \dfrac{(m-2)}{(m-1)a^2} \int \dfrac{dx}{x^{m-2}\sqrt{a^2 - x^2}}.$

221. $\int \dfrac{dx}{x^{2m}\sqrt{a^2 - x^2}} = -\sqrt{a^2 - x^2} \displaystyle\sum_{r=0}^{m-1} \dfrac{(m-1)!m!(2r)!2^{2m-2r-1}}{(r!)^2(2m)!a^{2m-2r}x^{2r+1}}.$

222. $\int \dfrac{dx}{x^{2m+1}\sqrt{a^2 - x^2}} = \dfrac{(2m)!}{(m!)^2} \left[-\dfrac{\sqrt{a^2 - x^2}}{a^2} \displaystyle\sum_{r=1}^{m} \dfrac{r!(r-1)!}{2(2r)!(4a^2)^{m-r}x^{2r}} \right.$

$$\left. + \dfrac{1}{2^{2m}a^{2m+1}} \log \dfrac{a - \sqrt{a^2 - x^2}}{x} \right].$$

223. $\int \dfrac{dx}{(b^2 - x^2)\sqrt{a^2 - x^2}} =$

$$\begin{cases} \dfrac{1}{2b\sqrt{a^2 - b^2}} \log \dfrac{(b\sqrt{a^2 - x^2} + x\sqrt{a^2 - b^2})^2}{b^2 - x^2}, & a^2 > b^2, \\[4mm] \text{or} \\[2mm] \dfrac{1}{b\sqrt{b^2 - a^2}} \tan^{-1} \dfrac{x\sqrt{b^2 - a^2}}{b\sqrt{a^2 - x^2}}, & b^2 > a^2. \end{cases}$$

224. $\int \dfrac{dx}{(b^2 + x^2)\sqrt{a^2 - x^2}} = \dfrac{1}{b\sqrt{a^2 + b^2}} \tan^{-1} \dfrac{x\sqrt{a^2 + b^2}}{b\sqrt{a^2 - x^2}}.$

225. $\int \dfrac{\sqrt{a^2 - x^2}}{b^2 + x^2} \, dx = \dfrac{\sqrt{a^2 + b^2}}{|b|} \sin^{-1} \dfrac{x\sqrt{a^2 + b^2}}{|a|\sqrt{x^2 + b^2}} - \sin^{-1} \dfrac{x}{|a|}, \quad b^2 > a^2.$

5.4.13 FORMS CONTAINING $\sqrt{a + bx + cx^2}$

$$X = a + bx + cx^2, \quad q = 4ac - b^2, \quad \text{and} \quad k = 4c/q.$$

$$\text{If } q = 0, \text{ then } \sqrt{X} = \sqrt{c}\left|x + \tfrac{b}{2c}\right|.$$

226. $\int \dfrac{dx}{\sqrt{X}} = \begin{cases} \dfrac{1}{\sqrt{c}} \log \dfrac{2\sqrt{cX} + 2cx + b}{\sqrt{q}}, & c > 0, \\[3mm] \text{or} \\[2mm] \dfrac{1}{\sqrt{c}} \sinh^{-1} \dfrac{2cx + b}{\sqrt{q}}, & c > 0, \\[3mm] \text{or} \\[2mm] -\dfrac{1}{\sqrt{-c}} \sin^{-1} \dfrac{2cx + b}{\sqrt{-q}}, & c < 0. \end{cases}$

227. $\int \dfrac{dx}{X\sqrt{X}} = \dfrac{2(2cx + b)}{q\sqrt{X}}.$

228. $\int \dfrac{dx}{X^2\sqrt{X}} = \dfrac{2(2cx + b)}{3q\sqrt{X}} \left(\dfrac{1}{X} + 2k \right).$

229. $\int \dfrac{dx}{X^n\sqrt{X}} = \begin{cases} \dfrac{2(2cx + b)\sqrt{X}}{(2n-1)q X^n} + \dfrac{2k(n-1)}{2n-1} \int \dfrac{dx}{X^{n-1}\sqrt{X}}, \\[3mm] \text{or} \\[2mm] \dfrac{(2cx + b)(n!)(n-1)!4^n k^{n-1}}{q(2n)!\sqrt{X}} \displaystyle\sum_{r=0}^{n-1} \dfrac{(2r)!}{(4kX)^r(r!)^2}. \end{cases}$

230. $\int \sqrt{X}\,dx = \dfrac{(2cx+b)\sqrt{X}}{4c} + \dfrac{1}{2k}\int \dfrac{dx}{\sqrt{X}}.$

231. $\int X\sqrt{X}\,dx = \dfrac{(2cx+b)\sqrt{X}}{8c}\left(X+\dfrac{3}{2k}\right) + \dfrac{3}{8k^2}\int \dfrac{dx}{\sqrt{X}}.$

232. $\int X^2\sqrt{X}\,dx = \dfrac{(2cx+b)\sqrt{X}}{12c}\left(X^2+\dfrac{5X}{4k}+\dfrac{15}{8k^2}\right) + \dfrac{5}{16k^3}\int \dfrac{dx}{\sqrt{X}}.$

233. $\int X^n\sqrt{X}\,dx =$

$$\begin{cases} \dfrac{(2cx+b)X^n\sqrt{X}}{4(n+1)c} + \dfrac{2n+1}{2(n+1)k}\int X^{n-1}\sqrt{X}\,dx, \\[4pt] \text{or} \\[4pt] \dfrac{(2n+2)!}{[(n+1)!]^2\,(4k)^{n+1}}\left[\dfrac{k(2cx+b)\sqrt{X}}{c}\sum_{r=0}^{n}\dfrac{r!(r+1)!(4kX)^r}{(2r+2)!} + \int \dfrac{dx}{\sqrt{X}}\right]. \end{cases}$$

234. $\int \dfrac{x\,dx}{\sqrt{X}} = \dfrac{\sqrt{X}}{c} - \dfrac{b}{2c}\int \dfrac{dx}{\sqrt{X}}.$

235. $\int \dfrac{x\,dx}{X\sqrt{X}} = -\dfrac{2(bx+2a)}{q\sqrt{X}}.$

236. $\int \dfrac{x\,dx}{X^n\sqrt{X}} = -\dfrac{\sqrt{X}}{(2n-1)cX^n} - \dfrac{b}{2c}\int \dfrac{dx}{X^n\sqrt{X}}.$

237. $\int \dfrac{x^2\,dx}{\sqrt{X}} = \left(\dfrac{x}{2c} - \dfrac{3b}{4c^2}\right)\sqrt{X} + \dfrac{3b^2-4ac}{8c^2}\int \dfrac{dx}{\sqrt{X}}.$

238. $\int \dfrac{x^2\,dx}{X\sqrt{X}} = \dfrac{(2b^2-4ac)x+2ab}{cq\sqrt{X}} + \dfrac{1}{c}\int \dfrac{dx}{\sqrt{X}}.$

239. $\int \dfrac{x^2\,dx}{X^n\sqrt{X}} = \dfrac{(2b^2-4ac)x+2ab}{(2n-1)cqX^{n-1}\sqrt{X}} + \dfrac{4ac+(2n-3)b^2}{(2n-1)cq}\int \dfrac{dx}{X^{n-1}\sqrt{X}}.$

240. $\int \dfrac{x^3\,dx}{\sqrt{X}} = \left(\dfrac{x^2}{3c} - \dfrac{5bx}{12c^2} + \dfrac{5b^2}{8c^3} - \dfrac{2a}{3c^2}\right)\sqrt{X} + \left(\dfrac{3ab}{4c^2} - \dfrac{5b^3}{16c^3}\right)\int \dfrac{dx}{\sqrt{X}}.$

241. $\int \dfrac{x^n\,dx}{\sqrt{X}} = \dfrac{1}{nc}x^{n-1}\sqrt{X} - \dfrac{(2n-1)b}{2nc}\int \dfrac{x^{n-1}\,dx}{\sqrt{X}} - \dfrac{(n-1)a}{nc}\int \dfrac{x^{n-2}\,dx}{\sqrt{X}}.$

242. $\int x\sqrt{X}\,dx = \dfrac{X\sqrt{X}}{3c} - \dfrac{b(2cx+b)}{8c^2}\sqrt{X} - \dfrac{b}{4ck}\int \dfrac{dx}{\sqrt{X}}.$

243. $\int xX\sqrt{X}\,dx = \dfrac{X^2\sqrt{X}}{5c} - \dfrac{b}{2c}\int X\sqrt{X}\,dx.$

244. $\int xX^n\sqrt{X}\,dx = \dfrac{X^{n+1}\sqrt{X}}{(2n+3)c} - \dfrac{b}{2c}\int X^n\sqrt{X}\,dx.$

245. $\int x^2\sqrt{X}\,dx = \left(x-\dfrac{5b}{6c}\right)\dfrac{X\sqrt{X}}{4c} + \dfrac{5b^2-4ac}{16c^2}\int \sqrt{X}\,dx.$

246. $\int \dfrac{dx}{x\sqrt{X}} = \begin{cases} \dfrac{1}{\sqrt{-a}}\sin^{-1}\left(\dfrac{bx+2a}{|x|\sqrt{-q}}\right), & a<0, \\[8pt] \text{or} \\[4pt] -\dfrac{2\sqrt{X}}{bx}, & a=0, \\[8pt] \text{or} \\[4pt] -\dfrac{1}{\sqrt{a}}\log\dfrac{2\sqrt{aX}+bx+2a}{x}, & a>0. \end{cases}$

247. $\displaystyle \int \frac{dx}{x^2\sqrt{X}} = -\frac{\sqrt{X}}{ax} - \frac{b}{2a}\int \frac{dx}{x\sqrt{X}}.$

248. $\displaystyle \int \frac{\sqrt{X}}{x}\,dx = \sqrt{X} + \frac{b}{2}\int \frac{dx}{\sqrt{X}} + a\int \frac{dx}{x\sqrt{X}}.$

249. $\displaystyle \int \frac{\sqrt{X}}{x^2}\,dx = -\frac{\sqrt{X}}{x} + \frac{b}{2}\int \frac{dx}{x\sqrt{X}} + c\int \frac{dx}{\sqrt{X}}.$

5.4.14   FORMS CONTAINING $\sqrt{2ax - x^2}$

250. $\displaystyle \int \sqrt{2ax - x^2}\,dx = \frac{1}{2}\left[(x - a)\sqrt{2ax - x^2} + a^2 \sin^{-1}\frac{x - a}{|a|} \right].$

251. $\displaystyle \int \frac{dx}{\sqrt{2ax - x^2}} = \begin{cases} \cos^{-1}\left(\dfrac{a - x}{|a|}\right), \\[2mm] \text{or} \\[2mm] \sin^{-1}\left(\dfrac{x - a}{|a|}\right). \end{cases}$

252. $\displaystyle \int x^n\sqrt{2ax - x^2}\,dx =$

$\begin{cases} \displaystyle -\frac{x^{n-1}\sqrt{(2ax - x^2)^3}}{n + 2} + \frac{(2n + 1)a}{n + 2}\int x^{n-1}\sqrt{2ax - x^2}\,dx, \\[3mm] \text{or} \\[3mm] \displaystyle \sqrt{2ax - x^2}\left[\frac{x^{n+1}}{n + 2} - \sum_{r=0}^{n}\frac{(2n + 1)!(r!)^2 a^{n-r+1}}{2^{n-r}(2r + 1)!(n + 2)!n!}x^r \right] + \frac{(2n + 1)!a^{n+2}}{2^n n!(n + 2)!}\sin^{-1}\left(\frac{x - a}{|a|}\right). \end{cases}$

253. $\displaystyle \int \frac{\sqrt{2ax - x^2}}{x^n}\,dx = \frac{\sqrt{(2ax - x^2)^3}}{(3 - 2n)ax^n} + \frac{n - 3}{(2n - 3)a}\int \frac{\sqrt{2ax - x^2}}{x^{n-1}}\,dx.$

254. $\displaystyle \int \frac{x^n\,dx}{\sqrt{2ax - x^2}} =$

$\begin{cases} \displaystyle -\frac{x^{n-1}\sqrt{2ax - x^2}}{n} + \frac{a(2n - 1)}{n}\int \frac{x^{n-1}}{\sqrt{2ax - x^2}}\,dx, \\[3mm] \text{or} \\[3mm] \displaystyle -\sqrt{2ax - x^2}\sum_{r=1}^{n}\frac{(2n)!r!(r - 1)!a^{n-r}}{2^{n-r}(2r)!(n!)^2}x^{r-1} + \frac{(2n)!a^n}{2^n(n!)^2}\sin^{-1}\left(\frac{x - a}{|a|}\right). \end{cases}$

255. $\displaystyle \int \frac{dx}{x^n\sqrt{2ax - x^2}} = \begin{cases} \displaystyle \frac{\sqrt{2ax - x^2}}{a(1 - 2n)x^n} + \frac{n - 1}{(2n - 1)a}\int \frac{dx}{x^{n-1}\sqrt{2ax - x^2}}, \\[3mm] \text{or} \\[3mm] \displaystyle -\sqrt{2ax - x^2}\sum_{r=0}^{n-1}\frac{2^{n-r}(n - 1)!n!(2r)!}{(2n)!(r!)^2 a^{n-r}x^{r+1}}. \end{cases}$

256. $\displaystyle \int \frac{dx}{\sqrt{(2ax - x^2)^3}} = \frac{x - a}{a^2\sqrt{2ax - x^2}}.$

257. $\displaystyle \int \frac{x\,dx}{\sqrt{(2ax - x^2)^3}} = \frac{x}{a\sqrt{2ax - x^2}}.$

5.4.15   MISCELLANEOUS ALGEBRAIC FORMS

258. $\displaystyle \int \frac{dx}{\sqrt{2ax + x^2}} = \log\left(x + a + \sqrt{2ax + x^2} \right).$

259. $\displaystyle \int \sqrt{ax^2 + c}\, dx = \begin{cases} \dfrac{x}{2}\sqrt{ax^2 + c} + \dfrac{c}{2\sqrt{-a}} \sin^{-1}\left(x\sqrt{-\dfrac{a}{c}}\right), & a < 0, \\[2ex] \text{or} \\[1ex] \dfrac{x}{2}\sqrt{ax^2 + c} + \dfrac{c}{2\sqrt{a}} \log\left(x\sqrt{a} + \sqrt{ax^2 + c}\right), & a > 0. \end{cases}$

260. $\displaystyle \int \sqrt{\dfrac{1+x}{1-x}}\, dx = \sin^{-1} x - \sqrt{1 - x^2}.$

261. $\displaystyle \int \dfrac{dx}{x\sqrt{ax^n + c}} = \begin{cases} \dfrac{1}{n\sqrt{c}} \log \dfrac{\sqrt{ax^n + c} - \sqrt{c}}{\sqrt{ax^n + c} + \sqrt{c}}, \\[1ex] \text{or} \\[1ex] \dfrac{2}{n\sqrt{c}} \log \dfrac{\sqrt{ax^n + c} - \sqrt{c}}{\sqrt{x^n}}, & c > 0, \\[1ex] \text{or} \\[1ex] \dfrac{2}{n\sqrt{-c}} \sec^{-1}\sqrt{-\dfrac{ax^n}{c}}, & c < 0. \end{cases}$

262. $\displaystyle \int \dfrac{dx}{\sqrt{ax^2 + c}} = \begin{cases} \dfrac{1}{\sqrt{-a}} \sin^{-1}\left(x\sqrt{-\dfrac{a}{c}}\right), & a < 0, \\[2ex] \text{or} \\[1ex] \dfrac{1}{\sqrt{a}} \log\left(x\sqrt{a} + \sqrt{ax^2 + c}\right), & a > 0. \end{cases}$

263. $\displaystyle \int (ax^2 + c)^{m+1/2}\, dx =$
$$\begin{cases} \dfrac{x(ax^2 + c)^{m+1/2}}{2(m+1)} + \dfrac{(2m+1)c}{2(m+1)} \int (ax^2 + c)^{m-1/2}\, dx, \\[2ex] \text{or} \\[1ex] x\sqrt{ax^2 + c} \displaystyle\sum_{r=0}^{m} \dfrac{(2m+1)!(r!)^2 c^{m-r}}{2^{2m-2r+1}m!(m+1)!(2r+1)!}(ax^2 + c)^r \\[2ex] \quad + \dfrac{(2m+1)!c^{m+1}}{2^{2m+1}m!(m+1)!} \displaystyle\int \dfrac{dx}{\sqrt{ax^2 + c}}. \end{cases}$$

264. $\displaystyle \int x(ax^2 + c)^{m+1/2}\, dx = \dfrac{(ax^2 + c)^{m+3/2}}{(2m+3)a}.$

265. $\displaystyle \int \dfrac{(ax^2 + c)^{m+1/2}}{x}\, dx =$
$$\begin{cases} \dfrac{(ax^2 + c)^{m+1/2}}{2m+1} + c \displaystyle\int \dfrac{(ax^2 + c)^{m-1/2}}{x}\, dx, \\[2ex] \text{or} \\[1ex] \sqrt{ax^2 + c} \displaystyle\sum_{r=0}^{m} \dfrac{c^{m-r}(ax^2 + c)^r}{2r+1} + c^{m+1} \displaystyle\int \dfrac{dx}{x\sqrt{ax^2 + c}}. \end{cases}$$

266. $\displaystyle \int \dfrac{dx}{(ax^2 + c)^{m+1/2}} =$
$$\begin{cases} \dfrac{x}{(2m-1)c(ax^2 + c)^{m-1/2}} + \dfrac{2m-2}{(2m-1)c} \displaystyle\int \dfrac{dx}{(ax^2 + c)^{m-1/2}}, \\[2ex] \text{or} \\[1ex] \dfrac{x}{\sqrt{ax^2 + c}} \displaystyle\sum_{r=0}^{m-1} \dfrac{2^{2m-2r-1}(m-1)!m!(2r)!}{(2m)!(r!)^2 c^{m-r}(ax^2 + c)^r}. \end{cases}$$

267. $\displaystyle \int \dfrac{dx}{x^m\sqrt{ax^2 + c}} = -\dfrac{\sqrt{ax^2 + c}}{(m-1)cx^{m-1}} - \dfrac{(m-2)a}{(m-1)c} \int \dfrac{dx}{x^{m-2}\sqrt{ax^2 + c}}.$

268. $\displaystyle\int \frac{1+x^2}{(1-x^2)\sqrt{1+x^4}}\, dx = \frac{1}{\sqrt{2}} \log \frac{x\sqrt{2}+\sqrt{1+x^4}}{1-x^2}.$

269. $\displaystyle\int \frac{1-x^2}{(1+x^2)\sqrt{1+x^4}}\, dx = \frac{1}{\sqrt{2}} \tan^{-1} \frac{x\sqrt{2}}{\sqrt{1+x^4}}.$

270. $\displaystyle\int \frac{dx}{x\sqrt{x^n+a^2}} = -\frac{2}{na} \log \frac{a+\sqrt{x^n+a^2}}{\sqrt{x^n}}.$

271. $\displaystyle\int \frac{dx}{x\sqrt{x^n-a^2}} = -\frac{2}{na} \sin^{-1} \frac{a}{\sqrt{x^n}}.$

272. $\displaystyle\int \sqrt{\frac{x}{a^3-x^3}}\, dx = \frac{2}{3} \sin^{-1} \left(\frac{x}{a}\right)^{3/2}.$

5.4.16   FORMS INVOLVING TRIGONOMETRIC FUNCTIONS

273. $\displaystyle\int \sin ax\, dx = -\frac{1}{a} \cos ax.$

274. $\displaystyle\int \cos ax\, dx = \frac{1}{a} \sin ax.$

275. $\displaystyle\int \tan ax\, dx = -\frac{1}{a} \log \cos ax = \frac{1}{a} \log \sec ax.$

276. $\displaystyle\int \cot ax\, dx = \frac{1}{a} \log \sin ax = -\frac{1}{a} \log \csc ax$

277. $\displaystyle\int \sec ax\, dx = \frac{1}{a} \log\,(\sec ax + \tan ax) = \frac{1}{a} \log \tan \left(\frac{\pi}{4}+\frac{ax}{2}\right)$

278. $\displaystyle\int \csc ax\, dx = \frac{1}{a} \log\,(\csc ax - \cot ax) = \frac{1}{a} \log \tan \frac{ax}{2}$

279. $\displaystyle\int \sin^2 ax\, dx = \frac{x}{2} - \frac{1}{2a} \cos ax \sin ax = \frac{x}{2} - \frac{1}{4a} \sin 2ax$

280. $\displaystyle\int \sin^3 ax\, dx = -\frac{1}{3a} (\cos ax)(\sin^2 ax + 2).$

281. $\displaystyle\int \sin^4 ax\, dx = \frac{3x}{8} - \frac{\sin 2ax}{4a} + \frac{\sin 4ax}{32a}.$

282. $\displaystyle\int \sin^n ax\, dx = -\frac{\sin^{n-1} ax \cos ax}{na} + \frac{n-1}{n} \int \sin^{n-2} ax\, dx.$

283. $\displaystyle\int \sin^{2m} ax\, dx = -\frac{\cos ax}{a} \sum_{r=0}^{m-1} \frac{(2m)!(r!)^2}{2^{2m-2r}(2r+1)!(m!)^2} \sin^{2r+1} ax + \frac{(2m)!}{2^{2m}(m!)^2}x.$

284. $\displaystyle\int \sin^{2m+1} ax\, dx = -\frac{\cos ax}{a} \sum_{r=0}^{m-1} \frac{2^{2m-2r}(m!)^2(2r)!}{(2m+1)!(r!)^2} \sin^{2r} ax.$

285. $\displaystyle\int \cos^2 ax\, dx = \frac{1}{2}x + \frac{1}{2a} \sin ax \cos ax = \frac{1}{2}x + \frac{1}{4a} \sin 2ax$

286. $\displaystyle\int \cos^3 ax\, dx = \frac{1}{3a} \sin ax\,(\cos^2 ax + 2).$

287. $\displaystyle\int \cos^4 ax\, dx = \frac{3}{8}x + \frac{\sin 2ax}{4a} + \frac{\sin 4ax}{32a}.$

288. $\displaystyle\int \cos^n ax\, dx = \frac{1}{na} \cos^{n-1} ax \sin ax + \frac{n-1}{n} \int \cos^{n-2} ax\, dx.$

289. $\displaystyle\int \cos^{2m} ax \, dx = \frac{\sin ax}{a} \sum_{r=0}^{m-1} \frac{(2m)!(r!)^2}{2^{2m-2r}(2r+1)!(m!)^2} \cos^{2r+1} ax + \frac{(2m)!}{2^{2m}(m!)^2} x.$

290. $\displaystyle\int \cos^{2m+1} ax \, dx = \frac{\sin ax}{a} \sum_{r=0}^{m} \frac{2^{2m-2r}(m!)^2(2r)!}{(2m+1)!(r!)^2} \cos^{2r} ax.$

291. $\displaystyle\int \frac{dx}{\sin^2 ax} = \int \operatorname{cosec}^2 ax \, dx = -\frac{1}{a} \cot ax.$

292. $\displaystyle\int \frac{dx}{\sin^m ax} = \int \operatorname{cosec}^m ax \, dx = -\frac{1}{a(m-1)} \frac{\cos ax}{\sin^{m-1} ax} + \frac{m-2}{m-1} \int \frac{dx}{\sin^{m-2} ax}.$

293. $\displaystyle\int \frac{dx}{\sin^{2m} ax} = \int \operatorname{cosec}^{2m} ax \, dx = -\frac{1}{a} \cos ax \sum_{r=0}^{m-1} \frac{2^{2m-2r-1}(m-1)!m!(2r)!}{(2m)!(r!)^2 \sin^{2r+1} ax}.$

294. $\displaystyle\int \frac{dx}{\sin^{2m+1} ax} = \int \operatorname{cosec}^{2m+1} ax \, dx =$

$$-\frac{1}{a} \cos ax \sum_{r=0}^{m-1} \frac{(2m)!(r!)^2}{2^{2m-2r}(2r+1)!(m!)^2 \sin^{2r+2} ax} + \frac{1}{a} \frac{(2m)!}{2^{2m}(m!)^2} \log \tan \frac{ax}{2}.$$

295. $\displaystyle\int \frac{dx}{\cos^2 ax} = \int \sec^2 ax \, dx = \frac{1}{a} \tan ax.$

296. $\displaystyle\int \frac{dx}{\cos^m ax} = \int \sec^m ax \, dx = \frac{1}{a(m-1)} \frac{\sin ax}{\cos^{m-1} ax} + \frac{m-2}{m-1} \int \frac{dx}{\cos^{m-2} ax}.$

297. $\displaystyle\int \frac{dx}{\cos^{2m} ax} = \int \sec^{2m} ax \, dx = \frac{1}{a} \sin ax \sum_{r=0}^{m-1} \frac{2^{2m-2r-1}(m-1)!m!(2r)!}{(2m)!(r!)^2 \cos^{2r+1} ax}.$

298. $\displaystyle\int \frac{dx}{\cos^{2m+1} ax} = \int \sec^{2m+1} ax \, dx = \frac{1}{a} \sin ax \sum_{r=0}^{m-1} \frac{(2m)!(r!)^2}{2^{2m-2r}(m!)^2(2r+1)! \cos^{2r+2} ax}$

$$+\frac{1}{a} \frac{(2m)!}{2^{2m}(m!)^2} \log (\sec ax + \tan ax).$$

299. $\displaystyle\int (\sin mx)(\sin nx) \, dx = \frac{\sin (m-n)x}{2(m-n)} - \frac{\sin (m+n)x}{2(m+n)}, \quad m^2 \neq n^2.$

300. $\displaystyle\int (\cos mx)(\cos nx) \, dx = \frac{\sin (m-n)x}{2(m-n)} + \frac{\sin (m+n)x}{2(m+n)}, \quad m^2 \neq n^2.$

301. $\displaystyle\int (\sin ax)(\cos ax) \, dx = \frac{1}{2a} \sin^2 ax.$

302. $\displaystyle\int (\sin mx)(\cos nx) \, dx = -\frac{\cos (m-n)x}{2(m-n)} - \frac{\cos (m+n)x}{2(m+n)}, \quad m^2 \neq n^2.$

303. $\displaystyle\int (\sin^2 ax)(\cos^2 ax) \, dx = -\frac{1}{32a} \sin 4ax + \frac{x}{8}.$

304. $\displaystyle\int (\sin ax)(\cos^m ax) \, dx = -\frac{\cos^{m+1} ax}{(m+1)a}.$

305. $\displaystyle\int (\sin^m ax)(\cos ax) \, dx = \frac{\sin^{m+1} ax}{(m+1)a}.$

306. $\displaystyle\int (\cos^m ax)(\sin^n ax) \, dx =$

$$\begin{cases} \dfrac{\cos^{m-1} ax \sin^{n+1} ax}{(m+n)a} + \dfrac{m-1}{m+n} \displaystyle\int (\cos^{m-2} ax)(\sin^n ax) \, dx, \\[2mm] \text{or} \\[2mm] -\dfrac{\cos^{m+1} ax \sin^{n-1} ax}{(m+n)a} + \dfrac{n-1}{m+n} \displaystyle\int (\cos^m ax)(\sin^{n-2} ax) \, dx. \end{cases}$$

307. $\displaystyle\int \frac{\cos^m ax}{\sin^n ax}\,dx = \begin{cases} -\dfrac{\cos^{m+1} ax}{a(n-1)\sin^{n-1} ax} - \dfrac{m-n+2}{n-1}\displaystyle\int \dfrac{\cos^m ax}{\sin^{n-2} ax}\,dx, \\[2ex] \text{or} \\[1ex] \dfrac{\cos^{m-1} ax}{a(m-n)\sin^{n-1} ax} + \dfrac{m-1}{m-n}\displaystyle\int \dfrac{\cos^{m-2} ax}{\sin^n ax}\,dx, \end{cases}$

308. $\displaystyle\int \frac{\sin^m ax}{\cos^n ax}\,dx = \begin{cases} \dfrac{\sin^{m+1} ax}{a(n-1)\cos^{n-1} ax} - \dfrac{m-n+2}{n-1}\displaystyle\int \dfrac{\sin^m ax}{\cos^{n-2} ax}\,dx, \\[2ex] \text{or} \\[1ex] -\dfrac{\sin^{m-1} ax}{a(m-n)\cos^{n-1} ax} + \dfrac{m-1}{m-n}\displaystyle\int \dfrac{\sin^{m-2} ax}{\cos^n ax}\,dx. \end{cases}$

309. $\displaystyle\int \frac{\sin ax}{\cos^2 ax}\,dx = \frac{1}{a\cos ax} = \frac{\sec ax}{a}$

310. $\displaystyle\int \frac{\sin^2 ax}{\cos ax}\,dx = -\frac{1}{a}\sin ax + \frac{1}{a}\log\tan\left(\frac{\pi}{4} + \frac{ax}{2}\right).$

311. $\displaystyle\int \frac{\cos ax}{\sin^2 ax}\,dx = -\frac{\csc ax}{a} = -\frac{1}{a\sin ax}$

312. $\displaystyle\int \frac{dx}{(\sin ax)(\cos ax)} = \frac{1}{a}\log\tan ax.$

313. $\displaystyle\int \frac{dx}{(\sin ax)(\cos^2 ax)} = \frac{1}{a}\left(\sec ax + \log\tan\frac{ax}{2}\right).$

314. $\displaystyle\int \frac{dx}{(\sin ax)(\cos^n ax)} = \frac{1}{a(n-1)\cos^{n-1} ax} + \int \frac{dx}{(\sin ax)(\cos^{n-2} ax)}.$

315. $\displaystyle\int \frac{dx}{(\sin^2 ax)(\cos ax)} = -\frac{1}{a}\csc ax + \frac{1}{a}\log\tan\left(\frac{\pi}{4} + \frac{ax}{2}\right).$

316. $\displaystyle\int \frac{dx}{(\sin^2 ax)(\cos^2 ax)} = -\frac{2}{a}\cot 2ax.$

317. $\displaystyle\int \frac{dx}{\sin^m ax \cos^n ax} =$
$\begin{cases} -\dfrac{1}{a(m-1)\sin^{m-1} ax \cos^{n-1} ax} + \dfrac{m+n-2}{m-1}\displaystyle\int \dfrac{dx}{\sin^{m-2} ax \cos^n ax}, \\[2ex] \text{or} \\[1ex] \dfrac{1}{a(n-1)\sin^{m-1} ax \cos^{n-1} ax} + \dfrac{m+n-2}{n-1}\displaystyle\int \dfrac{dx}{\sin^m ax \cos^{n-2} ax}. \end{cases}$

318. $\displaystyle\int \sin(a+bx)\,dx = -\frac{1}{b}\cos(a+bx).$

319. $\displaystyle\int \cos(a+bx)\,dx = \frac{1}{b}\sin(a+bx).$

320. $\displaystyle\int \frac{dx}{1 \pm \sin ax} = \mp\frac{1}{a}\tan\left(\frac{\pi}{4} \mp \frac{ax}{2}\right).$

321. $\displaystyle\int \frac{dx}{1 + \cos ax} = \frac{1}{a}\tan\frac{ax}{2}.$

322. $\displaystyle\int \frac{dx}{1 - \cos ax} = -\frac{1}{a}\cot\frac{ax}{2}.$

323. $\displaystyle\int \frac{dx}{a + b\sin x} = \begin{cases} \dfrac{2}{\sqrt{a^2 - b^2}}\tan^{-1}\left(\dfrac{a\tan\frac{x}{2} + b}{\sqrt{a^2 - b^2}}\right), \\[2ex] \text{or} \\[1ex] \dfrac{1}{\sqrt{b^2 - a^2}}\log\left(\dfrac{a\tan\frac{x}{2} + b - \sqrt{b^2 - a^2}}{a\tan\frac{x}{2} + b + \sqrt{b^2 - a^2}}\right). \end{cases}$

324. $\displaystyle\int \frac{dx}{a + b\cos x} = \begin{cases} \dfrac{2}{\sqrt{a^2 - b^2}} \tan^{-1} \dfrac{\sqrt{a^2 - b^2}\, \tan \frac{x}{2}}{a + b}, \\[2mm] \text{or} \\[2mm] \dfrac{1}{\sqrt{b^2 - a^2}} \log \left(\dfrac{\sqrt{b^2 - a^2}\, \tan \frac{x}{2} + a + b}{\sqrt{b^2 - a^2}\, \tan \frac{x}{2} - a - b} \right). \end{cases}$

325. $\displaystyle\int \frac{dx}{a + b\sin x + c\cos x} =$

$\begin{cases} \dfrac{1}{\sqrt{b^2 + c^2 - a^2}} \log \dfrac{b - \sqrt{b^2 + c^2 - a^2} + (a - c) \tan \frac{x}{2}}{b + \sqrt{b^2 + c^2 - a^2} + (a - c) \tan \frac{x}{2}}, & a \neq c,\ a^2 < b^2 + c^2, \\[3mm] \text{or} \\[2mm] \dfrac{2}{\sqrt{a^2 - b^2 - c^2}} \tan^{-1} \dfrac{b + (a - c) \tan \frac{x}{2}}{\sqrt{a^2 - b^2 - c^2}}, & a^2 > b^2 + c^2, \\[3mm] \text{or} \\[2mm] \dfrac{1}{a} \left[\dfrac{a - (b + c)\sin x - (b - c)\sin x}{a - (b + c)\sin x + (b - c)\sin x} \right], & a^2 = b^2 + c^2. \end{cases}$

326. $\displaystyle\int \frac{\sin^2 x}{a + b\cos^2 x}\, dx = \frac{1}{b}\sqrt{\frac{a + b}{a}} \tan^{-1}\left(\sqrt{\frac{a}{a + b}}\, \tan x\right) - \frac{x}{b},\quad ab > 0,\ |a| > |b|.$

327. $\displaystyle\int \frac{dx}{a^2 \cos^2 x + b^2 \sin^2 x} = \frac{1}{ab} \tan^{-1}\left(\frac{b\tan x}{a}\right).$

328. $\displaystyle\int \frac{\cos^2 cx}{a^2 + b^2 \sin^2 cx}\, dx = \frac{\sqrt{a^2 + b^2}}{ab^2 c} \tan^{-1} \frac{\sqrt{a^2 + b^2}\, \tan cx}{a} - \frac{x}{b^2}.$

329. $\displaystyle\int \frac{\sin cx \cos cx}{a \cos^2 cx + b \sin^2 cx}\, dx = \frac{1}{2c(b - a)} \log\left(a \cos^2 cx + b \sin^2 cx\right).$

330. $\displaystyle\int \frac{\cos cx}{a \cos cx + b \sin cx}\, dx =$

$\displaystyle\int \frac{dx}{a + b\tan cx} = \frac{1}{c(a^2 + b^2)}\left[acx + b\log\left(a\cos cx + b\sin cx\right)\right]$

331. $\displaystyle\int \frac{\sin cx}{a \cos cx + b \sin cx}\, dx =$

$\displaystyle\int \frac{dx}{b + a\cot cx} = \frac{1}{c(a^2 + b^2)}\left[bcx - a\log\left(a\cos cx + b\sin cx\right)\right]$

332. $\displaystyle\int \frac{dx}{a \cos^2 x + 2b \cos x \sin x + c \sin^2 x} =$

$\begin{cases} \dfrac{1}{2\sqrt{b^2 - ac}} \log \dfrac{c\tan x + b - \sqrt{b^2 - ac}}{c\tan x + b + \sqrt{b^2 - ac}}, & b^2 > ac, \\[3mm] \text{or} \\[2mm] \dfrac{1}{\sqrt{ac - b^2}} \tan^{-1} \dfrac{c\tan x + b}{\sqrt{ac - b^2}}, & b^2 < ac, \\[3mm] \text{or} \\[2mm] -\dfrac{1}{c\tan x + b}, & b^2 = ac. \end{cases}$

333. $\displaystyle\int \frac{\sin ax}{1 \pm \sin ax}\, dx = \pm x + \frac{1}{a} \tan\left(\frac{\pi}{4} \mp \frac{ax}{2}\right).$

334. $\displaystyle\int \frac{dx}{(\sin ax)(1 \pm \sin ax)} = \frac{1}{a} \tan\left(\frac{\pi}{4} \mp \frac{ax}{2}\right) + \frac{1}{a} \log \tan \frac{ax}{2}.$

335. $\displaystyle\int \frac{dx}{(1 + \sin ax)^2} = -\frac{1}{2a} \tan\left(\frac{\pi}{4} - \frac{ax}{2}\right) - \frac{1}{6a} \tan^3\left(\frac{\pi}{4} - \frac{ax}{2}\right).$

336. $\displaystyle\int \frac{dx}{(1 - \sin ax)^2} = \frac{1}{2a}\cot\left(\frac{\pi}{4} - \frac{ax}{2}\right) + \frac{1}{6a}\cot^3\left(\frac{\pi}{4} - \frac{ax}{2}\right).$

337. $\displaystyle\int \frac{\sin ax}{(1 + \sin ax)^2}\,dx = -\frac{1}{2a}\tan\left(\frac{\pi}{4} - \frac{ax}{2}\right) + \frac{1}{6a}\tan^3\left(\frac{\pi}{4} - \frac{ax}{2}\right).$

338. $\displaystyle\int \frac{\sin ax}{(1 - \sin ax)^2}\,dx = -\frac{1}{2a}\cot\left(\frac{\pi}{4} - \frac{ax}{2}\right) + \frac{1}{6a}\cot^3\left(\frac{\pi}{4} - \frac{ax}{2}\right).$

339. $\displaystyle\int \frac{\sin x}{a + b\sin x}\,dx = \frac{x}{b} - \frac{a}{b}\int \frac{dx}{a + b\sin x}.$

340. $\displaystyle\int \frac{dx}{(\sin x)(a + b\sin x)} = \frac{1}{a}\log\tan\frac{x}{2} - \frac{b}{a}\int \frac{dx}{a + b\sin x}.$

341. $\displaystyle\int \frac{dx}{(a + b\sin x)^2} = \begin{cases} \dfrac{b\cos x}{(a^2 - b^2)(a + b\sin x)} + \dfrac{a}{a^2 - b^2}\displaystyle\int \dfrac{dx}{a + b\sin x}, \\[4mm] \text{or} \\[2mm] \dfrac{a\cos x}{(b^2 - a^2)(a + b\sin x)} + \dfrac{b}{b^2 - a^2}\displaystyle\int \dfrac{dx}{a + b\sin x}. \end{cases}$

342. $\displaystyle\int \frac{dx}{a^2 + b^2\sin^2 cx} = \frac{1}{ac\sqrt{a^2 + b^2}}\tan^{-1}\frac{\sqrt{a^2 + b^2}\,\tan cx}{a}.$

343. $\displaystyle\int \frac{dx}{a^2 - b^2\sin^2 cx} = \begin{cases} \dfrac{1}{ac\sqrt{a^2 - b^2}}\tan^{-1}\dfrac{\sqrt{a^2 - b^2}\,\tan cx}{a}, & a^2 > b^2, \\[4mm] \text{or} \\[2mm] \dfrac{1}{2ac\sqrt{b^2 - a^2}}\log\dfrac{\sqrt{b^2 - a^2}\,\tan cx + a}{\sqrt{b^2 - a^2}\,\tan cx - a}, & a^2 < b^2. \end{cases}$

344. $\displaystyle\int \frac{\cos ax}{1 + \cos ax}\,dx = x - \frac{1}{a}\tan\frac{ax}{2}.$

345. $\displaystyle\int \frac{\cos ax}{1 - \cos ax}\,dx = -x - \frac{1}{a}\cot\frac{ax}{2}.$

346. $\displaystyle\int \frac{dx}{(\cos ax)(1 + \cos ax)} = \frac{1}{a}\log\tan\left(\frac{\pi}{4} + \frac{ax}{2}\right) - \frac{1}{a}\tan\frac{ax}{2}.$

347. $\displaystyle\int \frac{dx}{(\cos ax)(1 - \cos ax)} = \frac{1}{a}\log\tan\left(\frac{\pi}{4} + \frac{ax}{2}\right) - \frac{1}{a}\cot\frac{ax}{2}.$

348. $\displaystyle\int \frac{dx}{(1 + \cos ax)^2} = \frac{1}{2a}\tan\frac{ax}{2} + \frac{1}{6a}\tan^3\frac{ax}{2}.$

349. $\displaystyle\int \frac{dx}{(1 - \cos ax)^2} = -\frac{1}{2a}\cot\frac{ax}{2} - \frac{1}{6a}\cot^3\frac{ax}{2}.$

350. $\displaystyle\int \frac{\cos ax}{(1 + \cos ax)^2}\,dx = \frac{1}{2a}\tan\frac{ax}{2} - \frac{1}{6a}\tan^3\frac{ax}{2}.$

351. $\displaystyle\int \frac{\cos ax}{(1 - \cos ax)^2}\,dx = \frac{1}{2a}\cot\frac{ax}{2} - \frac{1}{6a}\cot^3\frac{ax}{2}.$

352. $\displaystyle\int \frac{\cos x}{a + b\cos x}\,dx = \frac{x}{b} - \frac{a}{b}\int \frac{dx}{a + b\cos x}.$

353. $\displaystyle\int \frac{dx}{(\cos x)(a + b\cos x)} = \frac{1}{a}\log\tan\left(\frac{x}{2} + \frac{\pi}{4}\right) - \frac{b}{a}\int \frac{dx}{a + b\cos x}.$

354. $\displaystyle\int \frac{dx}{(a + b\cos x)^2} = \frac{b\sin x}{(b^2 - a^2)(a + b\cos x)} - \frac{a}{b^2 - a^2}\int \frac{dx}{a + b\cos x}.$

355. $\displaystyle\int \frac{\cos x}{(a + b\cos x)^2}\,dx = \frac{a\sin x}{(a^2 - b^2)(a + b\cos x)} - \frac{b}{a^2 - b^2}\int \frac{dx}{a + b\cos x}.$

356. $\displaystyle\int \frac{dx}{a^2 + b^2 - 2ab\cos cx} = \frac{2}{c(a^2 - b^2)} \tan^{-1}\left(\frac{a+b}{a-b}\tan\frac{cx}{2}\right).$

357. $\displaystyle\int \frac{dx}{a^2 + b^2\cos^2 cx} = \frac{1}{ac\sqrt{a^2 + b^2}} \tan^{-1}\frac{a\tan cx}{\sqrt{a^2 + b^2}}.$

358. $\displaystyle\int \frac{dx}{a^2 - b^2\cos^2 cx} = \begin{cases} \dfrac{1}{ac\sqrt{a^2 - b^2}} \tan^{-1}\dfrac{a\tan cx}{\sqrt{a^2 - b^2}}, & a^2 > b^2, \\[2mm] \text{or} \\[2mm] \dfrac{1}{2ac\sqrt{b^2 - a^2}} \log\dfrac{a\tan cx - \sqrt{b^2 - a^2}}{a\tan cx + \sqrt{b^2 - a^2}}, & b^2 > a^2. \end{cases}$

359. $\displaystyle\int \frac{\sin ax}{1 \pm \cos ax}\, dx = \mp\frac{1}{a}\log(1 \pm \cos ax).$

360. $\displaystyle\int \frac{\cos ax}{1 \pm \sin ax}\, dx = \pm\frac{1}{a}\log(1 \pm \sin ax).$

361. $\displaystyle\int \frac{dx}{(\sin ax)(1 \pm \cos ax)} = \pm\frac{1}{2a(1 \pm \cos ax)} + \frac{1}{2a}\log\tan\frac{ax}{2}.$

362. $\displaystyle\int \frac{dx}{(\cos ax)(1 \pm \sin ax)} = \mp\frac{1}{2a(1 \pm \sin ax)} + \frac{1}{2a}\log\tan\left(\frac{ax}{2} + \frac{\pi}{4}\right).$

363. $\displaystyle\int \frac{\sin ax}{(\cos ax)(1 \pm \cos ax)}\, dx = \frac{1}{a}\log(\sec ax \pm 1).$

364. $\displaystyle\int \frac{\cos ax}{(\sin ax)(1 \pm \sin ax)}\, dx = -\frac{1}{a}\log(\csc ax \pm 1).$

365. $\displaystyle\int \frac{\sin ax}{(\cos ax)(1 \pm \sin ax)}\, dx = \frac{1}{2a(1 \pm \sin ax)} \pm \frac{1}{2a}\log\tan\left(\frac{ax}{2} + \frac{\pi}{4}\right).$

366. $\displaystyle\int \frac{\cos ax}{(\sin ax)(1 \pm \cos ax)}\, dx = -\frac{1}{2a(1 \pm \cos ax)} \pm \frac{1}{2a}\log\tan\frac{ax}{2}.$

367. $\displaystyle\int \frac{dx}{\sin ax \pm \cos ax} = \frac{1}{a\sqrt{2}}\log\tan\left(\frac{ax}{2} \pm \frac{\pi}{8}\right).$

368. $\displaystyle\int \frac{dx}{(\sin ax \pm \cos ax)^2} = \frac{1}{2a}\tan\left(ax \mp \frac{\pi}{4}\right).$

369. $\displaystyle\int \frac{dx}{1 + \cos ax \pm \sin ax} = \pm\frac{1}{a}\log\left(1 \pm \tan\frac{ax}{2}\right).$

370. $\displaystyle\int \frac{dx}{a^2\cos^2 cx - b^2\sin^2 cx} = \frac{1}{2abc}\log\frac{b\tan cx + a}{b\tan cx - a}.$

371. $\displaystyle\int x\sin ax\, dx = \frac{1}{a^2}\sin ax - \frac{x}{a}\cos ax.$

372. $\displaystyle\int x^2\sin ax\, dx = \frac{2x}{a^2}\sin ax + \frac{2 - a^2x^2}{a^3}\cos ax.$

373. $\displaystyle\int x^3\sin ax\, dx = \frac{3a^2x^2 - 6}{a^4}\sin ax + \frac{6x - a^2x^3}{a^3}\cos ax.$

374. $\displaystyle\int x^m\sin ax\, dx =$

$\begin{cases} -\dfrac{1}{a}x^m\cos ax + \dfrac{m}{a}\displaystyle\int x^{m-1}\cos ax\, dx, \\[2mm] \text{or} \\[2mm] \cos ax\displaystyle\sum_{r=0}^{\lfloor\frac{m}{2}\rfloor}(-1)^{r+1}\dfrac{m!}{(m-2r)!}\dfrac{x^{m-2r}}{a^{2r+1}} + \sin ax\displaystyle\sum_{r=0}^{\lfloor\frac{m-1}{2}\rfloor}(-1)^r\dfrac{m!}{(m-2r-1)!}\dfrac{x^{m-2r-1}}{a^{2r+2}}. \end{cases}$

375. $\displaystyle\int x\cos ax\,dx = \frac{1}{a^2}\cos ax + \frac{x}{a}\sin ax.$

376. $\displaystyle\int x^2\cos ax\,dx = \frac{2x}{a^2}\cos ax + \frac{a^2x^2-2}{a^3}\sin ax.$

377. $\displaystyle\int x^3\cos ax\,dx = \frac{3a^2x^2-6}{a^4}\cos ax + \frac{a^2x^3-6x}{a^3}\sin ax.$

378. $\displaystyle\int x^m\cos ax\,dx =$

$$\begin{cases} \dfrac{x^m}{a}\sin ax - \dfrac{m}{a}\displaystyle\int x^{m-1}\sin ax\,dx, \\[2mm] \quad\text{or} \\[2mm] \sin ax \displaystyle\sum_{r=0}^{\lfloor\frac{m}{2}\rfloor}(-1)^r\,\frac{m!}{(m-2r)!}\,\frac{x^{m-2r}}{a^{2r+1}} + \cos ax\displaystyle\sum_{r=0}^{\lfloor\frac{m-1}{2}\rfloor}(-1)^r\,\frac{m!}{(m-2r-1)!}\,\frac{x^{m-2r-1}}{a^{2r+2}}. \end{cases}$$

379. $\displaystyle\int \frac{\sin ax}{x}\,dx = \sum_{n=0}^{\infty}(-1)^n\,\frac{(ax)^{2n+1}}{(2n+1)(2n+1)!}.$

380. $\displaystyle\int \frac{\cos ax}{x}\,dx = \sum_{n=0}^{\infty}(-1)^n\,\frac{(ax)^{2n}}{(2n)(2n)!}.$

381. $\displaystyle\int x\sin^2 ax\,dx = \frac{x^2}{4} - \frac{x}{4a}\sin 2ax - \frac{1}{8a^2}\cos 2ax.$

382. $\displaystyle\int x^2\sin^2 ax\,dx = \frac{x^3}{6} - \left(\frac{x^2}{4a} - \frac{1}{8a^3}\right)\sin 2ax - \frac{x}{4a^2}\cos 2ax.$

383. $\displaystyle\int x\sin^3 ax\,dx = \frac{x}{12a}\cos 3ax - \frac{1}{36a^2}\sin 3ax - \frac{3x}{4a}\cos ax + \frac{3}{4a^2}\sin ax.$

384. $\displaystyle\int x\cos^2 ax\,dx = \frac{x^2}{4} + \frac{x}{4a}\sin 2ax + \frac{1}{8a^2}\cos 2ax.$

385. $\displaystyle\int x^2\cos^2 ax\,dx = \frac{x^3}{6} + \left(\frac{x^2}{4a} - \frac{1}{8a^3}\right)\sin 2ax + \frac{x}{4a^2}\cos 2ax.$

386. $\displaystyle\int x\cos^3 ax\,dx = \frac{x}{12a}\sin 3ax + \frac{1}{36a^2}\cos 3ax + \frac{3x}{4a}\sin ax + \frac{3}{4a^2}\cos ax.$

387. $\displaystyle\int \frac{\sin ax}{x^m}\,dx = \frac{\sin ax}{(1-m)x^{m-1}} + \frac{a}{m-1}\int \frac{\cos ax}{x^{m-1}}\,dx.$

388. $\displaystyle\int \frac{\cos ax}{x^m}\,dx = \frac{\cos ax}{(1-m)x^{m-1}} + \frac{a}{1-m}\int \frac{\sin ax}{x^{m-1}}\,dx.$

389. $\displaystyle\int \frac{x}{1\pm\sin ax}\,dx = \mp\frac{x\cos ax}{a(1\pm\sin ax)} + \frac{1}{a^2}\log(1\pm\sin ax).$

390. $\displaystyle\int \frac{x}{1+\cos ax}\,dx = \frac{x}{a}\tan\frac{ax}{2} + \frac{2}{a^2}\log\cos\frac{ax}{2}.$

391. $\displaystyle\int \frac{x}{1-\cos ax}\,dx = -\frac{x}{a}\cot\frac{ax}{2} + \frac{2}{a^2}\log\sin\frac{ax}{2}.$

392. $\displaystyle\int \frac{x+\sin x}{1+\cos x}\,dx = x\tan\frac{x}{2}.$

393. $\displaystyle\int \frac{x-\sin x}{1-\cos x}\,dx = -x\cot\frac{x}{2}.$

394. $\displaystyle\int \sqrt{1-\cos ax}\,dx = -\frac{2\sin ax}{a\sqrt{1-\cos ax}} = -\frac{2\sqrt{2}}{a}\cos\frac{ax}{2}.$

395. $\displaystyle \int \sqrt{1 + \cos ax}\, dx = \frac{2\sin ax}{a\sqrt{1 + \cos ax}} = \frac{2\sqrt{2}}{a}\sin\frac{ax}{2}$

For the following six integrals, each k represents an integer.

396. $* \displaystyle\int \sqrt{1 + \sin x}\, dx = \begin{cases} 2\left(\sin\dfrac{x}{2} - \cos\dfrac{x}{2}\right), & (8k-1)\dfrac{\pi}{2} < x \le (8k+3)\dfrac{\pi}{2}, \\ \text{or} \\ -2\left(\sin\dfrac{x}{2} - \cos\dfrac{x}{2}\right), & (8k+3)\dfrac{\pi}{2} < x \le (8k-1)\dfrac{\pi}{2}. \end{cases}$

397. $* \displaystyle\int \sqrt{1 - \sin x}\, dx = \begin{cases} 2\left(\sin\dfrac{x}{2} + \cos\dfrac{x}{2}\right), & (8k-3)\dfrac{\pi}{2} < x \le (8k+1)\dfrac{\pi}{2}, \\ \text{or} \\ -2\left(\sin\dfrac{x}{2} + \cos\dfrac{x}{2}\right), & (8k+1)\dfrac{\pi}{2} < x \le (8k-3)\dfrac{\pi}{2}. \end{cases}$

398. $* \displaystyle\int \frac{dx}{\sqrt{1 - \cos x}} = \begin{cases} \sqrt{2}\log\tan\dfrac{x}{4}, & 4k\pi < x \le (4k+2)\pi, \\ \text{or} \\ -\sqrt{2}\log\tan\dfrac{x}{4} & (4k+2)\pi < x \le 4k\pi. \end{cases}$

399. $* \displaystyle\int \frac{dx}{\sqrt{1 + \cos x}} = \begin{cases} \sqrt{2}\log\tan\left(\dfrac{x+\pi}{4}\right), & (4k-1)\pi < x \le (4k+1)\pi, \\ \text{or} \\ -\sqrt{2}\log\tan\left(\dfrac{x+\pi}{4}\right), & (4k+1)\pi < x \le (4k-1)\pi. \end{cases}$

400. $* \displaystyle\int \frac{dx}{\sqrt{1 - \sin x}} = \begin{cases} \sqrt{2}\log\tan\left(\dfrac{x}{4} - \dfrac{\pi}{8}\right), & (8k+1)\dfrac{\pi}{2} < x \le (8k+5)\dfrac{\pi}{2}, \\ \text{or} \\ -\sqrt{2}\log\tan\left(\dfrac{x}{4} - \dfrac{\pi}{8}\right), & (8k+5)\dfrac{\pi}{2} < x \le (8k+1)\dfrac{\pi}{2}. \end{cases}$

401. $* \displaystyle\int \frac{dx}{\sqrt{1 + \sin x}} = \begin{cases} \sqrt{2}\log\tan\left(\dfrac{x}{4} + \dfrac{\pi}{8}\right), & (8k-1)\dfrac{\pi}{2} < x \le (8k+3)\dfrac{\pi}{2}, \\ \text{or} \\ -\sqrt{2}\log\tan\left(\dfrac{x}{4} + \dfrac{\pi}{8}\right), & (8k+3)\dfrac{\pi}{2} < x \le (8k-1)\dfrac{\pi}{2}. \end{cases}$

402. $\displaystyle \int \tan^2 ax\, dx = \frac{1}{a}\tan ax - x.$

403. $\displaystyle \int \tan^3 ax\, dx = \frac{1}{2a}\tan^2 ax + \frac{1}{a}\log\cos ax.$

404. $\displaystyle \int \tan^4 ax\, dx = \frac{1}{3a}\tan^3 ax - \frac{1}{a}\tan ax + x.$

405. $\displaystyle \int \tan^n ax\, dx = \frac{1}{a(n-1)}\tan^{n-1} ax - \int \tan^{n-2} ax\, dx.$

406. $\displaystyle \int \cot^2 ax\, dx = -\frac{1}{a}\cot ax - x.$

407. $\displaystyle \int \cot^3 ax\, dx = -\frac{1}{2a}\cot^2 ax - \frac{1}{a}\log\sin ax.$

408. $\displaystyle \int \cot^4 ax\, dx = -\frac{1}{3a}\cot^3 ax + \frac{1}{a}\cot ax + x.$

409. $\displaystyle \int \cot^n ax\, dx = -\frac{1}{a(n-1)}\cot^{n-1} ax - \int \cot^{n-2} ax\, dx.$

410. $\displaystyle \int \frac{x}{\sin^2 ax}\, dx = \int x\csc^2 ax\, dx = -\frac{x\cot ax}{a} + \frac{1}{a^2}\log\sin ax$

411. $\displaystyle\int \frac{x}{\sin^n ax}\,dx = \int x\csc^n ax\,dx = -\frac{x\cos ax}{a(n-1)\sin^{n-1} ax}$

$$-\frac{1}{a^2(n-1)(n-2)\sin^{n-2} ax} + \frac{n-2}{n-1}\int \frac{x}{\sin^{n-2} ax}\,dx$$

412. $\displaystyle\int \frac{x}{\cos^2 ax}\,dx = \int x\sec^2 ax\,dx = \frac{x}{a}\tan ax + \frac{1}{a^2}\log\cos ax$

413. $\displaystyle\int \frac{x}{\cos^n ax}\,dx = \int x\sec^n ax\,dx = \frac{x\sin ax}{a(n-1)\cos^{n-1} ax}$

$$-\frac{1}{a^2(n-1)(n-2)\cos^{n-2} ax} + \frac{n-2}{n-1}\int \frac{x}{\cos^{n-2} ax}\,dx$$

414. $\displaystyle\int \frac{\sin ax}{\sqrt{1+b^2\sin^2 ax}}\,dx = -\frac{1}{ab}\sin^{-1}\frac{b\cos ax}{\sqrt{1+b^2}}.$

415. $\displaystyle\int \frac{\sin ax}{\sqrt{1-b^2\sin^2 ax}}\,dx = -\frac{1}{ab}\log\left(b\cos ax + \sqrt{1-b^2\sin^2 ax}\right).$

416. $\displaystyle\int (\sin ax)\sqrt{1+b^2\sin^2 ax}\,dx = -\frac{\cos ax}{2a}\sqrt{1+b^2\sin^2 ax} - \frac{1+b^2}{2ab}\sin^{-1}\frac{b\cos ax}{\sqrt{1+b^2}}.$

417. $\displaystyle\int (\sin ax)\sqrt{1-b^2\sin^2 ax}\,dx = -\frac{\cos ax}{2a}\sqrt{1-b^2\sin^2 ax}$

$$-\frac{1-b^2}{2ab}\log\left(b\cos ax + \sqrt{1-b^2\sin^2 ax}\right).$$

418. $\displaystyle\int \frac{\cos ax}{\sqrt{1+b^2\sin^2 ax}}\,dx = \frac{1}{ab}\log\left(b\sin ax + \sqrt{1+b^2\sin^2 ax}\right).$

419. $\displaystyle\int \frac{\cos ax}{\sqrt{1-b^2\sin^2 ax}}\,dx = \frac{1}{ab}\sin^{-1}(b\sin ax).$

420. $\displaystyle\int (\cos ax)\sqrt{1+b^2\sin^2 ax}\,dx = \frac{\sin ax}{2a}\sqrt{1+b^2\sin^2 ax}$

$$+\frac{1}{2ab}\log\left(b\sin ax + \sqrt{1+b^2\sin^2 ax}\right).$$

421. $\displaystyle\int (\cos ax)\sqrt{1-b^2\sin^2 ax}\,dx = \frac{\sin ax}{2a}\sqrt{1-b^2\sin^2 ax} + \frac{1}{2ab}\sin^{-1}(b\sin ax).$

For the following integral, k represents an integer and $a > |b|$

422. $*\displaystyle\int \frac{dx}{\sqrt{a+b\tan^2 cx}} =$

$$\begin{cases} \dfrac{1}{c\sqrt{a-b}}\sin^{-1}\left(\sqrt{\dfrac{a-b}{a}}\sin cx\right), & (2k-1)\frac{\pi}{2} < x \le (2k+1)\frac{\pi}{2}, \\[2mm] \text{or} \\[2mm] \dfrac{-1}{c\sqrt{a-b}}\sin^{-1}\left(\sqrt{\dfrac{a-b}{a}}\sin cx\right), & (2k+1)\frac{\pi}{2} < x \le (2k-1)\frac{\pi}{2}. \end{cases}$$

423. $\displaystyle\int \cos^n x\,dx = \frac{1}{2^{n-1}}\sum_{k=0}^{\frac{n}{2}-1}\binom{n}{k}\frac{\sin[(n-2k)x]}{(n-2k)} + \frac{1}{2^n}\binom{n}{\frac{n}{2}}x,$ n is an even integer.

424. $\displaystyle\int \cos^n x\,dx = \frac{1}{2^{n-1}}\sum_{k=0}^{\frac{n-1}{2}}\binom{n}{k}\frac{\sin[(n-2k)x]}{(n-2k)},$ n is an odd integer.

425. $\displaystyle\int \sin^n x\,dx = \frac{1}{2^{n-1}}\sum_{k=0}^{\frac{n}{2}-1}\binom{n}{k}\frac{\sin\left([(n-2k)(\frac{\pi}{2}-x)]\right)}{(2k-n)} + \frac{1}{2^n}\binom{n}{\frac{n}{2}}x,$ n is an even integer.

426. $\displaystyle\int \sin^n x \, dx = \frac{1}{2^{n-1}} \sum_{k=0}^{\frac{n-1}{2}} \binom{n}{k} \frac{\sin\left(\left[(n-2k)(\frac{\pi}{2}-x)\right]\right)}{(2k-n)}$, n is an odd integer.

5.4.17 FORMS INVOLVING INVERSE TRIGONOMETRIC FUNCTIONS

427. $\displaystyle\int \sin^{-1} ax \, dx = x \sin^{-1} ax + \frac{\sqrt{1-a^2x^2}}{a}$.

428. $\displaystyle\int \cos^{-1} ax \, dx = x \cos^{-1} ax - \frac{\sqrt{1-a^2x^2}}{a}$.

429. $\displaystyle\int \tan^{-1} ax \, dx = x \tan^{-1} ax - \frac{1}{2a} \log(1 + a^2x^2)$.

430. $\displaystyle\int \cot^{-1} ax \, dx = x \cot^{-1} ax + \frac{1}{2a} \log(1 + a^2x^2)$.

431. $\displaystyle\int \sec^{-1} ax \, dx = x \sec^{-1} ax - \frac{1}{a} \log\left(ax + \sqrt{a^2x^2 - 1}\right)$.

432. $\displaystyle\int \csc^{-1} ax \, dx = x \csc^{-1} ax + \frac{1}{a} \log\left(ax + \sqrt{a^2x^2 - 1}\right)$.

433. $\displaystyle\int \left(\sin^{-1} \frac{x}{a}\right) dx = x \sin^{-1} \frac{x}{a} + \sqrt{a^2 - x^2}$, $a > 0$.

434. $\displaystyle\int \left(\cos^{-1} \frac{x}{a}\right) dx = x \cos^{-1} \frac{x}{a} - \sqrt{a^2 - x^2}$, $a > 0$.

435. $\displaystyle\int \left(\tan^{-1} \frac{x}{a}\right) dx = x \tan^{-1} \frac{x}{a} - \frac{a}{2} \log(a^2 + x^2)$.

436. $\displaystyle\int \left(\cot^{-1} \frac{x}{a}\right) dx = x \cot^{-1} \frac{x}{a} + \frac{a}{2} \log(a^2 + x^2)$.

437. $\displaystyle\int x \sin^{-1}(ax) \, dx = \frac{1}{4a^2}\left((2a^2x^2 - 1)\sin^{-1}(ax) + ax\sqrt{1 - a^2x^2}\right)$.

438. $\displaystyle\int x \cos^{-1}(ax) \, dx = \frac{1}{4a^2}\left((2a^2x^2 - 1)\cos^{-1}(ax) - ax\sqrt{1 - a^2x^2}\right)$.

439. $\displaystyle\int x^n \sin^{-1}(ax) \, dx = \frac{x^{n+1}}{n+1} \sin^{-1}(ax) - \frac{a}{n+1} \int \frac{x^{n+1}}{\sqrt{1-a^2x^2}} \, dx$, $n \neq -1$.

440. $\displaystyle\int x^n \cos^{-1} ax \, dx = \frac{x^{n+1}}{n+1} \cos^{-1}(ax) + \frac{a}{n+1} \int \frac{x^{n+1}}{\sqrt{1-a^2x^2}} \, dx$, $n \neq -1$.

441. $\displaystyle\int x \tan^{-1}(ax) \, dx = \frac{1+a^2x^2}{2a^2} \tan^{-1}(ax) - \frac{x}{2a}$.

442. $\displaystyle\int x^n \tan^{-1}(ax) \, dx = \frac{x^{n+1}}{n+1} \tan^{-1}(ax) - \frac{a}{n+1} \int \frac{x^{n+1}}{1+a^2x^2} \, dx$.

443. $\displaystyle\int x \cot^{-1}(ax) \, dx = \frac{1+a^2x^2}{2a^2} \cot^{-1}(ax) + \frac{x}{2a}$.

444. $\displaystyle\int x^n \cot^{-1}(ax) \, dx = \frac{x^{n+1}}{n+1} \cot^{-1}(ax) + \frac{a}{n+1} \int \frac{x^{n+1}}{1+a^2x^2} \, dx$.

445. $\displaystyle\int \frac{\sin^{-1}(ax)}{x^2} \, dx = a \log\left(\frac{1-\sqrt{1-a^2x^2}}{x}\right) - \frac{\sin^{-1}(ax)}{x}$.

446. $\displaystyle\int \frac{\cos^{-1}(ax)}{x^2}\,dx = -\frac{1}{x}\cos^{-1}(ax) + a\log\frac{1+\sqrt{1-a^2x^2}}{x}.$

447. $\displaystyle\int \frac{\tan^{-1}(ax)}{x^2}\,dx = -\frac{1}{x}\tan^{-1}(ax) - \frac{a}{2}\log\frac{1+a^2x^2}{x^2}.$

448. $\displaystyle\int \frac{\cot^{-1}(ax)}{x^2}\,dx = -\frac{1}{x}\cot^{-1}(ax) - \frac{a}{2}\log\frac{x^2}{1+a^2x^2}.$

449. $\displaystyle\int (\sin^{-1}(ax))^2\,dx = x(\sin^{-1}(ax))^2 - 2x + \frac{2\sqrt{1-a^2x^2}}{a}\sin^{-1}(ax).$

450. $\displaystyle\int (\cos^{-1}(ax))^2\,dx = x(\cos^{-1}(ax))^2 - 2x - \frac{2\sqrt{1-a^2x^2}}{a}\cos^{-1}(ax).$

451. $\displaystyle\int (\sin^{-1}(ax))^n\,dx =$

$$\begin{cases} x(\sin^{-1}(ax))^n + \dfrac{n\sqrt{1-a^2x^2}}{a}(\sin^{-1}(ax))^{n-1} - n(n-1)\displaystyle\int (\sin^{-1}(ax))^{n-2}\,dx, \\[2mm] \text{or} \\[2mm] \displaystyle\sum_{r=0}^{\lfloor\frac{n}{2}\rfloor}(-1)^r \frac{n!}{(n-2r)!}x(\sin^{-1}ax)^{n-2r} + \sum_{r=0}^{\lfloor\frac{n-1}{2}\rfloor}(-1)^r \frac{n!\sqrt{1-a^2x^2}}{(n-2r-1)!a}(\sin^{-1}ax)^{n-2r-1}. \end{cases}$$

452. $\displaystyle\int (\cos^{-1}(ax))^n\,dx =$

$$\begin{cases} x(\cos^{-1}(ax))^n - \dfrac{n\sqrt{1-a^2x^2}}{a}(\cos^{-1}(ax))^{n-1} - n(n-1)\displaystyle\int (\cos^{-1}(ax))^{n-2}\,dx, \\[2mm] \text{or} \\[2mm] \displaystyle\sum_{r=0}^{\lfloor\frac{n}{2}\rfloor}(-1)^r \frac{n!}{(n-2r)!}x(\cos^{-1}ax)^{n-2r} - \sum_{r=0}^{\lfloor\frac{n-1}{2}\rfloor}(-1)^r \frac{n!\sqrt{1-a^2x^2}}{(n-2r-1)!a}(\cos^{-1}ax)^{n-2r-1}. \end{cases}$$

453. $\displaystyle\int \frac{\sin^{-1}ax}{\sqrt{1-a^2x^2}}\,dx = \frac{1}{2a}\left(\sin^{-1}ax\right)^2.$

454. $\displaystyle\int \frac{x^n \sin^{-1}ax}{\sqrt{1-a^2x^2}}\,dx = -\frac{x^{n-1}}{na^2}\sqrt{1-a^2x^2}\,\sin^{-1}ax + \frac{x^n}{n^2a}$
$$+\frac{n-1}{na^2}\int \frac{x^{n-2}\sin^{-1}ax}{\sqrt{1-a^2x^2}}\,dx.$$

455. $\displaystyle\int \frac{\cos^{-1}ax}{\sqrt{1-a^2x^2}}\,dx = -\frac{1}{2a}\left(\cos^{-1}ax\right)^2.$

456. $\displaystyle\int \frac{x^n \cos^{-1}ax}{\sqrt{1-a^2x^2}}\,dx = -\frac{x^{n-1}}{na^2}\sqrt{1-a^2x^2}\,\cos^{-1}ax - \frac{x^n}{n^2a}$
$$+\frac{n-1}{na^2}\int \frac{x^{n-2}\cos^{-1}ax}{\sqrt{1-a^2x^2}}\,dx.$$

457. $\displaystyle\int \frac{\tan^{-1}ax}{1+a^2x^2}\,dx = \frac{1}{2a}\left(\tan^{-1}ax\right)^2.$

458. $\displaystyle\int \frac{\cot^{-1}ax}{1+a^2x^2}\,dx = -\frac{1}{2a}\left(\cot^{-1}ax\right)^2.$

459. $\displaystyle\int x\sec^{-1}ax\,dx = \frac{x^2}{2}\sec^{-1}ax - \frac{1}{2a^2}\sqrt{a^2x^2-1}.$

460. $\displaystyle\int x^n\sec^{-1}ax\,dx = \frac{x^{n+1}}{n+1}\sec^{-1}ax - \frac{1}{n+1}\int \frac{x^n}{\sqrt{a^2x^2-1}}\,dx.$

461. $\displaystyle\int \frac{\sec^{-1} ax}{x^2}\, dx = -\frac{\sec^{-1} ax}{x} + \frac{\sqrt{a^2 x^2 - 1}}{x}.$

462. $\displaystyle\int x \csc^{-1} ax\, dx = \frac{x^2}{2}\csc^{-1} ax + \frac{1}{2a^2}\sqrt{a^2 x^2 - 1}.$

463. $\displaystyle\int x^n \csc^{-1} ax\, dx = \frac{x^{n+1}}{n+1}\csc^{-1} ax + \frac{1}{n+1}\int \frac{x^n}{\sqrt{a^2 x^2 - 1}}\, dx.$

464. $\displaystyle\int \frac{\csc^{-1} ax}{x^2}\, dx = -\frac{\csc^{-1} ax}{x} - \frac{\sqrt{a^2 x^2 - 1}}{x}.$

5.4.18   LOGARITHMIC FORMS

465. $\displaystyle\int \log x\, dx = x \log x - x.$

466. $\displaystyle\int x \log x\, dx = \frac{x^2}{2}\log x - \frac{x^2}{4}.$

467. $\displaystyle\int x^2 \log x\, dx = \frac{x^3}{3}\log x - \frac{x^3}{9}.$

468. $\displaystyle\int x^n \log x\, dx = \frac{x^{n+1}}{n+1}\log x - \frac{x^{n+1}}{(n+1)^2}.$

469. $\displaystyle\int (\log x)^2\, dx = x(\log x)^2 - 2x \log x + 2x.$

470. $\displaystyle\int (\log x)^n\, dx = \begin{cases} x(\log x)^n - n \displaystyle\int (\log x)^{n-1}\, dx, & n \neq -1, \\[2mm] \text{or} \\[2mm] (-1)^n n! x \displaystyle\sum_{r=0}^{n} \frac{(-\log x)^r}{r!}, & n \neq -1. \end{cases}$

471. $\displaystyle\int \frac{(\log x)^n}{x}\, dx = \frac{1}{n+1}(\log x)^{n+1}.$

472. *$\displaystyle\int \frac{dx}{\log x} = \log(\log x) + \log x + \frac{(\log x)^2}{2 \cdot 2!} + \frac{(\log x)^3}{3 \cdot 3!} + \cdots.$

473. $\displaystyle\int \frac{dx}{x \log x} = \log(\log x).$

474. $\displaystyle\int \frac{dx}{x(\log x)^n} = \frac{1}{(1-n)(\log x)^{n-1}}.$

475. $\displaystyle\int \frac{x^m\, dx}{(\log x)^n} = \frac{x^{m+1}}{(1-n)(\log x)^{n-1}} + \frac{m+1}{n-1}\int \frac{x^m\, dx}{(\log x)^{n-1}}.$

476. $\displaystyle\int x^m (\log x)^n\, dx = \begin{cases} \dfrac{x^{m+1}(\log x)^n}{m+1} - \dfrac{n}{m+1}\displaystyle\int x^m (\log x)^{n-1}\, dx, \\[2mm] \text{or} \\[2mm] (-1)^n \dfrac{n!}{m+1} x^{m+1} \displaystyle\sum_{r=0}^{n} \frac{(-\log x)^r}{r!(m+1)^{n-r}}. \end{cases}$

477. $\displaystyle\int x^p \cos(b \log x)\, dx = \frac{x^{p+1}}{(p+1)^2 + b^2}\left[b \sin(b \log x) + (p+1)\cos(b \log x)\right].$

478. $\displaystyle\int x^p \sin(b \log x)\, dx = \frac{x^{p+1}}{(p+1)^2 + b^2}\left[(p+1)\sin(b \log x) - b\cos(b \log x)\right].$

479. $\displaystyle\int \log(ax+b)\,dx = \frac{ax+b}{a}\log(ax+b) - x.$

480. $\displaystyle\int \frac{\log(ax+b)}{x^2}\,dx = \frac{a}{b}\log x - \frac{ax+b}{bx}\log(ax+b).$

481. $\displaystyle\int x^m \log(ax+b)\,dx = \frac{1}{m+1}\left[x^{m+1} - \left(-\frac{b}{a}\right)^{m+1}\right]\log(ax+b)$

$$-\frac{1}{m+1}\left(-\frac{b}{a}\right)^{m+1}\sum_{r=1}^{m+1}\frac{1}{r}\left(-\frac{ax}{b}\right)^r.$$

482. $\displaystyle\int \frac{\log(ax+b)}{x^m}\,dx = -\frac{1}{m-1}\frac{\log(ax+b)}{x^{m-1}} + \frac{1}{m-1}\left(-\frac{a}{b}\right)^{m-1}\log\frac{ax+b}{x}$

$$+\frac{1}{m-1}\left(-\frac{a}{b}\right)^{m-1}\sum_{r=1}^{m-2}\frac{1}{r}\left(-\frac{b}{ax}\right)^r, \quad m > 2.$$

483. $\displaystyle\int \log\frac{x+a}{x-a}\,dx = (x+a)\log(x+a) - (x-a)\log(x-a).$

484. $\displaystyle\int x^m \log\frac{x+a}{x-a}\,dx = \frac{x^{m+1}-(-a)^{m+1}}{m+1}\log(x+a) - \frac{x^{m+1}-a^{m+1}}{m+1}\log(x-a)$

$$+\frac{2a^{m+1}}{m+1}\sum_{r=1}^{\lfloor\frac{m+1}{2}\rfloor}\frac{1}{m-2r+2}\left(\frac{x}{a}\right)^{m-2r+2}.$$

485. $\displaystyle\int \frac{1}{x^2}\log\frac{x+a}{x-a}\,dx = \frac{1}{x}\log\frac{x-a}{x+a} - \frac{1}{a}\log\frac{x^2-a^2}{x^2}.$

For the following two integrals, $X = a + bx + cx^2$.

486. * $\displaystyle\int \log X\,dx =$

$$\begin{cases}\left(x+\dfrac{b}{2c}\right)\log X - 2x + \dfrac{\sqrt{4ac-b^2}}{c}\tan^{-1}\dfrac{2cx+b}{\sqrt{4ac-b^2}}, & b^2 - 4ac < 0,\\[2mm] \text{or}\\[2mm] \left(x+\dfrac{b}{2c}\right)\log X - 2x + \dfrac{\sqrt{b^2-4ac}}{c}\tanh^{-1}\dfrac{2cx+b}{\sqrt{b^2-4ac}}, & b^2 - 4ac > 0.\end{cases}$$

487. * $\displaystyle\int x^n \log X\,dx = \frac{x^{n+1}}{n+1}\log X - \frac{2c}{n+1}\int \frac{x^{n+2}}{X}\,dx - \frac{b}{n+1}\int \frac{x^{n+1}}{X}\,dx.$

488. $\displaystyle\int \log(x^2+a^2)\,dx = x\log(x^2+a^2) - 2x + 2a\tan^{-1}\frac{x}{a}.$

489. $\displaystyle\int \log(x^2-a^2)\,dx = x\log(x^2-a^2) - 2x + a\log\frac{x+a}{x-a}.$

490. $\displaystyle\int x\log(x^2+a^2)\,dx = \frac{1}{2}(x^2+a^2)\log(x^2+a^2) - \frac{1}{2}x^2.$

491. $\displaystyle\int \log\left(x+\sqrt{x^2\pm a^2}\right)dx = x\log\left(x+\sqrt{x^2\pm a^2}\right) - \sqrt{x^2\pm a^2}.$

492. $\displaystyle\int x\log\left(x+\sqrt{x^2\pm a^2}\right)dx = \left(\frac{x^2}{2}\pm\frac{a^2}{4}\right)\log\left(x+\sqrt{x^2\pm a^2}\right) - \frac{x\sqrt{x^2\pm a^2}}{4}.$

493. $\displaystyle\int x^m\log\left(x+\sqrt{x^2\pm a^2}\right)dx = \frac{x^{m+1}}{m+1}\log\left(x+\sqrt{x^2\pm a^2}\right)$

$$-\frac{1}{m+1}\int \frac{x^{m+1}}{\sqrt{x^2\pm a^2}}\,dx.$$

494. $\displaystyle \int \frac{\log\left(x + \sqrt{x^2 + a^2}\right)}{x^2}\, dx = -\frac{\log\left(x + \sqrt{x^2 + a^2}\right)}{x} - \frac{1}{a}\log\frac{a + \sqrt{x^2 + a^2}}{x}.$

495. $\displaystyle \int \frac{\log\left(x + \sqrt{x^2 - a^2}\right)}{x^2}\, dx = -\frac{\log\left(x + \sqrt{x^2 - a^2}\right)}{x} + \frac{1}{|a|}\sec^{-1}\frac{x}{a}.$

496. $\displaystyle \int x^n \log\left(x^2 - a^2\right) dx = \frac{1}{n+1}\left[x^{n+1}\log\left(x^2 - a^2\right) - a^{n+1}\log\left(x - a\right)\right.$
$$\left. -(-a)^{n+1}\log\left(x + a\right) - 2\sum_{r=0}^{\lfloor\frac{n}{2}\rfloor}\frac{a^{2r}x^{n-2r+1}}{n - 2r + 1}\right].$$

5.4.19   EXPONENTIAL FORMS

497. $\displaystyle \int e^x\, dx = e^x.$

498. $\displaystyle \int e^{-x}\, dx = -e^{-x}.$

499. $\displaystyle \int e^{ax}\, dx = \frac{e^{ax}}{a}.$

500. $\displaystyle \int xe^{ax}\, dx = \frac{e^{ax}}{a^2}(ax - 1).$

501. $\displaystyle \int x^m e^{ax}\, dx = \begin{cases} \dfrac{x^m e^{ax}}{a} - \dfrac{m}{a}\displaystyle\int x^{m-1} e^{ax}\, dx, \\[2mm] \text{or} \\[2mm] e^{ax}\displaystyle\sum_{r=0}^{m}(-1)^r\dfrac{m!x^{m-r}}{(m-r)!a^{r+1}}. \end{cases}$

502. * $\displaystyle \int \frac{e^{ax}}{x}\, dx = \log x + \frac{ax}{1!} + \frac{a^2 x^2}{2\cdot 2!} + \frac{a^3 x^3}{3\cdot 3!} + \cdots.$

503. $\displaystyle \int \frac{e^{ax}}{x^m}\, dx = \frac{1}{1 - m}\frac{e^{ax}}{x^{m-1}} + \frac{a}{m-1}\int \frac{e^{ax}}{x^{m-1}}\, dx.$

504. $\displaystyle \int e^{ax}\log x\, dx = \frac{e^{ax}\log x}{a} - \frac{1}{a}\int \frac{e^{ax}}{x}\, dx.$

505. $\displaystyle \int \frac{dx}{1 + e^x} = x - \log\left(1 + e^x\right) = \log\frac{e^x}{1 + e^x}.$

506. $\displaystyle \int \frac{dx}{a + be^{px}} = \frac{x}{a} - \frac{1}{ap}\log\left(a + be^{px}\right).$

507. $\displaystyle \int \frac{dx}{ae^{mx} + be^{-mx}} = \frac{1}{m\sqrt{ab}}\tan^{-1}\left(e^{mx}\sqrt{\frac{a}{b}}\right),\quad a > 0,\ b > 0.$

508. $\displaystyle \int \frac{dx}{ae^{mx} - be^{-mx}} = \begin{cases} \dfrac{1}{2m\sqrt{ab}}\log\dfrac{\sqrt{a}e^{mx} - \sqrt{b}}{\sqrt{a}e^{mx} + \sqrt{b}},\quad a > 0,\ b > 0, \\[2mm] \text{or} \\[2mm] \dfrac{-1}{m\sqrt{ab}}\tanh^{-1}\left(\sqrt{\dfrac{a}{b}}e^{mx}\right),\quad a > 0,\ b > 0. \end{cases}$

509. $\displaystyle \int \left(a^x - a^{-x}\right) dx = \frac{a^x + a^{-x}}{\log a}.$

510. $\displaystyle \int \frac{e^{ax}}{b + ce^{ax}}\, dx = \frac{1}{ac}\log\left(b + ce^{ax}\right).$

511. $\int \dfrac{xe^{ax}}{(1+ax)^2}\,dx = \dfrac{e^{ax}}{a^2(1+ax)}.$

512. $\int xe^{-x^2}\,dx = -\dfrac{1}{2}e^{-x^2}.$

513. $\int e^{ax}\sin(bx)\,dx = \dfrac{e^{ax}\,[a\sin(bx)-b\cos(bx)]}{a^2+b^2}.$

514. $\int e^{ax}\sin(bx)\sin(cx)\,dx = \dfrac{e^{ax}\,[(b-c)\sin(b-c)x + a\cos(b-c)x]}{2\left[a^2+(b-c)^2\right]}$
$$-\dfrac{e^{ax}\,[(b+c)\sin(b+c)x + a\cos(b+c)x]}{2\left[a^2+(b+c)^2\right]}.$$

515. $\int e^{ax}\sin(bx)\cos(cx)\,dx = \dfrac{e^{ax}\,[a\sin(b-c)x - (b-c)\cos(b-c)x]}{2\left[a^2+(b-c)^2\right]}$
$$+\dfrac{e^{ax}\,[a\sin(b+c)x - (b+c)\cos(b+c)x]}{2\left[a^2+(b+c)^2\right]}.$$

516. $\int e^{ax}\sin(bx)\sin(bx+c)\,dx = \dfrac{e^{ax}\cos c}{2a} - \dfrac{e^{ax}\,[a\cos 2bx + c + 2b\sin 2bx + c]}{2\left[a^2+4b^2\right]}.$

517. $\int e^{ax}\sin(bx)\cos(bx+c)\,dx = -\dfrac{e^{ax}\sin c}{2a} + \dfrac{e^{ax}\,[a\sin 2bx + c - 2b\cos 2bx + c]}{2\left[a^2+4b^2\right]}.$

518. $\int e^{ax}\cos(bx)\,dx = \dfrac{e^{ax}}{a^2+b^2}\,[a\cos(bx)+b\sin(bx)].$

519. $\int e^{ax}\cos(bx)\cos(cx)\,dx = \dfrac{e^{ax}\,[(b-c)\sin(b-c)x + a\cos(b-c)x]}{2\left[a^2+(b-c)^2\right]}$
$$+\dfrac{e^{ax}\,[(b+c)\sin(b+c)x + a\cos(b+c)x]}{2\left[a^2+(b+c)^2\right]}.$$

520. $\int e^{ax}\cos(bx)\cos(bx+c)\,dx = \dfrac{e^{ax}\cos c}{2a} + \dfrac{e^{ax}\,[a\cos 2bx + c + 2b\sin 2bx + c]}{2\left[a^2+4b^2\right]}.$

521. $\int e^{ax}\cos(bx)\sin(bx+c)\,dx = \dfrac{e^{ax}\sin c}{2a} + \dfrac{e^{ax}\,[a\sin 2bx + c - 2b\cos 2bx + c]}{2\left[a^2+4b^2\right]}.$

522. $\int e^{ax}\sin^n(bx)\,dx = \dfrac{1}{a^2+n^2b^2}\left[(a\sin(bx)-nb\cos(bx))e^{ax}\sin^{n-1}(bx)\right.$
$$\left.+n(n-1)b^2\int e^{ax}\sin^{n-2}(bx)\,dx\right].$$

523. $\int e^{ax}\cos^n(bx)\,dx = \dfrac{1}{a^2+n^2b^2}\left[(a\cos(bx)+nb\sin(bx))e^{ax}\cos^{n-1}(bx)\right.$
$$\left.+n(n-1)b^2\int e^{ax}\cos^{n-2}(bx)\,dx\right].$$

524. $\int x^m e^x \sin x\,dx = \dfrac{1}{2}x^m e^x(\sin x - \cos x) - \dfrac{m}{2}\int x^{m-1}e^x\sin x\,dx$
$$+\dfrac{m}{2}\int x^{m-1}e^x\cos x\,dx.$$

525. $\int x^m e^{ax}\sin bx\,dx = x^m e^{ax}\dfrac{a\sin(bx)-b\cos(bx)}{a^2+b^2}$
$$-\dfrac{m}{a^2+b^2}\int x^{m-1}e^{ax}(a\sin(bx)-b\cos(bx))\,dx.$$

526. $\int x^m e^x \cos x\,dx = \dfrac{1}{2}x^m e^x(\sin x + \cos x) - \dfrac{m}{2}\int x^{m-1}e^x\sin x\,dx$
$$-\dfrac{m}{2}\int x^{m-1}e^x\cos x\,dx.$$

527. $\displaystyle \int x^m e^{ax} \cos bx \, dx = x^m e^{ax} \frac{a \cos (bx) + b \sin (bx)}{a^2 + b^2}$

$$-\frac{m}{a^2 + b^2} \int x^{m-1} e^{ax} (a \cos (bx) + b \sin (bx)) \, dx.$$

528. $\displaystyle \int e^{ax} \cos^m x \sin^n x \, dx =$

$$\begin{cases}
\dfrac{e^{ax}(\cos^{m-1} x)(\sin^n x)\,[a\cos x + (m+n)\sin x]}{(m+n)^2 + a^2} \\[2mm]
\quad -\dfrac{na}{(m+n)^2 + a^2}\int e^{ax}(\cos^{m-1} x)(\sin^{n-1} x)\,dx \\[2mm]
\quad +\dfrac{(m-1)(m+n)}{(m+n)^2 + a^2}\int e^{ax}(\cos^{m-2} x)(\sin^n x)\,dx, \\[4mm]
\text{or} \\[2mm]
\dfrac{e^{ax}(\cos^m x)(\sin^{n-1} x)\,[a\sin x - (m+n)\cos x]}{(m+n)^2 + a^2} \\[2mm]
\quad +\dfrac{ma}{(m+n)^2 + a^2}\int e^{ax}(\cos^{m-1} x)(\sin^{n-1} x)\,dx \\[2mm]
\quad +\dfrac{(n-1)(m+n)}{(m+n)^2 + a^2}\int e^{ax}(\cos^m x)(\sin^{n-2} x)\,dx, \\[4mm]
\text{or} \\[2mm]
\dfrac{e^{ax}(\cos^{m-1} x)(\sin^{n-1} x)\left[a\sin x \cos x + m\sin^2 x - n\cos^2 x\right]}{(m+n)^2 + a^2} \\[2mm]
\quad +\dfrac{m(m-1)}{(m+n)^2 + a^2}\int e^{ax}(\cos^{m-2} x)(\sin^n x)\,dx \\[2mm]
\quad +\dfrac{n(n-1)}{(m+n)^2 + a^2}\int e^{ax}(\cos^m x)(\sin^{n-2} x)\,dx, \\[4mm]
\text{or} \\[2mm]
\dfrac{e^{ax}(\cos^{m-1} x)(\sin^{n-1} x)\left[a\sin x \cos x + m\sin^2 x - n\cos^2 x\right]}{(m+n)^2 + a^2} \\[2mm]
\quad +\dfrac{m(m-1)}{(m+n)^2 + a^2}\int e^{ax}(\cos^{m-2} x)(\sin^{n-2} x)\,dx \\[2mm]
\quad +\dfrac{(n-m)(n+m-1)}{(m+n)^2 + a^2}\int e^{ax}(\cos^m x)(\sin^{n-2} x)\,dx.
\end{cases}$$

529. $\displaystyle \int x e^{ax} \sin (bx) \, dx = \frac{x e^{ax}}{a^2 + b^2} [a \sin (bx) - b \cos (bx)]$

$$-\frac{e^{ax}}{\left(a^2 + b^2\right)^2} \left[\left(a^2 - b^2\right) \sin bx - 2ab \cos (bx)\right].$$

530. $\displaystyle \int x e^{ax} \cos (bx) \, dx = \frac{x e^{ax}}{a^2 + b^2} [a \cos (bx) + b \sin (bx)]$

$$-\frac{e^{ax}}{\left(a^2 + b^2\right)^2} \left[\left(a^2 - b^2\right) \cos bx + 2ab \sin (bx)\right].$$

531. $\displaystyle \int \frac{e^{ax}}{\sin^n x} \, dx = -\frac{e^{ax}\,[a \sin x + (n-2)\cos x]}{(n-1)(n-2)\sin^{n-1} x} + \frac{a^2 + (n-2)^2}{(n-1)(n-2)} \int \frac{e^{ax}}{\sin^{n-2} x} \, dx.$

532. $\displaystyle \int \frac{e^{ax}}{\cos^n x} \, dx = -\frac{e^{ax}\,[a \cos x - (n-2)\sin x]}{(n-1)(n-2)\cos^{n-1} x} + \frac{a^2 + (n-2)^2}{(n-1)(n-2)} \int \frac{e^{ax}}{\cos^{n-2} x} \, dx.$

533. $\displaystyle \int e^{ax} \tan^n x \, dx = e^{ax} \frac{\tan^{n-1} x}{n-1} - \frac{a}{n-1} \int e^{ax} \tan^{n-1} x \, dx - \int e^{ax} \tan^{n-2} x \, dx.$

5.4.20 HYPERBOLIC FORMS

534. $\displaystyle\int \sinh x \, dx = \cosh x.$

535. $\displaystyle\int \cosh x \, dx = \sinh x.$

536. $\displaystyle\int \tanh x \, dx = \log \cosh x.$

537. $\displaystyle\int \coth x \, dx = \log \sinh x.$

538. $\displaystyle\int \operatorname{sech} x \, dx = \tan^{-1}(\sinh x).$

539. $\displaystyle\int \operatorname{csch} x \, dx = \log \tanh \left(\frac{x}{2}\right).$

540. $\displaystyle\int x \sinh x \, dx = x \cosh x - \sinh x.$

541. $\displaystyle\int x^n \sinh x \, dx = x^n \cosh x - n \int x^{n-1}(\cosh x) \, dx.$

542. $\displaystyle\int x \cosh x \, dx = x \sinh x - \cosh x.$

543. $\displaystyle\int x^n \cosh x \, dx = x^n \sinh x - n \int x^{n-1}(\sinh x) \, dx.$

544. $\displaystyle\int \operatorname{sech} x \tanh x \, dx = -\operatorname{sech} x.$

545. $\displaystyle\int \operatorname{csch} x \coth x \, dx = -\operatorname{csch} x.$

546. $\displaystyle\int \sinh^2 x \, dx = \frac{\sinh 2x}{4} - \frac{x}{2}.$

547. $\displaystyle\int \sinh^m x \cosh^n x \, dx =$

$$
\begin{cases}
\dfrac{1}{m+n} \sinh^{m+1} x \cosh^{n-1} x + \dfrac{n-1}{m+n} \displaystyle\int \sinh^m x \cosh^{n-2} x \, dx, & m+n \neq 0, \\
\text{or} \\
\dfrac{1}{m+n} \sinh^{m-1} x \cosh^{n+1} x - \dfrac{m-1}{m+n} \displaystyle\int \sinh^{m-2} x \cosh^n x \, dx, & m+n \neq 0.
\end{cases}
$$

548. $\displaystyle\int \frac{dx}{(\sinh^m x)(\cosh^n x)} =$

$$
\begin{cases}
-\dfrac{1}{(m-1)(\sinh^{m-1} x)(\cosh^{n-1} x)} - \dfrac{m+n-2}{m-1} \displaystyle\int \dfrac{dx}{(\sinh^{m-2} x)(\cosh^n x)}, & m \neq 1, \\
\text{or} \\
\dfrac{1}{(n-1)(\sinh^{m-1} x)(\cosh^{n-1} x)} + \dfrac{m+n-2}{n-1} \displaystyle\int \dfrac{dx}{(\sinh^m x)(\cosh^{n-2} x)}, & n \neq 1.
\end{cases}
$$

549. $\displaystyle\int \tanh^2 x \, dx = x - \tanh x.$

550. $\displaystyle\int \tanh^n x \, dx = -\frac{\tanh^{n-1} x}{n-1} + \int (\tanh^{n-2} x) \, dx, \quad n \neq 1.$

551. $\displaystyle\int \operatorname{sech}^2 x \, dx = \tanh x.$

552. $\int \cosh^2 x \, dx = \dfrac{\sinh 2x}{4} + \dfrac{x}{2}$.

553. $\int \coth^2 x \, dx = x - \coth x$.

554. $\int \coth^n x \, dx = -\dfrac{\coth^{n-1} x}{n-1} + \int \coth^{n-2} x \, dx, \quad n \neq 1$.

555. $\int \operatorname{csch}^2 x \, dx = -\coth x$.

556. $\int (\sinh mx)(\sinh nx) \, dx = \dfrac{\sinh (m+n)x}{2(m+n)} - \dfrac{\sinh (m-n)x}{2(m-n)}, \quad m^2 \neq n^2$.

557. $\int (\cosh mx)(\cosh nx) \, dx = \dfrac{\sinh (m+n)x}{2(m+n)} + \dfrac{\sinh (m-n)x}{2(m-n)}, \quad m^2 \neq n^2$.

558. $\int (\sinh mx)(\cosh nx) \, dx = \dfrac{\cosh (m+n)x}{2(m+n)} + \dfrac{\cosh (m-n)x}{2(m-n)}, \quad m^2 \neq n^2$.

559. $\int \left(\sinh^{-1} \dfrac{x}{a} \right) dx = x \sinh^{-1} \dfrac{x}{a} - \sqrt{x^2 + a^2}, \quad a > 0$.

560. $\int x \left(\sinh^{-1} \dfrac{x}{a} \right) dx = \left(\dfrac{x^2}{2} + \dfrac{a^2}{4} \right) \sinh^{-1} \dfrac{x}{a} - \dfrac{x}{4}\sqrt{x^2 + a^2}, \quad a > 0$.

561. $\int x^n \sinh^{-1} x \, dx = \dfrac{x^{n+1}}{n+1} \sinh^{-1} x - \dfrac{1}{n+1} \int \dfrac{x^{n+1}}{\sqrt{1+x^2}} \, dx, \quad n \neq -1$.

562. $* \int^z \cosh^{-1} \dfrac{x}{a} \, dx = \begin{cases} z \cosh^{-1} \dfrac{z}{a} - \sqrt{z^2 - a^2}, & \cosh^{-1} \dfrac{z}{a} > 0, \\ \quad \text{or} \\ z \cosh^{-1} \dfrac{z}{a} + \sqrt{z^2 - a^2}, & \cosh^{-1} \dfrac{z}{a} < 0,\ a > 0. \end{cases}$

563. $\int x \left(\cosh^{-1} \dfrac{x}{a} \right) dx = \left(\dfrac{x^2}{2} - \dfrac{a^2}{4} \right) \cosh^{-1} \dfrac{x}{a} - \dfrac{x}{4}\sqrt{x^2 - a^2}$.

564. $\int x^n \cosh^{-1} x \, dx = \dfrac{x^{n+1}}{n+1} \cosh^{-1} x - \dfrac{1}{n+1} \int \dfrac{x^{n+1}}{\sqrt{x^2 - 1}} \, dx, \quad n \neq -1$.

565. $\int \left(\tanh^{-1} \dfrac{x}{a} \right) dx = x \tanh^{-1} \dfrac{x}{a} + \dfrac{a}{2} \log (a^2 - x^2), \quad \left| \dfrac{x}{a} \right| < 1$.

566. $\int \left(\coth^{-1} \dfrac{x}{a} \right) dx = x \coth^{-1} \dfrac{x}{a} + \dfrac{a}{2} \log (x^2 - a^2), \quad \left| \dfrac{x}{a} \right| > 1. \quad \bullet$

567. $\int x \left(\tanh^{-1} \dfrac{x}{a} \right) dx = \dfrac{x^2 - a^2}{2} \tanh^{-1} \dfrac{x}{a} + \dfrac{ax}{2}, \quad \left| \dfrac{x}{a} \right| < 1$.

568. $\int x^n \tanh^{-1} x \, dx = \dfrac{x^{n+1}}{n+1} \tanh^{-1} x - \dfrac{1}{n+1} \int \dfrac{x^{n+1}}{1-x^2} \, dx, \quad n \neq -1$.

569. $\int x \left(\coth^{-1} \dfrac{x}{a} \right) dx = \dfrac{x^2 - a^2}{2} \coth^{-1} \dfrac{x}{a} + \dfrac{ax}{2}, \quad \left| \dfrac{x}{a} \right| > 1$.

570. $\int x^n \coth^{-1} x \, dx = \dfrac{x^{n+1}}{n+1} \coth^{-1} x + \dfrac{1}{n+1} \int \dfrac{x^{n+1}}{x^2 - 1} \, dx, \quad n \neq -1$.

571. $\int \operatorname{sech}^{-1} x \, dx = x \operatorname{sech}^{-1} x + \sin^{-1} x$.

572. $\int x \operatorname{sech}^{-1} x \, dx = \dfrac{x^2}{2} \operatorname{sech}^{-1} x - \dfrac{1}{2}\sqrt{1 - x^2}$.

573. $\int x^n \operatorname{sech}^{-1} x \, dx = \dfrac{x^{n+1}}{n+1} \operatorname{sech}^{-1} x + \dfrac{1}{n+1} \int \dfrac{x^n}{\sqrt{1 - x^2}} \, dx, \quad n \neq -1$.

574. $\int \operatorname{csch}^{-1} x \, dx = x \operatorname{csch}^{-1} x + \dfrac{x}{|x|} \sinh^{-1} x.$

575. $\int x \operatorname{csch}^{-1} x \, dx = \dfrac{x^2}{2} \operatorname{csch}^{-1} x + \dfrac{1}{2} \dfrac{x}{|x|} \sqrt{1 + x^2}.$

576. $\int x^n \operatorname{csch}^{-1} x \, dx = \dfrac{x^{n+1}}{n+1} \operatorname{csch}^{-1} x + \dfrac{1}{n+1} \dfrac{x}{|x|} \int \dfrac{x^n}{\sqrt{1+x^2}} \, dx, \quad n \neq -1.$

5.4.21   BESSEL FUNCTIONS

$Z_p(x)$ represents any of the Bessel functions $\{J_p(x),\, Y_p(x),\, K_p(x),\, I_p(x)\}$.

577. $\int x^{p+1} Z_p(x) \, dx = x^{p+1} Z_{p+1}(x).$

578. $\int x^{-p+1} Z_p(x) \, dx = -x^{-p+1} Z_{p-1}(x).$

579. $\int x \left[Z_p(ax) \right]^2 dx = \dfrac{x^2}{2} \left[\left[Z_p(ax) \right]^2 - Z_{p-1}(ax) Z_{p+1}(ax) \right].$

580. $\int Z_1(x) \, dx = -Z_0(x).$

581. $\int x Z_0(x) \, dx = x Z_1(x).$

5.5   TABLE OF DEFINITE INTEGRALS

All integrals listed below that do not have stars next to their numbers have been automatically verified by computer.

582. $\displaystyle\int_0^\infty x^{n-1} e^{-x} \, dx = \Gamma(n), \quad n \text{ is a positive integer.}$

583. $\displaystyle\int_0^\infty x^n p^{-x} \, dx = \dfrac{n!}{(\log p)^{n+1}}, \quad p > 0, \ n \text{ is a non-negative integer.}$

584. $\displaystyle\int_0^\infty x^{n-1} e^{-(a+1)x} \, dx = \dfrac{\Gamma(n)}{(a+1)^n}, \quad n > 0, \ a > -1.$

585. $\displaystyle\int_0^1 x^m \left(\log \dfrac{1}{x} \right)^n dx = \dfrac{\Gamma(n+1)}{(m+1)^{n+1}}, \quad m > -1, \ n > -1.$

586. $\displaystyle\int_0^1 x^{m-1} (1-x)^{n-1} \, dx = \int_0^1 \dfrac{x^{m-1}}{(1+x)^{m+n}} = \dfrac{\Gamma(m)\,\Gamma(n)}{\Gamma(m+n)}, \quad n > 0, \ m > 0.$

587. $\displaystyle\int_a^b (x-a)^m (b-x)^n \, dx = (b-a)^{m+n+1} \dfrac{\Gamma(m+1)\,\Gamma(n+1)}{\Gamma(m+n+2)}, \quad m > -1, \ n > -1, \ b > a.$

588. $\displaystyle\int_1^\infty \dfrac{dx}{x^m} = \dfrac{1}{m-1}, \quad m > 1.$

589. $\displaystyle\int_0^\infty \dfrac{dx}{(1+x)x^p} = \pi \operatorname{cosec} p\pi, \quad 0 < p < 1.$

590. $\displaystyle\int_0^\infty \frac{dx}{(1-x)x^p} = -\pi \cot p\pi, \quad 0 < p < 1.$

591. $\displaystyle\int_0^1 \frac{x^p}{(1-x)^p} \, dx = p\pi \csc p\pi, \quad |p| < 1.$

592. $\displaystyle\int_0^1 \frac{x^p}{(1-x)^{p+1}} \, dx = \int_0^1 \frac{(1-x)^p}{x^{p+1}} \, dx = -\pi \csc p\pi, \quad -1 < p < 0.$

593. $\displaystyle\int_0^\infty \frac{x^{p-1}}{1+x} \, dx = \frac{\pi}{\sin p\pi}, \quad 0 < p < 1.$

594. $\displaystyle\int_0^\infty \frac{x^{m-1}}{1+x^n} \, dx = \frac{\pi}{n \sin \frac{m\pi}{n}}, \quad 0 < m < n.$

595. $\displaystyle\int_0^\infty \frac{x^a}{(m + x^b)^c} \, dx = \frac{m^{(a+1-bc)/b}}{b} \frac{\Gamma\left(\frac{a+1}{b}\right)\Gamma\left(c - \frac{a+1}{b}\right)}{\Gamma(c)}, \quad a > -1, \ b > 0, \ m > 0,$
$c > \frac{a+1}{b}.$

596. $\displaystyle\int_0^\infty \frac{dx}{(1+x)\sqrt{x}} = \pi.$

597. $\displaystyle\int_0^\infty \frac{a}{a^2 + x^2} \, dx = \begin{cases} \dfrac{\pi}{2}, & a > 0, \\ \text{or} \\ 0, & a = 0, \\ \text{or} \\ -\dfrac{\pi}{2}, & a < 0. \end{cases}$

598. $\displaystyle\int_0^a \left(a^2 - x^2\right)^{n/2} dx = \int_0^a \frac{1}{2} \left(a^2 - x^2\right)^{n/2} dx = \frac{n!!}{(n+1)!!} \frac{\pi}{2} a^{n+1}, \quad a > 0,$
n is an odd integer.

599. $\displaystyle\int_0^a x^m \left(a^2 - x^2\right)^{n/2} dx = \frac{1}{2} a^{m+n+1} \frac{\Gamma\left(\frac{m+1}{2}\right)\Gamma\left(\frac{n+2}{2}\right)}{\Gamma\left(\frac{m+n+3}{2}\right)}, \quad a > 0, \ m > -1, \ n > -2.$

600. $\displaystyle\int_0^{\pi/2} \sin^n x \, dx = \int_0^{\pi/2} \cos^n x \, dx = \begin{cases} \dfrac{\sqrt{\pi}}{2} \dfrac{\Gamma\left(\frac{n+1}{2}\right)}{\Gamma\left(\frac{n+2}{2}\right)}, & n > -1, \\ \text{or} \\ \dfrac{(n-1)!!}{n!!} \dfrac{\pi}{2}, & n \neq 0, \ n \text{ is an even integer,} \\ \text{or} \\ \dfrac{(n-1)!!}{n!!}, & n \neq 1, \ n \text{ is an odd integer.} \end{cases}$

601. $\displaystyle\int_0^\infty \frac{\sin ax}{x} \, dx = \begin{cases} \dfrac{\pi}{2}, & a > 0, \\ \text{or} \\ 0, & a = 0, \\ \text{or} \\ -\dfrac{\pi}{2}, & a < 0. \end{cases}$

602. * $\displaystyle\int_0^\infty \frac{\cos x}{x} \, dx = \infty.$

603. $\displaystyle\int_0^\infty \frac{\tan x}{x} \, dx = \frac{\pi}{2}.$

604. $\displaystyle\int_0^\infty \frac{\tan ax}{x} \, dx = \frac{\pi}{2}, \quad a > 0.$

605. $\displaystyle\int_0^\pi \sin nx \cdot \sin mx \, dx = \int_0^\pi \cos nx \cdot \cos mx \, dx = 0, \quad n \neq m, \ n \text{ is an integer,}$
m is an integer.

606. $\displaystyle\int_0^{\pi/n} \sin nx \cdot \cos nx \, dx = \int_0^{\pi/n} \sin nx \cdot \cos nx \, dx = 0, \quad n \text{ is an integer.}$

607. $*\displaystyle\int_0^\pi \sin ax \cos bx \, dx = \begin{cases} \dfrac{2a}{a^2 - b^2}, & a - b \text{ is an odd integer.} \\ \quad \text{or} \\ 0, & a - b \text{ is an even integer.} \end{cases}$

608. $\displaystyle\int_0^\infty \frac{\sin x \cos ax}{x} \, dx = \begin{cases} 0, & |a| > 1, \\ \quad \text{or} \\ \dfrac{\pi}{4}, & |a| = 1, \\ \quad \text{or} \\ \dfrac{\pi}{2}, & |a| < 1. \end{cases}$

609. $\displaystyle\int_0^\infty \frac{\sin ax \sin bx}{x^2} \, dx = \begin{cases} \dfrac{\pi a}{2}, & 0 < a \leq b, \\ \quad \text{or} \\ \dfrac{\pi b}{2}, & 0 < b \leq a. \end{cases}$

610. $\displaystyle\int_0^\pi \sin^2 mx \, dx = \int_0^\pi \cos^2 mx \, dx = \frac{\pi}{2}, \quad m \text{ is an integer.}$

611. $\displaystyle\int_0^\infty \frac{\sin^2 px}{x^2} \, dx = \frac{\pi \, |p|}{2}.$

612. $\displaystyle\int_0^\infty \frac{\sin x}{x^p} \, dx = \frac{\pi}{2\Gamma(p) \sin(p\pi/2)}, \quad 0 < p < 1.$

613. $\displaystyle\int_0^\infty \frac{\cos x}{x^p} \, dx = \frac{\pi}{2\Gamma(p) \cos(p\pi/2)}, \quad 0 < p < 1.$

614. $\displaystyle\int_0^\infty \frac{1 - \cos px}{x^2} \, dx = \frac{\pi \, |p|}{2}.$

615. $\displaystyle\int_0^\infty \frac{\sin px \cos qx}{x} \, dx = \begin{cases} 0 & q > p > 0, \\ \quad \text{or} \\ \dfrac{\pi}{2}, & p > q > 0, \\ \quad \text{or} \\ \dfrac{\pi}{4}, & p = q > 0. \end{cases}$

616. $\displaystyle\int_0^\infty \frac{\cos mx}{x^2 + a^2} \, dx = \frac{\pi}{2\,|a|} e^{-|ma|}.$

617. $*\displaystyle\int_0^\infty \cos x^2 \, dx = \int_0^\infty \sin x^2 \, dx = \frac{1}{2}\sqrt{\frac{\pi}{2}}.$

618. $*\displaystyle\int_0^\infty \sin(ax^n) \, dx = \frac{1}{na^{1/n}} \Gamma\!\left(\frac{1}{n}\right) \sin\frac{\pi}{2n}, \quad n > 1.$

619. $*\displaystyle\int_0^\infty \cos(ax^n) \, dx = \frac{1}{na^{1/n}} \Gamma\!\left(\frac{1}{n}\right) \cos\frac{\pi}{2n}, \quad n > 1.$

620. $\displaystyle\int_0^\infty \frac{\sin x}{\sqrt{x}} \, dx = \int_0^\infty \frac{\cos x}{\sqrt{x}} \, dx = \sqrt{\frac{\pi}{2}}.$

621. $\displaystyle\int_0^\infty \frac{\sin^3 x}{x} \, dx = \frac{\pi}{4}.$

622. $\displaystyle\int_0^\infty \frac{\sin^3 x}{x^2}\,dx = \frac{3}{4}\log 3.$

623. $\displaystyle\int_0^\infty \frac{\sin^3 x}{x^3}\,dx = \frac{3\pi}{8}.$

624. $\displaystyle\int_0^\infty \frac{\sin^4 x}{x^4}\,dx = \frac{\pi}{3}.$

625. $\displaystyle\int_0^{\pi/2} \frac{dx}{1+a\cos x}\,dx = \frac{\cos^{-1}a}{\sqrt{1-a^2}}, \quad |a| < 1.$

626. $\displaystyle\int_0^{\pi} \frac{dx}{a+b\cos x}\,dx = \frac{\pi}{\sqrt{a^2-b^2}}, \quad a > b \geq 0.$

627. $\displaystyle\int_0^{2\pi} \frac{dx}{1+a\cos x}\,dx = \frac{2\pi}{\sqrt{1-a^2}}, \quad |a| < 1.$

628. $\displaystyle\int_0^\infty \frac{\cos ax - \cos bx}{x}\,dx = \log\left|\frac{b}{a}\right|.$

629. $\displaystyle\int_0^{\pi/2} \frac{dx}{a^2\sin^2 x + b^2\cos^2 x}\,dx = \frac{\pi}{2\,|ab|}.$

630. $\displaystyle\int_0^{\pi/2} \frac{dx}{(a^2\sin^2 x + b^2\cos^2 x)^2}\,dx = \frac{\pi(a^2+b^2)}{4a^3b^3}, \quad a > 0,\ b > 0.$

631. $\displaystyle\int_0^{\pi/2} \sin^{n-1} x \cos^{m-1} x\,dx = \frac{1}{2}B\left(\frac{n}{2}\right)\frac{m}{2}, \quad m$ is a positive integer, n is a positive integer.

632. $\displaystyle\int_0^{\pi/2} \sin^{2n+1} x\,dx = \frac{(2n)!!}{(2n+1)!!}, \quad n$ is a positive integer.

633. $\displaystyle\int_0^{\pi/2} \sin^{2n} x\,dx = \frac{(2n-1)!!}{(2n)!!}\frac{\pi}{2}, \quad n$ is a positive integer.

634. $*\displaystyle\int_0^{\pi/2} \frac{x}{\sin x}\,dx = 2\left(\frac{1}{1^2} - \frac{1}{3^2} + \frac{1}{5^2} - \frac{1}{7^2} + \cdots\right).$

635. $\displaystyle\int_0^{\pi/2} \frac{dx}{1+\tan^m x}\,dx = \frac{\pi}{4}, \quad m$ is a non-negative integer.

636. $\displaystyle\int_0^{\pi/2} \sqrt{\cos x}\,dx = \frac{(2\pi)^{3/2}}{(\Gamma(1/4))^2}.$

637. $\displaystyle\int_0^{\pi/2} \tan^h x\,dx = \frac{\pi}{2\cos\left(\frac{h\pi}{2}\right)}, \quad 0 < h < 1.$

638. $\displaystyle\int_0^{\pi/2} \frac{\tan^{-1}ax - \tan^{-1}bx}{x}\,dx = \frac{\pi}{2}\log\frac{a}{b}, \quad a > 0,\ b > 0.$

639. $\displaystyle\int_0^\infty e^{-ax}\,dx = \frac{1}{a}, \quad a > 0.$

640. $\displaystyle\int_0^\infty \frac{e^{-ax} - e^{-bx}}{x}\,dx = \log\frac{b}{a}, \quad a > 0,\ b > 0.$

641. $\displaystyle\int_0^\infty x^n e^{-ax}\,dx = \begin{cases} \dfrac{\Gamma(n+1)}{a^{n+1}}, & a > 0,\ n > -1, \\ \quad\text{or} \\ \dfrac{n!}{a^{n+1}}, & a > 0,\ n \text{ is a positive integer.} \end{cases}$

642. $\displaystyle\int_0^\infty x^n e^{-ax^p}\,dx = \frac{\Gamma((n+1)/p)}{pa^{(n+1)/p}}, \quad a > 0,\ p > 0,\ n > -1.$

643. $\int_0^\infty e^{-a^2 x^2}\, dx = \dfrac{1}{2a}\sqrt{\pi}, \quad a > 0.$

644. $\int_0^b e^{-ax^2}\, dx = \dfrac{1}{2}\sqrt{\dfrac{\pi}{a}}\,\mathrm{erf}\left(b\sqrt{a}\right), \quad a > 0.$

645. $\int_b^\infty e^{-ax^2}\, dx = \dfrac{1}{2}\sqrt{\dfrac{\pi}{a}}\,\mathrm{erfc}\left(b\sqrt{a}\right), \quad a > 0.$

646. $\int_0^\infty x e^{-x^2}\, dx = \dfrac{1}{2}, \quad a > 0.$

647. $\int_0^\infty x^2 e^{-x^2}\, dx = \dfrac{\sqrt{\pi}}{4}.$

648. $\int_0^\infty x^n e^{-ax^2}\, dx = \dfrac{(n-1)!!}{2(2a)^{n/2}}\sqrt{\dfrac{\pi}{a}}, \quad a > 0,\ n > 0.$

649. $\int_0^\infty x^{2n+1} e^{-ax^2}\, dx = \dfrac{n!}{2a^{n+1}}, \quad a > 0,\ n > -1.$

650. $\int_0^1 x^m e^{-ax}\, dx = \dfrac{m!}{a^{m+1}}\left[1 - e^{-a}\displaystyle\sum_{r=0}^m \dfrac{a^r}{r!}\right].$

651. $\int_0^\infty e^{\left(-x^2 - a^2/x^2\right)}\, dx = \dfrac{e^{-2|a|}\sqrt{\pi}}{2}.$

652. $\int_0^\infty e^{\left(-ax^2 - b/x^2\right)}\, dx = \dfrac{1}{2}\sqrt{\dfrac{\pi}{a}}\,e^{-2\sqrt{ab}}, \quad a > 0,\ b > 0.$

653. $\int_0^\infty \sqrt{x}\,e^{-ax}\, dx = \dfrac{1}{2a}\sqrt{\dfrac{\pi}{a}}, \quad a > 0.$

654. $\int_0^\infty \dfrac{e^{-ax}}{\sqrt{x}}\, dx = \sqrt{\dfrac{\pi}{a}}, \quad a > 0.$

655. $\int_0^\infty e^{-ax}\cos mx\, dx = \dfrac{a}{a^2 + m^2}, \quad a > 0.$

656. $\int_0^\infty e^{-ax}\cos(bx + c)\, dx = \dfrac{a\cos c - b\sin c}{a^2 + b^2}, \quad a > 0.$

657. $\int_0^\infty e^{-ax}\sin mx\, dx = \dfrac{m}{a^2 + m^2}, \quad a > 0.$

658. $\int_0^\infty e^{-ax}\sin(bx + c)\, dx = \dfrac{b\cos c + a\sin c}{a^2 + b^2}, \quad a > 0.$

659. $\int_0^\infty x e^{-ax}\sin bx\, dx = \dfrac{2ab}{(a^2 + b^2)^2}, \quad a > 0.$

660. $\int_0^\infty x e^{-ax}\cos bx\, dx = \dfrac{a^2 - b^2}{(a^2 + b^2)^2}, \quad a > 0.$

661. $\int_0^\infty x^n e^{-ax}\sin bx\, dx = \dfrac{n!\left[(a + \imath b)^{n+1} - (a - \imath b)^{n+1}\right]}{2\imath (a^2 + b^2)^{n+1}}, \quad a > 0.$

662. $\int_0^\infty x^n e^{-ax}\cos bx\, dx = \dfrac{n!\left[(a - \imath b)^{n+1} + (a + \imath b)^{n+1}\right]}{2(a^2 + b^2)^{n+1}}, \quad a > 0,\ n > -1.$

663. $\int_0^\infty \dfrac{e^{-ax}\sin x}{x}\, dx = \cot^{-1} a, \quad a > 0.$

664. $\int_0^\infty e^{-a^2 x^2}\cos bx\, dx = \dfrac{\sqrt{\pi}}{2|a|}\exp^{-b^2/(4a^2)}, \quad ab > 0.$

665. $\int_0^\infty e^{-x\cos\phi} x^{b-1} \sin(x\sin\phi)\, dx = \Gamma(b)\sin(b\phi), \quad b > 0, \; -\frac{\pi}{2} < \phi < \frac{\pi}{2}.$

666. $\int_0^\infty e^{-x\cos\phi} x^{b-1} \cos(x\sin\phi)\, dx = \Gamma(b)\cos(b\phi), \quad b > 0, \; -\frac{\pi}{2} < \phi < \frac{\pi}{2}.$

667. $\int_0^\infty x^{b-1} \cos x\, dx = \Gamma(b)\cos\left(\frac{b\pi}{2}\right), \quad 0 < b < 1.$

668. $\int_0^\infty x^{b-1} \sin x\, dx = \Gamma(b)\sin\left(\frac{b\pi}{2}\right), \quad 0 < b < 1.$

669. $\int_0^1 (\log x)^n\, dx = (-1)^n n!, \quad n < -1.$

670. $\int_0^1 \sqrt{\log\frac{1}{x}}\, dx = \frac{\sqrt{\pi}}{2}.$

671. $\int_0^1 \left(\log\frac{1}{x}\right)^n dx = n!.$

672. $\int_0^1 x\log(1-x)\, dx = -\frac{3}{4}.$

673. $\int_0^1 x\log(1+x)\, dx = \frac{1}{4}.$

674. $\int_0^1 x^m (\log x)^n\, dx = \frac{(-1)^n \Gamma(n+1)}{(m+1)^{m+1}}, \quad m > -1, \; n \text{ is a positive integer.}$

675. $\int_0^1 \frac{\log x}{1+x}\, dx = -\frac{\pi^2}{12}.$

676. $\int_0^1 \frac{\log x}{1-x}\, dx = -\frac{\pi^2}{6}.$

677. $\int_0^1 \frac{\log(1+x)}{x}\, dx = \frac{\pi^2}{12}.$

678. $\int_0^1 \frac{\log(1-x)}{x}\, dx = -\frac{\pi^2}{6}.$

679. $\int_0^1 (\log x)\log(1+x)\, dx = 2 - 2\log 2 - \frac{\pi^2}{12}.$

680. $\int_0^1 (\log x)\log(1-x)\, dx = 2 - \frac{\pi^2}{6}.$

681. $\int_0^1 \frac{\log x}{1-x^2}\, dx = -\frac{\pi^2}{8}.$

682. $\int_0^1 \log\left(\frac{1+x}{1-x}\right)\frac{dx}{x} = \frac{\pi^2}{4}.$

683. $\int_0^1 \frac{\log x}{\sqrt{1-x^2}}\, dx = -\frac{\pi}{2}\log 2.$

684. $\int_0^1 x^m \left[\log\left(\frac{1}{x}\right)\right]^n dx = \frac{\Gamma(n+1)}{(m+1)^{n+1}}, \quad m > -1, \; n > -1.$

685. $\int_0^1 \frac{x^p - x^q}{\log x}\, dx = \log\left(\frac{p+1}{q+1}\right), \quad p > -1, \; q > -1.$

686. $\int_0^1 \frac{dx}{\sqrt{\log(-\log x)}} = \sqrt{\pi}.$

687. $\displaystyle\int_0^\infty \log\left(\frac{e^x+1}{e^x-1}\right) dx = \frac{\pi^2}{4}.$

688. $\displaystyle\int_0^{\pi/2} \log\sin x\, dx = \int_0^{\pi/2} \log\cos x\, dx = -\frac{\pi}{2}\log 2.$

689. $\displaystyle\int_0^{\pi/2} \log\sec x\, dx = \int_0^{\pi/2} \log\operatorname{cosec} x\, dx = \frac{\pi}{2}\log 2.$

690. $\displaystyle\int_0^\pi x\log\sin x\, dx = -\frac{\pi^2}{2}\log 2.$

691. $\displaystyle\int_0^{\pi/2} (\sin x)\log\sin x\, dx = \log 2 - 1.$

692. $\displaystyle\int_0^{\pi/2} \log\tan x\, dx = 0.$

693. $\displaystyle\int_0^\pi \log\,(a\pm b\cos x)\, dx = \pi\log\left(\frac{a+\sqrt{a^2-b^2}}{2}\right), \quad a\geq b.$

694. $\displaystyle\int_0^\pi \log\,(a^2 - 2ab\cos x + b^2)\, dx = \begin{cases} 2\pi\log a, & a\geq b>0, \\ \quad\text{or} \\ 2\pi\log b, & b\geq a>0. \end{cases}$

695. $\displaystyle\int_0^\infty \frac{\sin ax}{\sinh bx}\, dx = \frac{\pi}{2b}\tanh\frac{a\pi}{2\,|b|}.$

696. $\displaystyle\int_0^\infty \frac{\cos ax}{\cosh bx}\, dx = \frac{\pi}{2b}\operatorname{sech}\frac{a\pi}{2b}.$

697. $\displaystyle\int_0^\infty \frac{dx}{\cosh ax} = \frac{\pi}{2\,|a|}.$

698. $\displaystyle\int_0^\infty \frac{x}{\sinh ax}\, dx = \frac{\pi^2}{4a^2}, \quad a\geq 0.$

699. $\displaystyle\int_0^\infty e^{-ax}\cosh\,(bx)\, dx = \frac{a}{a^2-b^2}, \quad |b|<a.$

700. $\displaystyle\int_0^\infty e^{-ax}\sinh\,(bx)\, dx = \frac{b}{a^2-b^2}, \quad |b|<a.$

701. $\displaystyle\int_0^\infty \frac{\sinh ax}{e^{bx}+1}\, dx = \frac{\pi}{2b}\csc\frac{a\pi}{b} - \frac{1}{2a}, \quad b\geq 0.$

702. $\displaystyle\int_0^\infty \frac{\sinh ax}{e^{bx}-1}\, dx = \frac{1}{2a} - \frac{\pi}{2b}\cot\frac{a\pi}{b}, \quad b\geq 0.$

703. *$\displaystyle\int_0^{\pi/2} \frac{dx}{\sqrt{1-k^2\sin^2 x}} = \frac{\pi}{2}\left[1+\left(\frac{1}{2}\right)^2 k^2 + \left(\frac{1\cdot 3}{2\cdot 4}\right)^2 k^4 + \left(\frac{1\cdot 3\cdot 5}{2\cdot 4\cdot 6}\right)^2 k^6 + \dots\right],$
$k^2 < 1.$

704. *$\displaystyle\int_0^{\pi/2} \frac{dx}{(1-k^2\sin^2 x)^{3/2}} = \frac{\pi}{2}\left[1+\left(\frac{1}{2}\right)^2 3k^2 + \left(\frac{1\cdot 3}{2\cdot 4}\right)^2 5k^4\right.$
$\left. + \left(\frac{1\cdot 3\cdot 5}{2\cdot 4\cdot 6}\right)^2 7k^6 + \dots\right], \quad k^2 < 1.$

705. *$\displaystyle\int_0^{\pi/2} \sqrt{1-k^2\sin^2 x}\, dx = \frac{\pi}{2}\left[1-\left(\frac{1}{2}\right)^2 k^2 - \left(\frac{1\cdot 3}{2\cdot 4}\right)^2\frac{k^4}{3}\right.$
$\left. - \left(\frac{1\cdot 3\cdot 5}{2\cdot 4\cdot 6}\right)^2\frac{k^6}{5} - \dots\right], \quad k^2 < 1.$

706. $\displaystyle\int_0^\infty e^{-x} \log x \, dx = -\gamma.$

707. $\displaystyle\int_0^\infty e^{-x^2} \log x \, dx = -\frac{\sqrt{\pi}}{4}(\gamma + 2\log 2).$

708. $\displaystyle\int_0^\infty \left(\frac{1}{1 - e^{-x}} - \frac{1}{x}\right) e^{-x} \, dx = \gamma.$

709. $\displaystyle\int_0^\infty \frac{1}{x}\left(\frac{1}{1 - e^{-x}} - \frac{1}{x}\right) dx = \gamma.$

5.6 ORDINARY DIFFERENTIAL EQUATIONS

5.6.1 LINEAR DIFFERENTIAL EQUATIONS

Any linear differential equation can be written in the form

$$b_n(x)y^{(n)} + b_{n-1}(x)y^{(n-1)} + \cdots + b_1(x)y' + b_0(x)y = R(x) \tag{5.6.1}$$

or $p(D)y = R(x)$, where D is the differentiation operator $(Dy = dy/dx)$, $p(D)$ is a polynomial in D with coefficients $\{b_i\}$ depending on x, and $R(x)$ is an arbitrary function. In this notation, a power of D denotes repeated differentiation, that is, $D^n y = d^n y/dy^n$. For such an equation, the general solution has the form

$$y(x) = y_h(x) + y_p(x) \tag{5.6.2}$$

where $y_h(x)$ is the homogeneous solution and $y_p(x)$ is the particular solution. These functions satisfy $p(D)y_h = 0$ and $p(D)y_p = R(x)$.

Vector representation

Equation (5.6.1) can be written in the form $\dfrac{d\mathbf{y}}{dx} = A(x)\mathbf{y} + \mathbf{r}(x)$ where

$$\mathbf{y} = \begin{bmatrix} y \\ y' \\ y'' \\ \vdots \\ y^{(n-1)} \end{bmatrix}, \quad A(x) = \begin{bmatrix} 0 & 1 & 0 & \cdots & 0 \\ 0 & 0 & 1 & & 0 \\ \vdots & \vdots & & \ddots & \\ 0 & 0 & 0 & & 1 \\ -\frac{b_0}{b_n} & -\frac{b_1}{b_n} & -\frac{b_2}{b_n} & \cdots & -\frac{b_{n-1}}{b_n} \end{bmatrix}, \quad \mathbf{r}(x) = \begin{bmatrix} 0 \\ 0 \\ \vdots \\ 0 \\ \frac{R}{b_n} \end{bmatrix}.$$

Homogeneous solution

For the special case of a linear differential equation with constant coefficients (i.e., the $\{b_i\}$ in Equation (5.6.1) are constants), the procedure for finding the homogeneous solution is as follows:

1. Factor the polynomial $p(D)$ into real and complex linear factors, just as if D were a variable instead of an operator.

2. For each nonrepeated linear factor of the form $(D - a)$, where a is real, write a term of the form ce^{ax}, where c is an arbitrary constant.

3. For each repeated real linear factor of the form $(D - a)^m$, write m terms of the form

$$c_1 e^{ax} + c_2 x e^{ax} + c_3 x^2 e^{ax} + \cdots + c_m x^{m-1} e^{ax} \tag{5.6.3}$$

where the c_i's are arbitrary constants.

4. For each nonrepeated conjugate complex pair of factors of the form $(D - a + ib)(D - a - ib)$, write two terms of the form

$$c_1 e^{ax} \cos bx + c_2 e^{ax} \sin bx. \tag{5.6.4}$$

5. For each repeated conjugate complex pair of factors of the form $(D - a + ib)^m (D - a - ib)^m$, write $2m$ terms of the form

$$c_1 e^{ax} \cos bx + c_2 e^{ax} \sin bx + c_3 x e^{ax} \cos bx + c_4 x e^{ax} \sin bx + \ldots$$
$$+ c_{2m-1} x^{m-1} e^{ax} \cos bx + c_{2m} x^{m-1} e^{ax} \sin bx. \tag{5.6.5}$$

6. The sum of all the terms thus written is the homogeneous solution.

Example

For the linear equation

$$y^{(7)} - 14y^{(6)} + 80y^{(5)} - 242y^{(4)} + 419y^{(3)} - 416y'' + 220y' - 48y = 0,$$

$p(D)$ factors as $p(D) = (D - 1)^3 (D - 2)^2 (D - 3)(D - 4)$. The roots are thus $\{1, 1, 1, 2, 2, 3, 4\}$. Hence, the homogeneous solution has the form

$$y_h(x) = \left(c_0 + c_1 x + c_2 x^2\right) e^x + (c_3 + c_4 x) e^{2x} + c_5 e^{3x} + c_6 e^{4x}$$

where $\{c_0, \ldots, c_6\}$ are arbitrary constants.

Particular solutions

The following are solutions for some specific ordinary differential equations. In these tables we assume that $P(x)$ is a polynomial of degree n and $\{a, b, p, q, r, s\}$ are constants. In all of these tables, when using "cos" instead of "sin" in $R(x)$, use the given result, but replace "sin" by "cos", and replace "cos" by "$-$ sin".

If $R(x)$ is	A particular solution to $y' - ay = R(x)$ is
1. e^{rx}	$e^{rx}/(r - a)$.
2. $\sin sx$	$-\frac{a \sin sx + s \cos sx}{a^2 + s^2} = -\left(a^2 + s^2\right)^{-1/2} \sin\left(sx + \tan^{-1}\frac{s}{a}\right)$.
3. $P(x)$	$-\frac{1}{a}\left[P(x) + \frac{P'(x)}{a} + \frac{P''(x)}{a^2} + \cdots + \frac{P^{(n)}(x)}{a^n}\right]$.
4. $e^{rx}\sin sx$	Replace a by $a - r$ in formula 2 and multiply by e^{rx}.
5. $P(x)e^{rx}$	Replace a by $a - r$ in formula 3 and multiply by e^{rx}.
6. $P(x)\sin sx$	$-\sin sx\left[\frac{a}{a^2+s^2}P(x) + \frac{a^2-s^2}{(a^2+s^2)^2}P'(x)\right.$ $\left. + \cdots + \frac{a^k - \binom{k}{2}a^{k-2}s^2 + \binom{k}{4}a^{k-4}s^4 - \cdots}{(a^2+s^2)^k}P^{(k-1)}(x) + \cdots\right]$ $-\cos sx\left[\frac{s}{a^2+s^2}P(x) + \frac{2as}{(a^2+s^2)^2}P'(x)\right.$ $\left. + \cdots + \frac{\binom{k}{1}a^{k-1}s - \binom{k}{3}a^{k-3}s^3 + \cdots}{(a^2+s^2)^k}P^{(k-1)}(x) + \cdots\right]$.
7. $P(x)e^{rx}\sin sx$	Replace a by $a - r$ in formula 6 and multiply by e^{rx}.
8. e^{ax}	xe^{ax}.
9. $e^{ax}\sin sx$	$-e^{ax}\cos sx/s$.
10. $P(x)e^{ax}$	$e^{ax}\int^x P(z)\,dz$.
11. $P(x)e^{ax}\sin sx$	$\frac{e^{ax}\sin sx}{s}\left[\frac{P'(x)}{s} - \frac{P'''(x)}{s^3} + \frac{P^{(5)}(x)}{s^5} + \cdots\right]$ $-\frac{e^{ax}\cos sx}{s}\left[P(x) - \frac{P''(x)}{s^2} + \frac{P^{(4)}(x)}{s^4} + \cdots\right]$.

If $R(x)$ is	A particular solution to $y'' - 2ay' + a^2 y = R(x)$ is
12. e^{rx}	$e^{rx}/(r-a)^2$.
13. $\sin sx$	$\frac{(a^2-s^2)\sin sx + 2as\cos sx}{(a^2+s^2)^2} = \frac{1}{a^2+s^2}\sin\left(sx + \tan^{-1}\frac{2as}{a^2-s^2}\right)$.
14. $P(x)$	$\frac{1}{a^2}\left[P(x) + \frac{2P'(x)}{a} + \frac{3P''(x)}{a^2} + \cdots + \frac{(n+1)P^{(n)}(x)}{a^n}\right]$.
15. $e^{rx}\sin sx$	Replace a by $a-r$ in formula 13 and multiply by e^{rx}.
16. $P(x)e^{rx}$	Replace a by $a-r$ in formula 14 and multiply by e^{rx}.
17. $P(x)\sin sx$	$\sin sx\left[\frac{a^2-s^2}{(a^2+s^2)^2}P(x) + 2\frac{a^2-3as^2}{(a^2+s^2)^3}P'(x).\right.$ $\left. + \cdots + (k-1)\frac{a^k - \binom{k}{2}a^{k-2}s^2 + \binom{k}{4}a^{k-4}s^4 - \cdots}{(a^2+s^2)^k}P^{(k-2)}(x) + \cdots\right]$ $+ \cos sx\left[\frac{2as}{(a^2+s^2)^2}P(x) + 2\frac{3a^2s-s^3}{(a^2+s^2)^3}P'(x)\right.$ $\left. + \cdots + (k-1)\frac{\binom{k}{1}a^{k-1}s - \binom{k}{3}a^{k-3}s^3 + \cdots}{(a^2+s^2)^k}P^{(k-2)}(x) + \cdots\right]$.
18. $P(x)e^{rx}\sin sx$	Replace a by $a-r$ in formula 17 and multiply by e^{rx}.
19. e^{ax}	$x^2 e^{ax}/2$.
20. $e^{ax}\sin sx$	$-e^{ax}\sin sx/s^2$.
21. $P(x)e^{ax}$	$e^{ax}\int^x\int^y P(z)\,dz\,dy$
22. $P(x)e^{ax}\sin sx$	$-\frac{e^{ax}\sin sx}{s^2}\left[P(x) - \frac{3P''(x)}{s^2} + \frac{5P^{(4)}(x)}{s^4} + \cdots\right]$ $-\frac{e^{ax}\cos sx}{s^2}\left[\frac{2P(x)}{s} - -\frac{4P'''(x)}{s^3} + \frac{6P^{(5)}(x)}{s^5} + \cdots\right]$.

If $R(x)$ is	A particular solution to $y'' + qy = R(x)$ is
23. e^{rx}	$e^{rx}/(r^2 + q)$.
24. $\sin sx$	$\sin sx/(q - s^2)$.
25. $P(x)$	$\frac{1}{q}\left[P(x) - \frac{P''(x)}{q} + \frac{P^{(4)}(x)}{q^2} + \cdots + (-1)^k \frac{P^{(2k)}(x)}{q^k} + \cdots\right]$.
26. $e^{rx}\sin sx$	$\frac{(r^2 - s^2 + q)e^{rx}\sin sx - 2rse^{rx}\cos sx}{(r^2 - s^2 + q)^2 + (2rs)^2} =$ $\frac{e^{rx}}{\sqrt{(r^2 - s^2 + q)^2 + (2rs)^2}}\sin\left[sx - \tan^{-1}\frac{2rs}{r^2 - s^2 + q}\right]$.
27. $P(x)e^{rx}$	$\frac{e^{rx}}{q+r^2}\left[P(x) - \frac{2r}{q+r^2}P'(x) + \frac{3r^2 - q}{(q+r^2)^2}P''(x)\right.$ $\left. + \cdots + (-1)^{k-1}\frac{\binom{k}{1}r^{k-1} - \binom{k}{3}r^{k-3}q + \cdots}{(q+r^2)^{k-1}}P^{(k-1)}(x) + \cdots\right]$.
28. $P(x)\sin sx$	$\frac{\sin sx}{q-s^2}\left[P(x) - \frac{3s^2 + q}{(q-s^2)^2}P''(x)\right.$ $\left. + \cdots + (-1)^k\frac{\binom{2k+1}{1}s^{2k} + \binom{2k+1}{3}s^{2k-2}q + \cdots}{(q-s^2)^{2k}}P^{(2k)}(x) + \cdots\right]$ $- \frac{s\cos sx}{q-s^2}\left[\frac{2P'(x)}{(q-s^2)} - \frac{4s^2 + 4q}{(q-s^2)^3}P'''(x)\right.$ $\left. + \cdots + (-1)^{k+1}\frac{\binom{2k}{1}s^{2k-2} + \binom{2k}{3}s^{2k-4}q + \cdots}{(q-s^2)^{2k-1}}P^{(2k-1)}(x) + \cdots\right]$.

If $R(x)$ is	A particular solution to $y'' + b^2y = R(x)$ is
29. $\sin bx$	$-x\cos bx/2b$.
30. $P(x)\sin bx$	$\frac{\sin bx}{(2b)^2}\left[P(x) - \frac{P''(x)}{(2b)^2} + \frac{P^{(4)}(x)}{(2b)^4} + \cdots\right]$ $- \frac{\cos bx}{2b}\int\left[P(x) - \frac{P''(x)}{(2b)^2} + \cdots\right]dx$.

If $R(x)$ is	a particular solution to $y'' + py' + qy = R(x)$ is
31. e^{rx}	$e^{rx}/(r^2 + pr + q)$.
32. $\sin sx$	$\frac{(q-s^2)\sin sx - ps\cos sx}{(q-s^2)^2+(ps)^2} = \frac{1}{\sqrt{(q-s^2)^2+(ps)^2}}\sin\left(sx - \tan^{-1}\frac{ps}{q-s^2}\right)$.
33. $P(x)$	$\frac{1}{q}\left[P(x) - \frac{p}{q}P'(x) + \frac{p^2-q}{q^2}P''(x) - \frac{p^2-2pq}{q^2}P'''(x)\right.$ $\left. + \cdots + (-1)^n \frac{p^n - \binom{n-1}{1}p^{n-2}q + \binom{n-2}{2}p^{n-4}q^2 - \cdots}{q^n}P^{(n)}(x)\right]$.
34. $e^{rx}\sin sx$	Replace p by $p + 2r$, and q by $q + pr + r^2$ in formula 32 and multiply by e^{rx}.
35. $P(x)e^{rx}$	Replace p by $p + 2r$, and q by $q + pr + r^2$ in formula 33 and multiply by e^{rx}.

If $R(x)$ is	A particular solution to $(D - a)^n y = R(x)$ is
36. e^{rx}	$e^{rx}/(r - a)^n$.
37. $\sin sx$	$\frac{(-1)^n}{(a^2+s^2)^n}\left[\left(a^n - \binom{n}{2}a^{n-2}s^2 + \binom{n}{4}a^{n-4}s^4 - \cdots\right)\sin sx + \left(\binom{n}{1}a^{n-1}s + \binom{n}{3}a^{n-3}s^3 + \cdots\right)\cos sx\right]$.
38. $P(x)$	$\frac{(-1)^n}{a^n}\left[P(x) + \binom{n}{1}\frac{P'(x)}{a} + \binom{n+1}{2}\frac{P''(x)}{a^2} + \binom{n+2}{3}\frac{P'''(x)}{a^3} + \cdots\right]$.
39. $e^{rx}\sin sx$	Replace a by $a - r$ in formula 37 and multiply by e^{rx}.
40. $P(x)e^{rx}$	Replace a by $a - r$ in formula 38 and multiply by e^{rx}.

Second order linear constant coefficient equation

Consider $ay'' + by' + cy = 0$, where a, b, and c are real constants. Let m_1 and m_2 be the roots of $am^2 + bm + c = 0$. There are three forms of the solution:

1. If m_1 and m_2 are real and distinct, then $y(x) = c_1 e^{m_1 x} + c_2 e^{m_2 x}$
2. If m_1 and m_2 are real and equal, then $y(x) = c_1 e^{m_1 x} + c_2 x e^{m_1 x}$
3. If $m_1 = p + iq$ and $m_2 = p - iq$ (with $p = -b/2$ and $q = \sqrt{4ac - b^2}/2$), then $y(x) = e^{px}(c_1 \cos qx + c_2 \sin qx)$

Consider $ay'' + by' + cy = R(x)$, where a, b, and c are real constants. Let m_1 and m_2 be as above.

1. If m_1 and m_2 are real and distinct, then $y(x) = C_1 e^{m_1 x} + C_2 e^{m_2 x} + e^{m_1 x}/(m_1 - m_2) \int^x e^{-m_1 z} R(z)\, dz + e^{m_2 x}/(m_2 - m_1) \int^x e^{-m_2 z} R(z)\, dz$.

2. If m_1 and m_2 are real and equal, then $y(x) = C_1 e^{m_1 x} + C_2 x e^{m_1 x} + x e^{m_1 x} \int^x e^{-m_1 z} R(z)\, dz - e^{m_1 x} \int^x z e^{-m_1 z} R(z)\, dz$.

3. If $m_1 = p + iq$ and $m_2 = p - iq$, then $y(x) = e^{px}(c_1 \cos qx + c_2 \sin qx) + e^{px} \sin qx/q \int^x e^{-pz} R(z) \cos qz\, dz - e^{px} \cos qx/q \int^x e^{-pz} R(z) \sin qz\, dz$.

Damping: none, under, over, and critical

Consider the linear ordinary differential equation (ODE) $x'' + \mu x' + x = 0$. If the damping coefficient μ is positive, then all solutions decay to $x = 0$. If $\mu = 0$, the system is undamped and the solution oscillates without decaying. The value of μ such that the roots of the characteristic equation $\lambda^2 + \mu \lambda + 1 = 0$ are real and equal is the critical damping coefficient. If μ is less than (greater than) the critical damping coefficient, then the system is under (over) damped.

In the following figure all curves have the same initial values: $x(0) = 2$ and $x'(0) = -2.5$. Reading down, at the left-most depression, are the curves

- $x'' + 3x' + x = 0$ Overdamped
- $x'' + 2x' + x$ Critically damped
- $x'' + 0.2x' + x = 0$ Underdamped
- $x'' + x = 0$ Undamped

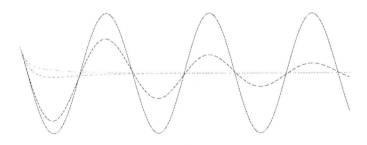

5.6.2 SOLUTION TECHNIQUES

Differential equation	Solution or solution technique
Autonomous equation $f(y^{(n)}, y^{(n-1)}, \ldots, y'', y', y) = 0$	Change dependent variable to $u(y) = y'(x)$
Bernoulli's equation $y' + f(x)y = g(x)y^n$	Change dependent variable to $v(x) = (y(x))^{1-n}$
Clairaut's equation $f(xy' - y) = g(y')$	One solution is $f(xC - y) = g(C)$
Constant coefficient equation $a_0 y^{(n)} + a_1 y^{(n-1)} + \ldots$ $\qquad + a_{n-1} y' + a_n y = 0$	There are solutions of the form $y = e^{\lambda x}$. See Section 5.6.1.
Dependent variable missing $f(y^{(n)}, y^{(n-1)}, \ldots, y'', y', x) = 0$	Change dependent variable to $u(x) = y'(x)$
Euler's equation $a_0 x^n y^{(n)} + a_1 x^{n-1} y^{(n-1)} + \ldots$ $\qquad + a_{n-1} xy + a_n y = 0$	Change independent variable to $x = e^t$
Exact equation $M(x, y)\, dx + N(x, y)\, dy = 0$ **with** $\frac{\partial M}{\partial y} = \frac{\partial N}{\partial x}$	Integrate $M(x, y)$ with respect to x holding y constant, call this $m(x, y)$. Then $m(x, y) + \int \left(N - \dfrac{\partial m}{\partial y} \right) dy = C$
Homogeneous equation $y' = f\left(\dfrac{y}{x}\right)$	$\ln x = \displaystyle\int \frac{dv}{f(v) - v} + C$ unless $f(v) = v$, in which case $y = Cx$.
Linear first order equation $y' + f(x)y = g(x)$	$y(x) =$ $e^{-\int^x f(t)\,dt} \left[\displaystyle\int^x e^{\int^z f(t)\,dt} g(z)\, dz + C \right]$
Reducible to homogeneous $(a_1 x + b_1 y + c_1)\, dx$ $\qquad + (a_2 x + b_2 y + c_2)\, dy = 0$ **with** $a_1/a_2 \neq b_1/b_2$	Change variables to $u = a_1 x + b_1 y + c$ and $v = a_2 x + b_2 y + c$
Reducible to separable $(a_1 x + b_1 y + c_1)\, dx$ $\qquad + (a_2 x + b_2 y + c_2)\, dy = 0$ **with** $a_1/a_2 = b_1/b_2$	Change dependent variable to $u(x) = a_1 x + b_1 y$
Separation of variables $y' = f(x)g(y)$	$\displaystyle\int \frac{dy}{g(y)} = \int f(x)\, dx + C$

5.6.3 INTEGRATING FACTORS

An integrating factor is a multiplicative term that makes a differential equation become exact. If the differential equation $M(x, y)\, dx + N(x, y)\, dy \neq 0$ is not exact (i.e., $M_y \neq N_x$) then it may always be made exact if you can find the integrating factor.

1. If $\frac{1}{N}\left(\frac{\partial M}{\partial y} - \frac{\partial N}{\partial x}\right) = f(x)$, a function of x alone, then $u = \exp\left(\int^x f(z)\,dz\right)$ is an integrating factor.

2. If $\frac{1}{M}\left(\frac{\partial M}{\partial y} - \frac{\partial N}{\partial x}\right) = g(y)$, a function of y alone, then $u = \exp\left(\int^y g(z)\,dz\right)$ is an integrating factor.

Example

The equation $\frac{y}{x}\,dx + dy = 0$ has $\{M = y/x,\ N = 1\}$ and $f(x) = 1/x$. Hence $u = \exp\left(\int^x \frac{1}{z}\,dz\right) = \exp(\log x) = x$ is an integrating factor. Multiplying the original equation by $u(x)$ results in $y\,dx + x\,dy = 0$ or $d(xy) = 0$.

5.6.4 VARIATION OF PARAMETERS

If the equation $L[y] = y'' + P(x)y' + Q(x)y = R(x)$ has the homogeneous solutions $y_1(x)$ and $y_2(x)$ (i.e., $L[y_i] = 0$), then the solution to the original equation is given by

$$y(x) = -y_1(x)\int \frac{y_2(x)R(x)}{W(y_1, y_2)}\,dx + y_2(x)\int \frac{y_1(x)R(x)}{W(y_1, y_2)}\,dx, \tag{5.6.6}$$

where $W(y_1, y_2) = y_1'y_2 - y_1 y_2'$ is the Wronskian.

Example

The homogeneous solutions to $y'' + y = \csc x$ are clearly $y_1(x) = \sin x$ and $y_2(x) = \cos x$. Here, $W(y_1, y_2) = -1$. Hence, $y(x) = \sin x \log(\sin x) - x \cos x$.

5.6.5 GREEN'S FUNCTIONS

Let $L[y] = f(x)$ be a linear differential equation for $y(x)$ with the linear homogeneous boundary conditions $\{B_i[y] = 0\}$, for $i = 1, 2, \ldots, n$. If there is a Green's function $G(x; z)$ that satisfies

$$\begin{aligned} L[G(x; z)] &= \delta(x - z), \\ B_i[G(x; z)] &= 0, \end{aligned} \tag{5.6.7}$$

where δ is Dirac's delta function, then the solution of the original system can be written as $y(x) = \int G(x; z)f(z)\,dz$, integrated over an appropriate region.

Example

To solve $y'' = f(x)$ with $y(0) = 0$ and $y(L) = 0$, the appropriate Green's function is

$$G(x; z) = \begin{cases} \dfrac{x(z - L)}{L} & \text{for } 0 \le x \le z, \\[2mm] \dfrac{z(x - L)}{L} & \text{for } z \le x \le L. \end{cases}$$

Hence, the solution is

$$y(x) = \int_0^L G(x; z)\, f(z)\, dz = \int_0^x \frac{z(x - L)}{L}\, f(z)\, dz + \int_x^L \frac{x(z - L)}{L}\, f(z)\, dz.$$

5.6.6 LIST OF GREEN'S FUNCTIONS

For the following, the Green's function is $G(x, \xi)$ when $x \le \xi$ and $G(\xi, x)$ when $x \ge \xi$.

1. For the equation $\dfrac{d^2 y}{dx^2} = f(x)$ with

    (a) $y(0) = y(1) = 0,$ $G(x, \xi) = -(1 - \xi)x,$

    (b) $y(0) = 0,\ y'(1) = 0,$ $G(x, \xi) = -x,$

    (c) $y(0) = -y(1),\ y'(0) = -y'(1),$ $G(x, \xi) = -\frac{1}{2}(x - \xi) - \frac{1}{4},$ and

    (d) $y(-1) = y(1) = 0,$ $G(x, \xi) = -\frac{1}{2}(x - \xi - x\xi + 1).$

2. For the equation $\dfrac{d^2 y}{dx^2} - y = f(x)$ with y finite in $(-\infty, \infty)$,

$$G(x, \xi) = -\tfrac{1}{2} e^{x - \xi}.$$

3. For the equation $\dfrac{d^2 y}{dx^2} + k^2 y = f(x)$ with

  (a) $y(0) = y(1) = 0,$ $G(x, \xi) = -\dfrac{\sin kx \sin k(1 - \xi)}{k \sin k},$

  (b) $y(-1) = y(1),\ y'(-1) = y'(1),$ and $G(x, \xi) = \dfrac{\cos k(x - \xi + 1)}{2k \sin k}.$

4. For the equation $\dfrac{d^2 y}{dx^2} - k^2 y = f(x)$ with

  (a) $y(0) = y(1) = 0,$ $G(x, \xi) = -\dfrac{\sinh kx \sinh k(1 - \xi)}{k \sinh k},$

  (b) $y(-1) = y(1),\ y'(-1) = y'(1),$ and $G(x, \xi) = -\dfrac{\cosh k(x - \xi + 1)}{2k \sinh k}.$

5. For the equation $\dfrac{d}{dx}\left(x \dfrac{dy}{dx}\right) = f(x),$ with $y(0)$ finite and $y(1) = 0,$ $G(x, \xi) = \ln \xi.$

6. For the equation $\dfrac{d}{dx}\left(x \dfrac{dy}{dx}\right) - \dfrac{m^2}{x} y = f(x),$ with $y(0)$ finite and $y(1) = 0,$ $G(x, \xi) = -\frac{1}{2m}\left[\left(\frac{x}{\xi}\right)^m - (x\xi)^m\right],\ (m = 1, 2, \ldots).$

7. For the equation $\dfrac{d}{dx}\left((1 - x^2)\dfrac{dy}{dx}\right) - \dfrac{m^2}{1 - x^2} y = f(x),$ with $y(-1)$ and $y(1)$ finite, $G(x, \xi) = -\frac{1}{2m}\left(\frac{1+x}{1-x}\frac{1-\xi}{1+\xi}\right)^{m/2},\ (m = 1, 2, \ldots).$

8. For the equation $\dfrac{d^4 y}{dx^4} = f(x)$, with $y(0) = y'(0) = y(1) = y'(1) = 0$,

$G(x, \xi) = -\dfrac{x^2(\xi-1)^2}{6}(2x\xi + x - 3\xi)$.

5.6.7 TRANSFORM TECHNIQUES

Transforms can sometimes be used to solve linear differential equations. Laplace transforms (page 539) are appropriate for initial value problems, while Fourier transforms (page 530) are appropriate for boundary value problems.

Example

Consider the linear second order equation $y'' + y = p(x)$, with the initial conditions $y(0) = 0$ and $y'(0) = 0$. Multiplying this equation by e^{-sx}, and integrating with respect to x from 0 to ∞, results in

$$\int_0^\infty e^{-sx} y''(x)\, dx + \int_0^\infty e^{-sx} y(x)\, dx = \int_0^\infty e^{-sx} p(x)\, dx.$$

Integrating by parts, and recognizing that $Y(s) = \mathcal{L}[y(x)] = \int_0^\infty e^{-sx} y(x)\, dx$ is the Laplace transform of y, this simplifies to

$$(s^2 + 1)Y(s) = \int_0^\infty e^{-sx} p(x)\, dx = \mathcal{L}[p(x)].$$

If $p(x) \equiv 1$, then $\mathcal{L}[p(x)] = s^{-1}$. The table of Laplace transforms shows that the $y(x)$ corresponding to $Y(s) = 1/[s(1 + s^2)]$ is $y(x) = \mathcal{L}^{-1}[Y(s)] = 1 - \cos x$.

5.6.8 NAMED ORDINARY DIFFERENTIAL EQUATIONS

1. Airy equation: $y'' = xy$
   Solution: $y = c_1 \operatorname{Ai}(x) + c_2 \operatorname{Bi}(x)$
2. Bernoulli equation: $y' = a(x)y^n + b(x)y$
3. Bessel equation: $x^2 y'' + xy' + (\lambda^2 x^2 - n^2)y = 0$
   Solution: $y = c_1 J_n(\lambda x) + c_2 Y_n(\lambda x)$
4. Bessel equation (transformed): $x^2 y'' + (2p + 1)xy' + (\lambda^2 x^{2r} + \beta^2)y = 0$
   Solution: $y = x^{-p}\left[c_1 J_{q/r}\left(\dfrac{\lambda}{r}x^r\right) + c_2 Y_{q/r}\left(\dfrac{\lambda}{r}x^r\right)\right] \qquad q \equiv \sqrt{p^2 - \beta^2}$
5. Bôcher equation: $y'' + \dfrac{1}{2}\left[\dfrac{m_1}{x-a_1} + \cdots + \dfrac{m_{n-1}}{x-a_{n-1}}\right] y'$
   $+\dfrac{1}{4}\left[\dfrac{A_0+A_1x+\cdots+A_lx^l}{(x-a_1)^{m_1}(x-a_2)^{m_2}\cdots(x-a_{n-1})^{m_{n-1}}}\right] y = 0$
6. Duffing's equation: $y'' + y + \epsilon y^3 = 0$
7. Emden–Fowler equation: $(x^p y')' \pm x^\sigma y^n = 0$

8. Hypergeometric equation: $y'' + \left(\frac{1-\alpha-\alpha'}{x-a} + \frac{1-\beta-\beta'}{x-b} + \frac{1-\gamma-\gamma'}{x-c} \right) y'$

$- \left(\frac{\alpha\alpha'}{(x-a)(b-c)} + \frac{\beta\beta'}{(x-b)(c-a)} + \frac{\gamma\gamma'}{(x-c)(a-b)} \right) \frac{(a-b)(b-c)(c-a)}{(x-a)(x-b)(x-c)} u = 0$

Solution: $y = P \begin{Bmatrix} a & b & c & \\ \alpha & \beta & \gamma & x \\ \alpha' & \beta' & \gamma' & \end{Bmatrix}$ (Riemann's P function)

9. Legendre equation: $(1 - x^2)y'' - 2xy' + n(n+1)y = 0$
   Solution: $y = c_1 P_n(x) + c_2 Q_n(x)$

10. Mathieu equation: $y'' + (a - 2q \cos 2x)y = 0$

11. Painlevé transcendent (first equation): $y'' = 6y^2 + x$

12. Parabolic cylinder equation: $y'' + (ax^2 + bx + c)y = 0$

13. Riccati equation: $y' = a(x)y^2 + b(x)y + c(x)$

5.6.9   LIAPUNOV'S DIRECT METHOD

If, as $\mathbf{x}(t)$ evolves, the function V depends on $\mathbf{x}$ so that $V(\mathbf{x}) > 0$ and $\frac{dV}{dt} < 0$, then the system is asymptotically stable: $V[\mathbf{x}(t)] \to 0$ as $x \to \infty$. For example, for the nonlinear system of differential equations with $a > 0$

$$\dot{x}_1 = -ax_1 - x_1 x_2^2, \qquad \dot{x}_2 = -ax_2 + x_1^2 x_2,$$

define $V(\mathbf{x}) = x_1^2 + x_2^2$. Since $\dot{V} = -2a(x_1^2 + x_2^2) = -2aV$, $V(t) = V_0 e^{-2at}$. Hence $x_1(t)$ and $x_2(t)$ both decay to 0.

5.6.10   LIE GROUPS

An algorithm for integrating second order ordinary differential equations is given by:

1. Determine the admitted Lie algebra L_r, where r is the dimension.

2. If $r > 2$, determine a subalgebra $L_2 \subset L_r$. If $r < 2$, then Lie groups are not useful for the given equation.

3. From the commutator and pseudoscalar product, change the basis to obtain one of the four cases in the table below.

4. Introduce canonical variables specified by the change of basis into the original differential equation. Integrate this new equation.

5. Rewrite the solution in terms of the original variables.

The invertible transformation $\{\bar{x} = \phi(x, y, a), \bar{y} = \psi(x, y, a)\}$ forms a one parameter group if $\phi(\bar{x}, \bar{y}, b) = \phi(x, y, a + b)$ and $\psi(\bar{x}, \bar{y}, b) = \psi(x, y, a + b)$. For small a, these transformations become

$$\bar{x} = x + a\xi(x, y) + O(a^2) \qquad \bar{y} = y + a\eta(x, y) + O(a^2). \qquad (5.6.8)$$

The infinitesimal generator is $X = \xi(x, y)\frac{\partial}{\partial x} + \eta(x, y)\frac{\partial}{\partial y}$. If $D = \frac{\partial}{\partial x} + y'\frac{\partial}{\partial y} + y''\frac{\partial}{\partial y'} + \ldots$, then the derivatives of the new variables are

$$\bar{y}' = \frac{d\bar{y}}{d\bar{x}} = \frac{D\psi}{D\phi} = \frac{\psi_x + y'\psi_y}{\phi_x + y'\phi_y} = P(x, y, y', a) = y' + a\zeta_1 + O(a^2), \quad \text{and}$$

$$\bar{y}'' = \frac{d\bar{y}'}{d\bar{x}} = \frac{DP}{D\phi} = \frac{P_x + y'P_y + y''P_{y'}}{\phi_x + y'\phi_y} = y'' + a\zeta_2 + O(a^2), \tag{5.6.9}$$

where

$$\zeta_1 = D(\eta) - y'D(\xi) = \eta_x + (\eta_y - \xi_x)y' - y'^2\xi_y, \quad \text{and}$$

$$\zeta_2 = D(\zeta_1) - y''D(\xi) = \eta_{xx} + (2\eta_{xy} - \xi_{xx})y' + (\eta_{yy} - 2\xi_{xy})y'^2$$
$$- y'^3\xi_{yy} + (\eta_y - 2\xi_x - 3y'\xi_y)y''. \tag{5.6.10}$$

The prolongations of X are $X^{(1)} = X + \zeta_1\frac{\partial}{\partial y'}$ and $X^{(2)} = X^{(1)} + \zeta_2\frac{\partial}{\partial y''}$. For a given differential equation, the different infinitesimal generators will generate an r-dimensional Lie group (L_r)

For the equation $F(x, y, y', y'') = 0$ to be invariant under the action of the above group, $X^{(2)}F \mid_{F=0} = 0$. When $F = y'' - f(x, y, y')$, this determining equation becomes

$$\eta_{xx} + (2\eta_{xy} - \xi_{xx})y' + (\eta_{yy} - 2\xi_{xy})y'^2 - y'^3\xi_y y$$
$$+ (\eta_y - 2\xi_x - 3y'\xi_y)f - \left[\eta_x + (\eta_y - \xi_x)y' - y'^2\right]f_{y'}$$
$$- \xi f_x - \eta f_y = 0. \tag{5.6.11}$$

Given the two generators $X_1 = \xi_1\frac{\partial}{\partial x} + \eta_1\frac{\partial}{\partial y}$ and $X_2 = \xi_2\frac{\partial}{\partial x} + \eta_2\frac{\partial}{\partial y}$, the pseudoscalar product is $X_1 \vee X_2 = \xi_1\eta_2 - \xi_2\eta_1$, and the commutator is $[X_1, X_2] = X_1X_2 - X_2X_1$. By a suitable choice of basis, any two-dimensional Lie algebra can be reduced to one of four types:

No.	Commutator	Pseudoscalar	Typified by
I	$[X_1, X_2] = 0$	$X_1 \vee X_2 \neq 0$	$\{X_1 = \frac{\partial}{\partial x}, \quad X_2 = \frac{\partial}{\partial y}\}$
II	$[X_1, X_2] = 0$	$X_1 \vee X_2 = 0$	$\{X_1 = \frac{\partial}{\partial y}, \quad X_2 = x\frac{\partial}{\partial y}\}$
III	$[X_1, X_2] = X_1$	$X_1 \vee X_2 \neq 0$	$\{X_1 = \frac{\partial}{\partial y}, \quad X_2 = x\frac{\partial}{\partial x} + y\frac{\partial}{\partial y}\}$
IV	$[X_1, X_2] = X_1$	$X_1 \vee X_2 = 0$	$\{X_1 = \frac{\partial}{\partial y}, \quad X_2 = y\frac{\partial}{\partial y}\}$

5.6.11 TYPES OF CRITICAL POINTS

An ODE may have several types of critical points; these include improper node, deficient improper node, proper node, saddle, center, and focus. See Figure 5.6.1.

FIGURE 5.6.1

Types of critical points. Clockwise from upper left: center, improper node, deficient improper node, spiral, star, saddle.

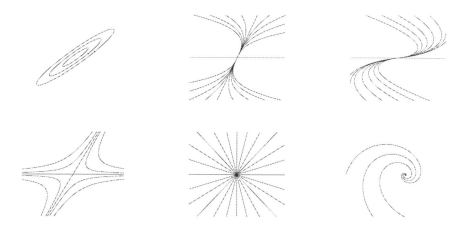

5.6.12   STOCHASTIC DIFFERENTIAL EQUATIONS

A stochastic differential equation has the form

$$dX(t) = a(X(t)) \, dt + b(X(t)) \, dB(t) \qquad (5.6.12)$$

where $B(t)$ is a random Brownian motion. Brownian motion has a Gaussian probability distribution and independent increments. The probability density function $f_{X(t)}$ for $X(t)$ satisfies the forward Kolmogorov equation

$$\tfrac{\partial}{\partial t} f_{X(t)}(x) = \tfrac{1}{2} \tfrac{\partial^2}{\partial x^2} \left[b^2(x) f_{X(t)}(x) \right] - \tfrac{\partial}{\partial x} \left[a(x) f_{X(t)}(x) \right]. \qquad (5.6.13)$$

The conditional expectation $u(t, x) = \mathrm{E}\left[\phi(X(t)) \mid X(0) = x\right]$ satisfies

$$\frac{\partial}{\partial t} u(t, x) = \frac{1}{2} b^2(x) \frac{\partial^2}{\partial x^2} u(t, x) + a(x) \frac{\partial}{\partial x} u(t, x) \quad \text{with} \quad u(0, x) = \phi(x).$$
$$(5.6.14)$$

5.7 PARTIAL DIFFERENTIAL EQUATIONS

5.7.1 CLASSIFICATIONS OF PDES

Consider second order partial differential equations, with two independent variables, of the form

$$A(x, y)\frac{\partial^2 u}{\partial x^2} + B(x, y)\frac{\partial^2 u}{\partial x \partial y} + C(x, y)\frac{\partial^2 u}{\partial y^2} = \Psi\left(u, \frac{\partial u}{\partial x}, \frac{\partial u}{\partial y}, x, y\right). \qquad (5.7.1)$$

If $\begin{bmatrix} B^2 - 4AC > 0 \\ B^2 - 4AC = 0 \\ B^2 - 4AC < 0 \end{bmatrix}$ at some point (x, y), then Equation (5.7.1) is $\begin{bmatrix} \text{hyperbolic} \\ \text{parabolic} \\ \text{elliptic} \end{bmatrix}$ at that point. If an equation is of the same type at all points, then the equation is simply of that type.

5.7.2 NAMED PARTIAL DIFFERENTIAL EQUATIONS

1. Biharmonic equation: $\quad \nabla^4 u = 0$

2. Burgers' equation: $\quad u_t + u u_x = \nu u_{xx}$

3. Diffusion (or heat) equation: $\quad \nabla(c(\mathbf{x}, t)\nabla u) = u_t$

4. Hamilton–Jacobi equation: $\quad V_t + H(t, \mathbf{x}, V_{x_1}, \ldots, V_{x_n}) = 0$

5. Helmholtz equation: $\quad \nabla^2 u + k^2 u = 0$

6. Korteweg de Vries equation: $\quad u_t + u_{xxx} - 6 u u_x = 0$

7. Laplace's equation: $\quad \nabla^2 u = 0$

8. Navier–Stokes equations: $\quad \mathbf{u}_t + (\mathbf{u} \cdot \nabla)\mathbf{u} = -\frac{\nabla P}{\rho} + \nu \nabla^2 \mathbf{u}$

9. Poisson equation: $\quad \nabla^2 u = -4\pi \rho(\mathbf{x})$

10. Schrödinger equation: $\quad -\frac{\hbar^2}{2m}\nabla^2 u + V(\mathbf{x})u = i\hbar u_t$

11. Sine–Gordon equation: $\quad u_{xx} - u_{yy} \pm \sin u = 0$

12. Tricomi equation: $\quad u_{yy} = y u_{xx}$

13. Wave equation: $\quad c^2 \nabla^2 u = u_{tt}$

14. Telegraph equation: $\quad u_{xx} = a u_{tt} + b u_t + c u$

5.7.3 WELL-POSEDNESS OF PDES

Partial differential equations involving $u(\mathbf{x})$ usually have the following types of boundary conditions:

1. Dirichlet conditions: $u = 0$ on the boundary

2. Neumann conditions: $\frac{\partial u}{\partial n} = 0$ on the boundary

3. Cauchy conditions: u and $\frac{\partial u}{\partial n}$ specified on the boundary

A well-posed differential equation meets these conditions:

1. The solution exists.

2. The solution is unique.

3. The solution is stable (i.e., the solution depends continuously on the boundary conditions and initial conditions).

Type of boundary conditions	Type of equation		
	Elliptic	Hyperbolic	Parabolic
Dirichlet			
Open (spacelike) surface	Undetermined	Undetermined	Unique, stable solution in one direction
Closed surface	Unique, stable solution	Undetermined	Undetermined
Neumann			
Open (spacelike) surface	Undetermined	Undetermined	Unique, stable solution in one direction
Closed surface	Overdetermined	Overdetermined	Overdetermined
Cauchy			
Open (spacelike) surface	Not physical results	Unique, stable solution	Overdetermined
Closed surface	Overdetermined	Overdetermined	Overdetermined

5.7.4 GREEN'S FUNCTIONS

In the following, $\mathbf{r} = (x, y, z)$, $\mathbf{r}_0 = (x_0, y_0, z_0)$, $R^2 = (x-x_0)^2+(y-y_0)^2+(z-z_0)^2$, $P^2 = (x - x_0)^2 + (y - y_0)^2$.

1. For the potential equation $\nabla^2 G + k^2 G = -4\pi \delta(\mathbf{r} - \mathbf{r}_0)$, with the radiation condition (outgoing waves only), the solution is

$$
G = \begin{cases} \frac{2\pi i}{k} e^{ik|x-x_0|} & \text{in one dimension,} \\ i\pi H_0^{(1)}(kP) & \text{in two dimensions, and} \\ \frac{e^{ikR}}{R} & \text{in three dimensions,} \end{cases}
$$

where $H_0^{(1)}(\cdot)$ is a Hankel function.

2. For the N-dimensional diffusion equation

$$\nabla^2 G - a^2 \frac{\partial G}{\partial t} = -4\pi \delta(\mathbf{r} - \mathbf{r}_0)\delta(t - t_0),$$

with the initial condition $G = 0$ for $t < t_0$, and the boundary condition $G = 0$ at $r = \infty$, the solution is

$$G = \frac{4\pi}{a^2} \left(\frac{a}{2\sqrt{\pi(t - t_0)}} \right)^N \exp\left(-\frac{a^2|\mathbf{r} - \mathbf{r}_0|^2}{4(t - t_0)} \right).$$

3. For the wave equation

$$\nabla^2 G - \frac{1}{c^2} \frac{\partial^2 G}{\partial t^2} = -4\pi \delta(\mathbf{r} - \mathbf{r}_0)\delta(t - t_0),$$

with the initial conditions $G = G_t = 0$ for $t < t_0$, and the boundary condition $G = 0$ at $r = \infty$, the solution is

$$G = \begin{cases} 2c\pi H\left[(t - t_0) - \frac{|x - x_0|}{c} \right] & \text{in one space dimension,} \\ \frac{2c}{\sqrt{c^2(t - t_0)^2 - P^2}} H\left[(t - t_0) - \frac{P}{c} \right] & \text{in two space dimensions, and} \\ \frac{1}{R}\delta\left[\frac{R}{c} - (t - t_0) \right] & \text{in three space dimensions.} \end{cases}$$

where $H(\cdot)$ is the Heaviside function.

5.7.5 QUASI-LINEAR EQUATIONS

Consider the quasi-linear differential equation for $u(\mathbf{x}) = u(x_1, x_2, \ldots, x_N)$,

$$a_1(\mathbf{x}, u)u_{x_1} + a_2(\mathbf{x}, u)u_{x_2} + \cdots + a_N(\mathbf{x}, u)u_{x_N} = b(\mathbf{x}, u).$$

Defining $\frac{\partial x_k}{\partial s} = a_k(\mathbf{x}, u)$, for $k = 1, 2, \ldots, N$, the original equation becomes $\frac{du}{ds} = b(\mathbf{x}, u)$. To solve the original system, the ordinary differential equations for $u(s, \mathbf{t})$ and the $\{x_k(s, \mathbf{t})\}$ must be solved. Their initial conditions can often be parameterized as (with $\mathbf{t} = (t_1, \ldots, t_{N-1})$)

$$u(s = 0, \mathbf{t}) = v(\mathbf{t}),$$
$$x_1(s = 0, \mathbf{t}) = h_1(\mathbf{t}),$$
$$x_2(s = 0, \mathbf{t}) = h_2(\mathbf{t}),$$
$$\vdots$$
$$x_N(s = 0, \mathbf{t}) = h_N(\mathbf{t}),$$

from which the solution follows. This results in an implicit solution.

Example

For the equation $u_x + x^2 u_y = -yu$ with $u = f(y)$ when $x = 0$, the corresponding equations are

$$\frac{\partial x}{\partial s} = 1, \qquad \frac{\partial y}{\partial s} = x^2, \qquad \frac{du}{ds} = -yu.$$

The original initial data can be written parametrically as $x(s = 0, t) = 0$, $y(s = 0, t_1) = t_1$, and $u(s = 0, t_1) = f(t_1)$. Solving for x results in $x(s, t_1) = s$. The equation for y can then be integrated to yield $y(s, t_1) = \frac{s^3}{3} + t_1$. Finally, the equation for u is integrated to obtain $u(s, t_1) = f(t_1) \exp\left(-\frac{s^4}{12} - st_1\right)$. These solutions constitute an implicit solution of the original system.

In this case, it is possible to eliminate the s and t_1 variables analytically to obtain the explicit solution: $u(x, y) = f\left(y - \frac{x^3}{3}\right) \exp\left(\frac{x^4}{4} - xy\right)$.

5.7.6 EXACT SOLUTIONS OF LAPLACE'S EQUATION

1. If $\nabla^2 u = 0$ in a circle of radius R and $u(R, \theta) = f(\theta)$, for $0 \le \theta < 2\pi$, then $u(r, \theta)$ is

$$u(r, \theta) = \frac{1}{2\pi} \int_0^{2\pi} \frac{R^2 - r^2}{R^2 - 2Rr \cos(\theta - \phi) + r^2} f(\phi) \, d\phi.$$

2. If $\nabla^2 u = 0$ in a sphere of radius one and $u(1, \theta, \phi) = f(\theta, \phi)$, then

$$u(r, \theta, \phi) = \frac{1}{4\pi} \int_0^\pi \int_0^{2\pi} f(\Theta, \Phi) \frac{1 - r^2}{(1 - 2r \cos \gamma + r^2)^{3/2}} \sin \Theta \, d\Theta \, d\Phi,$$

   where $\cos \gamma = \cos \theta \cos \Theta + \sin \theta \sin \Theta \cos(\phi - \Phi)$.

3. If $\nabla^2 u = 0$ in the half plane $y \ge 0$, and $u(x, 0) = f(x)$, then

$$u(x, y) = \frac{1}{\pi} \int_{-\infty}^{\infty} \frac{f(t)y}{(x - t)^2 + y^2} \, dt.$$

4. If $\nabla^2 u = 0$ in the half space $z \ge 0$, and $u(x, y, 0) = f(x, y)$, then

$$u(x, y, z) = \frac{z}{2\pi} \int_{-\infty}^{\infty} \int_{-\infty}^{\infty} \frac{f(\zeta, \eta)}{\left[(x - \zeta)^2 + (y - \eta)^2 + z^2\right]^{3/2}} \, d\zeta \, d\eta.$$

5.7.7 SOLUTIONS TO THE WAVE EQUATION

Consider the wave equation $\frac{\partial^2 u}{\partial t^2} = \nabla^2 u = \frac{\partial^2 u}{\partial x_1^2} + \cdots + \frac{\partial^2 u}{\partial x_n^2}$, with $\mathbf{x} = (x_1, \ldots, x_n)$ and the initial data $u(0, \mathbf{x}) = f(\mathbf{x})$ and $u_t(0, \mathbf{x}) = g(\mathbf{x})$. When n is odd (and $n \ge 3$), the solution is

$$u(t, \mathbf{x}) = \frac{1}{1 \cdot 3 \cdots (n - 2)} \left\{ \frac{\partial}{\partial t} \left(\frac{\partial}{t \, \partial t} \right)^{(n-3)/2} t^{n-2} \omega[f; \mathbf{x}, t] \right.$$

$$\left. + \left(\frac{\partial}{t \, \partial t} \right)^{(n-3)/2} t^{n-2} \omega[g; \mathbf{x}, t] \right\},$$

(5.7.2)

where $\omega[h; \mathbf{x}, t]$ is the average of the function $h(\mathbf{x})$ over the surface of an n-dimensional sphere of radius t centered at $\mathbf{x}$; that is, $\omega[h; \mathbf{x}, t] = \frac{1}{\sigma_{n-1}(t)} \int h(0, \zeta) \, d\Omega$, where $|\zeta - \mathbf{x}|^2 = t^2$, $\sigma_{n-1}(t)$ is the surface area of the n-dimensional sphere of radius t, and $d\Omega$ is an element of area.

When n is even, the solution is given by

$$u(t, \mathbf{x}) = \frac{1}{2 \cdot 4 \cdots (n-2)} \left\{ \frac{\partial}{\partial t} \left(\frac{\partial}{t \, \partial t} \right)^{(n-2)/2} \int_0^t \omega[f; \mathbf{x}, \rho] \frac{\rho^{n-1} \, d\rho}{\sqrt{t^2 - \rho^2}} \right.$$

$$\left. + \left(\frac{\partial}{t \, \partial t} \right)^{(n-2)/2} \int_0^t \omega[g; \mathbf{x}, \rho] \frac{\rho^{n-1} \, d\rho}{\sqrt{t^2 - \rho^2}} \right\}, \tag{5.7.3}$$

where $\omega[h; \mathbf{x}, t]$ is defined as above. Since this expression is integrated over ρ, the values of f and g must be known everywhere in the *interior* of the n-dimensional sphere.

Using u_n for the solution in n dimensions, the above simplify to

$$u_1(x, t) = \frac{1}{2} [f(x-t) + f(x+t)] + \frac{1}{2} \int_{x-t}^{x+t} g(\zeta) \, d\zeta, \tag{5.7.4}$$

$$u_2(\mathbf{x}, t) = \frac{1}{2\pi} \frac{\partial}{\partial t} \iint_{R(t)} \frac{f(x_1 + \zeta_1, x_2 + \zeta_2)}{\sqrt{t^2 - \zeta_1^2 - \zeta_2^2}} \, d\zeta_1 \, d\zeta_2$$

$$+ \frac{1}{2\pi} \iint_{R(t)} \frac{g(x_1 + \zeta_1, x_2 + \zeta_2)}{\sqrt{t^2 - \zeta_1^2 - \zeta_2^2}} \, d\zeta_1 \, d\zeta_2, \quad \text{and} \tag{5.7.5}$$

$$u_3(\mathbf{x}, t) = \frac{\partial}{\partial t} \left(t\omega[f; \mathbf{x}, t] \right) + t\omega[g; \mathbf{x}, t], \tag{5.7.6}$$

where $R(t)$ is the region $\{(\zeta_1, \zeta_2) \mid \zeta_1^2 + \zeta_2^2 \leq t^2\}$ and

$$\omega[h; \mathbf{x}, t] = \frac{1}{4\pi} \int_0^{2\pi} \int_0^{\pi} h(x_1 + t \sin\theta \cos\phi, x_2 + t \sin\theta \sin\phi, x_3 + t \cos\theta)$$

$$\times \sin\theta \, d\theta \, d\phi.$$

- The solution of the wave equation

$$\begin{aligned}
v_{tt} &= c^2 v_{xx}, \\
v(0, t) &= 0, \quad && \text{for } 0 < t < \infty, \\
v(x, 0) &= f(x), \quad && \text{for } 0 \leq x < \infty, \\
v_t(x, 0) &= g(x), \quad && \text{for } 0 \leq x < \infty,
\end{aligned}$$

is

$$v(x, t) = \begin{cases} \frac{1}{2} [f(x+ct) + f(x-ct)] + \frac{1}{2c} \int_{x-ct}^{x+ct} g(\zeta) \, d\zeta, & \text{for } x \geq ct, \\ \frac{1}{2} [f(x+ct) - f(ct-x)] + \frac{1}{2c} \int_{ct-x}^{x+ct} g(\zeta) \, d\zeta, & \text{for } x < ct. \end{cases}$$

- The solution of the inhomogeneous wave equation

$$\frac{\partial^2 u}{\partial t^2} - \frac{\partial^2 u}{\partial x^2} - \frac{\partial^2 u}{\partial y^2} - \frac{\partial^2 u}{\partial z^2} = F(t, x, y, z),$$

with the initial conditions $u(0, x, y, z) = 0$ and $u_t(0, x, y, z) = 0$, is

$$u(t, x, y, z) = \frac{1}{4\pi} \iiint\limits_{\rho \leq t} \frac{F(t - \rho, \zeta, \eta, \xi)}{\rho} \, d\zeta \, d\eta \, d\xi,$$

with $\rho = \sqrt{(x - \zeta)^2 + (y - \eta)^2 + (z - \xi)^2}$.

5.7.8 SEPARATION OF VARIABLES

A solution of a linear PDE is attempted in the form $u(\mathbf{x}) = u(x_1, x_2, \cdots, x_n) = X_1(x_1)X_2(x_2)\ldots X_n(x_n)$. Logical reasoning may determine the $\{X_i\}$.

- For example, the diffusion or heat equation in a circle is

$$\frac{\partial u}{\partial t} = \nabla^2 u = \frac{1}{r}\frac{\partial}{\partial r}\left(r\frac{\partial u}{\partial r}\right) + \frac{1}{r^2}\frac{\partial^2 u}{\partial \theta^2}$$

for $u(t, r, \theta)$. If $u(t, r, \theta) = T(t)R(r)\Theta(\theta)$, then

$$\frac{1}{rR}\frac{d}{dr}\left(r\frac{dR}{dr}\right) + \frac{1}{r^2\Theta}\frac{d^2\Theta}{d\theta^2} - \frac{1}{T}\frac{dT}{dt} = 0.$$

Logical reasoning leads to

$$\frac{1}{T}\frac{dT}{dt} = -\lambda, \qquad \frac{1}{\Theta}\frac{d^2\Theta}{d\theta^2} = -\rho, \qquad r\frac{d}{dr}\left(r\frac{dR}{dr}\right) + (-\rho + r^2\lambda)R = 0.$$

where λ and ρ are unknown constants. Solving these ordinary differential equations yields the general solution,

$$u(t, r, \theta) = \int_{-\infty}^{\infty} d\lambda \int_{-\infty}^{\infty} d\rho \, e^{-\lambda t}\Big[B(\lambda, \rho)\sin(\sqrt{\rho}\theta) + C(\lambda, \rho)\cos(\sqrt{\rho}\theta)\Big]$$
$$\times \Big[D(\lambda, \rho)J_{\sqrt{\rho}}(\sqrt{\lambda}r) + E(\lambda, \rho)Y_{\sqrt{\rho}}(\sqrt{\lambda}r)\Big].$$

Boundary conditions are required to determine $\{B, C, D, E\}$.

- A necessary and sufficient condition for a system with Hamiltonian $H = \frac{1}{2}(p_x^2 + p_y^2) + V(x, y)$, to be separable in elliptic, polar, parabolic, or Cartesian coordinates is that the expression,

$$(V_{yy} - V_{xx})(-2axy - b'y - bx + d) + 2V_{xy}(ay^2 - ax^2 + by - b'x + c - c')$$
$$+ V_x(6ay + 3b) + V_y(-6ax - 3b'),$$

vanishes for some constants $(a, b, b', c, c', d) \neq (0, 0, 0, c, c, 0)$.

- Consider the orthogonal coordinate system $\{u^1, u^2, u^3\}$, with the metric $\{g_{ii}\}$, and $g = g_{11}g_{22}g_{33}$. The Stäckel matrix is defined as

$$S = \begin{bmatrix} \Phi_{11}(u^1) & \Phi_{12}(u^1) & \Phi_{13}(u^1) \\ \Phi_{21}(u^2) & \Phi_{22}(u^2) & \Phi_{23}(u^2) \\ \Phi_{31}(u^3) & \Phi_{32}(u^3) & \Phi_{33}(u^3) \end{bmatrix},$$

where the $\{\Phi_{ij}\}$ are specified. The determinant of S can be written as $s = \Phi_{11}M_{11} + \Phi_{21}M_{21} + \Phi_{31}M_{33}$, where

$$M_{11} = \begin{vmatrix} \Phi_{22} & \Phi_{23} \\ \Phi_{32} & \Phi_{33} \end{vmatrix}, \quad M_{21} = -\begin{vmatrix} \Phi_{12} & \Phi_{13} \\ \Phi_{32} & \Phi_{33} \end{vmatrix} \quad M_{31} = \begin{vmatrix} \Phi_{12} & \Phi_{13} \\ \Phi_{22} & \Phi_{23} \end{vmatrix}.$$

If $g_{ii} = s/M_{i1}$ and $\sqrt{g}/s = f_1(u^1)f_2(u^2)f_3(u^3)$ then the Helmholtz equation $\nabla^2 W + \lambda^2 W = 0$ separates with $W = X_1(u^1)X_2(u_2)X_3(u^3)$. Here the $\{X_i\}$ are defined by

$$\frac{1}{f_i}\frac{d}{du^i}\left(f_i\frac{dX_i}{du^i}\right) + X_i\sum_{j=1}^{3}\alpha_j\Phi_{ij} = 0,$$

with $\alpha_1 = \lambda^2$, and α_2 and α_3 arbitrary. For example, in parabolic coordinates $\{\mu, \nu, \psi\}$ the metric coefficients are $g_{11} = g_{22} = \mu^2 + \nu^2$ and $g_{33} = \mu^2\nu^2$. Hence, $\sqrt{g} = \mu\nu(\mu^2 + \nu^2)$. For the Stäckel matrix

$$S = \begin{bmatrix} \mu^2 & -1 & 1/\mu^2 \\ \nu^2 & 1 & 1/\nu^2 \\ 0 & 0 & 1 \end{bmatrix}$$

(for which $s = \mu^2 + \nu^2$, $M_{11} = M_{21} = 1$, and $M_{21} = \mu^{-2} + \nu^{-2}$), the separation condition holds with $f_1 = \mu$, $f_2 = f_3 = 1$. Hence, the Helmholtz equation separates in parabolic coordinates. The separated equations are

$$\frac{1}{\mu}\frac{d}{d\mu}\left(\mu\frac{dX_1}{d\mu}\right) + X_1\left(\alpha_1\mu^2 - \alpha_2 + \frac{\alpha_1}{\mu^2}\right) = 0,$$

$$\frac{1}{\nu}\frac{d}{d\nu}\left(\nu\frac{dX_2}{d\nu}\right) + X_2\left(\alpha_1\nu^2 + \alpha_2 + \frac{\alpha_1}{\nu^2}\right) = 0, \text{ and}$$

$$\frac{d^2X_3}{d\psi^2} + \alpha_3 X_3 = 0,$$

where $W = X_1(\mu)X_2(\nu)X_3(\psi)$.

- Necessary and sufficient conditions for separation of the Laplace equation $(\nabla^2 W = 0)$ are

$$\frac{g_{ii}}{g_{jj}} = \frac{M_{j1}}{M_{i1}} \quad \text{and} \quad \frac{\sqrt{g}}{g_{ii}} = f_1(u^1)f_2(u^2)f_3(u^3)M_{i1}.$$

Particular solutions

In these tables, we assume that $P(x)$ is a polynomial of degree n.

If $R(x)$ is	A particular solution to $z_x + mz_y = R(x, y)$ is
1. e^{ax+by}	$e^{ax+by}/(a + mb)$.
2. $f(ax + by)$	$\int f(y)\, du/(a + mb)$, $u = ax + by$.
3. $f(y - mx)$	$xf(y - mx)$.
4. $\phi(x, y) f(y - mx)$	$f(y - mx) \int \phi(x, a + mx)\, dx$; then substitute $a = y - mx$.

If $R(x)$ is	A particular solution to $z_x + mz_y - kz = R(x, y)$ is
5. e^{ax+by}	$e^{ax+by}/(a + mb - k)$.
6. $\sin(ax + by)$	$-\dfrac{(a+bm)\cos(ax+by)+k\sin(ax+by)}{(a+bm)^2+k^2}$.
7. $e^{\alpha x+\beta y}\sin(ax + by)$	Replace k by $k - \alpha - m\beta$ in formula 6 and multiply by $e^{\alpha x+\beta y}$.
8. $e^{xk} f(ax + by)$	$e^{kx} \int f(y)\, du/(a + mb)$, $u = ax + by$.
9. $f(y - mx)$	$-f(y - mx)/k$.
10. $P(x) f(y - mx)$	$-\frac{1}{k} f(y - mx)\left[P(x) + \frac{P'(x)}{k} + \frac{P''(x)}{k^2} + \cdots + \frac{P^{(n)}(x)}{k^n}\right]$.
11. $e^{kx} f(y - mx)$	$xe^{kx} f(y - mx)$.

5.7.9 TRANSFORMING PARTIAL DIFFERENTIAL EQUATIONS

To transform a partial differential equation, construct a new function which depends upon new variables, and then differentiate with respect to the old variables to see how the derivatives transform. Consider transforming

$$f_{xx} + f_{yy} + xf_y = 0, \qquad (5.7.7)$$

from the $\{x, y\}$ variables to the $\{u, v\}$ variables, where $\{u = x, v = x/y\}$. Note that the inverse transformation is given by $\{x = u, y = u/v\}$.

First, define $g(u, v)$ as the function $f(x, y)$ when written in the new variables, that is

$$f(x, y) = g(u, v) = g\left(x, \frac{x}{y}\right). \qquad (5.7.8)$$

Now create the needed derivative terms, carefully applying the chain rule. For example, differentiating Equation (5.7.8) with respect to x results in

$$f_x(x, y) = g_u \frac{\partial}{\partial x}(u) + g_v \frac{\partial}{\partial x}(v) = g_1 \frac{\partial}{\partial x}(x) + g_2 \frac{\partial}{\partial x}\left(\frac{x}{y}\right)$$

$$= g_1 + g_2 \frac{1}{y} = g_1 + \frac{v}{u} g_2,$$

where a subscript of "1" ("2") indicates a derivative with respect to the first (second) argument of the function $g(u, v)$, that is, $g_1(u, v) = g_u(u, v)$. Use of this "slot notation" tends to minimize errors. In like manner

$$f_y(x, y) = g_u \frac{\partial}{\partial y}(u) + g_v \frac{\partial}{\partial y}(v) = g_1 \frac{\partial}{\partial y}(x) + g_2 \frac{\partial}{\partial y}\left(\frac{x}{y}\right)$$

$$= -\frac{x}{y^2}g_2 = -\frac{v^2}{u}g_2.$$

The second order derivatives can be calculated similarly:

$$f_{xx}(x, y) = \frac{\partial}{\partial x}(f_x(x, y)) = \frac{\partial}{\partial x}\left(g_1 + \frac{1}{y}g_2\right),$$

$$= g_{11} + \frac{2v}{u}g_{12} + \frac{v^2}{u^2}g_{22},$$

$$f_{xy}(x, y) = \frac{\partial}{\partial x}\left(-\frac{x}{y^2}g_2\right) = -\frac{u^2}{v^2}g_2 - \frac{u^3}{v^3}g_{12} - \frac{u^2}{v^2}g_{22}, \quad \text{and}$$

$$f_{yy}(x, y) = \frac{\partial}{\partial y}\left(-\frac{x}{y^2}g_2\right) = \frac{2v^3}{u^2}g_2 + \frac{v^4}{u^2}g_{22}.$$

Finally, Equation (5.7.7) in the new variables has the form,

$$0 = f_{xx} + f_{yy} + xf_y,$$

$$= \left(g_{11} + \frac{2v}{u}g_{12} + \frac{v^2}{u^2}g_{22}\right) + \left(\frac{2v^3}{u^2}g_2 + \frac{v^4}{u^2}g_{22}\right) + (u)\left(-\frac{v^2}{u}g_2\right),$$

$$= \frac{v^2(2v - u^2)}{u^2}g_v + g_{uu} + \frac{2v}{u}g_{uv} + \frac{v^2(1 + v^2)}{u^2}g_{vv}.$$

5.8 EIGENVALUES

The eigenvalues $\{\lambda_i\}$ of the differential operator L are the solutions of $L[u_i] = \lambda_i u_i$. Given a geometric shape, the eigenvalues of the Dirichlet problem are called eigenfrequencies (that is, $\nabla^2 u = \lambda u$ with $u = 0$ on the boundary).

- You cannot hear the shape of a drum. The following figures have the same eigenfrequencies.

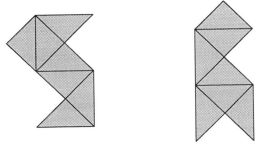

- You cannot hear the shape of a two-piece band. The following pairs of figures have the same eigenfrequencies.

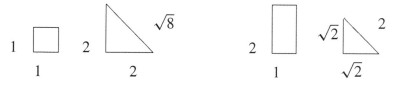

5.9   INTEGRAL EQUATIONS

5.9.1   DEFINITIONS

$$h(x)u(x) = f(x) + \lambda \int_a^{b(x)} k(x,t)G[u(t); t]\,dt. \qquad (5.9.1)$$

- $k(x,t)$ kernel

- $u(x)$ function to be determined

- $h(x)$, $f(x)$ given functions

- λ eigenvalue

Classification of integral equations

Linear	$G[u(x); x] = u(x)$.
Volterra	$b(x) = x$.
Fredholm	$b(x) = b$.
First kind	$h(x) = 0$.
Second kind	$h(x) = 1$.
Third kind	$h(x) \neq 0, 1$.
Homogeneous	$f(x) = 0$.
Singular	$a = -\infty, \ b = \infty$.

Classification of kernels

Symmetric	$k(x,t) = k(t,x)$.
Hermitian	$k(x,t) = \overline{k(t,x)}$.
Separable/degenerate	$k(x,t) = \sum_{i=1}^{n} a_i(x)b_i(t)$, $n < \infty$.
Difference	$k(x,t) = k(x-t)$.
Cauchy	$k(x,t) = \frac{1}{x-t}$.
Singular	$k(x,t) \to \infty$ as $t \to x$.
Hilbert–Schmidt	$\int_a^b \int_a^b |k(x,t)|^2 \, dx \, dt < \infty$.

5.9.2 CONNECTION TO DIFFERENTIAL EQUATIONS

The initial value problem

$$u''(x) + A(x)u'(x) + B(x)u(x) = g(x), \quad x > a,$$
$$u(a) = c_1, \quad u'(a) = c_2, \tag{5.9.2}$$

is equivalent to the Volterra integral equation,

$$u(x) = f(x) + \int_a^x k(x,t)u(t)\,dt, \quad x \geq a,$$

$$f(x) = \int_a^x (x-t)g(t)\,dt + (x-a)[A(a)c_1 + c_2] + c_1, \tag{5.9.3}$$

$$k(x,t) = (t-x)[B(t) - A'(t)] - A(t).$$

The boundary value problem

$$u''(x) + A(x)u'(x) + B(x)u(x) = g(x), a < x < b,$$
$$u(a) = c_1, u(b) = c_2, \tag{5.9.4}$$

is equivalent to the Fredholm integral equation

$$u(x) = f(x) + \int_a^b k(x,t)u(t)\,dt, \quad a \leq x \leq b,$$

$$f(x) = c_1 + \int_a^x (x-t)g(t)\,dt + \frac{x-a}{b-a}\left[c_2 - c_1 - \int_a^b (b-t)g(t)\,dt\right], \tag{5.9.5}$$

$$k(x,t) = \begin{cases} \frac{x-b}{b-a}\{A(t) - (a-t)[A'(t) - B(t)]\}, & x > t, \\ \frac{x-a}{b-a}\{A(t) - (b-t)[A'(t) - B(t)]\}, & x < t. \end{cases}$$

5.9.3 FREDHOLM ALTERNATIVE

For $u(x) = f(x) + \lambda \int_a^b k(x,t)u(t)\,dt$ with $\lambda \neq 0$, consider the solutions to $u_H(x) = \lambda \int_a^b k(x,t)u_H(t)\,dt$.

- If the only solution is $u_H(x) = 0$, then there is a unique solution $u(x)$.

- If $u_H(x) \neq 0$, then there is no solution unless $\int_a^b u_H^*(t) f(t)\, dt = 0$ for all $u_H^*(x)$ so that $u_H^*(x) = \lambda \int_a^b k(t, x) u_H^*(t)\, dt$. In this case, there are infinitely many solutions.

5.9.4 SPECIAL EQUATIONS WITH SOLUTIONS

1. Generalized Abel equation:

$$\int_0^x \frac{u(t)\, dt}{[h(x) - h(t)]^\alpha} = f(x),$$

$$u(x) = \frac{\sin(\alpha\pi)}{\pi} \frac{d}{dx} \int_0^x \frac{h'(t) f(t)\, dt}{[h(x) - h(t)]^{1-\alpha}}$$

(5.9.6)

where $0 \le x \le 1$, $0 \le \alpha < 1$, $0 \le h(x) \le 1$, $h'(x) > 0$, and $h'(x)$ is continuous.

2. Cauchy equation:

$$\mu u(x) = f(x) + \int_0^1 \frac{u(t)}{t - x}\, dt,$$

$$u(x) = \begin{cases} \dfrac{x^\gamma \sin^2(\pi\gamma)}{\pi^2} \dfrac{d}{dx} \int_x^1 \dfrac{ds}{(s-x)^\gamma} \int_0^s \dfrac{t^{-\gamma} f(t)}{(s-t)^{1-\gamma}}\, dt, & \mu < 0, \\[3mm] \dfrac{(1-x)^\gamma \sin^2(\pi\gamma)}{\pi^2} \dfrac{d}{dx} \int_0^x \dfrac{ds}{(x-s)^\gamma} \int_s^1 \dfrac{(1-t)^{-\gamma} f(t)}{(t-s)^{1-\gamma}}\, dt, & \mu > 0, \end{cases}$$

(5.9.7)

where $0 < x < 1$, μ is real, $\mu \neq 0$, $|\mu| = \pi \cot(\pi\gamma)$, $0 < \gamma < 1/2$, and the integral is a Cauchy principal value integral.

3. Volterra equation with difference kernel:

$$u(x) = f(x) + \lambda \int_0^x k(x - t) u(t)\, dt, \quad x \ge 0$$

$$u(x) = \mathcal{L}^{-1}\left[\frac{F(s)}{1 - \lambda K(s)} \right],$$

(5.9.8)

where $\mathcal{L}[f(x)] = F(s)$ and $\mathcal{L}[k(x)] = K(s)$ (see Section 6.26).

4. Fredholm equation with difference kernel:

$$u(x) = f(x) + \lambda \int_{-\infty}^{\infty} k(x - t)u(t)\, dt,$$

$$u(x) = \frac{1}{\sqrt{2\pi}} \int_{-\infty}^{\infty} e^{-i\alpha x} \frac{\mathcal{F}(\alpha)}{1 - \lambda K(\alpha)}\, d\alpha$$

(5.9.9)

where $-\infty < x < \infty$, $\mathcal{F}[f(x)] = \mathcal{F}(\alpha)$ and $\mathcal{F}[k(x)] = K(\alpha)$ (see Sections 5.9.3 and 6.22).

5. Fredholm equation with separable kernel:

$$u(x) = f(x) + \lambda \int_{a}^{b} \sum_{k=1}^{n} a_k(x)b_k(t)u(t)\, dt,$$

$$u(x) = f(x) + \lambda \sum_{k=1}^{n} c_k a_k(x), \quad \text{with}$$

$$c_m = \int_{a}^{b} b_m(t)f(t)\, dt + \lambda \sum_{k=1}^{n} c_k \int_{a}^{b} b_m(t)a_k(t)\, dt$$

(5.9.10)

where $a \le x \le b$, $n < \infty$, and $m = 1, 2, \ldots n$ (see Section 5.9.3).

6. Fredholm equation with symmetric kernel:

$$u(x) = f(x) + \lambda \int_{a}^{b} k(x, t)u(t)\, dt.$$

Solve $u_n(x) = \lambda_n \int_{a}^{b} k(x, t)u_n(t)\, dt$ for $\{u_n, \lambda_n\}$.

For $\lambda \ne \lambda_n$, $\quad u(x) = f(x) + \lambda \sum_{n=1}^{\infty} \frac{u_n(x) \int_{a}^{b} f(t)u_n(t)\, dt}{(\lambda_n - \lambda) \int_{a}^{b} u_n^2(t)\, dt}.$

For $\lambda = \lambda_n$ and $\int_{a}^{b} f(t)u_m(t)\, dt = 0$,

$$u(x) = f(x) + cu_m(x) + \lambda_m \sum_{\substack{n=1 \\ n\ne m}}^{\infty} \frac{u_n(x) \int_{a}^{b} f(t)u_n(t)\, dt}{(\lambda_n - \lambda_m) \int_{a}^{b} u_n^2(t)\, dt},$$

(5.9.11)

where $a \le x \le b$, and $k(x, t) = k(t, x)$ (see Section 5.9.3).

7. Volterra equation of second kind:

$$u(x) = f(x) + \lambda \int_a^x k(x, t)u(t)\, dt,$$

$$u(x) = f(x) + \lambda \int_a^x \sum_{n=0}^\infty \lambda^n k_{n+1}(x, t) f(t)\, dt,$$

$$k_1(x, t) = k(x, t), \tag{5.9.12}$$

$$\text{and } k_{n+1}(x, t) = \int_t^x k(x, s)k_n(s, t)\, ds$$

where $k(x, t)$ and $f(x)$ are continuous, $\lambda \neq 0$, and $x \geq a$.

8. Fredholm equation of second kind: resolvent kernel:

$$u(x) = f(x) + \lambda \int_a^b k(x, t)u(t)\, dt,$$

$$u(x) = f(x) + \lambda \int_a^b \frac{D(x, t; \lambda)}{D(\lambda)} f(t)\, dt,$$

$$D(\lambda) = \sum_{n=0}^\infty \frac{(-\lambda)^n c_n}{n!},$$

$$c_0 = 1, \qquad c_n = \int_a^b A_{n-1}(t, t)\, dt, \quad n = 1, 2, \ldots, \tag{5.9.13}$$

$$D(x, t; \lambda) = k(x, t) + \sum_{n=1}^\infty \frac{(-\lambda)^n}{n!} A_n(x, t),$$

$$A_0(x, t) = k(x, t), \quad \text{and } A_n(x, t) = c_n k(x, t)$$

$$- n \int_a^b k(x, s) A_{n-1}(s, t)\, ds$$

where $k(x, t)$ and $f(x)$ are continuous, $\lambda \neq 0$, $a \leq x \leq b$, and $D(\lambda) \neq 0$ (see Section 5.9.3).

9. Fredholm equation of second kind (Neumann series):

$$u(x) = f(x) + \lambda \int_a^b k(x, t)u(t)\, dt,$$

$$u(x) = f(x) + \sum_{n=1}^\infty \lambda^n \phi_n(x),$$

$$\phi_n(x) = \int_a^b k_n(x, s) f(s)\, ds, \tag{5.9.14}$$

$$k_1(x, s) = k(x, s),$$

$$\text{and } k_n(x, s) = \int_a^b k(x, t)k_{n-1}(t, s)\, dt, \quad n = 2, 3, \ldots,$$

where $|\lambda| < \left(\int_a^b \int_a^b k^2(x,t)\, dx\, dt \right)^{-1/2}$, $\lambda \neq 0$, and $a \leq x \leq b$ (see Section 5.9.3).

5.10 TENSOR ANALYSIS

5.10.1 DEFINITIONS

1. An *n-dimensional coordinate manifold* of class C^k, $k \geq 1$, is a point set M together with the totality of allowable coordinate systems on M. An *allowable coordinate system* (ϕ, U) on M is a one-to-one mapping $\phi : U \to M$, where U is an open subset of $\mathbb{R}^n$. The *n*-tuple $(x^1, \ldots, x^n) \in U$ give the *coordinates* of the corresponding point $\phi(x^1, \ldots, x^n) \in M$. If $(\tilde{\phi}, \tilde{U})$ is a second coordinate system on M, then the one-to-one correspondence $\tilde{\phi}^{-1} \circ \phi : U \to \tilde{U}$, called a *coordinate transformation* on M, is assumed to be of class C^k. It may be written as

$$\tilde{x}^i = \tilde{f}^i(x^1, \ldots, x^n), \quad i = 1, \ldots, n, \tag{5.10.1}$$

where the $\tilde{f}$ are defined by $(\tilde{\phi}^{-1} \circ \phi)(x^1, \ldots, x^n) = (\tilde{f}^1(x^1, \ldots, x^n), \ldots, \tilde{f}^n(x^1, \ldots, x^n))$. The coordinate transformation $\tilde{\phi}^{-1} \circ \phi$ has inverse $\phi^{-1} \circ \tilde{\phi}$, expressible in terms of the coordinates as

$$x^i = f^i(\tilde{x}^1, \ldots, \tilde{x}^n), \quad i = 1, \ldots, n. \tag{5.10.2}$$

2. The Jacobian matrix $\frac{\partial \tilde{x}^i}{\partial x^j}$ of the transformation satisfies $\frac{\partial \tilde{x}^i}{\partial x^k} \frac{\partial x^k}{\partial \tilde{x}^j} = \delta^i_j$ and $\frac{\partial x^i}{\partial \tilde{x}^k} \frac{\partial \tilde{x}^k}{\partial x^j} = \delta^i_j$, where a repeated upper and lower index signifies summation over the range $k = 1, \ldots, n$ (the *Einstein summation convention*) and $\delta^i_j = \begin{cases} 1, & i = j \\ 0, & i \neq j \end{cases}$ denotes the Kronecker delta. Note also that $\det\left(\frac{\partial \tilde{x}^i}{\partial x^j} \right) \neq 0$.

3. A function $F : M \to \mathbb{R}$ is called a *scalar invariant* on M. The coordinate representation of F in any coordinate system (ϕ, U) is defined by $f := F \circ \phi$. The coordinate representations $\tilde{f}$ of F with respect to a second coordinate system $(\tilde{\phi}, \tilde{U})$ is related to f by $\tilde{f}(\tilde{x}^1, \ldots, \tilde{x}^n) = f(f^1(\tilde{x}^1, \ldots, \tilde{x}^n), \ldots, f^n(\tilde{x}^1, \ldots, \tilde{x}^n))$.

4. A *parameterized curve* on M is a mapping $\gamma : I \to M$, where $I \subset \mathbb{R}$ is some interval. The coordinate representation of γ in any coordinate system (ϕ, U) is a mapping $g : I \to \mathbb{R}^n$ defined by $g = \phi^{-1} \circ \gamma$. The mapping g defines a parameterized curve in R^n. The component functions of g denoted by g^i (for $i = 1, \ldots, n$) are defined by $g(t) = (g^1(t), \cdots, g^n(t))$. The curve γ is C^k if, and only if, the functions g^i are C^k for every coordinate system on M. The

coordinate representation $\tilde{g}$ of γ with respect to a second coordinate system $(\tilde{\phi}, \tilde{u})$ is related to g by $\tilde{g}^i(t) = \tilde{f}^i(g^1(t), \cdots, g^n(t))$.

5. A *mixed tensor T of contravariant valence r, covariant valence s, and weight w at $p \in M$*, called a tensor of type (r, s, w), is an object which, with respect to each coordinate system on M, is represented by n^{r+s} real numbers whose values in any two coordinate systems, ϕ and $\tilde{\phi}$, are related by

$$\tilde{T}^{i_1 \cdots i_r}_{j_1 \cdots j_s} = \left[\det\left(\frac{\partial x}{\partial \tilde{x}} \right) \right]^w T^{k_1 \cdots k_r}_{\ell_1 \cdots \ell_s} \underbrace{\frac{\partial \tilde{x}^{i_1}}{\partial x^{k_1}} \cdots \frac{\partial \tilde{x}^{i_r}}{\partial x^{k_r}}}_{r \text{ factors}} \underbrace{\frac{\partial x^{\ell_1}}{\partial \tilde{x}^{j_1}} \cdots \frac{\partial x^{\ell_s}}{\partial \tilde{x}^{j_s}}}_{s \text{ factors}}.$$

The superscripts are called *contravariant indices* and the subscripts *covariant indices*. If $w \neq 0$, then T is said to be a *relative tensor*. If $w = 0$, then T is said to be an *absolute tensor* or a tensor of type (r, s). In the sequel only absolute tensors, which will be called tensors, will be considered unless otherwise indicated. A *tensor field T of type (r, s)* is an assignment of a tensor of type (r, s) to each point of M. A tensor field T is C^k if its component functions are C^k for every coordinate system on M.

5.10.2   ALGEBRAIC TENSOR OPERATIONS

1. *Addition and scalar multiplication:* The components of the *sum* of the tensors T_1 and T_2 of type (r, s) are given by

$$T_3{}^{i_1 \cdots i_r}_{j_1 \cdots j_s} = T_1{}^{i_1 \cdots i_r}_{j_1 \cdots j_s} + T_2{}^{i_1 \cdots i_r}_{j_1 \cdots j_s}. \tag{5.10.3}$$

2. *Multiplication:* The components of the *tensor* or *outer product* of a tensor T_1 of type (r, s) and a tensor T_2 of type (t, u) are given by

$$T_3{}^{i_1 \cdots i_r, k_1 \cdots k_t}_{j_1 \cdots j_s, \ell_1 \cdots \ell_u} = T_1{}^{i_1 \cdots i_r}_{j_1 \cdots j_s} T_2{}^{k_1 \cdots k_t}_{\ell_1 \cdots \ell_u}. \tag{5.10.4}$$

3. *Contraction:* The components of the *contraction* of the tth contravariant index with the uth covariant index of a tensor T of type (r, s), with $rs \geq 1$, is given by $T^{i_1 \cdots i_{t-1} k i_{t+1} \cdots i_r}_{j_1 \cdots j_{u-1} k j_{u+1} \cdots j_s}$.

4. *Permutation of indices:* Let T be any tensor of type $(0, r)$ and S_r the group of permutations of the set $\{1, \cdots, r\}$. The components of the tensor, obtained by permuting the indices of T with any $\sigma \in S_r$, are given by $(\sigma T)_{i_1 \cdots i_r} = T_{i_{\sigma(1)} \cdots i_{\sigma(r)}}$. The *symmetric part* of T, denoted by $\mathcal{S}(T)$, is the tensor whose components are given by

$$\mathcal{S}(T)_{i_1 \cdots i_r} = T_{(i_1 \cdots i_r)} = \frac{1}{r!} \sum_{\sigma \in S_r} T_{i_{\sigma(1)} \cdots i_{\sigma(r)}}. \tag{5.10.5}$$

The tensor T is said to be *symmetric* if, and only if, $T_{i_1 \cdots i_r} = T_{(i_1 \cdots i_r)}$. The *skew symmetric* part of T, denoted by $\mathcal{A}(T)$, is the tensor whose components are given by

$$\mathcal{A}(T)_{i_1 \cdots i_r} = T_{[i_1 \cdots i_r]} = \frac{1}{r!} \sum_{\sigma \in S_r} \operatorname{sgn}(\sigma) T_{i_{\sigma(1)} \cdots i_{\sigma(r)}}, \tag{5.10.6}$$

where sgn$(\sigma) = \pm 1$ according to whether σ is an even or odd permutation. The tensor T is said to be *skew symmetric* if, and only if, $T_{i_1 \cdots i_r} = T_{[i_1 \cdots i_r]}$. If $r = 2$, $\mathcal{S}(T)_{i_1 i_2} = \frac{1}{2}(T_{i_1 i_2} + T_{i_2 i_1})$ and $\mathcal{A}(T)_{i_1 i_2} = \frac{1}{2}(T_{i_1 i_2} - T_{i_2 i_1})$.

5.10.3 DIFFERENTIATION OF TENSORS

1. A *linear connection* ∇ at $p \in M$ is an object which, with respect to each coordinate system on M, is represented by n^3 real numbers $\Gamma^i_{\ jk}$, called the *connection coefficients*, whose values in any two coordinate systems ϕ and $\tilde{\phi}$ are related by

$$\tilde{\Gamma}^i_{\ jk} = \Gamma^\ell_{\ mn} \frac{\partial \tilde{x}^i}{\partial x^\ell} \frac{\partial x^m}{\partial \tilde{x}^j} \frac{\partial x^n}{\partial \tilde{x}^k} + \frac{\partial^2 x^\ell}{\partial \tilde{x}^j \partial \tilde{x}^k} \frac{\partial \tilde{x}^i}{\partial x^\ell} \tag{5.10.7}$$

The quantities $\Gamma^i_{\ jk}$ are *not* the components of a tensor of type $(1, 2)$. A linear connection ∇ on M is an assignment of a linear connection to each point of M. A connection ∇ is C^k if its connection coefficients $\Gamma^i_{\ jk}$ are C^k in every coordinate system on M.

2. The components of the *covariant derivative* of a tensor field T of type (r, s), with respect to a connection ∇, are given by

$$\nabla_k T^{i_1 \cdots i_r}_{\ \ j_1 \cdots j_s} = \partial_k T^{i_1 \cdots i_r}_{\ \ j_1 \cdots j_s} + \Gamma^{i_1}_{\ \ell k} T^{\ell i_2 \cdots i_r}_{\ \ j_1 \cdots j_s} + \cdots$$
$$\cdots + \Gamma^{i_r}_{\ \ell k} T^{i_1 \cdots i_{r-1}\ell}_{\ \ j_1 \cdots j_s} - \Gamma^\ell_{\ j_1 k} T^{i_1 \cdots i_r}_{\ \ell j_2 \cdots j_s} \cdots - \Gamma^\ell_{\ j_s k} T^{i_1 \cdots i_r}_{\ \ j_1 \cdots j_{s-1}\ell}, \tag{5.10.8}$$

where

$$\partial_k T^{i_1 \cdots i_r}_{\ \ j_i \cdots j_s} = T^{i_1 \cdots i_r}_{\ \ j_1 \cdots j_s, k} = \frac{\partial T^{i_1 \cdots i_r}_{\ \ j_1 \cdots j_s}}{\partial x^k}. \tag{5.10.9}$$

This formula has this structure:

- Apart from the partial derivative term, there is a negative affine term for each covariant index and a positive affine term for each contravariant index.

- The second subscript in the Γ-symbols is always the differentiated index (k in this case).

3. In tensor analysis, a comma is used to denote partial differentiation.

4. The quantity $\delta A_i = dA_i - \Gamma^k_{ij} A_k dx^j$ is called the *covariant differential* of A_i. If A_i is displaced in such a way that $\delta A_i = 0$, the displacement is said to be *parallel* with respect to the connection ∇.

5. A vector field $Y^i(t)$ is said to be *parallel along* a parameterized curve γ if the component functions satisfy the differential equation $\frac{dY^i}{dt} + Y^j \frac{dx^k}{dt} \Gamma^i_{\ jk} = 0$, where x^i denotes the component functions of γ in the coordinate system ϕ.

6. A parameterized curve γ in M is said to be an *affinely parameterized geodesic* if the component functions of γ satisfy the differential equation $\frac{d^2 x^i}{dt^2} + \Gamma^i_{jk} \frac{dx^j}{dt} \frac{dx^k}{dt} = 0$, which is equivalent to the statement that the tangent vector $\frac{dx^i}{dt}$ to γ is parallel along γ.

7. The components of the *torsion tensor* S of ∇ on M are defined by

$$S^i_{jk} = \Gamma^i_{jk} - \Gamma^i_{kj}. \tag{5.10.10}$$

8. The components of the *curvature tensor* R of ∇ on M are defined by

$$R^i_{jk\ell} = \partial_k \Gamma^i_{j\ell} - \partial_\ell \Gamma^i_{jk} + \Gamma^m_{j\ell} \Gamma^i_{mk} - \Gamma^m_{jk} \Gamma^i_{m\ell}. \tag{5.10.11}$$

In some references R is defined with the opposite sign.

9. The *Ricci tensor* of ∇ is defined by $R_{jk} = R^\ell_{jk\ell}$.

5.10.4   METRIC TENSOR

1. A *covariant metric tensor field* on M is a tensor field g_{ij} which satisfies $g_{ij} = g_{ji}$ and $g = |g_{ij}| \neq 0$ on M. The *contravariant metric* g^{ij} satisfies $g^{ik} g_{kj} = \delta^i_j$. The *line element* is expressible in terms of the metric tensor as $ds^2 = g_{ij} dx^i dx^j$.

2. *Signature of the metric:* For each $p \in M$, a coordinate system exists such that $g_{ij}(p) = \mathrm{diag}\,(\underbrace{1, \cdots, 1}_{r}, \underbrace{-1, \cdots, -1}_{n-r})$. The *signature* of g_{ij} is defined by $s = 2r - n$. It is independent of the coordinate system in which $g_{ij}(p)$ has the above diagonal form and is the same at every $p \in M$. A metric is said to be *positive definite* if $s = n$. A manifold, admitting a positive definite metric, is called a *Riemannian manifold*. A metric is said to be *indefinite* if $s \neq n$ and $s \neq -n$. A manifold, admitting an indefinite metric, is called a *pseudo-Riemannian manifold*. If $s = 2 - n$ or $n - 2$, the metric is said to be *Lorentzian* and the corresponding manifold is called a *Lorentzian manifold*.

3. The *inner product* of a pair of vectors X^i and Y^j is given by $g_{ij} X^i Y^j$. If $X^i = Y^i$, then $g_{ij} X^i X^j$ defines the "square" of the length of X^i. If g_{ij} is positive definite, then $g_{ij} X^i X^j \geq 0$ for all X^i, and $g_{ij} X^i X^j = 0$ if, and only if, $X^i = 0$. In the positive definite case, the *angle* θ between two tangent vectors X^i and Y^j is defined by $\cos\theta = g_{ij} X^i Y^j / (g_{k\ell} X^k X^\ell g_{mn} Y^m Y^n)^{\frac{1}{2}}$. If g is indefinite, $g_{ij} X^i X^j$ may have a positive, negative, or zero value. A nonzero vector X^i, satisfying $g_{ij} X^i X^j = 0$, is called a *null vector*. If g_{ij} is indefinite, it is not possible in general to define the angle between two tangent vectors.

4. *Operation of lowering indices:* The components of the tensor resulting from *lowering the tth contravariant index* of a tensor T of type (r, s), with $r \geq 1$, are given by

$$T^{i_1 \cdots i_{t-1} \cdot i_{t+1} \cdots i_r}_{i_t \ j_1 \cdots j_s} = g_{i_t k} T^{i_1 \cdots i_{t-1} k i_{t+1} \cdots i_r}_{j_1 \cdots j_s}. \tag{5.10.12}$$

5. *Operation of raising indices:* The components of the tensor from *raising the tth covariant index* of a tensor T of type (r, s), with $s \geq 1$, is given by

$$T^{i_1 \cdots i_r \; j_t}_{\; j_t \cdots j_{t-1} \cdot j_{t+1} \cdots j_s} = g^{j_t k} T^{i_1 \cdots i_r}_{\; j_1 \cdots j_{t-1} k j_{t+1} \cdots j_s}. \tag{5.10.13}$$

6. The *arc length* of a parameterized curve $\gamma : I \to M$, where $I = [a, b]$, and ϕ is any coordinate system, is defined by

$$L = \int_a^b \sqrt{\epsilon g_{ij}(x^1(t), \cdots, x^n(t)) \dot{x}^i \dot{x}^j} \, dt, \tag{5.10.14}$$

where $\epsilon = \mathrm{sgn}(g_{ij} \dot{x}^i \dot{x}^j) = \pm 1$ and $\dot{x}^i = \frac{dx^i}{dt}$.

5.10.5   RESULTS

The following results hold on any manifold M admitting any connection ∇:

1. The covariant derivative operator ∇_k is linear with respect to tensor addition, satisfies the product rule with respect to tensor multiplication, and commutes with contractions.

2. If T is any tensor of type $(0, r)$, then

$$\nabla_{[k} T_{i_1 \cdots i_r]} = T_{[i_1 \cdots i_r, k]} - \frac{1}{2} \left(S^{\ell}_{[i_1 k} T_{|\ell| i_2 \cdots i_r]} + \cdots + S^{\ell}_{[i_r k} T_{i_1 \cdots i_{r-1}|\ell]} \right), \tag{5.10.15}$$

where $|\;|$ indicates that the enclosed indices are excluded from the symmetrization. Thus $T_{[i_1 \cdots i_r, k]}$ defines a tensor of type $(0, r + 1)$, and $\nabla_{[k} T_{i_1 \cdots i_r]} = T_{[i_1 \cdots i_r, k]}$ in the torsion free case. If $T_j = \nabla_j f = f_{,j}$, where f is any scalar invariant, then $\nabla_{[i} \nabla_{j]} f = \frac{1}{2} f_{,k} S^k_{ij}$. In the torsion free case, $\nabla_i \nabla_j f = \nabla_j \nabla_i f$.

3. If X^i is any vector field on M, then the identity $2\nabla_{[j} \nabla_{k]} X^i + \nabla_{\ell} X^i S^{\ell}_{jk} = X^{\ell} R^i_{\ell jk}$, called the *Ricci identity*, reduces to $2\nabla_{[j} \nabla_{k]} X^i = R^i_{\ell jk} X^{\ell}$, in the torsion free case. If Y_i is any covariant vector field, the Ricci identity has the form $2\nabla_{[i} \nabla_{j]} Y_k - \nabla_{\ell} Y_k S^{\ell}_{ij} = -Y_{\ell} R^{\ell}_{kij}$. The Ricci identity may be extended to tensor fields of type (r, s). For the tensor field T^i_{jk}, it has the form

$$2\nabla_{[i} \nabla_{j]} T^k_{\ell m} - \nabla_n T^k_{\ell m} S^n_{ij} = T^n_{\ell m} R^k_{nij} - T^k_{nm} R^n_{kij} - T^k_{\ell n} R^n_{mij}. \tag{5.10.16}$$

If g is any metric tensor field, the above identity implies that $R_{(ij)k\ell} = \nabla_{[k} \nabla_{\ell]} g_{ij} - \frac{1}{2} \nabla_m g_{ij} S^m_{k\ell}$.

4. The torsion tensor S and curvature tensor R satisfy the following identities:

$$S^i_{(jk)} = 0, \qquad\qquad 0 = R^i_{j[k\ell;m]} - R^i_{jn[k} S^n_{\ell m]}, \tag{5.10.17}$$

$$R^i_{j(k\ell)} = 0, \qquad\qquad R^i_{[jk\ell]} = -S^i_{[jk;\ell]} + S^i_{m[j} S^m_{k\ell]}. \tag{5.10.18}$$

In the torsion free case, these identities reduce to the *cyclical identity* $R^i_{[jk\ell]} = 0$ and *Bianchi's identity* $R^i_{j[k\ell;m]} = 0$.

The following results hold for any pseudo-Riemannian manifold M with metric tensor field g_{ij}:

1. A unique connection ∇ called the *Levi–Civita or pseudo-Riemannian connection* with vanishing torsion ($S^i{}_{jk} = 0$) exists that satisfies $\nabla_i g_{jk} = 0$. It follows that $\nabla_i g^{jk} = 0$. The connection coefficients of ∇, called the *Christoffel symbols of the second kind*, are given by $\Gamma^i{}_{jk} = g^{i\ell}[jk, \ell]$, where $[jk, \ell] = \frac{1}{2}(g_{j\ell,k} + g_{k\ell,j} - g_{jk,\ell})$ are the *Christoffel symbols of the first kind*. $\Gamma^k{}_{jk} = \frac{1}{2}\partial_j(\log g) = |g|^{-\frac{1}{2}}\partial_j|g|^{\frac{1}{2}}$ and $g_{ij,k} = [ki, j] + [kj, i]$.

2. The operations of raising and lowering indices commute with the covariant derivative. For example if $X_i = g_{ij}X^j$, then $\nabla_k X_i = g_{ij}\nabla_k X^j$.

3. The *divergence* of a vector X^i is given by $\nabla_i X^i = |g|^{-\frac{1}{2}}\partial_i(|g|^{\frac{1}{2}}X^i)$. The *Laplacian* of a scalar invariant f is given by $\Delta f = g^{ij}\nabla_i\nabla_j f = \nabla_i(g^{ij}\nabla_j f) = |g|^{-\frac{1}{2}}\partial_i(|g|^{\frac{1}{2}}g^{ij}\partial_j f)$.

4. The equations of an affinely parameterized geodesic may be written as $\frac{d}{dt}(g_{ij}\dot{x}^j) - \frac{1}{2}g_{jk,i}\dot{x}^j\dot{x}^k = 0$.

5. Let X^i and Y^i be the components of any vector fields which are propagated in parallel along any parameterized curve γ. Then $\frac{d}{dt}(g_{ij}X^iY^j) = 0$, which implies that the inner product $g_{ij}X^iY^j$ is constant along γ. In particular, if $\dot{x}^i$ are the components of the tangent vector to γ, then $g_{ij}\dot{x}^i\dot{x}^j$ is constant along γ.

6. The *Riemann tensor*, defined by $R_{ijk\ell} = g_{im}R^m{}_{jk\ell}$, is given by

$$
\begin{aligned}
R_{ijk\ell} &= [j\ell, i]_{,k} - [jk, i]_{,\ell} + [i\ell, m]\Gamma^m{}_{jk} - [ik, m]\Gamma^m{}_{j\ell} \\
&= \frac{1}{2}(g_{i\ell,jk} + g_{jk,i\ell} - g_{j\ell,ik} - g_{ik,j\ell}) \\
&\quad + g^{mn}([i\ell, m][jk, n] - [ik, m][j\ell, n]).
\end{aligned}
\tag{5.10.19}
$$

It has the following symmetries:

$$
R_{ij(k\ell)} = R_{(ij)k\ell} = 0, \quad R_{ijk\ell} = R_{k\ell ij}, \quad \text{and} \quad R_{i[jk\ell]} = 0. \tag{5.10.20}
$$

Consequently it has a maximum of $n^2(n^2 - 1)/12$ independent components.

7. The equations $R_{ijk\ell} = 0$ are necessary and sufficient conditions for M to be a *flat* pseudo-Riemannian manifold, that is, a manifold for which a coordinate system exists so that the components g_{ij} are *constant* on M.

8. The Ricci tensor is given by

$$
\begin{aligned}
R_{ij} &= \partial_j\Gamma^k{}_{ik} - \partial_k\Gamma^k{}_{ij} + \Gamma^k{}_{i\ell}\Gamma^\ell{}_{kj} - \Gamma^k{}_{ij}\Gamma^\ell{}_{k\ell} \\
&= \frac{1}{2}\partial_i\partial_j(\log|g|) - \frac{1}{2}\Gamma^k{}_{ij}\partial_k(\log|g|) - \partial_k\Gamma^k{}_{ij} + \Gamma^k{}_{im}\Gamma^m{}_{kj}.
\end{aligned}
\tag{5.10.21}
$$

It possesses the symmetry $R_{ij} = R_{ji}$, and thus has a maximum of $n(n + 1)/2$ independent components.

9. The *scalar curvature* or *curvature invariant* is defined by $R = g^{ij}R_{ij}$.

10. The *Einstein tensor* is defined by $G_{ij} = R_{ij} - \frac{1}{2}Rg_{ij}$. In view of the Bianchi identity, it satisfies: $g^{jk}\nabla_j G_{ki} = 0$.

11. A *normal coordinate system* with origin $x_0 \epsilon M$ is defined by $\overset{0}{g}_{ij}\, x^j = g_{ij}x^j$, where a "0" affixed over a quantity indicates that the quantity is evaluated at x_0.

   The connection coefficients satisfy $\overset{0}{\Gamma}{}^i{}_{(j_1,j_2,j_3\cdots j_r)} = 0$ (for $r = 2, 3, 4, \ldots$) in any normal coordinate system. The equations of the geodesics through x_0 are given by $x^i = sk^i$, where s is an affine parameter and k^i is any constant vector.

5.10.6 EXAMPLES

1. The components of the *gradient* of a scalar invariant $\frac{\partial f}{\partial x^i}$ define a tensor of type $(0,1)$, since they transform as $\frac{\partial \tilde{f}}{\partial \tilde{x}^i} = \frac{\partial f}{\partial x^j}\frac{\partial x^j}{\partial \tilde{x}^i}$.

2. The components of the *tangent vector* to a parameterized curve $\frac{dx^i}{dt}$ define a tensor of type $(1,0)$, because they transform as $\frac{d\tilde{x}^i}{dt} = \frac{dx^j}{dt}\frac{\partial \tilde{x}^i}{\partial x^j}$.

3. The determinant of the metric tensor g defines a relative scalar invariant of weight of $w = 2$, because it transforms as $\tilde{g} = \left|\frac{\partial x^i}{\partial \tilde{x}^j}\right|^2 g$.

4. The Kronecker deltas δ_i^j are the components of a constant absolute tensor of type $(1, 1)$, because $\delta_j^i = \delta_\ell^k \frac{\partial \tilde{x}^i}{\partial x^k}\frac{\partial x^\ell}{\partial \tilde{x}^j}$.

5. The permutation symbol defined by

$$
e_{i_1\cdots i_n} = \begin{cases} 1, & \text{if } i_1\cdots i_n \text{ is an even permutation of } 1\cdots n, \\ -1, & \text{if } i_1\cdots i_n \text{ is an odd permutation of } 1\cdots n, \text{ and} \\ 0 & \text{otherwise,} \end{cases} \tag{5.10.22}
$$

   satisfies $\left|\frac{\partial x^i}{\partial \tilde{x}^i}\right| e_{j_1\cdots j_n} = e_{i_1\cdots i_n}\frac{\partial x^{i_1}}{\partial \tilde{x}^{j_1}}\cdots\frac{\partial x^{i_n}}{\partial \tilde{x}^{j_n}}$. Hence it defines a tensor of type $(0, n, -1)$, that is, it is a relative tensor of weight $w = -1$. The contravariant permutation symbol $e^{i_1\cdots i_n}$, defined in a similar way, is a relative tensor of weight $w = 1$.

6. The Levi–Civita symbol, $\epsilon_{i_1\cdots i_n} = |g|^{\frac{1}{2}} e_{i_1\cdots i_n}$, defines a covarient absolute tensor of valence n. The contravariant Levi–Civita tensor satisfies

$$
\epsilon^{i_1\cdots i_n} = g^{i_1 j_1}\cdots g^{i_n j_n}\epsilon_{j_1\cdots j_n} = (-1)^{\frac{n-x}{2}}|g|^{-\frac{1}{2}}e^{i_1\cdots i_n}. \tag{5.10.23}
$$

   Using this symbol, the *dual* of a covariant skew-symmetric tensor of valence r is defined by $*T_{i_1\cdots i_{n-r}} = \frac{1}{r!}\epsilon_{i_1\cdots i_{n-r}}^{j_1\cdots j_r} T_{j_1\cdots j_r}$.

7. *Cartesian tensors:* Let $M = E^3$ (i.e., Euclidean 3 space) with metric tensor $g_{ij} = \delta_{ij}$ with respect to Cartesian coordinates. The components of a *Cartesian tensor* of valence r transform as

$$
\tilde{T}_{i_1\cdots i_r} = T_{j_1\cdots j_r}O_{i_1 j_1}\cdots O_{i_r j_r}, \tag{5.10.24}
$$

where O_{ij} are the components of a constant orthogonal matrix which satisfies $(O^{-1})_{ij} = (O')_{ij} = O_{ji}$. For Cartesian tensors, all indices are written as covariant, because *no* distinction is required between covariant and contravariant indices.

An *oriented Cartesian tensor* is a Cartesian tensor where the orthogonal matrix in the transformation law is restricted by $\det(O_{ij}) = 1$. The Levi–Civita symbol ϵ_{ijk} is an example of an oriented Cartesian tensor as is the cross product, $(X \times Y)_i = \epsilon_{ijk}X_jY_k$, of two vectors. The connection coefficients satisfy $\Gamma^i{}_{jk} = 0$ in every Cartesian coordinate system on E^3. Thus the partial derivatives of Cartesian tensors are themselves Cartesian tensors, that is, if $T_{i_1\cdots i_r}$ is a Cartesian tensor, then so is $\partial_k T_{i_1\cdots i_r}$. A particular example is the curl of a vector field X_i given by $(\mathrm{curl}\, X)_i = \epsilon_{ijk}\partial_j X_k$ which defines an oriented Cartesian tensor.

8. Note the useful relations: $\epsilon_{ijk}\epsilon_{klm} = \delta_{il}\delta_{jm} - \delta_{im}\delta_{jl}$, $\epsilon_{ikl}\epsilon_{klm} = 2\delta_{im}$, and
$\epsilon_{ijk}\epsilon_{lmn} = \delta_{il}\delta_{jm}\delta_{kn} + \delta_{im}\delta_{jn}\delta_{kl} + \delta_{in}\delta_{jl}\delta_{km} - \delta_{in}\delta_{jm}\delta_{kl} - \delta_{im}\delta_{jl}\delta_{kn} - \delta_{il}\delta_{jn}\delta_{km}$.

9. The stress tensor E_{ij} and the strain tensor e_{ij} are examples of Cartesian tensors.

10. *Orthogonal curvilinear coordinates*: Let M be a 3-dimensional Riemannian manifold admitting a coordinate system $[x^1, x^2, x^3]$ such that the metric tensor has the form $g_{ii} = h_i{}^2(x^1, x^2, x^3)$ for $i = 1, \ldots, 3$ with $g_{ij} = g^{ij} = 0$ for $i \neq j$. The metric tensor on E^3 has this form with respect to orthogonal curvilinear coordinates. The nonzero components of various corresponding quantities corresponding to this metric are as follows:

- Covariant metric tensor,

$$g_{11} = h_1{}^2, \qquad g_{22} = h_2{}^2, \qquad g_{33} = h_3{}^2.$$

- Contravariant metric tensor,

$$g^{11} = h_1{}^{-2}, \qquad g^{22} = h_2{}^{-2}, \qquad g^{33} = h_3{}^{-2}.$$

- Christoffel symbols of the first kind (note that $[ij, k] = 0$ if i, j, and k are all different),

$$
\begin{array}{lll}
[11, 1] = h_1 h_{1,1} & [11, 2] = -h_1 h_{1,2} & [11, 3] = -h_1 h_{1,3} \\
[12, 1] = h_1 h_{1,2} & [12, 2] = h_2 h_{2,1} & [13, 1] = h_1 h_{1,3} \\
[13, 3] = h_3 h_{3,1} & [22, 1] = -h_2 h_{2,1} & [22, 2] = h_2 h_{2,2} \\
[22, 3] = -h_2 h_{2,3} & [23, 2] = h_2 h_{2,3} & [23, 3] = h_3 h_{3,2} \\
[33, 1] = -h_3 h_{3,1} & [33, 2] = -h_3 h_{3,2} & [33, 3] = h_3 h_{3,3}.
\end{array}
$$

- Christoffel symbols of the second kind (note that $\Gamma^k_{ij} = 0$ if i, j, and k are all different),

$$
\begin{array}{lll}
\Gamma^1_{11} = h_1{}^{-1} h_{1,1} & \Gamma^1_{12} = h_1{}^{-1} h_{1,2} & \Gamma^1_{13} = h_1{}^{-1} h_{1,3} \\
\Gamma^1_{22} = -h_1{}^{-2} h_2 h_{2,1} & \Gamma^1_{33} = -h_1{}^{-2} h_3 h_{3,1} & \Gamma^2_{11} = -h_1 h_2{}^{-2} h_{1,2} \\
\Gamma^2_{12} = h_2{}^{-1} h_{2,1} & \Gamma^2_{22} = h_2{}^{-1} h_{2,2} & \Gamma^2_{23} = h_2{}^{-1} h_{2,3} \\
\Gamma^2_{33} = -h_2{}^{-2} h_3 h_{3,2} & \Gamma^3_{11} = -h_1 h_3{}^{-2} h_{1,3} & \Gamma^3_{13} = h_3{}^{-1} h_{3,1} \\
\Gamma^3_{22} = -h_2 h_3{}^{-2} h_{2,3} & \Gamma^3_{23} = h_3{}^{-1} h_{3,2} & \Gamma^3_{33} = h_3{}^{-1} h_{3,3}.
\end{array}
$$

- Vanishing Riemann tensor conditions (Lamé equations),

$$h_{1,2,3} - h_2^{-1}h_{1,2}h_{2,3} - h_3^{-1}h_{1,3}h_{3,2} = 0,$$

$$h_{2,1,3} - h_1^{-1}h_{1,3}h_{2,1} - h_3^{-1}h_{3,1}h_{2,3} = 0,$$

$$h_{3,1,2} - h_1^{-1}h_{1,2}h_{3,1} - h_2^{-1}h_{2,1}h_{3,2} = 0,$$

$$h_2 h_{2,3,3} + h_3 h_{3,2,2} + h_1^{-2}h_2 h_3 h_{2,1} h_{3,1} - h_2^{-1}h_3 h_{2,2} h_{3,2}$$
$$- h_2 h_3^{-1}h_{2,3} h_{3,3} = 0,$$

$$h_1 h_{1,3,3} + h_3 h_{3,1,1} + h_1 h_2^{-2}h_3 h_{1,2} h_{3,2} - h_1^{-1}h_3 h_{1,1} h_{3,1}$$
$$- h_1 h_3^{-1}h_{1,3} h_{3,3} = 0,$$

$$h_1 h_{1,2,2} + h_2 h_{2,1,1} + h_1 h_2 h_3^{-2}h_{1,3} h_{2,3} - h_1^{-1}h_2 h_{1,1} h_{2,1}$$
$$- h_1 h_2^{-1}h_{1,2} h_{2,2} = 0.$$

11. *The 2-sphere*: A coordinate system $[\theta, \phi]$ for the 2-sphere $x^2 + y^2 + z^2 = r^2$ is given by $x = r \sin\theta \cos\phi$, $y = r \sin\theta \sin\phi$, $z = r \cos\theta$, where $[\theta, \phi] \in U = (0, \pi) \times (0, 2\pi)$. This is a non-Euclidean space. The nonzero independent components of various quantities defined on the sphere are given below:

- Covariant metric tensor components are $g_{11} = r^2$, $\quad g_{22} = r^2 \sin^2\theta$.
- Contravariant metric tensor components are $g^{11} = r^{-2}$, $\quad g^{22} = r^{-2} \csc^2\theta$.
- Christoffel symbols of the first kind are $[12, 2] = r^2 \sin\theta \cos\theta$, $\quad [22, 1] = -r^2 \sin\theta \cos\theta$.
- Christoffel symbols of the second kind are $\Gamma^1_{22} = -\sin\theta \cos\theta$, $\quad \Gamma^2_{12} = -\cos\theta \csc\theta$.
- Covariant Riemann tensor components are $R_{1212} = r^2 \sin^2\theta$.
- Covariant Ricci tensor components are $R_{11} = -1$, $\quad R_{22} = -\sin^2\theta$.
- Ricci scalar is $R = -2r^{-2}$.

12. *The 3-sphere*: A coordinate system $[\psi, \theta, \phi]$ for the 3-sphere $x^2 + y^2 + z^2 + w^2 = r^2$ is given by $x = r \sin\psi \sin\theta \cos\phi$, $y = r \sin\psi \sin\theta \sin\phi$, $z = r \sin\psi \cos\theta$, and $w = r \cos\psi$, where $[\psi, \theta, \phi] \in U = (0, \pi) \times (0, \pi) \times (0, 2\pi)$. The nonzero components of various quantities defined on the sphere are given below:

- Covariant metric tensor components,

$$g_{11} = r^2, \qquad g_{22} = r^2 \sin^2\psi, \qquad g_{33} = r^2 \sin^2\psi \sin^2\theta.$$

- Contravariant metric tensor components,

$$g^{11} = r^{-2}, \qquad g^{22} = r^{-2} \csc^2\psi, \qquad g^{33} = r^{-2} \csc^2\psi \csc^2\theta.$$

- Christoffel symbols of the first kind,

$$[22, 1] = -r^2 \sin\psi \cos\psi \qquad\qquad [33, 1] = -r^2 \sin\psi \cos\psi \sin^2\theta$$
$$[12, 2] = r^2 \sin\psi \cos\psi \qquad\qquad [33, 2] = -r^2 \sin^2\psi \sin\theta \cos\theta$$
$$[13, 3] = r^2 \sin\psi \cos\psi \sin^2\theta \qquad [23, 3] = r^2 \sin^2\psi \sin\theta \cos\theta.$$

- Christoffel symbols of the second kind,

$$\Gamma_{22}^1 = -\sin\psi\cos\psi \qquad \Gamma_{33}^1 = -\sin\psi\cos\psi\sin^2\theta$$
$$\Gamma_{12}^2 = \cot\psi \qquad \Gamma_{33}^2 = -\sin\theta\cos\theta$$
$$\Gamma_{13}^3 = \cot\psi \qquad \Gamma_{23}^3 = \cot\theta.$$

- Covariant Riemann tensor components,

$$R_{1212} = r^2\sin^2\psi, \quad R_{1313} = r^2\sin^2\psi\sin^2\theta, \quad R_{2323} = r^2\sin^4\psi\sin^2\theta.$$

- Covariant Ricci tensor components,
  $R_{11} = -2, \quad R_{22} = -2\sin^2\psi, \quad R_{33} = -2\sin^2\psi\sin^2\theta$. The Ricci scalar is $R = -6r^{-2}$.

- Covariant Einstein tensor components,

$$G_{11} = 1, \qquad G_{22} = \sin^2\psi, \qquad G_{33} = \sin^2\psi\sin^2\theta.$$

13. *Polar coordinates:* The line element is given by $ds^2 = dr^2 + r^2 d\theta^2$. Thus the metric tensor is $g_{ij} = \begin{pmatrix} 1 & 0 \\ 0 & r^2 \end{pmatrix}$, and the nonzero Christoffel symbols are $[21, 2] = [12, 2] = -[22, 1] = r$.

5.11   ORTHOGONAL COORDINATE SYSTEMS

In an orthogonal coordinate system, let $\{a_i\}$ denote the unit vectors in each of the three coordinate directions, and let $\{u_i\}$ denote distance along each of these axes. The coordinate system may be designated by the *metric coefficients* $\{g_{11}, g_{22}, g_{33}\}$, defined by

$$g_{ii} = \left(\frac{\partial x_1}{\partial u_i}\right)^2 + \left(\frac{\partial x_2}{\partial u_i}\right)^2 + \left(\frac{\partial x_3}{\partial u_i}\right)^2, \tag{5.11.1}$$

where $\{x_1, x_2, x_3\}$ represent rectangular coordinates. With these, we define $g = g_{11}g_{22}g_{33}$.

Operations for orthogonal coordinate systems are sometimes written in terms of $\{h_i\}$ functions, instead of the $\{g_{ii}\}$ terms. Here, $h_i = \sqrt{g_{ii}}$, so that $\sqrt{g} = h_1 h_2 h_3$. For example, in cylindrical polar coordinates, $\{x_1 = r\cos\theta, x_2 = r\sin\theta, x_3 = z\}$, so that $\{h_1 = 1, h_2 = r, h_3 = 1\}$.

In the following, ϕ represents a scalar, $\mathbf{E} = E_1\mathbf{a}_1 + E_2\mathbf{a}_2 + E_3\mathbf{a}_3$, and $\mathbf{F} = F_1\mathbf{a}_1 + F_2\mathbf{a}_2 + F_3\mathbf{a}_3$ represent vectors.

$$\operatorname{grad} \phi = \nabla \phi = \frac{\mathbf{a}_1}{\sqrt{g_{11}}} \frac{\partial \phi}{\partial u_1} + \frac{\mathbf{a}_2}{\sqrt{g_{22}}} \frac{\partial \phi}{\partial u_2} + \frac{\mathbf{a}_3}{\sqrt{g_{33}}} \frac{\partial \phi}{\partial u_3}, \qquad (5.11.2)$$

$$\operatorname{div} \mathbf{E} = \nabla \cdot \mathbf{E}$$

$$= \frac{1}{\sqrt{g}} \left\{ \frac{\partial}{\partial u_1} \left(\frac{g E_1}{g_{11}} \right) + \frac{\partial}{\partial u_2} \left(\frac{g E_2}{g_{22}} \right) + \frac{\partial}{\partial u_3} \left(\frac{g E_3}{g_{33}} \right) \right\}, \qquad (5.11.3)$$

$$\operatorname{curl} \mathbf{E} = \nabla \times \mathbf{E} = \mathbf{a}_1 \frac{\Gamma_1}{\sqrt{g_{11}}} + \mathbf{a}_2 \frac{\Gamma_2}{\sqrt{g_{22}}} + \mathbf{a}_3 \frac{\Gamma_3}{\sqrt{g_{33}}}, \qquad (5.11.4)$$

$$= \begin{vmatrix} \frac{\mathbf{a}_1}{h_2 h_3} & \frac{\mathbf{a}_2}{h_1 h_3} & \frac{\mathbf{a}_3}{h_1 h_2} \\ \frac{\partial}{\partial u_1} & \frac{\partial}{\partial u_2} & \frac{\partial}{\partial u_3} \\ h_1 E_1 & h_2 E_2 & h_3 E_3 \end{vmatrix}, \qquad (5.11.5)$$

$$[(\mathbf{F} \cdot \nabla) \mathbf{E}]_j = \sum_{i=1}^{3} \left[\frac{F_i}{h_i} \frac{\partial E_j}{\partial u_i} + \frac{E_i}{h_i h_j} \left(F_j \frac{\partial h_j}{\partial u_i} - F_i \frac{\partial h_i}{\partial u_j} \right) \right], \qquad (5.11.6)$$

$$\nabla^2 \phi = \frac{1}{h_1 h_2 h_3} \left\{ \frac{\partial}{\partial u_1} \left[\frac{h_2 h_3}{h_1} \frac{\partial \phi}{\partial u_1} \right] + \frac{\partial}{\partial u_2} \left[\frac{h_3 h_1}{h_2} \frac{\partial \phi}{\partial u_2} \right] + \frac{\partial}{\partial u_3} \left[\frac{h_1 h_2}{h_3} \frac{\partial \phi}{\partial u_3} \right] \right\},$$

$$= \frac{1}{\sqrt{g}} \left\{ \frac{\partial}{\partial u_1} \left[\frac{\sqrt{g}}{g_{11}} \frac{\partial \phi}{\partial u_1} \right] + \frac{\partial}{\partial u_2} \left[\frac{\sqrt{g}}{g_{22}} \frac{\partial \phi}{\partial u_2} \right] + \frac{\partial}{\partial u_3} \left[\frac{\sqrt{g}}{g_{33}} \frac{\partial \phi}{\partial u_3} \right] \right\}, \qquad (5.11.7)$$

$$\operatorname{grad} \operatorname{div} \mathbf{E} = \nabla (\nabla \cdot \mathbf{E}) = \frac{\mathbf{a}_1}{\sqrt{g_{11}}} \frac{\partial \Upsilon}{\partial x_1} + \frac{\mathbf{a}_2}{\sqrt{g_{22}}} \frac{\partial \Upsilon}{\partial x_2} + \frac{\mathbf{a}_3}{\sqrt{g_{33}}} \frac{\partial \Upsilon}{\partial x_3}, \qquad (5.11.8)$$

$$\operatorname{curl} \operatorname{curl} \mathbf{E} = \nabla \times (\nabla \times \mathbf{E})$$

$$= \mathbf{a}_1 \sqrt{\frac{g_{11}}{g}} \left[\frac{\partial \Gamma_3}{\partial x_2} - \frac{\partial \Gamma_2}{\partial x_3} \right] + \mathbf{a}_2 \sqrt{\frac{g_{22}}{g}} \left[\frac{\partial \Gamma_1}{\partial x_3} - \frac{\partial \Gamma_3}{\partial x_1} \right]$$

$$+ \mathbf{a}_3 \sqrt{\frac{g_{33}}{g}} \left[\frac{\partial \Gamma_2}{\partial x_1} - \frac{\partial \Gamma_1}{\partial x_2} \right], \qquad (5.11.9)$$

$$\diamondsuit \mathbf{E} = \operatorname{grad} \operatorname{div} \mathbf{E} - \operatorname{curl} \operatorname{curl} \mathbf{E}$$

$$= \nabla (\nabla \cdot \mathbf{E}) - \nabla \times (\nabla \times \mathbf{E})$$

$$= \mathbf{a}_1 \left\{ \frac{1}{\sqrt{g_{11}}} \frac{\partial \Upsilon}{\partial x_1} + \sqrt{\frac{g_{11}}{g}} \left[\frac{\partial \Gamma_2}{\partial x_3} - \frac{\partial \Gamma_3}{\partial x_2} \right] \right\}$$

$$+ \mathbf{a}_2 \left\{ \frac{1}{\sqrt{g_{22}}} \frac{\partial \Upsilon}{\partial x_2} + \sqrt{\frac{g_{22}}{g}} \left[\frac{\partial \Gamma_3}{\partial x_1} - \frac{\partial \Gamma_1}{\partial x_3} \right] \right\}$$

$$+ \mathbf{a}_3 \left\{ \frac{1}{\sqrt{g_{33}}} \frac{\partial \Upsilon}{\partial x_3} + \sqrt{\frac{g_{33}}{g}} \left[\frac{\partial \Gamma_1}{\partial x_2} - \frac{\partial \Gamma_2}{\partial x_1} \right] \right\}, \qquad (5.11.10)$$

where Υ and $\mathbf{\Gamma} = (\Gamma_1, \Gamma_2, \Gamma_3)$ are defined by

$$\Upsilon = \frac{1}{\sqrt{g}} \left\{ \frac{\partial}{\partial x_1} \left[E_1 \sqrt{\frac{g}{g_{11}}} \right] + \frac{\partial}{\partial x_2} \left[E_2 \sqrt{\frac{g}{g_{22}}} \right] + \frac{\partial}{\partial x_3} \left[E_3 \sqrt{\frac{g}{g_{33}}} \right] \right\},$$

$$\Gamma_1 = \frac{g_{11}}{\sqrt{g}} \left\{ \frac{\partial}{\partial x_2} \left(\sqrt{g_{33}} E_3 \right) - \frac{\partial}{\partial x_3} \left(\sqrt{g_{22}} E_2 \right) \right\},$$

$$\Gamma_2 = \frac{g_{22}}{\sqrt{g}} \left\{ \frac{\partial}{\partial x_3} \left(\sqrt{g_{11}} E_1 \right) - \frac{\partial}{\partial x_1} \left(\sqrt{g_{33}} E_3 \right) \right\},$$

$$\Gamma_3 = \frac{g_{22}}{\sqrt{g}} \left\{ \frac{\partial}{\partial x_1} \left(\sqrt{g_{22}} E_2 \right) - \frac{\partial}{\partial x_2} \left(\sqrt{g_{11}} E_1 \right) \right\}. \tag{5.11.11}$$

5.11.1 LIST OF ORTHOGONAL COORDINATE SYSTEMS

1. Rectangular coordinates $\{x, y, z\}$
   Ranges: $-\infty < x < \infty$, $-\infty < y < \infty$, $-\infty < z < \infty$.
   $g_{11} = g_{22} = g_{33} = \sqrt{g} = 1$,
   $h_1 = h_2 = h_3 = 1$.

$$\text{grad } f = \mathbf{a}_x \frac{\partial f}{\partial x} + \mathbf{a}_y \frac{\partial f}{\partial y} + \mathbf{a}_z \frac{\partial f}{\partial z}, \tag{5.11.12}$$

$$\text{div } \mathbf{E} = \frac{\partial}{\partial x}(E_x) + \frac{\partial}{\partial y}(E_y) + \frac{\partial}{\partial z}(E_z), \tag{5.11.13}$$

$$\text{curl } \mathbf{E} = \left(\frac{\partial E_z}{\partial y} - \frac{\partial E_y}{\partial z} \right) \mathbf{a}_x + \left(\frac{\partial E_x}{\partial z} - \frac{\partial E_z}{\partial x} \right) \mathbf{a}_y \tag{5.11.14}$$
$$+ \left(\frac{\partial E_y}{\partial x} - \frac{\partial E_x}{\partial y} \right) \mathbf{a}_z,$$

$$\nabla^2 f = \frac{\partial^2 f}{\partial x^2} + \frac{\partial^2 f}{\partial y^2} + \frac{\partial^2 f}{\partial z^2}, \text{ and} \tag{5.11.15}$$

$$[(\mathbf{F} \cdot \nabla) \mathbf{E}]_x = F_x \frac{\partial E_x}{\partial x} + F_y \frac{\partial E_x}{\partial y} + F_z \frac{\partial E_x}{\partial z}. \tag{5.11.16}$$

In this coordinate system the following notation is sometimes used: $\mathbf{i} = \mathbf{a}_x$, $\mathbf{j} = \mathbf{a}_y$, $\mathbf{k} = \mathbf{a}_z$.

2. Circular cylinder coordinates $\{r, \theta, z\}$
   Relations: $x = r \cos \theta, \ y = r \sin \theta, z = z.$
   Ranges: $0 < r < \infty, 0 < \theta < 2\pi, -\infty < z < \infty.$
   $g_{11} = g_{33} = 1, \ g_{22} = r^2, \ \sqrt{g} = r,$
   $h_1 = r, h_2 = h_3 = 1.$

$$\operatorname{grad} f = \mathbf{a}_r \frac{\partial f}{\partial r} + \frac{\mathbf{a}_\theta}{r} \frac{\partial f}{\partial \theta} + \mathbf{a}_z \frac{\partial f}{\partial z}, \tag{5.11.17}$$

$$\operatorname{div} \mathbf{E} = \frac{1}{r} \frac{\partial}{\partial r} (r E_r) + \frac{1}{r} \frac{\partial E_\theta}{\partial \theta} + \frac{\partial E_z}{\partial z}, \tag{5.11.18}$$

$$(\operatorname{curl} \mathbf{E})_r = \frac{1}{r} \frac{\partial E_z}{\partial \theta} - \frac{\partial E_\theta}{\partial z}, \tag{5.11.19}$$

$$(\operatorname{curl} \mathbf{E})_\theta = \frac{\partial E_r}{\partial z} - \frac{\partial E_z}{\partial r}, \tag{5.11.20}$$

$$(\operatorname{curl} \mathbf{E})_z = \frac{1}{r} \frac{\partial (r E_\theta)}{\partial r} - \frac{1}{r} \frac{\partial E_r}{\partial \theta}, \text{ and} \tag{5.11.21}$$

$$\nabla^2 f = \frac{1}{r} \frac{\partial}{\partial r} \left(r \frac{\partial f}{\partial r} \right) + \frac{1}{r^2} \frac{\partial^2 f}{\partial \theta^2} + \frac{\partial^2 f}{\partial z^2}. \tag{5.11.22}$$

3. Elliptic cylinder coordinates $\{\eta, \psi, z\}$
   Relations: $x = a \cosh \eta \cos \psi, \ y = a \sinh \eta \sin \psi, z = z.$
   Ranges: $0 < \eta < \infty, 0 < \psi < 2\pi, -\infty < z < \infty.$
   $g_{11} = g_{22} = a^2 (\cosh^2 \eta - \cos^2 \psi), g_{33} = 1, \sqrt{g} = a^2 (\cosh^2 \eta - \cos^2 \psi),$
   $h_1 = h_2 = h_3 = 1.$

4. Parabolic cylinder coordinates $\{\mu, \nu, z\}$
   Relations: $x = \frac{1}{2} (\mu^2 - \nu^2), \ y = \mu \nu, z = z.$
   Ranges: $0 \le \mu < \infty, -\infty < \nu < 2\pi, -\infty < z < \infty.$
   $g_{11} = g_{22} = \mu^2 + \nu^2, g_{33} = 1, \sqrt{g} = \mu^2 + \nu^2,$
   $h_1 = h_2 = h_3 = 1.$

5. Spherical coordinates $\{r, \theta, \psi\}$
   Relations: $x = r \sin \theta \cos \phi, \ y = r \sin \theta \sin \phi, z = r \cos \theta.$
   Ranges: $0 \le r < \infty, 0 \le \theta \le \pi, 0 \le \psi < 2\pi.$
   $g_{11} = 1, g_{22} = r^2, g_{33} = r^2 \sin^2 \theta, \sqrt{g} = r^2 \sin \theta,$
   $h_1 = r^2, h_2 = \sin \theta, h_3 = 1.$

$$\text{grad } f = \mathbf{e}_r \frac{\partial f}{\partial r} + \frac{\mathbf{e}_\theta}{r} \frac{\partial f}{\partial \theta} + \frac{\mathbf{e}_\phi}{r \sin \theta} \frac{\partial f}{\partial \phi}, \tag{5.11.23}$$

$$\text{div } \mathbf{E} = \frac{1}{r^2} \frac{\partial}{\partial r}(r^2 E_r) + \frac{1}{r \sin \theta} \frac{\partial}{\partial \theta}(E_\theta \sin \theta) \tag{5.11.24}$$
$$+ \frac{1}{r \sin \theta} \frac{\partial E_\phi}{\partial \phi}$$

$$(\text{curl } \mathbf{E})_r = \frac{1}{r \sin \theta} \left[\frac{\partial}{\partial \theta}(E_\phi \sin \theta) - \frac{\partial A_\theta}{\partial \phi} \right] \tag{5.11.25}$$

$$(\text{curl } \mathbf{E})_\theta = \frac{1}{r \sin \theta} \frac{\partial E_r}{\partial \phi} - \frac{1}{r} \frac{\partial (r E_\phi)}{\partial r} \tag{5.11.26}$$

$$(\text{curl } \mathbf{E})_\phi = \frac{1}{r} \frac{\partial (r E_\theta)}{\partial r} - \frac{1}{r} \frac{\partial E_r}{\partial \theta} \tag{5.11.27}$$

$$\nabla^2 f = \frac{1}{r^2} \frac{\partial}{\partial r} \left(r^2 \frac{\partial f}{\partial r} \right) + \frac{1}{r^2 \sin \theta} \frac{\partial}{\partial \theta} \left(\sin \theta \frac{\partial f}{\partial \theta} \right) \tag{5.11.28}$$
$$+ \frac{1}{r^2 \sin^2 \theta} \frac{\partial^2 f}{\partial \phi^2}$$

6. Prolate spheroidal coordinates $\{\eta, \theta, \psi\}$
   Relations: $x = a \sinh \eta \sin \theta \cos \psi, y = a \sinh \eta \sin \theta \sin \psi, z = a \cosh \eta \cos \theta$.
   Ranges: $0 \leq \eta < \infty, 0 \leq \theta \leq \pi, 0 \leq \psi < 2\pi$.
   $g_{11} = g_{22} = a^2(\sinh^2 \eta + \sin^2 \theta) \; g_{33} = a^2 \sinh^2 \eta \sin^2 \theta$,
   $\sqrt{g} = a^3(\sinh^2 \eta + \sin^2 \theta) \sinh \eta \sin \theta$.
   $h_1 = \sinh \eta, h_2 = \sin \theta, h_3 = a$.

7. Oblate spheroidal coordinates $\{\eta, \theta, \psi\}$
   Relations: $x = a \cosh \eta \sin \theta \cos \psi, y = a \cosh \eta \sin \theta \sin \psi, z = a \sinh \eta \cos \theta$.
   Ranges: $0 \leq \eta < \infty, 0 \leq \theta \leq \pi, 0 \leq \psi < 2\pi$.
   $g_{11} = g_{22} = a^2(\cosh^2 \eta - \sin^2 \theta) \; g_{33} = a^2 \cosh^2 \eta \sin^2 \theta$,
   $\sqrt{g} = a^3(\cosh^2 \eta - \sin^2 \theta) \cosh \eta \sin \theta$.
   $h_1 = \cosh \eta, h_2 = \sin \theta, h_3 = a$.

8. Parabolic coordinates $\{\mu, \nu, \psi\}$
   Relations: $x = \mu\nu \cos \psi, y = \mu\nu \sin \psi, z = \frac{1}{2}(\mu^2 - \nu^2)$.
   Ranges: $0 \leq \mu < \infty, 0 \leq \nu \leq \infty, 0 \leq \psi < 2\pi$.
   $g_{11} = g_{22} = \mu^2 + \nu^2 \; g_{33} = \mu^2\nu^2, \; \sqrt{g} = \mu\nu(\mu^2 + \nu^2)$.
   $h_1 = \mu, h_2 = \nu, h_3 = 1$.

9. Conical coordinates $\{r, \theta, \lambda\}$
   Relations: $x^2 = (r\theta\lambda/bc)^2, y^2 = r^2(\theta^2 - b^2)(b^2 - \lambda^2)/[b^2(c^2 - b^2)], z^2 = r^2(c^2 - \theta^2)(c^2 - \lambda^2)/[c^2(c^2 - b^2)]$.
   Ranges: $0 \leq r < \infty, b^2 < \theta^2 < c^2, 0 < \lambda^2 < b^2$.
   $g_{11} = 1, g_{22} = r^2(\theta^2 - \lambda^2)/((\theta^2 - b^2)(c^2 - \theta^2))$,
   $g_{33} = r^2(\theta^2 - \lambda^2)/((b^2 - \lambda^2)(c^2 - \lambda^2))$,
   $\sqrt{g} = r^2(\theta^2 - \lambda^2)/\sqrt{(\theta^2 - b^2)(c^2 - \theta^2)(b^2 - \lambda^2)(c^2 - \lambda^2)}$.

$$h_1 = r^2, h_2 = \sqrt{(\theta^2 - b^2)(c^2 - \theta^2)}, h_3 = \sqrt{(b^2 - \lambda^2)(c^2 - \lambda^2)}.$$

10. Ellipsoidal coordinates $\{\eta, \theta, \lambda\}$
    Relations: $x^2 = (\eta\theta\lambda/bc)^2$, $y^2 = (\eta^2 - b^2)(\theta^2 - b^2)(b^2 - \lambda^2)/[b^2(c^2 - b^2)]$,
    $z^2 = (\eta^2 - c^2)(c^2 - \theta^2)(c^2 - \lambda^2)/[c^2(c^2 - b^2)]$.
    Ranges: $c^2 \le \eta^2 < \infty, b^2 < \theta^2 < c^2, 0 < \lambda^2 < b^2$.
    $g_{11} = (\eta^2 - \theta^2)(\eta^2 - \lambda^2)/((\eta^2 - b^2)(\eta^2 - c^2))$,
    $g_{22} = (\theta^2 - \lambda^2)(\eta^2 - \theta^2)/((\theta^2 - b^2)(c^2 - \theta^2))$,
    $g_{33} = (\eta^2 - \lambda^2)(\theta^2 - \lambda^2)/((b^2 - \lambda^2)(c^2 - \lambda^2))$,
    $\sqrt{g} = \dfrac{(\eta^2 - \theta^2)(\eta^2 - \lambda^2)(\theta^2 - \lambda^2)}{\sqrt{(\eta^2 - b^2)(\eta^2 - c^2)(\theta^2 - b^2)(c^2 - \theta^2)(b^2 - \lambda^2)(c^2 - \lambda^2)}}$.
    $h_1 = \sqrt{(\eta^2 - b^2)(\eta^2 - c^2)}, h_2 = \sqrt{(\theta^2 - b^2)(c^2 - \theta^2)}, h_3 = \sqrt{(b^2 - \lambda^2)(c^2 - \lambda^2)}.$

11. Paraboloidal coordinates $\{\mu, \nu, \lambda\}$
    Relations: $x^2 = 4(\mu - b)(b - \nu)(b - \lambda)/(b - c)$,
    $y^2 = 4(\mu - c)(c - \nu)(\lambda - c)/(b - c), z^2 = \mu + \nu + \lambda - b - c$.
    Ranges: $b < \mu < \infty, 0 < \nu < c, c < \lambda < b$.
    $g_{11} = (\mu - \nu)(\mu - \lambda)/((\mu - b)(\mu - c)), g_{22} = (\mu - \nu)(\lambda - \nu)/((b - \nu)(c - \nu))$,
    $g_{33} = (\lambda - \nu)(\mu - \lambda)/((b - \lambda)(\lambda - c)), \sqrt{g} = \dfrac{(\mu - \nu)(\mu - \lambda)(\lambda - \nu)}{\sqrt{(\mu - b)(\mu - c)(b - \nu)(c - \nu)(b - \lambda)(\lambda - c)}}$.
    $h_1 = \sqrt{(\mu - b)(\mu - c)}, h_2 = \sqrt{(b - \nu)(c - \nu)}, h_3 = \sqrt{(b - \lambda)(\lambda - c)}.$

5.12   CONTROL THEORY

Let $\mathbf{x}$ be a state vector, let $\mathbf{y}$ be an observable vector, and let $\mathbf{u}$ be the control. Each of $\mathbf{x}, \mathbf{y}$, and $\mathbf{u}$ has n components. If a system evolves as

$$\dot{\mathbf{x}} = A\mathbf{x} + B\mathbf{u},$$

and

$$\dot{\mathbf{y}} = C\mathbf{x} + D\mathbf{u},$$

then, taking Laplace transforms, $\tilde{\mathbf{y}} = G(s)\tilde{\mathbf{u}}$ where $G(s)$ is the transfer function given by $G(s) = C(sI - A)^{-1}B + D$.

A system is said to be controllable if, and only if, for any times $\{t_0, t_1\}$ and any outputs $\{\mathbf{y}_0, \mathbf{y}_1\}$, a control $\mathbf{u}(t)$ exists so that $\mathbf{y}(t_0) = \mathbf{y}_0$ and $\mathbf{y}(t_1) = \mathbf{y}_1$. The system is not controllable if $\text{rank}[B \ AB \ A^2B \ \ldots \ A^{n-1}B] < n$.

If, given $\mathbf{u}(t)$ and $\mathbf{y}(t)$ on some interval $t_0 < t < t_1$, the value of $\mathbf{x}(t)$ can be deduced on that interval, then the system is said to be observable. Observability requires $\text{rank}[C^T \ A^T C^T \ \ldots \ \left(A^{(n-1)}\right)^T C^T] = n$

If the control is bounded (say $u_i^- < u_i < u_i^+$), then a "bang–bang" control is one for which $u_i = u_i^-$ or $u_i = u_i^+$. A "bang–off–bang" control is one for which $u_i = 0$, $u_i = u_i^-$ or $u_i = u_i^+$.

A second frequently studied control problem is $\dot{\mathbf{x}} = \mathbf{f}(\mathbf{x}, \mathbf{u}, t)$, where $\mathbf{x}(t_0)$ and $\mathbf{x}(t_f)$ are specified, and there is a cost function, $J = \int_{t_0}^{t_f} \phi(\mathbf{x}, \mathbf{u}, t)$. The goal is to minimize the cost function. Defining the Hamiltonian $H(\mathbf{x}, \mathbf{u}, t) = \phi + \mathbf{z} \cdot \mathbf{f}$, the optimal control satisfies

$$\dot{\mathbf{x}} = \frac{\partial H}{\partial \mathbf{z}}, \quad \dot{\mathbf{z}} = -\frac{\partial H}{\partial \mathbf{x}}, \quad \mathbf{0} = \frac{\partial H}{\partial \mathbf{u}}.$$

Example: In the one-dimensional case, with $\dot{x} = -ax + u$, $x(0) = x_0$, $x(\infty) = 0$, and $J = \int_0^\infty (x^2 + u^2) \, dt$; the optimal control is given by $u = (a - \sqrt{1 + a^2})x^*(t)$ where $x^*(t) = x_0 e^{-\sqrt{1+a^2}t}$.

References

1. A. G. Butkovskiy, *Green's Functions and Transfer Functions Handbook*, Halstead Press, John Wiley & Sons, New York, 1982.

2. I. S. Gradshteyn and I. M. Rhizik, *Tables of Integrals, Series, and Products*, A. Jeffrey, Ed., Academic Press, New York, 1994.

3. N. H. Ibragimov, Ed., *CRC Handbook of Lie Group Analysis of Differential Equations*, CRC Press, Boca Raton, FL, 1994, Volume 1.

4. A. J. Jerri, *Introduction to Integral Equations with Applications*, Marcel Dekker, New York, 1985.

5. A. D. Polyanin and V. F. Zaitsev, *Handbook of Exact Solution for Ordinary Differential Equations*, CRC Press, Boca Raton, FL, 1995.

6. J. A. Schouten, *Ricci-Calculus*, Springer-Verlag, Berlin, 1954.

7. J. L. Synge and A. Schild, *Tensor Calculus*, University of Toronto Press, Toronto, 1949.

8. D. Zwillinger, *Handbook of Differential Equations*, 2nd ed., Academic Press, New York, 1992.

9. D. Zwillinger, *Handbook of Integration*, A. K. Peters, Boston, 1992.

Chapter **6**

Special Functions

0-8493-2479-3/96/$0.00+$.50
© 1996 CRC Press, Inc.

6.1   TRIGONOMETRIC OR CIRCULAR FUNCTIONS

6.1.1   DEFINITION OF ANGLES

If two lines intersect and one line is rotated about the point of intersection, the angle of rotation is designated positive if the angle of rotation is counterclockwise. Angles are commonly measured in units of radians or degrees. Degrees are a historical unit related to the calendar defined by a complete revolution equalling 360 degrees (the approximate number of days in a year). Radians are the angular unit usually used for mathematics and science. Radians are specified by the arc length traced by the tip of a rotating line divided by the length of that line. Thus a complete rotation of a line about the origin corresponds to 2π radians of rotation. It is a convenient convention that a full rotation of 2π radians is divided into four angular segments of $\pi/2$ each and that these are referred to as the four quadrants using Roman numerals I, II, III, and IV to designate them (see Figure 6.1.1).

6.1.2   CHARACTERIZATION OF ANGLES

A "right" angle is the angle between two perpendicular lines. It is equal to $\pi/2$ radians or 90 degrees. An acute angle is an angle less than $\pi/2$ radians. An obtuse angle is one between $\pi/2$ and π radians.

6.1.3   RELATION BETWEEN RADIANS AND DEGREES

The angle π radians corresponds to 180 degrees. Therefore,

$$\text{one radian} = \frac{180}{\pi} = 57.30 \,\text{degrees},$$
$$\text{one degree} = \frac{\pi}{180} = 0.01745 \,\text{radians.}$$

(6.1.1)

6.1.4   CIRCULAR FUNCTIONS

Consider the rectangular coordinate system shown in Figure 6.1.1. The coordinate x is positive to the right of the origin and the coordinate y is positive above the origin. The radius vector $\mathbf{r}$ shown terminating on the point $P(x, y)$ is shown rotated by the angle α up from the x axis. The radius vector $\mathbf{r}$ has component vectors $\mathbf{x}$ and $\mathbf{y}$.

The trigonometric or circular functions of the angle α are defined in terms of the signed coordinates x and y and the length r, always positive. Note that the coordinate x is negative in quadrants II and III and the coordinate y is negative in quadrants III and IV. The definitions of the trigonometric functions in terms of the Cartesian coordinates x and y of the point $P(x, y)$ are shown below. The angle α can be specified in radians, degrees, or any other unit.

FIGURE 6.1.1
The four quadrants (left) and notation for trigonometric functions (right).

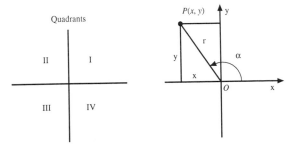

$$\text{sine } \alpha \quad = \sin \alpha = y/r,$$
$$\text{cosine } \alpha \quad = \cos \alpha = x/r,$$
$$\text{tangent } \alpha \quad = \tan \alpha = y/x,$$
$$\text{cotangent } \alpha = \cot \alpha = x/y,$$
$$\text{cosecant } \alpha \quad = \csc \alpha = r/y,$$
$$\text{secant } \alpha \quad = \sec \alpha = r/x.$$

There are also the following seldom used functions:

versed sine of A = versine of A = vers $A = 1 - \cos A$,
coversed sine of A = versed cosine of A = covers $A = 1 - \sin A$,
exsecant of A = exsec A = sec $A - 1$,
haversine of A = hav $A = \frac{1}{2}$ vers A.

6.1.5 PERIODICITY RELATIONSHIPS

When n is any integer,

$$\sin (\alpha + n2\pi) = \sin \alpha,$$
$$\cos (\alpha + n2\pi) = \cos \alpha, \qquad\qquad (6.1.2)$$
$$\tan (\alpha + n\pi) = \tan \alpha.$$

6.1.6 SYMMETRY RELATIONSHIPS

$$\sin (-\alpha) = - \sin \alpha, \qquad \cos (-\alpha) = + \cos \alpha, \qquad \tan (-\alpha) = - \tan \alpha.$$

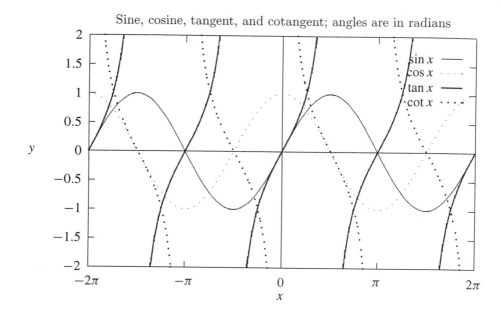

Sine, cosine, tangent, and cotangent; angles are in radians

6.1.7   SIGNS IN THE FOUR QUADRANTS

Quadrant	sin	cos	tan	csc	sec	cot
I	+	+	+	+	+	+
II	+	−	−	+	−	−
III	−	−	+	−	−	+
IV	−	+	−	−	+	−

6.1.8   FUNCTIONS IN TERMS OF ANGLES IN THE FIRST QUADRANT

For $0 \le \alpha \le \pi/2$, with n any integer

	$-\alpha$	$\dfrac{\pi}{2} \pm \alpha$	$\pi \pm \alpha$	$\dfrac{3\pi}{2} \pm \alpha$	$2n\pi \pm \alpha$
sin	$-\sin\alpha$	$\cos\alpha$	$\mp\sin\alpha$	$-\cos\alpha$	$\pm\sin\alpha$
cos	$\cos\alpha$	$\mp\sin\alpha$	$-\cos\alpha$	$\pm\sin\alpha$	$+\cos\alpha$
tan	$-\tan\alpha$	$\mp\cot\alpha$	$\pm\tan\alpha$	$\mp\cot\alpha$	$\pm\tan\alpha$
csc	$-\csc\alpha$	$\sec\alpha$	$\mp\csc\alpha$	$-\sec\alpha$	$\pm\csc\alpha$
sec	$\sec\alpha$	$\mp\csc\alpha$	$-\sec\alpha$	$\pm\csc\alpha$	$\sec\alpha$
cot	$-\cot\alpha$	$\mp\tan\alpha$	$\pm\cot\alpha$	$\mp\tan\alpha$	$\pm\cot\alpha$

6.1.9 CIRCULAR FUNCTIONS OF SOME SPECIAL ANGLES

Angle	$0 = 0°$	$\pi/12 = 15°$	$\pi/6 = 30°$	$\pi/4 = 45°$	$\pi/3 = 60°$
sin	0	$\frac{\sqrt{2}}{4}(\sqrt{3}-1)$	1/2	$\sqrt{2}/2$	$\sqrt{3}/2$
cos	1	$\frac{\sqrt{2}}{4}(\sqrt{3}+1)$	$\sqrt{3}/2$	$\sqrt{2}/2$	1/2
tan	0	$2-\sqrt{3}$	$\sqrt{3}/3$	1	$\sqrt{3}$
csc	∞	$\sqrt{2}(\sqrt{3}+1)$	2	$\sqrt{2}$	$2\sqrt{3}/3$
sec	1	$\sqrt{2}(\sqrt{3}-1)$	$2\sqrt{3}/3$	$\sqrt{2}$	2
cot	∞	$2+\sqrt{3}$	$\sqrt{3}$	1	$\sqrt{3}/3$

Angle	$5\pi/12 = 75°$	$\pi/2 = 90°$	$7\pi/12 = 105°$	$2\pi/3 = 120°$
sin	$\frac{\sqrt{2}}{4}(\sqrt{3}+1)$	1	$\frac{\sqrt{2}}{4}(\sqrt{3}+1)$	1/2
cos	$\frac{\sqrt{2}}{4}(\sqrt{3}-1)$	0	$-\frac{\sqrt{2}}{4}(\sqrt{3}-1)$	$-1/2$
tan	$2+\sqrt{3}$	∞	$-(2+\sqrt{3})$	$-\sqrt{3}$
csc	$\sqrt{2}(\sqrt{3}-1)$	1	$\sqrt{2}(\sqrt{3}-1)$	$2\sqrt{3}/3$
sec	$\sqrt{2}(\sqrt{3}+1)$	∞	$-\sqrt{2}(\sqrt{3}+1)$	-2
cot	$2-\sqrt{3}$	0	$-(2-\sqrt{3})$	$-\sqrt{3}/3$

Angle	$3\pi/4 = 135°$	$5\pi/6 = 150°$	$11\pi/12 = 165°$	$\pi = 180°$
sin	$\sqrt{2}/2$	$\sqrt{3}/2$	$\frac{\sqrt{2}}{4}(\sqrt{3}-1)$	0
cos	$-\sqrt{2}/2$	$-\sqrt{3}/2$	$-\frac{\sqrt{2}}{4}(\sqrt{3}+1)$	-1
tan	-1	$-\sqrt{3}/3$	$-(2-\sqrt{3})$	0
csc	$\sqrt{2}$	2	$\sqrt{2}(\sqrt{3}+1)$	∞
sec	$-\sqrt{2}$	$-2\sqrt{3}/3$	$-\sqrt{2}(\sqrt{3}-1)$	-1
cot	-1	$-\sqrt{3}$	$-(2+\sqrt{3})$	∞

6.1.10 ONE CIRCULAR FUNCTION IN TERMS OF ANOTHER

For $0 \le x \le \pi/2$,

	$\sin x$	$\cos x$	$\tan x$
$\sin x =$	$\sin x$	$\sqrt{1 - \cos^2 x}$	$\dfrac{\tan x}{\sqrt{1 + \tan^2 x}}$
$\cos x =$	$\sqrt{1 - \sin^2 x}$	$\cos x$	$\dfrac{1}{\sqrt{1 + \tan^2 x}}$
$\tan x =$	$\dfrac{\sin x}{\sqrt{1 - \sin^2 x}}$	$\dfrac{\sqrt{1 - \cos^2 x}}{\cos x}$	$\tan x$
$\csc x =$	$\dfrac{1}{\sin x}$	$\dfrac{1}{\sqrt{1 - \cos^2 x}}$	$\dfrac{\sqrt{1 + \tan^2 x}}{\tan x}$
$\sec x =$	$\dfrac{1}{\sqrt{1 - \sin^2 x}}$	$\dfrac{1}{\cos x}$	$\sqrt{1 + \tan^2 x}$
$\cot x =$	$\dfrac{\sqrt{1 - \sin^2 x}}{\sin x}$	$\dfrac{\cos x}{\sqrt{1 - \cos^2 x}}$	$\dfrac{1}{\tan x}$

	$\csc x$	$\sec x$	$\cot x$
$\sin x =$	$\dfrac{1}{\csc x}$	$\dfrac{\sqrt{\sec^2 x - 1}}{\sec x}$	$\dfrac{1}{\sqrt{1 + \cot^2 x}}$
$\cos x =$	$\dfrac{\sqrt{\csc^2 x - 1}}{\csc x}$	$\dfrac{1}{\sec x}$	$\dfrac{\cot x}{\sqrt{1 + \cot^2 x}}$
$\tan x =$	$\dfrac{1}{\sqrt{\csc^2 x - 1}}$	$\sqrt{\sec^2 x - 1}$	$\dfrac{1}{\cot x}$
$\csc x =$	$\csc x$	$\dfrac{\sec x}{\sqrt{\sec^2 x - 1}}$	$\sqrt{1 + \cot^2 x}$
$\sec x =$	$\dfrac{\csc x}{\sqrt{\csc^2 x - 1}}$	$\sec x$	$\dfrac{\sqrt{1 + \cot^2 x}}{\cot x}$
$\cot x =$	$\sqrt{\csc^2 x - 1}$	$\dfrac{1}{\sqrt{\sec^2 x - 1}}$	$\cot x$

6.1.11 DEFINITIONS IN TERMS OF EXPONENTIALS

$$\cos z = \frac{e^{iz} + e^{-iz}}{2}.$$

$$\sin z = \frac{e^{iz} - e^{-iz}}{2i}.$$

$$\tan z = \frac{\sin z}{\cos z} = \frac{e^{iz} - e^{-iz}}{i(e^{iz} + e^{-iz})}.$$

$$e^{iz} = \cos z + i \sin z.$$

$$e^{-iz} = \cos z - i \sin z.$$

6.1.12   FUNDAMENTAL IDENTITIES

Reciprocal relations

$$\sin\alpha = \frac{1}{\csc\alpha}, \qquad \cos\alpha = \frac{1}{\sec\alpha}, \qquad \tan\alpha = \frac{\sin\alpha}{\cos\alpha} = \frac{1}{\cot\alpha},$$

$$\csc\alpha = \frac{1}{\sin\alpha}, \qquad \sec\alpha = \frac{1}{\cos\alpha}, \qquad \cot\alpha = \frac{\cos\alpha}{\sin\alpha} = \frac{1}{\tan\alpha}.$$

Pythagorean theorem

$$\sin^2 z + \cos^2 z = 1.$$
$$\sec^2 z - \tan^2 z = 1.$$
$$\csc^2 z - \cot^2 z = 1.$$

Product relations

$$\sin\alpha = \tan\alpha\cos\alpha, \qquad\qquad \cos\alpha = \cot\alpha\sin\alpha,$$
$$\tan\alpha = \sin\alpha\sec\alpha, \qquad\qquad \cot\alpha = \cos\alpha\csc\alpha,$$
$$\sec\alpha = \csc\alpha\tan\alpha, \qquad\qquad \csc\alpha = \sec\alpha\cot\alpha.$$

Quotient relations

$$\sin\alpha = \frac{\tan\alpha}{\sec\alpha}, \qquad \cos\alpha = \frac{\cot\alpha}{\csc\alpha}, \qquad \tan\alpha = \frac{\sin\alpha}{\cos\alpha},$$

$$\csc\alpha = \frac{\sec\alpha}{\tan\alpha}, \qquad \sec\alpha = \frac{\csc\alpha}{\cot\alpha}, \qquad \cot\alpha = \frac{\cos\alpha}{\sin\alpha}.$$

6.1.13   ANGLE SUM AND DIFFERENCE RELATIONSHIPS

$$\sin(\alpha \pm \beta) = \sin\alpha\cos\beta \pm \cos\alpha\sin\beta.$$
$$\cos(\alpha \pm \beta) = \cos\alpha\cos\beta \mp \sin\alpha\sin\beta.$$
$$\tan(\alpha \pm \beta) = \frac{\tan\alpha \pm \tan\beta}{1 \mp \tan\alpha\tan\beta}.$$
$$\cot(\alpha \pm \beta) = \frac{\cot\alpha\cot\beta \mp 1}{\cot\beta \pm \cot\alpha}.$$

6.1.14   DOUBLE ANGLE FORMULAE

$$\sin 2\alpha = 2\sin\alpha\cos\alpha = \frac{2\tan\alpha}{1+2\tan^2\alpha}.$$

$$\cos 2\alpha = 2\cos^2\alpha - 1 = 1 - 2\sin^2\alpha = \cos^2\alpha - \sin^2\alpha = \frac{1-\tan^2\alpha}{1+\tan^2\alpha}.$$

$$\tan 2\alpha = \frac{2\tan\alpha}{1-\tan^2\alpha}.$$

$$\cot 2\alpha = \frac{\cot^2\alpha - 1}{2\cot\alpha}.$$

6.1.15   MULTIPLE ANGLE FORMULAE

$$\sin 3\alpha = -4\sin^3\alpha + 3\sin\alpha.$$

$$\sin 4\alpha = -8\sin^3\alpha\cos\alpha + 4\sin\alpha\cos\alpha.$$

$$\sin 5\alpha = 16\sin^5\alpha - 20\sin^3\alpha + 5\sin\alpha.$$

$$\sin 6\alpha = 32\sin\alpha\cos^5\alpha - 32\sin\alpha\cos^3\alpha + 6\sin\alpha\cos\alpha.$$

$$\sin n\alpha = 2\sin(n-1)\alpha\cos\alpha - \sin(n-2)\alpha.$$

$$\cos 3\alpha = 4\cos^3\alpha - 3\cos\alpha.$$

$$\cos 4\alpha = 8\cos^4\alpha - 8\cos^2\alpha + 1.$$

$$\cos 5\alpha = 16\cos^5\alpha - 20\cos^3\alpha + 5\cos\alpha.$$

$$\cos 6\alpha = 32\cos^6\alpha - 48\cos^4\alpha + 18\cos^2\alpha - 1.$$

$$\cos n\alpha = 2\cos(n-1)\alpha\cos\alpha - \cos(n-2)\alpha.$$

$$\tan 3\alpha = \frac{-\tan^3\alpha + 3\tan\alpha}{-3\tan^2\alpha + 1}.$$

$$\tan 4\alpha = \frac{-4\tan^3\alpha + 4\tan\alpha}{\tan^4\alpha - 6\tan^2\alpha + 1}.$$

$$\tan n\alpha = \frac{\tan(n-1)\alpha + \tan\alpha}{-\tan(n-1)\alpha\tan\alpha + 1}.$$

6.1.16 HALF ANGLE FORMULAE

$$\cos\frac{\alpha}{2} = \pm\sqrt{\frac{1+\cos\alpha}{2}}$$

(positive if $\alpha/2$ is in quadrant I or IV, negative if in II or III).

$$\sin\frac{\alpha}{2} = \pm\sqrt{\frac{1-\cos\alpha}{2}}$$

(positive if $\alpha/2$ is in quadrant I or II, negative if in III or IV).

$$\tan\frac{\alpha}{2} = \frac{1-\cos\alpha}{\sin\alpha} = \frac{\sin\alpha}{1+\cos\alpha} = \pm\sqrt{\frac{1-\cos\alpha}{1+\cos\alpha}}$$

(positive if $\alpha/2$ is in quadrant I or III, negative if in II or IV).

$$\cot\frac{\alpha}{2} = \frac{1+\cos\alpha}{\sin\alpha} = \frac{\sin\alpha}{1-\cos\alpha} = \pm\sqrt{\frac{1+\cos\alpha}{1-\cos\alpha}}$$

(positive if $\alpha/2$ is in quadrant I or III, negative if in II or IV).

6.1.17 POWERS OF CIRCULAR FUNCTIONS

$$\sin^2\alpha = \frac{1}{2}(1-\cos 2\alpha). \qquad\qquad \cos^2\alpha = \frac{1}{2}(1+\cos 2\alpha).$$

$$\sin^3\alpha = \frac{1}{4}(-\sin 3\alpha + 3\sin\alpha). \qquad \cos^3\alpha = \frac{1}{4}(\cos 3\alpha + 3\cos\alpha).$$

$$\sin^4\alpha = \frac{1}{8}(3 - 4\cos 2\alpha + \cos 4\alpha). \qquad \cos^4\alpha = \frac{1}{8}(3 + 4\cos 2\alpha + \cos 4\alpha).$$

$$\tan^2\alpha = \frac{1-\cos 2\alpha}{1+\cos 2\alpha}.$$

$$\cot^2\alpha = \frac{1+\cos 2\alpha}{1-\cos 2\alpha}.$$

6.1.18 PRODUCTS OF SINE AND COSINE

$$\cos\alpha\cos\beta = \frac{1}{2}\cos(\alpha-\beta) + \frac{1}{2}\cos(\alpha+\beta).$$

$$\sin\alpha\sin\beta = \frac{1}{2}\cos(\alpha-\beta) - \frac{1}{2}\cos(\alpha+\beta). \qquad (6.1.3)$$

$$\sin\alpha\cos\beta = \frac{1}{2}\sin(\alpha-\beta) + \frac{1}{2}\sin(\alpha+\beta).$$

6.1.19   SUMS OF CIRCULAR FUNCTIONS

$$\sin\alpha \pm \sin\beta = 2\sin\frac{\alpha\pm\beta}{2}\cos\frac{\alpha\mp\beta}{2}.$$

$$\cos\alpha + \cos\beta = 2\cos\frac{\alpha+\beta}{2}\cos\frac{\alpha-\beta}{2}.$$

$$\cos\alpha - \cos\beta = -2\sin\frac{\alpha+\beta}{2}\sin\frac{\alpha-\beta}{2}.$$

$$\tan\alpha \pm \tan\beta = \frac{\sin\alpha\pm\beta}{\cos\alpha\cos\beta}.$$

$$\cot\alpha \pm \cot\beta = \frac{\sin\beta\pm\alpha}{\sin\alpha\sin\beta}. \tag{6.1.4}$$

$$\frac{\sin\alpha+\sin\beta}{\sin\alpha-\sin\beta} = \frac{\tan\frac{\alpha+\beta}{2}}{\tan\frac{\alpha-\beta}{2}}.$$

$$\frac{\sin\alpha+\sin\beta}{\cos\alpha-\cos\beta} = \cot\frac{-\alpha+\beta}{2}.$$

$$\frac{\sin\alpha+\sin\beta}{\cos\alpha+\cos\beta} = \tan\frac{\alpha+\beta}{2}.$$

$$\frac{\sin\alpha-\sin\beta}{\cos\alpha+\cos\beta} = \tan\frac{\alpha-\beta}{2}.$$

6.1.20   EVALUATING SINES AND COSINES

The following table is useful for evaluating sines and cosines in multiples of π:

	n an integer	n even	n odd	$n/2$ odd	$n/2$ even
$\sin n\pi$	0	0	0	0	0
$\cos n\pi$	$(-1)^n$	$+1$	-1	$+1$	$+1$
$\sin n\pi/2$		0	$(-1)^{(n-1)/2}$	0	0
$\cos n\pi/2$		$(-1)^{n/2}$	0	-1	$+1$

	n odd	$n/2$ odd	$n/2$ even
$\sin n\pi/4$	$(-1)^{(n^2+4n+11)/8}/\sqrt{2}$	$(-1)^{(n-2)/4}$	0

Note the useful formulae (where $i^2 = -1$)

$$\sin\frac{n\pi}{2} = \frac{i^{n+1}}{2}\left[(-1)^n - 1\right], \quad \text{and}$$

$$\cos\frac{n\pi}{2} = \frac{i^n}{2}\left[(-1)^n + 1\right]. \tag{6.1.5}$$

6.2   CIRCULAR FUNCTIONS AND PLANAR TRIANGLES

6.2.1   RIGHT TRIANGLES

Let A, B, and C designate the vertices of a right triangle with C the right angle and a, b, and c the lengths of the sides opposite the corresponding vertices:

$$\sin A = \frac{a}{c} = \frac{1}{\csc A},$$

$$\cos A = \frac{b}{c} = \frac{1}{\sec A},$$

$$\tan A = \frac{a}{b} = \frac{1}{\cot A}.$$

The Pythagorean theorem states that $a^2 + b^2 = c^2$.
The sum of the interior angles equals π, i.e., $A + B + C = \pi$.

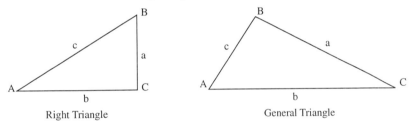

Right Triangle   General Triangle

6.2.2   GENERAL PLANE TRIANGLES

Let A, B, and C designate the interior angles of a general triangle and let a, b, and c be the length of the sides opposite those angles.

Radius of the inscribed circle:

$$r = \sqrt{\frac{(s-a)(s-b)(s-c)}{s}},$$

where $s = \frac{1}{2}(a + b + c)$, the semiperimeter.

Radius of the circumscribed circle:

$$R = \frac{a}{2 \sin A} = \frac{b}{2 \sin B} = \frac{c}{2 \sin C} = \frac{abc}{4(\text{Area})}. \qquad (6.2.1)$$

Law of sines:

$$\frac{a}{\sin A} = \frac{b}{\sin B} = \frac{c}{\sin C}.$$

Law of cosines:

$$a^2 = c^2 + b^2 - 2bc \cos A, \qquad \cos A = \frac{c^2 + b^2 - a^2}{2bc}.$$

$$b^2 = a^2 + c^2 - 2ca \cos B, \qquad \cos B = \frac{a^2 + c^2 - b^2}{2ca}.$$

$$c^2 = b^2 + a^2 - 2ab \cos C, \qquad \cos C = \frac{b^2 + a^2 - c^2}{2ab}.$$

Triangle sides in terms of other components:

$$a = b \cos C + c \cos B,$$
$$c = a \cos A + b \cos C,$$
$$b = c \cos B + a \cos A.$$

Law of tangents:

$$\frac{a+b}{a-b} = \frac{\tan \frac{A+B}{2}}{\tan \frac{A-B}{2}},$$

$$\frac{b+c}{b-c} = \frac{\tan \frac{B+C}{2}}{\tan \frac{B-C}{2}}, \qquad (6.2.2)$$

$$\frac{a+c}{a-c} = \frac{\tan \frac{A+C}{2}}{\tan \frac{A-C}{2}}.$$

Area of general triangle:

$$\text{Area} = \frac{bc \sin A}{2} = \frac{ac \sin B}{2} = \frac{ab \sin C}{2},$$

$$= \frac{c^2 \sin A \sin B}{2 \sin C} = \frac{b^2 \sin A \sin C}{2 \sin B} = \frac{a^2 \sin B \sin C}{2 \sin A},$$

$$= \sqrt{s(s-a)(s-b)(s-c)} = rs = \frac{abc}{4R} \qquad \text{(Heron's formula)}.$$

Mollweide's formulae:

$$\frac{b-c}{a} = \frac{\sin\frac{1}{2}(B-C)}{\cos\frac{1}{2}A},$$

$$\frac{c-a}{b} = \frac{\sin\frac{1}{2}(C-A)}{\cos\frac{1}{2}B}, \qquad (6.2.3)$$

$$\frac{a-b}{c} = \frac{\sin\frac{1}{2}(A-B)}{\cos\frac{1}{2}C}.$$

Newton's formulae:

$$\frac{b+c}{a} = \frac{\cos\frac{1}{2}(B-C)}{\sin\frac{1}{2}A},$$

$$\frac{c+a}{b} = \frac{\cos\frac{1}{2}(C-A)}{\sin\frac{1}{2}B}, \qquad (6.2.4)$$

$$\frac{a+b}{c} = \frac{\cos\frac{1}{2}(A-B)}{\sin\frac{1}{2}C}.$$

6.2.3 HALF ANGLE FORMULAE

$$\tan\frac{A}{2} = \frac{r}{s-a} \qquad \tan\frac{B}{2} = \frac{r}{s-b} \qquad \tan\frac{C}{2} = \frac{r}{s-c}$$

$$\sin\frac{A}{2} = \sqrt{\frac{(s-b)(s-c)}{bc}} \qquad\qquad \cos\frac{A}{2} = \sqrt{\frac{s(s-a)}{bc}}$$

$$\sin\frac{B}{2} = \sqrt{\frac{(s-c)(s-a)}{ca}} \qquad\qquad \cos\frac{B}{2} = \sqrt{\frac{s(s-b)}{ca}}$$

$$\sin\frac{C}{2} = \sqrt{\frac{(s-a)(s-b)}{ab}} \qquad\qquad \cos\frac{C}{2} = \sqrt{\frac{s(s-c)}{ab}}$$

6.2.4 SOLUTION OF TRIANGLES

A triangle is totally described by specifying any side and two additional parameters: either the remaining two sides, another side and the included angle, or two specified angles. Two angles alone specify the shape of a triangle, but not its size, which requires specification of a side.

Three sides given

Formulae for any one of the angles:

$$\cos A = \frac{c^2 + b^2 - a^2}{2bc}, \qquad \sin A = \frac{2}{bc}\sqrt{s(s-a)(s-b)(s-c)},$$

$$\sin \frac{A}{2} = \sqrt{\frac{(s-b)(s-c)}{bc}}, \qquad \cos \frac{A}{2} = \sqrt{\frac{s(s-a)}{bc}},$$

$$\tan \frac{A}{2} = \sqrt{\frac{(s-b)(s-c)}{s(s-a)}} = \frac{r}{s-a}.$$

Given two sides (b, c) and the included angle (A)

See Figure 6.2.2, left. The remaining side and angles can be determined by repeated use of the law of cosines. For example,

Nonlogarithmic solution; perform these steps sequentially:

$$a^2 = b^2 + c^2 - 2bc \cos A$$
$$\cos B = (a^2 + c^2 - b^2)/2ca \qquad (6.2.5)$$
$$\cos C = (a^2 + b^2 - c^2)/2ba$$

FIGURE 6.2.2
Different triangles requiring solution.

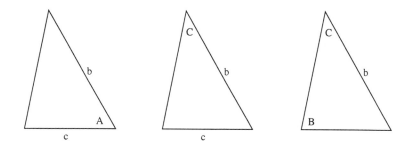

Logarithmic solution; perform these steps sequentially:

$$B + C = \pi - A$$
$$\tan \frac{(B-C)}{2} = \frac{b-c}{b+c} \tan \frac{(B+C)}{2}$$
$$B = \frac{B+C}{2} + \frac{B-C}{2}$$
$$C = \frac{B+C}{2} - \frac{B-C}{2} \qquad (6.2.6)$$
$$a = \frac{b \sin A}{\sin B}$$

Given two sides (b, c) and an angle (C), not the included angle

See Figure 6.2.2, middle. The remaining angles and side are determined by use of the law of sines. and the fact that the sum of the angles is π, $A + B + C = \pi$.

$$\sin B = \frac{b \sin C}{c}, \qquad A = \pi - B - C, \qquad a = \frac{b \sin A}{\sin B}.$$

Given one side (b) and two angles (B, C)

See Figure 6.2.2, right. The third angle is specified by $A = \pi - B - C$. The remaining sides are found by

$$a = \frac{b \sin A}{\sin B}, \qquad c = \frac{b \sin C}{\sin B}.$$

6.3 INVERSE CIRCULAR FUNCTIONS

6.3.1 DEFINITION IN TERMS OF AN INTEGRAL

$$\sin^{-1} z = \int_0^z \frac{dt}{\sqrt{1 - t^2}},$$

$$\cos^{-1} z = \int_z^1 \frac{dt}{\sqrt{1 - t^2}} = \frac{\pi}{2} - \sin^{-1} z,$$

$$\tan^{-1} z = \int_0^z \frac{dt}{1 + t^2} = \frac{\pi}{2} - \cot^{-1} z,$$

where z can be complex. The path of integration must not cross the real axis in the first two cases. In the third case, it must not cross the imaginary axis except possibly inside the unit circle. If $-1 \le x \le 1$, then $\sin^{-1} x$ and $\cos^{-1} x$ are real, $-\frac{\pi}{2} \le \sin^{-1} x \le \frac{\pi}{2}$, and $0 \le \cos^{-1} x \le \pi$.

$$\csc^{-1} z = \sin^{-1}(1/z),$$

$$\sec^{-1} z = \cos^{-1}(1/z),$$

$$\cot^{-1} z = \tan^{-1}(1/z),$$

$$\sec^{-1} z + \csc^{-1} z = \pi/2.$$

6.3.2   FUNDAMENTAL PROPERTIES

The general solutions of the equations $\{\sin t = z, \cos t = z, \tan t = z\}$ are, respectively, (where k is an arbitrary integer):

$$t = \sin^{-1} z = (-1)^k \sin^{-1} z + k\pi,$$
$$t = \cos^{-1} z = \pm \cos^{-1} z + 2k\pi,$$
$$t = \tan^{-1} z = \tan^{-1} z + k\pi, \, (z^2 \neq -1).$$

6.3.3   PRINCIPAL VALUES OF THE INVERSE CIRCULAR FUNCTIONS

The notation $\sin^{-1} x$ is used to denote any angle whose sin is x. The function $\sin^{-1} x$ is usually used to denote the *principal value*. Similar notation is used for the other inverse trigonometric functions. The principal values of the inverse trigonometric functions are defined as follows:

1. When $-1 \leq x \leq 1$,   then $-\pi/2 \leq \sin^{-1} x \leq \pi/2$.
2. When $-1 \leq x \leq 1$,   then $0 \leq \cos^{-1} x \leq \pi$.
3. When $-\infty \leq x \leq \infty$,   then $-\pi/2 \leq \tan^{-1} x \leq \pi/2$.
4. When $1 \leq x$,   then $0 \leq \csc^{-1} x \leq \pi/2$.
   When $x \leq -1$,   then $-\pi/2 \leq \csc^{-1} x \leq 0$.
5. When $1 \leq x$,   then $0 \leq \sec^{-1} x \leq \pi/2$.
   When $x \leq -1$,   then $\pi/2 \leq \sec^{-1} x \leq \pi$.
6. When $-\infty \leq x \leq \infty$,   then $0 \leq \cot^{-1} x \leq \pi$.

6.3.4   FUNDAMENTAL IDENTITIES

$$\sin^{-1} x + \cos^{-1} x = \pi/2.$$
$$\tan^{-1} x + \cot^{-1} x = \pi/2.$$

(6.3.1)

If $\alpha = \sin^{-1} x$, then

$$\sin \alpha = x, \qquad \cos \alpha = \sqrt{1 - x^2}, \qquad \tan \alpha = \frac{x}{\sqrt{1 - x^2}},$$

$$\csc \alpha = \frac{1}{x}, \qquad \sec \alpha = \frac{1}{\sqrt{1 - x^2}}, \qquad \cot \alpha = \frac{\sqrt{1 - x^2}}{x}.$$

If $\alpha = \cos^{-1} x$, then

$$\sin \alpha = \sqrt{1 - x^2}, \qquad \cos \alpha = x, \qquad \tan \alpha = \frac{\sqrt{1 - x^2}}{x},$$

$$\csc \alpha = \frac{1}{\sqrt{1 - x^2}}, \qquad \sec \alpha = \frac{1}{x}, \qquad \cot \alpha = \frac{x}{\sqrt{1 - x^2}}.$$

If $\alpha = \tan^{-1} x$, then

$$\sin \alpha = \frac{x}{\sqrt{1+x^2}}, \qquad \cos \alpha = \frac{1}{\sqrt{1+x^2}}, \qquad \tan \alpha = x,$$

$$\csc \alpha = \frac{\sqrt{1+x^2}}{x}, \qquad \sec \alpha = \sqrt{1+x^2}, \qquad \cot \alpha = \frac{1}{x}.$$

6.3.5 FUNCTIONS OF NEGATIVE ARGUMENTS

$$\sin^{-1}(-z) = -\sin^{-1} z, \qquad\qquad \sec^{-1}(-z) = \pi - \sec^{-1} z,$$

$$\cos^{-1}(-z) = \pi - \cos^{-1} z, \qquad\quad\; \csc^{-1}(-z) = -\csc^{-1} z,$$

$$\tan^{-1}(-z) = -\tan^{-1} z, \qquad\quad\; \cot^{-1}(-z) = \pi - \cot^{-1} z.$$

6.3.6 RELATIONSHIP TO INVERSE HYPERBOLIC FUNCTIONS

$$\sin^{-1} z = -i \sinh^{-1}(iz), \qquad\qquad \sec^{-1} z = \pm i \operatorname{sech}^{-1}(iz),$$

$$\cos^{-1} z = \pm i \cosh^{-1}(iz), \qquad\qquad \csc^{-1} z = i \operatorname{csch}^{-1}(iz),$$

$$\tan^{-1} z = -i \tanh^{-1}(iz), \qquad\qquad \cot^{-1} z = i \coth^{-1}(iz).$$

6.3.7 SUM AND DIFFERENCE OF TWO INVERSE TRIGONOMETRIC FUNCTIONS

$$\sin^{-1} z_1 \pm \sin^{-1} z_2 = \sin^{-1}\left(z_1\sqrt{1 - z_2^2} \pm z_2\sqrt{1 - z_1^2} \right).$$

$$\cos^{-1} z_1 \pm \cos^{-1} z_2 = \cos^{-1}\left(z_1 z_2 \mp \sqrt{(1 - z_2^2)(1 - z_1^2)} \right).$$

$$\tan^{-1} z_1 \pm \tan^{-1} z_2 = \tan^{-1}\left(\frac{z_1 \pm z_2}{1 \mp z_1 z_2} \right).$$

$$\sin^{-1} z_1 \pm \cos^{-1} z_2 = \sin^{-1}\left(z_1 z_2 \pm \sqrt{(1 - z_1^2)(1 - z_2^2)} \right),$$

$$= \cos^{-1}\left(z_2\sqrt{1 - z_1^2} \mp z_1\sqrt{1 - z_2^2} \right).$$

$$\tan^{-1} z_1 \pm \cot^{-1} z_2 = \tan^{-1}\left(\frac{z_1 z_2 \pm 1}{z_2 \mp z_1} \right) = \cot^{-1}\left(\frac{z_2 \mp z_1}{z_1 z_2 \pm 1} \right).$$

6.4 SPHERICAL GEOMETRY AND TRIGONOMETRY

6.4.1 RIGHT SPHERICAL TRIANGLES

Let a, b, and c be the sides of a right spherical triangle with opposite angles A, B, and C, respectively, where each side is measured by the angle subtended at the center of the sphere. Assume that $C = \pi/2 = 90°$ (see Figure 6.4.3). Then,

$$\sin a = \tan b \cot B, \qquad\qquad \sin a = \sin A \sin c,$$
$$\sin b = \tan a \cot A, \qquad\qquad \sin b = \sin B \sin c,$$
$$\cos A = \tan b \cot c, \qquad\qquad \cos A = \cos a \sin B,$$
$$\cos B = \tan a \cot c, \qquad\qquad \cos B = \cos b \sin A,$$
$$\cos c = \cos A \cot B, \qquad\qquad \cos c = \cos a \cos b.$$

FIGURE 6.4.3
Right spherical triangle (left) and diagram for Napier's rule (right).

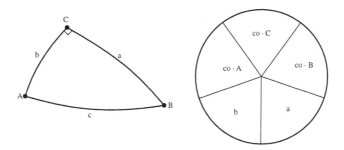

Napier's rules of circular parts

Arrange the five quantities a, b, co-A (complement of A), co-C, co-B of a right spherical triangle with right angle at C, in cyclic order as pictured in Figure 6.4.3. If any one of these quantities is designated a *middle part*, then two of the other parts are *adjacent* to it, and the remaining two parts are *opposite* to it. The formulae above for a right spherical triangle may be recalled by the following two rules:

1. The sine of any middle part is equal to the product of the *tangents* of the two *adjacent* parts.

2. The sine of any middle part is equal to the product of the *cosines* of the two *opposite* parts.

Rules for determining quadrant

1. A leg and the angle opposite to it are always of the same quadrant.

2. If the hypotenuse is less than 90°, the legs are of the same quadrant.

3. If the hypotenuse is greater than 90°, the legs are of unlike quadrants.

6.4.2 OBLIQUE SPHERICAL TRIANGLES

In the following:

- a, b, c represent the sides of any spherical triangle.

- A, B, C represent the corresponding opposite angles.

- a', b', c', A', B', C' are the corresponding parts of the polar triangle.

- $s = (a + b + c)/2$.

- $S = (A + B + C)/2$.

- Δ is the area of spherical triangle.

- E is the spherical excess of the triangle.

- R is the radius of the sphere upon which the triangle lies.

$$0° < a + b + c < 360°, \qquad 180° < A + B + C < 540°,$$
$$E = A + B + C - 180°, \qquad \Delta = \pi R^2 E / 180.$$
$$\tan \frac{1}{4} E = \sqrt{\tan \frac{s}{2} \tan \frac{1}{2}(s - a) \tan \frac{1}{2}(s - b) \tan \frac{1}{2}(s - c)}.$$

$$A = 180° - a', \qquad B = 180° - b', \qquad C = 180° - c',$$
$$a = 180° - A', \qquad b = 180° - B', \qquad c = 180° - C'.$$

Spherical law of sines

$$\frac{\sin a}{\sin A} = \frac{\sin b}{\sin B} = \frac{\sin c}{\sin C}.$$

Spherical law of cosines for sides

$$\cos a = \cos b \cos c + \sin b \sin c \cos A,$$
$$\cos b = \cos c \cos a + \sin c \sin a \cos B, \qquad (6.4.1)$$
$$\cos c = \cos a \cos b + \sin a \sin b \cos C.$$

Spherical law of cosines for angles

$$\cos A = -\cos B \cos C + \sin B \sin C \cos a,$$
$$\cos B = -\cos C \cos A + \sin C \sin A \cos b,$$
$$\cos C = -\cos A \cos B + \sin A \sin B \cos c.$$

Spherical law of tangents

$$\frac{\tan \frac{1}{2}(B-C)}{\tan \frac{1}{2}(B+C)} = \frac{\tan \frac{1}{2}(b-c)}{\tan \frac{1}{2}(b+c)},$$

$$\frac{\tan \frac{1}{2}(C-A)}{\tan \frac{1}{2}(C+A)} = \frac{\tan \frac{1}{2}(c-a)}{\tan \frac{1}{2}(c+a)}, \qquad (6.4.2)$$

$$\frac{\tan \frac{1}{2}(A-B)}{\tan \frac{1}{2}(A+B)} = \frac{\tan \frac{1}{2}(a-b)}{\tan \frac{1}{2}(a+b)}.$$

Spherical half angle formulae

Define $k^2 = (\tan r)^2 = \dfrac{\sin(s-a)\sin(s-b)\sin(s-c)}{\sin s}$. Then

$$\tan\left(\frac{A}{2}\right) = \frac{k}{\sin(s-a)},$$

$$\tan\left(\frac{B}{2}\right) = \frac{k}{\sin(s-b)}, \qquad (6.4.3)$$

$$\tan\left(\frac{C}{2}\right) = \frac{k}{\sin(s-c)}.$$

Spherical half side formulae

Define $K^2 = (\tan R)^2 = \dfrac{-\cos S}{\cos(S-A)\cos(S-B)\cos(S-C)}$. Then

$$\tan(a/2) = K \cos(S-A),$$
$$\tan(b/2) = K \cos(S-B), \qquad (6.4.4)$$
$$\tan(c/2) = K \cos(S-C).$$

Gauss's formulae

$$\frac{\sin \frac{1}{2}(a-b)}{\sin \frac{1}{2}c} = \frac{\sin \frac{1}{2}(A-B)}{\cos \frac{1}{2}C}, \qquad \frac{\cos \frac{1}{2}(a-b)}{\cos \frac{1}{2}c} = \frac{\sin \frac{1}{2}(A+B)}{\cos \frac{1}{2}C},$$

$$\frac{\sin \frac{1}{2}(a+b)}{\sin \frac{1}{2}c} = \frac{\cos \frac{1}{2}(A-B)}{\sin \frac{1}{2}C}, \qquad \frac{\cos \frac{1}{2}(a+b)}{\cos \frac{1}{2}c} = \frac{\cos \frac{1}{2}(A+B)}{\sin \frac{1}{2}C}.$$

Napier's analogs

$$\frac{\sin\frac{1}{2}(A-B)}{\sin\frac{1}{2}(A+B)} = \frac{\tan\frac{1}{2}(a-b)}{\tan\frac{1}{2}c}, \qquad \frac{\sin\frac{1}{2}(a-b)}{\sin\frac{1}{2}(a+b)} = \frac{\tan\frac{1}{2}(A-B)}{\cot\frac{1}{2}C},$$

$$\frac{\cos\frac{1}{2}(A-B)}{\cos\frac{1}{2}(A+B)} = \frac{\tan\frac{1}{2}(a+b)}{\tan\frac{1}{2}c}, \qquad \frac{\cos\frac{1}{2}(a-b)}{\cos\frac{1}{2}(a+b)} = \frac{\tan\frac{1}{2}(A+B)}{\cot\frac{1}{2}C}.$$

Haversine formulae

$$\text{hav } a = \text{hav}(b-c) + \sin b \sin c \,\text{hav } A.$$

$$\text{hav } A = \frac{\sin(s-b)\sin(s-c)}{\sin b \sin c},$$

$$= \frac{\text{hav } a - \text{hav}(b-c)}{\sin b \sin c}, \qquad (6.4.5)$$

$$= \text{hav}[180° - (B+C)] + \sin B \sin C \,\text{hav } a.$$

Rules for determining quadrant

1. If $A > B > C$, then $a > b > c$.
2. A side (angle) which differs by more than 90° from another side (angle) is in the same quadrant as its opposite angle (side).
3. Half the sum of any two sides and half the sum of the opposite angles are in the same quadrant.

Summary of solution of oblique spherical triangles

Given	Solution	Check
Three sides	Half-angle formulae	Law of sines
Three angles	Half-side formulae	Law of sines
Two sides and included angle	Napier's analogies (to find sum and difference of unknown angles); then law of sines (to find remaining side).	Gauss's formulae
Two angles and included side	Napier's analogies (to find sum and difference of unknown sides); then law of sines (to find remaining angle).	Gauss's formulae
Two sides and an opposite angle	Law of sines (to find an angle); then Napier's analogies (to find remaining angle and side). Note number of solutions.	Gauss's formulae
Two angles and an opposite side	Law of sines (to find a side); then Napier's analogies (to find remaining side and angle). Note number of solutions.	Gauss's formulae

6.4.3   TABLE OF TRIGONOMETRIC FUNCTIONS

x (radians)	$\sin x$	$\cos x$	$\tan x$	$\cot x$	$\sec x$	$\csc x$
0	0	1	0	$\pm\infty$	1	$\pm\infty$
0.1	0.0998	0.9950	0.1003	9.9666	1.0050	10.0167
0.2	0.1987	0.9801	0.2027	4.9332	1.0203	5.0335
0.3	0.2955	0.9553	0.3093	3.2327	1.0468	3.3839
0.4	0.3894	0.9211	0.4228	2.3652	1.0857	2.5679
0.5	0.4794	0.8776	0.5463	1.8305	1.1395	2.0858
0.6	0.5646	0.8253	0.6841	1.4617	1.2116	1.7710
0.7	0.6442	0.7648	0.8423	1.1872	1.3075	1.5523
0.8	0.7174	0.6967	1.0296	0.9712	1.4353	1.3940
0.9	0.7833	0.6216	1.2602	0.7936	1.6087	1.2766
1.0	0.8415	0.5403	1.5574	0.6421	1.8508	1.1884
1.1	0.8912	0.4536	1.9648	0.5090	2.2046	1.1221
1.2	0.9320	0.3624	2.5722	0.3888	2.7597	1.0729
1.3	0.9636	0.2675	3.6021	0.2776	3.7383	1.0378
1.4	0.9854	0.1700	5.7979	0.1725	5.8835	1.0148
1.5	0.9975	0.0707	14.1014	0.0709	14.1368	1.0025
$\pi/2$	1	0	$\pm\infty$	0	$\pm\infty$	1
1.6	0.9996	−0.0292	−34.2325	−0.0292	−34.2471	1.0004
1.7	0.9917	−0.1288	−7.6966	−0.1299	−7.7613	1.0084
1.8	0.9738	−0.2272	−4.2863	−0.2333	−4.4014	1.0269
1.9	0.9463	−0.3233	−2.9271	−0.3416	−3.0932	1.0567
2.0	0.9093	−0.4161	−2.1850	−0.4577	−2.4030	1.0998
2.1	0.8632	−0.5048	−1.7098	−0.5848	−1.9808	1.1585
2.2	0.8085	−0.5885	−1.3738	−0.7279	−1.6992	1.2369
2.3	0.7457	−0.6663	−1.1192	−0.8935	−1.5009	1.3410
2.4	0.6755	−0.7374	−0.9160	−1.0917	−1.3561	1.4805
2.5	0.5985	−0.8011	−0.7470	−1.3386	−1.2482	1.6709
2.6	0.5155	−0.8569	−0.6016	−1.6622	−1.1670	1.9399
2.7	0.4274	−0.9041	−0.4727	−2.1154	−1.1061	2.3398
2.8	0.3350	−0.9422	−0.3555	−2.8127	−1.0613	2.9852
2.9	0.2392	−0.9710	−0.2464	−4.0584	−1.0299	4.1797
3.0	0.1411	−0.9900	−0.1425	−7.0153	−1.0101	7.0862
3.1	0.0416	−0.9991	−0.0416	−24.0288	−1.0009	24.0496
π	0	−1	0	$\pm\infty$	−1	$\pm\infty$

6.5 EXPONENTIAL FUNCTION

6.5.1 EXPONENTIATION

For a any real number and m a positive integer, the exponential a^m is defined as

$$a^m = \underbrace{a \cdot a \cdot a \cdots a}_{m \text{ terms}}. \qquad (6.5.1)$$

The following three laws of exponents follow:

1. $a^n \cdot a^m = a^{m+n}$.

2. $\dfrac{a^m}{a^n} = \begin{cases} a^{m-n}, & \text{if } m > n, \\ 1, & \text{if } m = n, \\ \frac{1}{a^{n-m}}, & \text{if } m < n. \end{cases}$

3. $(a^m)^n = a^{(mn)}$.

The nth root function is defined as the inverse of the nth power function:

$$\text{If } b^n = a, \text{ then } b = \sqrt[n]{a} = a^{(1/n)}. \qquad (6.5.2)$$

If n is odd, there will be a unique real number satisfying the above definition of $\sqrt[n]{a}$, for any real value of a. If n is even, for positive values of a there will be two real values for $\sqrt[n]{a}$, one positive and one negative. By convention, the symbol $\sqrt[n]{a}$ means the positive value. If n is even and a is negative, then there are no real values for $\sqrt[n]{a}$.

To extend the definition to include a^t (for t not necessarily an integer), so as to maintain the laws of exponents, the following definitions are required (where we now restrict a to be positive, p to be an odd number, and q to be an even number):

$$a^0 = 1 \qquad a^{p/q} = \sqrt[q]{a^p} \qquad a^{-t} = \frac{1}{a^t}$$

With these restrictions, the second law of exponents can be written as $\dfrac{a^m}{a^n} = a^{m-n}$.

If $a > 1$, then the function a^x is monotone increasing while, if $0 < a < 1$ then the function a^x is monotone decreasing.

6.5.2 DEFINITION OF e^z

$$\exp(z) = e^z = \lim_{m \to \infty} \left(1 + \frac{z}{m}\right)^m$$

$$= 1 + z + \frac{z^2}{2!} + \frac{z^3}{3!} + \frac{z^4}{4!} + \cdots.$$

If $z = x + iy$, then $e^z = e^x e^{iy} = e^x(\cos y + i \sin y)$.

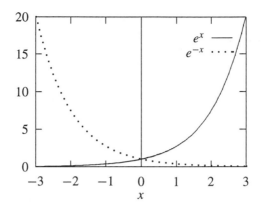

6.5.3   DERIVATIVE AND INTEGRAL OF e^x

The derivative of e^x is e^x. The integral of e^x is e^x.

6.5.4   CIRCULAR FUNCTIONS IN TERMS OF EXPONENTIALS

$$\cos z = \frac{e^{iz} + e^{-iz}}{2}, \qquad\qquad e^{iz} = \cos z + i \sin z.$$

$$\sin z = \frac{e^{iz} - e^{-iz}}{2i}, \qquad\qquad e^{-iz} = \cos z - i \sin z.$$

6.6   LOGARITHMIC FUNCTIONS

6.6.1   DEFINITION OF THE NATURAL LOG

The natural logarithm (also known as the Napierian logarithm) of z is written as $\ln z$ or as $\log_e z$. It is sometimes written $\log z$ (this is also used to represent a "generic" logarithm, a logarithm to any base). One definition is

$$\ln z = \int_1^z \frac{dt}{t},$$

where the integration path from 1 to z does not cross the origin or the negative real axis.

For complex values of z the natural logarithm, as defined above, can be represented in terms of its magnitude and phase. If $z = x + iy = re^{i\theta}$, then $\ln z = \ln r + i\theta$, where $r = \sqrt{x^2 + y^2}$, $x = r\cos\theta$, and $y = r\sin\theta$.

6.6.2 SPECIAL VALUES

$$\ln 0 = -\infty, \qquad\qquad \ln 1 = 0, \qquad\qquad \ln e = 1,$$

$$\ln(-1) = i\pi + 2\pi ik, \qquad \ln(\pm i) = \pm\frac{i\pi}{2} + 2\pi ik,$$

(e is given numerically on page 14).

6.6.3 LOGARITHMS TO A BASE OTHER THAN e

The logarithmic function to the base a, written $\log_a$, is defined as

$$\log_a z = \frac{\log_b z}{\log_b a} = \frac{\ln z}{\ln a}$$

Note the properties:

- $\log_a a^p = p.$

- $\log_a b = \dfrac{1}{\log_b a}.$

- $\log_{10} z = \dfrac{\ln z}{\ln 10} = (\log_{10} e)\ln z \approx (0.4342944819\ldots)\ln z.$

- $\ln z = (\ln 10)\log_{10} z \approx (2.3025850929\ldots)\log_{10} z.$

6.6.4 RELATIONSHIP OF THE LOGARITHM TO THE EXPONENTIAL

For real values of z the logarithm is a monotonic function, as is the exponential. Any monotonic function has a single-valued inverse function; the natural logarithm is the inverse of the exponential. If $x = e^y$, then $y = \ln x$, and $x = e^{\ln x}$. The same inverse relations exist for bases other than e. For example, if $u = a^w$, then $w = \log_a u$, and $u = a^{\log_a u}$.

6.6.5   IDENTITIES

$$\log_a z_1 z_2 = \log_a z_1 + \log_a z_2, \qquad \text{for } (-\pi < \arg z_1 + \arg z_2 < \pi).$$

$$\log_a \frac{z_1}{z_2} = \log_a z_1 - \log_a z_2, \qquad \text{for } (-\pi < \arg z_1 - \arg z_2 < \pi).$$

$$\log_a z^n = n \log_a z, \qquad \text{for } (-\pi < n \arg z < \pi), \text{ when } n \text{ is an integer.}$$

6.6.6   SERIES EXPANSIONS FOR THE NATURAL LOGARITHM

$$\ln(1+z) = z - \frac{1}{2}z^2 + \frac{1}{3}z^3 - \dots, \qquad \text{for } |z| < 1.$$

$$\ln z = \left(\frac{z-1}{z}\right) + \frac{1}{2}\left(\frac{z-1}{z}\right)^2 + \frac{1}{3}\left(\frac{z-1}{z}\right)^3 + \dots, \qquad \text{for } \operatorname{Re} z \geq \frac{1}{2}.$$

6.6.7   DERIVATIVE AND INTEGRATION FORMULAE

$$\frac{d\ln z}{dz} = \frac{1}{z}, \qquad \int \frac{dz}{z} = \ln z, \qquad \int \ln z \, dz = z \ln z - z.$$

6.7   HYPERBOLIC FUNCTIONS

6.7.1   DEFINITIONS OF THE HYPERBOLIC FUNCTIONS

$$\sinh z = \frac{e^z - e^{-z}}{2}, \qquad \operatorname{csch} z = \frac{1}{\sinh z},$$

$$\cosh z = \frac{e^z + e^{-z}}{2}, \qquad \operatorname{sech} z = \frac{1}{\cosh z},$$

$$\tanh z = \frac{e^z - e^{-z}}{e^z + e^{-z}} = \frac{\sinh z}{\cosh z}, \qquad \coth z = \frac{1}{\tanh z}.$$

The curve $y = \cosh x$ is called a *catenary*.

When $z = x + iy$,

$$\sinh z = \sinh x \cos y + i \cosh x \sin y,$$

$$\cosh z = \cosh x \cos y + i \sinh x \sin y,$$

$$\tanh z = \frac{\sinh 2x + i \sin 2y}{\cosh 2x + \cos 2y},$$

$$\coth z = \frac{\sinh 2x - i \sin 2y}{\cosh 2x - \cos 2y}.$$

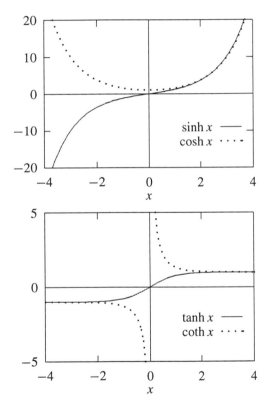

6.7.2   RANGE OF VALUES

Function	Domain (interval of u)	Range (interval of function)	Remarks
$\sinh u$	$(-\infty, +\infty)$	$(-\infty, +\infty)$	
$\cosh u$	$(-\infty, +\infty)$	$[1, +\infty)$	
$\tanh u$	$(-\infty, +\infty)$	$(-1, +1)$	
$\operatorname{csch} u$	$(-\infty, 0)$	$(0, -\infty)$	Two branches,
	$(0, +\infty)$	$(+\infty, 0)$	pole at $u = 0$.
$\operatorname{sech} u$	$(-\infty, +\infty)$	$(0, 1]$	
$\coth u$	$(-\infty, 0)$	$(-1, -\infty)$	Two branches,
	$(0, +\infty)$	$(+\infty, 1)$	pole at $u = 0$.

6.7.3   SERIES EXPANSIONS

$$\cosh z = 1 + \frac{z^2}{2!} + \frac{z^4}{4!} + \frac{z^6}{6!} + \dots, \qquad |z| < \infty.$$

$$\sinh z = z + \frac{z^3}{3!} + \frac{z^5}{5!} + \frac{z^7}{7!} + \dots, \qquad |z| < \infty.$$

$$\tanh z = z - \frac{z^3}{3} + \frac{2z^5}{15} + \dots, \qquad |z| < \frac{\pi}{2}.$$

6.7.4   SYMMETRY RELATIONSHIPS

$$\cosh(-z) = +\cosh z, \qquad \sinh(-z) = -\sinh z, \qquad \tanh(-z) = -\tanh z.$$

6.7.5   INTERRELATIONSHIPS AMONG THE HYPERBOLIC FUNCTIONS

$$e^z = \cosh z + \sinh z, \qquad e^{-z} = \cosh z - \sinh z,$$

$$(\cosh z)^2 - (\sinh z)^2 = (\tanh z)^2 + (\operatorname{sech} z)^2 = (\coth z)^2 - (\operatorname{csch} z)^2 = 1.$$

6.7.6   RELATIONSHIP TO CIRCULAR FUNCTIONS

$$\cosh z = \cos iz, \qquad \sinh z = -i \sin iz, \qquad \tanh z = -i \tan iz.$$

6.7.7 HYPERBOLIC FUNCTIONS IN TERMS OF ONE ANOTHER

Function	$\sinh x$	$\cosh x$	$\tanh x$
$\sinh x =$	$\sinh x$	$\pm\sqrt{(\cosh x)^2 - 1}$	$\dfrac{\tanh x}{\sqrt{1 - (\tanh x)^2}}$
$\cosh x =$	$\sqrt{1 + (\sinh x)^2}$	$\cosh x$	$\dfrac{1}{\sqrt{1 - (\tanh x)^2}}$
$\tanh x =$	$\dfrac{\sinh x}{\sqrt{1 + (\sinh x)^2}}$	$\pm\dfrac{\sqrt{(\cosh x)^2 - 1}}{\cosh x}$	$\tanh x$
$\operatorname{csch} x =$	$\dfrac{1}{\sinh x}$	$\pm\dfrac{1}{\sqrt{(\cosh x)^2 - 1}}$	$\dfrac{\sqrt{1 - (\tanh x)^2}}{\tanh x}$
$\operatorname{sech} x =$	$\dfrac{1}{\sqrt{1 + (\sinh x)^2}}$	$\dfrac{1}{\cosh x}$	$\sqrt{1 - (\tanh x)^2}$
$\coth x =$	$\dfrac{\sqrt{1 + (\sinh x)^2}}{\sinh x}$	$\pm\dfrac{\cosh x}{\sqrt{(\cosh x)^2 - 1}}$	$\dfrac{1}{\tanh x}$

Function	$\operatorname{csch} x$	$\operatorname{sech} x$	$\coth x$
$\sinh x =$	$\dfrac{1}{\operatorname{csch} x}$	$\pm\dfrac{\sqrt{1 - (\operatorname{sech} x)^2}}{\operatorname{sech} x}$	$\pm\dfrac{1}{\sqrt{(\coth x)^2 - 1}}$
$\cosh x =$	$\pm\dfrac{\sqrt{(\operatorname{csch} x)^2 + 1}}{\operatorname{csch} x}$	$\dfrac{1}{\operatorname{sech} x}$	$\pm\dfrac{\coth x}{\sqrt{(\coth x)^2 - 1}}$
$\tanh x =$	$\dfrac{1}{\sqrt{(\operatorname{csch} x)^2 + 1}}$	$\pm\sqrt{1 - (\operatorname{sech} x)^2}$	$\dfrac{1}{\coth x}$
$\operatorname{csch} x =$	$\operatorname{csch} x$	$\pm\dfrac{\operatorname{sech} x}{\sqrt{1 - (\operatorname{sech} x)^2}}$	$\pm\sqrt{(\coth x)^2 - 1}$
$\operatorname{sech} x =$	$\pm\dfrac{\operatorname{csch} x}{\sqrt{(\operatorname{csch} x)^2 + 1}}$	$\operatorname{sech} x$	$\pm\dfrac{\sqrt{(\coth x)^2 - 1}}{\coth x}$
$\coth x =$	$\sqrt{(\operatorname{csch} x)^2 + 1}$	$\pm\dfrac{1}{\sqrt{1 - (\operatorname{sech} x)^2}}$	$\coth x$

6.7.8 SUM AND DIFFERENCE FORMULAE

$$\cosh(z_1 \pm z_2) = \cosh z_1 \cosh z_2 \pm \sinh z_1 \sinh z_2,$$
$$\sinh(z_1 \pm z_2) = \sinh z_1 \cosh z_2 \pm \cosh z_1 \sinh z_2,$$
$$\tanh(z_1 \pm z_2) = \frac{\tanh z_1 \pm \tanh z_2}{1 \pm \tanh z_1 \tanh z_2} = \frac{\sinh 2z_1 \pm \sinh 2z_2}{\cosh 2z_1 \pm \cosh 2z_2},$$
$$\coth(z_1 \pm z_2) = \frac{1 \pm \coth z_1 \coth z_2}{\coth z_1 \pm \coth z_2} = \frac{\sinh 2z_1 \mp \sinh 2z_2}{\cosh 2z_1 - \cosh 2z_2}. \qquad (6.7.1)$$

6.7.9   MULTIPLE ARGUMENT RELATIONS

$$\sinh 2\alpha = 2 \sinh \alpha \cosh \alpha = \frac{2 \tanh \alpha}{1 - \tanh^2 \alpha}.$$

$$\sinh 3\alpha = +3 \sinh \alpha + 4 \sinh^3 \alpha = \sinh \alpha (4 \cosh^2 \alpha - 1).$$

$$\sinh 4\alpha = 4 \sinh^3 \alpha \cosh \alpha + 4 \cosh^3 \alpha \sinh \alpha.$$

$$\cosh 2\alpha = \cosh^2 \alpha + \sinh^2 \alpha = 2 \cosh^2 \alpha - 1,$$

$$= 1 + 2 \sinh^2 \alpha = \frac{1 + \tanh^2 \alpha}{1 - \tanh^2 \alpha}.$$

$$\cosh 3\alpha = -3 \cosh \alpha + 4 \cosh^3 \alpha = \cosh \alpha (4 \sinh^2 \alpha + 1).$$

$$\cosh 4\alpha = \cosh^4 \alpha + 6 \sinh^2 \alpha \cosh^2 \alpha + 6 \sinh^4 \alpha.$$

$$\tanh 2\alpha = \frac{2 \tanh \alpha}{1 + \tanh^2 \alpha}.$$

$$\tanh 3\alpha = \frac{3 \tanh \alpha + \tanh^3 \alpha}{1 + 3 \tanh^2 \alpha}.$$

$$\coth 2\alpha = \frac{1 + \coth^2 \alpha}{2 \coth \alpha}.$$

$$\coth 3\alpha = \frac{3 \coth \alpha + \coth^3 \alpha}{1 + 3 \coth^2 \alpha}.$$

6.7.10   SUMS OF FUNCTIONS

$$\sinh u \pm \sinh w = 2 \sinh \frac{u \pm w}{2} \cosh \frac{u \mp w}{2},$$

$$\cosh u + \cosh w = 2 \cosh \frac{u + w}{2} \cosh \frac{u - w}{2},$$

$$\cosh u - \cosh w = 2 \sinh \frac{u + w}{2} \sinh \frac{u - w}{2},$$

$$\tanh u \pm \tanh w = \frac{\sinh u \pm w}{\cosh u \cosh w},$$

$$\coth u \pm \coth w = \frac{\sinh u \pm w}{\sinh u \sinh w}.$$

6.7.11   PRODUCTS OF FUNCTIONS

$$\sinh u \sinh w = \frac{1}{2} \left(\cosh(u + w) - \cosh(u - w) \right),$$

$$\sinh u \cosh w = \frac{1}{2} \left(\sinh(u + w) + \sinh(u - w) \right),$$

$$\cosh u \cosh w = \frac{1}{2} \left(\cosh(u + w) + \cosh(u - w) \right).$$

6.7.12 HALF-ARGUMENT FORMULAE

$$\sinh \frac{z}{2} = \pm \sqrt{\frac{\cosh z - 1}{2}},$$

$$\cosh \frac{z}{2} = +\sqrt{\frac{\cosh z + 1}{2}},$$

$$\tanh \frac{z}{2} = \pm \sqrt{\frac{\cosh z - 1}{\cosh z + 1}} = \frac{\sinh z}{\cosh z + 1},$$

$$\coth \frac{z}{2} = \pm \sqrt{\frac{\cosh z + 1}{\cosh z - 1}} = \frac{\sinh z}{\cosh z - 1}.$$

6.7.13 DIFFERENTIATION FORMULAE

$$\frac{d\sinh z}{dz} = \cosh z, \qquad\qquad \frac{d\cosh z}{dz} = \sinh z,$$

$$\frac{d\tanh z}{dz} = (\operatorname{sech} z)^2, \qquad\qquad \frac{d\operatorname{csch} z}{dz} = -\operatorname{csch} z \coth z,$$

$$\frac{d\operatorname{sech} z}{dz} = -\operatorname{sech} z \tanh z, \qquad\qquad \frac{d\coth z}{dz} = -(\operatorname{csch} z)^2.$$

6.8 INVERSE HYPERBOLIC FUNCTIONS

When $z = x + iy$,

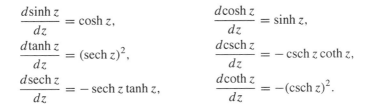

$$\cosh^{-1} z = \int_0^z \frac{dt}{\sqrt{t^2 - 1}}, \qquad \sinh^{-1} z = \int_0^z \frac{dt}{\sqrt{1 + t^2}}, \qquad \tanh^{-1} z = \int_0^z \frac{dt}{1 - t^2}.$$

6.8.1 RANGE OF VALUES

Function	Domain	Range	Remarks
$\sinh^{-1} u$	$(-\infty, +\infty)$	$(-\infty, +\infty)$	Odd function
$\cosh^{-1} u$	$[1, +\infty)$	$(-\infty, +\infty)$	Even function, double valued
$\tanh^{-1} u$	$(-1, +1)$	$(-\infty, +\infty)$	Odd function
$\operatorname{csch}^{-1} u$	$(-\infty, 0), (0, \infty)$	$(0, -\infty), (\infty, 0)$	Odd function, two branches, Pole at $u = 0$
$\operatorname{sech}^{-1} u$	$(0, 1]$	$(-\infty, +\infty)$	Double valued
$\coth^{-1} u$	$(-\infty, -1), (1, \infty)$	$(-\infty, 0), (\infty, 0)$	Odd function, two branches

6.8.2 RELATIONSHIPS AMONG INVERSE HYPERBOLIC FUNCTIONS

Function	$\sinh^{-1} x$	$\cosh^{-1} x$	$\tanh^{-1} x$
$\sinh^{-1} x =$	$\sinh^{-1} x$	$\pm \cosh^{-1} \sqrt{x^2 + 1}$	$\tanh^{-1} \dfrac{x}{\sqrt{1 + x^2}}$
$\cosh^{-1} x =$	$\pm \sinh^{-1} \sqrt{x^2 - 1}$	$\cosh^{-1} x$	$\pm \tanh^{-1} \dfrac{\sqrt{x^2 - 1}}{x}$
$\tanh^{-1} x =$	$\sinh^{-1} \dfrac{x}{\sqrt{1 - x^2}}$	$\pm \cosh^{-1} \dfrac{1}{\sqrt{1 - x^2}}$	$\tanh^{-1} x$
$\operatorname{csch}^{-1} x =$	$\sinh^{-1} \dfrac{1}{x}$	$\pm \cosh^{-1} \dfrac{\sqrt{1 + x^2}}{x}$	$\tanh^{-1} \dfrac{1}{\sqrt{1 + x^2}}$
$\operatorname{sech}^{-1} x =$	$\pm \sinh^{-1} \dfrac{\sqrt{1 - x^2}}{x}$	$\cosh^{-1} \dfrac{1}{x}$	$\pm \tanh^{-1} \sqrt{1 - x^2}$
$\coth^{-1} x =$	$\sinh^{-1} \dfrac{1}{\sqrt{x^2 - 1}}$	$\pm \cosh^{-1} \dfrac{x}{\sqrt{x^2 - 1}}$	$\tanh^{-1} \dfrac{1}{x}$

Function	$\operatorname{csch}^{-1} x$	$\operatorname{sech}^{-1} x$	$\coth^{-1} x$
$\sinh^{-1} x =$	$\operatorname{csch}^{-1} \dfrac{1}{x}$	$\pm \operatorname{sech}^{-1} \dfrac{1}{\sqrt{1 + x^2}}$	$\coth^{-1} \dfrac{\sqrt{1 + x^2}}{x}$
$\cosh^{-1} x =$	$\pm \operatorname{csch}^{-1} \dfrac{1}{\sqrt{x^2 - 1}}$	$\operatorname{sech}^{-1} \dfrac{1}{x}$	$\pm \coth^{-1} \dfrac{x}{\sqrt{x^2 - 1}}$
$\tanh^{-1} x =$	$\operatorname{csch}^{-1} \dfrac{\sqrt{1 - x^2}}{x}$	$\pm \operatorname{sech}^{-1} \sqrt{1 - x^2}$	$\coth^{-1} \dfrac{1}{x}$
$\operatorname{csch}^{-1} x =$	$\operatorname{csch}^{-1} x$	$\pm \operatorname{sech}^{-1} \dfrac{x}{\sqrt{1 + x^2}}$	$\coth^{-1} \sqrt{1 + x^2}$
$\operatorname{sech}^{-1} x =$	$\pm \operatorname{csch}^{-1} \dfrac{x}{\sqrt{1 - x^2}}$	$\operatorname{sech}^{-1} x$	$\pm \coth^{-1} \dfrac{1}{\sqrt{1 - x^2}}$
$\coth^{-1} x =$	$\operatorname{csch}^{-1} \sqrt{x^2 - 1}$	$\operatorname{sech}^{-1} \dfrac{\sqrt{x^2 - 1}}{x}$	$\coth^{-1} x$

6.8.3 RELATIONSHIPS WITH LOGARITHMIC FUNCTIONS

$$\sinh^{-1} x = \log\left(x + \sqrt{x^2 + 1}\right), \qquad \operatorname{csch}^{-1} x = \log\left(\frac{1 \pm \sqrt{1 + x^2}}{x}\right),$$

$$\cosh^{-1} x = \log\left(x \pm \sqrt{x^2 - 1}\right), \qquad \operatorname{sech}^{-1} x = \log\left(\frac{1 \pm \sqrt{1 - x^2}}{x}\right),$$

$$\tanh^{-1} x = \frac{1}{2}\log\left(\frac{1 + x}{1 - x}\right), \qquad \coth^{-1} x = \frac{1}{2}\log\left(\frac{x + 1}{x - 1}\right).$$

6.8.4 RELATIONSHIPS WITH CIRCULAR FUNCTIONS

$$\sinh^{-1} x = -i\,\sin^{-1} ix, \qquad\qquad \sinh^{-1} ix = +i\,\sin^{-1} x,$$

$$\cosh^{-1} x = \pm i\,\cos^{-1} ix, \qquad\qquad \cosh^{-1} ix = \pm i\,\cos^{-1} ix,$$

$$\tanh^{-1} x = -i\,\tan^{-1} ix, \qquad\qquad \tanh^{-1} ix = +i\,\tan^{-1} x,$$

$$\operatorname{csch}^{-1} x = +i\,\csc^{-1} ix, \qquad\qquad \operatorname{csch}^{-1} ix = -i\,\csc^{-1} x,$$

$$\operatorname{sech}^{-1} x = \pm i\,\sec^{-1} ix, \qquad\qquad \operatorname{sech}^{-1} ix = \pm i\,\sec^{-1} ix,$$

$$\coth^{-1} x = +i\,\cot^{-1} ix, \qquad\qquad \coth^{-1} ix = -i\,\cot^{-1} x.$$

6.8.5 SUM AND DIFFERENCE OF FUNCTIONS

$$\sinh^{-1} x \pm \sinh^{-1} y = \sinh^{-1} x\sqrt{1 + y^2} \pm y\sqrt{1 + x^2},$$

$$\cosh^{-1} x \pm \cosh^{-1} y = \cosh^{-1} xy \pm \sqrt{(y^2 - 1)(x^2 - 1)},$$

$$\tanh^{-1} x \pm \tanh^{-1} y = \tanh^{-1} \frac{x \pm y}{xy \pm 1},$$

$$\sinh^{-1} x \pm \cosh^{-1} y = \sinh^{-1} xy \pm \sqrt{(1 + x^2)(y^2 - 1)},$$

$$= \cosh^{-1} y\sqrt{1 + x^2} \pm x\sqrt{y^2 - 1},$$

$$\tanh^{-1} x \pm \coth^{-1} y = \tanh^{-1}\left(\frac{xy \pm 1}{y \pm x}\right),$$

$$= \coth^{-1}\left(\frac{y \pm x}{xy \pm 1}\right).$$

6.9 GUDERMANNIAN FUNCTION

This function relates circular and hyperbolic functions without the use of functions of imaginary argument. The Gudermannian is a monotonic odd function which is asymptotic to $\mp\frac{\pi}{2}$ at $x = \mp\infty$. It is zero at the origin.

$$\text{gd}\, x = \text{ the Gudermannian of } x$$

$$= \int_0^x \frac{dt}{\cosh t} = 2\tan^{-1}\left(\tanh\frac{x}{2}\right) = 2\tan^{-1} e^x - \frac{\pi}{2}.$$

$$\text{gd}^{-1}\, x = \text{ the inverse Gudermannian of } x$$

$$= \int_0^x \frac{dt}{\cos t} = \log\left[\tan\left(\frac{\pi}{4} + \frac{x}{2}\right)\right] = \log\left(\sec x + \tan x\right).$$

If $\text{gd}(x + iy) = \alpha + i\beta$, then

$$\tan\alpha = \frac{\sinh x}{\cos y}, \qquad\qquad \tanh\beta = \frac{\sin y}{\cosh x},$$

$$\tanh x = \frac{\sin\alpha}{\cosh\beta}, \qquad\qquad \tan y = \frac{\sin\beta}{\cosh\alpha}.$$

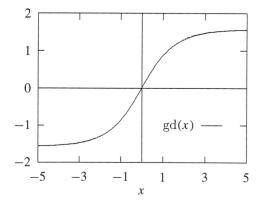

6.9.1   FUNDAMENTAL IDENTITIES

$$\tanh\left(\frac{x}{2}\right) = \tan\left(\frac{\text{gd}\,x}{2}\right),$$

$$e^x = \cosh x + \sinh x = \sec \text{gd}\,x + \tan \text{gd}\,x,$$

$$= \tan\left(\frac{\pi}{4} + \frac{\text{gd}\,x}{2}\right) = \frac{1 + \sin(\text{gd}\,x)}{\cos(\text{gd}\,x)},$$

$$i\,\text{gd}^{-1}\,x = \text{gd}^{-1}(ix), \quad \text{where } i = \sqrt{-1}.$$

6.9.2   DERIVATIVES OF GUDERMANNIAN

$$\frac{d(\text{gd}\,x)}{dx} = \text{sech}\,x \qquad \frac{d(\text{gd}^{-1}\,x)}{dx} = \sec x.$$

6.9.3   RELATIONSHIP TO HYPERBOLIC AND CIRCULAR FUNCTIONS

$$\sinh x = \tan(\text{gd}\,x), \qquad \qquad \text{csch}\,x = \cot(\text{gd}\,x),$$
$$\cosh x = \sec(\text{gd}\,x), \qquad \qquad \text{sech}\,x = \cos(\text{gd}\,x),$$
$$\tanh x = \sin(\text{gd}\,x), \qquad \qquad \coth x = \text{cosec}(\text{gd}\,x).$$

x	e^x	$\log x$	$\text{gd}\,x$	$\sinh x$	$\cosh x$	$\tanh x$
0	1	$-\infty$	0	0	1	0
0.1	1.1052	-2.3026	0.0998	0.1002	1.0050	0.0997
0.2	1.2214	-1.6094	0.1987	0.2013	1.0201	0.1974
0.3	1.3499	-1.2040	0.2956	0.3045	1.0453	0.2913
0.4	1.4918	-0.9163	0.3897	0.4108	1.0811	0.3799
0.5	1.6487	-0.6931	0.4804	0.5211	1.1276	0.4621

x	e^x	$\log x$	$\operatorname{gd} x$	$\sinh x$	$\cosh x$	$\tanh x$
0.6	1.8221	−0.5108	0.5669	0.6367	1.1855	0.5370
0.7	2.0138	−0.3567	0.6490	0.7586	1.2552	0.6044
0.8	2.2255	−0.2231	0.7262	0.8881	1.3374	0.6640
0.9	2.4596	−0.1054	0.7985	1.0265	1.4331	0.7163
1.0	2.7183	−0.0000	0.8658	1.1752	1.5431	0.7616
1.1	3.0042	0.0953	0.9281	1.3356	1.6685	0.8005
1.2	3.3201	0.1823	0.9857	1.5095	1.8107	0.8337
1.3	3.6693	0.2624	1.0387	1.6984	1.9709	0.8617
1.4	4.0552	0.3365	1.0872	1.9043	2.1509	0.8854
1.5	4.4817	0.4055	1.1317	2.1293	2.3524	0.9051
1.6	4.9530	0.4700	1.1724	2.3756	2.5775	0.9217
1.7	5.4739	0.5306	1.2094	2.6456	2.8283	0.9354
1.8	6.0496	0.5878	1.2432	2.9422	3.1075	0.9468
1.9	6.6859	0.6419	1.2739	3.2682	3.4177	0.9562
2.0	7.3891	0.6931	1.3018	3.6269	3.7622	0.9640
2.1	8.1662	0.7419	1.3271	4.0219	4.1443	0.9705
2.2	9.0250	0.7885	1.3501	4.4571	4.5679	0.9757
2.3	9.9742	0.8329	1.3709	4.9370	5.0372	0.9801
2.4	11.0232	0.8755	1.3899	5.4662	5.5569	0.9837
2.5	12.1825	0.9163	1.4070	6.0502	6.1323	0.9866
2.6	13.4637	0.9555	1.4225	6.6947	6.7690	0.9890
2.7	14.8797	0.9933	1.4366	7.4063	7.4735	0.9910
2.8	16.4446	1.0296	1.4493	8.1919	8.2527	0.9926
2.9	18.1741	1.0647	1.4609	9.0596	9.1146	0.9940
3.0	20.0855	1.0986	1.4713	10.0179	10.0677	0.9951
3.1	22.1980	1.1314	1.4808	11.0765	11.1215	0.9959
3.2	24.5325	1.1632	1.4893	12.2459	12.2866	0.9967
3.3	27.1126	1.1939	1.4971	13.5379	13.5748	0.9973
3.4	29.9641	1.2238	1.5041	14.9654	14.9987	0.9978
3.5	33.1155	1.2528	1.5104	16.5426	16.5728	0.9982
3.6	36.5982	1.2809	1.5162	18.2855	18.3128	0.9985
3.7	40.4473	1.3083	1.5214	20.2113	20.2360	0.9988
3.8	44.7012	1.3350	1.5261	22.3394	22.3618	0.9990
3.9	49.4024	1.3610	1.5303	24.6911	24.7113	0.9992
4.0	54.5982	1.3863	1.5342	27.2899	27.3082	0.9993

6.10 ORTHOGONAL POLYNOMIALS

6.10.1 HERMITE POLYNOMIALS

Symbol: $H_n(x)$.

Interval: $[-\infty, \infty]$.

Differential Equation: $y'' - 2xy' + 2ny = 0$.

Explicit Expression: $H_n(x) = \displaystyle\sum_{m=0}^{\lfloor n/2 \rfloor} \frac{(-1)^m n! (2x)^{n-2m}}{m!(n-2m)!}$.

Recurrence Relation: $H_{n+1}(x) = 2x H_n(x) - 2n H_{n-1}(x)$.

Weight: e^{-x^2}.

Standardization: $H_n(x) = 2^n x^n + \dots$.

Norm: $\displaystyle\int_{-\infty}^{\infty} e^{-x^2} [H_n(x)]^2 \, dx = 2^n n! \sqrt{\pi}$.

Rodrigues' Formula: $H_n(x) = (-1)^n e^{x^2} \dfrac{d^n}{dx^n}(e^{-x^2})$.

Generating Function: $\displaystyle\sum_{n=0}^{\infty} H_n(x) \frac{z^n}{n!} = e^{-z^2 + 2zx}$.

Inequality: $|H_n(x)| < \sqrt{2^n e^{x^2} n!}$.

6.10.2 JACOBI POLYNOMIALS

Symbol: $P_n^{(\alpha,\beta)}(x)$.

Interval: $[-1, 1]$.

Differential Equation:
$(1 - x^2)y'' + [\beta - \alpha - (\alpha + \beta + 2)x]y' + n(n + \alpha + \beta + 1)y = 0$.

Explicit Expression:

$$P_n^{(\alpha,\beta)}(x) = \frac{1}{2^n} \sum_{m=0}^{n} \binom{n+\alpha}{m}\binom{n+\beta}{n-m}(x-1)^{n-m}(x+1)^m.$$

Recurrence Relation: $2(n+1)(n+\alpha+\beta+1)(2n+\alpha+\beta)P_{n+1}^{(\alpha,\beta)}(x) = (2n+\alpha+\beta+1)[(\alpha^2-\beta^2)+(2n+\alpha+\beta+2)(2n+\alpha+\beta)x]P_n^{(\alpha,\beta)}(x) - 2(n+\alpha)(n+\beta)(2n+\alpha+\beta+2)P_{n-1}^{(\alpha,\beta)}(x)$.

Weight: $(1-x)^\alpha (1+x)^\beta$.

Standardization: $P_n^{(\alpha,\beta)}(1) = \dbinom{n+\alpha}{n}$.

Norm: $\displaystyle\int_{-1}^{1} (1-x)^\alpha (1+x)^\beta \left[P_n^{(\alpha,\beta)}(x)\right]^2 dx = \frac{2^{\alpha+\beta+1}\Gamma(n+\alpha+1)\Gamma(n+\beta+1)}{(2n+\alpha+\beta+1)n!\Gamma(n+\alpha+\beta+1)}$.

Rodrigues' Formula:

$$P_n^{(\alpha,\beta)}(x) = \frac{(-1)^n}{2^n n!(1-x)^\alpha(1+x)^\beta}\frac{d^n}{dx^n}\left[(1-x)^{n+\alpha}(1+x)^{n+\beta}\right].$$

Generating Function: $\displaystyle\sum_{n=0}^{\infty} P_n^{(\alpha,\beta)}(x)z^n = 2^{\alpha+\beta}R^{-1}(1-z+R)^{-\alpha}(1+z+R)^{-\beta}$,

where $R = \sqrt{1-2xz+z^2}$ and $|z| < 1$.

Inequality: $\displaystyle\max_{-1\leq x\leq 1}\left|P_n^{(\alpha,\beta)}(x)\right| = \begin{cases} \binom{n+q}{n} \sim n^q, & \text{if } q = \max(\alpha,\beta) \geq -\frac{1}{2}, \\ \left|P_n^{(\alpha,\beta)}(x')\right| \sim n^{-1/2}, & \text{if } q = \max(\alpha,\beta) < -\frac{1}{2}, \end{cases}$

where $\alpha, \beta > 1$ and x' (in the second result) is one of the two maximum points nearest $(\beta-\alpha)/(\alpha+\beta+1)$.

6.10.3   LAGUERRE POLYNOMIALS

Symbol: $L_n(x)$.
Interval: $[0, \infty]$.

$L_n(x)$ is the same as $L_n^{(0)}(x)$ (see the generalized Laguerre polynomials).

6.10.4   GENERALIZED LAGUERRE POLYNOMIALS

Symbol: $L_n^{(\alpha)}(x)$.
Interval: $[0, \infty]$.
Differential Equation: $xy'' + (\alpha+1-x)y' + ny = 0$.
Explicit Expression: $\displaystyle L_n^{(\alpha)}(x) = \sum_{m=0}^{n}\frac{(-1)^m}{m!}\binom{n+\alpha}{n-m}x^m$.

Recurrence Relation:
$$(n+1)L_{n+1}^{(\alpha)}(x) = [(2n+\alpha+1)-x]L_n^{(\alpha)}(x) - (n+\alpha)L_{n-1}^{(\alpha)}(x).$$

Weight: $x^\alpha e^{-x}$.

Standardization: $\displaystyle L_n^{(\alpha)}(x) = \frac{(-1)^n}{n!}x^n + \dots$.

Norm: $\displaystyle\int_0^\infty x^\alpha e^{-x}\left[L_n^{(\alpha)}(x)\right]^2 dx = \frac{\Gamma(n+\alpha+1)}{n!}$.

Rodrigues' Formula: $\displaystyle L_n^{(\alpha)}(x) = \frac{1}{n!x^\alpha e^{-x}}\frac{d^n}{dx^n}[x^{n+\alpha}e^{-x}]$.

Generating Function: $\displaystyle\sum_{n=0}^{\infty} L_n^{(\alpha)}(x)z^n = (1-z)^{-\alpha-1}\exp\left(\frac{xz}{z-1}\right)$.

Inequality: $\displaystyle\left|L_n^{(\alpha)}(x)\right| \leq \begin{cases} \frac{\Gamma(n+\alpha+1)}{n!\Gamma(\alpha+1)}e^{x/2}, & \text{if } x \geq 0 \text{ and } \alpha > 0, \\ \left[2 - \frac{\Gamma(n+\alpha+1)}{n!\Gamma(\alpha+1)}\right]e^{x/2}, & \text{if } x \geq 0 \text{ and } -1 < \alpha < 0, \end{cases}$

Note that $\displaystyle L_n^{(m)}(x) = (-1)^m\frac{d^m}{dx^m}\left[L_{n+m}(x)\right]$.

6.10.5   LEGENDRE POLYNOMIALS

Symbol: $P_n(x)$.
Interval: $[-1, 1]$.
Differential Equation: $(1 - x^2)y'' - 2xy' + n(n+1)y = 0$.
Explicit Expression: $P_n(x) = \dfrac{1}{2^n} \displaystyle\sum_{m=0}^{\lfloor n/2 \rfloor} (-1)^m \binom{n}{m}\binom{2n-2m}{n} x^{n-2m}$.
Recurrence Relation: $(n+1)P_{n+1}(x) = (2n+1)x P_n(x) - n P_{n-1}(x)$.
Weight: 1.
Standardization: $P_n(1) = 1$.
Norm: $\displaystyle\int_{-1}^{1} [P_n(x)]^2 \, dx = \dfrac{2}{2n+1}$.
Rodrigues' Formula: $P_n(x) = \dfrac{(-1)^n}{2^n n!} \dfrac{d^n}{dx^n}[(1-x^2)^n]$.
Generating Function: $\displaystyle\sum_{n=0}^{\infty} P_n(x)z^n = (1 - 2xz + z^2)^{-1/2}$, and $-1 < x < 1, |z| < 1$.
Inequality: $|P_n(x)| \leq 1$ for $-1 \leq x \leq 1$.

The Legendre polynomials satisfy $\displaystyle\int_{-1}^{1} P_n(x) P_m(x) \, dx = \dfrac{2}{2m+1}\delta_{nm}$.
The Legendre series representation is

$$f(x) = \sum_{n=0}^{\infty} A_n P_n(x), \qquad A_n = \frac{2n+1}{2} \int_{-1}^{1} f(x) P_n(x) \, dx.$$
$$\tag{6.10.1}$$

The associated Legendre functions $P_\ell^m(x)$ are

$$P_\ell^m(x) = (-1)^m (1 - x^2)^{m/2} \frac{d^m}{dx^m} P_\ell(x),$$
$$= \frac{(-1)^m}{2^\ell \ell!}(1 - x^2)^{m/2} \frac{d^{\ell+m}}{dx^{\ell+m}}(x^2 - 1)^\ell.$$
$$\tag{6.10.2}$$

6.10.6   TSCHEBYSHEFF POLYNOMIALS, FIRST KIND

Symbol: $T_n(x)$.
Interval: $[-1, 1]$.
Differential Equation: $(1 - x^2)y'' - xy' + n^2 y = 0$.
Explicit Expression: $T_n(x) = \cos\left(n \cos^{-1} x\right)$,
$$= \frac{n}{2}\sum_{m=0}^{\lfloor n/2 \rfloor}(-1)^m \frac{(n-m-1)!}{m!(n-2m)!}(2x)^{n-2m}.$$
Recurrence Relation: $T_{n+1}(x) = 2x T_n(x) - T_{n-1}(x)$.
Weight: $(1 - x^2)^{-1/2}$.
Standardization: $T_n(1) = 1$.

$$Norm: \int_{-1}^{1} (1 - x^2)^{-1/2} [T_n(x)]^2 \, dx = \begin{cases} \pi, & n = 0, \\ \pi/2, & n \neq 0. \end{cases}$$

$$Rodrigues'\ Formula:\ T_n(x) = \frac{\sqrt{\pi(1 - x^2)}}{(-2)^n \Gamma(n + \frac{1}{2})} \frac{d^n}{dx^n} \left[(1 - x^2)^{n-1/2} \right].$$

$$Generating\ Function:\ \sum_{n=0}^{\infty} T_n(x)z^n = \frac{1 - xz}{1 - 2xz + z^2}, \text{ for } -1 < x < 1 \text{ and } |z| < 1.$$

Inequality: $|T_n(x)| \leq 1$, for $-1 \leq x \leq 1$.

Note that $T_n(x) = \frac{n!\sqrt{\pi}}{\Gamma(n+\frac{1}{2})} P_n^{(-1/2,-1/2)}(x)$.

6.10.7 TSCHEBYSHEFF POLYNOMIALS, SECOND KIND

Symbol: $U_n(x)$.

Interval: $[-1, 1]$.

Differential Equation: $(1 - x^2)y'' - 3xy' + n(n + 2)y = 0$.

$$Explicit\ Expression:\ U_n(x) = \sum_{m=0}^{\lfloor n/2 \rfloor} \frac{(-1)^m (m - n)!}{m!(n - 2m)!} (2x)^{n-2m}$$

$$U_n(\cos\theta) = \frac{\sin[(n + 1)\theta]}{\sin\theta}.$$

Recurrence Relation: $U_{n+1}(x) = 2xU_n(x) - U_{n-1}(x)$.

Weight: $(1 - x^2)^{1/2}$.

Standardization: $U_n(1) = n + 1$.

$$Norm: \int_{-1}^{1} (1 - x^2)^{1/2} [U_n(x)]^2 \, dx = \frac{\pi}{2}.$$

$$Rodrigues'\ Formula:\ U_n(x) = \frac{(-1)^n (n + 1)\sqrt{\pi}}{(1 - x^2)^{1/2} 2^{n+1} \Gamma(n + \frac{3}{2})} \frac{d^n}{dx^n} [(1 - x^2)^{n+(1/2)}].$$

$$Generating\ Function:\ \sum_{n=0}^{\infty} U_n(x)z^n = \frac{1}{1 - 2xz + z^2}, \text{ for } -1 < x < 1 \text{ and } |z| < 1.$$

Inequality: $|U_n(x)| \leq n + 1$, for $-1 \leq x \leq 1$.

Note that $U_n(x) = \frac{(n+1)!\sqrt{\pi}}{2\Gamma(n+\frac{3}{2})} P_n^{(1/2,1/2)}(x)$.

6.10.8   TABLES OF ORTHOGONAL POLYNOMIALS

$H_0 = 1$
$H_1 = 2x$
$H_2 = 4x^2 - 2$
$H_3 = 8x^3 - 12x$
$H_4 = 16x^4 - 48x^2 + 12$
$H_5 = 32x^5 - 160x^3 + 120x$
$H_6 = 64x^6 - 480x^4 + 720x^2 - 120$
$H_7 = 128x^7 - 1344x^5 + 3360x^3 - 1680x$
$H_8 = 256x^8 - 3584x^6 + 13440x^4 - 13440x^2 + 1680$
$H_9 = 512x^9 - 9216x^7 + 48384x^5 - 80640x^3 + 30240x$
$H_{10} = 1024x^{10} - 23040x^8 + 161280x^6 - 403200x^4 + 302400x^2 - 30240$

$x^{10} = (30240H_0 + 75600H_2 + 25200H_4 + 2520H_6 + 90H_8 + H_{10})/1024$
$x^9 = (15120H_1 + 10080H_3 + 1512H_5 + 72H_7 + H_9)/512$
$x^8 = (1680H_0 + 3360H_2 + 840H_4 + 56H_6 + H_8)/256$
$x^7 = (840H_1 + 420H_3 + 42H_5 + H_7)/128$
$x^6 = (120H_0 + 180H_2 + 30H_4 + H_6)/64$
$x^5 = (60H_1 + 20H_3 + H_5)/32$
$x^4 = (12H_0 + 12H_2 + H_4)/16$
$x^3 = (6H_1 + H_3)/8$
$x^2 = (2H_0 + H_2)/4$
$x = (H_1)/2$
$1 = H_0$

$L_0 = 1$
$L_1 = -x + 1$
$L_2 = (x^2 - 4x + 2)/2$
$L_3 = (-x^3 + 9x^2 - 18x + 6)/6$
$L_4 = (x^4 - 16x^3 + 72x^2 - 96x + 24)/24$
$L_5 = (-x^5 + 25x^4 - 200x^3 + 600x^2 - 600x + 120)/120$
$L_6 = (x^6 - 36x^5 + 450x^4 - 2400x^3 + 5400x^2 - 4320x + 720)/720$

$x^6 = 720L_0 - 4320L_1 + 10800L_2 - 14400L_3 + 10800L_4 - 4320L_5 + 720L_6$
$x^5 = 120L_0 - 600L_1 + 1200L_2 - 1200L_3 + 600L_4 - 120L_5$
$x^4 = 24L_0 - 96L_1 + 144L_2 - 96L_3 + 24L_4$
$x^3 = 6L_0 - 18L_1 + 18L_2 - 6L_3$
$x^2 = 2L_0 - 4L_1 + 2L_2$
$x = L_0 - L_1$
$1 = L_0$

$P_0 = 1$
$P_1 = x$
$P_2 = (3x^2 - 1)/2$
$P_3 = (5x^3 - 3x)/2$
$P_4 = (35x^4 - 30x^2 + 3)/8$
$P_5 = (63x^5 - 70x^3 + 15x)/8$
$P_6 = (231x^6 - 315x^4 + 105x^2 - 5)/16$
$P_7 = (429x^7 - 693x^5 + 315x^3 - 35x)/16$
$P_8 = (6435x^8 - 12012x^6 + 6930x^4 - 1260x^2 + 35)/128$
$P_9 = (12155x^9 - 25740x^7 + 18018x^5 - 4620x^3 + 315x)/128$
$P_{10} = (46189x^{10} - 109395x^8 + 90090x^6 - 30030x^4 + 3465x^2 - 63)/256$

$x^{10} = (4199P_0 + 16150P_2 + 15504P_4 + 7904P_6 + 2176P_8 + 256P_{10})/46189$
$x^9 = (3315P_1 + 4760P_3 + 2992P_5 + 960P_7 + 128P_9)/12155$
$x^8 = (715P_0 + 2600P_2 + 2160P_4 + 832P_6 + 128P_8)/6435$
$x^7 = (143P_1 + 182P_3 + 88P_5 + 16P_7)/429$
$x^6 = (33P_0 + 110P_2 + 72P_4 + 16P_6)/231$
$x^5 = (27P_1 + 28P_3 + 8P_5)/63$
$x^4 = (7P_0 + 20P_2 + 8P_4)/35$
$x^3 = (3P_1 + 2P_3)/5$
$x^2 = (P_0 + 2P_2)/3$
$x = P_1$
$1 = P_0$

$T_0 = 1$
$T_1 = x$
$T_2 = 2x^2 - 1$
$T_3 = 4x^3 - 3x$
$T_4 = 8x^4 - 8x^2 + 1$
$T_5 = 16x^5 - 20x^3 + 5x$
$T_6 = 32x^6 - 48x^4 + 18x^2 - 1$
$T_7 = 64x^7 - 112x^5 + 56x^3 - 7x$
$T_8 = 128x^8 - 256x^6 + 160x^4 - 32x^2 + 1$
$T_9 = 256x^9 - 576x^7 + 432x^5 - 120x^3 + 9x$
$T_{10} = 512x^{10} - 1280x^8 + 1120x^6 - 400x^4 + 50x^2 - 1$

$x^{10} = (126T_0 + 210T_2 + 120T_4 + 45T_6 + 10T_8 + T_{10})/512$
$x^9 = (126T_1 + 84T_3 + 36T_5 + 9T_7 + T_9)/256$
$x^8 = (35T_0 + 56T_2 + 28T_4 + 8T_6 + T_8)/128$
$x^7 = (35T_1 + 21T_3 + 7T_5 + T_7)/64$
$x^6 = (10T_0 + 15T_2 + 6T_4 + T_6)/32$
$x^5 = (10T_1 + 5T_3 + T_5)/16$
$x^4 = (3T_0 + 4T_2 + T_4)/8$
$x^3 = (3T_1 + T_3)/4$
$x^2 = (T_0 + T_2)/2$
$x = T_1$
$1 = T_0$

$U_0 = 1$
$U_1 = 2x$
$U_2 = 4x^2 - 1$
$U_3 = 8x^3 - 4x$
$U_4 = 16x^4 - 12x^2 + 1$
$U_5 = 32x^5 - 32x^3 + 6x$
$U_6 = 64x^6 - 80x^4 + 24x^2 - 1$
$U_7 = 128x^7 - 192x^5 + 80x^3 - 8x$
$U_8 = 256x^8 - 448x^6 + 240x^4 - 40x^2 + 1$
$U_9 = 512x^9 - 1024x^7 + 672x^5 - 160x^3 + 10x$
$U_{10} = 1024x^{10} - 2304x^8 + 1792x^6 - 560x^4 + 60x^2 - 1$

$x^{10} = (42U_0 + 90U_2 + 75U_4 + 35U_6 + 9U_8 + U_{10})/1024$
$x^9 = (42U_1 + 48U_3 + 27U_5 + 8U_7 + U_9)/512$
$x^8 = (14U_0 + 28U_2 + 20U_4 + 7U_6 + U_8)/256$
$x^7 = (14U_1 + 14U_3 + 6U_5 + U_7)/128$
$x^6 = (5U_0 + 9U_2 + 5U_4 + U_6)/64$
$x^5 = (5U_1 + 4U_3 + U_5)/32$
$x^4 = (2U_0 + 3U_2 + U_4)/16$
$x^3 = (2U_1 + U_3)/8$
$x^2 = (U_0 + U_2)/4$
$x = (U_1)/2$
$1 = U_0$

6.10.9   TABLE OF JACOBI POLYNOMIALS

Notation: $(m)_n = m(m+1)\ldots(m+n-1)$.

$P_0^{(\alpha,\beta)}(x) = 1.$

$P_1^{(\alpha,\beta)}(x) = \dfrac{1}{2}\Big(2(\alpha+1) + (\alpha+\beta+2)(x-1)\Big).$

$P_2^{(\alpha,\beta)}(x) = \dfrac{1}{8}\Big(4(\alpha+1)_2 + 4(\alpha+\beta+3)(\alpha+2)(x-1) + (\alpha+\beta+3)_2(x-1)^2\Big).$

$P_3^{(\alpha,\beta)}(x) = \dfrac{1}{48}\Big(8(\alpha+1)_3 + 12(\alpha+\beta+4)(\alpha+2)_2(x-1)$

$\qquad\qquad + 6(\alpha+\beta+4)_2(\alpha+3)(x-1)^2 + (\alpha+\beta+4)_3(x-1)^3\Big).$

$P_4^{(\alpha,\beta)}(x) = \dfrac{1}{384}\Big(16(\alpha+1)_4 + 32(\alpha+\beta+5)(\alpha+2)_3(x-1)$

$\qquad\qquad + 24(\alpha+\beta+5)_2(\alpha+3)_2(x-1)^2 + 8(\alpha+\beta+5)_3(\alpha+4)(x-1)^3$

$\qquad\qquad + (\alpha+\beta+5)_4(x-1)^4\Big).$

6.10.10   SPHERICAL HARMONICS

The spherical harmonics are defined by

$$Y_{lm}(\theta,\phi) = \sqrt{\frac{2l+1}{4\pi}\frac{(l-m)!}{(l+m)!}}\, P_l^m(\cos\theta)e^{im\phi}. \tag{6.10.3}$$

They satisfy

$$Y_{l,-m}(\theta,\phi) = (-1)^m Y_{l,m}^*(\theta,\phi), \tag{6.10.4}$$

$$Y_{l0}(\theta,\phi) = \sqrt{\frac{2l+1}{4\pi}}\, P_l(\cos\theta), \tag{6.10.5}$$

$$Y_{lm}\left(\frac{\pi}{2},\phi\right) = \begin{cases} \sqrt{\dfrac{(2l+1)(l-m)!(l+m)!}{4\pi}}\,\dfrac{(-1)^{(l+m)/2}e^{im\phi}}{2^l(\frac{l-m}{2})!(\frac{l+m}{2})!}, & \frac{l+m}{2}\ \text{integral}, \\ 0, & \frac{l+m}{2}\ \text{not integral}. \end{cases} \tag{6.10.6}$$

The normalization and orthogonality conditions are

$$\int_0^{2\pi} d\phi \int_0^\pi \sin\theta\, d\theta\, Y_{l'm'}^*(\theta,\phi)Y_{lm}(\theta,\phi) = \delta_{ll'}\delta_{mm'}, \tag{6.10.7}$$

and

$$\int_0^{2\pi} d\phi \int_0^\pi \sin\theta\, d\theta\, Y_{l_1 m_1}^*(\theta,\phi)Y_{l_2 m_2}(\theta,\phi)Y_{l_3 m_3}(\theta,\phi),$$

$$= \sqrt{\frac{(2l_2+1)(2l_3+1)}{4\pi(2l_1+1)}}\begin{pmatrix} l_1 & l_3 & l_1 \\ m_2 & m_3 & m_1 \end{pmatrix}\begin{pmatrix} l_1 & l_3 & l_1 \\ 0 & 0 & 0 \end{pmatrix}, \tag{6.10.8}$$

where the terms on the right hand side are Clebsch–Gordan coefficients (see page 527).
Because of the (distributional) completeness relation,

$$\sum_{l=0}^{\infty} \sum_{m=-l}^{l} Y_{lm}(\theta, \phi) Y_{lm}^{*}(\theta', \phi') = \delta(\phi - \phi')\delta(\cos\theta - \cos\theta'),$$

(6.10.9)

an arbitrary function $g(\theta, \phi)$ can be expanded in spherical harmonics as

$$g(\theta, \phi) = \sum_{l=0}^{\infty} \sum_{m=-l}^{l} A_{lm} Y_{lm}(\theta, \phi), \qquad A_{lm} = \int Y_{lm}^{*}(\theta, \phi) g(\theta, \phi)\, d\Omega.$$

(6.10.10)

In spherical coordinates,

$$\nabla^2 [f(r)Y_{lm}(\theta, \phi)] = \left[\frac{1}{r^2} \frac{d}{dr}\left(r^2 \frac{df}{dr} \right) - l(l+1)\frac{f(r)}{r^2} \right] Y_{lm}(\theta, \phi).$$

(6.10.11)

6.10.11 TABLE OF SPHERICAL HARMONICS

$$l = 0 \qquad Y_{00} = \frac{1}{\sqrt{4\pi}}.$$

$$l = 1 \quad \begin{cases} Y_{11} = -\sqrt{\dfrac{3}{8\pi}}\, \sin\theta\, e^{i\phi}, \\[2mm] Y_{10} = \sqrt{\dfrac{3}{4\pi}}\, \cos\theta. \end{cases}$$

$$l = 2 \quad \begin{cases} Y_{22} = \dfrac{1}{4}\sqrt{\dfrac{15}{2\pi}}\, \sin^2\theta\, e^{2i\phi}, \\[2mm] Y_{21} = -\sqrt{\dfrac{15}{8\pi}}\, \sin\theta\cos\theta\, e^{i\phi}, \\[2mm] Y_{20} = \dfrac{1}{2}\sqrt{\dfrac{5}{4\pi}}(3\cos^2\theta - 1). \end{cases}$$

$$l = 3 \quad \begin{cases} Y_{33} = -\dfrac{1}{4}\sqrt{\dfrac{105}{4\pi}}\, \sin^3\theta\, e^{3i\phi}, \\[2mm] Y_{32} = \dfrac{1}{4}\sqrt{\dfrac{105}{2\pi}}\, \sin^2\theta\cos\theta\, e^{2i\phi}, \\[2mm] Y_{31} = -\dfrac{1}{4}\sqrt{\dfrac{21}{4\pi}}\, \sin\theta(5\cos^2\theta - 1)\, e^{i\phi}, \\[2mm] Y_{30} = \dfrac{1}{2}\sqrt{\dfrac{7}{4\pi}}(5\cos^3\theta - 3\cos\theta). \end{cases}$$

6.11   GAMMA FUNCTION

$$\Gamma(z) = \int_0^\infty t^{z-1} e^{-t}\, dt, \quad z = x + iy, \quad x > 0.$$

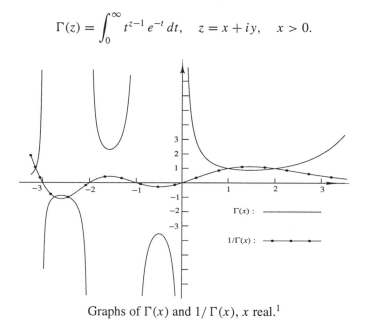

Graphs of $\Gamma(x)$ and $1/\Gamma(x)$, x real.[1]

6.11.1   RECURSION FORMULA

$$\Gamma(z + 1) = z\,\Gamma(z).$$

The relation $\Gamma(z) = \Gamma(z + 1)/z$ can be used to define the gamma function in the left half plane, $z \neq 0, -1, -2, \ldots$.

6.11.2   SINGULAR POINTS

The gamma function has simple poles at $z = -n$, (for $n = 0, 1, 2, \ldots$), with the respective residues $(-1)^n/n!$; that is,

$$\lim_{z \to -n} (z + n)\Gamma(z) = \frac{(-1)^n}{n!}.$$

[1] From Temme, N.M., *Special Functions: An Introduction to the Classical Functions of Mathematical Physics*, John Wiley & Sons, New York, 1996. With permission.

6.11.3   SPECIAL VALUES

$$\Gamma(n+1) = n! \quad \text{if } n = 0, 1, 2, \ldots, \text{ where } 0! = 1,$$

$$\Gamma(1) = 1, \quad \Gamma(2) = 1, \quad \Gamma(3) = 2, \quad \Gamma(\tfrac{1}{2}) = \sqrt{\pi},$$

$$\Gamma(m + \tfrac{1}{2}) = \frac{1 \cdot 3 \cdot 5 \cdots (2m-1)}{2^m} \sqrt{\pi}, \quad m = 1, 2, 3, \ldots ,$$

$$\Gamma(-m + \tfrac{1}{2}) = \frac{(-1)^m 2^m}{1 \cdot 3 \cdot 5 \cdots (2m-1)} \sqrt{\pi}, \quad m = 1, 2, 3, \ldots .$$

$$\Gamma(\tfrac{1}{4}) = 3.62560\,99082, \qquad \Gamma(\tfrac{1}{3}) = 2.67893\,85347,$$

$$\Gamma(\tfrac{1}{2}) = \sqrt{\pi} = 1.77245\,38509, \qquad \Gamma(\tfrac{2}{3}) = 1.35411\,79394,$$

$$\Gamma(\tfrac{3}{4}) = 1.22541\,67024, \qquad \Gamma(\tfrac{3}{2}) = \sqrt{\pi}/2 = 0.88622\,69254.$$

6.11.4   DEFINITION BY PRODUCTS

$$\Gamma(z) = \lim_{n \to \infty} \frac{n!\,n^z}{z(z+1)\cdots(z+n)},$$

$$\frac{1}{\Gamma(z)} = z\,e^{\gamma z} \prod_{n=1}^{\infty} \left[(1 + z/n)\,e^{-z/n} \right], \quad \gamma \text{ is Euler's constant.}$$

6.11.5   OTHER INTEGRALS

$$\Gamma(z)\,\cos \tfrac{1}{2}\pi z = \int_0^{\infty} t^{z-1} \cos t\,dt, \quad 0 < \operatorname{Re} z < 1,$$

$$\Gamma(z)\,\sin \tfrac{1}{2}\pi z = \int_0^{\infty} t^{z-1} \sin t\,dt, \quad -1 < \operatorname{Re} z < 1.$$

6.11.6   PROPERTIES

$$\Gamma'(1) = \int_0^{\infty} \ln t\, e^{-t}\,dt = -\gamma.$$

Multiplication formula:

$$\Gamma(2z) = \pi^{-1/2}\, 2^{2z-1}\, \Gamma(z)\, \Gamma(z + 1/2).$$

Reflection formulas:

$$\Gamma(z)\,\Gamma(1-z) = \frac{\pi}{\sin \pi z},$$

$$\Gamma(\tfrac{1}{2}+z)\,\Gamma(\tfrac{1}{2}-z) = \frac{\pi}{\cos \pi z},$$

$$\Gamma(z-n) = (-1)^n \Gamma(z)\frac{\Gamma(1-z)}{\Gamma(n+1-z)} = \frac{(-1)^n \pi}{\sin \pi z\, \Gamma(n+1-z)}.$$

6.11.7 ASYMPTOTIC EXPANSION

For $z \to \infty$, $|\arg z| < \pi$:

$$\Gamma(z) \sim \sqrt{2\pi/z}\, z^z\, e^{-z}\left[1 + \frac{1}{12\,z} + \frac{1}{288\,z^2} - \frac{139}{51\,840\,z^3} + \cdots\right].$$

$$\ln \Gamma(z) \sim \ln\!\left(\sqrt{2\pi/z}\,z^z e^{-z}\right) + \sum_{n=1}^{\infty} \frac{B_{2n}}{2n\,(2n-1)}\frac{1}{z^{2n-1}},$$

$$\sim \ln\!\left(\sqrt{2\pi/z}\,z^z e^{-z}\right) + \frac{1}{12z} - \frac{1}{360z^3} + \frac{1}{1\,260z^5} - \frac{1}{1\,680z^7} + \cdots,$$

where B_n are the Bernoulli numbers. If we let $z = n$ a large positive integer, then a useful approximation for $n!$ is given by Stirling's formula,

$$n! \sim \sqrt{2\pi n}\, n^n\, e^{-n}, \quad n \to \infty.$$

6.11.8 LOGARITHMIC DERIVATIVE

Logarithmic derivative of the gamma function

$$\psi(z) = \frac{d}{dz}\ln \Gamma(z) = -\gamma + \sum_{n=0}^{\infty}\left(\frac{1}{n+1} - \frac{1}{z+n}\right), \quad z \neq 0, -1, -2, \ldots.$$

6.11.9 SPECIAL VALUES

$$\psi(1) = -\gamma, \quad \psi(\tfrac{1}{2}) = -\gamma - 2\ln 2.$$

6.11.10 ASYMPTOTIC EXPANSION

For $z \to \infty$, $|\arg z| < \pi$:

$$\psi(z) \sim \ln z - \frac{1}{2z} - \sum_{n=1}^{\infty}\frac{B_{2n}}{2nz^{2n}},$$

$$\sim \ln z - \frac{1}{2\,z} - \frac{1}{12\,z^2} + \frac{1}{120\,z^4} - \frac{1}{252\,z^6} + \cdots.$$

6.11.11   NUMERICAL VALUES

x	$\Gamma(x)$	$\ln\Gamma(x)$	$\psi(x)$	$\psi'(x)$
1.00	1.00000000	0.00000000	−0.57721566	1.64493407
1.04	0.97843820	−0.02179765	−0.51327488	1.55371164
1.08	0.95972531	−0.04110817	−0.45279934	1.47145216
1.12	0.94359019	−0.05806333	−0.39545533	1.39695222
1.16	0.92980307	−0.07278247	−0.34095315	1.32920818
1.20	0.91816874	−0.08537409	−0.28903990	1.26737721
1.24	0.90852106	−0.09593721	−0.23949368	1.21074707
1.28	0.90071848	−0.10456253	−0.19211890	1.15871230
1.32	0.89464046	−0.11133336	−0.14674236	1.11075532
1.36	0.89018453	−0.11632650	−0.10321006	1.06643142
1.40	0.88726382	−0.11961291	−0.06138454	1.02535659
1.44	0.88580506	−0.12125837	−0.02114267	0.98719773
1.48	0.88574696	−0.12132396	0.01762627	0.95166466
1.52	0.88703878	−0.11986657	0.05502211	0.91850353
1.56	0.88963920	−0.11693929	0.09113519	0.88749142
1.60	0.89351535	−0.11259177	0.12604745	0.85843189
1.64	0.89864203	−0.10687051	0.15983345	0.83115118
1.68	0.90500103	−0.09981920	0.19256120	0.80549511
1.72	0.91258058	−0.09147889	0.22429289	0.78132645
1.76	0.92137488	−0.08188828	0.25508551	0.75852269
1.80	0.93138377	−0.07108387	0.28499143	0.73697414
1.84	0.94261236	−0.05910015	0.31405886	0.71658233
1.88	0.95507085	−0.04596975	0.34233226	0.69725865
1.92	0.96877431	−0.03172361	0.36985272	0.67892313
1.96	0.98374254	−0.01639106	0.39665832	0.66150345
2.00	1.00000000	0.00000000	0.42278434	0.64493407

6.12   BETA FUNCTION

$$B(p,q) = \int_0^1 t^{p-1}(1-t)^{q-1}\,dt, \quad \mathrm{Re}\,p > 0, \quad \mathrm{Re}\,q > 0.$$

6.12.1   RELATION WITH GAMMA FUNCTION

$$B(p, q) = \frac{\Gamma(p)\,\Gamma(q)}{\Gamma(p+q)}.$$

6.12.2   PROPERTIES

$$B(p, q) = B(q, p),$$

$$B(p, q + 1) = \frac{q}{p}\, B(p + 1, q) = \frac{q}{p+q}\, B(p, q),$$

$$B(p, q)\, B(p + q, r) = \frac{\Gamma(p)\,\Gamma(q)\,\Gamma(r)}{\Gamma(p+q+r)}.$$

6.12.3   OTHER INTEGRALS

(In all cases Re $p > 0$, Re $q > 0$.)

$$
\begin{aligned}
B(p, q) &= 2\int_0^{\pi/2} \sin^{2p-1}\theta \, \cos^{2q-1}\theta \, d\theta, \\
&= \int_0^{\infty} \frac{t^{p-1}}{(t+1)^{p+q}}\, dt, \\
&= \int_0^{\infty} e^{-pt}\left(1 - e^{-t}\right)^{q-1} dt, \\
&= r^q (r+1)^p \int_0^1 \frac{t^{p-1}(1-t)^{q-1}}{(r+t)^{p+q}}\, dt, \quad r > 0.
\end{aligned}
$$

6.13   ERROR FUNCTIONS AND FRESNEL INTEGRALS

$$
\begin{aligned}
\operatorname{erf} x &= \frac{2}{\sqrt{\pi}} \int_0^x e^{-t^2}\, dt, \\
\operatorname{erfc} x &= \frac{2}{\sqrt{\pi}} \int_x^{\infty} e^{-t^2}\, dt.
\end{aligned}
$$

The function erfc x is known as the complementary error function.

6.13.1   SERIES EXPANSIONS

$$\operatorname{erf} x \;=\; \frac{2}{\sqrt{\pi}} \sum_{n=0}^{\infty} \frac{(-1)^n \, x^{2n+1}}{(2n+1)\,n!} = \frac{2}{\sqrt{\pi}} \left(x - \frac{x^3}{3} + \frac{1}{2!}\frac{x^5}{5} - \frac{1}{3!}\frac{x^7}{7} + \cdots \right),$$

$$= \frac{2}{\sqrt{\pi}} \sum_{n=0}^{\infty} \frac{\Gamma(3/2)\, e^{-x^2}}{\Gamma(n + 3/2)}\, x^{2n+1} = \frac{2}{\sqrt{\pi}}\, e^{-x^2} \left(x + \frac{2}{3} x^3 + \frac{4}{15} x^5 \cdots \right).$$

6.13.2   PROPERTIES

$$\operatorname{erf} x + \operatorname{erfc} x = 1, \qquad \operatorname{erf}(-x) = -\operatorname{erf} x, \qquad \operatorname{erfc}(-x) = 2 - \operatorname{erfc} x.$$

6.13.3   RELATIONSHIP WITH NORMAL PROBABILITY FUNCTION

$$\int_0^x f(t)\, dt = \tfrac{1}{2} \operatorname{erf}\,(x/\sqrt{2}), \qquad f(t) = \frac{1}{\sqrt{2\pi}}\, e^{-\frac{1}{2} t^2}.$$

6.13.4   SPECIAL VALUES

$$\operatorname{erf}(\pm\infty) = \pm 1, \quad \operatorname{erfc}(-\infty) = 2, \quad \operatorname{erfc} \infty = 0,$$

$$\operatorname{erf} x_0 = \operatorname{erfc} x_0 = \tfrac{1}{2} \quad \text{if} \quad x_0 = 0.476936\ldots.$$

6.13.5   ASYMPTOTIC EXPANSION

For $z \to \infty$, $|\arg z| < \frac{3}{4}\pi$,

$$\operatorname{erfc} z \;\sim\; \frac{2}{\sqrt{\pi}} \frac{e^{-z^2}}{2z} \sum_{n=0}^{\infty} \frac{(-1)^n\,(2n)!}{n!(2z)^{2n}},$$

$$\sim\; \frac{2}{\sqrt{\pi}} \frac{e^{-z^2}}{2z} \left(1 - \frac{1}{2\,z^2} + \frac{6}{4\,z^4} - \frac{15}{8\,z^6} + \cdots \right).$$

6.13.6 OTHER FUNCTIONS

Plasma dispersion function

$$
\begin{aligned}
w(z) &= e^{-z^2}\operatorname{erfc}(-iz), \\
&= \frac{1}{\pi i}\int_{-\infty}^{\infty}\frac{e^{-t^2}}{t-z}\,dt, \quad \operatorname{Im} z > 0, \\
&= 2\,e^{-z^2} - w(-z), \\
&= \sum_{n=0}^{\infty}\frac{(iz)^n}{\Gamma(n/2+1)}.
\end{aligned}
$$

Dawson's integral

$$
F(x) = e^{-x^2}\int_0^x e^{t^2}\,dt = -\tfrac{1}{2}i\sqrt{\pi}\,e^{-x^2}\,\operatorname{erf} ix.
$$

Fresnel integrals

$$
C(z) = \sqrt{\frac{2}{\pi}}\int_0^z \cos t^2\,dt, \quad S(z) = \sqrt{\frac{2}{\pi}}\int_0^z \sin t^2\,dt.
$$

Relations

$$
C(z) + iS(z) = \frac{1+i}{2}\,\operatorname{erf}\frac{(1-i)z}{\sqrt{2}}.
$$

Limits

$$
\lim_{z\to\infty} C(z) = \tfrac{1}{2}, \quad \lim_{z\to\infty} S(z) = \tfrac{1}{2}.
$$

Representations

$$C(z) = \tfrac{1}{2} + f(z)\,\sin(z^2) - g(z)\,\cos(z^2),$$
$$S(z) = \tfrac{1}{2} - f(z)\,\cos(z^2) - g(z)\,\sin(z^2),$$

where

$$f(z) = \frac{1}{\pi\sqrt{2}} \int_0^\infty \frac{e^{-z^2 t}}{\sqrt{t}(t^2+1)}\,dt, \quad g(z) = \frac{1}{\pi\sqrt{2}} \int_0^\infty \frac{\sqrt{t}\,e^{-z^2 t}}{(t^2+1)}\,dt.$$

And for $z \to \infty$, $|\arg z| < \tfrac{1}{2}\pi$,

$$f(z) \sim \frac{1}{\pi\sqrt{2}} \sum_{n=0}^\infty (-1)^n \frac{\Gamma(2n+1/2)}{z^{2n+1/2}}$$

$$\sim \frac{1}{\sqrt{2\pi z}}\left[1 - \frac{3}{4\,z^2} + \frac{105}{16\,z^4} - \cdots\right],$$

$$g(z) \sim \frac{1}{\pi\sqrt{2}} \sum_{n=0}^\infty (-1)^n \frac{\Gamma(2n+3/2)}{z^{2n+3/2}},$$

$$\sim \frac{1}{2z\sqrt{2\pi z}}\left[1 - \frac{15}{4\,z^2} + \frac{945}{16\,z^4} - \cdots\right].$$

6.13.7 PROPERTIES

$$\sqrt{\frac{2}{\pi}} \int_z^\infty e^{it^2}\,dt = [g(z) + if(z)]\,e^{iz^2}.$$

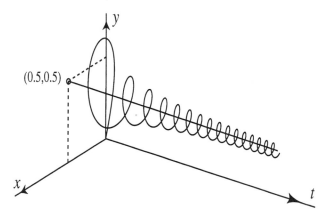

Cornu's spiral, formed from Fresnel functions,
is the set $\{x, y, t\}$ where $x = C(t)$, $y = S(t)$, $t \geq 0$.[2]

---

[2]From Temme, N.M., *Special Functions: An Introduction to the Classical Functions of Mathematical Physics,* John Wiley & Sons, New York, 1996. With permission.

6.13.8   NUMERICAL VALUES

x	$\mathrm{erf}(x)$	$e^{x^2}\mathrm{erfc}(x)$	$C(x)$	$S(x)$
0.0	0.00000000	1.00000000	0.00000000	0.00000000
0.2	0.22270259	0.80901952	0.15955138	0.00212745
0.4	0.42839236	0.67078779	0.31833776	0.01699044
0.6	0.60385609	0.56780472	0.47256350	0.05691807
0.8	0.74210096	0.48910059	0.61265370	0.13223984
1.0	0.84270079	0.42758358	0.72170592	0.24755829
1.2	0.91031398	0.37853742	0.77709532	0.39584313
1.4	0.95228512	0.33874354	0.75781398	0.55244498
1.6	0.97634838	0.30595299	0.65866707	0.67442706
1.8	0.98909050	0.27856010	0.50694827	0.71289443
2.0	0.99532227	0.25539568	0.36819298	0.64211874
2.2	0.99813715	0.23559296	0.32253723	0.49407286
2.4	0.99931149	0.21849873	0.40704642	0.36532279
2.6	0.99976397	0.20361325	0.55998756	0.36073841
2.8	0.99992499	0.19054888	0.64079292	0.48940140
3.0	0.99997791	0.17900115	0.56080398	0.61721360
3.2	0.99999397	0.16872810	0.41390216	0.58920847
3.4	0.99999848	0.15953536	0.39874249	0.44174492
3.6	0.99999964	0.15126530	0.53845493	0.39648758
3.8	0.99999992	0.14378884	0.60092662	0.52778933
4.0	0.99999998	0.13699946	0.47431072	0.59612656
4.2	1.00000000	0.13080849	0.41041217	0.46899697
4.4	1.00000000	0.12514166	0.54218734	0.41991084
4.6	1.00000000	0.11993626	0.56533023	0.55685845
4.8	1.00000000	0.11513908	0.42894668	0.54293254
5.0	1.00000000	0.11070464	0.48787989	0.42121705

6.14   SINE, COSINE, AND EXPONENTIAL INTEGRALS

6.14.1   SINE AND COSINE INTEGRALS

$$\text{Si}(z) = \int_0^z \frac{\sin t}{t}\, dt, \quad \text{Ci}(z) = \gamma + \ln z + \int_0^z \frac{\cos t - 1}{t}\, dt,$$

where γ is Euler's constant.

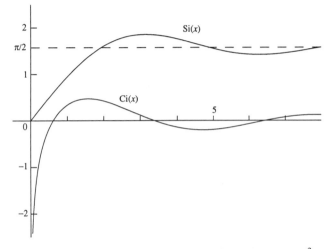

Sine and cosine integrals $\text{Si}(x)$ and $\text{Ci}(x)$, $0 \le x \le 8$.[3]

6.14.2   ALTERNATIVE DEFINITIONS

$$\text{Si}(z) = \tfrac{1}{2}\pi - \int_z^\infty \frac{\sin t}{t}\, dt, \quad \text{Ci}(z) = -\int_z^\infty \frac{\cos t}{t}\, dt.$$

6.14.3   LIMITS

$$\lim_{z \to \infty} \text{Si}(z) = \tfrac{1}{2}\pi, \quad \lim_{z \to \infty} \text{Ci}(z) = 0.$$

---

[3]From Temme, N.M., *Special Functions: An Introduction to the Classical Functions of Mathematical Physics,* John Wiley & Sons, New York, 1996. With permission.

6.14.4   REPRESENTATIONS

$$\mathrm{Si}(z) = -f(z)\cos z - g(z)\sin z + \tfrac{1}{2}\pi,$$
$$\mathrm{Ci}(z) = +f(z)\sin z - g(z)\cos z,$$

where

$$f(z) = \int_0^\infty \frac{e^{-zt}}{t^2+1}\,dt, \quad g(z) = \int_0^\infty \frac{te^{-zt}}{t^2+1}\,dt.$$

6.14.5   ASYMPTOTIC EXPANSION

For $z \to \infty$, $|\arg z| < \pi$,

$$f(z) \sim \frac{1}{z}\sum_{n=0}^\infty (-1)^n \frac{(2n)!}{z^{2n}}, \qquad g(z) \sim \frac{1}{z^2}\sum_{n=0}^\infty (-1)^n \frac{(2n+1)!}{z^{2n}}.$$

6.14.6   EXPONENTIAL INTEGRALS

$$
\begin{aligned}
E_n(z) &= \int_1^\infty \frac{e^{-zt}}{t^n}\,dt, \quad \mathrm{Re}\,z > 0, \quad n = 1, 2, \dots . \\
&= \frac{z^{n-1}e^{-z}}{\Gamma(n)}\int_0^\infty \frac{e^{-zt}t^{n-1}}{t+1}\,dt, \quad \mathrm{Re}\,z > 0.
\end{aligned}
$$

6.14.7   SPECIAL CASE

$$E_1(z) = \int_z^\infty \frac{e^{-t}}{t}\,dt, \quad |\arg z| < \pi.$$

This function is also written as $-\mathrm{Ei}(-z)$. For real values of $z = x$,

$$\mathrm{Ei}(x) = \int_{-\infty}^x \frac{e^t}{t}\,dt,$$

where for $x > 0$ the integral should be interpreted as a Cauchy principal value integral.

6.14.8   LOGARITHMIC INTEGRAL

$$\mathrm{li}(x) = \int_0^x \frac{dt}{\ln t} = \mathrm{Ei}(\ln x),$$

where for $x > 1$ the integral should be interpreted as a Cauchy principal value integral.

6.14.9 REPRESENTATIONS

$$E_1(z) = -\gamma - \ln z + \int_0^z \frac{1 - e^{-t}}{t} \, dt,$$

$$E_1\left(z e^{\frac{1}{2}\pi i}\right) = -\gamma - \ln z - \text{Ci}(z) + i\left[-\tfrac{1}{2}\pi + \text{Si}(z)\right].$$

6.14.10 NUMERICAL VALUES

$\text{Si}(x)$, $\text{Ci}(x)$, $e^x E_1(x)$, $e^{-x} \text{Ei}(x)$, for $0 \le x \le 5$

x	$\text{Si}(x)$	$\text{Ci}(x)$	$e^x E_1(x)$	$e^{-x} \text{Ei}(x)$
0.0	0.00000000	$-\infty$	∞	$-\infty$
0.2	0.19955609	−1.04220560	1.49334875	−0.67280066
0.4	0.39646146	−0.37880935	1.04782801	0.07022623
0.6	0.58812881	−0.02227071	0.82793344	0.42251981
0.8	0.77209579	0.19827862	0.69124540	0.60542430
1.0	0.94608307	0.33740392	0.59634736	0.69717488
1.2	1.10804720	0.42045918	0.52593453	0.73554406
1.4	1.25622673	0.46200659	0.47129255	0.74156823
1.6	1.38918049	0.47173252	0.42748798	0.72790154
1.8	1.50581678	0.45681113	0.39149162	0.70249838
2.0	1.60541298	0.42298083	0.36132862	0.67048271
2.2	1.68762483	0.37507460	0.33565051	0.63519181
2.4	1.75248550	0.31729162	0.31350201	0.59879930
2.6	1.80039445	0.25333662	0.29418566	0.56270515
2.8	1.83209659	0.18648839	0.27717933	0.52778864
3.0	1.84865253	0.11962979	0.26208374	0.49457640
3.2	1.85140090	0.05525741	0.24858794	0.46335631
3.4	1.84191398	−0.00451808	0.23644592	0.43425550
3.6	1.82194812	−0.05797435	0.22546029	0.40729435
3.8	1.79339035	−0.10377815	0.21547074	0.38242392
4.0	1.75820314	−0.14098170	0.20634565	0.35955201
4.2	1.71836856	−0.16901316	0.19797586	0.33856115
4.4	1.67583396	−0.18766029	0.19027005	0.31932101
4.6	1.63246035	−0.19704708	0.18315120	0.30169680
4.8	1.58997528	−0.19760361	0.17655390	0.28555486
5.0	1.54993124	−0.19002975	0.17042218	0.27076626

6.15 POLYLOGARITHMS

$$\mathrm{Li}_1(z) = \int_0^z \frac{dt}{1-t} = -\ln(1-z), \quad \text{logarithm,}$$

$$\mathrm{Li}_2(z) = \int_0^z \frac{\mathrm{Li}_1(t)}{t}\, dt = -\int_0^z \frac{\ln(1-t)}{t}\, dt, \quad \text{dilogarithm,}$$

$$\mathrm{Li}_n(z) = \int_0^z \frac{\mathrm{Li}_{n-1}(t)}{t}\, dt, \quad n \geq 2, \quad \text{polylogarithm.}$$

6.15.1 ALTERNATIVE DEFINITION

For any complex ν

$$\mathrm{Li}_\nu(z) = \sum_{k=1}^{\infty} \frac{z^k}{k^\nu}, \quad |z| < 1.$$

6.15.2 SINGULAR POINTS

$z = 1$ is a singular point of $\mathrm{Li}_\nu(z)$.

6.15.3 INTEGRAL

$$\mathrm{Li}_\nu(z) = \frac{z}{\Gamma(\nu)} \int_0^\infty \frac{t^{\nu-1}}{e^t - z}\, dt, \quad \mathrm{Re}\,\nu > 0, \quad z \notin [1, \infty).$$

6.15.4 GENERATING FUNCTION

$$\sum_{n=2}^{\infty} w^{n-1} \mathrm{Li}_n(z) = z \int_0^\infty \frac{e^{wt} - 1}{e^t - z}\, dt, \quad z \notin [1, \infty).$$

The series converges for $|w| < 1$, the integral is defined for $\mathrm{Re}\,w < 1$.

6.15.5 SPECIAL VALUES

$$\mathrm{Li}_2(1) = \tfrac{1}{6}\pi^2, \quad \mathrm{Li}_2(-1) = -\tfrac{1}{12}\pi^2, \quad \mathrm{Li}_2(\tfrac{1}{2}) = \tfrac{1}{12}\pi^2 - \tfrac{1}{2}(\ln 2)^2,$$

$$\mathrm{Li}_\nu(1) = \zeta(\nu), \quad \mathrm{Re}\,\nu > 1 \quad \text{(Riemann zeta function).}$$

6.15.6   FUNCTIONAL EQUATIONS FOR DILOGARITHMS

$$\text{Li}_2(z) + \text{Li}_2(1 - z) = \tfrac{1}{6}\pi^2 - \ln z \, \ln(1 - z),$$
$$\tfrac{1}{2}\text{Li}_2(x^2) = \text{Li}_2(x) + \text{Li}_2(-x),$$
$$\text{Li}_2(-1/x) + \text{Li}_2(-x) = -\tfrac{1}{6}\pi^2 - \tfrac{1}{2}(\ln x)^2,$$
$$2\text{Li}_2(x) + 2\text{Li}_2(y) + 2\text{Li}_2(z) =$$
$$\text{Li}_2(-xy/z) + \text{Li}_2(-yz/x) + \text{Li}_2(-zx/y),$$

where $1/x + 1/y + 1/z = 1$.

6.16   HYPERGEOMETRIC FUNCTIONS

Recall the geometric series and binomial expansion ($|z| < 1$),

$$(1 - z)^{-1} = \sum_{n=0}^{\infty} z^n, \quad (1 - z)^{-a} = \sum_{n=0}^{\infty} \binom{-a}{n}(-z)^n = \sum_{n=0}^{\infty} \frac{(a)_n}{n!} z^n.$$

where the shifted factorial, $(a)_n$, is defined in Section 1.2.6.

6.16.1   DEFINITION OF THE F-FUNCTION

Gauss hypergeometric function

$$F(a, b; c; z) = \sum_{n=0}^{\infty} \frac{(a)_n\,(b)_n}{(c)_n\,n!}\, z^n,$$
$$= 1 + \frac{ab}{c}z + \frac{a(a+1)\,b(b+1)}{c(c+1)\,2!}z^2 + \ldots, \quad |z| < 1,$$
$$= F(a, b; c; z) = F(b, a; c; z)$$

where a, b and c may assume all complex values, $c \neq 0, -1, -2, \ldots$.

6.16.2   POLYNOMIAL CASE

For $m = 0, 1, 2, \ldots$

$$F(-m, b; c; z) = \sum_{n=0}^{m} \frac{(-m)_n\,(b)_n}{(c)_n\,n!}\, z^n = \sum_{n=0}^{m}(-1)^n \binom{m}{n} \frac{(b)_n}{(c)_n} z^n.$$

6.16.3   SPECIAL CASES

$$F(a, b; b; z) = (1 - z)^{-a},$$

$$F(1, 1; 2; z) = -\frac{\ln(1 - z)}{z},$$

$$F\left(\tfrac{1}{2}, 1; \tfrac{3}{2}; z^2\right) = \frac{1}{2z} \ln\left(\frac{1 + z}{1 - z}\right),$$

$$F\left(\tfrac{1}{2}, 1; \tfrac{3}{2}; -z^2\right) = \frac{\tan^{-1} z}{z},$$

$$F\left(\tfrac{1}{2}, \tfrac{1}{2}; \tfrac{3}{2}; z^2\right) = \frac{\sin^{-1} z}{z},$$

$$F\left(\tfrac{1}{2}, \tfrac{1}{2}; \tfrac{3}{2}; -z^2\right) = \frac{\ln(z + \sqrt{1 + z^2})}{z}.$$

6.16.4   SPECIAL VALUES

When Re $(c - a - b) > 0$,

$$F(a, b; c; 1) = \frac{\Gamma(c)\Gamma(c - a - b)}{\Gamma(c - a)\Gamma(c - b)}.$$

6.16.5   INTEGRAL

When Re $c >$ Re $b > 0$,

$$F(a, b; c; z) = \frac{\Gamma(c)}{\Gamma(b)\Gamma(c - b)} \int_0^1 t^{b-1}(1 - t)^{c-b-1}(1 - tz)^{-a}\, dt.$$

6.16.6   FUNCTIONAL RELATIONSHIPS

$$
\begin{aligned}
F(a, b; c; z) &= (1 - z)^{-a} F\left(a, c - b; c; \frac{z}{z - 1}\right), \\
&= (1 - z)^{-b} F\left(c - a, b; c; \frac{z}{z - 1}\right), \\
&= (1 - z)^{c-a-b} F(c - a, c - b; c; z).
\end{aligned}
$$

6.16.7   DIFFERENTIAL EQUATION

$$z(1 - z)F'' + [(c - (a + b + 1)z]F' - abF = 0,$$

with (regular) singular points $z = 0, 1, \infty$.

6.16.8 PROPERTIES

$$\frac{d}{dz}F(a,b;c;z) = \frac{ab}{c}F(a+1,b+1;c+1;z),$$

$$\frac{d^n}{dz^n}F(a,b;c;z) = \frac{(a)_n\,(b)_n}{(c)_n}F(a+n,b+n;c+n;z).$$

6.16.9 RECURSION FORMULAE

Notation: F is $F\,(a,b;c;z)$; $F(a+)$, $F(a-)$ are $F\,(a+1,b;c;z)$, $F\,(a-1,b;c;z)$, respectively, etc.

$$(c-a)F(a-) + (2a-c-az+bz)F + a(z-1)F(a+) = 0,$$

$$c(c-1)(z-1)F(c-) + c[c-1-(2c-a-b-1)z]F$$
$$+(c-a)(c-b)zF(c+) = 0,$$

$$c[a+(b-c)z]F - ac(1-z)F(a+) + (c-a)(c-b)zF(c+) = 0,$$

$$c(1-z)F - cF(a-) + (c-b)zF(c+) = 0,$$

$$(b-a)F + aF(a+) - bF(b+) = 0,$$

$$(c-a-b)F + a(1-z)F(a+) - (c-b)F(b-) = 0,$$

$$(c-a-1)F + aF(a+) - (c-1)F(c-) = 0,$$

$$(b-a)(1-z)F - (c-a)F(a-) + (c-b)F(b-) = 0,$$

$$[a-1+(b+1-c)z]F + (c-a)F(a-) - (c-1)(1-z)F(c-) = 0.$$

6.17 LEGENDRE FUNCTIONS

6.17.1 DIFFERENTIAL EQUATION

The Legendre differential equation is,

$$(1-z^2)w'' - 2zw' + \nu(\nu+1)w = 0.$$

The solutions $P_\nu(z)$, $Q_\nu(z)$ can be given in terms of Gaussian hypergeometric functions.

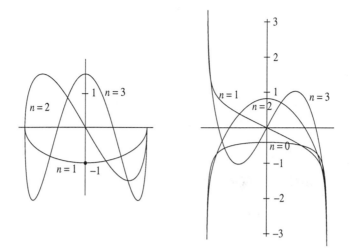

Legendre functions $P_n(x), n = 1, 2, 3$ (left) and
$Q_n(x), n = 0, 1, 2, 3$, on the interval $[-1, 1]$.[4]

6.17.2 DEFINITION

$$P_\nu(z) = F\left(-\nu, \nu + 1; 1; \tfrac{1}{2} - \tfrac{1}{2} z\right),$$

$$Q_\nu(z) = \frac{\sqrt{\pi}\ \Gamma(\nu + 1)}{\Gamma(\nu + \tfrac{3}{2})\ (2z)^{\nu+1}} F\left(\tfrac{1}{2}\nu + 1,\ \tfrac{1}{2}\nu + \tfrac{1}{2};\ \nu + \tfrac{3}{2};\ z^{-2}\right).$$

The Q-function is not defined if $\nu = -1, -2, \ldots$.

6.17.3 POLYNOMIAL CASE

Legendre polynomial $\nu = n = 0, 1, 2, \ldots$,

$$\begin{aligned}
P_n(x) &= F\left(-n, n + 1; 1; \tfrac{1}{2} - \tfrac{1}{2}x\right) \\
&= \sum_{k=0}^{m} \frac{(-1)^k (2n - 2k)!}{2^k\ k!\ (n - k)!\ (n - 2k)!} x^{n-2k}, \quad m = \begin{cases} \tfrac{1}{2}n, & \text{if } n \text{ even,} \\[2mm] \tfrac{1}{2}(n - 1), & \text{if } n \text{ odd.} \end{cases}
\end{aligned}$$

6.17.4 SINGULAR POINTS

$P_\nu(z)$ has a singular point at $z = -1$ and is analytic in the remaining part of the complex z-plane, with a branch cut along $(-\infty, -1]$. $Q_\nu(z)$ has singular points at $z = \pm 1$ and is analytic in the remaining part of the complex z-plane, with a branch cut along $(-\infty, +1]$.

---

[4]From Temme, N.M., *Special Functions: An Introduction to the Classical Functions of Mathematical Physics,* John Wiley & Sons, New York, 1996. With permission.

6.17.5 RELATIONSHIPS

$$P_{-\nu-1}(z) = P_\nu(z),$$
$$Q_{-\nu-1}(z) = Q_\nu(z) - \pi \cot \nu\pi \, P_\nu(z).$$

6.17.6 SPECIAL CASE

The function $Q_n(z)$. We distinguish two cases

$$Q_n(x), \quad x \in (-1, 1), \quad Q_n(z), \quad z \notin [-1, 1].$$

$$Q_0(z) = \tfrac{1}{2} \ln \frac{z+1}{z-1}, \quad Q_1(z) = \tfrac{1}{2} z \ln \frac{z+1}{z-1} - 1,$$

$$Q_n(z) = P_n(z)Q_0(z) - \sum_{k=0}^{n-1} \frac{(2k+1)[1-(-1)^{n+k}]}{(n+k+1)(n-k)} P_k(z),$$

$$Q_0(x) = \tfrac{1}{2} \ln \frac{1+x}{1-x}, \quad Q_1(x) = \tfrac{1}{2} x \ln \frac{1+x}{1-x} - 1,$$

$$Q_n(x) = P_n(x)Q_0(x) - \sum_{k=0}^{n-1} \frac{(2k+1)[1-(-1)^{n+k}]}{(n+k+1)(n-k)} P_k(x).$$

n	P_n	Q_n
0	1	$\tfrac{1}{2} \ln[(1+x)/(1-x)]$
1	x	$P_1(x)Q_0(x) - 1$
2	$\tfrac{1}{2}(3x^2 - 1)$	$P_2(x)Q_0(x) - \tfrac{3}{2}x$
3	$\tfrac{1}{2}x(5x^2 - 3)$	$P_3(x)Q_0(x) - \tfrac{5}{2}x^2 + \tfrac{2}{3}$
4	$\tfrac{1}{8}(35x^4 - 30x^2 + 3)$	$P_4(x)Q_0(x) - \tfrac{35}{8}x^3 + \tfrac{55}{24}x$
5	$\tfrac{1}{8}x(63x^4 - 70x^2 + 15)$	$P_5(x)Q_0(x) - \tfrac{63}{8}x^4 + \tfrac{49}{8}x^2 - \tfrac{8}{15}$

Legendre polynomials $P_n(x)$ and functions $Q_n(x)$, $x \in (-1, 1)$.

6.17.7 RECURSION RELATIONSHIPS

$$
\begin{aligned}
(\nu + 1)P_{\nu+1}(z) &= (2\nu + 1)z P_\nu(z) - \nu P_{\nu-1}(z), \\
(2\nu + 1)P_\nu(z) &= P'_{\nu+1}(z) - P'_{\nu-1}(z), \\
(\nu + 1)P_\nu(z) &= P'_{\nu+1}(z) - z P'_\nu(z), \\
\nu P_\nu(z) &= z P'_\nu(z) - P'_{\nu-1}(z), \\
(1 - z^2)P'_\nu(z) &= \nu P_{\nu-1}(z) - \nu z P_\nu(z).
\end{aligned}
$$

The functions $Q_\nu(z)$ satisfy the same relations.

6.17.8   INTEGRALS

$$
\begin{aligned}
P_\nu(\cosh\alpha) &= \frac{2}{\pi}\int_0^\alpha \frac{\cosh(\nu+\tfrac12)\theta}{\sqrt{2\cosh\alpha - 2\cosh\theta}}\, d\theta, \\
&= \frac{1}{\pi}\int_{-\alpha}^\alpha \frac{e^{-(\nu+1/2)\theta}}{\sqrt{2\cosh\alpha - 2\cosh\theta}}\, d\theta, \\
&= \frac{1}{\pi}\int_0^\pi \frac{d\psi}{(\cosh\alpha + \sinh\alpha\,\cos\psi)^{\nu+1}}, \\
&= \frac{1}{\pi}\int_0^\pi (\cosh\alpha + \sinh\alpha\,\cos\psi)^\nu\, d\psi.
\end{aligned}
$$

$$
\begin{aligned}
P_\nu(\cos\beta) &= \frac{2}{\pi}\int_0^\beta \frac{\cos(\nu+\tfrac12)\theta}{\sqrt{2\cos\theta - 2\cos\beta}}\, d\theta, \\
&= \frac{1}{\pi}\int_0^\pi \frac{d\psi}{(\cos\beta + i\sin\beta\,\cos\psi)^{\nu+1}}, \\
&= \frac{1}{\pi}\int_0^\pi (\cos\beta + i\sin\beta\,\cos\psi)^\nu\, d\psi.
\end{aligned}
$$

$$
\begin{aligned}
Q_\nu(z) &= 2^{-\nu-1}\int_{-1}^1 \frac{(1-t^2)^\nu}{(z-t)^{\nu+1}}\, dt, \quad \operatorname{Re}\nu > -1,\ |\arg z| < \pi,\ z\notin[-1,1], \\
&= \int_0^\infty \left[z + \sqrt{z^2-1}\,\cosh\phi\right]^{-\nu-1} d\phi, \\
&= \int_\alpha^\infty \frac{e^{-(\nu+1/2)\theta}}{\sqrt{2\cosh\theta - 2\cosh\alpha}}\, d\theta, \quad z = \cosh\alpha.
\end{aligned}
$$

6.17.9   DIFFERENTIAL EQUATION

The associated Legendre differential equation is,

$$
(1-z^2)y'' - 2zy' + \left[\nu(\nu+1) - \frac{\mu^2}{1-z^2}\right]y = 0.
$$

The solutions $P_\nu^\mu(z)$, $Q_\nu^\mu(z)$, the associated Legendre functions, can be given in terms of Gauss hypergeometric functions. We only consider integer values of μ, ν, and replace them with m, n, respectively. Then the associated differential equation follows from the Legendre differential equation after it has been differentiated m times.

6.17.10   RELATIONSHIPS BETWEEN THE ASSOCIATED AND ORDINARY LEGENDRE FUNCTIONS

$$P_n^m(z) = (1 - z^2)^{\frac{1}{2}m} \frac{d^m}{dz^m} P_n(z), \quad P_n^{-m}(z) = \frac{(n-m)!}{(n+m)!} P_n^m(z),$$

$$Q_n^m(z) = (1 - z^2)^{\frac{1}{2}m} \frac{d^m}{dz^m} Q_n(z), \quad Q_n^{-m}(z) = \frac{(n-m)!}{(n+m)!} Q_n^m(z),$$

$$P_n^{-m}(z) = (1 - z^2)^{-\frac{1}{2}m} \int_1^z \cdots \int_1^z P_n(z) \, (dz)^m,$$

$$Q_n^{-m}(z) = (-1)^m (1 - z^2)^{-\frac{1}{2}m} \int_z^\infty \cdots \int_z^\infty Q_n(z) \, (dz)^m,$$

$$P_{-n-1}^m(z) = P_n^m(z).$$

6.17.11   ORTHOGONALITY RELATIONSHIP

Let $n \geq m$.

$$\int_{-1}^1 P_n^m(x) P_k^m(x) \, dx = \begin{cases} 0, & \text{if } k \neq n, \\[2mm] \dfrac{2}{2n+1} \dfrac{(n+m)!}{(n-m)!}, & \text{if } k = n. \end{cases}$$

6.17.12   RECURSION RELATIONSHIPS

$$P_n^{m+1}(z) + \frac{2mz}{\sqrt{z^2 - 1}} P_n^m(z) = (n - m + 1)(n + m) P_n^{m-1}(z),$$

$$(z^2 - 1) \frac{d P_n^m(z)}{dz} = mz P_n^m(z) + \sqrt{z^2 - 1} P_n^{m+1}(z),$$

$$(2n + 1)z P_n^m(z) = (n - m + 1) P_{n+1}^m(z) + (n + m) P_{n-1}^m(z),$$

$$(z^2 - 1) \frac{d P_n^m(z)}{dz} = (n - m + 1) P_{n+1}^m(z) - (n + 1)z P_n^m(z),$$

$$P_{n-1}^m(z) - P_{n+1}^m(z) = -(2n + 1)\sqrt{z^2 - 1} P_n^{m-1}(z).$$

The functions $Q_n^m(z)$ satisfy the same relations.

6.18   BESSEL FUNCTIONS

6.18.1   DIFFERENTIAL EQUATION

The Bessel differential equation,

$$z^2 y'' + z y' + (z^2 - \nu^2) y = 0.$$

The solutions are denoted with

$$J_\nu(z), \quad Y_\nu(z) \quad \text{(the ordinary Bessel functions)}$$

and

$$H_\nu^{(1)}(z), \quad H_\nu^{(2)}(z) \quad \text{(the Hankel functions)}.$$

Further solutions are

$$J_{-\nu}(z), \quad Y_{-\nu}(z), \quad H_{-\nu}^{(1)}(z), \quad H_{-\nu}^{(2)}(z).$$

When ν is an integer,

$$J_{-n}(z) = (-1)^n J_n(z), \quad n = 0, 1, 2, \ldots .$$

Bessel functions $J_0(x)$, $J_1(x)$, $Y_0(x)$, $Y_1(x)$, $0 \le x \le 12$.

6.18.2   SINGULAR POINTS

The Bessel differential equation has a regular singularity at $z = 0$ and an irregular singularity at $z = \infty$.

6.18.3 RELATIONSHIPS

$$H_\nu^{(1)}(z) = J_\nu(z) + i Y_\nu(z), \quad H_\nu^{(2)}(z) = J_\nu(z) - i Y_\nu(z).$$

Neumann function: If $\nu \neq 0, \pm 1, \pm 2, \ldots$

$$Y_\nu(z) = \frac{\cos \nu\pi \; J_\nu(z) - J_{-\nu}(z)}{\sin \nu\pi}.$$

When $\nu = n$ (integer) then the limit $\nu \to n$ should be taken in the right-hand side of this equation. Complete solutions to Bessel's equation may be written as

$$c_1 J_\nu(z) + c_2 J_{-\nu}(z), \qquad \text{if } \nu \text{ is not an integer,}$$
$$c_1 J_\nu(z) + c_2 Y_\nu(z), \qquad \text{for any value of } \nu,$$
$$c_1 H_\nu^{(1)}(z) + c_2 H_\nu^{(2)}(z), \qquad \text{for any value of } \nu.$$

6.18.4 SERIES EXPANSIONS

For any complex z,

$$J_\nu(z) = (\tfrac{1}{2}z)^\nu \sum_{n=0}^{\infty} \frac{(-1)^n (\tfrac{1}{2}z)^{2n}}{\Gamma(n + \nu + 1) n!}.$$

$$J_0(z) = 1 - (\tfrac{1}{2}z)^2 + \frac{1}{2! \, 2!}(\tfrac{1}{2}z)^4 - \frac{1}{3! \, 3!}(\tfrac{1}{2}z)^6 + \cdots,$$

$$J_1(z) = \tfrac{1}{2}z \left[1 - \frac{1}{1! \, 2!}(\tfrac{1}{2}z)^2 + \frac{1}{2! \, 3!}(\tfrac{1}{2}z)^4 - \frac{1}{3! \, 4!}(\tfrac{1}{2}z)^6 + \cdots \right],$$

$$Y_n(z) = \frac{2}{\pi} J_n(z) \ln(\tfrac{1}{2}z) - \frac{(\tfrac{1}{2}z)^{-n}}{\pi} \sum_{k=0}^{n-1} \frac{(n - k - 1)!}{k!}(\tfrac{1}{2}z)^{2k} -$$
$$\frac{(\tfrac{1}{2}z)^n}{\pi} \sum_{k=0}^{\infty} [\psi(k + 1) + \psi(n + k + 1)] \frac{(-1)^k (\tfrac{1}{2}z)^{2k}}{k! \, (n + k)!},$$

where ψ is the logarithmic derivative of the gamma function.

6.18.5 RECURRENCE RELATIONSHIPS

$$C_{\nu-1}(z) + C_{\nu+1}(z) = \frac{2\nu}{z} C_\nu(z),$$
$$C_{\nu-1}(z) - C_{\nu+1}(z) = 2 C_\nu'(z),$$
$$C_\nu'(z) = C_{\nu-1}(z) - \frac{\nu}{z} C_\nu(z),$$
$$C_\nu'(z) = -C_{\nu+1}(z) + \frac{\nu}{z} C_\nu(z),$$

where $C_\nu(z)$ denotes one of the functions $J_\nu(z)$, $Y_\nu(z)$, $H_\nu^{(1)}(z)$, $H_\nu^{(2)}(z)$.

6.18.6   BEHAVIOR AS $z \to 0$

Let Re $\nu > 0$.

$$J_\nu(z) \sim \frac{(\tfrac{1}{2}z)^\nu}{\Gamma(\nu+1)}, \qquad Y_\nu(z) \sim -\frac{1}{\pi}\Gamma(\nu)\left(\frac{2}{z}\right)^\nu,$$

$$H_\nu^{(1)}(z) \sim \frac{1}{\pi i}\Gamma(\nu)\left(\frac{2}{z}\right)^\nu, \qquad H_\nu^{(2)}(z) \sim -\frac{1}{\pi i}\Gamma(\nu)\left(\frac{2}{z}\right)^\nu.$$

The same relations hold as Re $\nu \to \infty$, with z fixed.

6.18.7   INTEGRALS

Let Re $z > 0$ and ν be any complex number.

$$J_\nu(z) = \frac{1}{\pi}\int_0^\pi \cos(\nu\theta - z\sin\theta)\,d\theta - \frac{\sin\nu\pi}{\pi}\int_0^\infty e^{-\nu t - z\sinh t}\,dt,$$

$$Y_\nu(z) = \frac{1}{\pi}\int_0^\pi \sin(z\sin\theta - \nu\theta)\,d\theta - \int_0^\infty \left(e^{\nu t} + e^{-\nu t}\cos\nu\pi\right)e^{-z\sinh t}\,dt.$$

When $\nu = n$ (integer), the second integral in the first relation disappears.

6.18.8   FOURIER EXPANSION

For any complex z,

$$e^{-iz\sin t} = \sum_{n=-\infty}^{\infty} e^{-int} J_n(z),$$

with Parseval relation

$$\sum_{n=-\infty}^{\infty} J_n^2(z) = 1.$$

6.18.9   AUXILIARY FUNCTIONS

Let $\chi = z - (\tfrac{1}{2}\nu + \tfrac{1}{4})\pi$ and define

$$P(\nu, z) = \sqrt{\pi z/2}\,[\ J_\nu(z)\cos\chi + Y_\nu(z)\sin\chi],$$
$$Q(\nu, z) = \sqrt{\pi z/2}\,[-J_\nu(z)\sin\chi + Y_\nu(z)\cos\chi].$$

6.18.10   INVERSE RELATIONSHIPS

$$J_\nu(z) = \sqrt{2/(\pi z)}\,[P(\nu, z)\cos\chi - Q(\nu, z)\sin\chi],$$
$$Y_\nu(z) = \sqrt{2/(\pi z)}\,[P(\nu, z)\sin\chi + Q(\nu, z)\cos\chi]$$

For the Hankel functions,

$$H_\nu^{(1)}(z) = \sqrt{2/(\pi z)}\,[P(\nu, z) + iQ(\nu, z)]e^{i\chi},$$
$$H_\nu^{(2)}(z) = \sqrt{2/(\pi z)}\,[P(\nu, z) - iQ(\nu, z)]e^{-i\chi}.$$

The functions $P(\nu, z)$, $Q(\nu, z)$ are the slowly varying components in the asymptotic expansions of the oscillatory Bessel and Hankel functions.

6.18.11   ASYMPTOTIC EXPANSIONS

Let (α, n) be defined by

$$
\begin{aligned}
(\alpha, n) &= \frac{2^{-2n}}{n!}\{(4\alpha^2 - 1)(4\alpha^2 - 3^2)\cdots[4\alpha^2 - (2n-1)^2]\}, \\
&= \frac{\Gamma(\tfrac{1}{2} + \alpha + n)}{n!\,\Gamma(\tfrac{1}{2} + \alpha - n)}, \qquad n = 0, 1, 2, \ldots, \\
&= \frac{(-1)^n \cos(\pi\alpha)}{\pi n!}\Gamma(\tfrac{1}{2} + \alpha + n)\Gamma(\tfrac{1}{2} - \alpha + n),
\end{aligned}
$$

with recursion

$$(\alpha, n+1) = -\frac{(n + \tfrac{1}{2})^2 - \alpha^2}{n+1}\,(\alpha, n), \quad n = 1, 2, 3, \ldots, \quad (\alpha, 0) = 1.$$

Then, for $z \to \infty$,

$$P(\nu, z) \sim \sum_{n=0}^{\infty}(-1)^n\frac{(\nu, 2n)}{(2z)^{2n}}, \qquad Q(\nu, z) \sim \sum_{n=0}^{\infty}(-1)^n\frac{(\nu, 2n+1)}{(2z)^{2n+1}}.$$

With $\mu = 4\nu^2$,

$$P(\nu, z) \sim 1 - \frac{(\mu - 1)(\mu - 9)}{2!\,(8z)^2} + \frac{(\mu - 1)(\mu - 9)(\mu - 25)(\mu - 49)}{4!\,(8z)^4} - \cdots,$$
$$Q(\nu, z) \sim \frac{\mu - 1}{8z} - \frac{(\mu - 1)(\mu - 9)(\mu - 25)}{3!\,(8z)^3} + \cdots.$$

For large positive values of x,

$$J_\nu(x) = \sqrt{2/(\pi x)}\,\left[\cos(x - \tfrac{1}{2}\nu\pi - \tfrac{1}{4}\pi) + \mathcal{O}(x^{-1})\right],$$
$$Y_\nu(x) = \sqrt{2/(\pi x)}\,\left[\sin(x - \tfrac{1}{2}\nu\pi - \tfrac{1}{4}\pi) + \mathcal{O}(x^{-1})\right].$$

6.18.12   ZEROS OF BESSEL FUNCTIONS

For $\nu \geq 0$, the zeros $j_{\nu,k}$, $y_{\nu,k}$ of $J_\nu(x)$, $Y_\nu(x)$ can be arranged as sequences

$$0 < j_{\nu,1} < j_{\nu,2} < \cdots < j_{\nu,n} < \cdots, \quad \lim_{n\to\infty} j_{\nu,n} = \infty,$$

$$0 < y_{\nu,1} < y_{\nu,2} < \cdots < y_{\nu,n} < \cdots, \quad \lim_{n\to\infty} y_{\nu,n} = \infty.$$

Between two consecutive positive zeros of $J_\nu(x)$, there is exactly one zero of $J_{\nu+1}(x)$. Conversely, between two consecutive positive zeros of $J_{\nu+1}(x)$, there is exactly one zero of $J_\nu(x)$. The same holds for the zeros of $Y_\nu(z)$. Moreover, between each pair of consecutive positive zeros of $J_\nu(x)$, there is exactly one zero of $Y_\nu(x)$, and conversely.

6.18.13   ASYMPTOTICS OF THE ZEROS

When ν is fixed, $s \gg \nu$, and $\mu = 4\nu^2$,

$$j_{\nu,s} \sim \alpha - \frac{\mu-1}{8\alpha}\left[1 - \frac{4(7\mu^2 - 31)}{3(8\alpha)^2} - \frac{32(83\mu^2 - 982\mu + 3779)}{15(8\alpha)^4} + \cdots\right]$$

where $\alpha = (s + \frac{1}{2}\nu - \frac{1}{4})\pi$; $y_{\nu,s}$ has the same asymptotic expansion with $\alpha = (s + \frac{1}{2}\nu - \frac{3}{4})\pi$.

n	$j_{0,n}$	$j_{1,n}$	$y_{0,n}$	$y_{1,n}$
1	2.40483	3.83171	0.89358	2.19714
2	5.52008	7.01559	3.95768	5.42968
3	8.65373	10.17347	7.08605	8.59601
4	11.79153	13.32369	10.22235	11.74915
5	14.93092	16.47063	13.36110	14.89744
6	18.07106	19.61586	16.50092	18.04340
7	21.21164	22.76008	19.64131	21.18807

Positive zeros $j_{\nu,n}$, $y_{\nu,n}$ of Bessel functions $J_\nu(x)$, $Y_\nu(x)$, $\nu = 0, 1$.

6.18.14   HALF ORDER BESSEL FUNCTIONS

For integer values of n, let

$$j_n(z) = \sqrt{\pi/(2z)}\ J_{n+\frac{1}{2}}(z), \quad y_n(z) = \sqrt{\pi/(2z)}\ Y_{n+\frac{1}{2}}(z).$$

Then

$$j_0(z) = y_{-1}(z) = \frac{\sin z}{z}, \quad y_0(z) = -j_{-1}(z) = -\frac{\cos z}{z},$$

and, for $n = 0, 1, 2, \dots$,

$$j_n(z) = (-z)^n \left[\frac{1}{z}\frac{d}{dz}\right]^n \frac{\sin z}{z}, \quad y_n(z) = -(-z)^n \left[\frac{1}{z}\frac{d}{dz}\right]^n \frac{\cos z}{z}.$$

Recursion relationships

The functions $j_n(z)$, $y_n(z)$ both satisfy

$$z[f_{n-1}(z) + f_{n+1}(z)] = (2n + 1)f_n(z),$$
$$nf_{n-1}(z) - (n + 1)f_{n+1}(z) = (2n + 1)f_n'(z).$$

Differential equation

$$z^2 f'' + 2zf' + [z^2 - n(n + 1)]f = 0.$$

6.18.15   MODIFIED BESSEL FUNCTIONS

Differential equation

$$z^2 y'' + zy' - (z^2 + v^2)y = 0.$$

With solutions $I_v(z)$, $K_v(z)$,

$$I_v(z) = \left(\frac{z}{2}\right)^v \sum_{n=0}^{\infty} \frac{(z/2)^{2n}}{\Gamma(n + v + 1)\,n!},$$

$$K_v(z) = \frac{\pi}{2} \frac{I_{-v}(z) - I_v(z)}{\sin v\pi},$$

where the right-hand side should be determined by a limiting process when v assumes integer values. When $n = 0, 1, 2, \dots$,

$$K_n(z) = (-1)^{n+1} I_n(z) \ln \frac{z}{2} + \frac{1}{2}\left(\frac{2}{z}\right)^n \sum_{k=0}^{n-1} \frac{(n - k - 1)!}{k!}\left(-\frac{z^2}{4}\right)^k$$

$$+ \frac{(-1)^n}{2}\left(\frac{z}{2}\right)^n \sum_{k=0}^{\infty} [\psi(k + 1) + \psi(n + k + 1)]\frac{(z/2)^{2k}}{k!\,(n + k)!}.$$

Relations with the ordinary Bessel functions

$$I_\nu(z) = e^{-\frac{1}{2}\nu\pi i} J_\nu\left(ze^{\frac{1}{2}\pi i}\right), \qquad -\pi < \arg z \le \frac{1}{2}\pi,$$

$$I_\nu(z) = e^{\frac{3}{2}\nu\pi i} J_\nu\left(ze^{-\frac{3}{2}\pi i}\right), \qquad \frac{1}{2}\pi < \arg z \le \pi,$$

$$K_\nu(z) = \frac{1}{2}\pi i e^{\frac{1}{2}\nu\pi i} H_\nu^{(1)}\left(ze^{\frac{1}{2}\pi i}\right), \qquad -\pi < \arg z \le \frac{1}{2}\pi,$$

$$K_\nu(z) = -\frac{1}{2}\pi i e^{-\frac{1}{2}\nu\pi i} H_\nu^{(2)}\left(ze^{-\frac{1}{2}\pi i}\right), \qquad -\frac{1}{2}\pi < \arg z \le \pi,$$

$$Y_\nu\left(ze^{\frac{1}{2}\pi i}\right) = e^{\frac{1}{2}(\nu+1)\pi i} I_\nu(z) - \frac{2}{\pi}e^{-\frac{1}{2}\nu\pi i} K_\nu(z), \qquad -\pi < \arg z \le \frac{1}{2}\pi.$$

For $n = 0, 1, 2, \dots$,

$$I_n(z) = i^{-n} J_n(iz), \quad Y_n(iz) = i^{n+1} I_n(z) - \frac{2}{\pi} i^{-n} K_n(z),$$

$$I_{-n}(z) = I_n(z), \quad K_{-\nu}(z) = K_\nu(z), \quad \text{for any } \nu.$$

Recursion relationships

$$I_{\nu-1}(z) - I_{\nu+1}(z) = \frac{2\nu}{z} I_\nu(z), \qquad K_{\nu+1}(z) - K_{\nu-1}(z) = \frac{2\nu}{z} K_\nu(z)$$

$$I_{\nu-1}(z) + I_{\nu+1}(z) = 2I_\nu'(z), \qquad K_{\nu-1}(z) + K_{\nu+1}(z) = -2K_\nu'(z).$$

Integrals

$$I_\nu(z) = \frac{1}{\pi} \int_0^\pi e^{z\cos\theta} \cos(\nu\theta)\, d\theta - \frac{\sin\nu\pi}{\pi} \int_0^\infty e^{-\nu t - z\cosh t}\, dt,$$

$$K_\nu(z) = \int_0^\infty e^{-z\cosh t} \cosh(\nu t)\, dt.$$

When $\nu = n$ (integer), the second integral in the first relation disappears.

6.18.16   NUMERICAL VALUES

x	$J_0(x)$	$J_1(x)$	$Y_0(x)$	$Y_1(x)$
0.0	1.00000000	0.00000000	$-\infty$	$-\infty$
0.2	0.99002497	0.09950083	-1.08110532	-3.32382499
0.4	0.96039823	0.19602658	-0.60602457	-1.78087204
0.6	0.91200486	0.28670099	-0.30850987	-1.26039135
0.8	0.84628735	0.36884205	-0.08680228	-0.97814418
1.0	0.76519769	0.44005059	0.08825696	-0.78121282
1.2	0.67113274	0.49828906	0.22808350	-0.62113638
1.4	0.56685512	0.54194771	0.33789513	-0.47914697
1.6	0.45540217	0.56989594	0.42042690	-0.34757801
1.8	0.33998641	0.58151695	0.47743171	-0.22366487
2.0	0.22389078	0.57672481	0.51037567	-0.10703243
2.2	0.11036227	0.55596305	0.52078429	0.00148779
2.4	0.00250768	0.52018527	0.51041475	0.10048894
2.6	-0.09680495	0.47081827	0.48133059	0.18836354
2.8	-0.18503603	0.40970925	0.43591599	0.26354539
3.0	-0.26005195	0.33905896	0.37685001	0.32467442
3.2	-0.32018817	0.26134325	0.30705325	0.37071134
3.4	-0.36429560	0.17922585	0.22961534	0.40101529
3.6	-0.39176898	0.09546555	0.14771001	0.41539176
3.8	-0.40255641	0.01282100	0.06450325	0.41411469
4.0	-0.39714981	-0.06604333	-0.01694074	0.39792571
4.2	-0.37655705	-0.13864694	-0.09375120	0.36801281
4.4	-0.34225679	-0.20277552	-0.16333646	0.32597067
4.6	-0.29613782	-0.25655284	-0.22345995	0.27374524
4.8	-0.24042533	-0.29849986	-0.27230379	0.21356517
5.0	-0.17759677	-0.32757914	-0.30851763	0.14786314

x	$e^{-x} I_0(x)$	$e^{-x} I_1(x)$	$e^x K_0(x)$	$e^x K_1(x)$
0.0	1.00000000	0.00000000	∞	∞
0.2	0.82693855	0.08228312	2.14075732	5.83338603
0.4	0.69740217	0.13676322	1.66268209	3.25867388
0.6	0.59932720	0.17216442	1.41673762	2.37392004
0.8	0.52414894	0.19449869	1.25820312	1.91793030
1.0	0.46575961	0.20791042	1.14446308	1.63615349
1.2	0.41978208	0.21525686	1.05748453	1.44289755
1.4	0.38306252	0.21850759	0.98807000	1.30105374
1.6	0.35331500	0.21901949	0.93094598	1.19186757
1.8	0.32887195	0.21772628	0.88283353	1.10480537
2.0	0.30850832	0.21526929	0.84156822	1.03347685
2.2	0.29131733	0.21208773	0.80565398	0.97377017
2.4	0.27662232	0.20848109	0.77401814	0.92291367
2.6	0.26391400	0.20465225	0.74586824	0.87896728
2.8	0.25280553	0.20073741	0.72060413	0.84053006
3.0	0.24300035	0.19682671	0.69776160	0.80656348
3.2	0.23426883	0.19297862	0.67697511	0.77628028
3.4	0.22643140	0.18922985	0.65795227	0.74907206
3.6	0.21934622	0.18560225	0.64045596	0.72446066
3.8	0.21290013	0.18210758	0.62429158	0.70206469
4.0	0.20700192	0.17875084	0.60929767	0.68157595
4.2	0.20157738	0.17553253	0.59533899	0.66274241
4.4	0.19656556	0.17245023	0.58230127	0.64535587
4.6	0.19191592	0.16949973	0.57008720	0.62924264
4.8	0.18758620	0.16667571	0.55861332	0.61425660
5.0	0.18354081	0.16397227	0.54780756	0.60027386

6.19   ELLIPTIC INTEGRALS

6.19.1   DEFINITIONS

Any integral of the type $\int R(x, y)\, dx$, where $R(x, y)$ is a rational function of x and y, with

$$y^2 = a_0 x^4 + a_1 x^3 + a_2 x^2 + a_3 x + a_4, \quad |a_0| + |a_1| > 0,$$

a polynomial of the third or fourth degree in x, is called an *elliptic integral*.

$$F(\phi, k) = \int_0^\phi \frac{d\theta}{\sqrt{1 - k^2 \sin^2 \theta}},$$

$$= \int_0^x \frac{dt}{\sqrt{(1 - t^2)(1 - k^2 t^2)}}, \quad x = \sin \phi, \quad k^2 < 1.$$

$$E(\phi, k) = \int_0^\phi \sqrt{1 - k^2 \sin^2 \theta}\, d\theta,$$

$$= \int_0^x \frac{\sqrt{1 - k^2 t^2}}{\sqrt{1 - t^2}}\, dt, \quad x = \sin \phi, \quad k^2 < 1.$$

$$\Pi(n; \phi, k) = \int_0^\phi \frac{1}{1 + n \sin^2 \theta} \frac{d\theta}{\sqrt{1 - k^2 \sin^2 \theta}},$$

$$= \int_0^x \frac{1}{1 + n t^2} \frac{dt}{\sqrt{(1 - t^2)(1 - k^2 t^2)}}, \quad x = \sin \phi, \quad k^2 < 1.$$

If $n > 1$, this integral should be interpreted as a Cauchy principal value integral.

6.19.2 COMPLETE ELLIPTIC INTEGRAL OF THE FIRST AND SECOND KIND

In terms of the Gauss hypergeometric function,

$$K = F(\tfrac{1}{2}\pi, k) = \tfrac{1}{2}\pi F\left(\tfrac{1}{2}, \tfrac{1}{2}; 1; k^2\right),$$
$$E = E(\tfrac{1}{2}\pi, k) = \tfrac{1}{2}\pi F\left(-\tfrac{1}{2}, \tfrac{1}{2}; 1; k^2\right).$$

6.19.3 COMPLEMENTARY INTEGRALS

In these expressions, primes do not mean derivatives.

$$K' = F\left(k', \tfrac{1}{2}\pi\right), \quad E' = E\left(k', \tfrac{1}{2}\pi\right), \quad k' = \sqrt{1 - k^2}.$$

k is called the *modulus*, k' is called the *complementary modulus*.
    The Legendre relation is,

$$K E' + E K' - K K' = \tfrac{1}{2}\pi.$$

α	K	E
0°	1.5707963268	1.5707963268
5	1.5737921309	1.5678090740
10	1.5828428043	1.5588871966
15	1.5981420021	1.5441504969
20	1.6200258991	1.5237992053
25	1.6489952185	1.4981149284
30	1.6857503548	1.4674622093
35	1.7312451757	1.4322909693
40	1.7867691349	1.3931402485
45	1.8540746773	1.3506438810
50	1.9355810960	1.3055390943
55	2.0347153122	1.2586796248
60	2.1565156475	1.2110560276
65	2.3087867982	1.1638279645
70	2.5045500790	1.1183777380
75	2.7680631454	1.0764051131
80	3.1533852519	1.0401143957
85	3.8317419998	1.0126635062
90	∞	1.0000000000

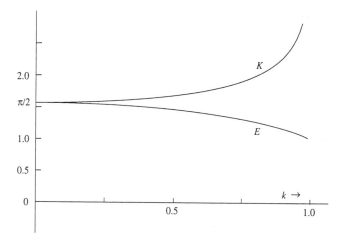

The complete elliptic integrals E and K, $0 \le k \le 1$.[5]

---

[5]From Temme, N.M., *Special Functions: An Introduction to the Classical Functions of Mathematical Physics*, John Wiley & Sons, New York, 1996. With permission.

6.19.4   EXTENSION OF THE RANGE OF ϕ

$$F(\pi, k) = 2K, \quad E(\pi, k) = 2E,$$

and, for $m = 0, 1, 2, \ldots$,

$$
\begin{aligned}
F(\phi + m\pi, k) &= mF(\pi, k) + F(\phi, k) = 2mK + F(\phi, k), \\
E(\phi + m\pi, k) &= mE(\pi, k) + E(\phi, k) = 2mE + E(\phi, k).
\end{aligned}
$$

6.19.5   DEFINITION

Elliptic functions are the inverses of elliptic integrals. If $u = F(\phi, k)$ (the elliptic integral of the first kind), that is,

$$
\begin{aligned}
u &= \int_0^\phi \frac{d\theta}{\sqrt{1 - k^2 \sin^2 \theta}} \\
&= \int_0^x \frac{dt}{\sqrt{(1 - t^2)(1 - k^2 t^2)}}, \quad x = \sin \phi, \quad k^2 < 1,
\end{aligned}
$$

then $x(u)$, the inverse function, is an elliptic function. The inverse relation is written as

$$x = \sin \phi = \mathrm{sn}(u, k).$$

ϕ is called the *amplitude* of u and denoted by am u. Two other functions are defined by

$$\mathrm{cn}(u, k) = \cos \phi, \quad \mathrm{dn}(u, k) = \sqrt{1 - k^2 \sin^2 \phi} = \sqrt{1 - k^2 \mathrm{sn}^2(u, k)} = \Delta(\phi).$$

Analogous definitions of these functions are

$$u = \int_1^{\mathrm{cn}(u,k)} \frac{dt}{\sqrt{(1 - t^2)(k'^2 + k^2 t^2)}},$$

$$u = \int_1^{\mathrm{dn}(u,k)} \frac{dt}{\sqrt{(1 - t^2)(t^2 - k'^2)}}.$$

6.19.6   PROPERTIES

$$
\begin{aligned}
&\mathrm{sn}^2(u, k) + \mathrm{cn}^2(u, k) = 1, \\
&\mathrm{dn}^2(u, k) + k^2 \mathrm{sn}^2(u, k) = 1, \\
&\mathrm{dn}^2(u, k) - k^2 \mathrm{cn}^2(u, k) = 1 - k^2 = k'^2.
\end{aligned}
$$

6.19.7   PERIODS OF THE ELLIPTIC FUNCTIONS

The elliptic functions are *doubly periodic functions* with respect to the variable u.
The periods of

$$
\begin{aligned}
\operatorname{sn}(u, k) &\quad \text{are} \quad 4K \quad \text{and} \quad 2iK', \\
\operatorname{cn}(u, k) &\quad \text{are} \quad 4K \quad \text{and} \quad 2K + 2iK', \\
\operatorname{dn}(u, k) &\quad \text{are} \quad 2K \quad \text{and} \quad 4iK'.
\end{aligned}
$$

6.19.8   SERIES EXPANSIONS

$$
\begin{aligned}
\operatorname{sn}(u, k) = {}& u - (1 + k^2)\frac{u^3}{3!} + (1 + 14k^2 + k^4)\frac{u^5}{5!} \\
& - (1 + 135k^2 + 135k^4 + k^6)\frac{u^7}{7!} + \dots, \\
\operatorname{cn}(u, k) = {}& 1 - \frac{u^2}{2!} + (1 + 4k^2)\frac{u^4}{4!} \\
& - (1 + 44k^2 + 16k^4)\frac{u^6}{6!} + \dots, \\
\operatorname{dn}(u, k) = {}& 1 - k^2\frac{u^2}{2!} + k^2(4 + k^2)\frac{u^4}{4!} \\
& - k^2(16 + 44k^2 + k^4)\frac{u^6}{6!} + \dots.
\end{aligned}
$$

Let the *nome q* be defined by $q = e^{-\pi K/K'}$ and $v = \pi u/(2K)$. Then

$$
\operatorname{sn}(u, k) = \frac{2\pi}{kK} \sum_{n=0}^{\infty} \frac{q^{n+\frac{1}{2}}}{1 - q^{2n+1}} \sin[(2n + 1)v],
$$

$$
\operatorname{cn}(u, k) = \frac{2\pi}{kK} \sum_{n=0}^{\infty} \frac{q^{n+\frac{1}{2}}}{1 + q^{2n+1}} \cos[(2n + 1)v],
$$

$$
\operatorname{dn}(u, k) = \frac{\pi}{2K} + \frac{2\pi}{K} \sum_{n=1}^{\infty} \frac{q^n}{1 + q^{2n}} \cos(2nv).
$$

6.20 CLEBSCH–GORDAN COEFFICIENTS

$$\begin{pmatrix} j_1 & j_2 \\ m_1 & m_2 \end{pmatrix}\begin{matrix} j \\ m \end{matrix}\!\!\bigg) = \delta_{m,m_1+m_2} \sqrt{\frac{(j_1 + j_2 - j)!(j + j_1 - j_2)!(j + j_2 - j_1)!(2j + 1)}{(j + j_1 + j_2 + 1)!}}$$

$$\times \sum_k \frac{(-1)^k \sqrt{(j_1 + m_1)!(j_1 - m_1)!(j_2 + m_2)!(j_2 - m_2)!(j + m)!(j - m)!}}{k!(j_1 + j_2 - j - k)!(j_1 - m_1 - k)!(j_2 + m_2 - k)!(j - j_2 + m_1 + k)!(j - j_1 - m_2 + k)!}.$$

Conditions:

- Each of $\{j_1, j_2, j, m_1, m_2, m\}$ may be an integer, or half an integer. Additionally: $j > 0$, $j_1 > 0$, $j_2 > 0$ and $j + j_1 + j_2$ is an integer.

- $j_1 + j_2 - j \geq 0$.

- $j_1 - j_2 + j \geq 0$.

- $-j_1 + j_2 + j \geq 0$.

- $|m_1| \leq j_1$, $|m_2| \leq j_2$, $|m| \leq j$.

- $\begin{pmatrix} j_1 & j_2 \\ m_1 & m_2 \end{pmatrix}\begin{matrix} j \\ m \end{matrix}\!\!\bigg) = 0$ if $m_1 + m_2 \neq m$.

Special values:

- $\begin{pmatrix} j_1 & 0 \\ m_1 & 0 \end{pmatrix}\begin{matrix} j \\ m \end{matrix}\!\!\bigg) = \delta_{j_1,j}\delta_{m_1,m}$.

- $\begin{pmatrix} j_1 & j_2 \\ 0 & 0 \end{pmatrix}\begin{matrix} j \\ 0 \end{matrix}\!\!\bigg) = 0$ when $j_1 + j_2 + j$ is an odd integer.

- $\begin{pmatrix} j_1 & j_1 \\ m_1 & m_1 \end{pmatrix}\begin{matrix} j \\ m \end{matrix}\!\!\bigg) = 0$ when $2j_1 + j$ is an odd integer.

Symmetry relations: all of the following are equal to $\begin{pmatrix} j_1 & j_2 \\ m_1 & m_2 \end{pmatrix}\begin{matrix} j \\ m \end{matrix}\!\!\bigg)$:

- $\begin{pmatrix} j_2 & j_1 & j \\ -m_2 & -m_1 & -m \end{pmatrix}$,

- $(-1)^{j_1+j_2-j} \begin{pmatrix} j_2 & j_1 & j \\ m_1 & m_2 & m \end{pmatrix}$,

- $(-1)^{j_1+j_2-j} \begin{pmatrix} j_1 & j_2 & j \\ -m_1 & -m_2 & -m \end{pmatrix}$,

- $\sqrt{\dfrac{2j+1}{2j_1+1}}(-1)^{j_2+m_2} \begin{pmatrix} j & j_2 & j_1 \\ -m & m_2 & -m_1 \end{pmatrix}$,

- $\sqrt{\dfrac{2j+1}{2j_1+1}}(-1)^{j_1-m_1+j-m} \begin{pmatrix} j & j_2 & j_1 \\ m & -m_2 & m_1 \end{pmatrix}$,

- $\sqrt{\dfrac{2j+1}{2j_1+1}}(-1)^{j-m+j_1-m_1} \begin{pmatrix} j_2 & j & j_1 \\ m_2 & -m & -m_1 \end{pmatrix}$,

- $\sqrt{\dfrac{2j+1}{2j_2+1}}(-1)^{j_1-m_1} \begin{pmatrix} j_1 & j & j_2 \\ m_1 & -m & -m_2 \end{pmatrix}$,

- $\sqrt{\dfrac{2j+1}{2j_2+1}}(-1)^{j_1-m_1} \begin{pmatrix} j & j_1 & j_2 \\ m & -m_1 & m_2 \end{pmatrix}$.

By use of the symmetry relations, Clebsch–Gordan coefficients may be put in the standard form $j_1 \le j_2 \le j$ and $m \ge 0$.

m_2	m	j_1	j	$\begin{pmatrix} j_1 & j_2 & j \\ m_1 & m_2 & m \end{pmatrix}$	
				$j_2 = 1/2$	
$-1/2$	0	1/2	1	0.707105	$\frac{\sqrt{2}}{2}$
1/2	0	1/2	1	0.707105	$\frac{\sqrt{2}}{2}$
0	1/2	1/2	1	0.866025	$\frac{\sqrt{3}}{2}$
1/2	1/2	1/2	1	0.866025	$\frac{\sqrt{3}}{2}$
1/2	1	1/2	1	1.000000	1

m_2	m	j_1	j	$\begin{pmatrix} j_1 & j_2 & j \\ m_1 & m_2 & m \end{pmatrix}$	
				$j_2 = 1$	
-1	0	1	1	0.707105	$\frac{\sqrt{2}}{2}$
1	0	1	1	-0.707105	$-\frac{\sqrt{2}}{2}$
$-1/2$	$1/2$	1	1	0.750000	$3/4$
0	$1/2$	1	1	0.353553	$\frac{\sqrt{2}}{4}$
$1/2$	$1/2$	1	1	-0.353553	$-\frac{\sqrt{2}}{4}$
1	$1/2$	1	1	-0.750000	$-3/4$
0	1	1	1	0.707105	$\frac{\sqrt{2}}{2}$
1	1	1	1	-0.707105	$-\frac{\sqrt{2}}{2}$
$-1/2$	0	$1/2$	$3/2$	0.707105	$\frac{\sqrt{2}}{2}$
0	0	$1/2$	$3/2$	0.866025	$\frac{\sqrt{3}}{2}$
$1/2$	0	$1/2$	$3/2$	0.707105	$\frac{\sqrt{2}}{2}$
0	$1/2$	$1/2$	$3/2$	0.816496	$\frac{\sqrt{6}}{3}$
1	$1/2$	$1/2$	$3/2$	0.577349	$\frac{\sqrt{3}}{3}$
$1/2$	1	$1/2$	$3/2$	0.912873	$\frac{\sqrt{30}}{6}$
1	1	$1/2$	$3/2$	0.790570	$\frac{\sqrt{10}}{4}$
1	$3/2$	$1/2$	$3/2$	1.000000	1
-1	0	1	2	0.408249	$\frac{\sqrt{6}}{6}$
0	0	1	2	0.816496	$\frac{\sqrt{6}}{3}$
1	0	1	2	0.408249	$\frac{\sqrt{6}}{6}$
$-1/2$	$1/2$	1	2	0.559018	$\frac{\sqrt{5}}{4}$
0	$1/2$	1	2	0.790570	$\frac{\sqrt{10}}{4}$
$1/2$	$1/2$	1	2	0.790570	$\frac{\sqrt{10}}{4}$
1	$1/2$	1	2	0.559018	$\frac{\sqrt{5}}{4}$
0	1	1	2	0.707105	$\frac{\sqrt{2}}{2}$
1	1	1	2	0.707105	$\frac{\sqrt{2}}{2}$
$1/2$	$3/2$	1	2	0.853916	$\frac{\sqrt{105}}{12}$
1	$3/2$	1	2	0.853916	$\frac{\sqrt{105}}{12}$
1	2	1	2	1.000000	1

6.21 INTEGRAL TRANSFORMS: PRELIMINARIES

- $I = (a, b)$ is an interval, where $-\infty \leq a < b \leq \infty$.

- $L^1(I)$ is the set of all absolutely integrable functions on I. In particular, $L^1(\mathbb{R})$ is the set of all absolutely integrable functions on the real line $\mathbb{R}$.

- $L^2(I)$ is the set of all square integrable functions on I.

- If f is integrable over every finite closed subinterval of I, but not necessarily on I itself, we say that f is locally integrable on I. For example, the function $f(x) = 1/x$ is not integrable on the interval $I = (0, 1)$, yet it is locally integrable on it.

- A function $f(x)$, defined on a closed interval $[a, b]$, is said to be of bounded variation if there is a positive number M so that, for any partition $a = x_0 < x_1 < x_2 < \cdots , x_n = b$, the following relation holds: $\displaystyle\sum_{i=1}^{n} |f(x_i) - f(x_{i-1})| \leq M$.

- If f has a derivative f' at every point of $[a, b]$, then by the mean value theorem, for any $a \leq x < y \leq b$, we have $f(x) - f(y) = f'(z)(x - y)$, for some $x < z < y$. If f' is bounded, then f is of bounded variation.

- The left limit of a function $f(x)$ at a point t (if it exists) will be denoted by $\lim_{x \to t^-} f(x) = f(t-)$, and likewise the right limit at t will be denoted by $\lim_{x \to t^+} f(x) = f(t+)$.

6.22 FOURIER INTEGRAL TRANSFORM

The origin of the Fourier integral transformation can be traced to Fourier's celebrated work on the *Analytical Theory of Heat*, which appeared in 1822. Fourier's major finding was to show that an "arbitrary" function defined on a finite interval could be expanded in a trigonometric series (series of sinusoidal functions). In an attempt to extend his results to functions defined on the infinite interval $(0, \infty)$, Fourier introduced what is now known as the Fourier integral transform.

The Fourier integral transform of a function $f(t)$ is defined by

$$\mathcal{F}(f)(\omega) = \hat{f}(\omega) = F(\omega) = \frac{1}{\sqrt{2\pi}} \int_{-\infty}^{\infty} f(t)e^{it\omega} \, dt, \tag{6.22.1}$$

whenever the integral exists.

There is no universal agreement on the definition of the Fourier integral transform. Some authors take the kernel of the transformation as $e^{-it\omega}$, so that the kernel of the inverse transformation is $e^{it\omega}$. In either case, if we define the Fourier transform as

$$\hat{f}(\omega) = a \int_{-\infty}^{\infty} f(t)e^{\pm it\omega}\, dt,$$

then its inverse is $f(t) = b \int_{-\infty}^{\infty} \hat{f}(\omega)e^{\mp it\omega}\, d\omega,$ (6.22.2)

for some constants a and b, with $ab = 1/2\pi$. Again there is no agreement on the choice of the constants; sometimes one of them is taken as 1 so that the other is $1/(2\pi)$. For the sake of symmetry, we choose $a = b = 1/\sqrt{2\pi}$. The functions f and $\hat{f}$ are called a Fourier transform pair.

Another definition that is popular in the engineering literature is the one in which the kernel of the transform is taken as $e^{2\pi it\omega}$ (or $e^{-2\pi it\omega}$) so that the kernel of the inverse transform is $e^{-2\pi it\omega}$ (or $e^{2\pi it\omega}$). The main advantage of this definition is that the constants a and b disappear and the Fourier transform pair becomes

$$\hat{f}(\omega) = \int_{-\infty}^{\infty} f(t)e^{\pm 2\pi it\omega}\, dt \qquad \text{and} \qquad f(t) = \int_{-\infty}^{\infty} \hat{f}(\omega)e^{\mp 2\pi it\omega}\, d\omega.$$
(6.22.3)

The Fourier cosine and sine coefficients of $f(t)$ are defined by

$$a(\omega) = \frac{1}{\pi}\int_{-\infty}^{\infty} f(t)\cos\omega t\, dt \quad \text{and} \quad b(\omega) = \frac{1}{\pi}\int_{-\infty}^{\infty} f(t)\sin\omega t\, dt.$$
(6.22.4)

The Fourier cosine and sine coefficients are related to the Fourier cosine and sine integral transforms. For example, if f is even, then $a(\omega) = \sqrt{2/\pi}\, F_c(\omega)$ and, if f is odd, $b(\omega) = \sqrt{2/\pi}\, F_s(\omega)$ (see Section 6.22.7).

Two other integrals related to the Fourier integral transform are Fourier's repeated integral and the allied integral. Fourier's repeated integral, $S(f, t)$, of $f(t)$ is defined by

$$S(f, t) = \int_0^{\infty} (a(\omega)\cos t\omega + b(\omega)\sin t\omega)\, d\omega,$$
$$= \frac{1}{\pi}\int_0^{\infty} d\omega \int_{-\infty}^{\infty} f(x)\cos\omega(t - x)\, dx.$$
(6.22.5)

The allied Fourier integral, $\tilde{S}(f, t)$, of f is defined by

$$\tilde{S}(f, t) = \int_0^{\infty} (b(\omega)\cos t\omega - a(\omega)\sin t\omega)\, d\omega,$$
$$= \frac{1}{\pi}\int_0^{\infty} d\omega \int_{-\infty}^{\infty} f(x)\sin\omega(x - t)\, dx.$$
(6.22.6)

6.22.1 EXISTENCE

For the Fourier integral transform to exist, it is sufficient that f be absolutely integrable on $(-\infty, \infty)$, i.e., $f \in L^1(\mathbb{R})$.

THEOREM 6.22.1   *(Riemann–Lebesgue lemma)*

If $f \in L^1(\mathbb{R})$, then its Fourier transform $\hat{f}(\omega)$ is defined everywhere, uniformly continuous, and tends to zero as $\omega \to \pm\infty$.

The uniform continuity follows from the relationship

$$\left| \hat{f}(\omega + h) - \hat{f}(\omega) \right| \leq \frac{1}{\sqrt{2\pi}} \int_{-\infty}^{\infty} |f(t)| \left| e^{iht} - 1 \right| dt,$$

and the tendency toward zero at $\pm\infty$ is a consequence of the Riemann–Lebesgue lemma.

THEOREM 6.22.2   *(Riemann–Lebesgue lemma)*

Let $f \in L^1(I)$, where $I = (a, b)$ is finite or infinite and let ω be a real variable. Let $a \leq a' < b' \leq b$ and $\hat{f}_\omega(\lambda, a', b') = \int_{a'}^{b'} f(t)e^{i\lambda\omega t}\, dt$. Then $\lim_{\omega \to \pm\infty} \hat{f}_\omega(\lambda, a', b') = 0$, and the convergence is uniform in a' and b'. In particular, $\lim_{\omega \to \pm\infty} \int_{-\infty}^{\infty} f(t)e^{i\omega t}\, dt = 0$.

6.22.2   PROPERTIES

1. *Linearity*: The Fourier transform is linear,

   $$\mathcal{F}\left[af(t) + bg(t)\right](\omega) = a\mathcal{F}\left[f(t)\right](\omega) + b\mathcal{F}\left[g(t)\right](\omega) = a\hat{f}(\omega) + b\hat{g}(\omega),$$

   where a and b are complex numbers.

2. *Translation*: $\mathcal{F}\left[f(t - b)\right](\omega) = e^{ib\omega}\hat{f}(\omega).$

3. *Dilation (scaling)*: $\mathcal{F}\left[f(at)\right](\omega) = \frac{1}{a}\hat{f}(\frac{\omega}{a}), \quad a \neq 0.$

4. *Translation and dilation*:

   $$\mathcal{F}\left[f(at - b)\right](\omega) = \frac{1}{a}e^{ib\omega/a}\hat{f}\left(\frac{\omega}{a}\right), \quad a > 0.$$

5. *Complex conjugation*: $\mathcal{F}\left[\bar{f}(t)\right](\omega) = \overline{\hat{f}(-\omega)}.$

6. *Modulation*: $\mathcal{F}\left[e^{iat}f(t)\right](\omega) = \hat{f}(\omega + a)$, and

   $$\mathcal{F}\left[e^{iat}f(bt)\right](\omega) = \frac{1}{b}\hat{f}\left(\frac{\omega + a}{b}\right), \quad b > 0. \tag{6.22.7}$$

7. *Differentiation*: If $f^{(k)} \in L^1(\mathbb{R})$, for $k = 0, 1, 2, \cdots, n$ and $\lim_{|t| \to \infty} f^{(k)}(t) = 0$ for $k = 0, 1, 2, \cdots, n - 1$, then

   $$\mathcal{F}\left[f^{(n)}(t)\right](\omega) = (-i\omega)^n \hat{f}(\omega). \tag{6.22.8}$$

8. *Integration*: Let $f \in L^1(\mathbb{R})$, and define $g(x) = \int_{-\infty}^{x} f(t)\, dt$. If $g \in L^1(\mathbb{R})$, then $\hat{g}(\omega) = -\hat{f}(\omega)/(i\omega).$

9. *Multiplication by polynomials*: If $t^n f(t) \in L^1(\mathbb{R})$, then

$$\mathcal{F}\left[t^k f(t)\right](\omega) = \frac{1}{(i)^k} \hat{f}^{(k)}(\omega), \qquad (6.22.9)$$

and hence,

$$\mathcal{F}\left[\left(\sum_{k=0}^{n} a_k t^k\right) f(t)\right](\omega) = \sum_{k=0}^{n} \frac{a_k}{(i)^k} \hat{f}^{(k)}(\omega). \qquad (6.22.10)$$

10. *Convolution*: The convolution operation, $\star$, associated with the Fourier transform is defined as

$$h(t) = (f \star g)(t) = \frac{1}{\sqrt{2\pi}} \int_{-\infty}^{\infty} f(x)g(t-x)dx,$$

where f and g are defined over the whole real line.

THEOREM 6.22.3

If f and g belong to $L^1(\mathbb{R})$, then so does h. Moreover, $\hat{h}(\omega) = \hat{f}(\omega)\hat{g}(\omega)$. If $\hat{f}$ and $\hat{g}$ belong to $L^1(\mathbb{R})$, then $(\hat{f} \star \hat{g})(\omega) = \widehat{(fg)}(\omega)$.

11. *Parseval's relation*: If F and G are the Fourier transforms of f and g respectively, then Parseval's relation is

$$\int_{-\infty}^{\infty} F(\omega)G(\omega)\, d\omega = \int_{-\infty}^{\infty} f(t)g(-t)\, dt. \qquad (6.22.11)$$

Replacing G by $\bar{G}$ (so that $g(-t)$ is replaced by $\bar{g}(t)$) results in a more convenient form of Parseval's relation

$$\int_{-\infty}^{\infty} F(\omega)\bar{G}(\omega)\, d\omega = \int_{-\infty}^{\infty} f(t)\bar{g}(t)\, dt. \qquad (6.22.12)$$

In particular, for $f = g$,

$$\int_{-\infty}^{\infty} |F(\omega)|^2\, d\omega = \int_{-\infty}^{\infty} |f(t)|^2\, dt. \qquad (6.22.13)$$

6.22.3 INVERSION FORMULA

Many of the theorems on the inversion of the Fourier transform are based on *Dini's condition* which can be stated as follows:

If $f \in L^1(\mathbb{R})$, then a necessary and sufficient condition that

$$S(f, x) = \lim_{\lambda \to \infty} \frac{1}{\pi} \int_{-\infty}^{\infty} f(t) \frac{\sin \lambda(x-t)}{(x-t)}\, dt = a$$

is that

$$\lim_{\lambda \to \infty} \int_0^\delta (f(x+y) + f(x-y) - 2a) \frac{\sin \lambda y}{y} dy = 0,$$

(6.22.14)

for any fixed $\delta > 0$.

By the Riemann–Lebesgue lemma, this condition is satisfied if

$$\int_0^\delta \left| \frac{f(x+y) + f(x-y) - 2a}{y} \right| dy < \infty,$$

(6.22.15)

for some $\delta > 0$. In particular, condition (6.22.15) holds for $a = f(x)$, if f is differentiable at x, and for $a = [f(x+0) + f(x-0)]/2$, if f is of bounded variation in a neighborhood of x.

THEOREM 6.22.4   *(Inversion theorem)*

Let f be a locally integrable function, of bounded variation in a neighborhood of the point x. If f satisfies either one of the following conditions:

1. *$f(t) \in L^1(\mathbb{R})$, or*
2. *$f(t)/(1 + |t|) \in L^1(\mathbb{R})$, and the integral $\int_{-\infty}^{\infty} f(t) e^{i\omega t} dt$ converges uniformly on every finite interval of ω,*

then

$$\frac{1}{\sqrt{2\pi}} \int_{-\infty}^{\infty} \hat{f}(\omega) e^{-ix\omega} d\omega = \lim_{\lambda \to \infty} \frac{1}{\sqrt{2\pi}} \int_{-\lambda}^{\lambda} \hat{f}(\omega) e^{-ix\omega} d\omega$$

is equal to $[f(x+0) + f(x-0)]/2$ whenever the expression has meaning, to $f(x)$ whenever $f(x)$ is continuous at x, and to $f(x)$ almost everywhere. If f is continuous and of bounded variation in the interval (a, b), then the convergence is uniform in any interval interior to (a, b).

6.22.4   POISSON SUMMATION FORMULA

The Poisson summation formula may be written in the form

$$\frac{1}{\sqrt{2\pi}} \sum_{k=-\infty}^{\infty} f\left(t + \frac{k\pi}{\sigma}\right) = \frac{\sigma}{\pi} \sum_{k=-\infty}^{\infty} \hat{f}(2k\sigma) e^{-2ikt\sigma}, \quad \sigma > 0,$$

(6.22.16)

provided that the two series converge. A sufficient condition for the validity of Equation (6.22.16) is that $f = O(1 + |t|)^{-\alpha}$ as $|t| \to \infty$, and $\hat{f} = O\left((1 + |\omega|)^{-\alpha}\right)$ as $|\omega| \to \infty$ for some $\alpha > 1$.

Another version of the Poisson summation formula is

$$\sum_{k=-\infty}^{\infty} \hat{f}(\omega + k\sigma) \overline{\hat{g}}(\omega + k\sigma) = \frac{1}{\sigma} \sum_{k=-\infty}^{\infty} \left(\int_{-\infty}^{\infty} f(t) \overline{g}\left(t - \frac{2\pi k}{\sigma}\right) dt \right) e^{2\pi ik\omega/\sigma}.$$

(6.22.17)

6.22.5   SHANNON'S SAMPLING THEOREM

If f is a function band-limited to $[-\sigma, \sigma]$, i.e.,

$$f(t) = \frac{1}{\sqrt{2\pi}} \int_{-\sigma}^{\sigma} F(\omega) e^{it\omega} \, d\omega,$$

with $F \in L^2(-\sigma, \sigma)$, then it can be reconstructed from its sample values at the points $t_k = (k\pi)/\sigma, k = 0, \pm 1, \pm 2, \cdots$, via the formula

$$f(t) = \sum_{k=-\infty}^{\infty} f(t_k) \frac{\sin \sigma (t - t_k)}{\sigma (t - t_k)}, \qquad (6.22.18)$$

with the series absolutely and uniformly convergent on compact sets.

The series on the right-hand side of Equation (6.22.18) can be written as $\sin \sigma t \sum_{k=-\infty}^{\infty} f(t_k) \frac{(-1)^k}{(\sigma t - k\pi)}$, which is a special case of a Cardinal series (these series have the form $\sin \sigma t \sum_{k=-\infty}^{\infty} C_k \frac{(-1)^k}{(\sigma t - k\pi)}$).

6.22.6   UNCERTAINTY PRINCIPLE

Let T and W be two real numbers defined by

$$T^2 = \frac{1}{E} \int_{-\infty}^{\infty} t^2 |f(t)|^2 \, dt \quad \text{and} \quad W^2 = \frac{1}{E} \int_{-\infty}^{\infty} \omega^2 |\hat{f}(\omega)|^2 \, d\omega,$$

where

$$E = \int_{-\infty}^{\infty} |f(t)|^2 \, dt = \int_{-\infty}^{\infty} |\hat{f}(\omega)|^2 \, d\omega.$$

Assuming that f is differentiable and $\lim_{|t| \to \infty} t f^2(t) = 0$, then $2TW \geq 1$, or

$$\left(\int_{-\infty}^{\infty} t^2 |f(t)|^2 \, dt \right)^{1/2} \left(\int_{-\infty}^{\infty} \omega^2 |\hat{f}(\omega)|^2 \, d\omega \right)^{1/2} \geq \frac{1}{2} \int_{-\infty}^{\infty} |f(t)|^2 \, dt.$$

This means that f and $\hat{f}$ cannot both be very small. Another related property of the Fourier transform is that, if either one of the functions f or $\hat{f}$ vanishes outside some finite interval, then the other one must trail on to infinity. In other words, they can not both vanish outside any finite interval.

6.22.7   FOURIER SINE AND COSINE TRANSFORMS

The Fourier cosine transform, $F_c(\omega)$, and the Fourier sine transform, $F_s(\omega)$, of $f(t)$ are defined as

$$F_c(\omega) = \sqrt{\frac{2}{\pi}} \int_0^{\infty} f(t) \cos \omega t \, dt \quad \text{and} \quad F_s(\omega) = \sqrt{\frac{2}{\pi}} \int_0^{\infty} f(t) \sin \omega t \, dt. \qquad (6.22.19)$$

The inverse transforms have the same functional form:

$$f(t) = \sqrt{\frac{2}{\pi}} \int_0^\infty F_c(\omega) \cos \omega t \, d\omega = \sqrt{\frac{2}{\pi}} \int_0^\infty F_s(\omega) \sin \omega t \, d\omega.$$

$$(6.22.20)$$

If f is even, i.e., $f(t) = f(-t)$, then $F(\omega) = F_c(\omega)$, and if f is odd, i.e., $f(t) = -f(-t)$, then $F(\omega) = i F_s(\omega)$.

6.23   DISCRETE FOURIER TRANSFORM (DFT)

The discrete Fourier transform of the sequence $\{a_n\}_{n=0}^{N-1}$, where $N \geq 1$, is a sequence $\{A_m\}_{m=0}^{N-1}$, defined by

$$A_m = \sum_{n=0}^{N-1} a_n (W_N)^{mn}, \qquad \text{for} \quad m = 0, 1, \cdots, N-1,$$

$$(6.23.1)$$

where $W_N = e^{2\pi i / N}$. Note that $\sum_{m=0}^{N-1} W_N^{m(k-n)} = N\delta_{kn}$. For example, the DFT of the sequence $\{1, 0, 1, 1\}$ is $\{3, -i, 1, i\}$.

The inversion formula is

$$a_n = \frac{1}{N} \sum_{m=0}^{N-1} A_m W_N^{-mn}, \qquad n = 0, 1, \cdots, N-1.$$

$$(6.23.2)$$

Equations (6.23.1) and (6.23.2) are called a discrete Fourier transform (DFT) pair of order N. The factor $1/N$ and the negative sign in the exponent of W_N that appear in Equation (6.23.2) are sometimes introduced in Equation (6.23.1) instead. We use the notation

$$\mathcal{F}_N[(a_n)] = A_m \qquad \mathcal{F}_N^{-1}[(A_m)] = a_n,$$

to indicate that the discrete Fourier transform of order N of the sequence $\{a_n\}$ is $\{A_m\}$ and that the inverse transform of $\{A_m\}$ is $\{a_n\}$.

Because $W_N^{\pm(m+N)n} = W_N^{\pm mn}$, Equations (6.23.1) and (6.23.2) can be used to extend the sequences $\{a_n\}_{n=0}^{N-1}$ and $\{A_m\}_{m=0}^{N-1}$, as periodic sequences with period N. This means that $A_{m+N} = A_m$, and $a_{n+N} = a_n$. Using this, the summation limits, 0 and $N-1$, can be replaced with n_1 and $n_1 + N - 1$, respectively, where n_1 is any integer. In the special case where $n_1 = -M$ and $N = 2M + 1$, Equations (6.23.1) and (6.23.2) become

$$A_m = \sum_{n=-M}^{M} a_n W_N^{mn}, \qquad \text{for} \quad m = -M, -M+1, \cdots, M-1, M,$$

$$(6.23.3)$$

and

$$a_n = \frac{1}{2M+1} \sum_{m=-M}^{M} A_m W_N^{-mn}, \qquad \text{for} \quad n = -M, -M+1, \cdots, M-1, M.$$

$$(6.23.4)$$

6.23.1 PROPERTIES

1. *Linearity:* The discrete Fourier transform is linear, that is

$$\mathcal{F}_N[\alpha(a_n) + \beta(b_n)] = \alpha A_m + \beta B_m,$$

for any complex numbers α and β, where the sum of two sequences is defined as $(a_n) + (b_n) = (a_n + b_n)$.

2. *Translation:* $\mathcal{F}_N[(a_{n-k})] = W_N^{mk} A_m$, or $e^{2\pi i mk/N} A_m = \sum_{n=0}^{N-1} a_{n-k} W_N^{mn}$.

3. *Modulation:* $\mathcal{F}_N[(W_N^{nk} a_n)] = A_{m+k}$, or $A_{m+k} = \sum_{n=0}^{N-1} e^{2\pi i nk/N} a_n W_N^{mn}$.

4. *Complex Conjugation:* $\mathcal{F}_N[(\bar{a}_{-n})] = \bar{A}_m$, or $\bar{A}_m = \sum_{n=0}^{N-1} \bar{a}_{-n} W_N^{mn}$.

5. *Symmetry:* $\mathcal{F}_N[(a_{-n})] = A_{-m}$, or $A_{-m} = \sum_{n=0}^{N-1} a_{-n} W_N^{mn}$.

6. *Convolution:* The convolution of the sequences $\{a_n\}_{n=0}^{N-1}$ and $\{b_n\}_{n=0}^{N-1}$ is the sequence $\{c_n\}_{n=0}^{N-1}$ given by

$$c_n = \sum_{k=0}^{N-1} a_k b_{n-k}. \tag{6.23.5}$$

The *convolution relation of the DFT* is $\mathcal{F}_N[(c_n)] = \mathcal{F}_N[(a_n)]\mathcal{F}_N[(b_n)]$, or $C_m = A_m B_m$. A consequence of this and Equation (6.23.2), is the relation

$$\sum_{k=0}^{N-1} a_k b_{n-k} = \frac{1}{N} \sum_{m=0}^{N-1} A_m B_m W_N^{-mn}. \tag{6.23.6}$$

7. *Parseval's relation:*

$$\sum_{n=0}^{N-1} a_n \bar{d}_n = \frac{1}{N} \sum_{m=0}^{N-1} A_m \bar{D}_m. \tag{6.23.7}$$

In particular,

$$\sum_{n=0}^{N-1} |a_n|^2 = \frac{1}{N} \sum_{m=0}^{N-1} |A_m|^2. \tag{6.23.8}$$

In (4) and (5), the fact that $\bar{W}_N = W_N^{-1}$ has been used. A sequence $\{a_n\}$ is said to be even if $\{a_{-n}\} = \{a_n\}$ and is said to be odd if $\{a_{-n}\} = \{-a_n\}$. The following are consequences of (4) and (5):

1. If $\{a_n\}$ is a sequence of real numbers, i.e., $\bar{a}_n = a_n$, then $\bar{A}_m = A_{-m}$.

2. $\{a_n\}$ is real and even if and only if $\{A_m\}$ is real and even.

3. $\{a_n\}$ is real and odd if and only if $\{A_m\}$ is pure imaginary and odd.

6.24   FAST FOURIER TRANSFORM (FFT)

To determine A_m for each $m = 0, 1, \cdots, M - 1$ (using Equation (6.23.1)), $M - 1$ multiplications are required. Hence the total number of multiplications required to determine all the A_m's is $(M - 1)^2$. This number can be reduced by using decimation.

Assuming M is even, we put $M = 2N$ and write

$$\mathcal{F}_{2N}[(a_n)] = A_m. \tag{6.24.1}$$

Now split $\{a_n\}$ into two sequences, one consisting of terms with even subscripts ($b_n = a_{2n}$) and one with odd subscripts ($c_n = a_{2n+1}$). Then

$$A_m = B_m + W_{2N}^m C_m. \tag{6.24.2}$$

For the evaluation of B_m and C_m, the total number of multiplications required is $2(N - 1)^2$. To determine A_m from Equation (6.24.2), we must calculate the product $W_{2N}^m C_m$, for each fixed m. Therefore, the total number of multiplications required to determine A_m from Equation (6.24.2) is $2(N - 1)^2 + 2N - 1 = 2N^2 - 2N + 1$.

But had we determined A_m from (6.24.1), we would have performed $(2N - 1)^2 = 4N^2 - 4N + 1$ multiplications. Thus, splitting the sequence $\{a_n\}$ into two sequences and then applying the discrete Fourier transform, reduces the number of multiplications required to evaluate A_m approximately by a factor of 2.

If N is even, this process can be repeated. Split $\{b_n\}$ and $\{c_n\}$ into four sequences, each of length $N/2$. Then B_m and C_m are determined in terms of four discrete Fourier transforms, each of order $N/2$. This process can be continued $k - 1$ times if $M = 2^k$ for some positive integer k.

If we denote the required number of multiplications for the discrete Fourier transform of order $N = 2^k$ by $F(N)$, then $F(2N) = 2F(N) + N$ and $F(2) = 1$, which leads to $F(N) = \frac{N}{2} \log_2 N$.

6.25   MULTIDIMENSIONAL FOURIER TRANSFORMS

If $\mathbf{x} = (x_1, x_2, \ldots, x_n)$ and $\mathbf{u} = (u_1, u_2, \ldots, u_n)$, then

1. Fourier transform
$$F(\mathbf{u}) = (2\pi)^{-n/2} \int \cdots \int_{\mathbb{R}^n} f(\mathbf{x}) e^{-i(\mathbf{x} \cdot \mathbf{u})} \, d\mathbf{x}.$$

2. Inverse Fourier transform
$$f(\mathbf{x}) = (2\pi)^{-n/2} \int \cdots \int_{\mathbb{R}^n} F(\mathbf{u}) e^{i(\mathbf{x} \cdot \mathbf{u})} \, d\mathbf{u}.$$

3. Parseval's relation
$$\int \cdots \int_{\mathbb{R}^n} f(\mathbf{x}) \overline{g(\mathbf{x})} \, d\mathbf{x} = (2\pi)^{-n} \int \cdots \int_{\mathbb{R}^n} F(\mathbf{u}) \overline{G(\mathbf{u})} \, d\mathbf{u}.$$

6.26 LAPLACE TRANSFORM

The Laplace transformation dates back to the work of the French mathematician, Pierre Simon Marquis de Laplace (1749–1827), who used it in his work on probability theory in the 1780's.

The Laplace transform of a function $f(t)$ is defined as

$$F(s) = (\mathcal{L}f)(s) = \int_0^\infty f(t)e^{-st}\, dt, \qquad (6.26.1)$$

whenever the integral exists for at least one value of s. The transform variable, s, can be taken as a complex number. We say that f is Laplace transformable or the Laplace transformation is applicable to f if $(\mathcal{L}f)$ exists for at least one value of s. The integral on the right-hand side of Equation (6.26.1) is called the Laplace integral of f.

6.26.1 EXISTENCE AND DOMAIN OF CONVERGENCE

Sufficient conditions for the existence of the Laplace transform are

1. f is a locally integrable function, i.e., $\int_0^a |f(t)|\, dt < \infty$, for any $a > 0$.
2. f is of (real) exponential type, i.e., for some constants $M, t_0 > 0$ and real γ, f satisfies

$$|f(t)| \le Me^{\gamma t}, \qquad \text{for all } t \ge t_0. \qquad (6.26.2)$$

If f is a locally integrable function on $[0, \infty)$ and of (real) exponential type γ, then the Laplace integral of f, $\int_0^\infty f(t)e^{-st}\, dt$, converges absolutely for $\operatorname{Re} s > \gamma$ and uniformly for $\operatorname{Re} s \ge \gamma_1 > \gamma$. Consequently, $F(s)$ is analytic in the half-plane $\Omega = \{s \in \mathbb{C} : \operatorname{Re} s > \gamma\}$. It can be shown that if $F(s)$ exists for some s_0, then it also exists for any s for which $\operatorname{Re} s > \operatorname{Re} s_0$. The actual domain of existence of the Laplace transform may be larger than the one given above. For example, the function $f(t) = \cos e^t$ is of real exponential type zero, but $F(s)$ exists for $\operatorname{Re} s > -1$.

If $f(t)$ is a locally integrable function on $[0, \infty)$, not of exponential type, and

$$\int_0^\infty f(t)e^{-s_0 t}\, dt \qquad (6.26.3)$$

converges for some complex number s_0, then the Laplace integral

$$\int_0^\infty f(t)e^{-st}\, dt \qquad (6.26.4)$$

converges in the region $\operatorname{Re} s > \operatorname{Re} s_0$ and converges uniformly in the region $|\arg(s - s_0)| \le \theta' < \frac{\pi}{2}$. Moreover, if Equation (6.26.3) diverges, then so does Equation (6.26.4) for $\operatorname{Re} s < \operatorname{Re} s_0$.

6.26.2 PROPERTIES

1. *Linearity:* $\mathcal{L}(\alpha f + \beta g) = \alpha \mathcal{L}(f) + \beta \mathcal{L}(g) = \alpha F + \beta G$, for any constants α and β.

2. *Dilation:* $[\mathcal{L}(f(at))](s) = \dfrac{1}{a} F\left(\dfrac{s}{a}\right)$, for $a > 0$.

3. *Multiplication by Exponential Functions:*

$$\left[\mathcal{L}\left(e^{at} f(t)\right)\right](s) = F(s - a).$$

4. *Translation:* $[\mathcal{L}(f(t - a) H(t - a))](s) = e^{-as} F(s)$ for $a > 0$. This can be put in the form

$$[\mathcal{L}(f(t) H(t - a))](s) = e^{-as} [\mathcal{L}(f(t + a))](s),$$

where H is the Heaviside function. Examples:

   (a) If

$$g(t) = \begin{cases} 0, & 0 \le t \le a, \\ (t - a)^{\nu}, & a \le t, \end{cases}$$

then $g(t) = f(t - a) H(t - a)$ where $f(t) = t^{\nu} (Re\ \nu > -1)$. Since $\mathcal{L}(t^{\nu}) = \Gamma(\nu + 1)/s^{\nu+1}$, it follows that $(\mathcal{L}g)(s) = e^{-as} \Gamma(\nu + 1)/s^{\nu+1}$, for $Re\ s > 0$.

   (b) If

$$g(t) = \begin{cases} t, & 0 \le t \le a, \\ 0, & a < t, \end{cases}$$

we may write $g(t) = t [H(t) - H(t - a)] = t H(t) - (t - a) H(t - a) - a H(t - a)$. Thus by properties (1) and (4),

$$G(s) = \frac{1}{s^2} - \frac{1}{s^2} e^{-as} - \frac{a}{s} e^{-as}.$$

5. *Differentiation of the transformed function:* If f is a differentiable function of exponential type, $\lim_{t \to 0^+} f(t) = f(0^+)$ exists, and f' is locally integrable on $[0, \infty)$, then the Laplace transform of f' exists, and

$$(\mathcal{L}f')(s) = s F(s) - f(0). \tag{6.26.5}$$

Note that although f is assumed to be of exponential type, f' need not be. For example, $f(t) = \sin e^{t^2}$, but $f'(t) = 2t e^{t^2} \cos e^{t^2}$.

6. *Differentiation of higher orders:* Let f be an n differentiable function so that $f^{(k)}$ (for $k = 0, 1, \ldots, n - 1$) are of exponential type with the additional assumption that $\lim_{t \to 0^+} f^{(k)}(t) = f^{(k)}(0+)$ exists. If $f^{(n)}$ is locally integrable on $[0, \infty)$, then its Laplace transform exists, and

$$\left[\mathcal{L}\left(f^{(n)}\right)\right](s) = s^n F(s) - s^{n-1} f(0) - s^{n-2} f'(0) - \cdots - f^{(n-1)}(0). \tag{6.26.6}$$

7. *Integration*: If $g(t) = \int_0^t f(x)\, dx$, then (if the transforms exist) $G(s) = F(s)/s$. Repeated applications of this rule result in

$$\left[\mathcal{L}\left(f^{(-n)}\right)\right](s) = \frac{1}{s^n} F(s), \tag{6.26.7}$$

where $f^{(-n)}$ is the nth antiderivative of f defined by $f^{(-n)}(t) = \int_0^t dt_n \int_0^{t_n} dt_{n-1}$ $\ldots \int_0^{t_2} f(t_1)\, dt_1$. Section 6.26.1 shows that the Laplace transform is an analytic function in a half-plane. Hence it has derivatives of all orders at any point in that half-plane. The next property shows that we can evaluate these derivatives by direct differentiation.

8. *Multiplication by powers of t*: Let f be a locally integrable function whose Laplace integral converges absolutely and uniformly for Re $s > \sigma$. Then F is analytic in Re $s > \sigma$, and (for $n = 0, 1, 2, \ldots$, with Re $s > \sigma$)

$$\left[\mathcal{L}\left(t^n f(t)\right)\right](s) = \left(-\frac{d}{ds}\right)^n F(s),$$

$$\left[\mathcal{L}\left(\left(t\frac{d}{dt}\right)^n f(t)\right)\right](s) = \left(-\frac{d}{ds}s\right)^n F(s), \tag{6.26.8}$$

where $\left(t\frac{d}{dt}\right)^n$ is the operator $\left(t\frac{d}{dt}\right)$ applied n times.

9. *Division by powers of t*: If f is a locally integrable function of exponential type so that $f(t)/t$ is a Laplace transformable function, then

$$\left[\mathcal{L}\left(\frac{f(t)}{t}\right)\right](s) = \int_s^\infty F(u)\, du, \tag{6.26.9}$$

or, more generally,

$$\left[\mathcal{L}\left(\frac{f(t)}{t^n}\right)\right](s) = \int_s^\infty \cdots \int_s^\infty F(s)\, (ds)^n \tag{6.26.10}$$

is the nth repeated integral. It follows from properties (7) and (9) that

$$\left[\mathcal{L}\left(\int_0^t \frac{f(x)}{x}\, dx\right)\right](s) = \frac{1}{s}\int_s^\infty F(u)\, du. \tag{6.26.11}$$

10. *Periodic functions*: Let f be a locally integrable function that is periodic with period T. Then

$$[\mathcal{L}(f)](s) = \frac{1}{(1 - e^{-Ts})}\int_0^T f(t)e^{-st}\, dt. \tag{6.26.12}$$

11. *Hardy's theorem*: If $f(t) = \sum_{n=0}^\infty c_n t^n$ for $t \geq 0$ and $\sum_{n=0}^\infty \frac{c_n n!}{s_0^n}$ converges for some $s_0 > 0$, then $[\mathcal{L}(f)](s) = \sum_{n=0}^\infty \frac{c_n n!}{s^n}$ for Re $s > s_0$.

6.26.3   INVERSION FORMULAE

Inversion by integration

If $f(t)$ is a locally integrable function on $[0, \infty)$ such that

1. f is of bounded variation in a neighborhood of a point $t_0 \geq 0$ (a right-hand neighborhood if $t_0 = 0$),

2. The Laplace integral of f converges absolutely on the line Re $s = c$, then

$$\lim_{T \to \infty} \frac{1}{2\pi i} \int_{c-iT}^{c+iT} F(s)e^{st_0} ds = \begin{cases} 0, & \text{if } t_0 < 0, \\ f(0+)/2 & \text{if } t_0 = 0, \\ \left[f(t_0+) + f(t_0-) \right]/2 & \text{if } t_0 > 0. \end{cases}$$

In particular, if f is differentiable on $(0, \infty)$ and satisfies the above conditions, then

$$\lim_{T \to \infty} \frac{1}{2\pi i} \int_{c-iT}^{c+iT} F(s)e^{st} ds = f(t), \quad 0 < t < \infty.$$

The integral here is taken to be a Cauchy principal value since, in general, this integral may be divergent. For example, if $f(t) = 1$, then $F(s) = 1/s$ and, for $c = 1$ and $t = 0$, the integral $\int_{1-i\infty}^{1+i\infty} \frac{1}{s} ds$ diverges.

Inversion by partial fractions

Suppose that F is a rational function $F(x) = P(s)/Q(s)$ in which the degree of the denominator Q is greater than that of the numerator P. For instance, let F be represented in its most reduced form where P and Q have no common zeros, and assume that Q has only simple zeros at $a_1, \ldots, a_n$, then

$$f(t) = \mathcal{L}^{-1}\left(F(s) \right)(t) = \mathcal{L}^{-1}\left(\frac{P(s)}{Q(s)} \right)(t) = \sum_{k=1}^{n} \frac{P(a_k)}{Q'(a_k)} e^{a_k t}. \tag{6.26.13}$$

For example, if $P(s) = s - 5$ and $Q(s) = s^2 + 6s + 13$, then $a_1 = -3 + 2i$, $a_2 = -3 - 2i$, and it follows that

$$f(t) = \mathcal{L}^{-1}\left(\frac{s - 5}{s^2 + 6s + 13} \right) = \frac{(2i - 8)}{4i} e^{(-3+2i)t} + \frac{(2i + 8)}{4i} e^{(-3-2i)t}$$

$$= e^{-3t}(\cos 2t - 4 \sin 2t).$$

6.26.4   CONVOLUTION

Let $f(t)$ and $g(t)$ be locally integrable functions on $[0, \infty)$, and assume that their Laplace integrals converge absolutely in some half-plane Re $s > \alpha$. Then the convolution operation, $\star$, associated with the Laplace transform, is defined by

$$h(t) = (f \star g)(t) = \int_0^t f(x)g(t-x)dx. \qquad (6.26.14)$$

The convolution of f and g is a locally integrable function on $[0, \infty)$ that is continuous if either f or g is continuous. Additionally, it has a Laplace transform given by

$$H(s) = (\mathcal{L}h)(s) = F(s)G(s), \qquad (6.26.15)$$

where $(\mathcal{L}f)(s) = F(s)$ and $(\mathcal{L}g)(s) = G(s)$.

6.27 Z-TRANSFORM

The Z-transform of a sequence $\{f(n)\}_{-\infty}^{\infty}$ is defined by

$$\mathcal{Z}[f(n)] = F(z) = \sum_{n=-\infty}^{\infty} f(n)z^{-n}, \qquad (6.27.1)$$

for all complex numbers z for which the series converges.

The series converges at least in a ring of the form $0 \leq r_1 < z < r_2 \leq \infty$, whose radii, r_1 and r_2, depend on the behavior of $f(n)$ at $\pm\infty$:

$$r_1 = \limsup_{n\to\infty} \sqrt[n]{|f(n)|}, \qquad r_2 = \liminf_{n\to\infty} \frac{1}{\sqrt[n]{|f(-n)|}}. \qquad (6.27.2)$$

If there is more than one sequence involved, we may denote r_1 and r_2 by $r_1(f)$ and $r_2(f)$ respectively. The function $F(z)$ is analytic in this ring, but it may be possible to continue it analytically beyond the boundaries of the ring. If $f(n) = 0$ for $n < 0$, then $r_2 = \infty$, and if $f(n) = 0$ for $n \geq 0$, then $r_1 = 0$.

Let $z = re^{i\theta}$. Then the Z-transform evaluated at $r = 1$ is the Fourier transform of the sequence $\{f(n)\}_{-\infty}^{\infty}$,

$$\sum_{n=-\infty}^{\infty} f(n)e^{-in\theta}. \qquad (6.27.3)$$

Examples:

1. Let a be a complex number and define $f(n) = a^n$, for $n \geq 0$, and zero otherwise, then

$$\mathcal{Z}[f(n)] = \sum_{n=0}^{\infty} a^n z^{-n} = \frac{z}{z-a} \quad , \quad |z| > |a|. \qquad (6.27.4)$$

2. If $f(n) = na^n$, for $n \geq 0$, and zero otherwise, then

$$\mathcal{Z}[f(n)] = \sum_{n=0}^{\infty} na^n z^{-n} = \frac{az}{(z-a)^2} \quad , \quad |z| > |a|.$$

3. Let $u(n) = \begin{cases} 1, & n \geq 0, \\ 0, & n < 0, \end{cases}$ then $\mathcal{Z}[u(n)] = \frac{z}{z-1}$.

4. Let $\delta(n) = \begin{cases} 1, & n = 0, \\ 0, & \text{otherwise}, \end{cases}$ then $\mathcal{Z}[\delta(n-k)] = z^{-k}$ for $k = 0, \pm 1, \pm 2, \cdots$.

6.27.1 PROPERTIES

Let the region of convergence of the Z-transform of the sequence $\{f(n)\}$ be denoted by D_f.

1. *Linearity:*

$$\mathcal{Z}[af(n)+bg(n)] = a\mathcal{Z}[f(n)]+b\mathcal{Z}[g(n)] = aF(z)+bG(z), \quad z \in D_f \cap D_g.$$

The region $D_f \cap D_g$ contains the ring $r_1 < |z| < r_2$, where
$r_1 = \text{maximum } \{r_1(f), r_1(g)\}$ and $r_2 = \text{minimum } \{r_2(f), r_2(g)\}$.

2. *Translation:* $\mathcal{Z}[f(n-k)] = z^{-k} F(z)$.

3. *Multiplication by exponentials:*
$\mathcal{Z}[(a^n f(n))] = F(z/a)$ when $ar_1 < |z| < ar_2$.

4. *Multiplication by powers of n:* For $k = 0, 1, 2, \cdots$ and $z \in D_f$,

$$\mathcal{Z}[(n^k f(n))] = (-1)^k \left(z\frac{d}{dz} \right)^k F(z). \tag{6.27.5}$$

5. *Conjugation:* $\mathcal{Z}[\bar{f}(-n)] = \bar{F}\left(\frac{1}{\bar{z}} \right)$.

6. *Initial and final values:* If $f(n) = 0$ for $n < 0$, then $\lim_{z \to \infty} F(z) = f(0)$ and, conversely, if $F(z)$ is defined for $r_1 < |z|$ and for some integer m, $\lim_{z \to \infty} z^m F(z) = A$, then $f(m) = A$ and $f(n) = 0$, for $n < m$.

7. *Parseval's relation:* Let $F(z)$ and $G(z)$ be the Z-transforms of $\{f(n)\}$ and $\{g(n)\}$, respectively. Then

$$\sum_{n=-\infty}^{\infty} f(n)\bar{g}(n) = \frac{1}{2\pi} \int_{-\pi}^{\pi} F(e^{i\omega})\bar{G}(e^{i\omega}) \, d\omega. \tag{6.27.6}$$

In particular,

$$\sum_{n=-\infty}^{\infty} |f(n)|^2 = \frac{1}{2\pi} \int_{-\pi}^{\pi} |F(e^{i\omega})|^2 \, d\omega. \tag{6.27.7}$$

6.27.2 INVERSION FORMULA

Consider the sequences

$$f(n) = u(n) = \begin{cases} 1, & n \geq 0, \\ 0, & n < 0, \end{cases} \quad \text{and} \quad g(n) = -u(-n-1) = \begin{cases} -1, & n < 0, \\ 0, & n \geq 0. \end{cases}$$

Note that $F(z) = \dfrac{z}{z-1}$ for $|z| > 1$, and $G(z) = \dfrac{z}{z-1}$ for $|z| < 1$. Hence, the inverse Z-transform of the function $z/(z-1)$ is not unique. In general, the inverse Z-transform is not unique, unless its region of convergence is specified.

1. *Inversion by using series representation:*
   If $F(z)$ is given by its series

$$F(z) = \sum_{n=-\infty}^{\infty} a_n z^{-n}, \quad r_1 < z < r_2,$$

   then its inverse Z-transform is unique and equals $\{f(n) = a_n\}$ for all n.

2. *Inversion by using complex integration:*
   If $F(z)$ is given in a closed form as an algebraic expression and its domain of analyticity is known, then its inverse Z-transform can be obtained by using the relationship

$$f(n) = \frac{1}{2\pi i} \oint_\gamma F(z) z^{n-1} dz, \tag{6.27.8}$$

   where γ is a closed contour surrounding the origin in the domain of analyticity of $F(z)$.

3. *Inversion by using Fourier series:*
   If the domain of analyticity of F contains the unit circle, $|r| = 1$, and if F is single valued therein, then $F(e^{i\theta})$ is a periodic function with period 2π, and, consequently, it can be expanded in a Fourier series. The coefficients of the series form the inverse Z-transform of F and they are given explicitly by

$$f(n) = \frac{1}{2\pi} \int_{-\pi}^{\pi} F(e^{i\theta}) e^{in\theta} d\theta. \tag{6.27.9}$$

4. *Inversion by using partial fractions:*
   Dividing Equation (6.27.4) by z and differentiating both sides with respect to z, results in

$$\mathcal{Z}^{-1}\left[(z-a)^{-k}\right] = \binom{n-1}{n-k} a^{n-k} u(n-k), \tag{6.27.10}$$

   for $k = 1, 2, \cdots$ and $|z| > |a| > 0$. Moreover, from the example on page 544,

$$\mathcal{Z}^{-1}\left[z^{-k}\right] = \delta(n-k). \tag{6.27.11}$$

Let $F(z)$ be a rational function of the form

$$F(z) = \frac{P(z)}{Q(z)} = \frac{a_N z^N + \cdots + a_1 z + a_0}{b_M z^M + \cdots + b_1 z + b_0}.$$

- Consider the case $N < M$. The denominator $Q(z)$ can be factored over the field of complex numbers as $Q(z) = c(z - z_1)^{k_1} \cdots (z - z_m)^{k_m}$, where c is a constant and $k_1 \cdots, k_m$ are positive integers satisfying $k_1 + \cdots + k_m = M$. Hence, F can be written in the form

$$F(z) = \sum_{i=1}^{m} \sum_{j=1}^{k_i} \frac{A_{i,j}}{(z - z_i)^j}, \tag{6.27.12}$$

where

$$A_{i,j} = \frac{1}{(k_i - j)!} \lim_{z \to z_i} \frac{d^{k_i - j}}{dz^{k_i - j}} (z - z_i)^{k_i} F(z). \tag{6.27.13}$$

The inverse Z-transform of the fractional decomposition Equation (6.27.12) in the region that is exterior to the smallest circle containing all the zeros of $Q(z)$ can be obtained by using Equation (6.27.10).

- Consider the case $N \geq M$. We must divide until F can be reduced to the form

$$F(z) = H(z) + \frac{R(z)}{Q(z)},$$

where the remainder polynomial, $R(z)$, has degree less than or equal to $M - 1$, and the quotient, $H(z)$, is a polynomial of degree, at most, $N - M$. The inverse Z-transform of the quotient polynomial can be obtained by using Equation (6.27.11) and that of $R(z)/Q(z)$ can be obtained as in the case $N < M$.

Example: to find the inverse Z-transform of the function,

$$F(z) = \frac{z^4 + 5}{(z - 1)^2(z - 2)}, \qquad |z| > 2,$$

the partial fraction expansion,

$$\frac{z^4 + 5}{(z - 1)^2(z - 2)} = z + 4 - \frac{1}{(z - 1)^2} - \frac{5}{(z - 1)} + \frac{16}{(z - 2)},$$

is created. With the aid of Equation (6.27.10) and Equation (6.27.11),

$$\mathcal{Z}^{-1}[F(z)] = \delta(n+1) + 4\delta(n) - (n-1)u(n-2) - 5u(n-1) + 16 \cdot 2^{n-1}u(n-1),$$

or $f(n) = -n - 4 + 16 \cdot 2^{n-1}$, for $n \geq 2$, with the initial values $f(-1) = 1$, $f(0) = 4$, and $f(1) = 11$.

6.27.3 CONVOLUTION AND PRODUCT

The convolution of two sequences, $\{f(n)\}_{-\infty}^{\infty}$ and $\{g(n)\}_{-\infty}^{\infty}$, is a sequence $\{h(n)\}_{-\infty}^{\infty}$ defined by $h(n) = \sum_{k=-\infty}^{\infty} f(k)g(n-k)$. The Z-transform of the convolution of two sequences is the product of their Z-transforms,

$$\mathcal{Z}[h(n)] = \mathcal{Z}[f(n)]\mathcal{Z}[g(n)],$$

for $z \in D_f \bigcap D_g$, or $H(z) = F(z)G(z)$.

The Z-transform of the product of two sequences is given by

$$\mathcal{Z}[f(n)g(n)] = \frac{1}{2\pi i} \oint_{\gamma} F(\omega)G\left(\frac{z}{\omega}\right)\frac{d\omega}{\omega}, \qquad (6.27.14)$$

where γ is a closed contour surrounding the origin in the domain of convergence of $F(\omega)$ and $G(z/\omega)$.

6.28 HILBERT TRANSFORM

The Hilbert transform of f is defined as

$$(\mathcal{H}f)(x) = \tilde{f}(x) = \frac{1}{\pi} \int_{-\infty}^{\infty} \frac{f(t)}{t-x}\,dt = \frac{1}{\pi} \int_{-\infty}^{\infty} \frac{f(x+t)}{t}\,dt \qquad (6.28.1)$$

where the integral is a Cauchy principal value.

Since the definition is given in terms of a singular integral, it is sometimes impractical to use. An alternative definition is given below. First, let f be an integrable function, and define $a(t)$ and $b(t)$ by

$$a(t) = \frac{1}{\pi} \int_{-\infty}^{\infty} f(x)\cos txdx, \qquad b(t) = \frac{1}{\pi} \int_{-\infty}^{\infty} f(x)\sin tx\,dx. \qquad (6.28.2)$$

Consider the function $F(z)$, defined by the Fourier integral

$$F(z) = \int_{0}^{\infty} (a(t) - ib(t))e^{izt}\,dt = U(z) + i\tilde{U}(z), \qquad (6.28.3)$$

where $z = x + iy$. The real and imaginary parts of F are

$$U(z) = \int_{0}^{\infty} (a(t)\cos xt + b(t)\sin xt)e^{-yt}\,dt, \quad \text{and}$$

$$\tilde{U}(z) = \int_{0}^{\infty} (a(t)\sin xt - b(t)\cos xt)e^{-yt}\,dt.$$

Formally,

$$\lim_{y \to 0} U(z) = f(x) = \int_0^\infty (a(t) \cos xt + b(t) \sin xt) \, dt,$$

(6.28.4)

and

$$\lim_{y \to 0} \tilde{U}(z) = -\tilde{f}(x) = \int_0^\infty (a(t) \sin xt - b(t) \cos xt) \, dt,$$

(6.28.5)

The Hilbert transform of a function f, given by Equation (6.28.4), is defined as the function $\tilde{f}$ given by Equation (6.28.5).

6.28.1 EXISTENCE

If $f \in L^1(\mathbb{R})$, then its Hilbert transform $(\mathcal{H}f)(x)$ exists for almost all x. For $f \in L^p(\mathbb{R})$, $p > 1$, there is the following stronger result:

THEOREM 6.28.1

Let $f \in L^p(\mathbb{R})$, $p > 1$. Then $(\mathcal{H}f)(x)$ exists for almost all x and defines a function that also belongs to $L^p(\mathbb{R})$ with

$$\int_{-\infty}^\infty |(\mathcal{H}f)(x)|^p \, dx \le C_p \int_{-\infty}^\infty |f(x)|^p \, dx.$$

In the special case of $p = 2$, we have

$$\int_{-\infty}^\infty |(\mathcal{H}f)(x)|^2 \, dx = \int_{-\infty}^\infty |f(x)|^2 \, dx.$$

(6.28.6)

The theorem is not valid if $p = 1$ because, although it is true that $(\mathcal{H}f)(x)$ is defined almost everywhere, it is not necessarily in $L^1(\mathbb{R})$. The function $f(t) = (t \log^2 t)^{-1} H(t)$ provides a counterexample.

6.28.2 PROPERTIES

1. *Translation:* The Hilbert transformation commutes with the translation operator $(\mathcal{H}f)(x + a) = \mathcal{H}(f(t + a))(x)$.

2. *Dilation:* The Hilbert transformation also commutes with the dilation operator

$$(\mathcal{H}f)(ax) = \mathcal{H}(f(at))(x) \quad a > 0,$$

but

$$(\mathcal{H}f)(ax) = -\mathcal{H}(f(at))(x) \quad \text{for} \quad a < 0.$$

3. *Multiplication by t:* $\mathcal{H}(tf(t))(x) = x(\mathcal{H}f)(x) + \dfrac{1}{\pi}\displaystyle\int_{-\infty}^{\infty} f(t)\,dt.$

4. *Differentiation:* $\mathcal{H}(f'(t))(x) = (\mathcal{H}f)'(x),$ provided that $f(t) = O(t)$ as $|t| \to \infty.$

5. *Orthogonality:* The Hilbert transform of $f \in L^2(\mathbb{R})$ is orthogonal to f in the sense $\int_{-\infty}^{\infty} f(x)(\mathcal{H}f)(x)dx = 0.$

6. *Parity:* The Hilbert transform of an even function is odd and that of an odd function is even.

7. *Inversion formula:* If $(\mathcal{H}f)(x) = \dfrac{1}{\pi}\displaystyle\int_{-\infty}^{\infty}\dfrac{f(t)}{t-x}\,dt,$ then

$$f(t) = -\frac{1}{\pi}\int_{-\infty}^{\infty}\frac{(\mathcal{H}f)(x)}{x-t}dx \text{ or, symbolically,}$$

$$\mathcal{H}(\mathcal{H}f)(x) = -f(x), \tag{6.28.7}$$

that is, applying the Hilbert transform twice returns the negative of the original function. Moreover, if $f \in L^1(\mathbb{R})$ has a bounded derivative, then the allied integral (see Equation 6.22.6) equals $(\mathcal{H}f)(x).$

6.28.3   RELATIONSHIP WITH THE FOURIER TRANSFORM

From Equations (6.28.3)–(6.28.5), we obtain

$$\lim_{y\to 0} F(z) = F(x) = \int_0^{\infty}(a(t) - ib(t))e^{ixt}\,dt = f(x) - i(\mathcal{H}f)(x),$$

where $a(t)$ and $b(t)$ are given by Equation (6.28.2).

Let g be a real-valued integrable function and consider its Fourier transform $\hat{g}(x) = \dfrac{1}{\sqrt{2\pi}}\int_{-\infty}^{\infty}g(t)e^{ixt}\,dt.$ If we denote the real and imaginary parts of $\hat{g}$ by f and $\tilde{f},$ respectively, then

$$f(x) = \frac{1}{\sqrt{2\pi}}\int_{-\infty}^{\infty}g(t)\cos xt\,dt, \quad\text{ and}$$

$$\tilde{f}(x) = \frac{1}{\sqrt{2\pi}}\int_{-\infty}^{\infty}g(t)\sin xt\,dt.$$

Splitting g into its even and odd parts, g_e and $g_o,$ respectively, we obtain

$$g_e(t) = \frac{g(t) + g(-t)}{2} \quad\text{and}\quad g_o(t) = \frac{g(t) - g(-t)}{2};$$

hence

$$f(x) = \sqrt{\frac{2}{\pi}}\int_0^{\infty}g_e(t)\cos xt\,dt, \quad\text{and}\quad \tilde{f}(x) = \sqrt{\frac{2}{\pi}}\int_0^{\infty}g_o(t)\sin xt\,dt,$$

or

$$f(x) = \frac{1}{\sqrt{2\pi}} \int_{-\infty}^{\infty} g_e(t)e^{ixt}\, dt, \quad \text{and} \quad \tilde{f}(x) = \frac{-i}{\sqrt{2\pi}} \int_{-\infty}^{\infty} g_o(t)e^{ixt}\, dt.$$

This shows that, if the Fourier transform of the even part of a real-valued function represents a function $f(x)$, then the Fourier transform of the odd part represents the Hilbert transform of f (up to multiplication by i).

THEOREM 6.28.2

Let $f \in L^1(\mathbb{R})$ and assume that $\mathcal{H}f$ is also in $L^1(\mathbb{R})$. Then

$$\mathcal{F}(\mathcal{H}f)(\omega) = -i\, sgn(\omega)\mathcal{F}(f)(\omega), \tag{6.28.8}$$

where $\mathcal{F}$ denotes the Fourier transformation. Similarly, if $f \in L^2(\mathbb{R})$, then $(\mathcal{H}f) \in L^2(\mathbb{R})$, and Equation (6.28.8) remains valid.

6.29 HANKEL TRANSFORM

The Hankel transform of order ν of a function $f(x)$ is defined as

$$\mathcal{H}_\nu(f)(y) = F_\nu(y) = \int_0^{\infty} f(x)\sqrt{xy}J_\nu(yx)dx, \tag{6.29.1}$$

for $y > 0$ and $\nu > -1/2$, where $J_\nu(z)$ is the Bessel function of the first kind of order ν.

The Hankel transforms of order $1/2$ and $-1/2$ are equal to the Fourier sine and cosine transforms, respectively, because

$$J_{1/2}(x) = \sqrt{\frac{2}{\pi x}} \sin x, \qquad J_{-1/2}(x) = \sqrt{\frac{2}{\pi x}} \cos x.$$

As with the Fourier transform, there are many variations on the definition of the Hankel transform. Some authors define it as

$$G_\nu(y) = \int_0^{\infty} xg(x)J_\nu(yx)dx; \tag{6.29.2}$$

however, the two definitions are equivalent; we only need to replace $f(x)$ by $\sqrt{x}g(x)$ and $F_\nu(y)$ by $\sqrt{y}G_\nu(y)$.

6.29.1   PROPERTIES

1. *Existence*: Since $\sqrt{x}\,J_\nu(x)$ is bounded on the positive real axis, the Hankel transform of f exists if $f \in L^1(0, \infty)$.

2. *Multiplication by x^m*:

$$\mathcal{H}_\nu \left(x^m f(x) \right)(y) = y^{1/2-\nu} \left(\frac{1}{y}\frac{d}{dy} \right)^m \left[y^{\nu+m-1/2} F_{\nu+m}(y) \right].$$

3. *Division by x*:

$$\mathcal{H}_\nu \left(\frac{2\nu}{x} f(x) \right)(y) = y \left[F_{\nu-1}(y) + F_{\nu+1}(y) \right],$$

and also

$$\mathcal{H}_\nu \left(\frac{f(x)}{x} \right)(y) = y^{1/2-\nu} \int_0^y t^{\nu-1/2} F_{\nu-1}(t)\, dt.$$

4. *Differentiation*:

$$\mathcal{H}_\nu \left(2\nu f'(x) \right)(y) = (\nu - 1/2) y F_{\nu+1}(y) - (\nu + 1/2) y F_{\nu-1}(y).$$

5. *Differentiation and multiplication by powers of x*:

$$\mathcal{H}_\nu \left[x^{1/2-\nu} \left(\frac{1}{x}\frac{d}{dx} \right)^m \left(x^{\nu+m-1/2} f(x) \right) \right](y) = y^m F_{\nu+m}(y).$$

6. *Parseval's relation*: Let F_ν and G_ν denote the Hankel transforms of order ν of f and g, respectively. Then

$$\int_0^\infty F_\nu(y) G_\nu(y)\, dy = \int_0^\infty f(x) g(x)\, dx. \tag{6.29.3}$$

In particular,

$$\int_0^\infty |F_\nu(y)|^2\, dy = \int_0^\infty |f(x)|^2\, dx. \tag{6.29.4}$$

7. *Inversion formula*: If f is absolutely integrable on $(0, \infty)$ and of bounded variation in a neighborhood of point x, then

$$\int_0^\infty F_\nu(y) \sqrt{xy}\, J_\nu(yx)\, dy = \frac{f(x+0) + f(x-0)}{2}, \tag{6.29.5}$$

whenever the expression on the right-hand side of the equation has a meaning; the integral converges to $f(x)$ whenever f is continuous at x.

6.30   TABLES OF TRANSFORMS

Finite sine transforms

$$f_s(n) = \int_0^\pi F(x) \sin nx \, dx, \ \text{ for } n = 1, 2, \dots.$$

No.	$f_s(n)$	$F(x)$
1	$(-1)^{n+1} f_s(n)$	$F(\pi - x)$
2	$1/n$	$\pi - x/\pi$
3	$(-1)^{n+1}/n$	x/π
4	$1 - (-1)^n/n$	1
5	$\dfrac{2}{n^2} \sin \dfrac{n\pi}{2}$	$\begin{cases} x & \text{when } 0 < x < \pi/2 \\ \pi - x & \text{when } \pi/2 < x < \pi \end{cases}$
6	$(-1)^{n+1}/n^3$	$x(\pi^2 - x^2)/6\pi$
7	$1 - (-1)^n/n^3$	$x(\pi - x)/2$
8	$\dfrac{\pi^2(-1)^{n-1}}{n} - \dfrac{2[1 - (-1)^n]}{n^3}$	x^2
9	$\pi(-1)^n \left(\dfrac{6}{n^3} - \dfrac{\pi^2}{n} \right)$	x^3
10	$\dfrac{n}{n^2 + c^2} \left[1 - (-1)^n e^{c\pi} \right]$	e^{cx}
11	$\dfrac{n}{n^2 + c^2}$	$\dfrac{\sinh c(\pi - x)}{\sinh c\pi}$
12	$\dfrac{n}{n^2 - k^2}$ with $k \neq 0, 1, 2, \dots$	$\dfrac{\sin k(\pi - x)}{\sin k\pi}$
13	$\begin{cases} \pi/2 & \text{when } n = m \\ 0 & \text{when } n \neq m, m = 1, 2, \dots \end{cases}$	$\sin mx$
14	$\dfrac{n}{n^2 - k^2}[1 - (-1)^n \cos k\pi]$ with $k \neq 1, 2, \dots$	$\cos kx$
15	$\dfrac{n}{n^2 - m^2}[1 - (-1)^{n+m}]$ when $n \neq m = 1, 2, \dots$ (0 when $n = m$)	$\cos mx$
16	$\dfrac{n}{(n^2 - k^2)^2}$ with $k \neq 0, 1, 2, \dots$	$\dfrac{\pi \sin kx}{2k \sin^2 k\pi} - \dfrac{x \cos k(\pi - x)}{2k \sin k\pi}$
17	b^n/n with $|b| \leq 1$	$\dfrac{2}{\pi} \tan^{-1} \dfrac{b \sin x}{1 - b \cos x}$
18	$\dfrac{1 - (-1)^n}{n} b^n$ with $|b| \leq 1$	$\dfrac{2}{\pi} \tan^{-1} \dfrac{2b \sin x}{1 - b^2}$

Finite cosine transforms

$$f_c(n) = \int_0^\pi F(x)\cos nx\,dx,\ \text{for } n = 0, 1, 2, \ldots.$$

No.	$f_c(n)$	$F(x)$
1	$(-1)^n f_c(n)$	$F(\pi - x)$
2	$\begin{cases} \pi & n = 0 \\ 0 & n = 1, 2, \ldots \end{cases}$	1
3	$\begin{cases} 0 & n = 0 \\ \dfrac{2}{n}\sin\dfrac{n\pi}{2} & n = 1, 2, \ldots \end{cases}$	$\begin{cases} 1 & \text{for } 0 < x < \pi/2 \\ -1 & \text{for } \pi/2 < x < \pi \end{cases}$
4	$\begin{cases} \dfrac{\pi^2}{2} & n = 0 \\ (-1)^n - 1/n^2 & n = 1, 2, \ldots \end{cases}$	x
5	$\begin{cases} \dfrac{\pi^2}{6} & n = 0 \\ (-1)^n/n^2 & n = 1, 2, \ldots \end{cases}$	$\dfrac{x^2}{2\pi}$
6	$\begin{cases} 0 & n = 0 \\ 1/n^2 & n = 1, 2, \ldots \end{cases}$	$\dfrac{(x-\pi)^2}{2\pi} - \dfrac{\pi}{6}$
7	$\begin{cases} \dfrac{\pi^4}{4} & n = 0 \\ 3\pi^2\dfrac{(-1)^n}{n^2} & n = 1, 2, \ldots \\ \quad - 6\dfrac{1 - (-1)^n}{n^4} \end{cases}$	x^3
8	$\dfrac{(-1)^n e^c \pi - 1}{n^2 + c^2}$	$\dfrac{1}{c}e^{cx}$
9	$\dfrac{1}{n^2 + c^2}$	$\dfrac{\cosh c(\pi - x)}{c \sinh c\pi}$
10	$\dfrac{k}{n^2 - k^2}[(-1)^n \cos\pi k - 1]$ with $k \neq 0, 1, 2, \ldots$	$\sin kx$
11	$\begin{cases} 0 & m = 1, 2, \ldots \\ \dfrac{(-1)^{n+m} - 1}{n^2 - m^2} & m \neq 1, 2, \ldots \end{cases}$	$\dfrac{1}{m}\sin mx$
12	$\dfrac{1}{n^2 - k^2}$ with $k \neq 0, 1, 2, \ldots$	$-\dfrac{\cos k(\pi - x)}{k \sin k\pi}$
13	$\begin{cases} \pi/2 & \text{when } n = m \\ 0 & \text{when } n \neq m \end{cases}$	$\cos mx \qquad (m = 1, 2, \ldots)$

Fourier sine transforms

$$F(\omega) = F_s(f)(\omega) = \sqrt{\frac{2}{\pi}} \int_0^\infty f(x) \sin(\omega x)\, dx, \quad \omega > 0$$

No.	$f(x)$	$F(\omega)$
1	$\begin{cases} 1 & 0 < x < a \\ 0 & x > a \end{cases}$	$\sqrt{\frac{2}{\pi}}\left(\frac{1-\cos\omega a}{\omega}\right)$
2	$x^{p-1} \qquad (0 < p < 1)$	$\sqrt{\frac{2}{\pi}}\,\frac{\Gamma(p)}{\omega^p}\sin\frac{p\pi}{2}$
3	$\begin{cases} \sin x & 0 < x < a \\ 0 & x > a \end{cases}$	$\frac{1}{\sqrt{2\pi}}\left(\frac{\sin[a(1-\omega)]}{1-\omega} - \frac{\sin[a(1+\omega)]}{1+\omega}\right)$
4	e^{-x}	$\sqrt{\frac{2}{\pi}}\,\frac{\omega}{1+\omega^2}$
5	$xe^{-x^2/2}$	$\omega e^{-\omega^2/2}$
6	$\cos\frac{x^2}{2}$	$\sqrt{2}\left[\sin\frac{\omega^2}{2}C\left(\frac{\omega^2}{2}\right) - \cos\frac{\omega^2}{2}S\left(\frac{\omega^2}{2}\right)\right]$
7	$\sin\frac{x^2}{2}$	$\sqrt{2}\left[\cos\frac{\omega^2}{2}C\left(\frac{\omega^2}{2}\right) + \sin\frac{\omega^2}{2}S\left(\frac{\omega^2}{2}\right)\right]$

Fourier cosine transforms

$$F(\omega) = F_c(f)(\omega) = \sqrt{\frac{2}{\pi}} \int_0^\infty f(x) \cos(\omega x)\, dx, \quad \omega > 0.$$

No.	$f(x)$	$F(\omega)$
1	$\begin{cases} 1 & 0 < x < a \\ 0 & x > a \end{cases}$	$\sqrt{\frac{2}{\pi}}\,\frac{\sin a\omega}{\omega}$
2	$x^{p-1} \qquad (0 < p < 1)$	$\sqrt{\frac{2}{\pi}}\,\frac{\Gamma(p)}{\omega^p}\cos\frac{p\pi}{2}$
3	$\begin{cases} \cos x & 0 < x < a \\ 0 & x > a \end{cases}$	$\frac{1}{\sqrt{2\pi}}\left(\frac{\sin[a(1-\omega)]}{1-\omega} + \frac{\sin[a(1+\omega)]}{1+\omega}\right)$
4	e^{-x}	$\sqrt{\frac{2}{\pi}}\,\frac{1}{1+\omega^2}$
5	$e^{-x^2/2}$	$e^{-\omega^2/2}$
6	$\cos\frac{x^2}{2}$	$\cos\left(\frac{\omega^2}{2} - \frac{\pi}{4}\right)$
7	$\sin\frac{x^2}{2}$	$\cos\left(\frac{\omega^2}{2} + \frac{\pi}{4}\right)$

Fourier transforms: functional relations

$$F(\omega) = \mathcal{F}(f)(\omega) = \frac{1}{\sqrt{2\pi}} \int_{-\infty}^{\infty} f(x) e^{i\omega x} \, dx, \quad \omega > 0.$$

No.	$f(x)$		$F(\omega)$
1	$ag(x) + bh(x)$		$aG(\omega) + bH(\omega)$
2	$f(ax)$	$a \neq 0$, Im $a = 0$	$\frac{1}{|a|} F\left(\frac{\omega}{a}\right)$
3	$f(-x)$		$F(-\omega)$
4	$\overline{f(x)}$		$\overline{F(-\omega)}$
5	$f(x - \tau)$	Im $\tau = 0$	$e^{-i\omega\tau} F(\omega)$
6	$e^{i\Omega x} f(x)$	Im $\Omega = 0$	$F(\omega - \Omega)$
7	$F(x)$		$2\pi f(-\omega)$
8	$\frac{d^n}{dx^n} f(x)$		$(i\omega)^n F(\omega)$
9	$(-ix)^n f(x)$		$\frac{d^n}{d\omega^n} F(\omega)$
10	$\frac{\partial}{\partial a} f(x, a)$		$\frac{\partial}{\partial a} F(\omega, a)$

Fourier transforms

$$F(\omega) = \mathcal{F}(f)(\omega) = \frac{1}{\sqrt{2\pi}} \int_{-\infty}^{\infty} f(x)e^{i\omega x}\, dx, \quad \omega > 0.$$

No.	$f(x)$	$F(\omega)$
1	$\delta(x)$	$1/\sqrt{2\pi}$
2	$\delta(x - \tau)$	$e^{i\omega\tau}/\sqrt{2\pi}$
3	$\delta^{(n)}(x)$	$(-i\omega)^n/\sqrt{2\pi}$
4	$H(x) = \begin{cases} 1 & x > 0 \\ 0 & x < 0 \end{cases}$	$-\dfrac{1}{i\omega\sqrt{2\pi}} + \sqrt{\dfrac{\pi}{2}}\delta(\omega)$
5	$\text{sgn}(x) = \begin{cases} 1 & x > 0 \\ -1 & x < 0 \end{cases}$	$-\sqrt{\dfrac{2}{\pi}}\dfrac{1}{i\omega}$
6	$\begin{cases} 1 & \|x\| < a \\ 0 & \|x\| > a \end{cases}$	$\sqrt{\dfrac{2}{\pi}}\dfrac{\sin a\omega}{\omega}$
7	$\begin{cases} e^{i\Omega t} & \|x\| < a \\ 0 & \|x\| > a \end{cases}$	$\sqrt{\dfrac{2}{\pi}}\dfrac{\sin a(\Omega + \omega)}{\Omega + \omega}$
8	$e^{-a\|x\|} \qquad a > 0$	$-\sqrt{\dfrac{2}{\pi}}\dfrac{a}{a^2+\omega^2}$
9	$\dfrac{\sin \Omega x}{x}$	$\sqrt{\dfrac{\pi}{2}}\left[H(\Omega - \omega) - H(-\Omega - \omega)\right]$

Fourier transforms

$$F(\omega) = \mathcal{F}(f)(\omega) = \frac{1}{\sqrt{2\pi}} \int_{-\infty}^{\infty} f(x)e^{i\omega x}\, dx, \quad \omega > 0.$$

No.	$f(x)$	$F(\omega)$
10	$\sin ax/x$	$\begin{cases} \sqrt{\frac{\pi}{2}} & \lvert\omega\rvert < a \\ 0 & \lvert\omega\rvert > a \end{cases}$
11	$\begin{cases} e^{iax} & p < x < q \\ 0 & x < p, x > q \end{cases}$	$\dfrac{i}{\sqrt{2\pi}} e^{ip(\omega+a)} - e^{iq(\omega+a)}/\omega + a$
12	$\begin{cases} e^{-cx+iax} & x > 0 \\ 0 & x < 0 \end{cases} \quad (c > 0)$	$\dfrac{i}{\sqrt{2\pi}(\omega + a + ic)}$
13	$e^{-px^2} \qquad \text{Re } p > 0$	$\dfrac{1}{\sqrt{2p}} e^{-\omega^2/4p}$
14	$\cos px^2$	$\dfrac{1}{\sqrt{2p}} \cos\left(\dfrac{\omega^2}{4p} - \dfrac{\pi}{4}\right)$
15	$\sin px^2$	$\dfrac{1}{\sqrt{2p}} \cos\left(\dfrac{\omega^2}{4p} + \dfrac{\pi}{4}\right)$
16	$\lvert x\rvert^{-p} \qquad (0 < p < 1)$	$\sqrt{\dfrac{2}{\pi}} \dfrac{\Gamma(1-p)\sin\frac{p\pi}{2}}{\lvert\omega\rvert^{1-p}}$
17	$e^{-a\lvert x\rvert}/\sqrt{\lvert x\rvert}$	$\dfrac{\sqrt{\sqrt{a^2+\omega^2}+a}}{\sqrt{\omega^2+a^2}}$
18	$\dfrac{\cosh ax}{\cosh \pi x} \qquad (-\pi < a < \pi)$	$\sqrt{\dfrac{2}{\pi}} \dfrac{\cos\frac{a}{2}\cosh\frac{\omega}{2}}{\cos a+\cosh \omega}$
19	$\dfrac{\sinh ax}{\sinh \pi x} \qquad (-\pi < a < \pi)$	$\dfrac{1}{\sqrt{2\pi}} \dfrac{\sin a}{\cos a+\cosh \omega}$
20	$\begin{cases} \dfrac{1}{\sqrt{a^2-x^2}} & \lvert x\rvert < a \\ 0 & \lvert x\rvert > a \end{cases}$	$\sqrt{\dfrac{\pi}{2}} J_0(a\omega)$
21	$\dfrac{\sin[b\sqrt{a^2+x^2}]}{\sqrt{a^2+x^2}}$	$\begin{cases} 0 & \lvert\omega\rvert > b \\ \sqrt{\dfrac{\pi}{2}} J_0(a\sqrt{b^2 - \omega^2}) & \lvert\omega\rvert < b \end{cases}$
22	$\begin{cases} P_n(x) & \lvert x\rvert < 1 \\ 0 & \lvert x\rvert > 1 \end{cases}$	$\dfrac{i^n}{\sqrt{\omega}} J_{n+1/2}(\omega)$
23	$\begin{cases} \dfrac{\cos[b\sqrt{a^2-x^2}]}{\sqrt{a^2-x^2}} & \lvert x\rvert < a \\ 0 & \lvert x\rvert > a \end{cases}$	$\sqrt{\dfrac{\pi}{2}} J_0(a\sqrt{\omega^2 + b^2})$
24	$\begin{cases} \dfrac{\cosh[b\sqrt{a^2-x^2}]}{\sqrt{a^2-x^2}} & \lvert x\rvert < a \\ 0 & \lvert x\rvert > a \end{cases}$	$\sqrt{\dfrac{\pi}{2}} J_0(a\sqrt{\omega^2 - b^2})$

Multidimensional Fourier transforms

No.	$f(\mathbf{x})$	$F(\mathbf{u})$
	In n-dimensions	
1	$f(a\mathbf{x})$ $\qquad$ Im $a = 0$	$\|a\|^{-n} F(a^{-1}\mathbf{u})$
2	$f(\mathbf{x} - \mathbf{a})$	$e^{-i\mathbf{a}\cdot\mathbf{u}} F(\mathbf{u})$
3	$e^{i\mathbf{a}\cdot\mathbf{x}} f(\mathbf{x})$	$F(\mathbf{v} - \mathbf{a})$
4	$F(\mathbf{x})$	$(2\pi)^n f(-\mathbf{u})$
	Two dimensions: let $\mathbf{x} = (x, y)$ and $\mathbf{u} = (u, v)$.	
5	$f(ax, by)$	$\frac{1}{\|ab\|} F\left(\frac{u}{a}, \frac{v}{b}\right)$
6	$f(x - a, y - b)$	$e^{i(au+bv)} F(u, v)$
7	$e^{i(ax+by)} f(x, y)$	$F(u - a, v - b)$
8	$F(x, y)$	$(2\pi)^2 F f(-u, -v)$
9	$\delta(x - a)\delta(y - b)$	$\frac{1}{2\pi} e^{-i(au+bv)}$
10	$e^{-x^2/4a - y^2/4b}$ $\qquad$ $a, b > 0$	$2\sqrt{ab}\, e^{-au^2 - bv^2}$
11	$\begin{cases} 1 & \|x\| < a,\ \|y\| < b \\ 0 & \text{otherwise (rectangle)} \end{cases}$	$\dfrac{2\sin au \sin bv}{\pi uv}$
12	$\begin{cases} 1 & \|x\| < a \\ 0 & \text{otherwise (strip)} \end{cases}$	$\dfrac{2\sin au}{\pi uv}\delta(v)$
13	$\begin{cases} 1 & x^2 + y^2 < a^2 \\ 0 & \text{otherwise (circle)} \end{cases}$	$\dfrac{aJ_1(a\sqrt{u^2 + v^2})}{\sqrt{u^2 + v^2}}$
	Three dimensions: let $\mathbf{x} = (x, y, z)$ and $\mathbf{u} = (u, v, w)$.	
14	$\delta(x - a)\delta(y - b)\delta(z - c)$	$\frac{1}{(2\pi)^{3/2}} e^{-i(au+bv+cw)}$
15	$e^{-x^2/4a - y^2/4b - z^2/4c}$ $\qquad$ $a, b, c > 0$	$2^{3/2}\sqrt{abc}\, e^{-au^2 - bv^2 - cw^2}$
16	$\begin{cases} 1 & \|x\| < a,\ \|y\| < b,\ \|z\| < c \\ 0 & \text{otherwise (box)} \end{cases}$	$\left(\dfrac{2}{\pi}\right)^{3/2} \dfrac{\sin au \sin bv \sin cw}{uvw}$
17	$\begin{cases} 1 & x^2 + y^2 + z^2 < a^2 \\ 0 & \text{otherwise (ball)} \end{cases}$	$\frac{\sin a\rho - a\rho\cos a\rho}{\sqrt{2\pi}\rho^3}$ $\qquad$ $\rho^2 = u^2 + v^2 + w^2$

Laplace transforms: functional relations

$$F(s) = \mathcal{L}(f)(s) = \int_0^\infty f(t)e^{-st}\,dt.$$

No.	$f(t)$	$F(s)$
1	$af(t) + bg(t)$	$aF(s) + bG(s)$
2	$f'(t)$	$sF(s) - F(0+)$
3	$f''(t)$	$s^2 F(s) - sF(0+) - F'(0+)$
4	$f^{(n)}(t)$	$s^n F(s) - \sum_{k=0}^{n-1} s^{n-1-k} F^{(k)}(0+)$
5	$\int_0^t f(\tau)\,d\tau$	$\frac{1}{s} F(s)$
6	$\int_0^t \int_0^\tau f(u)\,du\,d\tau$	$\frac{1}{s^2} F(s)$
7	$\int_0^t f_1(t-\tau)f_2(\tau)\,d\tau = f_1 * f_2$	$F_1(s)F_2(s)$
8	$tf(t)$	$-F'(s)$
9	$t^n f(t)$	$(-1)^n F^{(n)}(s)$
10	$\frac{1}{t} f(t)$	$\int_s^\infty F(z)\,dz$
11	$e^{at} f(t)$	$F(s-a)$
12	$f(t-b)$ with $f(t) = 0$ for $t < 0$	$e^{-bt} F(s)$
13	$\frac{1}{c} f\left(\frac{t}{c}\right)$	$F(cs)$
14	$\frac{1}{c} e^{bt/c} f\left(\frac{t}{c}\right)$	$F(cs - b)$
15	$f(t+a) = f(t)$	$\int_0^a e^{-st} f(t)\,dt / 1 - e^{-as}$
16	$f(t+a) = -f(t)$	$\int_0^a e^{-st} f(t)\,dt / 1 + e^{-as}$
17	$\sum_{k=1}^n \frac{p(a_n)}{q'(a_n)} e^{a_n t}$ with $q(t) = (t - a_1) \cdots (t - a_n)$	$\dfrac{p(s)}{q(s)}$
18	$e^{at} \sum_{k=1}^n \frac{\phi^{(n-k)}(a)}{(n-k)!} \frac{t^{k-1}}{(k-1)!}$	$\phi(s)/(s-a)^n$

Laplace transforms

$$F(s) = \mathcal{L}(f)(s) = \int_0^\infty f(t)e^{-st}\,dt.$$

No.	$F(s)$		$f(t)$
1	1		$\delta(t)$, delta function
2	$1/s$		$H(t)$, unit step function
3	$1/s^2$		t
4	$1/s^n$	$(n = 1, 2, \ldots)$	$\frac{t^{n-1}}{(n-1)!}$
5	$1/\sqrt{s}$		$1/\sqrt{\pi t}$
6	$s^{-3/2}$		$2\sqrt{t/\pi}$
7	$s^{-(n+1/2)}$	$(n = 1, 2, \ldots)$	$\frac{2^n t^{n-1/2}}{\sqrt{\pi}(2n-1)!!}$
8	$\frac{\Gamma(k)}{s^k}$	$(k > 0)$	t^{k-1}
9	$\frac{1}{s-a}$		e^{at}
10	$\frac{1}{(s-a)^2}$		te^{at}
11	$\frac{1}{(s-a)^n}$	$(n = 1, 2, \ldots)$	$\frac{1}{(n-1)!}t^{n-1}e^{at}$
12	$\frac{\Gamma(k)}{(s-a)^k}$	$(k > 0)$	$t^{k-1}e^{at}$
13	$\frac{1}{(s-a)(s-b)}$	$(a \neq b)$	$\frac{1}{a-b}\left(e^{at} - e^{bt}\right)$
14	$\frac{s}{(s-a)(s-b)}$	$(a \neq b)$	$\frac{1}{a-b}\left(ae^{at} - be^{bt}\right)$
15	$\frac{1}{(s-a)(s-b)(s-c)}$	$(a, b, c$ distinct$)$	$-\frac{(b-c)e^{at}+(c-a)e^{bt}+(a-b)e^{ct}}{(a-b)(b-c)(c-a)}$
16	$\frac{1}{s^2+a^2}$		$\frac{1}{a}\sin at$
17	$\frac{s}{s^2+a^2}$		$\cos at$
18	$\frac{1}{s^2-a^2}$		$\frac{1}{a}\sinh at$
19	$\frac{s}{s^2-a^2}$		$\cosh at$
20	$\frac{1}{s(s^2+a^2)}$		$\frac{1}{a^2}(1 - \cos at)$
21	$\frac{1}{s^2(s^2+a^2)}$		$\frac{1}{a^3}(at - \sin at)$
22	$\frac{1}{(s^2+a^2)^2}$		$\frac{1}{2a^3}(\sin at - at\cos at)$
23	$\frac{s}{(s^2+a^2)^2}$		$\frac{t}{2a}\sin at$
24	$\frac{s^2}{(s^2+a^2)^2}$		$\frac{1}{2a}(\sin at + at\cos at)$

Laplace transforms

$$F(s) = \mathcal{L}(f)(s) = \int_0^\infty f(t)e^{-st}\, dt.$$

No.	$F(s)$		$f(t)$
25	$\dfrac{s^2-a^2}{(s^2+a^2)^2}$		$t\cos at$
26	$\dfrac{s}{(s^2+a^2)(s^2+b^2)}$	$(a^2 \neq b^2)$	$\dfrac{\cos at - \cos bt}{b^2-a^2}$
27	$\dfrac{1}{(s-a)^2+b^2}$		$\dfrac{1}{b}e^{at}\sin bt$
28	$\dfrac{s-a}{(s-a)^2+b^2}$		$e^{at}\cos bt$
29	$\dfrac{1}{\big[(s-a)^2+b^2\big]^n}$		$-\dfrac{e^{-at}}{4^{n-1}b^{2n}}\sum_{k=1}^n \binom{2n-k-1}{n-1}$ $\times (-2t)^{n-1}\dfrac{d^k}{dt^k}[\cos bt]$
30	$\dfrac{s}{\big[(s-a)^2+b^2\big]^n}$		$\dfrac{e^{-at}}{4^{n-1}b^{2n}}\bigg\{\sum_{k=1}^n \binom{2n-k-1}{n-1}\dfrac{(-2t)^{k-1}}{(k-1)!}$ $\times \dfrac{d^k}{dt^k}[a\cos bt + b\sin at]$ $-2b\sum_{k=1}^n \binom{2n-k-2}{n-1}\dfrac{(-2t)^{k-1}}{(k-1)!}$ $\times \dfrac{\partial^k}{\partial t^k}[\sin bt]\bigg\}$
31	$\dfrac{3a^2}{s^3+a^3}$		e^{-at} $-e^{at/2}\left(\cos\dfrac{at\sqrt3}{2} - \sqrt3\sin\dfrac{at\sqrt3}{2}\right)$
32	$\dfrac{s}{s^4+4a^4}$		$\dfrac{1}{2a^2}\sin at\sinh at$
33	$\dfrac{4a^3}{s^4+4a^4}$		$\sin at\cosh at - \cos at\sinh at$
34	$\dfrac{1}{s^4-a^4}$		$\dfrac{1}{2a^3}(\sinh at - \sin at)$
35	$\dfrac{s}{s^4-a^4}$		$\dfrac{1}{2a^2}(\cosh at - \cos at)$
36	$\dfrac{8a^3s^2}{(s^2+a^2)^3}$		$(1+a^2t^2)\sin at - at\cos at$
37	$\dfrac{1}{s}\left(\dfrac{s-1}{s}\right)^n$		$L_n(t) = \dfrac{e^t}{n!}\dfrac{d^n}{dt^n}(t^n e^{-t})$
38	$\dfrac{s}{(s-a)^{3/2}}$		$\dfrac{1}{\sqrt{\pi t}}e^{at}(1+2at)$
39	$\sqrt{s-a}-\sqrt{s-b}$		$\dfrac{1}{2\sqrt{\pi t^3}}(e^{bt}-e^{at})$
40	$\dfrac{1}{\sqrt{s}+a}$		$\dfrac{1}{\sqrt{\pi t}} - ae^{a^2t}\,\mathrm{erfc}(a\sqrt t)$
41	$\dfrac{\sqrt{s}}{s-a^2}$		$\dfrac{1}{\sqrt{\pi t}} + ae^{a^2t}\,\mathrm{erf}(a\sqrt t)$
42	$\dfrac{\sqrt{s}}{s+a^2}$		$\dfrac{1}{\sqrt{\pi t}} - \dfrac{2a}{\sqrt\pi}e^{-a^2t}\int_0^{a\sqrt t} e^{\tau^2}\,d\tau$
43	$\dfrac{1}{\sqrt{s}(s-a^2)}$		$\dfrac{1}{a}e^{a^2t}\,\mathrm{erf}(a\sqrt t)$
44	$\dfrac{1}{\sqrt{s}(s+a^2)}$		$\dfrac{2}{a\sqrt\pi}e^{-a^2t}\int_0^{a\sqrt t} e^{\tau^2}\,d\tau$

Laplace transforms

$$F(s) = \mathcal{L}(f)(s) = \int_0^\infty f(t)e^{-st}\, dt.$$

No.	$F(s)$	$f(t)$
45	$\dfrac{b^2 - a^2}{(s - a^2)(b + \sqrt{s})}$	$e^{a^2 t}[b - a\operatorname{erf}(a\sqrt{t})]$ $-be^{b^2 t}\operatorname{erfc}(b\sqrt{t})$
46	$\dfrac{1}{\sqrt{s}(\sqrt{s}+a)}$	$e^{a^2 t}\operatorname{erfc}(a\sqrt{t})$
47	$\dfrac{1}{(s+a)\sqrt{s+b}}$	$\dfrac{1}{\sqrt{b-a}}e^{-at}\operatorname{erf}(\sqrt{b-a}\sqrt{t})$
48	$\dfrac{b^2-a^2}{\sqrt{s}(s-a^2)(\sqrt{s}+b)}$	$e^{a^2 t}\left[\frac{b}{a}\operatorname{erf}(a\sqrt{t}) - 1\right]$ $+e^{b^2 t}\operatorname{erfc}(b\sqrt{t})$
49	$\dfrac{(1-s)^n}{s^{n+1/2}}$	$\dfrac{n!}{(2n)!\sqrt{\pi t}} H_{2n}(\sqrt{t})$
50	$\dfrac{(1-s)^n}{s^{n+3/2}}$	$-\dfrac{n!}{(2n+1)!\sqrt{\pi}} H_{2n+1}(\sqrt{t})$
51	$\dfrac{\sqrt{s+2a}}{\sqrt{s}} - 1$	$ae^{-at}\left[I_1(at) + I_0(at)\right]$
52	$\dfrac{1}{\sqrt{s+a}\sqrt{s+b}}$	$e^{-(a+b)t/2}I_0\left(\frac{a-b}{2}t\right)$
53	$\dfrac{\Gamma(k)}{(s + a)^k(s + b)^k}$ $(k \geq 0)$	$\sqrt{\pi}\left(\frac{t}{a-b}\right)^{k-1/2}e^{-(a+b)t/2}$ $\times I_{k-1/2}\left(\frac{a-b}{2}t\right)$
54	$\dfrac{1}{\sqrt{s + a}(s + b)^{3/2}}$	$te^{-(a+b)t/2}\left[I_0\left(\frac{a-b}{2}t\right)\right.$ $\left. + I_1\left(\frac{a-b}{2}t\right)\right]$
55	$\dfrac{\sqrt{s+2a}-\sqrt{s}}{\sqrt{s+2a}+\sqrt{s}}$	$\frac{1}{t}e^{-at}I_1(at)$
56	$\dfrac{1}{\sqrt{s^2+a^2}}$	$J_0(at)$
57	$\dfrac{(\sqrt{s^2+a^2}-s)^k}{\sqrt{s^2+a^2}}$ $(k > -1)$	$a^k J_k(at)$
58	$\dfrac{1}{(s^2+a^2)^k}$ $(k > 0)$	$\dfrac{\sqrt{\pi}}{\Gamma(k)}\left(\frac{t}{2a}\right)^{k-1/2} J_{k-1/2}(at)$
59	$(\sqrt{s^2 + a^2} - s)^k$ $(k > 0)$	$\frac{ka^k}{t} J_k(at)$
60	$\dfrac{(s-\sqrt{s^2-a^2})^k}{\sqrt{s^2-a^2}}$ $(k > -1)$	$a^k I_k(at)$
61	$\dfrac{1}{(s^2-a^2)^k}$ $(k > 0)$	$\dfrac{\sqrt{\pi}}{\Gamma(k)}\left(\frac{t}{2a}\right)^{k-1/2} I_{k-1/2}(at)$

Laplace transforms

$$F(s) = \mathcal{L}(f)(s) = \int_0^\infty f(t)e^{-st}\,dt.$$

No.	$F(s)$		$f(t)$
62	$\dfrac{e^{-ks}}{s}$		$\begin{cases} 0 & \text{when } 0 < t < k \\ 1 & \text{when } t > k \end{cases}$
63	$\dfrac{e^{-ks}}{s^2}$		$\begin{cases} 0 & \text{when } 0 < t < k \\ t - k & \text{when } t > k \end{cases}$
64	$\dfrac{e^{-ks}}{s^p}$	$(p > 0)$	$\begin{cases} 0 & \text{when } 0 < t < k \\ \frac{(t-k)^{p-1}}{\Gamma(p)} & \text{when } t > k \end{cases}$
65	$\dfrac{1 - e^{-ks}}{s}$		$\begin{cases} 1 & \text{when } 0 < t < k \\ 0 & \text{when } t > k \end{cases}$
66	$\dfrac{a}{s^2+a^2} \coth \frac{\pi s}{2a}$		$|\sin at|$
67	$\frac{1}{s}e^{-a/s}$		$J_0(2\sqrt{at})$
68	$\frac{1}{\sqrt{s}}e^{-a/s}$		$\frac{1}{\sqrt{\pi t}} \cos 2\sqrt{at}$
69	$\frac{1}{\sqrt{s}}e^{a/s}$		$\frac{1}{\sqrt{\pi t}} \cosh 2\sqrt{at}$
70	$\frac{1}{s^{3/2}}e^{-a/s}$		$\frac{1}{\sqrt{\pi a}} \sin 2\sqrt{at}$
71	$\frac{1}{s^{3/2}}e^{a/s}$		$\frac{1}{\sqrt{\pi a}} \sinh 2\sqrt{at}$
72	$\frac{1}{s^k}e^{-a/s}$	$(k > 0)$	$\left(\frac{t}{a}\right)^{(k-1)/2} J_{k-1}(2\sqrt{at})$
73	$\frac{1}{s^k}e^{a/s}$	$(k > 0)$	$\left(\frac{t}{a}\right)^{(k-1)/2} I_{k-1}(2\sqrt{at})$
74	$e^{-a\sqrt{s}}$	$(a > 0)$	$\frac{a}{2\sqrt{\pi t}}e^{-a^2/4t}$
75	$\frac{1}{s}e^{-a\sqrt{s}}$	$(a \geq 0)$	$\operatorname{erfc}\left(\frac{a}{2\sqrt{t}}\right)$
76	$\frac{1}{\sqrt{s}}e^{-a\sqrt{s}}$	$(a \geq 0)$	$\frac{1}{\sqrt{\pi t}}e^{-a^2/4t}$
77	$s^{-3/2}e^{-a\sqrt{s}}$	$(a \geq 0)$	$t\sqrt{\frac{t}{\pi}}e^{-a^2/4t} - a\operatorname{erfc}\left(\frac{a}{2\sqrt{t}}\right)$
78	$\dfrac{e^{-k\sqrt{s}}}{\sqrt{s}(a+\sqrt{s})}$	$(k \geq 0)$	$e^{ak+a^2t}\operatorname{erfc}\left(a\sqrt{t} + \frac{k}{2\sqrt{t}}\right)$

Laplace transforms

$$F(s) = \mathcal{L}(f)(s) = \int_0^\infty f(t)e^{-st}\,dt.$$

No.	$F(s)$		$f(t)$
79	$\dfrac{e^{-k(\sqrt{s^2+a^2}-s)}}{\sqrt{s^2+a^2}}$	$(k \geq 0)$	$J_0(a\sqrt{t^2+2kt})$
80	$\frac{1}{s}\log s$		$\Gamma'(1) - \log t$
81	$\frac{1}{s^k}\log s$	$(k > 0)$	$t^{k-1}\left[\dfrac{\Gamma'(k)}{|\Gamma(k)|^2} - \dfrac{\log t}{\Gamma(k)}\right]$
82	$\frac{\log s}{s-a}$	$(a > 0)$	$e^{at}[\log a - \text{Ei}\,(-at)]$
83	$\frac{\log s}{s^2+1}$		$\cos t\,\text{Si}(t) - \sin t\,\text{Ci}(t)$
84	$\frac{s\log s}{s^2+1}$		$-\sin t\,\text{Si}(t) - \cos t\,\text{Ci}(t)$
85	$\frac{1}{s}\log(1 + as)$	$(a > 0)$	$-\text{Ei}\left(-\frac{t}{a}\right)$
86	$\log\frac{s-a}{s-b}$		$\frac{1}{t}(e^{bt} - e^{at})$
87	$\frac{1}{s}\log(1 + a^2s^2)$		$-2\,\text{Ci}\left(-\frac{t}{a}\right)$
88	$\frac{1}{s}\log(s^2 + a^2)$	$(a > 0)$	$2\log a - 2\,\text{Ci}(at)$
89	$\frac{1}{s^2}\log(s^2 + a^2)$	$(a > 0)$	$\frac{2}{a}[at\log a + \sin at - at\,\text{Ci}(at)]$
90	$\log\frac{s^2+a^2}{s^2}$		$\frac{2}{t}(1 - \cos at)$
91	$\log\frac{s^2-a^2}{s^2}$		$\frac{2}{t}(1 - \cosh at)$
92	$\tan^{-1}\frac{a}{s}$		$\frac{1}{t}\sin at$
93	$e^{k^2s^2}\,\text{erfc}(ks)$	$(k > 0)$	$\frac{1}{k\sqrt{\pi}}e^{-t^2/4k^2}$
94	$\frac{1}{s}e^{k^2s^2}\,\text{erfc}(ks)$	$(k > 0)$	$\text{erf}\left(\frac{t}{2k}\right)$
95	$e^{ks}\,\text{erfc}(\sqrt{ks})$	$(k > 0)$	$\frac{\sqrt{k}}{\pi\sqrt{t}(t+k)}$
96	$\frac{1}{\sqrt{s}}e^{ks}\,\text{erfc}(\sqrt{ks})$	$(k > 0)$	$\frac{1}{\sqrt{\pi}(t+k)}$
97	$\text{erf}\left(\frac{a}{\sqrt{s}}\right)$		$\frac{1}{\pi t}\sin(2a\sqrt{t})$
98	$-e^{as}\text{Ei}\,(-as)$	$(a > 0)$	$\frac{1}{t+a}$
99	$\frac{1}{a} + se^{as}\text{Ei}\,(-as)$	$(a > 0)$	$\frac{1}{(t+a)^2}$
100	$\left[\frac{\pi}{2} - \text{Si}(s)\right]\cos s + \text{Ci}(s)\sin s$		$\frac{1}{t^2+1}$
101	$K_0(as)$		$\begin{cases} 0 & \text{when } 0 < t < k \\ (t^2 - k^2)^{-1/2} & \text{when } t > k \end{cases}$

Hankel transforms

$$\mathcal{H}_\nu(f)(y) = F_\nu(y) = \int_0^\infty f(x)\sqrt{xy}\,J_\nu(yx)\,dx, \quad y > 0.$$

No.	$f(x)$	$F_\nu(y)$
1	$\begin{cases} x^{\nu+1/2}, & 0 < x < 1 \\ 0, & 1 < x \end{cases}$, $\operatorname{Re}\nu > -1$	$y^{-1/2}J_{\nu+1}(y)$
2	$\begin{cases} x^{\nu+1/2}(a^2 - x^2)^\mu, & 0 < x < a \\ 0, & a < x; \end{cases}$, $\operatorname{Re}\nu, \quad \operatorname{Re}\mu > -1,$	$2^\mu\Gamma(\mu+1)a^{\nu+\mu+1}y^{-\mu-1/2}$ $\times J_{\nu+\mu+1}(ay)$
3	$x^{\nu+1/2}(x^2 + a^2)^{-\nu-1/2}$, $\operatorname{Re}a > 0, \quad \operatorname{Re}\nu > -1/2$	$\sqrt{\pi}\,y^{\nu-1/2}2^{-\nu}e^{-ay}$ $\times [\Gamma(\nu+1/2)]^{-1}$
4	$x^{\nu+1/2}e^{-ax}$, $\operatorname{Re}a > 0, \quad \operatorname{Re}\nu > -1$	$a(\pi)^{-1/2}2^{\nu+1}y^{\nu+1/2}\Gamma(\nu+3/2)$ $\times (a^2 + y^2)^{-\nu-3/2}$
5	$x^{\nu+1/2}e^{-ax^2}$, $\operatorname{Re}a > 0, \quad \operatorname{Re}\nu > -1$	$y^{\nu+1/2}(2a)^{-\nu-1}\exp\left(-y^2/4a\right)$
6	$e^{-ax}/\sqrt{x}$, $\operatorname{Re}a > 0, \quad \operatorname{Re}\nu > -1$	$y^{-\nu+1/2}\left[\sqrt{(a^2 + y^2)} - a\right]^\nu$ $\times (a^2 + y^2)^{-1/2}$
7	$x^{-\nu-1/2}\cos(ax)$, $a > 0, \quad \operatorname{Re}\nu > -1/2$	$\sqrt{\pi}\,2^{-\nu}y^{-\nu+1/2}[\Gamma(\nu+1/2)]^{-1}$ $\times (y^2 - a^2)^{\nu-1/2}H(y-a)$
8	$x^{1/2-\nu}\sin(ax)$, $a > 0, \quad \operatorname{Re}\nu > 1/2$	$a2^{1-\nu}\sqrt{\pi}\,y^{\nu+1/2}[\Gamma(\nu-1/2)]^{-1}$ $\times (y^2 - a^2)^{\nu-3/2}H(y-a)$
9	$x^{-1/2}J_{\nu-1}(ax)$, $a > 0, \quad \operatorname{Re}\nu > -1$	$a^{\nu-1}y^{-\nu+1/2}H(y-a)$
10	$x^{-1/2}J_{\nu+1}(ax)$, $a > 0, \quad \operatorname{Re}\nu > -3/2$	$\begin{cases} a^{-\nu-1}y^{\nu+1/2}, & 0 < y < a \\ 0, & a < y \end{cases}$

Hilbert transforms

$$\mathcal{H}(f)(y) = F(y) = \frac{1}{\pi} \int_{-\infty}^{\infty} \frac{f(x)}{x - y} \, dx.$$

No.	$f(x)$	$F(y)$
1	1	0
2	$\begin{cases} 0, & -\infty < x < a \\ 1, & a < x < b \\ 0, & b < x < \infty \end{cases}$	$\dfrac{1}{\pi} \log \left\lvert (b - y)(a - y)^{-1} \right\rvert$
3	$\begin{cases} 0, & -\infty < x < a \\ x^{-1}, & a < x < \infty \end{cases}$	$(\pi y)^{-1} \log \left\lvert a(a - y)^{-1} \right\rvert,$ $0 \neq y \neq a, \quad a > 0$
4	$(x + a)^{-1} \qquad\qquad \mathrm{Im}\, a > 0$	$i(y + a)^{-1}$
5	$\dfrac{1}{1 + x^2}$	$-y/1 + y^2$
6	$\dfrac{1}{1 + x^4}$	$-\dfrac{y(1 + y^2)}{\sqrt{2}(1 + y^4)}$
7	$\sin(ax), \qquad\qquad a > 0$	$\cos(ay)$
8	$\sin(ax)/x, \qquad\qquad a > 0$	$[\cos(ay) - 1]/y$
9	$\cos(ax), \qquad\qquad a > 0$	$-\sin(ay)$
10	$[1 - \cos(ax)]/x, \qquad a > 0$	$\sin(ay)/y$
11	$\mathrm{sgn}(x)\sin(a\lvert x \rvert^{1/2}) \qquad a > 0$	$\cos(a\lvert y \rvert^{1/2}) + \exp(-a\lvert y \rvert^{1/2})$
12	$e^{iax} \qquad\qquad a > 0$	$i e^{iay}$

Mellin transforms

$$f^*(s) = \mathcal{M}[f(x); s] = \int_0^\infty f(x) x^{s-1}\, dx.$$

No.	$f(x)$	$f^*(s)$
1	$ag(x) + bh(x)$	$ag^*(s) + bh^*(s)$
2	$f^{(n)}(x)$†	$(-1)^n \frac{\Gamma(s)}{\Gamma(s-n)} f^*(s-n)$
3	$x^n f^{(n)}(x)$†	$(-1)^n \frac{\Gamma(s+n)}{\Gamma(s)} f^*(s)$
4	$I_n f(x)$‡	$(-1)^n \frac{\Gamma(s)}{\Gamma(s+n)} f^*(s+n)$
5	e^{-x}	$\Gamma(s)$ $\qquad\qquad$ Re $s > 0$
6	e^{-x^2}	$\frac{1}{2}\Gamma(\frac{1}{2}s)$ $\qquad\quad$ Re $s > 0$
7	$\cos x$	$\Gamma(s)\cos(\frac{1}{2}\pi s)$ $\quad$ $0 < $ Re $s < 1$
8	$\sin x$	$\Gamma(s)\sin(\frac{1}{2}\pi s)$ $\quad$ $0 < $ Re $s < 1$
9	$(1-x)^{-1}$	$\pi\cot(\pi s)$ $\qquad$ $0 < $ Re $s < 1$
10	$(1+x)^{-1}$	$\pi\,\mathrm{cosec}(\pi s)$ $\qquad$ $0 < $ Re $s < 1$
11	$(1+x^a)^{-b}$	$\frac{\Gamma(s/a)\Gamma(b-s/a)}{a\Gamma(b)}$ $\quad$ $0 < $ Re $s < ab$
12	$\log(1+ax)$ $\qquad$ $\lvert\arg a\rvert < \pi$	$\pi s^{-1} a^{-s}\,\mathrm{cosec}(\pi s)$ $\qquad\qquad\qquad -1 < $ Re $s < 0$
13	$\tan^{-1} x$	$-\frac{1}{2}\pi s^{-1}\sec(\frac{1}{2}\pi s)$ $\qquad\qquad\qquad -1 < $ Re $s < 0$
14	$\cot^{-1} x$	$\frac{1}{2}\pi s^{-1}\sec(\frac{1}{2}\pi s)$ $\quad$ $0 < $ Re $s < 1$
15	$\mathrm{csch}\, ax$ $\qquad$ Re $a > 0$	$2(1 - 2^{-s})a^{-s}\Gamma(s)\zeta(s)$ $\ $ Re $s > 1$
16	$\mathrm{sech}^2\, ax$ $\qquad$ Re $a > 0$	$4(2a)^{-s}\Gamma(s)\zeta(s-1)$ $\quad$ Re $s > 2$
17	$\mathrm{csch}^2\, ax$ $\qquad$ Re $a > 0$	$4(2a)^{-s}\Gamma(s)\zeta(s-1)$ $\quad$ Re $s > 2$
18	$K_\nu(ax)$	$a^{-s}2^{s-2}\Gamma((s-\nu)/2)$ $\qquad \times\, \Gamma((s+\nu)/2)$ $\quad$ Re $s > \lvert$Re $\nu\rvert$

†Assuming that $\lim_{x\to 0} x^{s-r-1} f^{(r)}(x) = 0$ for $r = 0, 1, \ldots, n-1$.

‡Where I_n denotes the nth repeated integral of $f(x)$: $I_0 f(x) = f(x)$, $I_n f(x) = \int_0^x I_{n-1}(t)\, dt$.

References

1. W. Magnus, F. Oberhettinger, and R.P. Soni, *Formulas and Theorems for the Special Functions of Mathematical Physics*, Springer–Verlag, New York, 1966.

2. Staff of the Bateman Manuscript Project, A. Erdélyi, Ed., *Tables of Integral Transforms*, in 3 volumes, McGraw-Hill, New York, 1954.

3. N.I.A. Vilenkin, *Special Functions and the Theory of Group Representations*, American Mathematical Society, Providence, RI, 1968.

4. I.S. Gradshteyn and I.M. Ryzhik, *Tables of Integrals, Series, and Products,* 5th ed., Academic Press, New York, 1994.

Chapter 7

Probability and Statistics

0-8493-2479-3/96/$0.00+$.50
© 1996 CRC Press, Inc.

7.1 PROBABILITY THEORY

7.1.1 INTRODUCTION

A sample space S associated with an experiment is a set S of elements such that any outcome of the experiment corresponds to a unique element of the set. An event E is a subset of a sample space S. An element in a sample space is called a sample point or a simple event.

Definition of probability

If an experiment can occur in n mutually exclusive and equally likely ways, and if exactly m of these ways correspond to an event E, then the probability of E is given by

$$P(E) = \frac{m}{n}.$$

If E is a subset of S, and if to each unit subset of S, a nonnegative number, called the probability, is assigned, and if E is the union of two or more different simple events, then the probability of E, denoted $P(E)$, is the sum of the probabilities of those simple events whose union is E.

Marginal and conditional probability

Suppose a sample space S is partitioned into rs disjoint subsets where the general subset is denoted $E_i \cap F_j$ (with $i = 1, 2, \ldots, r$ and $j = 1, 2, \ldots, s$). Then the marginal probability of E_i is defined as

$$P(E_i) = \sum_{j=1}^{s} P(E_i \cap F_j), \tag{7.1.1}$$

and the marginal probability of F_j is defined as

$$P(F_j) = \sum_{i=1}^{r} P(E_i \cap F_j). \tag{7.1.2}$$

The conditional probability of E_i, given that F_j has occurred, is defined as

$$P(E_i \mid F_j) = \frac{P(E_i \cap F_j)}{P(F_j)}, \qquad \text{when } P(F_j) \neq 0 \tag{7.1.3}$$

and that of F_j, given that E_i has occurred, is defined as

$$P(F_j \mid E_i) = \frac{P(E_i \cap F_j)}{P(E_i)}, \qquad \text{when } P(E_i) \neq 0. \tag{7.1.4}$$

Probability theorems

1. If $\emptyset$ is the null set, then $P(\emptyset) = 0$.

2. If S is the sample space, then $P(S) = 1$.

3. If E and F are two events, then

$$P(E \cup F) = P(E) + P(F) - P(E \cap F). \tag{7.1.5}$$

4. If E and F are mutually exclusive events, then

$$P(E \cup F) = P(E) + P(F). \tag{7.1.6}$$

5. If E and E' are complementary events, then

$$P(E) = 1 - P(E'). \tag{7.1.7}$$

6. Two events are said to be independent if and only if

$$P(E \cap F) = P(E)\,P(F). \tag{7.1.8}$$

The event E is said to be statistically independent of the event F if $P(E \mid F) = P(E)$ and $P(F \mid E) = P(F)$.

7. The events $\{E_1, \ldots, E_n\}$ are called mutually independent for all combinations if and only if every combination of these events taken any number of times is independent.

8. *Bayes' rule*: If $\{E_1, \ldots, E_n\}$ are n mutually exclusive events whose union is the sample space S, and if E is any arbitrary event of S such that $P(E) \neq 0$, then

$$P(E_k \mid E) = \frac{P(E_k)\,P(E \mid E_k)}{P(E)} = \frac{P(E_k)\,P(E \mid E_k)}{\sum_{j=1}^{n} P(E_j)\,P(E \mid E_j)}. \tag{7.1.9}$$

9. For a uniform probability distribution,

$$P(A) = \frac{\text{Number of outcomes in event } A}{\text{Total number of outcomes}}$$

Terminology

1. A function whose domain is a sample space S and whose range is some set of real numbers is called a random variable. This random variable is called discrete if it assumes only a finite or denumerable number of values. It is called continuous if it assumes a continuum of values.

2. "iid" or "i.i.d." is often used for the phrase "independent and identically distributed".

3. Random variables are usually represented by capital letters.

4. Many probability distribution have special representations:

    (a) χ_n^2: chi-square random variable with n degrees of freedom

    (b) $E(\lambda)$: exponential distribution with parameter λ

    (c) $N(\mu, \sigma)$: normal random variable with mean μ and standard deviation σ

    (d) $P(\lambda)$: Poisson distribution with parameter λ

    (e) $U[a, b]$: uniform random variable on the interval $[a, b)$

Characterizing random variables

When X is a discrete random variable, let p_k for $k = 0, 1, \ldots$ be the probability that $X = x_k$ (with $p_k \geq 0$ and $\sum_k p_k = 1$). For any event E,

$$P(E) = P(X \text{ is in } E) = \sum_{x_k \in E} p_k. \tag{7.1.10}$$

In the continuous case, $f(x)\,dx$ is used to denote the probability that X lies in the region $[x, x + dx]$; it is called the *probability density function* (with $f(x) \geq 0$ and $\int f(x)\,dx = 1$). For any event E,

$$P(E) = P(X \text{ is in } E) = \int_E f(x)\,dx. \tag{7.1.11}$$

The *cumulative distribution function*, or simply the *distribution function*, is defined by

$$F(x) = \text{Probability}(X \leq x) = \begin{cases} \sum_{x_k \leq x} p_k, & \text{in the discrete case,} \\ \int^x f(t)\,dt, & \text{in the continuous case.} \end{cases} \tag{7.1.12}$$

Note that $F(-\infty) = 0$ and $F(\infty) = 1$. The probability that X is between a and b is

$$P(a \leq X \leq b) = P(X \leq b) - P(X \leq a) = F(b) - F(a). \tag{7.1.13}$$

Let $g(X)$ be a function of X. The expected value of $g(X)$, denoted by $\mathrm{E}\,[g(X)]$, is defined by

$$\mathrm{E}\,[g(X)] = \begin{cases} \sum_k p_k g(x_k), & \text{in the discrete case,} \\ \int g(t) f(t)\,dt, & \text{in the continuous case.} \end{cases} \tag{7.1.14}$$

1. $\mathrm{E}\,[aX + bY] = a\mathrm{E}\,[X] + b\mathrm{E}\,[Y]$.
2. $\mathrm{E}\,[XY] = \mathrm{E}\,[X]\mathrm{E}\,[Y]$ if X and Y are statistically independent.

The *moments* of X are defined by $\mu_k' = \mathrm{E}\,[X^k]$. The first moment, μ_1', is called the *mean* of X; it is usually denoted by $\mu = \mu_1' = \mathrm{E}\,[X]$. The *centered moments* of X are defined by $\mu_k = \mathrm{E}\,[(X - \mu)^k]$. The second centered moment is called the *variance* and is denoted by $\sigma^2 = \mu_2 = \mathrm{E}\,[(X - \mu)^2]$. Here, σ is called the *standard deviation*. The *skewness* is $\gamma_1 = \mu_3/\sigma^3$, and the *excess* or *kurtosis* is $\gamma_2 = (\mu_4/\sigma^4) - 3$.

Using σ_Z^2 to denote the variance for the random variable Z,

1. $\sigma_{cX}^2 = c^2 \sigma_X^2$.
2. $\sigma_{c+X}^2 = \sigma_X^2$.
3. $\sigma_{aX+b}^2 = a^2 \sigma_X^2$.

Generating and characteristic functions

In the case of a discrete distribution, the *generating function* corresponding to X (when it exists) is given by $G(s) = G_X(s) = \mathrm{E}\left[s^X\right] = \sum_{k=0}^{\infty} p_k s^{x_k}$. From this function, the moments may be found from

$$\mu_n' = \left(s \frac{\partial}{\partial s}\right)^n G(s)\Bigg|_{s=1}. \tag{7.1.15}$$

1. If c is a constant, then the generating function of $c + X$ is $s^c G(s)$.
2. If c is a constant, then the generating function of cX is $G(cs)$.
3. If $Z = X + Y$ where X and Y are independent discrete random variables, then $G_Z(s) = G_X(s)G_Y(s)$.
4. If $Y = \sum_{i=1}^{n} X_i$, the $\{X_i\}$ are independent, and each X_i has the common generating function $G_X(s)$, then the generating function of Y is $[G_X(s)]^n$.

In the case of a continuous distribution, the *characteristic function* corresponding to X is given by $\phi(t) = \mathrm{E}\left[e^{itX}\right] = \int_{-\infty}^{\infty} e^{itx} f(x)\,dx$. From this function, the moments may be found: $\mu_n' = i^{-n}\phi^{(n)}(0)$. If $Z = X + Y$ where X and Y are independent continuous random variables, then $\phi_Z(t) = \phi_X(t)\phi_Y(t)$. The *cumulant function* is defined as the logarithm of the characteristic function. The nth cumulant, κ_n, is defined as a certain term in the Taylor series of the cumulant function,

$$\log \phi(t) = \sum_{n=0}^{\infty} \kappa_n \frac{(it)^n}{n!}.$$

Note that $\kappa_1 = \mu$, $\kappa_2 = \sigma^2$, $\kappa_3 = \mu_3$, and $\kappa_4 = \mu_4 - 3\mu_2^2$. For a normal probability distribution, $\kappa_n = 0$ for $n \geq 3$. The centered moments in terms of cumulants are

$$\begin{aligned}
\mu_2 &= \kappa_2, \\
\mu_3 &= \kappa_3, \\
\mu_4 &= \kappa_4 + 3\kappa_2^2, \\
\mu_5 &= \kappa_5 + 10\kappa_3\kappa_2, \\
\mu_6 &= \kappa_6 + 15\kappa_4\kappa_2 + 10\kappa_3^2 + 15\kappa_2^3.
\end{aligned} \tag{7.1.16}$$

7.1.2 MULTIVARIATE DISTRIBUTIONS

Discrete case

The k-dimensional random variable $(X_1, \ldots, X_k)$ is a k-dimensional discrete random variable if it assumes values only at a finite or denumerable number of points $(x_1, \ldots, x_k)$. Define

$$P(X_1 = x_1, X_2 = x_2, \ldots, X_k = x_k) = f(x_1, x_2, \ldots, x_k) \qquad (7.1.17)$$

for every value that the random variable can assume. The function $f(x_1, \ldots, x_k)$ is called the joint density of the k-dimensional random variable. If E is any subset of the set of values that the random variable can assume, then

$$P(E) = P[(X_1, \ldots, X_k) \text{ is in } E] = \sum_E f(x_1, \ldots, x_k) \qquad (7.1.18)$$

where the sum is over all those points in E. The cumulative distribution function is defined as

$$F(x_1, x_2, \ldots, x_k) = \sum_{z_1 \leq x_1} \sum_{z_2 \leq x_2} \cdots \sum_{z_k \leq x_k} f(z_1, z_2, \ldots, z_k). \qquad (7.1.19)$$

Continuous case

The k random variables $(X_1, \ldots, X_k)$ are said to be jointly distributed if a function f exists so that $f(x_1, \ldots, x_k) \geq 0$ for all $-\infty < x_i < \infty$ $(i = 1, \ldots, k)$ and so that, for any given event E,

$$P(E) = P[(X_1, X_2, \ldots, X_k) \text{ is in } E]$$
$$= \int \cdots \int_E f(x_1, x_2, \ldots, x_k) \, dx_1 \, dx_2 \cdots dx_k. \qquad (7.1.20)$$

The function $f(x_1, \ldots, x_k)$ is called the joint density of the random variables $X_1, X_2, \ldots, X_k$. The cumulative distribution function is defined as

$$F(x_1, x_2, \ldots, x_k) = \int_{-\infty}^{x_1} \int_{-\infty}^{x_2} \cdots \int_{-\infty}^{x_k} f(z_1, z_2, \ldots, z_k) \, dz_1 \, dz_2 \cdots dz_k. \qquad (7.1.21)$$

Given the cumulative distribution function, the probability density may be found from

$$f(x_1, x_2, \ldots, x_k) = \frac{\partial}{\partial x_1} \frac{\partial}{\partial x_2} \cdots \frac{\partial}{\partial x_k} F(x_1, x_2, \ldots, x_k). \qquad (7.1.22)$$

Moments

The rth moment of X_i is defined as

$$E[X_i^r] = \begin{cases} \sum_{x_1} \cdots \sum_{x_k} x_i^r f(x_1, \ldots, x_k), & \text{in the discrete case,} \\ \int_{-\infty}^{\infty} \cdots \int x_i^r f(x_1, \ldots, x_k) \, dx_1 \cdots dx_k & \text{in the continuous case.} \end{cases} \qquad (7.1.23)$$

Joint moments about the origin are defined as $\mathrm{E}\left[X_1^{r_1} X_2^{r_2} \cdots X_k^{r_k}\right]$ where $r_1 + r_2 + \cdots + r_k$ is the order of the moment. Joint moments about the mean are defined as $\mathrm{E}\left[(X_1 - \mu_1)^{r_1}(X_2 - \mu_2)^{r_2} \cdots (X_k - \mu_k)^{r_k}\right]$, where $\mu_k = \mathrm{E}[X_k]$.

Marginal and conditional distributions

If the random variables $X_1, X_2, \ldots, X_k$ have the joint density function $f(x_1, x_2, \ldots, x_k)$, then the marginal distribution of the subset of the random variables, say, $X_1, X_2, \ldots, X_p$ (with $p < k$), is given by

$$
g(x_1, x_2, \ldots, x_p) =
$$

$$
\begin{cases}
\sum_{x_{p+1}} \sum_{x_{p+2}} \cdots \sum_{x_k} f(x_1, x_2, \ldots, x_k), & \text{in the discrete case,} \\
\int_{-\infty}^{\infty} \cdots \int f(x_1, \ldots, x_k)\, dx_{p+1} \cdots dx_k, & \text{in the continuous case.}
\end{cases}
\tag{7.1.24}
$$

The conditional distribution of a certain subset of the random variables is the joint distribution of this subset under the condition that the remaining variables are given certain values. The conditional distribution of $X_1, X_2, \ldots, X_p$, given $X_{p+1}, X_{p+2}, \ldots, X_k$, is

$$
h(x_1, \ldots, x_p \mid x_{p+1}, \ldots, x_k) = \frac{f(x_1, x_2, \ldots, x_k)}{g(x_{p+1}, x_{p+2}, \ldots, x_k)}
\tag{7.1.25}
$$

if $g(x_{p+1}, x_{p+2}, \ldots, x_k) \neq 0$.

The variance σ_{ii} of X_i and the covariance σ_{ij} of X_i and X_j are given by

$$
\begin{aligned}
\sigma_{ii}^2 &= \sigma_i^2 = \mathrm{E}\left[(X_i - \mu_i)^2\right], \\
\sigma_{ij}^2 &= \rho_{ij}\sigma_i\sigma_j = \mathrm{E}\left[(X_i - \mu_i)(X_j - \mu_j)\right],
\end{aligned}
\tag{7.1.26}
$$

where ρ_{ij} is the correlation coefficient, and σ_i and σ_j are the standard deviations of X_i and X_j.

7.1.3   RANDOM SUMS OF RANDOM VARIABLES

If $T = \sum_{i=1}^{N} X_i$, N is an integer-valued random variable with generating function $G_N(s)$, and if the $\{X_i\}$ are discrete independent and identically distributed random variables with generating function $G_X(s)$, and the $\{X_i\}$ are independent of N, then the generating function for T is $G_T(s) = G_N(G_X(s))$. (If the $\{X_i\}$ are continuous random variables, then $\phi_T(\xi) = G_N(\phi_X(\xi))$.) Hence,

- $\mu_T = \mu_N \mu_X$.
- $\sigma_T^2 = \mu_N \sigma_X^2 + \mu_X^2 \sigma_N^2$.

7.1.4 TRANSFORMING VARIABLES

1. Suppose that the random variable X has the probability density function $f_X(x)$ and the random variable Y is defined by $Y = g(X)$. If g is measurable and one-to-one, then

$$f_Y(y) = f_X(h(y)) \left| \frac{dh}{dy} \right| \tag{7.1.27}$$

where $h(y) = g^{-1}(y)$.

2. If the random variables X and Y are independent and if their densities f_X and f_Y, respectively, exist almost everywhere, then the probability density of their sum, $Z = X + Y$, is given by the formula,

$$f_Z(z) = \int_{-\infty}^{\infty} f_X(x) f_Y(z - x) \, dx. \tag{7.1.28}$$

3. If the random variables X and Y are independent and if their densities f_X and f_Y, respectively, exist almost everywhere, then the probability density of their product, $Z = XY$, is given by the formula,

$$f_Z(z) = \int_{-\infty}^{\infty} \frac{1}{|x|} f_X(x) f_Y \left(\frac{z}{x} \right) dx. \tag{7.1.29}$$

7.1.5 CENTRAL LIMIT THEOREM

If $\{X_i\}$ are independent and identically distributed random variables with mean μ and finite variance σ^2, then the random variable

$$Z = \frac{(X_1 + X_2 + \cdots + X_n) - n\mu}{\sqrt{n}\sigma} \tag{7.1.30}$$

tends (as $n \to \infty$) to a normal random variable with mean zero and variance one.

7.1.6 AVERAGES OVER VECTORS

Let $\overline{f(\mathbf{n})}$ denote the average of the function f as the unit vector $\mathbf{n}$ varies uniformly in all directions in three dimensions. If $\mathbf{a}$, $\mathbf{b}$, $\mathbf{c}$, and $\mathbf{d}$ are constant vectors, then

$$\overline{|\mathbf{a} \cdot \mathbf{n}|^2} = |\mathbf{a}|^2 / 3,$$

$$\overline{(\mathbf{a} \cdot \mathbf{n})(\mathbf{b} \cdot \mathbf{n})} = (\mathbf{a} \cdot \mathbf{b})/3,$$

$$\overline{(\mathbf{a} \cdot \mathbf{n})\mathbf{n}} = \mathbf{a}/3,$$

$$\overline{|\mathbf{a} \times \mathbf{n}|^2} = 2 |\mathbf{a}|^2 / 3, \tag{7.1.31}$$

$$\overline{(\mathbf{a} \times \mathbf{n}) \cdot (\mathbf{b} \times \mathbf{n})} = 2\mathbf{a} \cdot \mathbf{b}/3,$$

$$\overline{(\mathbf{a} \cdot \mathbf{n})(\mathbf{b} \cdot \mathbf{n})(\mathbf{c} \cdot \mathbf{n})(\mathbf{d} \cdot \mathbf{n})} = [(\mathbf{a} \cdot \mathbf{b})(\mathbf{c} \cdot \mathbf{d}) + (\mathbf{a} \cdot \mathbf{c})(\mathbf{b} \cdot \mathbf{d}) + (\mathbf{a} \cdot \mathbf{d})(\mathbf{b} \cdot \mathbf{c})] /15.$$

Now let $\overline{f(\mathbf{n})}$ denote the average of the function f as the unit vector $\mathbf{n}$ varies uniformly in all directions in two dimensions. If $\mathbf{a}$ and $\mathbf{b}$ are constant vectors, then

$$\overline{|\mathbf{a} \cdot \mathbf{n}|^2} = |\mathbf{a}|^2/2,$$
$$\overline{(\mathbf{a} \cdot \mathbf{n})(\mathbf{b} \cdot \mathbf{n})} = (\mathbf{a} \cdot \mathbf{b})/2, \qquad (7.1.32)$$
$$\overline{(\mathbf{a} \cdot \mathbf{n})\mathbf{n}} = \mathbf{a}/2.$$

7.1.7   INEQUALITIES

1. *Markov's Inequality:* If X is a random variable which takes only nonnegative values, then for any $a > 0$,

$$P(X \geq a) \leq \frac{\mathrm{E}[X]}{a}. \qquad (7.1.33)$$

2. *Cauchy–Schwartz Inequality:* Let X and Y be random variables for which $\mathrm{E}[X^2]$ and $\mathrm{E}[Y^2]$ exist, then

$$(\mathrm{E}[XY])^2 \leq \mathrm{E}[X^2]\mathrm{E}[Y^2]. \qquad (7.1.34)$$

3. *One-Sided Chebyshev Inequality:* Let X be a random variable with zero mean (i.e., $\mathrm{E}[X] = 0$) and variance σ^2. Then, for any positive a,

$$P(X > a) \leq \frac{\sigma^2}{\sigma^2 + a^2}. \qquad (7.1.35)$$

4. *Chebyshev's Inequality:* Let c be any real number and let X be a random variable for which $\mathrm{E}[(X - c)^2]$ is finite. Then, for every $\epsilon > 0$ the following holds:

$$P(|X - c| \geq \epsilon) \leq \frac{1}{\epsilon^2}\mathrm{E}[(X - c)^2]. \qquad (7.1.36)$$

5. *Bienaymé–Chebyshev's Inequality:* If $E[|X|^r] < \infty$ for all $r > 0$ (r not necessarily an integer) then, for every $a > 0$,

$$P(|X| \geq a) \leq \frac{E[|X|^r]}{a^r}. \qquad (7.1.37)$$

6. *Generalized Bienaymé–Chebyshev's Inequality:* Let $g(x)$ be a non-decreasing nonnegative function defined on $(0, \infty)$. Then, for $a \geq 0$,

$$P(|X| \geq a) \leq \frac{E[g(|X|)]}{g(a)}. \qquad (7.1.38)$$

7. *Chernoff bound:* This bound is useful for sums of random variables. Let $Y_n = \sum_{i=1}^{n} X_i$ where each of the X_i is iid. Let $M(t) = \mathrm{E}_x[e^{tX}]$ be the common moment generating function for the $\{X_i\}$, and define $g(t) = \log M(t)$. Then,

$$P\left(Y_n \geq ng'(t)\right) \leq e^{-n[tg'(t)-g(t)]}, \qquad \text{if } t \geq 0,$$
$$P\left(Y_n \leq ng'(t)\right) \leq e^{-n[tg'(t)-g(t)]}, \qquad \text{if } t \leq 0.$$

8. *Kolmogorov's Inequality:* Let $X_1, X_2, \ldots, X_n$ be n independent random variables such that $E[X_i] = 0$ and $\mathrm{Var}(X_i) = \sigma_{X_i}^2$ is finite. Then, for all $a > 0$,

$$P\left(\max_{i=1,\ldots,n} |X_1 + X_2 + \cdots + X_i| > a\right) \leq \sum_{i=1}^{n} \frac{\sigma_i^2}{a^2}.$$

9. *Jensen's Inequality:* If $E[X]$ exists, and if $f(x)$ is a convex $\cup$ ("convex cup") function, then

$$E[f(X)] \geq f(E[X]). \tag{7.1.39}$$

7.1.8   GEOMETRIC PROBABILITY

1. Points on a finite line
   If A and B are uniformly chosen from the interval $[0, 1)$, and X is the distance between A and B (that is, $X = |A - B|$) then the probability density of X is $f_X(x) = 2(1 - x)$.

2. Points on a finite line
   Uniformly and independently choose $n - 1$ random values in the interval $[0, 1)$. This creates n intervals.

   $P_k(x)$ = Probability (exactly k intervals have length larger than x)

   $$= \binom{n}{k}\left\{[1 - kx]^{n-1} - \binom{n-1}{1}[1 - (k+1)x]^{n-1} + \right.$$

   $$\left. \cdots + (-1)^s \binom{n-k}{s}[1 - (k+s)x]^{n-1}\right\},$$

   where $s = \left\lfloor \frac{1}{x} - k \right\rfloor$. From this, the probability that the largest interval length exceeds x is

   $$1 - P_0(x) = \binom{n}{1}(1 - x)^{n-1} - \binom{n}{2}(1 - 2x)^{n-1} + \ldots.$$

3. Points in the plane
   Assume that the number of points in any region A of the plane is a Poisson variate with mean λA (λ is the "density" of the points). Given a fixed point P define $R_1, R_2, \ldots$, to be the distance to the point nearest to P, second nearest to P, etc. Then

   $$f_{R_s}(r) = \frac{2(\lambda \pi)^s}{(s-1)!} r^{2s-1} e^{-\lambda \pi r^2}.$$

4. Buffon's needle problem
   A needle of length L is placed at random on a plane on which are ruled parallel lines at unit distance apart. Assume that $L < 1$ so that only one intersection is possible. The probability P that the needle intersects a line is

   $$P = \frac{2}{\pi}\left[\frac{\pi}{2} - \sin^{-1} L^{-1} + L - \sqrt{L^2 - 1}\right].$$

5. Points in three-dimensional space

Assume that the number of points in any volume V is a Poisson variate with mean λV (λ is the "density" of the points). Given a fixed point P define R_1, R_2, ..., to be the distance to the point nearest to P, second nearest to P, etc. Then

$$f_{R_s}(r) = \frac{3\left(\frac{4}{3}\lambda\pi\right)^s}{\Gamma(s)} r^{3s-1} e^{-\frac{4}{3}\lambda\pi r^3}.$$

7.1.9   CLASSIC PROBABILITY PROBLEMS

1. Birthday problem: The probability that n people all have different birthdays is $q_n = \frac{364}{365}\frac{363}{365}\cdots\frac{366-n}{365}$. Let $p_n = 1 - q_n$. For 23 people the probability of at least two people having the same birthday is $p_{23} = 1 - q_{23} > 1/2$; more than half.

n	10	20	23	30	40	50
p_n	0.117	0.411	0.507	0.706	0.891	0.970

2. Raisin cookie problem: A baker creates enough cookie dough for 1000 raisin cookies. The number of raisins to be added to the dough, R, is to be determined.

- If you want to be 99% certain that the *first* cookie will have at least one raisin, then $1 - \left(\frac{999}{1000}\right)^R \geq 0.99$, or $R \geq 4603$.

- If you want to be 99% certain that *every* cookie will have at least one raisin, then $P(C, R) \geq 0.99$, where C is the number of cookies and $P(C, R) = C^{-R} \sum_{i=0}^{C} \binom{C}{i}(-1)^i (C-i)^R$. Hence $R \geq 11508$.

7.2   PROBABILITY DISTRIBUTIONS

7.2.1   DISCRETE DISTRIBUTIONS

1. *Discrete uniform distribution*: If the random variable X has a probability density function given by

$$P(X = x) = f(x) = \frac{1}{n}, \qquad \text{for } x = x_1, x_2, \ldots, x_n,$$

$$(7.2.1)$$

then the variable X is said to possess a discrete uniform probability distribution.

Properties: When $x_i = i$ for $i = 1, 2, \ldots, n$ then

$$\text{Mean} = \mu = \frac{n+1}{2},$$

$$\text{Variance} = \sigma^2 = \frac{n^2 - 1}{12},$$

$$\text{Standard deviation} = \sigma = \sqrt{\frac{n^2 - 1}{12}}, \qquad (7.2.2)$$

$$\text{Moment generating function} = G(t) = \frac{e^t(1 - e^{nt})}{n(1 - e^t)}.$$

2. *Binomial distribution*: If the random variable X has a probability density function given by

$$P(X = x) = f(x) = \binom{n}{x}\theta^x(1 - \theta)^{n-x}, \qquad \text{for } x = 0, 1, \ldots, n, \qquad (7.2.3)$$

then the variable X is said to possess a binomial distribution. Note that $f(x)$ is the general term in the expansion of $[\theta + (1 - \theta)]^n$.
Properties:

$$\text{Mean} = \mu = n\theta,$$

$$\text{Variance} = \sigma^2 = n\theta(1 - \theta),$$

$$\text{Standard deviation} = \sigma = \sqrt{n\theta(1 - \theta)}, \qquad (7.2.4)$$

$$\text{Moment generating function} = G(t) = [\theta e^t + (1 - \theta)]^n.$$

3. *Geometric distribution*: If the random variable X has a probability density function given by

$$P(X = x) = f(x) = \theta(1 - \theta)^{x-1} \qquad \text{for } x = 1, 2, 3, \ldots, \qquad (7.2.5)$$

then the variable X is said to possess a geometric distribution.
Properties:

$$\text{Mean} = \mu = \frac{1}{\theta},$$

$$\text{Variance} = \sigma^2 = \frac{1 - \theta}{\theta^2},$$

$$\text{Standard deviation} = \sigma = \sqrt{\frac{1 - \theta}{\theta^2}}, \qquad (7.2.6)$$

$$\text{Moment generating function} = G(t) = \frac{\theta e^t}{1 - e^t(1 - \theta)}.$$

4. *Hypergeometric distribution*: If the random variable X has a probability density function given by

$$P(X = x) = f(x) = \frac{\binom{k}{x}\binom{N-k}{n-x}}{\binom{N}{n}} \qquad \text{for } x = 1, 2, 3, \ldots, \min(n, k) \qquad (7.2.7)$$

then the variable X is said to possess a hypergeometric distribution.
Properties:

$$\text{Mean} = \mu = \frac{kn}{N},$$

$$\text{Variance} = \sigma^2 = \frac{k(N-k)n(N-n)}{N^2(N-1)}, \qquad (7.2.8)$$

$$\text{Standard deviation} = \sigma = \sqrt{\frac{k(N-k)n(N-n)}{N^2(N-1)}}.$$

5. *Negative binomial distribution*: If the random variable X has a probability density function given by

$$P(X = x) = f(x) = \binom{x+r-1}{r-1} \theta^r (1-\theta)^x \qquad \text{for } x = 0, 1, 2, \ldots,$$
$$(7.2.9)$$

then the variable X is said to possess a negative binomial distribution (also known as a Pascal or Polya distribution).
Properties:

$$\text{Mean} = \mu = \frac{r}{\theta},$$

$$\text{Variance} = \sigma^2 = \frac{r}{\theta}\left(\frac{1}{\theta} - 1\right) = \frac{r(1-\theta)}{\theta^2},$$

$$\text{Standard deviation} = \sqrt{\frac{r}{\theta}\left(\frac{1}{\theta} - 1\right)} = \sqrt{\frac{r(1-\theta)}{\theta^2}}, \qquad (7.2.10)$$

$$\text{Moment generating function} = G(t) = e^{tr}\theta^r[1 - (1-\theta)e^t]^{-r}.$$

6. *Poisson distribution*: If the random variable X has a probability density function given by

$$P(X = x) = f(x) = \frac{e^{-\lambda}\lambda^x}{x!} \qquad \text{for } x = 0, 1, 2, \ldots, \qquad (7.2.11)$$

with $\lambda > 0$, then the variable X is said to possess a Poisson distribution.
Properties:

$$\text{Mean} = \mu = \lambda,$$

$$\text{Variance} = \sigma^2 = \lambda,$$

$$\text{Standard deviation} = \sigma = \sqrt{\lambda}, \qquad (7.2.12)$$

$$\text{Moment generating function} = G(t) = e^{\lambda(e^t - 1)}.$$

7. *Multinomial distribution*: If a set of random variables $X_1, X_2, \ldots, X_n$ has a probability function given by

$$P(X_1 = x_1, X_2 = x_2, \ldots, X_n = x_n) = f(x_1, x_2, \ldots, x_n)$$

$$= N! \prod_{i=1}^{n} \frac{\theta_i^{x_i}}{x_i!} \qquad (7.2.13)$$

where the $\{x_i\}$ are positive integers, each $\theta_i > 0$, and

$$\sum_{i=1}^{n} \theta_i = 1 \quad \text{and} \quad \sum_{i=1}^{n} x_i = N, \tag{7.2.14}$$

then the joint distribution of X_1, X_2, ..., X_n is called the multinomial distribution. Note that $f(x_1, x_2, \ldots, x_n)$ is the general term in the expansion of $(\theta_1 + \theta_2 + \cdots + \theta_n)^N$.

Properties:

$$\text{Mean of } X_i = \mu_i = N\theta_i,$$
$$\text{Variance of } X_i = \sigma_i^2 = N\theta_i(1 - \theta_i),$$
$$\text{Covariance of } X_i \text{ and } X_j = \sigma_{ij}^2 = -N\theta_i\theta_j, \tag{7.2.15}$$
$$\text{Joint moment generating function} = (\theta_1 e^{t_1} + \cdots + \theta_n e^{t_n})^N.$$

7.2.2 CONTINUOUS DISTRIBUTIONS

1. *Uniform distribution*: If the random variable X has a density function of the form

$$f(x) = \frac{1}{\beta - \alpha}, \quad \text{for } \alpha < x < \beta, \tag{7.2.16}$$

then the variable X is said to possess a uniform distribution.

Properties:

$$\text{Mean} = \mu = \frac{\alpha + \beta}{2},$$
$$\text{Variance} = \sigma^2 = \frac{(\beta - \alpha)^2}{12},$$
$$\text{Standard deviation} = \sigma = \sqrt{\frac{(\beta - \alpha)^2}{12}},$$
$$\text{Moment generating function} = G(t) = \frac{e^{\beta t} - e^{\alpha t}}{(\beta - \alpha)t}, \tag{7.2.17}$$
$$= \frac{2}{(\beta - \alpha)t} \sinh\left[\frac{(\beta - \alpha)t}{2}\right] e^{(\alpha + \beta)t/2}.$$

2. *Normal distribution*: If the random variable X has a density function of the form

$$f(x) = \frac{1}{\sqrt{2\pi}\sigma} \exp\left(-\frac{(x - \mu)^2}{2\sigma^2}\right), \quad \text{for } -\infty < x < \infty, \tag{7.2.18}$$

then the variable X is said to possess a uniform distribution.

Properties:

$$\text{Mean} = \mu,$$

$$\text{Variance} = \sigma^2,$$

$$\text{Standard deviation} = \sigma,$$

$$\text{Moment generating function} = G(t) = \exp\left(\mu t + \frac{\sigma^2 t^2}{2}\right). \tag{7.2.19}$$

- Set $y = \frac{x-\mu}{\sigma}$ to obtain a standard normal distribution.
- The cumulative distribution function is

$$F(x) = \Phi(x) = \frac{1}{\sqrt{2\pi}\sigma} \int_{-\infty}^{x} \exp\left(-\frac{(t-\mu)^2}{2\sigma^2}\right) dt.$$

3. *Multidimensional normal distribution*:
   The random vector $\mathbf{X}$ is said to be *multivariate normal* if and only if the linear combination $\mathbf{a}^T\mathbf{X}$ is normal for all vectors $\mathbf{a}$. If the mean of $\mathbf{X}$ is $\boldsymbol{\mu}$, and if the second moment matrix $R = \mathrm{E}\left[(\mathbf{X}-\boldsymbol{\mu})(\mathbf{X}-\boldsymbol{\mu})^T\right]$ is nonsingular, the density function of $\mathbf{X}$ is

$$p(\mathbf{x}) = \frac{1}{(2\pi)^{n/2}\sqrt{\det R}} \exp\left[-\frac{1}{2}(\mathbf{x}-\boldsymbol{\mu})^T R^{-1}(\mathbf{x}-\boldsymbol{\mu})\right]. \tag{7.2.20}$$

Sometimes integrals of the form $I_n = \int_{-\infty}^{\infty} \cdots \int (\mathbf{x}^T M \mathbf{x})^n \, p(\mathbf{x}) \, d\mathbf{x}$ are desired.

Defining $a_k = \mathrm{tr}\,(MR)^k$, we find:

$$I_0 = 1,$$
$$I_1 = a_1,$$
$$I_2 = a_1^2 + 2a_2,$$
$$I_3 = a_1^3 + 6a_1 a_2 + 8a_3, \tag{7.2.21}$$
$$I_4 = a_1^4 + 12a_1^2 a_2 + 32a_1 a_3 + 12a_2^2 + 48a_4.$$

4. *Gamma distribution*: If the random variable X has a density function of the form

$$f(x) = \frac{1}{\Gamma(1+\alpha)\beta^{1+\alpha}} x^\alpha e^{-x/\beta}, \qquad \text{for } 0 < x < \infty, \tag{7.2.22}$$

with $\alpha > -1$ and $\beta > 0$, then the variable X is said to possess a gamma distribution.
Properties:

$$\text{Mean} = \mu = \beta(1+\alpha),$$

$$\text{Variance} = \sigma^2 = \beta^2(1+\alpha),$$

$$\text{Standard deviation} = \sigma = \beta\sqrt{1+\alpha}$$

$$\text{Moment generating function} = G(t) = (1-\beta t)^{-1-\alpha}, \qquad \text{for } t < \beta^{-1}. \tag{7.2.23}$$

5. *Exponential distribution*: If the random variable X has a density function of the form

$$f(x) = \frac{e^{-x/\theta}}{\theta}, \qquad \text{for } 0 < x < \infty, \qquad (7.2.24)$$

where $\theta > 0$, then the variable X is said to possess an exponential distribution.
Properties:

$$\text{Mean} = \mu = \theta,$$
$$\text{Variance} = \sigma^2 = \theta^2,$$
$$\text{Standard deviation} = \sigma = \theta, \qquad (7.2.25)$$
$$\text{Moment generating function} = G(t) = (1 - \theta t)^{-1}.$$

6. *Beta distribution*: If the random variable X has a density function of the form

$$f(x) = \frac{\Gamma(\alpha + \beta + 2)}{\Gamma(1 + \alpha)\Gamma(1 + \beta)} x^\alpha (1 - x)^\beta, \qquad \text{for } 0 < x < 1,$$
$$(7.2.26)$$

where $\alpha > -1$ and $\beta > -1$, then the variable X is said to possess a beta distribution.
Properties:

$$\text{Mean} = \mu = \frac{1 + \alpha}{2 + \alpha + \beta},$$
$$\text{Variance} = \sigma^2 = \frac{(1 + \alpha)(1 + \beta)}{(2 + \alpha + \beta)^2 (3 + \alpha + \beta)}, \qquad (7.2.27)$$
$$r^{\text{th}} \text{ moment about the origin} = \nu_r = \frac{\Gamma(2 + \alpha + \beta)\Gamma(1 + \alpha + r)}{\Gamma(2 + \alpha + \beta + r)\Gamma(1 + \alpha)}.$$

7. *Chi-square distribution*: If the random variable X has a density function of the form

$$f(x) = \frac{x^{(n-2)/2} e^{-x/2}}{2^{n/2} \Gamma(n/2)} \qquad \text{for } 0 < x < \infty \qquad (7.2.28)$$

then the variable X is said to possess a chi-square (χ^2) distribution with n degrees of freedom.
Properties:

$$\text{Mean} = \mu = n,$$
$$\text{Variance} = \sigma^2 = 2n. \qquad (7.2.29)$$

(a) If $Y_1, Y_2, \ldots, Y_n$ are independent and identically distributed normal random variables with a mean of 0 and a variance of 1, then $\chi^2 = \sum_{i=1}^{n} Y_i^2$ is distributed as chi-square with n degrees of freedom.

(b) If $\chi_1^2, \chi_2^2, \dots, \chi_k^2$, are independent random variables and have chi-square distributions with $n_1, n_2, \dots, n_k$ degrees of freedom, then $\sum_{i=1}^{k} \chi_i^2$ has a chi-squared distribution with $n = \sum_{i=1}^{k} n_i$ degrees of freedom.

8. *Snedecor's F-distribution*: If the random variable X has a density function of the form

$$f(x) = \frac{\Gamma\left(\frac{n+m}{2}\right) \left(\frac{m}{n}\right)^{m/2} x^{(m-2)/2}}{\Gamma\left(\frac{m}{2}\right) \Gamma\left(\frac{n}{2}\right) \left(1 + \frac{m}{n}x\right)^{(n+m)/2}}, \qquad \text{for } 0 < x < \infty, \qquad (7.2.30)$$

then the variable X is said to possess a F-distribution with m and n degrees of freedom.

Properties:

$$\text{Mean} = \mu = \frac{n}{n-2}, \qquad \text{for } n > 2,$$

$$\text{Variance} = \frac{2n^2(m+n-2)}{m(n-2)^2(n-4)}, \qquad \text{for } n > 4. \qquad (7.2.31)$$

(a) The transformation $w = \dfrac{mx/n}{1 + \frac{mx}{n}}$ transforms the F-density to the beta density.

(b) If the random variable X has a χ^2-distribution with m degrees of freedom, the random variable Y has a χ^2-distribution with n degrees of freedom, and X and Y are independent, then $F = \dfrac{X/m}{Y/n}$ is distributed as an F-distribution with m and n degrees of freedom.

9. *Student's t-distribution*: If the random variable X has a density function of the form

$$f(x) = \frac{\Gamma\left(\frac{n+1}{2}\right)}{\sqrt{n\pi}\, \Gamma\left(\frac{n}{2}\right) \left(1 + \frac{t^2}{n}\right)^{(n+1)/2}}, \qquad \text{for } -\infty < x < \infty. \qquad (7.2.32)$$

then the variable X is said to possess a t-distribution with n degrees of freedom.

Properties:

$$\text{Mean} = \mu = 0,$$

$$\text{Variance} = \sigma^2 = \frac{n}{n-2}, \qquad \text{for } n > 2. \qquad (7.2.33)$$

• If the random variable X is normally distributed with mean 0 and variance σ^2, and if Y^2/σ^2 has a χ^2 distribution with n degrees of freedom, and if X and Y are independent, then $t = \dfrac{X\sqrt{n}}{Y}$ is distributed as a t-distribution with n degrees of freedom.

7.3 QUEUING THEORY

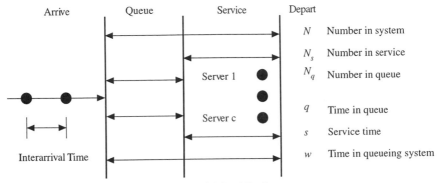

A queue is represented as $A/B/c/K/m/Z$ where

- A and B represent the interarrival times and service times:

  GI general independent interarrival time,
  G general service time distribution,
  H_k k-stage hyperexponential interarrival or service time distribution,
  E_k Erlang-k interarrival or service time distribution,
  M exponential interarrival or service time distribution,
  D deterministic (constant) interarrival or service time distribution.

- c is the number of identical servers.

- K is the system capacity.

- m is the number in the source.

- Z is the queue discipline:

  FCFS first come, first served (also known as FIFO),
  LIFO last in, first out,
  RSS random,
  PRI priority service.

When not all variables are present, the trailing ones have the default values, $K = \infty$, $m = \infty$, Z is RSS.

The variable of concern are

1. a_n: proportion of customers that find n customers already in the system when they arrive
2. d_n: proportion of customers leaving behind n customers in the system
3. p_n: proportion of time the system contains n customers
4. L: average number of customers in the system
5. L_Q: average number of customers in the queue
6. W: average time for customer in system

7. W_Q: average time for customer in the queue
8. λ: average arrival rate of customers to the system (number per unit time)
9. μ: average service rate per server (number per unit time)
10. u: traffic intensity, $u = \lambda/\mu$
11. ρ: server utilization, the probability that any particular server is busy, $\rho = u/c = (\lambda/\mu)/c$

Theorems:

1. Little's formula: $L = \lambda W$ and $L_Q = \lambda W_Q$.
2. For Poisson arrivals: $p_n = a_n$.
3. If customers arrive one at a time and are served one at a time: $a_n = d_n$.
4. For an $M/M/1$ queue with $\lambda < \mu$,
   - $p_n = (1 - u)u^n$
   - $L = u/(1 - u)$
   - $L_Q = L - (1 - p_0)$
   - $L_Q = u^2/(1 - u)$
   - $W = 1/(\mu - \lambda)$
   - $W_Q = \lambda/\mu(\mu - \lambda)$

5. For an $M/M/c$ queue (so that $\mu_n = n\mu$ for $n = 1, 2, \ldots, c$ and $\mu_n = c\mu$ for $n \geq c$),

   - $$p_0 = \left[\frac{u^c}{c!(1 - \rho)} + \sum_{n=0}^{c-1} \frac{u^n}{n!} \right]^{-1}$$
   - $p_n = p_0 u^n/n!$ for $n = 0, 1, \ldots, c$
   - $p_n = p_0 u^n/c!c^{n-c}$ for $n \geq c$
   - $L_Q = p_0 u^c \rho/c!(1 - \rho)^2$
   - $W_Q = L_Q/\lambda$
   - $W = W_Q + 1/\mu$
   - $L = \lambda W$

7.4 MARKOV CHAINS

A *discrete parameter stochastic process* is a collection of random variables $\{X(t), t = 0,1,2,\ldots\}$. The values of $X(t)$ are called the *states* of the process. The collection of states is called the *state space*. The values of t usually represent points in time. The number of states is either finite or countably infinite. A discrete parameter stochastic process is called a *Markov chain* if, for any set of n time points $t_1 < t_2 < \cdots < t_n$, the conditional distribution of $X(t_n)$ given values for $X(t_1), X(t_2), \ldots, X(t_{n-1})$ depends only on $X(t_{n-1})$. It is expressed by

$$P\left[X(t_n) \leq x_n \mid X(t_1) = x_1, \ldots, X(t_{n-1}) = x_{n-1}\right]$$
$$= P\left[X(t_n) \leq x_n \mid X(t_{n-1}) = x_{n-1}\right]. \quad (7.4.1)$$

A Markov chain is said to be *stationary* if the value of the conditional probability $P\left[X(t_{n+1}) = x_{n+1} \mid X(t_n) = x_n\right]$ is independent of n. This discussion will be restricted to stationary Markov chains.

7.4.1 TRANSITION FUNCTION

Let x and y be states and let $\{t_n\}$ be time points in $T = \{0, 1, 2, \ldots\}$. The *transition function*, $P(x, y)$, is defined by

$$P(x, y) = P_{n,n+1}(x, y) = P\left[X(t_{n+1}) = y \mid X(t_n) = x\right], \qquad t_n, t_{n+1} \in T. \quad (7.4.2)$$

$P(x, y)$ is the probability that a Markov chain in state x at time n will be in state y at time $n + 1$. Some properties of the transition function are that $P(x, y) \geq 0$ and $\sum_y P(x, y) = 1$. The values of $P(x, y)$ are commonly called the *one-step transition probabilities*.

The function $\pi_0(x) = P(X(0) = x)$, with $\pi_0(x) \geq 0$ and $\sum_x \pi_0(x) = 1$ is called the *initial distribution* of the Markov chain. It is the probability distribution when the chain is started. Thus,

$$P[X(0) = x_0, X(1) = x_1, \ldots, X(n) = x_n]$$
$$= \pi_0(x_0) P_{0,1}(x_0, x_1) P_{1,2}(x_1, x_2) \cdots P_{n-1,n}(x_{n-1}, x_n). \quad (7.4.3)$$

7.4.2 TRANSITION MATRIX

A convenient way to summarize the transition function of a Markov chain is by using the *one-step transition matrix*. It is defined as

$$\mathbf{P} = \begin{bmatrix} P(0,0) & P(0,1) & \cdots & P(0,n) & \cdots \\ P(1,0) & P(1,1) & \cdots & P(1,n) & \cdots \\ \vdots & \vdots & \ddots & \vdots & \\ P(n,0) & P(n,1) & \cdots & P(n,n) & \cdots \\ \vdots & \vdots & & \vdots & \end{bmatrix}.$$

Define the *n–step transition matrix* by $\mathbf{P}^{(n)}$ as the matrix with entries

$$P^n(x, y) = P\left[X(t_{m+n}) = y \mid X(t_m) = x\right]. \tag{7.4.4}$$

This can be written in terms of the one-step transition matrix as $\mathbf{P}^{(n)} = \mathbf{P}^n$.

Suppose the state space is finite. The one-step transition matrix is said to be *regular* if, for some positive power m, all of the elements of $\mathbf{P}^m$ are strictly positive.

THEOREM 7.4.1   *(Chapman–Kolmogorov equation)*

Let $P(x, y)$ be the one-step transition function of a Markov chain and define $P^0(x, y)$ = 1, if $x = y$, and 0, otherwise. Then, for any pair of nonnegative integers, s and t, such that $s + t = n$,

$$P^n(x, y) = \sum_z P^s(x, z) P^t(z, y).$$

7.4.3   RECURRENCE

Define the probability that a Markov chain starting in state x returns to state x for the first time after n steps by

$$f^n(x, x) = P\left[X(t_n) = x, X(t_{n-1}) \neq x, \ldots, X(t_1) \neq x \mid X(t_0) = x\right].$$

It follows that $P^n(x, x) = \sum_{k=0}^{n} f^k(x, x) P^{n-k}(x, x)$. A state x is said to be *recurrent* if $\sum_{n=0}^{\infty} f^n(x, x) = 1$. This means that a state x is recurrent if, after starting in x, the probability of returning to it after some finite length of time is one. A state which is not recurrent is said to be *transient*.

THEOREM 7.4.2

A state x of a Markov chain is recurrent if and only if $\sum_{n=1}^{\infty} P^n(x, x) = \infty$.

Two states, x and y, are said to *communicate* if, for some $n \geq 0$, $P^n(x, y) > 0$. This theorem implies that, if x is a recurrent state and x communicates with y, y is also a recurrent state. A Markov chain is said to be *irreducible* if every state communicates with every other state and with itself.

Let x be a recurrent state and define T_x the *(return time)* as the number of stages for a Markov chain to return to state x, having begun there. A recurrent state x is said to be *null recurrent* if $\mathrm{E}[T_x] = \infty$. A recurrent state that is not null recurrent is said to be *positive recurrent*.

7.4.4   STATIONARY DISTRIBUTIONS

Let $\{X(t), t = 0, 1, 2, \ldots\}$ be a Markov chain having a one-step transition function of $P(x, y)$. A function $\pi(x)$ where each $\pi(x)$ is nonnegative, $\sum_x \pi(x) P(x, y) = \pi(y)$, and $\sum_y \pi(y) = 1$, is called a *stationary distribution*. If a Markov chain has a stationary distribution and $\lim_{n\to\infty} P^n(x, y) = \pi(y)$, then, regardless of the initial distribution, $\pi_0(x)$, the distribution of $X(t_n)$ approaches $\pi(x)$ as n becomes infinite. When this happens, $\pi(x)$ is often referred to as the *steady state distribution*. The following categorizes those Markov chains with stationary distributions.

THEOREM 7.4.3

Let X_P denote the set of positive recurrent states of a Markov chain.

1. *If X_P is empty, the chain has no stationary distribution.*

2. *If X_P is a nonempty irreducible set, the chain has a unique stationary distribution.*

3. *If X_P is nonempty but not irreducible, the chain has an infinite number of distinct stationary distributions.*

The *period* of a state x is denoted by $d(x)$ and is defined as the greatest common divisor of all integers, $n \geq 1$, for which $P^n(x, x) > 0$. If $P^n(x, x) = 0$ for all $n \geq 1$, then define $d(x) = 0$. If each state of a Markov chain has $d(x) = 1$, the chain is said to be *aperiodic*. If each state has period $d > 1$, the chain is said to be *periodic* with period d. The vast majority of Markov chains encountered in practice are aperiodic. An irreducible, positive recurrent, aperiodic Markov chain always possesses a steady-state distribution. An important special case occurs when the state space is finite. Suppose that $X = \{1, 2, \ldots, K\}$. Let $\pi_0 = \{\pi_0(1), \pi_0(2), \ldots, \pi_0(K)\}$.

THEOREM 7.4.4

Let $\mathbf{P}$ be a regular one-step transition matrix and π_0 be an arbitrary vector of initial probabilities. Then $\lim_{n\to\infty} \pi_0(x)\,\mathbf{P}^n = \mathbf{y}$, where $\mathbf{yP} = \mathbf{y}$, and $\sum_{i=1}^{K} \pi_0(t_i) = 1$.

A simple three-state Markov chain

A Markov chain having three states $\{0, 1, 2\}$ with a one-step transition matrix of

$$P = \begin{bmatrix} \frac{1}{2} & 0 & \frac{1}{2} \\ \frac{1}{4} & \frac{3}{4} & 0 \\ 0 & \frac{3}{4} & \frac{1}{4} \end{bmatrix}$$ is diagrammed below.

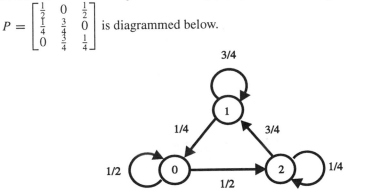

The one-step transition matrix gives a two–step transition matrix of

$$
P^{(2)} = P^2 = \begin{bmatrix} \frac{1}{4} & \frac{3}{8} & \frac{3}{8} \\[4pt] \frac{5}{16} & \frac{9}{16} & \frac{1}{8} \\[4pt] \frac{3}{16} & \frac{9}{16} & \frac{1}{8} \end{bmatrix}
$$

The one-step transition matrix is regular. This Markov chain is irreducible, and all three states are recurrent. In addition, all three states are positive recurrent. Since all states have period 1, the chain is aperiodic. The steady state distribution is $\pi(0) = 3/11$, $\pi(1) = 6/11$, and $\pi(2) = 2/11$.

7.4.5 RANDOM WALKS

Let $\eta(t_1)$, $\eta(t_2)$, ... be independent random variables having a common density $f(x)$, and let $t_1, t_2, \ldots$ be integers. Let $X(t_0)$ be an integer–valued random variable that is independent of $\eta(t_1)$, $\eta(t_2)$, ..., and $X(t_n) = X_0 + \sum_{i=1}^{n} \eta(t_i)$. The sequence $\{X(t_i), i = 0, 1, \ldots\}$ is called a *random walk*. An important special case is a *simple random walk*. It is defined by

$$
P(x, y) = \begin{cases} p, & \text{if } y = x - 1, \\ r, & \text{if } y = x, \\ q, & \text{if } y = x + 1, \end{cases} \quad \text{where} \quad p+q+r = 1, \quad \text{and} \quad P(0,0) = p+r.
$$

Here, an object begins at a certain point in a lattice and at each step either stays at that point or moves to a neighboring lattice point. In the case of a one- or two-dimensional lattice, it turns out that, if a random walk begins at a lattice point x, it will return to that point with probability 1. In the case of a three-dimensional lattice, the probability that it will return to its starting point is only about 0.3405.

7.4.6 EHRENFEST CHAIN

A simple model of gas exchange between two isolated bodies is as follows. Suppose that there are two boxes, Box I and Box II, where Box I contains K molecules numbered $1, 2, \ldots, K$ and Box II contains $N - K$ molecules numbered $K + 1, K + 2, \ldots, N$. A number is chosen at random from $\{1, 2, \ldots, N\}$, and the molecule with that number is transferred from its box to the other one. Let $X(t_n)$ be the number of molecules in Box I after n trials. Then the sequence $\{X(t_n), n = 0, 1, \ldots\}$ is a Markov chain with one-stage transition function of

$$
P(x, y) = \begin{cases} \frac{x}{K}, & y = x - 1, \\ 1 - \frac{x}{K}, & y = x + 1, \\ 0, & \text{otherwise.} \end{cases}
$$

7.5 RANDOM NUMBER GENERATION

7.5.1 METHODS OF PSEUDORANDOM NUMBER GENERATION

Depending on the application, either integers in some range or floating point numbers in $[0, 1)$ are the desired output from a pseudorandom number generator (PRNG). Since most PRNGs use integer recursions, a conversion into integers in a desired range or into a floating point number in $[0, 1)$ is required. If x_n is an integer produced by some PRNG in the range $0 \leq x_n \leq M - 1$, then an integer in the range $0 \leq x_n \leq N - 1$, with $N \leq M$, is given by $y_n = \lfloor \frac{Nx_n}{M} \rfloor$. If $N \ll M$, then $y_n = x_n \pmod{N}$ may be used. Alternately, if a floating point value in $[0, 1)$ is desired, let $y_n = x_n/M$.

Linear congruential generators

Perhaps the oldest generator still in use is the linear congruential generator (LCG). The underlying integer recursion for LCGs is

$$x_n = ax_{n-1} + b \pmod{M}. \tag{7.5.1}$$

Equation (7.5.1) defines a periodic sequence of integers modulo M starting with x_0, the initial seed. The constants of the recursion are referred to as the *modulus* M, *multiplier* a, and *additive constant* b. If $M = 2^m$, a very efficient implementation is possible. Alternately, there are theoretical reasons why choosing M prime is optimal. Hence, the only moduli that are used in practical implementations are $M = 2^m$ or the prime $M = 2^p - 1$ (i.e., M is a Mersenne prime). With a Mersenne prime, modular multiplication can be implemented at about twice the computational cost of multiplication modulo 2^p.

Equation (7.5.1) yields a sequence $\{x_n\}$ whose period, denoted $\mathrm{Per}(x_n)$, depends on M, a, and b. The values of the maximal period for the three most common cases used and the conditions required to obtain them are

a	b	M	$\mathrm{Per}(x_n)$
Primitive root of M	Anything	Prime	$M - 1$
3 or 5 (mod 8)	0	2^m	2^{m-2}
1 (mod 4)	1 (mod 2)	2^m	2^m

A major shortcoming of LCGs modulo a power-of-two compared with prime modulus LCGs derives from the following theorem for LCGs:

THEOREM 7.5.1

Define the following LCG sequence: $x_n = ax_{n-1} + b \pmod{M_1}$. *If M_2 divides M_1 then $y_n = x_n \pmod{M_2}$ satisfies $y_n = ay_{n-1} + b \pmod{M_2}$.*

Theorem 7.5.1 implies that the k least-significant bits of any power-of-two modulus LCG with $\mathrm{Per}(x_n) = 2^m = M$ has $\mathrm{Per}(y_n) = 2^k, 0 < k \leq m$. Since a long period is crucial in PRNGs, when these types of LCGs are employed in a manner that makes use of only a few least-significant-bits, their quality may be compromised. When M is prime, no such problem arises.

Since LCGs are in such common usage, here is a list of parameter values mentioned in the literature. The Park–Miller LCG is widely considered a minimally acceptable PRNG.

a	b	M	Source
7^5	0	$2^{31} - 1$	Park–Miller
131	0	2^{35}	Neave
16333	25887	2^{15}	Oakenfull
3432	6789	9973	Oakenfull
171	0	30269	Wichman–Hill

Shift register generators

Another popular method of generating pseudorandom numbers is using binary shift register sequences to produce pseudorandom bits. A binary shift register sequence (SRS) is defined by a binary recursion of the type,

$$x_n = x_{n-j_1} \oplus x_{n-j_2} \oplus \cdots \oplus x_{n-j_k}, \qquad j_1 < j_2 < \cdots < j_k = \ell, \qquad (7.5.2)$$

where $\oplus$ is the exclusive "or" operation. Note that $x \oplus y \equiv x + y$ (mod 2). Thus the new bit, x_n, is produced by adding k previously computed bits together modulo 2. The implementation of this recurrence requires keeping the last ℓ bits from the sequence in a shift register, hence the name. The longest possible period is equal to the number of nonzero ℓ-dimensional binary vectors, namely $2^\ell - 1$.

A sufficient condition for achieving $\text{Per}(x_n) = 2^\ell - 1$ is that the characteristic polynomial, corresponding to Equation (7.5.2), be primitive modulo 2. Since primitive trinomials of nearly all degrees of interest have been found, SRSs are usually implemented using two-term recursions of the form,

$$x_n = x_{n-k} \oplus x_{n-\ell}, \qquad 0 < k < \ell. \qquad (7.5.3)$$

In these two-term recursions, k is the lag and ℓ is the register length. Proper choice of the pair (ℓ, k) leads to SRSs with $\text{Per}(x_n) = 2^\ell - 1$. Here is a list with suitable (ℓ, k) pairs:

Primitive trinomial exponents					
(5,2)	(7,1)	(7,3)	(17,3)	(17,5)	(17,6)
(31,3)	(31,6)	(31,7)	(31,13	(127,1)	(521,32)

Lagged-Fibonacci generators

Another way of producing pseudorandom numbers uses lagged-Fibonacci generators. The term "lagged-Fibonacci" refers to two-term recurrences of the form,

$$x_n = x_{n-k} \diamond x_{n-\ell}, \qquad 0 < k < \ell, \qquad (7.5.4)$$

where $\diamond$ refers to three common methods of combination: (1) addition modulo 2^m, (2) multiplication modulo 2^m, or (3) bitwise exclusive 'OR'ing of m-long bit vectors. Combination method (3) can be thought of as a special implementation of a two-term SRS.

Using combination method (1) leads to additive lagged-Fibonacci sequences (ALFSs). If x_n satisfies

$$x_n = x_{n-k} + x_{n-\ell} \quad (\text{mod } 2^m), \qquad 0 < k < \ell, \qquad (7.5.5)$$

then the maximal period is $\text{Per}(x_n) = (2^\ell - 1)2^{m-1}$.

ALFS are especially suitable for producing floating point deviates using the real-valued recursion $y_n = y_{n-k} + y_{n-\ell}$ (mod 1). This circumvents the need to convert from integers to floating point values and allows floating point hardware to be used. One caution with ALFS is that Theorem 7.5.1 holds, and so the low-order bits have periods that are shorter than the maximal period. However, this is not nearly the problem as in the LCG case. With ALFSs, the j least-significant bits will have period $(2^\ell - 1)2^{j-1}$, so, if ℓ is large, there really is no problem. Note that one can use the table of primitive trinomial exponents to find (ℓ, k) pairs that give maximal period ALF sequences.

7.5.2 GENERATING NONUNIFORM RANDOM VARIABLES

Suppose we want deviates from a distribution with probability density function $f(x)$ and distribution function $F(x) = \int_{-\infty}^{x} f(u) \, du$. In the following y is $U[0, 1)$ means y is uniformly distributed on $[0, 1)$.

Two general techniques for converting uniform random variables into those from other distributions are as follows:

1. The inverse transform method:
   If y is $U[0, 1)$, then the random variable $F^{-1}(y)$ will have its density equal to $f(x)$ (since $0 \leq F(x) \leq 1$).

2. The acceptance-rejection method:
   Suppose the density can be written as $f(x) = Ch(x)g(x)$ where $h(x)$ is the density of a computable random variable, the function $0 < g(x) \leq 1$, and $C^{-1} = \int_{-\infty}^{\infty} h(u)g(u) \, du$ is a normalization constant. If x is $U[0, 1)$, y has density $h(x)$, and if $x < g(y)$, then x has density $f(x)$. Thus one generates $\{x, y\}$ pairs, rejecting both if $x \geq g(y)$ and returning x if $x < g(y)$.

Examples of the inverse transform method:

1. (Exponential distribution) The exponential distribution with rate λ is $f(x) = \lambda e^{-\lambda x}$ (for $x \geq 0$) and $F(x) = 1 - e^{-\lambda x}$. Thus $u = F(x)$ can be solved to give $x = F^{-1}(u) = -\lambda^{-1} \ln(1 - u)$. If u is $U[0, 1)$, then so is $1 - u$. Hence $x = -\lambda^{-1} \ln u$ is exponentially distributed with rate λ.

2. (Normal distribution) Let z_i be normally distributed with $f(z) = \frac{1}{\sqrt{2\pi}} e^{-z^2/2}$. If each of the pair (z_1, z_2) is normally distributed, then the polar transformation gives random variables $r = \sqrt{z_1^2 + z_2^2}$ (exponentially distributed with

$\lambda = 2$) and $\theta = \tan^{-1}(z_2/z_1)$ (uniformly distributed on $[0, 2\pi)$). Inverting, $z_1 = \sqrt{-2\ln x_1}\cos 2\pi x_2$ and $z_2 = \sqrt{-2\ln x_1}\sin 2\pi x_2$ are normally distributed when x_1 and x_2 are $U[0, 1)$.

Examples of the rejection method:

1. (Exponential distribution with $\lambda = 1$)

    (a) Generate random numbers $\{U_i\}_{i=1}^N$ uniform on $[0, 1]$), stopping at $N = \min\{n \mid U_1 \geq U_2 \geq U_{n-1} < U_n\}$.

    (b) If N is even, accept that run, and go to step (c). If N is odd reject the run, and return to step (a).

    (c) Set X equal to the number of failed runs plus the first random number in the successful run.

2. (Normal distribution)

    (a) Select two random variables (V_1, V_2) from $U[0, 1)$. Form $R = V_1^2 + V_2^2$.

    (b) If $R > 1$, then reject the (V_1, V_2) pair, and select another pair.

    (c) If $R < 1$, then $x = V_1\sqrt{-2\dfrac{\ln R}{R}}$ has a $N(0, 1)$ distribution.

3. (Normal distribution)

    (a) Select two exponentially distributed random variables with rate 1: (V_1, V_2).

    (b) If $V_2 \geq (V_1 - 1)^2/2$, then reject the (V_1, V_2) pair, and select another pair.

    (c) Otherwise, V_1 has a $N(0, 1)$ distribution.

4. (Cauchy distribution) To generate values of X from $f(x) = \frac{1}{\pi(1+x^2)}$ on $-\infty < x < \infty$,

    (a) Generate random numbers U_1, U_2 (uniform on $[0, 1)$), and set $Y_1 = U_1 - \frac{1}{2}$, $Y_2 = U_2 - \frac{1}{2}$.

    (b) If $Y_1^2 + Y_2^2 \leq \frac{1}{4}$, then return $X = Y_1/Y_2$. Otherwise return to step (a).

To generate values of X from a Cauchy distribution with parameters β and θ,
$$f(x) = \frac{\beta}{\pi\left[\beta^2 + (x - \theta)^2\right]}, \text{ for } -\infty < x < \infty, \text{ construct } X \text{ as above, and then}$$
use $\beta X + \theta$.

Discrete random variables

In general, the density function of a discrete random variable can be represented as a vector $\mathbf{p} = (p_0, p_1, \ldots, p_{n-1}, p_n)$ by defining the probabilities $P(x = j) = p_j$ (for $j = 0, \ldots, n$). The distribution function can be defined by the vector $\mathbf{c} = (c_0, c_1, \ldots, c_{n-1}, 1)$, where $c_j = \sum_{i=0}^{j} p_i$. Given this representation of $F(x)$, we can apply the inverse transform by computing x to be $U[0, 1)$, and then finding the index j so that $c_j \leq x < c_{j+1}$. In this case event j will have occurred. Examples:

1. (Binomial distribution) The binomial distribution with n trials of mean p has $p_j = \binom{n}{j} p^j (1-p)^{n-j}$, for $j = 0, \ldots, n$.

   - As an example, consider the result of flipping a fair coin. In 2 flips, the probability of obtaining $(0, 1, 2)$ heads is $\mathbf{p} = (\frac{1}{4}, \frac{1}{2}, \frac{3}{4})$. Hence $\mathbf{c} = (\frac{1}{4}, \frac{3}{4}, 1)$. If x (chosen from $U[0, 1)$) turns out to be say, 0.4, then "1 head" is returned (since $\frac{1}{4} < 0.4 < \frac{3}{4}$).

   - Note that, when n is large, it is costly to compute the density and distribution vectors. When n is large and relatively few binomially distributed pseudorandom numbers are desired, an alternative is to use the normal approximation to the binomial.

   - Alternately, one can form the sum $\sum_{i=1}^{n} \lfloor u_i + p \rfloor$, where each u_i is $U[0, 1)$.

2. (Geometric distribution) To simulate a value from $P(X = i) = p(1-p)^{i-1}$ for $i \geq 1$, use $X = 1 + \left\lceil \dfrac{\log U}{\log(1-p)} \right\rceil$.

3. (Poisson distribution) The Poisson distribution with mean λ has $p_j = \lambda^j e^{\lambda}/j!$ for $j \geq 0$. The Poisson distribution counts the number of events in a unit time interval if the times are exponentially distributed with rate λ. Thus if the times t_i are exponentially distributed with rate λ, then j will be Poisson distributed with mean λ when $\sum_{i=0}^{j} t_i \leq 1 \leq \sum_{i=0}^{j+1} t_i$. Since $t_i = -\lambda^{-1} \ln u_i$, where u_i is $U[0, 1)$, the previous equation may be written as $\prod_{i=0}^{j} u_i \geq e^{-\lambda} \geq \prod_{i=0}^{j+1} u_i$. This allows us to compute Poisson random variables by iteratively computing $P_j = \prod_{i=0}^{j} u_i$ until $P_j < e^{-\lambda}$. The first such j that makes this inequality true will have the desired distribution.

Random variables can be simulated using the following table (each U and U_i is uniform on the interval $[0, 1)$):

Distribution	Density	Formula for deviate
Binomial	$p_j = \binom{n}{j} p^j (1-p)^{n-j}$	$\sum_{i=1}^{n} \lfloor U_i + p \rfloor$
Cauchy	$f(x) = \dfrac{\sigma}{\pi(x^2 + \sigma^2)}$	$\sigma \tan(\pi U)$
Exponential	$f(x) = \lambda e^{-\lambda x}$	$-\lambda^{-1} \ln U$
Pareto	$f(x) = ab^a/x^{a+1}$	$b/U^{1/a}$
Rayleigh	$f(x) = x/\sigma e^{-x^2/2\sigma^2}$	$\sigma \sqrt{-\ln U}$

Testing pseudorandom numbers

The prudent way to check a complicated computation that makes use of pseudorandom numbers is to run it several times with different types of pseudorandom number generators and see if the results appear consistent across the generators. The fact that this is not always possible or practical has led researchers to develop statistical tests of randomness that should be passed by general purpose pseudorandom number generators. Some common tests are the spectral test, the equidistribution test, the serial test, the runs test, the coupon collector test, and the birthday spacing test.

7.6   CONTROL CHARTS

Control charts are graphical tools used to assess and maintain the stability of a process. They are used to separate random variation from specific causes. Data measurements are plotted versus time along with upper and lower control limits and a center line. If the process is in control and the underlying distribution is normal, then the control limits represent three standard deviations from the center line (mean).

If all of the data points are contained within the control limits, the process is considered stable and the mean and standard deviations can be reliably calculated. The variations between data points occur from random causes. Data outside the control limits or forming abnormal patterns point to unstable, out-of-control processes.

In the tables, k denotes the number of samples taken, i is an index for the samples ($i = 1 \ldots k$), n is the sample size (number of elements in each sample), and R is the range of the values in a sample (maximum element value minus minimum element value). The mean is μ and the standard deviation is σ. Control chart upper and lower control limits are denoted UCL and LCL.

Types of Control Charts, Their Statistics, and Uses

Chart	Statistics	Statistical quantity
	Applications	
$\bar{x} - R$	Gaussian	Average value and range
	Charts continuous measurable quantities. Measurements taken on small sample sets.	
$\tilde{x} - R$	Gaussian	Median value and range
	Similar to $\bar{x} - R$ chart but fewer calculations needed for plotting.	
$x - Rs$	Gaussian	Individual measured values
	Similar to $\bar{x} - R$ chart but single measurements are made. Used when measurements are expensive or dispersion of measured values is small. $Rs = |x_i - x_{i-1}|$	
pn	Binomial	Number of defective units
	Charts number of defective units in sets of fixed size.	
p	Binomial	Percent defective
	Charts number of defective units in sets of varying size.	
c	Poisson	Number of defects
	Charts number of flaws in a product of fixed size.	
u	Poisson	Defect density (defects per quantity unit)
	Charts the defect density on a product of varying size.	

Types of Control Charts and Limits ("*P*" stands for parameter)

Chart	(μ, σ) known?	P	Centerline	UCL	LCL
$\bar{x} - R$	No	$\bar{x}$	$\bar{\bar{x}} = \frac{\sum \bar{x}}{k}$	$\bar{\bar{x}} + A_2\bar{R}$	$\bar{\bar{x}} - A_2\bar{R}$
$\bar{x} - R$	No	R	$\bar{R} = \frac{\sum R}{k}$	$D_4\bar{R}$	$D_3\bar{R}$
$\bar{x} - R$	Yes	$\bar{x}$	$\bar{\bar{x}} = \mu$	$\mu + \frac{3\sigma}{\sqrt{n}}$	$\mu - \frac{3\sigma}{\sqrt{n}}$
$\bar{x} - R$	Yes	R	$\bar{R} = d_2\sigma$	$D_2\sigma$	$D_1\sigma$
$\tilde{x} - R$	No	$\tilde{x}$	$\bar{\tilde{x}} = \frac{\sum \tilde{x}}{k}$	$\bar{\tilde{x}} + m_3A_2$	$\bar{\tilde{x}} - m_3A_2$
$\tilde{x} - R$	No	R	$\bar{R} = \frac{\sum R}{k}$	$D_4\bar{R}$	$D_3\bar{R}$
$x - Rs$	No	x	$\bar{x} = \frac{\sum x}{k}$	$\bar{x} + 2.66\bar{R}s$	$\bar{x} - 2.66\bar{R}s$
$x - Rs$	No	Rs	$\bar{R}s = \frac{\sum \bar{R}s}{k}$	$3.27\bar{R}s$	–
pn	No	pn	$\bar{p}n = \frac{\sum pn}{k}$	$\bar{p}n + \sqrt{\bar{p}n(1-\bar{p})}$	$\bar{p}n - \sqrt{\bar{p}n(1-\bar{p})}$
p	No	p	$\bar{p} = \frac{\sum pn}{\sum n}$	$\bar{p}n + 3\sqrt{\frac{\bar{p}(1-\bar{p})}{n}}$	$\bar{p}n - 3\sqrt{\frac{\bar{p}(1-\bar{p})}{n}}$
c	No	c	$\bar{c} = \frac{\sum c}{k}$	$\bar{c} + 3\sqrt{\bar{c}}$	$\bar{c} - 3\sqrt{\bar{c}}$
u	No	u	$\bar{u} = \frac{\sum c}{\sum n}$	$\bar{u} + 3\sqrt{\bar{u}/n}$	$\bar{u} - 3\sqrt{\bar{u}/n}$

Sample size n	A_2	d_2	D_1	D_2	D_3	D_4	m_3	$m_3 A_2$
2	1.880	1.128	0	3.686	–	3.267	1.000	1.880
3	1.023	1.693	0	4.358	–	2.575	1.160	1.187
4	0.729	2.059	0	4.698	–	2.282	1.092	0.796
5	0.577	2.326	0	4.918	–	2.115	1.198	0.691
6	0.483	2.534	0	5.078	–	2.004	1.135	0.549
7	0.419	2.704	0.205	5.203	0.076	1.924	1.214	0.509
8	0.373	2.847	0.387	5.307	0.136	1.864	1.160	0.432
9	0.337	2.970	0.546	5.394	0.184	1.816	1.223	0.412
10	0.308	3.078	0.687	5.469	0.223	1.777	1.176	0.363
11	0.285	3.173	0.812	5.534	0.256	1.744		
12	0.266	3.258	0.924	5.592	0.284	1.716		
13	0.249	3.336	1.026	5.646	0.308	1.692		
14	0.235	3.407	1.121	5.693	0.329	1.671		
15	0.223	3.472	1.207	5.737	0.348	1.652		
16	0.212	3.532	1.285	5.779	0.364	1.636		
17	0.203	3.588	1.359	5.817	0.379	1.621		
18	0.194	3.640	1.426	5.854	0.392	1.608		
19	0.187	3.689	1.490	5.888	0.404	1.596		
20	0.180	3.735	1.548	5.922	0.414	1.586		
21	0.173	3.778	1.605	5.951	0.425	1.575		
22	0.167	3.819	1.659	5.979	0.434	1.566		
23	0.162	3.858	1.710	6.006	0.443	1.557		
24	0.157	3.895	1.759	6.031	0.452	1.548		
25	0.153	3.931	1.806	6.056	0.459	1.541		

Abnormal Distributions of Points in Control Charts

Abnormality	Description
Sequence	Seven or more consecutive points on one side of the center line. Denotes the average value has shifted.
Bias	Fewer than seven consecutive points on one side of the center line, but most of the points are on that side. • 10 of 11 consecutive points • 12 or more of 14 consecutive points • 14 or more of 17 consecutive points • 16 or more of 20 consecutive points
Trend	Seven or more consecutive rising or falling points.
Approaching the limit	Two out of three or three or more out of seven consecutive points are more than two-thirds the distance between the center line and a control limit.
Periodicity	The data points vary in a regular periodic pattern.

7.7 STATISTICS

7.7.1 DESCRIPTIVE STATISTICS

1. Sample distribution and density functions
   - Sample distribution function:

$$\hat{F}(x) = \frac{1}{n} \sum_{i=1}^{n} u(x - x_i) \qquad (7.7.1)$$

where $u(x)$ be the unit step function defined by $u(x) = 0$ for $x \le 0$ and $u(x) = 1$ for $x > 0$.

   - Sample density function or histogram:

$$\hat{f}(x) = \frac{\hat{F}(x_0 + (i + 1)w) - \hat{F}(x_0 + iw)}{w} \qquad (7.7.2)$$

for $x \in [x_0 + iw, x_0 + (i + 1)w)$. The interval $[x_0 + iw, x_0 + (i + 1)w)$ is called the ith bin, w is the bin width, and $f_i = \hat{F}(x_0 + (i+1)w) - \hat{F}(x_0 + iw)$ is the bin frequency.

2. Order statistics and quantiles
   - Order statistics are obtained by arranging the sample values $\{x_1, x_2, \ldots, x_n\}$ in increasing order, denoted by

$$x_{(1)} \le x_{(2)} \le \cdots \le x_{(n)}. \qquad (7.7.3)$$

   (a) $x_{(1)}$ and $x_{(n)}$ are the minimum and maximum data values, respectively.
   (b) For $i = 1, \ldots, n$, $x_{(i)}$ is called the ith order statistic.

   - *Quantiles*: If $0 < p < 1$, then the quantile of order p, ξ_p, is given by the $p(n + 1)^{\text{th}}$ order statistic. It may be necessary to interpolate between successive values.
   (a) If $p = j/4$ for $j = 1, 2$, or 3, then $\xi_{\frac{j}{4}}$ is called the jth quartile.
   (b) If $p = j/10$ for $j = 1, 2, \ldots, 9$, then $\xi_{\frac{j}{10}}$ is called the jth decile.
   (c) If $p = j/100$ for $j = 1, 2, \ldots, 99$, then $\xi_{\frac{j}{100}}$ is called the jth percentile.

3. Measures of central tendency
   - Arithmetic mean:

$$\bar{x} = \frac{1}{n} \sum_{i=1}^{n} x_i = \frac{x_1 + x_2 + \cdots + x_n}{n}. \qquad (7.7.4)$$

- α-trimmed mean:

$$\bar{x}_\alpha = \frac{1}{n(1-2\alpha)} \left((1-r)\left(x_{(k+1)} + x_{(n-k)}\right) + \sum_{i=k+2}^{n-k-1} x_{(i)} \right), \tag{7.7.5}$$

where $k = \lfloor \alpha n \rfloor$ is the greatest integer less than or equal to αn, and $r = \alpha n - k$. If $\alpha = 0$ then $\bar{x}_\alpha = \bar{x}$.

- *Weighted mean*: If to each x_i is associated a weight $w_i \geq 0$ so that

$$\sum_{i=1}^{n} w_i = 1, \quad \text{then} \quad \bar{x}_w = \sum_{i=1}^{n} w_i x_i.$$

- Geometric mean:

$$\text{G.M.} = \left(\prod_{i=1}^{n} x_i \right)^{\frac{1}{n}} = (x_1 x_2 \cdots x_n)^{\frac{1}{n}}. \tag{7.7.6}$$

- Harmonic mean:

$$\text{H.M.} = \frac{n}{\sum_{i=1}^{n} \frac{1}{x_i}} = \frac{n}{\frac{1}{x_1} + \frac{1}{x_2} + \cdots + \frac{1}{x_n}}. \tag{7.7.7}$$

- Relationship between arithmetic, geometric, and harmonic means:

$$\text{H.M.} \leq \text{G.M.} \leq \bar{x} \tag{7.7.8}$$

with equality holding only when all sample values are equal.

- The mode is the data value that occurs with the greatest frequency. Note that the mode may not be unique.

- Median:
  (a) If n is odd and $n = 2k + 1$, then $M = x_{(k+1)}$.
  (b) If n is even and $n = 2k$, then $M = (x_{(k)} + x_{(k+1)})/2$.

- Midrange:

$$\text{mid} = \frac{x_{(1)} + x_{(n)}}{2}. \tag{7.7.9}$$

4. Measures of dispersion

- Mean deviation or absolute deviation:

$$\text{M.D.} = \frac{1}{n} \sum_{i=1}^{n} |x_i - M|, \quad \text{or} \quad \text{M.D.} = \frac{1}{n} \sum_{i=1}^{n} |x_i - \bar{x}|. \tag{7.7.10}$$

- Sample standard deviation:

$$s = \sqrt{\frac{1}{n-1} \sum_{i=1}^{n} (x_i - \bar{x})^2} = \sqrt{\frac{\sum_{i=1}^{n} x_i^2 - n\bar{x}^2}{n-1}}. \tag{7.7.11}$$

- The sample variance is the square of the sample standard deviation.

- Root mean square: $\text{R.M.S.} = \sqrt{\frac{1}{n} \sum_{i=1}^{n} x_i^2}.$

- Sample range: $x_{(n)} - x_{(1)}$.

- Interquartile range: $\xi_{\frac{3}{4}} - \xi_{\frac{1}{4}}$.

- The quartile deviation or semi-interquartile range is one half the interquartile range.

5. Higher-order statistics

- Sample moments: $m_k = \frac{1}{n} \sum_{i=1}^{n} x_i^k.$

- Sample central moments, or sample moments about the mean:

$$\mu_k = \frac{1}{n} \sum_{i=1}^{n} (x_i - \bar{x})^k. \tag{7.7.12}$$

7.7.2 STATISTICAL ESTIMATORS

Definitions

1. A function of a set of random variables is a *statistic*. It is a function of observable random variables that does not contain any unknown parameters. A statistic is itself an observable random variable.

2. Let θ be a parameter appearing in the density function for the random variable X. Suppose that we know a formula for computing an approximate value $\hat{\theta}$ of θ from a given sample $\{x_1, \ldots, x_n\}$ (call such a function g). Then $\hat{\theta} = g(x_1, x_2, \ldots, x_n)$ can be considered as a single observation of the random variable $\hat{\Theta} = g(X_1, X_2, \ldots, X_n)$. The random variable $\hat{\Theta}$ is an *estimator* for the parameter θ.

3. A *hypothesis* is an assumption about the distribution of a random variable X. This may usually be cast into the form $\theta \in \Theta_0$. We use H_0 to denote the *null hypothesis* and H_1 to denote an *alternative hypothesis*.

4. In *significance testing*, a test statistic $T = T(X_1, \ldots, X_n)$ is used to *reject H_0*, or to *not reject H_0*. Generally, if $T \in C$, where C is a *critical region*, then H_0 is rejected.

5. A *type I error*, denoted α, is to reject H_0 when it should not be rejected. A *type II error*, denoted β, is to not reject H_0 when it should be rejected.

6. The power of a test is $\eta = 1 - \beta$.

	Unknown truth	
	H_0	H_1
Do not reject H_0	True decision. Probability is $1 - \alpha$	Type II error. Probability is β
Reject H_0	Type I error. Probability is α	True decision. Probability is $\eta = 1 - \beta$

Consistent estimators

Let $\widehat{\Theta} = g(X_1, X_2, \ldots, X_n)$ be an estimator for the parameter θ, and suppose that g is defined for arbitrarily large values of n. If the estimator has the property, $\mathrm{E}\left[(\widehat{\Theta} - \theta)^2\right] \to 0$, as $n \to \infty$, then the estimator is called a *consistent estimator*.

1. A consistent estimator is not unique.

2. A consistent estimator may be meaningless.

3. A consistent estimator is not necessarily unbiased.

Efficient estimators

An unbiased estimator $\widehat{\Theta} = g(X_1, X_2, \ldots, X_n)$ for a parameter θ is said to be *efficient* if it has finite variance $(\mathrm{E}\left[(\widehat{\Theta} - \Theta)^2\right] < \infty)$ and if there does not exist another estimator $\widehat{\Theta}^* = g^*(X_1, X_2, \ldots, X_n)$ for θ, whose variance is smaller than that of $\widehat{\Theta}$. The *efficiency* of an unbiased estimator is the ratio,

$$\frac{\text{Cramér–Rao lower bound}}{\text{Actual variance}}.$$

The relative efficiency of two unbiased estimators is the ratio of their variances.

Maximum likelihood estimators (MLE)

Suppose X is a random variable whose density function is $f(x; \boldsymbol{\theta})$, where $\boldsymbol{\theta} = (\theta_1, \ldots, \theta_r)$. If the independent sample values $x_1, \ldots, x_n$ are obtained, then define the likelihood function as $L = \prod_{i=1}^{n} f(x_i; \boldsymbol{\theta})$. The MLE estimate for $\boldsymbol{\theta}$ is the solution of the simultaneous equations, $\frac{\partial L}{\partial \theta_i} = 0$, for $i = 1, \ldots, r$.

1. A MLE need not be consistent.

2. A MLE may not be unbiased.

3. A MLE need not be unique.

4. If a single sufficient statistic T exists for the parameter θ, the MLE of θ must be a function of T.

5. Let $\widehat{\Theta}$ be a MLE of θ. If $\tau(\cdot)$ is a function with a single-valued inverse, then a MLE of $\tau(\theta)$ is $\tau(\widehat{\Theta})$.

Define $\bar{x} = \sum_{i=1}^{n} X_i/n$ and $S^2 = \sum_{i=1}^{n}(X_i - \bar{x})^2/n$ (note that $S \neq s$). Then:

Distribution	Estimated parameter	MLE estimate of parameter
Exponential $E(\lambda)$	$1/\lambda$	$1/\bar{x}$
Exponential $E(\lambda)$	$\lambda^2 = \sigma^2$	$\bar{x}^2$
Normal $N(\mu, \sigma)$	μ	$\bar{x}$
Normal $N(\mu, \sigma)$	σ^2	S^2
Poisson $P(\lambda)$	λ	$\bar{x}$
Uniform $U(0, \theta)$	θ	X_{max}

Method of moments (MOM)

Let $\{X_i\}$ be independent and identically distributed random variables with density $f(x; \boldsymbol{\theta})$. Let $\mu'_r(\boldsymbol{\theta}) = E[X^r]$ be the rth population moment (if it exists). Let $m'_r = \frac{1}{n}\sum_{i=1}^{n} x_i^r$ be the rth sample moment. Form the k equations, $\mu'_r = m'_r$, and solve to obtain an estimate of $\boldsymbol{\theta}$.

1. MOM estimators are not necessarily uniquely defined.
2. MOM estimators may not be functions of sufficient or complete statistics.

Sufficient statistics

A statistic $G = g(X_1, \ldots, X_n)$ is defined as a *sufficient statistic* if, and only if, the conditional distribution of H, given G, does not depend on θ for any statistic $H = h(X_1, \ldots, X_n)$.

Let $\{X_i\}$ be independent and identically distributed random variables, with density $f(x; \theta)$. The statistics $\{G_1, \ldots, G_r\}$ are defined as *jointly sufficient statistics* if, and only if, the conditional distribution of $X_1, X_2, \ldots, X_n$ given $G_1 = g_1, G_1 = g_2$, $\ldots G_r = g_r$ does not depend on θ.

1. A single sufficient statistic may not exist.

Unbiased estimators

An estimator $g(X_1, X_2, \ldots, X_n)$ for a parameter θ is said to be *unbiased* if

$$E[g(X_1, X_2, \ldots, X_n)] = \theta.$$

1. An unbiased estimator may not exist.
2. An unbiased estimator is not unique.
3. An unbiased estimator may be meaningless.
4. An unbiased estimator is not necessarily consistent.

UMVU estimators

A *uniformly minimum variance unbiased* estimator, called a UMVU estimator, is unbiased and has the minimum variance among all unbiased estimators.

Define, as usual, $\bar{x} = \sum_{i=1}^{n} X_i/n$ and $s^2 = \sum_{i=1}^{n}(X_i - \bar{x})^2/(n-1)$. Then:

Distribution	Estimated parameter	UMVU estimate of parameter	Variance of estimator
Exponential $E(\lambda)$	λ	$\dfrac{n-1}{s}$	$\dfrac{\lambda^2}{n-2}$
Exponential $E(\lambda)$	$\dfrac{1}{\lambda}$	$\bar{x}$	$\dfrac{1}{n\lambda^2}$
Normal $N(\mu, \sigma)$	μ	$\bar{x}$	$\dfrac{\sigma^2}{n}$
Normal $N(\mu, \sigma)$	σ^2	s^2	$\dfrac{2\sigma^4}{n-1}$
Poisson $P(\lambda)$	λ	$\bar{x}$	$\dfrac{\lambda^2}{n}$
Uniform $U(0, \theta)$	θ	$\dfrac{n+1}{n}X_{\max}$	$\dfrac{\theta^2}{n(n+2)}$

7.7.3   CRAMER–RAO BOUND

The Cramer–Rao bound gives a lower bound on the variance of an unknown unbiased statistical parameter, when n samples are taken. When the single unknown parameter is θ,

$$\sigma^2(\theta) \geq \frac{1}{-n\mathrm{E}\left[\frac{\partial^2}{\partial\theta^2}\log f(x;\theta)\right]} = \frac{1}{n\mathrm{E}\left[\left(\frac{\partial}{\partial\theta}\log f(x;\theta)\right)^2\right]}. \qquad (7.7.13)$$

Examples

1. For a normal random variable with unknown mean θ and known variance σ^2, the density is $f(x;\theta) = \frac{1}{\sqrt{2\pi}\sigma}\exp\left(-\frac{(x-\theta)^2}{2\sigma^2}\right)$. Hence, $\frac{\partial}{\partial\theta}\log f(x;\theta) = (x-\theta)/\sigma^2$. The computation

$$\mathrm{E}\left[\frac{(x-\theta)^2}{\sigma^4}\right] = \int_{-\infty}^{\infty} \frac{(x-\theta)^2}{\sigma^4}\frac{1}{\sqrt{2\pi}\sigma}e^{-(x-\theta)^2/2\sigma^2}\,dx = \frac{1}{\sigma^2}$$

results in $\sigma^2(\theta) \geq \frac{\sigma^2}{n}$.

2. For a normal random variable with known mean μ and unknown variance $\theta = \sigma^2$, the density is $f(x;\theta) = \frac{1}{\sqrt{2\pi\theta}}\exp\left(-\frac{(x-\mu)^2}{2\theta^2}\right)$. Hence, $\frac{\partial}{\partial\theta}\log f(x;\theta) = ((x-\mu)^2 - 2\theta)/(2\theta)^2$. The computation $E\left[\frac{(x-\mu)^2 - 2\theta}{(2\theta)^2}\right] = \frac{1}{2\theta^2} = \frac{1}{2\sigma^4}$ results in $\sigma^2(\theta) \geq 2\sigma^4/n$.

3. For a Poisson random variable with unknown mean θ, the density is $f(x;\theta) = \theta^x e^{-\theta}/x!$. Hence, $\frac{\partial}{\partial\theta}\log f(x;\theta) = x/\theta - 1$. The computation $E\left[\left(\frac{x}{\theta} - 1\right)^2\right] = \sum_{x=0}^{\infty}\left(\frac{x}{\theta} - 1\right)^2 \frac{\theta^x e^{-\theta}}{x!} = \frac{1}{\theta}$ results in $\sigma^2(\theta) \geq \theta/n$.

7.7.4 ORDER STATISTICS

When $\{X_i\}$ are n independent and identically distributed random variables with the common distribution function $F_X(x)$, let Z_m be the mth largest of the values ($m = 0, 1, \ldots, n$). Hence Z_1 is the maximum of the n values and Z_n is the minimum of the n values. Then $F_{Z_m}(x) = \sum_{m=1}^{n}\binom{n}{i}[F_X(x)]^i [1 - F_X(x)]^{n-i}$. Hence

$$F_{\min}(z) = [F_X(z)]^n, \qquad\qquad f_{\min}(z) = n[F_X(z)]^{n-1} f_X(z),$$
$$F_{\max}(z) = 1 - [1 - F_X(z)]^n, \qquad f_{\max}(z) = n[1 - F_X(z)]^{n-1} f_X(z).$$

The expected value of the ith order statistic is given by

$$E\left[x_{(i)}\right] = \frac{n!}{(i-1)!(n-i)!}\int_{-\infty}^{\infty} xf(x)F^{i-1}(x)[1 - F(x)]^{n-i}\, dx.$$
$$(7.7.14)$$

Uniform distribution: If X is uniformly distributed on the interval $[0, 1]$ then $E\left[x_{(i)}\right] = \frac{n!}{(i-1)!(n-i)!}\int_0^1 x^i(1 - x)^{n-i}\, dx$. The expected value of the largest of n samples is $\frac{n}{n+1}$; the expected value of the least of n samples is $\frac{1}{n+1}$.

Normal distribution: The following table gives values of $E\left[x_{(i)}\right]$ for a standard normal distribution. Missing values (indicated by a dash) may be obtained from $E\left[x_{(i)}\right] = -E\left[x_{(n-i+1)}\right]$.

For example, if an average person takes five intelligence tests (each test having a normal distribution with a mean of 100 and a standard deviation of 20), then the expected value of the largest score is $100 + (1.1630)(20) \approx 123$.

i	$n=2$	3	4	5	6	7	8	10
1	0.5642	0.8463	1.0294	1.1630	1.2672	1.3522	1.4236	1.5388
2	—	0.0000	0.2970	0.4950	0.6418	0.7574	0.8522	1.0014
3		—	—	0.0000	0.2016	0.3527	0.4728	0.6561
4			—	—	—	0.0000	0.1522	0.3756
5				—	—	—	—	0.1226
6					—	—	—	—
7						—	—	—

7.7.5   CLASSIC STATISTICS PROBLEMS

Sample size problem

Suppose that a Bernoulli random variable is to be estimated from a population. What sample size n is required so that, with 99% certainty, the error is no more than $e = 5$ percentage points (i.e., $\text{Prob}(|\hat{p} - p| < 0.05) > 0.99$)?

If an *a priori* estimate of p is available, then the minimum sample size is $n_p = z_{\alpha/2}^2 p(1 - p)/e^2$. If no *a priori* estimate is available, then $n_n = z_{\alpha/2}^2/4e^2 \geq n_p$. For the numbers above, $n \geq n_n = 664$.

Large scale testing with infrequent success

Suppose that a disease occurs in one person out of every 1000. Suppose that a test for this disease has a type I and a type II error of 1% (that is, $\alpha = \beta = 0.01$). Imagine that 100,000 people are tested. Of the 100 people who have the disease, 99 will be diagnosed as having it. Of the 99,900 people who do not have the disease, 999 will be diagnosed as having it. Hence, only $\frac{99}{1098} \approx 9\%$ of the people who test positive for the disease actually have it.

7.8   CONFIDENCE INTERVALS

A probability distribution may have one or more unknown parameters. A confidence interval is an assertion that an unknown parameter lies in a computed range, with a specified probability. Before constructing a confidence interval, first select a confidence coefficient, denoted $1 - \alpha$. Typically, $1 - \alpha = 0.95, 0.99$, or the like. For the definitions of z_α, t_α, and χ_α^2 see Section 7.12.1.

7.8.1   CONFIDENCE INTERVAL: SAMPLE FROM ONE POPULATION

The following confidence intervals assume a random sample of size n, given by $\{x_1, x_2, \ldots, x_n\}$.

1. Find mean μ of the normal distribution with known variance σ^2.

   - Determine the critical value $z_{\alpha/2}$ such that $\Phi\left(z_{\alpha/2}\right) = 1 - \alpha/2$, where $\Phi(z)$ is the standard normal distribution function.

   - Compute the mean $\bar{x}$ of the sample.

   - Compute $k = z_{\alpha/2}\sigma/\sqrt{n}$.

   - The $100(1-\alpha)$ percent confidence interval for μ is given by $[\bar{x} - k, \bar{x} + k]$.

2. Find mean μ of the normal distribution with unknown variance σ^2.

- Determine the critical value $t_{\alpha/2}$ such that $F\left(t_{\alpha/2}\right) = 1 - \alpha/2$, where $F(t)$ is the t-distribution with $n - 1$ degrees of freedom.

- Compute the mean $\bar{x}$ and standard deviation s of the sample.

- Compute $k = t_{\alpha/2}s/\sqrt{n}$.

- The $100(1-\alpha)$ percent confidence interval for μ is given by $[\bar{x} - k, \bar{x} + k]$.

3. Find the probability of success p for Bernoulli trials with large sample size.

- Determine the critical value $z_{\alpha/2}$ such that $\Phi\left(z_{\alpha/2}\right) = 1 - \alpha/2$, where $\Phi(z)$ is the standard normal distribution function.

- Compute the proportion $\hat{p}$ of "successes" out of n trials.

- Compute $k = z_{\alpha/2}\sqrt{\dfrac{\hat{p}(1 - \hat{p})}{n}}$.

- The $100(1-\alpha)$ percent confidence interval for $\hat{p}$ is given by $[\hat{p} - k, \hat{p} + k]$.

4. Find variance σ^2 of the normal distribution.

- Determine the critical values $\chi^2_{\alpha/2}$ and $\chi^2_{1-\alpha/2}$ such that $F\left(\chi^2_{\alpha/2}\right) = 1 - \alpha/2$ and $F\left(\chi^2_{1-\alpha/2}\right) = \alpha/2$, where $F(z)$ is the chi-square distribution function with $n - 1$ degrees of freedom.

- Compute the standard deviation s.

- Compute $k_1 = \dfrac{(n - 1)s^2}{\chi^2_{\alpha/2}}$ and $k_2 = \dfrac{(n - 1)s^2}{\chi^2_{1-\alpha/2}}$.

- The $100(1 - \alpha)$ percent confidence interval for σ^2 is given by $[k_1, k_2]$.

- The $100(1 - \alpha)$ percent confidence interval for the standard deviation σ is given by $\left[\sqrt{k_1}, \sqrt{k_2}\right]$.

5. Find quantile ξ_p of order p for large sample sizes.

- Determine the critical value $z_{\alpha/2}$ such that $\Phi\left(z_{\alpha/2}\right) = 1 - \alpha/2$, where $\Phi(z)$ is the standard normal distribution function.

- Compute the order statistics $x_{(1)}, x_{(2)}, \ldots, x_{(n)}$.

- Compute $k_1 = \left\lfloor np - z_{\alpha/2}\sqrt{np(1 - p)} \right\rfloor$ and $k_2 = \left\lceil np + z_{\alpha/2}\sqrt{np(1 - p)} \right\rceil$.

- The $100(1 - \alpha)$ percent confidence interval for ξ_p is given by $\left[x_{(k_1)}, x_{(k_2)}\right]$.

6. Find median M based on the Wilcoxon one-sample statistic for a large sample.

- Determine the critical value $z_{\alpha/2}$ such that $\Phi\left(z_{\alpha/2}\right) = 1 - \alpha/2$, where $\Phi(z)$ is the standard normal distribution function.

- Compute the order statistics $w_{(1)}, w_{(2)}, \ldots, w_{(N)}$ of the $N = n(n-1)/2$ averages $(x_i + x_j)/2$, for $1 \le i < j \le n$.

- Compute $k_1 = \left\lfloor \dfrac{N}{2} - \dfrac{z_{\alpha/2} N}{\sqrt{3n}} \right\rfloor$ and $k_2 = \left\lceil \dfrac{N}{2} + \dfrac{z_{\alpha/2} N}{\sqrt{3n}} \right\rceil$.

- The $100(1-\alpha)$ percent confidence interval for M is given by $\left[w_{(k_1)}, w_{(k_2)} \right]$.

7.8.2   CONFIDENCE INTERVAL: SAMPLES FROM TWO POPULATIONS

The following confidence intervals assume random samples from two large populations: one sample of size n, given by $\{x_1, x_2, \ldots, x_n\}$, and one sample of size m, given by $\{y_1, y_2, \ldots, y_m\}$.

1. Find the difference in population means μ_x and μ_y from independent samples with known variances σ_x^2 and σ_y^2.

    - Determine the critical value $z_{\alpha/2}$ such that $\Phi(z_{\alpha/2}) = 1 - \alpha/2$, where $\Phi(z)$ is the standard normal distribution function.

    - Compute the means $\bar{x}$ and $\bar{y}$.

    - Compute $k = z_{\alpha/2} \sqrt{\dfrac{\sigma_x^2}{n} + \dfrac{\sigma_y^2}{m}}$.

    - The $100(1-\alpha)$ percent confidence interval for $\mu_x - \mu_y$ is given by $[(\bar{x} - \bar{y}) - k, (\bar{x} - \bar{y}) + k]$.

2. Find the difference in population means μ_x and μ_y from independent samples with unknown variances σ_x^2 and σ_y^2.

    - Determine the critical value $z_{\alpha/2}$ such that $\Phi(z_{\alpha/2}) = 1 - \alpha/2$, where $\Phi(z)$ is the standard normal distribution function.

    - Compute the means $\bar{x}$ and $\bar{y}$, and the standard deviations s_x and s_y.

    - Compute $k = z_{\alpha/2} \sqrt{\dfrac{s_x^2}{n} + \dfrac{s_y^2}{m}}$.

    - The $100(1-\alpha)$ percent confidence interval for $\mu_x - \mu_y$ is given by $[(\bar{x} - \bar{y}) - k, (\bar{x} - \bar{y}) + k]$.

3. Find the difference in population means μ_x and μ_y from independent samples with unknown but equal variances $\sigma_x^2 = \sigma_y^2$.

    - Determine the critical value $t_{\alpha/2}$ such that $F(t_{\alpha/2}) = 1 - \alpha/2$, where $F(t)$ is the t-distribution with $n + m - 2$ degrees of freedom.

- Compute the means $\bar{x}$ and $\bar{y}$, the standard deviations s_x and s_y, and the pooled standard deviation estimate,

$$s = \sqrt{\frac{(n-1)s_x^2 + (m-1)s_y^2}{n+m-2}}. \tag{7.8.1}$$

- Compute $k = t_{\alpha/2}\, s\, \sqrt{\dfrac{1}{n} + \dfrac{1}{m}}$.

- The $100(1-\alpha)$ percent confidence interval for $\mu_x - \mu_y$ is given by $[(\bar{x} - \bar{y}) - k, (\bar{x} - \bar{y}) + k]$.

4. Find the difference in population means μ_x and μ_y for paired samples with unknown but equal variances $\sigma_x^2 = \sigma_y^2$.

- Determine the critical value $t_{\alpha/2}$ such that $F\left(t_{\alpha/2}\right) = 1 - \alpha/2$, where $F\left(t\right)$ is the t-distribution with $n - 1$ degrees of freedom.

- Compute the mean $\bar{\mu}_d$ and standard deviation s_d of the paired differences $x_1 - y_1, x_2 - y_2, \ldots, x_n - y_n$.

- Compute $k = t_{\alpha/2}\, s_d / \sqrt{n}$.

- The $100(1-\alpha)$ percent confidence interval for $\mu_d = \mu_x - \mu_y$ is given by $[\bar{\mu}_d - k, \bar{\mu}_d + k]$.

5. Find the difference in Bernoulli trial success rates, $p_x - p_y$, for large, independent samples.

- Determine the critical value $z_{\alpha/2}$ such that $\Phi\left(z_{\alpha/2}\right) = 1 - \alpha/2$, where $\Phi\left(z\right)$ is the standard normal distribution function.

- Compute the proportions $\hat{p}_x$ and $\hat{p}_y$ of "successes" for the samples.

- Compute $k = z_{\alpha/2}\sqrt{\dfrac{\hat{p}_x\left(1 - \hat{p}_x\right)}{n} + \dfrac{\hat{p}_y\left(1 - \hat{p}_y\right)}{m}}$.

- The $100(1-\alpha)$ percent confidence interval for $p_x - p_y$ is given by $\left[\left(\hat{p}_x - \hat{p}_y\right) - k, \left(\hat{p}_x - \hat{p}_y\right) + k\right]$.

6. Find the difference in medians $M_x - M_y$ based on the Mann–Whitney–Wilcoxon procedure.

- Determine the critical value $z_{\alpha/2}$ such that $\Phi\left(z_{\alpha/2}\right) = 1 - \alpha/2$, where $\Phi\left(z\right)$ is the standard normal distribution function.

- Compute the order statistics $w_{(1)}, w_{(2)}, \ldots, w_{(N)}$ of the $N = nm$ differences $x_i - y_j$, for $1 \le i \le n$ and $1 \le j \le m$.

- Compute

$$k_1 = \frac{nm}{2} + \left[0.5 - z_{\alpha/2}\sqrt{\frac{nm\,(n+m+1)}{12}}\right]$$

and

$$k_2 = \left\lceil \frac{nm}{2} - 0.5 + z_{\alpha/2} \sqrt{\frac{nm\,(n+m+1)}{12}} \right\rceil.$$

- The $100(1-\alpha)$ percent confidence interval for $M_x - M_y$ is given by $\left[w_{(k_1)}, w_{(k_2)} \right]$.

7. Find the ratio of variances σ_x^2/σ_y^2, for independent samples.

- Determine the critical values $F_{\alpha/2}$ and $F_{1-\alpha/2}$ such that $F\left(F_{\alpha/2}\right) = 1-\alpha/2$ and $F\left(F_{1-\alpha/2}\right) = \alpha/2$, where $F\,(F)$ is the F-distribution with $m-1$ and $n-1$ degrees of freedom.

- Compute the standard deviations s_x and s_y of the samples.

- Compute $k_1 = F_{1-\alpha/2}$ and $k_2 = F_{\alpha/2}$

- The $100(1-\alpha)$ percent confidence interval for σ_x^2/σ_y^2 is given by $\left[\dfrac{s_x^2}{s_y^2} k_1, \dfrac{s_x^2}{s_y^2} k_2 \right]$.

7.9   TESTS OF HYPOTHESES

A statistical hypothesis is a an assumption about the distribution of a random variable. A statistical test of a hypothesis is a procedure in which a sample is used to determine whether we should "reject" or "not reject" the hypothesis. Before employing a hypothesis test, first select a significance level α. Typically, $\alpha = 0.05, 0.01$, or the like.

7.9.1   HYPOTHESIS TESTS: PARAMETER FROM ONE POPULATION

The following hypothesis tests assume a random sample of size n, given by $\{x_1, x_2, \ldots, x_n\}$.

1. Test of the hypothesis $\mu = \mu_0$ against the alternative $\mu \neq \mu_0$ of the mean of a normal distribution with known variance σ^2:

- Determine the critical value $z_{\alpha/2}$ such that $\Phi\left(z_{\alpha/2}\right) = 1 - \alpha/2$, where $\Phi\,(z)$ is the standard normal distribution function.

- Compute the mean $\bar{x}$ of the sample.

- Compute the test statistic $z = \dfrac{(\bar{x} - \mu_0)\sqrt{n}}{\sigma}$.

- If $|z| > z_{\alpha/2}$, then reject the hypothesis. If $|z| \leq z_{\alpha/2}$, then do not reject the hypothesis.

2. Test of the hypothesis $\mu = \mu_0$ against the alternative $\mu > \mu_0$ (or $\mu < \mu_0$) of the mean of a normal distribution with known variance σ^2:

   - Determine the critical value z_α such that $\Phi(z_\alpha) = 1 - \alpha$, where $\Phi(z)$ is the standard normal distribution function.

   - Compute the mean $\bar{x}$ of the sample.

   - Compute the test statistic $z = \dfrac{(\bar{x} - \mu_0)\sqrt{n}}{\sigma}$. (For the alternative $\mu < \mu_0$, multiply z by -1.)

   - If $z > z_\alpha$, then reject the hypothesis. If $z \leq z_\alpha$, then do not reject the hypothesis.

3. Test of the hypothesis $\mu = \mu_0$ against the alternative $\mu \neq \mu_0$ of the mean of a normal distribution with unknown variance σ^2:

   - Determine the critical value $t_{\alpha/2}$ such that $F(t_{\alpha/2}) = 1 - \alpha/2$, where $F(t)$ is the t-distribution with $n - 1$ degrees of freedom.

   - Compute the mean $\bar{x}$ and standard deviation s of the sample.

   - Compute the test statistic $t = \dfrac{(\bar{x} - \mu_0)\sqrt{n}}{s}$.

   - If $|t| > t_{\alpha/2}$, then reject the hypothesis. If $|t| \leq t_{\alpha/2}$, then do not reject the hypothesis.

4. Test of the hypothesis $\mu = \mu_0$ against the alternative $\mu > \mu_0$ (or $\mu < \mu_0$) of the mean of a normal distribution with unknown variance σ^2:

   - Determine the critical value t_α such that $F(t_\alpha) = 1 - \alpha$, where $F(t)$ is the t-distribution with $n - 1$ degrees of freedom.

   - Compute the mean $\bar{x}$ and standard deviation s of the sample.

   - Compute the test statistic $t = \dfrac{(\bar{x} - \mu_0)\sqrt{n}}{s}$. (For the alternative $\mu < \mu_0$, multiply t by -1.)

   - If $t > t_\alpha$, then reject the hypothesis. If $t \leq t_\alpha$, then do not reject the hypothesis.

5. Test of the hypothesis $p = p_0$ against the alternative $p \neq p_0$ of the probability of success for a binomial distribution, large sample:

   - Determine the critical value $z_{\alpha/2}$ such that $\Phi(z_{\alpha/2}) = 1 - \alpha/2$, where $\Phi(z)$ is the standard normal distribution function.

   - Compute the proportion $\hat{p}$ of "successes" for the sample.

   - Compute the test statistic $z = \dfrac{\hat{p} - p_0}{\sqrt{\dfrac{p_0(1-p_0)}{n}}}$.

- If $|z| > z_{\alpha/2}$, then reject the hypothesis. If $|z| \le z_{\alpha/2}$, then do not reject the hypothesis.

6. Test of the hypothesis $p = p_0$ against the alternative $p > p_0$ (or $p < p_0$) of the probability of success for a binomial distribution, large sample:

  - Determine the critical value z_α such that $\Phi(z_\alpha) = 1 - \alpha$, where $\Phi(z)$ is the standard normal distribution function.

  - Compute the proportion $\hat{p}$ of "successes" for the sample.

  - Compute the test statistic $z = \dfrac{\hat{p} - p_0}{\sqrt{\dfrac{p_0(1-p_0)}{n}}}$. (For the alternative $p < p_0$, multiply z by -1.)

  - If $z > z_\alpha$, then reject the hypothesis. If $z \le z_\alpha$, then do not reject the hypothesis.

7. Wilcoxon signed rank test of the hypothesis $M = M_0$ against the alternative $M \ne M_0$ of the median of a population, large sample:

  - Determine the critical value $z_{\alpha/2}$ such that $\Phi\left(z_{\alpha/2}\right) = 1 - \alpha/2$, where $\Phi(z)$ is the standard normal distribution.

  - Compute the quantities $|x_i - M_0|$, and keep track of the sign of $x_i - M_0$. If $|x_i - M_0| = 0$, then remove it from the list and reduce n by one.

  - Order the $|x_i - M_0|$ from smallest to largest, assigning rank 1 to the smallest and rank n to the largest; $|x_i - M_0|$ has rank r_i if it is the r_i^{th} entry in the ordered list. If $|x_i - M_0| = |x_j - M_0|$, then assign each the average of their ranks.

  - Compute the sum of the signed ranks $R = \displaystyle\sum_{i=1}^{n} \text{sign}\,(x_i - M_0)\, r_i$.

  - Compute the test statistic $z = \dfrac{R}{\sqrt{\dfrac{n(n+1)(2n+1)}{6}}}$.

  - If $|z| > z_{\alpha/2}$, then reject the hypothesis. If $|z| \le z_{\alpha/2}$, then do not reject the hypothesis.

8. Wilcoxon signed rank test of the hypothesis $M = M_0$ against the alternative $M > M_0$ (or $M < M_0$) of the median of a population, large sample:

  - Determine the critical value z_α such that $\Phi(z_\alpha) = 1 - \alpha$, where $\Phi(z)$ is the standard normal distribution.

  - Compute the quantities $|x_i - M_0|$, and keep track of the sign of $x_i - M_0$. If $|x_i - M_0| = 0$, then remove it from the list and reduce n by one.

  - Order the $|x_i - M_0|$ from smallest to largest, assigning rank 1 to the smallest and rank n to the largest; $|x_i - M_0|$ has rank r_i if it is the r_i^{th} entry in the ordered list. If $|x_i - M_0| = |x_j - M_0|$, then assign each the average of their ranks.

- Compute the sum of the signed ranks $R = \sum_{i=1}^{n} \text{sign} (x_i - M_0) \, r_i$.

- Compute the test statistic $z = \dfrac{R}{\sqrt{\frac{n(n+1)(2n+1)}{6}}}$. (For the alternative $M < M_0$,

  multiply the test statistic by -1.)

- If $z > z_\alpha$, then reject the hypothesis. If $z \leq z_\alpha$, then do not reject the hypothesis.

9. Test of the hypothesis $\sigma^2 = \sigma_0^2$ against the alternative $\sigma^2 \neq \sigma_0^2$ of the variance of a normal distribution:

   - Determine the critical values $\chi_{\alpha/2}^2$ and $\chi_{1-\alpha/2}^2$ such that $F\left(\chi_{\alpha/2}^2\right) = 1 - \alpha/2$

     and $F\left(\chi_{1-\alpha/2}^2\right) = \alpha/2$, where $F(x)$ is the chi-square distribution function with $n - 1$ degrees of freedom.

   - Compute the standard deviation s of the sample.

   - Compute the test statistic $\chi^2 = \dfrac{(n-1)s^2}{\sigma_0^2}$.

   - If $\chi^2 < \chi_{1-\alpha/2}^2$ or $\chi^2 > \chi_{\alpha/2}^2$, then reject the hypothesis.

   - If $\chi_{1-\alpha/2}^2 \leq \chi^2 \leq \chi_{\alpha/2}^2$, then do not reject the hypothesis.

10. Test of the hypothesis $\sigma^2 = \sigma_0^2$ against the alternative $\sigma^2 > \sigma_0^2$ (or $\sigma^2 < \sigma_0^2$) of the variance of a normal distribution:

    - Determine the critical value χ_α^2 ($\chi_{1-\alpha}^2$ for the alternative $\sigma^2 < \sigma_0^2$) such that $F\left(\chi_\alpha^2\right) = 1 - \alpha$ ($F\left(\chi_{1-\alpha}^2\right) = \alpha$), where $F(x)$ is the chi-square distribution function with $n - 1$ degrees of freedom.

    - Compute the standard deviation s of the sample.

    - Compute the test statistic $\chi^2 = \dfrac{(n-1)s^2}{\sigma_0^2}$.

    - If $\chi^2 > \chi_\alpha^2$ ($\chi^2 < \chi_{1-\alpha}^2$), then reject the hypothesis.

    - If $\chi^2 \leq \chi_\alpha^2$ ($\chi_{1-\alpha}^2 \leq \chi^2$), then do not reject the hypothesis.

7.9.2 HYPOTHESIS TESTS: PARAMETERS FROM TWO POPULATIONS

The following hypothesis tests assume a random sample of size n, given by $\{x_1, x_2, \dots, x_n\}$, and a random sample of size m, given by $\{y_1, y_2, \dots, y_m\}$.

1. Test of the hypothesis $\mu_x = \mu_y$ against the alternative $\mu_x \neq \mu_y$ of the means of independent normal distributions with known variances σ_x^2 and σ_y^2:

- Determine the critical value $z_{\alpha/2}$ such that $\Phi\left(z_{\alpha/2}\right) = 1 - \alpha/2$, where $\Phi(z)$ is the standard normal distribution function.

- Compute the means, $\bar{x}$ and $\bar{y}$, of the samples.

- Compute the test statistic $z = \dfrac{\bar{x} - \bar{y}}{\sqrt{\dfrac{\sigma_x^2}{n} + \dfrac{\sigma_y^2}{m}}}$.

- If $|z| > z_{\alpha/2}$, then reject the hypothesis. If $|z| \leq z_{\alpha/2}$, then do not reject the hypothesis.

2. Test of the hypothesis $\mu_x = \mu_y$ against the alternative $\mu_x > \mu_y$ (or $\mu_x < \mu_y$) of the means of independent normal distributions with known variances σ_x^2 and σ_y^2 :

- Determine the critical value z_α such that $\Phi(z_\alpha) = 1 - \alpha$, where $\Phi(z)$ is the standard normal distribution function.

- Compute the means $\bar{x}$ and $\bar{y}$ of the samples.

- Compute the test statistic $z = \dfrac{\bar{x} - \bar{y}}{\sqrt{\dfrac{\sigma_x^2}{n} + \dfrac{\sigma_y^2}{m}}}$. (For the alternative $\mu_x < \mu_y$, multiply z by -1.)

- If $z > z_\alpha$, then reject the hypothesis. If $z \leq z_\alpha$, then do not reject the hypothesis.

3. Test of the hypothesis $\mu_x = \mu_y$ against the alternative $\mu_x \neq \mu_y$ of the means of independent normal distributions with unknown variances σ_x^2 and σ_y^2, large sample:

- Determine the critical value $z_{\alpha/2}$ such that $\Phi\left(z_{\alpha/2}\right) = 1 - \alpha/2$, where $\Phi(z)$ is the standard normal distribution.

- Compute the means, $\bar{x}$ and $\bar{y}$, and standard deviations, s_x^2 and s_y^2, of the samples.

- Compute the test statistic $z = \dfrac{\bar{x} - \bar{y}}{\sqrt{\dfrac{s_x^2}{n} + \dfrac{s_y^2}{m}}}$.

- If $|z| > z_{\alpha/2}$, then reject the hypothesis. If $|z| \leq z_{\alpha/2}$, then do not reject the hypothesis.

4. Test of the hypothesis $\mu_x = \mu_y$ against the alternative $\mu_x > \mu_y$ (or $\mu_x < \mu_y$) of the means of independent normal distributions with unknown variances, σ_x^2 and σ_y^2, large sample:

- Determine the critical value z_α such that $\Phi(z_\alpha) = 1 - \alpha$, where $\Phi(z)$ is the standard normal distribution function.

- Compute the means, $\bar{x}$ and $\bar{y}$, and standard deviations, s_x^2 and s_y^2, of the samples.

- Compute the test statistic $z = \dfrac{\bar{x} - \bar{y}}{\sqrt{\frac{s_x^2}{n} + \frac{s_y^2}{m}}}$. (For the alternative $\mu_x < \mu_y$, multiply z by -1.)

- If $z > z_\alpha$, then reject the hypothesis. If $z \leq z_\alpha$, then do not reject the hypothesis.

5. Test of the hypothesis $\mu_x = \mu_y$ against the alternative $\mu_x \neq \mu_y$ of the means of independent normal distributions with unknown variances $\sigma_x^2 = \sigma_y^2$:

   - Determine the critical value $t_{\alpha/2}$ such that $F\left(t_{\alpha/2}\right) = 1 - \alpha/2$, where $F(t)$ is the t-distribution with $n + m - 2$ degrees of freedom.

   - Compute the means, $\bar{x}$ and $\bar{y}$, and standard deviations, s_x^2 and s_y^2, of the samples.

   - Compute the test statistic $t = \dfrac{\bar{x} - \bar{y}}{\sqrt{\frac{(n-1)s_x^2 + (m-1)s_y^2}{n+m-2}} \sqrt{\frac{1}{n} + \frac{1}{m}}}$.

   - If $|t| > t_{\alpha/2}$, then reject the hypothesis. If $|t| \leq t_{\alpha/2}$, then do not reject the hypothesis.

6. Test of the hypothesis $\mu_x = \mu_y$ against the alternative $\mu_x > \mu_y$ (or $\mu_x < \mu_y$) of the means of independent normal distributions with unknown variances $\sigma_x^2 = \sigma_y^2$:

   - Determine the critical value t_α such that $F(t_\alpha) = 1 - \alpha$, where $F(t)$ is the t-distribution with $n + m - 2$ degrees of freedom.

   - Compute the means, $\bar{x}$ and $\bar{y}$, and standard deviations, s_x^2 and s_y^2, of the samples.

   - Compute the test statistic $t = \dfrac{\bar{x} - \bar{y}}{\sqrt{\frac{(n-1)s_x^2 + (m-1)s_y^2}{n+m-2}} \sqrt{\frac{1}{n} + \frac{1}{m}}}$. (For the alternative $\mu_x < \mu_y$, multiply t by -1.)

   - If $t > t_\alpha$, then reject the hypothesis. If $t \leq t_\alpha$, then do not reject the hypothesis.

7. Test of the hypothesis $\mu_x = \mu_y$ against the alternative $\mu_x \neq \mu_y$ of the means of paired normal samples:

   - Determine the critical value $t_{\alpha/2}$ so that $F\left(t_{\alpha/2}\right) = 1 - \alpha/2$, where $F(t)$ is the t-distribution with $n - 1$ degrees of freedom.

   - Compute the mean, $\hat{\mu}_d$, and standard deviation, s_d, of the differences $x_1 - y_1, x_2 - y_2, \ldots, x_n - y_n$.

   - Compute the test statistic $t = \dfrac{\hat{\mu}_d \sqrt{n}}{s_d}$.

   - If $|t| > t_{\alpha/2}$, then reject the hypothesis. If $|t| \leq t_{\alpha/2}$, then do not reject the hypothesis.

8. Test of the hypothesis $\mu_x = \mu_y$ against the alternative $\mu_x > \mu_y$ (or $\mu_x < \mu_y$) of the means of paired normal samples:

   - Determine the critical value t_α so that $F(t_\alpha) = 1 - \alpha$, where $F(t)$ is the t-distribution with $n + m - 2$ degrees of freedom.

   - Compute the mean, $\hat{\mu}_d$, and standard deviation, s_d, of the differences $x_1 - y_1, x_2 - y_2, \ldots, x_n - y_n$.

   - Compute the test statistic $t = \dfrac{\hat{\mu}_d \sqrt{n}}{s_d}$. (For the alternative $\mu_x < \mu_y$, multiply t by -1.)

   - If $t > t_\alpha$, then reject the hypothesis. If $t \le t_\alpha$, then do not reject the hypothesis.

9. Test of the hypothesis $p_x = p_y$ against the alternative $p_x \ne p_y$ of the probability of success for a binomial distribution, large sample:

   - Determine the critical value $z_{\alpha/2}$ such that $\Phi(z_{\alpha/2}) = 1 - \alpha/2$, where $\Phi(z)$ is the standard normal distribution function.

   - Compute the proportions, $\hat{p}_x$ and $\hat{p}_y$, of "successes" for the samples.

   - Compute the test statistic $z = \dfrac{\hat{p}_x - \hat{p}_y}{\sqrt{\frac{\hat{p}_x(1-p_x)}{n} + \frac{\hat{p}_y(1-p_y)}{m}}}$.

   - If $|z| > z_{\alpha/2}$, then reject the hypothesis. If $|z| \le z_{\alpha/2}$, then do not reject the hypothesis.

10. Test of the hypothesis $p_x = p_y$ against the alternative $p_x > p_y$ (or $p_x < p_y$) of the probability of success for a binomial distribution, large sample:

   - Determine the critical value z_α such that $\Phi(z_\alpha) = 1 - \alpha$, where $\Phi(z)$ is the standard normal distribution function.

   - Compute the proportions, $\hat{p}_x$ and $\hat{p}_y$, of "successes" for the samples.

   - Compute the test statistic $z = \dfrac{\hat{p}_x - \hat{p}_y}{\sqrt{\frac{\hat{p}_x(1-p_x)}{n} + \frac{\hat{p}_y(1-p_y)}{m}}}$.

   - If $z > z_\alpha$, then reject the hypothesis. If $z \le z_\alpha$, then do not reject the hypothesis.

11. Mann–Whitney–Wilcoxon test of the hypothesis $M_x = M_y$ against the alternative $M_x \ne M_y$ of the medians of independent samples, large sample:

   - Determine the critical value $z_{\alpha/2}$ such that $\Phi(z_{\alpha/2}) = 1 - \alpha/2$, where $\Phi(z)$ is the standard normal distribution.

   - Pool the $N = m + n$ observations, but keep track of which sample the observation was drawn from.

- Order the pooled observations from smallest to largest, assigning rank 1 to the smallest and rank N to the largest; an observation has rank r_i if it is the r_i^{th} entry in the ordered list. If two observations are equal, then assign each the average of their ranks.

- Compute the sum of the ranks from the first sample T_x.

- Compute the test statistic $z = \dfrac{T_x - \frac{m(N+1)}{2}}{\sqrt{\frac{mn(N+1)}{12}}}$.

- If $|z| > z_{\alpha/2}$, then reject the hypothesis. If $|z| \le z_{\alpha/2}$, then do not reject the hypothesis.

12. Mann–Whitney–Wilcoxon test of the hypothesis $M_x = M_y$ against the alternative $M_x > M_y$ (or $M_x < M_y$) of the medians of independent samples, large sample:

- Determine the critical value z_α such that $\Phi(z_\alpha) = 1 - \alpha$, where $\Phi(z)$ is the standard normal distribution.

- Pool the $N = m + n$ observations, but keep track of which sample the observation was drawn from.

- Order the pooled observations from smallest to largest, assigning rank 1 to the smallest and rank N to the largest; an observation has rank r_i if it is the r_i^{th} entry in the ordered list. If two observations are equal, then assign each the average of their ranks.

- Compute the sum of the ranks from the first sample T_x.

- Compute the test statistic $z = \dfrac{T_x - \frac{m(N+1)}{2}}{\sqrt{\frac{mn(N+1)}{12}}}$. (For the alternative $M_x < M_y$, multiply the test statistic by -1.)

- If $|z| > z_\alpha$, then reject the hypothesis. If $|z| \le z_\alpha$, then do not reject the hypothesis.

13. Wilcoxon signed rank test of the hypothesis $M_x = M_y$ against the alternative $M_x \ne M_y$ of the medians of paired samples, large sample:

- Determine the critical value $z_{\alpha/2}$ such that $\Phi(z_{\alpha/2}) = 1 - \alpha/2$, where $\Phi(z)$ is the standard normal distribution.

- Compute the paired differences $d_i = x_i - y_i$, for $i = 1, 2, \ldots, n$.

- Compute the quantities $|d_i|$ and keep track of the sign of d_i. If $d_i = 0$, then remove it from the list and reduce n by one.

- Order the $|d_i|$ from smallest to largest, assigning rank 1 to the smallest and rank n to the largest; $|d_i|$ has rank r_i if it is the r_i^{th} entry in the ordered list. If $|d_i| = |d_j|$, then assign each the average of their ranks.

- Compute the sum of the signed ranks $R = \sum\limits_{i=1}^{n} \mathrm{sign}(d_i)\, r_i$.

- Compute the test statistic $z = \dfrac{R}{\sqrt{\dfrac{n(n+1)(2n+1)}{6}}}$.

- If $|z| > z_{\alpha/2}$, then reject the hypothesis. If $|z| \le z_{\alpha/2}$, then do not reject the hypothesis.

14. Wilcoxon signed rank test of the hypothesis $M_x = M_y$ against the alternative $M_x > M_y$ (or $M_x < M_y$) of the medians of paired samples, large sample:

- Determine the critical value z_α such that $\Phi(z_\alpha) = 1 - \alpha$, where $\Phi(z)$ is the standard normal distribution.

- Compute the paired differences $d_i = x_i - y_i$, for $i = 1, 2, \ldots, n$.

- Compute the quantities $|d_i|$ and keep track of the sign of d_i. If $d_i = 0$, then remove it from the list and reduce n by one.

- Order the $|d_i|$ from smallest to largest, assigning rank 1 to the smallest and rank n to the largest; $|d_i|$ has rank r_i if it is the r_i^{th} entry in the ordered list. If $|d_i| = |d_j|$, then assign each the average of their ranks.

- Compute the sum of the signed ranks $R = \displaystyle\sum_{i=1}^{n} \text{sign}(d_i)\, r_i$.

- Compute the test statistic $z = \dfrac{R}{\sqrt{\dfrac{n(n+1)(2n+1)}{6}}}$. (For the alternative $M_x < M_y$, multiply the test statistic by -1.)

- If $z > z_\alpha$, then reject the hypothesis. If $z \le z_\alpha$, then do not reject the hypothesis.

15. Test of the hypothesis $\sigma_x^2 = \sigma_y^2$ against the alternative $\sigma_x^2 \ne \sigma_y^2$ (or $\sigma_x^2 > \sigma_y^2$) of the variances of independent normal samples:

- Determine the critical value $F_{\alpha/2}$ (F_α for the alternative $\sigma_x^2 > \sigma_y^2$) such that $F(F_{\alpha/2}) = 1 - \alpha/2$ ($F(F_\alpha) = 1 - \alpha$), where $F(F)$ is the F-distribution function with $n - 1$ and $m - 1$ degrees of freedom.

- Compute the standard deviations s_x and s_y of the samples.

- Compute the test statistic $F = \dfrac{s_x^2}{s_y^2}$. (For the two-sided test, put the larger value in the numerator.)

- If $F > F_{\alpha/2}$ ($F > F_\alpha$), then reject the hypothesis. If $F \le F_{\alpha/2}$ ($F \le F_\alpha$), then do not reject the hypothesis.

7.9.3   HYPOTHESIS TESTS: DISTRIBUTION OF A POPULATION

The following hypothesis tests assume a random sample of size n, given by $\{x_1, x_2, \ldots, x_n\}$.

1. Run test for randomness of a sample of binary values, large sample:

   - Determine the critical value $z_{\alpha/2}$ such that $\Phi\left(z_{\alpha/2}\right) = 1 - \alpha/2$, where $\Phi(z)$ is the standard normal distribution function.

   - Since the data are binary, denote the possible values of x_i by 0 and 1. Count the total number of zeros, and call this n_1; count the total number of ones, and call this n_2. Group the data into maximal sub-sequences of zeros and ones, and call each such sub-sequence a run. Let R be the number of runs in the sample.

   - Compute $\mu_R = \dfrac{2n_1 n_2}{n_1 + n_2} + 1$, and $\sigma_R^2 = \dfrac{(\mu_R - 1)(\mu_R - 2)}{n_1 + n_2 - 1}$.

   - Compute the test statistic $z = \dfrac{R - \mu_R}{\sigma_R}$.

   - If $|z| > z_{\alpha/2}$, then reject the hypothesis. If $|z| \le z_{\alpha/2}$, then do not reject the hypothesis.

2. Run test for randomness against an alternative that a trend is present in a sample of binary values, large sample:

   - Determine the critical value z_α such that $\Phi(z_\alpha) = 1 - \alpha$, where $\Phi(z)$ is the standard normal distribution function.

   - Since the data are binary, denote the possible values of x_i by 0 and 1. Count the total number of zeros, and call this n_1; count the total number of ones, and call this n_2. Group the data into maximal sub-sequences of zeros and ones, and call each such sub-sequence a run. Let R be the number of runs in the sample.

   - Compute $\mu_R = \dfrac{2n_1 n_2}{n_1 + n_2} + 1$, and $\sigma_R^2 = \dfrac{(\mu_R - 1)(\mu_R - 2)}{n_1 + n_2 - 1}$.

   - Compute the test statistic $z = \dfrac{R - \mu_R}{\sigma_R}$.

   - If $z < -z_\alpha$, then reject the hypothesis (this suggests the presence of a trend in the data). If $z \ge -z_\alpha$, then do not reject the hypothesis.

3. Run test for randomness against an alternative that the data are periodic for a sample of binary values, large sample:

   - Determine the critical value z_α such that $\Phi(z_\alpha) = 1 - \alpha$, where $\Phi(z)$ is the standard normal distribution function.

   - Since the data are binary, denote the possible values of x_i by 0 and 1. Count the total number of zeros, and call this n_1; count the total number of ones, and call this n_2. Group the data into maximal sub-sequences of zeros and ones, and call each such sub-sequence a run. Let R be the number of runs in the sample.

- Compute $\mu_R = \dfrac{2n_1 n_2}{n_1 + n_2} + 1$, and $\sigma_R^2 = \dfrac{(\mu_R - 1)(\mu_R - 2)}{n_1 + n_2 - 1}$.

- Compute the test statistic $z = \dfrac{R - \mu_R}{\sigma_R}$.

- If $z > z_\alpha$, then reject the hypothesis (this suggests the data are periodic). If $z \le z_\alpha$, then do not reject the hypothesis.

4. Chi-square test that the data are drawn from a specific k-parameter multinomial distribution, large sample:

- Determine the critical value χ_α^2 such that $F\left(\chi_\alpha^2\right) = 1 - \alpha$, where $F(x)$ is the chi-square distribution with $k - 1$ degrees of freedom.

- The k-parameter multinomial has k possible outcomes $A_1, A_2, \ldots, A_k$ with probabilities $p_1, p_2, \ldots, p_k$. For $i = 1, 2, \ldots, k$, compute n_i, the number of x_js corresponding to A_i.

- For $i = 1, 2, \ldots, k$, compute the sample multinomial parameters $\hat{p}_i = n_i / n$.

- Compute the test statistic $\chi^2 = \displaystyle\sum_{i=1}^{k} \dfrac{(n_i - np_i)^2}{np_i}$.

- If $\chi^2 > \chi_\alpha^2$, then reject the hypothesis. If $\chi^2 \le \chi_\alpha^2$, then do not reject the hypothesis.

5. Chi-square test for independence of attributes A and B having possible outcomes $A_1, A_2, \ldots, A_k$ and $B_1, B_2, \ldots, B_m$:

- Determine the critical value χ_α^2 such that $F\left(\chi_\alpha^2\right) = 1 - \alpha$, where $F(x)$ is the chi-square distribution with $(k - 1)(m - 1)$ degrees of freedom.

- For $i = 1, 2, \ldots, k$ and $j = 1, 2, \ldots, m$, define o_{ij} to be the number of observations having attributes A_i and B_j, and define $o_{i\cdot} = \displaystyle\sum_{j=1}^{m} o_{ij}$ and $o_{\cdot j} = \sum_{i=1}^{k} o_{ij}$.

- The variables defined above are often collected into a table, called a contingency table:

Attribute	B_1	B_2	$\cdots$	B_m	Totals
A_1	o_{11}	o_{12}	$\cdots$	o_{1m}	$o_{1\cdot}$
A_2	o_{21}	o_{22}	$\cdots$	o_{2m}	$o_{2\cdot}$
$\vdots$	$\vdots$	$\vdots$	$\ddots$	$\vdots$	$\vdots$
A_k	o_{k1}	o_{k2}	$\cdots$	o_{km}	$o_{k\cdot}$
Totals	$o_{\cdot 1}$	$o_{\cdot 2}$	$\cdots$	$o_{\cdot m}$	n

- For $i = 1, 2, \ldots, k$ and $j = 1, 2, \ldots, m$, compute the sample mean number of observations in the ij^{th} cell of the contingency table $e_{ij} = \dfrac{o_{i}.o._{j}}{n}$.

- Compute the test statistic, $\chi^2 = \displaystyle\sum_{i=1}^{k} \sum_{j=1}^{m} \dfrac{\left(o_{ij} - e_{ij}\right)^2}{e_{ij}}$.

- If $\chi^2 > \chi_\alpha^2$, then reject the hypothesis (that is, conclude that the attributes are not independent). If $\chi^2 \le \chi_\alpha^2$, then do not reject the hypothesis.

6. Kolmogorov–Smirnov test that $F_0(x)$ is the distribution of the population from which the sample was drawn:

- Determine the critical value D_α such that $Q\left(D_\alpha\right) = 1 - \alpha$, where $Q\left(D\right)$ is the distribution function for the Kolmogorov–Smirnov test statistic D.

- Compute the sample distribution function $\hat{F}(x)$.

- Compute the test statistic, given the maximum deviation of the sample and target distribution functions $D = \max\left|\hat{F}(x) - F_0(x)\right|$.

- If $D > D_\alpha$, then reject the hypothesis (this suggests the data are periodic). If $D \le D_\alpha$, then do not reject the hypothesis.

7.9.4 HYPOTHESIS TESTS: DISTRIBUTIONS OF TWO POPULATIONS

The following hypothesis tests assume a random sample of size n, given by $\{x_1, x_2, \ldots, x_n\}$, and a random sample of size m, given by $\{y_1, y_2, \ldots, y_m\}$.

1. Chi-square test that two k-parameter multinomial distributions are equal, large sample:

- Determine the critical value χ_α^2 such that $F\left(\chi_\alpha^2\right) = 1 - \alpha$, where $F\left(x\right)$ is the chi-square distribution with $k - 1$ degrees of freedom.

- The k-parameter multinomials have k possible outcomes $A_1, A_2, \ldots, A_k$. For $i = 1, 2, \ldots, k$, compute n_i, the number of x_js corresponding to A_i, and compute m_i, the number of y_js corresponding to A_i.

- For $i = 1, 2, \ldots, k$, compute the sample multinomial parameters $\hat{p}_i = \dfrac{n_i + m_i}{n + m}$.

- Compute the test statistic,

$$\chi^2 = \sum_{i=1}^{k} \frac{(n_i - n\hat{p}_i)^2}{n\hat{p}_i} + \sum_{i=1}^{k} \frac{(m_i - m\hat{p}_i)^2}{m\hat{p}_i}. \tag{7.9.1}$$

- If $\chi^2 > \chi_\alpha^2$, then reject the hypothesis. If $\chi^2 \le \chi_\alpha^2$, then do not reject the hypothesis.

2. Mann–Whitney–Wilcoxon test for equality of independent continuous distributions, large sample:

- Determine the critical value $z_{\alpha/2}$ such that $\Phi\left(z_{\alpha/2}\right) = 1 - \alpha$, where $\Phi(z)$ is the normal distribution function.

- For $i = 1, 2, \ldots, n$ and $j = 1, 2, \ldots, m$, define $S_{ij} = 1$ if $x_i < y_j$ and $S_{ij} = 0$ if $x_i > y_j$.

- Compute $U = \sum_{i=1}^{n} \sum_{j=1}^{m} S_{ij}$.

- Compute the test statistic $z = \dfrac{U - \frac{mn}{2}}{\sqrt{\frac{mn(m+n+1)}{12}}}$.

- If $|z| > z_{\alpha/2}$, then reject the hypothesis. If $|z| \leq z_{\alpha/2}$, then do not reject the hypothesis.

3. Spearman rank correlation coefficient for independence of paired samples, large sample:

- Determine the critical value $R_{\alpha/2}$ such that $F\left(R_{\alpha/2}\right) = 1 - \alpha$, where $F(R)$ is the distribution function for the Spearman rank correlation coefficient.

- The samples are ordered, with the smallest x_i assigned the rank r_1 and the largest assigned the rank r_n; for $i = 1, 2, \ldots, n$, x_i is assigned rank r_i if it occupies the ith position in the ordered list. Similarly the y_is are assigned ranks s_i. In case of a tie within a sample, the ranks are averaged.

- Compute the test statistic

$$R = \frac{n \sum_{i=1}^{n} r_i s_i - \left(\sum_{i=1}^{n} r_i\right)\left(\sum_{i=1}^{n} s_i\right)}{\sqrt{\left(n \sum_{i=1}^{n} r_i^2 - \left(\sum_{i=1}^{n} r_i\right)^2\right)\left(n \sum_{i=1}^{n} s_i^2 - \left(\sum_{i=1}^{n} s_i\right)^2\right)}}.$$

- If $|R| > R_{\alpha/2}$, then reject the hypothesis. If $|R| \leq R_{\alpha/2}$, then do not reject the hypothesis.

7.9.5   SEQUENTIAL PROBABILITY RATIO TESTS

Given two simple hypotheses and m observations, compute:

- $P_{0m} = \text{Prob (observations} \mid H_0)$.
- $P_{1m} = \text{Prob (observations} \mid H_1)$.
- $v_m = P_{1m}/P_{0m}$.

and then make one of the following decisions:

- If $v_m \geq \dfrac{1-\beta}{\alpha}$ then reject H_0.

- If $v_m \leq \dfrac{\beta}{1-\alpha}$ then reject H_1.

- If $\dfrac{\beta}{1-\alpha} < v_m < \dfrac{1-\beta}{\alpha}$ then make another observation.

Hence, the number of samples taken is not fixed *a priori*, but determined as sampling occurs. For example:

- Let θ denote the fraction of defective items. Two simple hypotheses are H_0: $\theta = \theta_0 = 0.05$ and H_1: $\theta = \theta_1 = 0.15$. Choose $\alpha = 5\%$ and $\beta = 10\%$ (i.e., reject lot with $\theta = \theta_0$ about 5% of the time; accept lot with $\theta = \theta_1$ about 10% of the time). If, after m observations, there are d defective items, then

$$P_{im} = \binom{m}{d}\theta_i^d (1-\theta_i)^{m-d} \quad \text{and} \quad v_m = \left(\frac{\theta_1}{\theta_0}\right)^d \left(\frac{1-\theta_1}{1-\theta_0}\right)^{m-d}$$

or $v_m = 3^d (0.895)^{m-d}$, using the above numbers. The critical values are $\dfrac{\beta}{1-\alpha} = 0.105$ and $\dfrac{1-\beta}{\alpha} = 18$. The decision to perform another observation depends on whether or not

$$0.105 \leq 3^d (0.895)^{m-d} \leq 18.$$

Taking logarithms, a $(m-d, d)$ control chart can be drawn with the following lines: $d = 0.101(m-d) - 2.049$ and $d = 0.101(m-d) + 2.63$. On the figure below, a sample path leading to rejection of H_0 has been indicated:

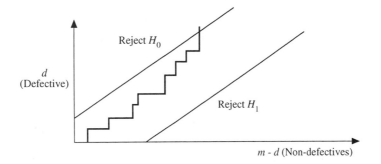

- Let X be normally distributed with unknown mean μ and known standard deviation σ. Consider the two simple hypotheses, $H_0 : \mu = \mu_0$ and $H_1 : \mu = \mu_1$. If Y is the sum of the first m observations of X, then a (Y, m) control chart is constructed with the two lines:

$$Y = \frac{\mu_0 + \mu_1}{2}m + \frac{\sigma^2}{\mu_1 - \mu_0}\log\frac{\beta}{1-\alpha},$$

$$Y = \frac{\mu_0 + \mu_1}{2}m + \frac{\sigma^2}{\mu_1 - \mu_0}\log\frac{1-\beta}{\alpha}. \tag{7.9.2}$$

7.10   LINEAR REGRESSION

1. The general linear statistical model assumes that the observed data values $\{y_1, y_2, \ldots, y_m\}$ are of the form

$$y_i = \beta_0 + \beta_1 x_{i1} + \beta_2 x_{i2} + \cdots + \beta_n x_{in} + \epsilon_i, \qquad (7.10.1)$$

for $i = 1, 2, \ldots, m$.

2. For $i = 1, 2, \ldots, m$ and $j = 1, 2, \ldots, n$, the independent variables x_{ij} are known (nonrandom).

3. $\{\beta_0, \beta_1, \beta_2, \cdots, \beta_n\}$ are unknown parameters.

4. For each i, ϵ_i is a zero-mean normal random variable with unknown variance σ^2.

7.10.1   LINEAR MODEL $y = \beta_0 + \beta_1 x + \epsilon$

1. Point estimate of β_1:

$$\hat{\beta}_1 = \frac{m \sum_{i=1}^{m} x_i y_i - \left(\sum_{i=1}^{m} x_i \right) \left(\sum_{i=1}^{m} y_i \right)}{m \left(\sum_{i=1}^{m} x_i^2 \right) - \left(\sum_{i=1}^{m} x_i \right)^2}. \qquad (7.10.2)$$

2. Point estimate of β_0:

$$\hat{\beta}_0 = \bar{y} - \hat{\beta}_1 \bar{x}. \qquad (7.10.3)$$

3. Point estimate of the correlation coefficient:

$$r = \hat{\rho} = \frac{m \sum_{i=1}^{m} x_i y_i - \left(\sum_{i=1}^{m} x_i \right) \left(\sum_{i=1}^{m} y_i \right)}{\sqrt{m \left(\sum_{i=1}^{m} x_i^2 \right) - \left(\sum_{i=1}^{m} x_i \right)^2} \sqrt{m \left(\sum_{i=1}^{m} y_i^2 \right) - \left(\sum_{i=1}^{m} y_i \right)^2}}. $$

$$\qquad (7.10.4)$$

4. Point estimate of error variance σ^2:

$$\hat{\sigma}^2 = \frac{\sum_{i=1}^{m} \left(y_i - \hat{\beta}_0 - \hat{\beta}_1 x_i \right)^2}{m - 2}. \qquad (7.10.5)$$

5. The standard error of the estimate is defined as $s_e = \sqrt{\hat{\sigma}^2}$.

6. Least-squares regression line: $\hat{y} = \hat{\beta}_0 + \hat{\beta}_1 x$.

7. Confidence interval for β_0:

   - Determine the critical value $t_{\alpha/2}$ such that $F\left(t_{\alpha/2}\right) = 1 - \alpha/2$, where $F(t)$ is the t-distribution with $m - 2$ degrees of freedom.

   - Compute the point estimate $\hat{\beta}_0$.

- Compute $k = t_{\alpha/2}s_e\sqrt{\dfrac{1}{m} + \dfrac{\bar{x}^2}{\sum_{i=1}^{m}(x_i - \bar{x})^2}}$.
- The $100(1-\alpha)$ percent confidence interval for β_0 is given by $\left[\hat{\beta}_0 - k, \hat{\beta}_0 + k\right]$.

8. Confidence interval for β_1:

- Determine the critical value $t_{\alpha/2}$ such that $F\left(t_{\alpha/2}\right) = 1 - \alpha/2$, where $F(t)$ is the t-distribution with $m - 2$ degrees of freedom.
- Compute the point estimate $\hat{\beta}_1$.
- Compute $k = t_{\alpha/2}\dfrac{s_e}{\sqrt{\sum_{i=1}^{m}(x_i - \bar{x})^2}}$.
- The $100(1-\alpha)$ percent confidence interval for β_1 is given by $\left[\hat{\beta}_1 - k, \hat{\beta}_1 + k\right]$.

9. Confidence interval for σ^2:

- Determine the critical values $\chi^2_{\alpha/2}$ and $\chi^2_{1-\alpha/2}$ such that $F\left(\chi^2_{\alpha/2}\right) = 1 - \alpha/2$ and $F\left(\chi^2_{1-\alpha/2}\right) = \alpha/2$, where $F(z)$ is the chi-square distribution function with $m - 2$ degrees of freedom.
- Compute the point estimate $\hat{\sigma}^2$.
- Compute $k_1 = \dfrac{(n-2)\hat{\sigma}^2}{\chi^2_{\alpha/2}}$ and $k_2 = \dfrac{(n-2)\hat{\sigma}^2}{\chi^2_{1-\alpha/2}}$.
- The $100(1-\alpha)$ percent confidence interval for σ^2 is given by $[k_1, k_2]$.

10. Confidence interval (predictive interval) for y, given x_0:

- Determine the critical value $t_{\alpha/2}$ such that $F\left(t_{\alpha/2}\right) = 1 - \alpha/2$, where $F(t)$ is the t-distribution with $m - 2$ degrees of freedom.
- Compute the point estimates $\hat{\beta}_0$, $\hat{\beta}_1$, and s_e.
- Compute $k = t_{\alpha/2}s_e\sqrt{\dfrac{1}{m} + \dfrac{(x_0 - \bar{x})^2}{\sum_{i=1}^{m}(x_i - \bar{x})^2}}$ and $\hat{y} = \hat{\beta}_0 + \hat{\beta}_1 x_0$.
- The $100(1-\alpha)$ percent confidence interval for β_1 is given by $[\hat{y} - k, \hat{y} + k]$.

11. Test of the hypothesis $\beta_1 = 0$ against the alternative $\beta_1 \neq 0$:

- Determine the critical value $t_{\alpha/2}$ such that $F\left(t_{\alpha/2}\right) = 1 - \alpha/2$, where $F(t)$ is the t-distribution with $m - 2$ degrees of freedom.
- Compute the point estimates $\hat{\beta}_1$ and s_e.
- Compute the test statistic $t = \dfrac{\hat{\beta}_1}{s_e}\sqrt{\sum_{i=1}^{m}(x_i - \bar{x})^2}$.
- If $|t| > t_{\alpha/2}$, then reject the hypothesis. If $|t| \leq t_{\alpha/2}$, then do not reject the hypothesis.

7.10.2   GENERAL MODEL $y = \beta_0 + \beta_1 x_1 + \beta_2 x_2 + \cdots + \beta_n x_n + \epsilon$

1. The m equations $(i = 1, 2, \ldots, m)$

$$y_i = \beta_0 + \beta_1 x_{i1} + \beta_2 x_{i2} + \cdots + \beta_n x_{in} + \epsilon_i \qquad (7.10.6)$$

can be written in matrix notation as $\mathbf{y} = \mathbf{X}\boldsymbol{\beta} + \boldsymbol{\epsilon}$ where

$$\mathbf{y} = \begin{bmatrix} y_1 \\ y_2 \\ \vdots \\ y_m \end{bmatrix}, \qquad \boldsymbol{\beta} = \begin{bmatrix} \beta_0 \\ \beta_1 \\ \vdots \\ \beta_n \end{bmatrix}, \qquad \boldsymbol{\epsilon} = \begin{bmatrix} \epsilon_1 \\ \epsilon_2 \\ \vdots \\ \epsilon_m \end{bmatrix}, \qquad (7.10.7)$$

and

$$\mathbf{X} = \begin{bmatrix} 1 & x_{11} & x_{12} & \cdots & x_{1n} \\ 1 & x_{21} & x_{22} & \cdots & x_{2n} \\ \vdots & \vdots & \vdots & \ddots & \vdots \\ 1 & x_{m1} & x_{m2} & \cdots & x_{mn} \end{bmatrix}. \qquad (7.10.8)$$

2. Throughout the remainder of the section, we assume $\mathbf{X}$ has full column rank.
3. The least-squares estimate $\hat{\boldsymbol{\beta}}$ satisfies the *normal equations* $\mathbf{X}^T\mathbf{X}\hat{\boldsymbol{\beta}} = \mathbf{X}^T\mathbf{y}$. That is, $\hat{\boldsymbol{\beta}} = \left(\mathbf{X}^T\mathbf{X}\right)^{-1} \mathbf{X}^T\mathbf{y}$.
4. Point estimator of σ^2:

$$\hat{\sigma}^2 = \frac{1}{m - n - 1} \left(\mathbf{y}^T\mathbf{y} - \hat{\boldsymbol{\beta}}^T (\mathbf{X}^T\mathbf{y}) \right). \qquad (7.10.9)$$

5. The standard error of the estimate is defined as $s_e = \sqrt{\hat{\sigma}^2}$.
6. Least-squares regression line: $\hat{y} = \mathbf{x}^T\hat{\boldsymbol{\beta}}$.
7. In the following, let c_{ij} denote the $(i, j)^{\text{th}}$ entry in the matrix $\left(\mathbf{X}^T\mathbf{X}\right)^{-1}$.
8. Confidence interval for β_i:

   - Determine the critical value $t_{\alpha/2}$ such that $F\left(t_{\alpha/2}\right) = 1 - \alpha/2$, where $F(t)$ is the t-distribution with $m - n - 1$ degrees of freedom.
   - Compute the point estimate $\hat{\beta}_i$ by solving the normal equations, and compute s_e.
   - Compute $k_i = t_{\alpha/2} s_e \sqrt{c_{ii}}$.
   - The $100(1-\alpha)$ percent confidence interval for β_i is given by $\left[\hat{\beta}_i - k_i, \hat{\beta}_i + k_i\right]$.

9. Confidence interval for σ^2:

   - Determine the critical values $\chi^2_{\alpha/2}$ and $\chi^2_{1-\alpha/2}$ such that $F\left(\chi^2_{\alpha/2}\right) = 1 - \alpha/2$ and $F\left(\chi^2_{1-\alpha/2}\right) = \alpha/2$, where $F(z)$ is the chi-square distribution function with $m - n - 1$ degrees of freedom.

- Compute the point estimate $\hat{\sigma}^2$.

- Compute $k_1 = \dfrac{(m - n - 1)\hat{\sigma}^2}{\chi^2_{\alpha/2}}$ and $k_2 = \dfrac{(m - n - 1)\hat{\sigma}^2}{\chi^2_{1-\alpha/2}}$.

- The $100(1 - \alpha)$ percent confidence interval for σ^2 is given by $[k_1, k_2]$.

10. Confidence interval (predictive interval) for y, given $\mathbf{x}_0$:

- Determine the critical value $t_{\alpha/2}$ such that $F\left(t_{\alpha/2}\right) = 1 - \alpha/2$, where $F(t)$ is the t-distribution with $m - 2$ degrees of freedom.

- Compute the point estimate $\hat{\beta}_i$ by solving the normal equations, and compute s_e.

- Compute $k = t_{\alpha/2}\, s_e \sqrt{1 + \mathbf{x}_0^{\mathrm{T}} \left(\mathbf{X}^{\mathrm{T}}\mathbf{X}\right)^{-1} \mathbf{x}_0}$ and $\hat{y} = \mathbf{x}_0^{\mathrm{T}}\hat{\boldsymbol{\beta}}$.

- The $100(1-\alpha)$ percent confidence interval for β_1 is given by $[\hat{y} - k, \hat{y} + k]$.

11. Test of the hypothesis $\beta_i = 0$ against the alternative $\beta_i \neq 0$:

- Determine the critical value $t_{\alpha/2}$ such that $F\left(t_{\alpha/2}\right) = 1 - \alpha/2$, where $F(t)$ is the t-distribution with $m - n - 1$ degrees of freedom.

- Compute the point estimates $\hat{\beta}_i$ and s_e by solving the normal equations.

- Compute the test statistic $t = \dfrac{\hat{\beta}_i}{s_e\sqrt{c_{ii}}}$.

- If $|t| > t_{\alpha/2}$, then reject the hypothesis. If $|t| \leq t_{\alpha/2}$, then do not reject the hypothesis.

7.11 ANALYSIS OF VARIANCE (ANOVA)

7.11.1 ONE-FACTOR ANOVA

1. Suppose we have k samples from k populations, with the jth population consisting of n_j observations,

$$y_{11}, y_{21}, \ldots, y_{n_1 1}$$
$$y_{12}, y_{22}, \ldots, y_{n_2 2}$$
$$\vdots$$
$$y_{1k}, y_{2k}, \ldots, y_{n_k k}.$$

2. One-factor model:

- The one-factor ANOVA assumes that the ith observation from the jth sample is of the form $y_{ij} = \mu + \tau_j + e_{ij}$.

- For $j = 1, 2, \ldots, k$, the parameter $\mu_j = \mu + \tau_j$ is the unknown mean of the jth population, and $\sum_{j=1}^{k} \tau_j = 0$.

- For $j = 1, 2, \ldots, k$ and $i = 1, 2, \ldots, n_j$, the random variable e_{ij} is normally distributed with mean zero and variance σ^2.

- For $j = 1, 2, \ldots, k$ and $i = 1, 2, \ldots, n_j$, the random variables e_{ij} are independent.

- The total number of observations is $n = n_1 + n_2 + \cdots + n_k$.

3. Point estimates of means:

- Total sample mean $\hat{y} = \dfrac{1}{n} \sum_{j=1}^{k} \sum_{i=1}^{n_j} y_{ij}$.

- Sample mean of jth sample $\hat{y}_j = \dfrac{1}{n_j} \sum_{i=1}^{n_j} y_{ij}$.

4. Sums of squares:

- Sum of squares between samples $\text{SS}_b = \sum_{j=1}^{k} n_j \left(\hat{y}_j - \hat{y} \right)^2$.

- Sum of squares within samples $\text{SS}_w = \sum_{j=1}^{k} \sum_{i=1}^{n_j} \left(y_{ij} - \hat{y}_j \right)^2$.

- Total sum of squares Total $\text{SS} = \sum_{j=1}^{k} \sum_{i=1}^{n_j} \left(y_{ij} - \hat{y} \right)^2$.

- Partition of total sum of squares Total $\text{SS} = \text{SS}_b + \text{SS}_w$.

5. Degrees of freedom:

- Between samples, $k - 1$.

- Within samples, $n - k$.

- Total, $n - 1$.

6. Mean squares:

   - Obtained by dividing sums of squares by their respective degrees of freedom.

   - Between samples, $MS_b = \dfrac{SS_b}{k-1}$.

   - Within samples (also called the residual mean square),
   $$MS_w = \frac{SS_w}{n-k}.$$

7. Test of the hypothesis $\mu_1 = \mu_2 = \cdots = \mu_k$ against the alternative $\mu_i \neq \mu_j$ for some i and j; equivalently, test the null hypothesis $\tau_1 = \tau_2 = \cdots = \tau_k = 0$ against the hypothesis $\tau_j \neq 0$ for some j:

   - Determine the critical value F_α such that $F(F_\alpha) = 1 - \alpha$, where $F(F)$ is the F-distribution with $k-1$ and $n-k$ degrees of freedom.

   - Compute the point estimates $\hat{y}$ and $\hat{y}_j$ for $j = 1, 2, \ldots, k$.

   - Compute the sums of squares SS_b and SS_w.

   - Compute the mean squares MS_b and MS_w.

   - Compute the test statistic $F = \dfrac{MS_b}{MS_w}$.

   - If $F > F_\alpha$, then reject the hypothesis. If $F \leq F_\alpha$, then do not reject the hypothesis.

   - The above computations are often organized into an ANOVA table:

Source	SS	D.O.F.	MS	F Ratio
Between samples	SS_b	$k-1$	MS_b	$F = \frac{MS_b}{MS_w}$
Within samples	SS_w	$n-k$	MS_w	
Total	Total SS	$n-1$		

8. Confidence interval for $\mu_i - \mu_j$, for $i \neq j$:

   - Determine the critical value $t_{\alpha/2}$ such that $F(t_{\alpha/2}) = 1 - \alpha/2$, where $F(t)$ is the t-distribution with $n-k$ degrees of freedom.

   - Compute the point estimates $\hat{y}_i$ and $\hat{y}_j$.

   - Compute the residual mean square MS_w.

   - Compute $k = t_{\alpha/2} \sqrt{MS_w \left(\dfrac{1}{n_i} + \dfrac{1}{n_j} \right)}$.

   - The $100(1 - \alpha)$ percent confidence interval for $\mu_i - \mu_j$ is given by
   $$\left[(\hat{y}_i - y_j) - k, (\hat{y}_i - y_j) + k \right].$$

9. Confidence interval for contrast in the means, defined by $C = c_1\mu_1 + c_2\mu_2 + \cdots + c_k\mu_k$, where $c_1 + c_2 + \cdots + c_k = 0$:

- Determine the critical value F_α such that $F(F_\alpha) = 1 - \alpha$, where $F(F)$ is the F-distribution with $k - 1$ and $n - k$ degrees of freedom.
- Compute the point estimates $\hat{y}_j$ for $j = 1, 2, \ldots, k$.
- Compute the residual mean square $\mathrm{MS_w}$.
- Compute $k = \sqrt{F_\alpha \mathrm{MS_w} \left(\dfrac{k-1}{n} \displaystyle\sum_{j=1}^{k} c_j^2 \right)}$.
- The $100(1 - \alpha)$ percent confidence interval for the contrast C is given by
$$\left[\sum_{j=1}^{k} c_j \hat{y}_j - k, \sum_{j=1}^{k} c_j \hat{y}_j + k \right].$$

7.11.2   UNREPLICATED TWO-FACTOR ANOVA

1. Suppose we have a sample of observations y_{ij} indexed by two factors $i = 1, 2, \ldots, m$ and $j = 1, 2, \ldots, n$.

2. Unreplicated two-factor model:

   - The unreplicated two-factor ANOVA assumes that the ij^{th} observation is of the form $y_{ij} = \mu + \beta_i + \tau_j + e_{ij}$.
   - μ is the overall mean, β_i is the ith differential effect of factor one, τ_j is the j differential effect of factor two, and
   $$\sum_{i=1}^{m} \beta_i = \sum_{j=1}^{n} \tau_j = 0.$$
   - For $i = 1, 2, \ldots, m$ and $j = 1, 2, \ldots, n$, the random variable e_{ij} is normally distributed with mean zero and variance σ^2.
   - For $j = 1, 2, \ldots, m$ and $j = 1, 2, \ldots, n$, the random variables e_{ij} are independent.
   - Total number of observations is mn.

3. Point estimates of means:

   - Total sample mean $\hat{y} = \dfrac{1}{mn} \displaystyle\sum_{i=1}^{m} \sum_{j=1}^{n} y_{ij}$.
   - i^{th} factor-one sample mean $\hat{y}_{i \cdot} = \dfrac{1}{n} \displaystyle\sum_{j=1}^{n} y_{ij}$.
   - j^{th} factor-two sample mean $\hat{y}_{\cdot j} = \dfrac{1}{m} \displaystyle\sum_{i=1}^{m} y_{ij}$.

4. Sums of squares:

- Factor-one sum of squares $SS_1 = n \sum_{i=1}^{m} (\hat{y}_{i\cdot} - \hat{y})^2$.

- Factor-two sum of squares $SS_2 = m \sum_{j=1}^{n} (\hat{y}_{\cdot j} - \hat{y})^2$.

- Residual sum of squares $SS_r = \sum_{i=1}^{m} \sum_{j=1}^{n} (y_{ij} - \hat{y}_{i\cdot} - \hat{y}_{\cdot j} + \hat{y})^2$.

- Total sum of squares Total $SS = \sum_{j=1}^{k} \sum_{i=1}^{n_j} (y_{ij} - \hat{y})^2$.

- Partition of total sum of squares Total $SS = SS_1 + SS_2 + SS_r$.

5. Degrees of freedom:

- Factor one, $m - 1$.
- Factor two, $n - 1$.
- Residual, $(m - 1)(n - 1)$.
- Total, $mn - 1$.

6. Mean squares:

- Obtained by dividing sums of squares by their respective degrees of freedom.
- Factor-one mean square $MS_1 = \dfrac{SS_1}{m - 1}$.
- Factor-two mean square $MS_2 = \dfrac{SS_2}{n - 1}$.
- Residual mean square $MS_r = \dfrac{SS_r}{(m - 1)(n - 1)}$.

7. Test of the null hypothesis $\beta_1 = \beta_2 = \cdots = \beta_m = 0$ (no factor-one effects) against the alternative hypothesis $\beta_i \neq 0$ for some i:

- Determine the critical value F_α such that $F(F_\alpha) = 1 - \alpha$, where $F(F)$ is the F-distribution with $m - 1$ and $(m - 1)(n - 1)$ degrees of freedom.
- Compute the point estimates $\hat{y}$ and $\hat{y}_{i\cdot}$ for $i = 1, 2, \ldots, m$.
- Compute the sums of squares SS_1 and SS_r.
- Compute the mean squares MS_1 and MS_r.
- Compute the test statistic $F = \dfrac{MS_1}{MS_r}$.
- If $F > F_\alpha$, then reject the hypothesis. If $F \leq F_\alpha$, then do not reject the hypothesis.

8. Test of the null hypothesis $\tau_1 = \tau_2 = \cdots = \tau_n = 0$ (no factor-two effects) against the alternative hypothesis $\tau_j \neq 0$ for some j:

   - Determine the critical value F_α such that $F(F_\alpha) = 1 - \alpha$, where $F(F)$ is the F-distribution with $n - 1$ and $(m - 1)(n - 1)$ degrees of freedom.

   - Compute the point estimates $\hat{y}$ and $\hat{y}_{.j}$ for $j = 1, 2, \ldots, n$.

   - Compute the sums of squares SS_2 and SS_r.

   - Compute the mean squares MS_2 and MS_r.

   - Compute the test statistic $F = \dfrac{MS_2}{MS_r}$.

   - If $F > F_\alpha$, then reject the hypothesis. If $F \leq F_\alpha$, then do not reject the hypothesis.

   - The above computations are often organized into an ANOVA table:

Source	SS	D.O.F.	MS	F Ratio
Factor one	SS_1	$m - 1$	MS_1	$F = \frac{MS_1}{MS_r}$
Factor two	SS_2	$n - 1$	MS_2	$F = \frac{MS_2}{MS_r}$
Residual	SS_r	$(m - 1)(n - 1)$	MS_r	
Total	Total SS	$mn - 1$		

9. Confidence interval for contrast in the factor-one means, defined by $C = c_1\beta_1 + c_2\beta_2 + \cdots + c_m\beta_m$, where $c_1 + c_2 + \cdots + c_m = 0$:

   - Determine the critical value F_α such that $F(F_\alpha) = 1 - \alpha$, where $F(F)$ is the F-distribution with $m - 1$ and $(m - 1)(n - 1)$ degrees of freedom.

   - Compute the point estimates $\hat{y}_{i.}$ for $i = 1, 2, \ldots, m$.

   - Compute the residual mean square MS_r.

   - Compute $k = \sqrt{F_\alpha MS_r \left(\dfrac{m - 1}{n} \displaystyle\sum_{i=1}^{m} c_i^2\right)}$.

   - The $100(1 - \alpha)$ percent confidence interval for the contrast C is given by

   $$\left[\sum_{i=1}^{m} c_i \hat{y}_{i.} - k, \ \sum_{i=1}^{m} c_i \hat{y}_{i.} + k\right].$$

10. Confidence interval for contrast in the factor-two means, defined by $C = c_1\tau_1 + c_2\tau_2 + \cdots + c_n\tau_n$, where $c_1 + c_2 + \cdots + c_n = 0$:

    - Determine the critical value F_α such that $F(F_\alpha) = 1 - \alpha$, where $F(F)$ is the F-distribution with $n - 1$ and $(m - 1)(n - 1)$ degrees of freedom.

    - Compute the point estimates $\hat{y}_{.j}$ for $j = 1, 2, \ldots, n$.

- Compute the residual mean square MS_r.

- Compute $k = \sqrt{F_\alpha MS_r \left(\dfrac{n-1}{m} \displaystyle\sum_{j=1}^{n} c_j^2 \right)}.$

- The $100(1 - \alpha)$ percent confidence interval for the contrast C is given by

$$\left[\sum_{j=1}^{n} c_j \hat{y}_{\cdot j} - k, \sum_{j=1}^{n} c_j \hat{y}_{\cdot j} + k \right].$$

7.11.3 REPLICATED TWO-FACTOR ANOVA

1. Suppose we have a sample of observations y_{ijk} indexed by two factors $i = 1, 2, \ldots, m$ and $j = 1, 2, \ldots, n$. Moreover, there are p observations per factor pair (i, j), indexed by $k = 1, 2, \ldots, p$.

2. Replicated two-factor model:

   - The replicated two-factor ANOVA assumes that the ijk^{th} observation is of the form $y_{ijk} = \mu + \beta_i + \tau_j + \gamma_{ij} + e_{ijk}$.

   - μ is the overall mean, β_i is the ith differential effect of factor one, τ_j is the j differential effect of factor two, and

$$\sum_{i=1}^{m} \beta_i = \sum_{j=1}^{n} \tau_j = 0.$$

   - For $i = 1, 2, \ldots, m$ and $j = 1, 2, \ldots, n$, γ_{ij} is the ij^{th} interaction effect of factors one and two.

   - For $i = 1, 2, \ldots, m$, $j = 1, 2, \ldots, n$, and $k = 1, 2, \ldots, p$, the random variable e_{ijk} is normally distributed with mean zero and variance σ^2.

   - For $j = 1, 2, \ldots, m$, $j = 1, 2, \ldots, n$, and $k = 1, 2, \ldots, p$, the random variables e_{ijk} are independent.

   - Total number of observations is mnp.

3. Point estimates of means:

   - Total sample mean $\hat{y} = \dfrac{1}{mnp} \displaystyle\sum_{i=1}^{m} \sum_{j=1}^{n} \sum_{k=1}^{p} y_{ijk}.$

   - i^{th} factor-one sample mean $\hat{y}_{i\cdot\cdot} = \dfrac{1}{np} \displaystyle\sum_{j=1}^{n} \sum_{k=1}^{p} y_{ijk}.$

   - j^{th} factor-two sample mean $\hat{y}_{\cdot j\cdot} = \dfrac{1}{mp} \displaystyle\sum_{i=1}^{m} \sum_{k=1}^{p} y_{ijk}.$

- ij^{th} interaction mean $\hat{y}_{ij\cdot} = \dfrac{1}{p} \displaystyle\sum_{k=1}^{p} y_{ijk}.$

4. Sums of squares:

- Factor-one sum of squares $SS_1 = np \displaystyle\sum_{i=1}^{m} (\hat{y}_{i\cdot\cdot} - \hat{y})^2.$

- Factor-two sum of squares $SS_2 = mp \displaystyle\sum_{j=1}^{n} (\hat{y}_{\cdot j\cdot} - \hat{y})^2.$

- Interaction sum of squares $SS_{12} = p \displaystyle\sum_{i=1}^{m} \sum_{j=1}^{n} (\hat{y}_{ij\cdot} - \hat{y})^2.$

- Residual sum of squares $SS_r = \displaystyle\sum_{i=1}^{m} \sum_{j=1}^{n} \sum_{k=1}^{p} (y_{ijk} - \hat{y}_{i\cdot\cdot} - \hat{y}_{\cdot j\cdot} + \hat{y})^2.$

- Total sum of squares Total $SS = \displaystyle\sum_{i=1}^{m} \sum_{j=1}^{n} \sum_{k=1}^{p} (y_{ijk} - \hat{y})^2.$

- Partition of total sum of squares Total $SS = SS_1 + SS_2 + SS_{12} + SS_r.$

5. Degrees of freedom:

- Factor one, $m - 1$.
- Factor two, $n - 1$.
- Interaction, $(m - 1)(n - 1)$.
- Residual, $mn(p - 1)$.
- Total, $mnp - 1$.

6. Mean squares:

- Obtained by dividing sums of squares by their respective degrees of freedom.
- Factor-one mean square $MS_1 = \dfrac{SS_1}{m - 1}.$
- Factor-two mean square $MS_2 = \dfrac{SS_2}{n - 1}.$
- Interaction mean square $MS_{12} = \dfrac{SS_{12}}{(m - 1)(n - 1)}.$
- Residual mean square $MS_r = \dfrac{SS_r}{mn(p - 1)}.$

7. Test of the null hypothesis $\beta_1 = \beta_2 = \cdots = \beta_m = 0$ (no factor-one effects) against the alternative hypothesis $\beta_i \neq 0$ for some i:

- Determine the critical value F_α such that $F(F_\alpha) = 1 - \alpha$, where $F(F)$ is the F-distribution with $m - 1$ and $mn(p - 1)$ degrees of freedom.
- Compute the point estimates $\hat{y}$ and $\hat{y}_{i..}$ for $i = 1, 2, \ldots, m$.
- Compute the sums of squares SS_1 and SS_r.
- Compute the mean squares MS_1 and MS_r.
- Compute the test statistic $F = \dfrac{MS_1}{MS_r}$.
- If $F > F_\alpha$, then reject the hypothesis. If $F \leq F_\alpha$, then do not reject the hypothesis.

8. Test of the null hypothesis $\tau_1 = \tau_2 = \cdots = \tau_n = 0$ (no factor-two effects) against the alternative hypothesis $\tau_j \neq 0$ for some j:

- Determine the critical value F_α such that $F(F_\alpha) = 1 - \alpha$, where $F(F)$ is the F-distribution with $n - 1$ and $mn(p - 1)$ degrees of freedom.
- Compute the point estimates $\hat{y}$ and $\hat{y}_{.j.}$ for $j = 1, 2, \ldots, n$.
- Compute the sums of squares SS_2 and SS_r.
- Compute the mean squares MS_2 and MS_r.
- Compute the test statistic $F = \dfrac{MS_2}{MS_r}$.
- If $F > F_\alpha$, then reject the hypothesis. If $F \leq F_\alpha$, then do not reject the hypothesis.

9. Test of the null hypothesis $\gamma_{ij} = 0$ for $i = 1, 2, \ldots, m$ and $j = 1, 2, \ldots, n$ (no factor-one effects) against the alternative hypothesis $\gamma_{ij} \neq 0$ for some i and j:

- Determine the critical value F_α such that $F(F_\alpha) = 1 - \alpha$, where $F(F)$ is the F-distribution with $(m-1)(n-1)$ and $mn(p-1)$ degrees of freedom.
- Compute the point estimates $\hat{y}$, $\hat{y}_{i..}$, $\hat{y}_{.j.}$, and $\hat{y}_{ij}$ for $i = 1, 2, \ldots, m$ and $j = 1, 2, \ldots, n$.
- Compute the sums of squares SS_{12} and SS_r.
- Compute the mean squares MS_{12} and MS_r.
- Compute the test statistic $F = \dfrac{MS_{12}}{MS_r}$.
- If $F > F_\alpha$, then reject the hypothesis. If $F \leq F_\alpha$, then do not reject the hypothesis.

• The above computations are often organized into an ANOVA table:

Source	SS	D.O.F.	MS	F Ratio
Factor one	SS_1	$m - 1$	MS_1	$F = MS_1/MS_r$
Factor two	SS_2	$n - 1$	MS_2	$F = MS_2/MS_r$
Interaction	SS_{12}	$(m - 1)(n - 1)$	MS_{12}	$F = MS_{12}/MS_r$
Residual	SS_r	$mn(p - 1)$	MS_r	
Total	Total SS	$mnp - 1$		

10. Confidence interval for contrast in the factor-one means, defined by $C = c_1\beta_1 + c_2\beta_2 + \cdots + c_m\beta_m$, where $c_1 + c_2 + \cdots + c_m = 0$:

   • Determine the critical value F_α such that $F(F_\alpha) = 1 - \alpha$, where $F(F)$ is the F-distribution with $m - 1$ and $mn(p - 1)$ degrees of freedom.

   • Compute the point estimates $\hat{y}_{i..}$ for $i = 1, 2, \ldots, m$.

   • Compute the residual mean square MS_r.

   • Compute $k = \sqrt{F_\alpha MS_r \left(\dfrac{m - 1}{np} \sum_{i=1}^{m} c_i^2 \right)}$.

   • The $100(1 - \alpha)$ percent confidence interval for the contrast C is given by

$$\left[\sum_{i=1}^{m} c_i \hat{y}_{i..} - k, \sum_{i=1}^{m} c_i \hat{y}_{i..} + k \right].$$

11. Confidence interval for contrast in the factor-two means, defined by $C = c_1\tau_1 + c_2\tau_2 + \cdots + c_n\tau_n$, where $c_1 + c_2 + \cdots + c_n = 0$:

   • Determine the critical value F_α such that $F(F_\alpha) = 1 - \alpha$, where $F(F)$ is the F-distribution with $n - 1$ and $mn(p - 1)$ degrees of freedom.

   • Compute the point estimates $\hat{y}_{.j.}$ for $j = 1, 2, \ldots, n$.

   • Compute the residual mean square MS_r.

   • Compute $k = \sqrt{F_\alpha MS_r \left(\dfrac{n - 1}{mp} \sum_{j=1}^{n} c_j^2 \right)}$.

   • The $100(1 - \alpha)$ percent confidence interval for the contrast C is given by

$$\left[\sum_{j=1}^{n} c_j \hat{y}_{.j.} - k, \sum_{j=1}^{n} c_j \hat{y}_{.j.} + k \right].$$

7.12 PROBABILITY TABLES

7.12.1 CRITICAL VALUES

The critical value

- z_α satisfies $\Phi(z_\alpha) = 1 - \alpha$ (where, as usual, $\Phi(z)$ is the distribution function for the standard normal).

- t_α satisfies $F(t_\alpha) = 1 - \alpha$ where $F(t)$ is the distribution function for the t-distribution (with some specified number of degrees of freedom).

- χ_α^2 satisfies $F(\chi_\alpha^2) = 1 - \alpha$ where $F(t)$ is the distribution function for the χ^2-distribution (with some specified number of degrees of freedom).

7.12.2 TABLE OF THE NORMAL DISTRIBUTION

For a standard normal random variable:

Limits		Proportional of the total area (%)	Remaining area (%)
$\mu - \lambda\sigma$	$\mu + \lambda\sigma$	(%)	(%)
$\mu - \sigma$	$\mu + \sigma$	68.26	31.74
$\mu - 1.65\sigma$	$\mu + 1.65\sigma$	90	10
$\mu - 1.96\sigma$	$\mu + 1.96\sigma$	95	5
$\mu - 2\sigma$	$\mu + 2\sigma$	95.44	4.56
$\mu - 2.58\sigma$	$\mu + 2.58\sigma$	99	1
$\mu - 3\sigma$	$\mu + 3\sigma$	99.73	0.27
$\mu - 3.09\sigma$	$\mu + 3.09\sigma$	99.8	0.2
$\mu - 3.29\sigma$	$\mu + 3.29\sigma$	99.9	0.1

x	1.282	1.645	1.960	2.326	2.576	3.090
$\Phi(x)$	0.90	0.95	0.975	0.99	0.995	0.999
$2[1 - \Phi(x)]$	0.20	0.10	0.05	0.02	0.01	0.002

x	3.09	3.72	4.26	4.75	5.20	5.61	6.00	6.36
$1 - \Phi(x)$	10^{-3}	10^{-4}	10^{-5}	10^{-6}	10^{-7}	10^{-8}	10^{-9}	10^{-10}

For large values of x:

$$\left[\frac{e^{-x^2/2}}{\sqrt{2\pi}}\left(\frac{1}{x} - \frac{1}{x^3}\right)\right] < 1 - \Phi(x) < \left[\frac{e^{-x^2/2}}{\sqrt{2\pi}}\left(\frac{1}{x}\right)\right]$$

x	$F(x)$	$1-F(x)$	$f(x)$	x	$F(x)$	$1-F(x)$	$f(x)$
0.00	0.5000	0.5000	0.3989	0.50	0.6915	0.3085	0.3521
0.01	0.5040	0.4960	0.3989	0.51	0.6950	0.3050	0.3503
0.02	0.5080	0.4920	0.3989	0.52	0.6985	0.3015	0.3485
0.03	0.5120	0.4880	0.3988	0.53	0.7019	0.2981	0.3467
0.04	0.5160	0.4840	0.3986	0.54	0.7054	0.2946	0.3448
0.05	0.5199	0.4801	0.3984	0.55	0.7088	0.2912	0.3429
0.06	0.5239	0.4761	0.3982	0.56	0.7123	0.2877	0.3411
0.07	0.5279	0.4721	0.3980	0.57	0.7157	0.2843	0.3391
0.08	0.5319	0.4681	0.3977	0.58	0.7190	0.2810	0.3372
0.09	0.5359	0.4641	0.3973	0.59	0.7224	0.2776	0.3352
0.10	0.5398	0.4602	0.3970	0.60	0.7258	0.2742	0.3332
0.11	0.5438	0.4562	0.3965	0.61	0.7291	0.2709	0.3312
0.12	0.5478	0.4522	0.3961	0.62	0.7324	0.2676	0.3292
0.13	0.5517	0.4483	0.3956	0.63	0.7357	0.2643	0.3271
0.14	0.5557	0.4443	0.3951	0.64	0.7389	0.2611	0.3251
0.15	0.5596	0.4404	0.3945	0.65	0.7421	0.2579	0.3230
0.16	0.5636	0.4364	0.3939	0.66	0.7454	0.2546	0.3209
0.17	0.5675	0.4325	0.3932	0.67	0.7486	0.2514	0.3187
0.18	0.5714	0.4286	0.3925	0.68	0.7518	0.2482	0.3166
0.19	0.5754	0.4247	0.3918	0.69	0.7549	0.2451	0.3144
0.20	0.5793	0.4207	0.3910	0.70	0.7580	0.2420	0.3123
0.21	0.5832	0.4168	0.3902	0.71	0.7611	0.2389	0.3101
0.22	0.5871	0.4129	0.3894	0.72	0.7642	0.2358	0.3079
0.23	0.5909	0.4091	0.3885	0.73	0.7673	0.2327	0.3056
0.24	0.5948	0.4052	0.3876	0.74	0.7703	0.2296	0.3034
0.25	0.5987	0.4013	0.3867	0.75	0.7734	0.2266	0.3011
0.26	0.6026	0.3974	0.3857	0.76	0.7764	0.2236	0.2989
0.27	0.6064	0.3936	0.3847	0.77	0.7793	0.2207	0.2966
0.28	0.6103	0.3897	0.3836	0.78	0.7823	0.2177	0.2943
0.29	0.6141	0.3859	0.3825	0.79	0.7852	0.2148	0.2920
0.30	0.6179	0.3821	0.3814	0.80	0.7881	0.2119	0.2897
0.31	0.6217	0.3783	0.3802	0.81	0.7910	0.2090	0.2874
0.32	0.6255	0.3745	0.3790	0.82	0.7939	0.2061	0.2850
0.33	0.6293	0.3707	0.3778	0.83	0.7967	0.2033	0.2827
0.34	0.6331	0.3669	0.3765	0.84	0.7995	0.2004	0.2803
0.35	0.6368	0.3632	0.3752	0.85	0.8023	0.1977	0.2780
0.36	0.6406	0.3594	0.3739	0.86	0.8051	0.1949	0.2756
0.37	0.6443	0.3557	0.3725	0.87	0.8078	0.1921	0.2732
0.38	0.6480	0.3520	0.3711	0.88	0.8106	0.1894	0.2709
0.39	0.6517	0.3483	0.3697	0.89	0.8133	0.1867	0.2685
0.40	0.6554	0.3446	0.3683	0.90	0.8159	0.1841	0.2661
0.41	0.6591	0.3409	0.3668	0.91	0.8186	0.1814	0.2637
0.42	0.6628	0.3372	0.3653	0.92	0.8212	0.1788	0.2613
0.43	0.6664	0.3336	0.3637	0.93	0.8238	0.1762	0.2589
0.44	0.6700	0.3300	0.3621	0.94	0.8264	0.1736	0.2565
0.45	0.6736	0.3264	0.3605	0.95	0.8289	0.1711	0.2541
0.46	0.6772	0.3228	0.3589	0.96	0.8315	0.1685	0.2516
0.47	0.6808	0.3192	0.3572	0.97	0.8340	0.1660	0.2492
0.48	0.6844	0.3156	0.3555	0.98	0.8365	0.1635	0.2468
0.49	0.6879	0.3121	0.3538	0.99	0.8389	0.1611	0.2444
0.50	0.6915	0.3085	0.3521	1.00	0.8413	0.1587	0.2420

x	$F(x)$	$1 - F(x)$	$f(x)$	x	$F(x)$	$1 - F(x)$	$f(x)$
1.00	0.8413	0.1587	0.2420	1.50	0.9332	0.0668	0.1295
1.01	0.8438	0.1562	0.2396	1.51	0.9345	0.0655	0.1276
1.02	0.8461	0.1539	0.2371	1.52	0.9357	0.0643	0.1257
1.03	0.8485	0.1515	0.2347	1.53	0.9370	0.0630	0.1238
1.04	0.8508	0.1492	0.2323	1.54	0.9382	0.0618	0.1219
1.05	0.8531	0.1469	0.2299	1.55	0.9394	0.0606	0.1200
1.06	0.8554	0.1446	0.2275	1.56	0.9406	0.0594	0.1182
1.07	0.8577	0.1423	0.2251	1.57	0.9418	0.0582	0.1163
1.08	0.8599	0.1401	0.2226	1.58	0.9429	0.0570	0.1145
1.09	0.8621	0.1379	0.2203	1.59	0.9441	0.0559	0.1127
1.10	0.8643	0.1357	0.2178	1.60	0.9452	0.0548	0.1109
1.11	0.8665	0.1335	0.2155	1.61	0.9463	0.0537	0.1091
1.12	0.8686	0.1314	0.2131	1.62	0.9474	0.0526	0.1074
1.13	0.8708	0.1292	0.2107	1.63	0.9485	0.0515	0.1057
1.14	0.8729	0.1271	0.2083	1.64	0.9495	0.0505	0.1040
1.15	0.8749	0.1251	0.2059	1.65	0.9505	0.0495	0.1023
1.16	0.8770	0.1230	0.2036	1.66	0.9515	0.0485	0.1006
1.17	0.8790	0.1210	0.2012	1.67	0.9525	0.0475	0.0989
1.18	0.8810	0.1190	0.1989	1.68	0.9535	0.0465	0.0973
1.19	0.8830	0.1170	0.1965	1.69	0.9545	0.0455	0.0957
1.20	0.8849	0.1151	0.1942	1.70	0.9554	0.0446	0.0940
1.21	0.8869	0.1131	0.1919	1.71	0.9564	0.0436	0.0925
1.22	0.8888	0.1112	0.1895	1.72	0.9573	0.0427	0.0909
1.23	0.8907	0.1094	0.1872	1.73	0.9582	0.0418	0.0893
1.24	0.8925	0.1075	0.1849	1.74	0.9591	0.0409	0.0878
1.25	0.8943	0.1056	0.1827	1.75	0.9599	0.0401	0.0863
1.26	0.8962	0.1038	0.1804	1.76	0.9608	0.0392	0.0848
1.27	0.8980	0.1020	0.1781	1.77	0.9616	0.0384	0.0833
1.28	0.8997	0.1003	0.1759	1.78	0.9625	0.0375	0.0818
1.29	0.9015	0.0985	0.1736	1.79	0.9633	0.0367	0.0804
1.30	0.9032	0.0968	0.1714	1.80	0.9641	0.0359	0.0790
1.31	0.9049	0.0951	0.1691	1.81	0.9648	0.0352	0.0775
1.32	0.9066	0.0934	0.1669	1.82	0.9656	0.0344	0.0761
1.33	0.9082	0.0918	0.1647	1.83	0.9664	0.0336	0.0748
1.34	0.9099	0.0901	0.1626	1.84	0.9671	0.0329	0.0734
1.35	0.9115	0.0885	0.1604	1.85	0.9678	0.0322	0.0721
1.36	0.9131	0.0869	0.1582	1.86	0.9686	0.0314	0.0707
1.37	0.9147	0.0853	0.1561	1.87	0.9693	0.0307	0.0694
1.38	0.9162	0.0838	0.1540	1.88	0.9699	0.0301	0.0681
1.39	0.9177	0.0823	0.1518	1.89	0.9706	0.0294	0.0669
1.40	0.9192	0.0808	0.1497	1.90	0.9713	0.0287	0.0656
1.41	0.9207	0.0793	0.1476	1.91	0.9719	0.0281	0.0644
1.42	0.9222	0.0778	0.1456	1.92	0.9726	0.0274	0.0632
1.43	0.9236	0.0764	0.1435	1.93	0.9732	0.0268	0.0619
1.44	0.9251	0.0749	0.1415	1.94	0.9738	0.0262	0.0608
1.45	0.9265	0.0735	0.1394	1.95	0.9744	0.0256	0.0596
1.46	0.9278	0.0722	0.1374	1.96	0.9750	0.0250	0.0584
1.47	0.9292	0.0708	0.1354	1.97	0.9756	0.0244	0.0573
1.48	0.9306	0.0694	0.1334	1.98	0.9761	0.0238	0.0562
1.49	0.9319	0.0681	0.1315	1.99	0.9767	0.0233	0.0551
1.50	0.9332	0.0668	0.1295	2.00	0.9772	0.0227	0.0540

x	$F(x)$	$1 - F(x)$	$f(x)$	x	$F(x)$	$1 - F(x)$	$f(x)$
2.00	0.9772	0.0227	0.0540	2.50	0.9938	0.0062	0.0175
2.01	0.9778	0.0222	0.0529	2.51	0.9940	0.0060	0.0171
2.02	0.9783	0.0217	0.0519	2.52	0.9941	0.0059	0.0167
2.03	0.9788	0.0212	0.0508	2.53	0.9943	0.0057	0.0163
2.04	0.9793	0.0207	0.0498	2.54	0.9945	0.0055	0.0158
2.05	0.9798	0.0202	0.0488	2.55	0.9946	0.0054	0.0155
2.06	0.9803	0.0197	0.0478	2.56	0.9948	0.0052	0.0151
2.07	0.9808	0.0192	0.0468	2.57	0.9949	0.0051	0.0147
2.08	0.9812	0.0188	0.0459	2.58	0.9951	0.0049	0.0143
2.09	0.9817	0.0183	0.0449	2.59	0.9952	0.0048	0.0139
2.10	0.9821	0.0179	0.0440	2.60	0.9953	0.0047	0.0136
2.11	0.9826	0.0174	0.0431	2.61	0.9955	0.0045	0.0132
2.12	0.9830	0.0170	0.0422	2.62	0.9956	0.0044	0.0129
2.13	0.9834	0.0166	0.0413	2.63	0.9957	0.0043	0.0126
2.14	0.9838	0.0162	0.0404	2.64	0.9959	0.0042	0.0122
2.15	0.9842	0.0158	0.0396	2.65	0.9960	0.0040	0.0119
2.16	0.9846	0.0154	0.0387	2.66	0.9961	0.0039	0.0116
2.17	0.9850	0.0150	0.0379	2.67	0.9962	0.0038	0.0113
2.18	0.9854	0.0146	0.0371	2.68	0.9963	0.0037	0.0110
2.19	0.9857	0.0143	0.0363	2.69	0.9964	0.0036	0.0107
2.20	0.9861	0.0139	0.0355	2.70	0.9965	0.0035	0.0104
2.21	0.9865	0.0135	0.0347	2.71	0.9966	0.0034	0.0101
2.22	0.9868	0.0132	0.0339	2.72	0.9967	0.0033	0.0099
2.23	0.9871	0.0129	0.0332	2.73	0.9968	0.0032	0.0096
2.24	0.9875	0.0126	0.0325	2.74	0.9969	0.0031	0.0094
2.25	0.9878	0.0122	0.0317	2.75	0.9970	0.0030	0.0091
2.26	0.9881	0.0119	0.0310	2.76	0.9971	0.0029	0.0089
2.27	0.9884	0.0116	0.0303	2.77	0.9972	0.0028	0.0086
2.28	0.9887	0.0113	0.0296	2.78	0.9973	0.0027	0.0084
2.29	0.9890	0.0110	0.0290	2.79	0.9974	0.0026	0.0081
2.30	0.9893	0.0107	0.0283	2.80	0.9974	0.0026	0.0079
2.31	0.9896	0.0104	0.0277	2.81	0.9975	0.0025	0.0077
2.32	0.9898	0.0102	0.0271	2.82	0.9976	0.0024	0.0075
2.33	0.9901	0.0099	0.0264	2.83	0.9977	0.0023	0.0073
2.34	0.9904	0.0096	0.0258	2.84	0.9977	0.0023	0.0071
2.35	0.9906	0.0094	0.0252	2.85	0.9978	0.0022	0.0069
2.36	0.9909	0.0091	0.0246	2.86	0.9979	0.0021	0.0067
2.37	0.9911	0.0089	0.0241	2.87	0.9980	0.0021	0.0065
2.38	0.9913	0.0087	0.0235	2.88	0.9980	0.0020	0.0063
2.39	0.9916	0.0084	0.0229	2.89	0.9981	0.0019	0.0061
2.40	0.9918	0.0082	0.0224	2.90	0.9981	0.0019	0.0060
2.41	0.9920	0.0080	0.0219	2.91	0.9982	0.0018	0.0058
2.42	0.9922	0.0078	0.0213	2.92	0.9982	0.0018	0.0056
2.43	0.9925	0.0076	0.0208	2.93	0.9983	0.0017	0.0054
2.44	0.9927	0.0073	0.0203	2.94	0.9984	0.0016	0.0053
2.45	0.9929	0.0071	0.0198	2.95	0.9984	0.0016	0.0051
2.46	0.9930	0.0069	0.0194	2.96	0.9985	0.0015	0.0050
2.47	0.9932	0.0068	0.0189	2.97	0.9985	0.0015	0.0049
2.48	0.9934	0.0066	0.0184	2.98	0.9986	0.0014	0.0047
2.49	0.9936	0.0064	0.0180	2.99	0.9986	0.0014	0.0046
2.50	0.9938	0.0062	0.0175	3.00	0.9987	0.0014	0.0044

7.12.3 PERCENTAGE POINTS, STUDENT'S t-DISTRIBUTION

For a given value of n this table gives the value of t such that

$$F(t) = \int_{-\infty}^{t} \frac{\Gamma((n+1)/2)}{\sqrt{n\pi}\,\Gamma(n/2)} \left(1 + \frac{x^2}{n}\right)^{-(n+1)/2} dx$$

is a specified number. The t-distribution is symmetrical, so that $F(-t) = 1 - F(t)$.

n	$F = $ 0.6000	0.7500	0.9000	0.9500	0.9750	0.9900	0.9950	0.9990	0.9995
1	0.325	1.000	3.078	6.314	12.706	31.821	63.657	318.309	636.619
2	0.289	0.816	1.886	2.920	4.303	6.965	9.925	22.327	31.599
3	0.277	0.765	1.638	2.353	3.182	4.541	5.841	10.215	12.924
4	0.271	0.741	1.533	2.132	2.776	3.747	4.604	7.173	8.610
5	0.267	0.727	1.476	2.015	2.571	3.365	4.032	5.893	6.869
6	0.265	0.718	1.440	1.943	2.447	3.143	3.707	5.208	5.959
7	0.263	0.711	1.415	1.895	2.365	2.998	3.499	4.785	5.408
8	0.262	0.706	1.397	1.860	2.306	2.896	3.355	4.501	5.041
9	0.261	0.703	1.383	1.833	2.262	2.821	3.250	4.297	4.781
10	0.260	0.700	1.372	1.812	2.228	2.764	3.169	4.144	4.587
11	0.260	0.697	1.363	1.796	2.201	2.718	3.106	4.025	4.437
12	0.259	0.695	1.356	1.782	2.179	2.681	3.055	3.930	4.318
13	0.259	0.694	1.350	1.771	2.160	2.650	3.012	3.852	4.221
14	0.258	0.692	1.345	1.761	2.145	2.624	2.977	3.787	4.140
15	0.258	0.691	1.341	1.753	2.131	2.602	2.947	3.733	4.073
16	0.258	0.690	1.337	1.746	2.120	2.583	2.921	3.686	4.015
17	0.257	0.689	1.333	1.740	2.110	2.567	2.898	3.646	3.965
18	0.257	0.688	1.330	1.734	2.101	2.552	2.878	3.610	3.922
19	0.257	0.688	1.328	1.729	2.093	2.539	2.861	3.579	3.883
20	0.257	0.687	1.325	1.725	2.086	2.528	2.845	3.552	3.850
25	0.256	0.684	1.316	1.708	2.060	2.485	2.787	3.450	3.725
50	0.255	0.679	1.299	1.676	2.009	2.403	2.678	3.261	3.496
100	0.254	0.677	1.290	1.660	1.984	2.364	2.626	3.174	3.390
∞	0.253	0.674	1.282	1.645	1.960	2.326	2.576	3.091	3.291

7.12.4   PERCENTAGE POINTS, CHI-SQUARE DISTRIBUTION

For a given value of n this table gives the value of χ^2 such that

$$F(\chi^2) = \int_0^{\chi^2} \frac{x^{(n-2)/2}e^{-x/2}}{2^{n/2}\Gamma(n/2)}\,dx$$

is a specified number.

n	0.005	0.010	0.025	0.050	0.100	0.250	0.500	0.750	0.900	0.950	0.975	0.990	0.995
1	0.0000393	0.0001571	0.0009821	0.00393	0.0158	0.102	0.455	1.32	2.71	3.84	5.02	6.63	7.88
2	0.0100	0.0201	0.0506	0.103	0.211	0.575	1.39	2.77	4.61	5.99	7.38	9.21	10.6
3	0.0717	0.115	0.216	0.352	0.584	1.21	2.37	4.11	6.25	7.81	9.35	11.3	12.8
4	0.207	0.297	0.484	0.711	1.06	1.92	3.36	5.39	7.78	9.49	11.1	13.3	14.9
5	0.412	0.554	0.831	1.15	1.61	2.67	4.35	6.63	9.24	11.1	12.8	15.1	16.7
6	0.676	0.872	1.24	1.64	2.20	3.45	5.35	7.84	10.6	12.6	14.4	16.8	18.5
7	0.989	1.24	1.69	2.17	2.83	4.25	6.35	9.04	12.0	14.1	16.0	18.5	20.3
8	1.34	1.65	2.18	2.73	3.49	5.07	7.34	10.2	13.4	15.5	17.5	20.1	22.0
9	1.73	2.09	2.70	3.33	4.17	5.90	8.34	11.4	14.7	16.9	19.0	21.7	23.6
10	2.16	2.56	3.25	3.94	4.87	6.74	9.34	12.5	16.0	18.3	20.5	23.2	25.2
11	2.60	3.05	3.82	4.57	5.58	7.58	10.3	13.7	17.3	19.7	21.9	24.7	26.8
12	3.07	3.57	4.40	5.23	6.30	8.44	11.3	14.8	18.5	21.0	23.3	26.2	28.3
13	3.57	4.11	5.01	5.89	7.04	9.30	12.3	16.0	19.8	22.4	24.7	27.7	29.8
14	4.07	4.66	5.63	6.57	7.79	10.2	13.3	17.1	21.1	23.7	26.1	29.1	31.3
15	4.60	5.23	6.26	7.26	8.55	11.0	14.3	18.2	22.3	25.0	27.5	30.6	32.8
16	5.14	5.81	6.91	7.96	9.31	11.9	15.3	19.4	23.5	26.3	28.8	32.0	34.3
17	5.70	6.41	7.56	8.67	10.1	12.8	16.3	20.5	24.8	27.6	30.2	33.4	35.7
18	6.26	7.01	8.23	9.39	10.9	13.7	17.3	21.6	26.0	28.9	31.5	34.8	37.2
19	6.84	7.63	8.91	10.1	11.7	14.6	18.3	22.7	27.2	30.1	32.9	36.2	38.6
20	7.43	8.26	9.59	10.9	12.4	15.5	19.3	23.8	28.4	31.4	34.2	37.6	40.0
21	8.03	8.90	10.3	11.6	13.2	16.3	20.3	24.9	29.6	32.7	35.5	38.9	41.4
22	8.64	9.54	11.0	12.3	14.0	17.2	21.3	26.0	30.8	33.9	36.8	40.3	42.8
23	9.26	10.2	11.7	13.1	14.8	18.1	22.3	27.1	32.0	35.2	38.1	41.6	44.2
24	9.89	10.9	12.4	13.8	15.7	19.0	23.3	28.2	33.2	36.4	39.4	43.0	45.6
25	10.5	11.5	13.1	14.6	16.5	19.9	24.3	29.3	34.4	37.7	40.6	44.3	46.9
30	13.8	15.0	16.8	18.5	20.6	24.5	29.3	34.8	40.3	43.8	47.0	50.9	53.7
35	17.2	18.5	20.6	22.5	24.8	29.1	34.3	40.2	46.1	49.8	53.2	57.3	60.3
50	28.0	29.7	32.4	34.8	37.7	42.9	49.3	56.3	63.2	67.5	71.4	76.2	79.5

7.12.5   PERCENTAGE POINTS, F-DISTRIBUTION

Given n and m this gives the value of f such that

$$F(f) = \int_0^f \frac{\Gamma((n+m)/2)}{\Gamma(m/2)\Gamma(n/2)} m^{m/2} n^{n/2} x^{m/2-1} (n+mx)^{-(m+n)/2}\, dx = 0.9.$$

$m =$

n	1	2	3	4	5	6	7	8	9	10	50	100	∞
1	39.86	49.50	53.59	55.83	57.24	58.20	58.91	59.44	59.86	60.19	62.69	63.01	63.33
2	8.53	9.00	9.16	9.24	9.29	9.33	9.35	9.37	9.38	9.39	9.47	9.48	9.49
3	5.54	5.46	5.39	5.34	5.31	5.28	5.27	5.25	5.24	5.23	5.15	5.14	5.13
4	4.54	4.32	4.19	4.11	4.05	4.01	3.98	3.95	3.94	3.92	3.80	3.78	3.76
5	4.06	3.78	3.62	3.52	3.45	3.40	3.37	3.34	3.32	3.30	3.15	3.13	3.10
6	3.78	3.46	3.29	3.18	3.11	3.05	3.01	2.98	2.96	2.94	2.77	2.75	2.72
7	3.59	3.26	3.07	2.96	2.88	2.83	2.78	2.75	2.72	2.70	2.52	2.50	2.47
8	3.46	3.11	2.92	2.81	2.73	2.67	2.62	2.59	2.56	2.54	2.35	2.32	2.29
9	3.36	3.01	2.81	2.69	2.61	2.55	2.51	2.47	2.44	2.42	2.22	2.19	2.16
10	3.29	2.92	2.73	2.61	2.52	2.46	2.41	2.38	2.35	2.32	2.12	2.09	2.06
11	3.23	2.86	2.66	2.54	2.45	2.39	2.34	2.30	2.27	2.25	2.04	2.01	1.97
12	3.18	2.81	2.61	2.48	2.39	2.33	2.28	2.24	2.21	2.19	1.97	1.94	1.90
13	3.14	2.76	2.56	2.43	2.35	2.28	2.23	2.20	2.16	2.14	1.92	1.88	1.85
14	3.10	2.73	2.52	2.39	2.31	2.24	2.19	2.15	2.12	2.10	1.87	1.83	1.80
15	3.07	2.70	2.49	2.36	2.27	2.21	2.16	2.12	2.09	2.06	1.83	1.79	1.76
16	3.05	2.67	2.46	2.33	2.24	2.18	2.13	2.09	2.06	2.03	1.79	1.76	1.72
17	3.03	2.64	2.44	2.31	2.22	2.15	2.10	2.06	2.03	2.00	1.76	1.73	1.69
18	3.01	2.62	2.42	2.29	2.20	2.13	2.08	2.04	2.00	1.98	1.74	1.70	1.66
19	2.99	2.61	2.40	2.27	2.18	2.11	2.06	2.02	1.98	1.96	1.71	1.67	1.63
20	2.97	2.59	2.38	2.25	2.16	2.09	2.04	2.00	1.96	1.94	1.69	1.65	1.61
25	2.92	2.53	2.32	2.18	2.09	2.02	1.97	1.93	1.89	1.87	1.61	1.56	1.52
50	2.81	2.41	2.20	2.06	1.97	1.90	1.84	1.80	1.76	1.73	1.44	1.39	1.34
100	2.76	2.36	2.14	2.00	1.91	1.83	1.78	1.73	1.69	1.66	1.35	1.29	1.20
∞	2.71	2.30	2.08	1.94	1.85	1.77	1.72	1.67	1.63	1.60	1.24	1.17	1.00

Given n and m this gives the value of f such that

$$F(f) = \int_0^f \frac{\Gamma((n+m)/2)}{\Gamma(m/2)\Gamma(n/2)} m^{m/2} n^{n/2} x^{m/2-1}(n+mx)^{-(m+n)/2}\, dx = 0.95.$$

n	1	2	3	4	5	6	7	8	9	10	50	100	∞
1	161.4	199.5	215.7	224.6	230.2	234.0	236.8	238.9	240.5	241.9	251.8	253.0	254.3
2	18.51	19.00	19.16	19.25	19.30	19.33	19.35	19.37	19.38	19.40	19.48	19.49	19.50
3	10.13	9.55	9.28	9.12	9.01	8.94	8.89	8.85	8.81	8.79	8.58	8.55	8.53
4	7.71	6.94	6.59	6.39	6.26	6.16	6.09	6.04	6.00	5.96	5.70	5.66	5.63
5	6.61	5.79	5.41	5.19	5.05	4.95	4.88	4.82	4.77	4.74	4.44	4.41	4.36
6	5.99	5.14	4.76	4.53	4.39	4.28	4.21	4.15	4.10	4.06	3.75	3.71	3.67
7	5.59	4.74	4.35	4.12	3.97	3.87	3.79	3.73	3.68	3.64	3.32	3.27	3.23
8	5.32	4.46	4.07	3.84	3.69	3.58	3.50	3.44	3.39	3.35	3.02	2.97	2.93
9	5.12	4.26	3.86	3.63	3.48	3.37	3.29	3.23	3.18	3.14	2.80	2.76	2.71
10	4.96	4.10	3.71	3.48	3.33	3.22	3.14	3.07	3.02	2.98	2.64	2.59	2.54
11	4.84	3.98	3.59	3.36	3.20	3.09	3.01	2.95	2.90	2.85	2.51	2.46	2.40
12	4.75	3.89	3.49	3.26	3.11	3.00	2.91	2.85	2.80	2.75	2.40	2.35	2.30
13	4.67	3.81	3.41	3.18	3.03	2.92	2.83	2.77	2.71	2.67	2.31	2.26	2.21
14	4.60	3.74	3.34	3.11	2.96	2.85	2.76	2.70	2.65	2.60	2.24	2.19	2.13
15	4.54	3.68	3.29	3.06	2.90	2.79	2.71	2.64	2.59	2.54	2.18	2.12	2.07
16	4.49	3.63	3.24	3.01	2.85	2.74	2.66	2.59	2.54	2.49	2.12	2.07	2.01
17	4.45	3.59	3.20	2.96	2.81	2.70	2.61	2.55	2.49	2.45	2.08	2.02	1.96
18	4.41	3.55	3.16	2.93	2.77	2.66	2.58	2.51	2.46	2.41	2.04	1.98	1.92
19	4.38	3.52	3.13	2.90	2.74	2.63	2.54	2.48	2.42	2.38	2.00	1.94	1.88
20	4.35	3.49	3.10	2.87	2.71	2.60	2.51	2.45	2.39	2.35	1.97	1.91	1.84
25	4.24	3.39	2.99	2.76	2.60	2.49	2.40	2.34	2.28	2.24	1.84	1.78	1.71
50	4.03	3.18	2.79	2.56	2.40	2.29	2.20	2.13	2.07	2.03	1.60	1.52	1.45
100	3.94	3.09	2.70	2.46	2.31	2.19	2.10	2.03	1.97	1.93	1.48	1.39	1.28
∞	3.84	3.00	2.60	2.37	2.21	2.10	2.01	1.94	1.88	1.83	1.35	1.25	1.00

$m =$

Given n and m this gives the value of f such that

$$F(f) = \int_0^f \frac{\Gamma((n+m)/2)}{\Gamma(m/2)\Gamma(n/2)} m^{m/2} n^{n/2} x^{m/2-1} (n+mx)^{-(m+n)/2}\, dx = 0.975.$$

n	$m=$ 1	2	3	4	5	6	7	8	9	10	50	100	∞
1	647.8	799.5	864.2	899.6	921.8	937.1	948.2	956.7	963.3	968.6	1008	1013	1018
2	38.51	39.00	39.17	39.25	39.30	39.33	39.36	39.37	39.39	39.40	39.48	39.49	39.50
3	17.44	16.04	15.44	15.10	14.88	14.73	14.62	14.54	14.47	14.42	14.01	13.96	13.90
4	12.22	10.65	9.98	9.60	9.36	9.20	9.07	8.98	8.90	8.84	8.38	8.32	8.26
5	10.01	8.43	7.76	7.39	7.15	6.98	6.85	6.76	6.68	6.62	6.14	6.08	6.02
6	8.81	7.26	6.60	6.23	5.99	5.82	5.70	5.60	5.52	5.46	4.98	4.92	4.85
7	8.07	6.54	5.89	5.52	5.29	5.12	4.99	4.90	4.82	4.76	4.28	4.21	4.14
8	7.57	6.06	5.42	5.05	4.82	4.65	4.53	4.43	4.36	4.30	3.81	3.74	3.67
9	7.21	5.71	5.08	4.72	4.48	4.32	4.20	4.10	4.03	3.96	3.47	3.40	3.33
10	6.94	5.46	4.83	4.47	4.24	4.07	3.95	3.85	3.78	3.72	3.22	3.15	3.08
11	6.72	5.26	4.63	4.28	4.04	3.88	3.76	3.66	3.59	3.53	3.03	2.96	2.88
12	6.55	5.10	4.47	4.12	3.89	3.73	3.61	3.51	3.44	3.37	2.87	2.80	2.72
13	6.41	4.97	4.35	4.00	3.77	3.60	3.48	3.39	3.31	3.25	2.74	2.67	2.60
14	6.30	4.86	4.24	3.89	3.66	3.50	3.38	3.29	3.21	3.15	2.64	2.56	2.49
15	6.20	4.77	4.15	3.80	3.58	3.41	3.29	3.20	3.12	3.06	2.55	2.47	2.40
16	6.12	4.69	4.08	3.73	3.50	3.34	3.22	3.12	3.05	2.99	2.47	2.40	2.32
17	6.04	4.62	4.01	3.66	3.44	3.28	3.16	3.06	2.98	2.92	2.41	2.33	2.25
18	5.98	4.56	3.95	3.61	3.38	3.22	3.10	3.01	2.93	2.87	2.35	2.27	2.19
19	5.92	4.51	3.90	3.56	3.33	3.17	3.05	2.96	2.88	2.82	2.30	2.22	2.13
20	5.87	4.46	3.86	3.51	3.29	3.13	3.01	2.91	2.84	2.77	2.25	2.17	2.09
25	5.69	4.29	3.69	3.35	3.13	2.97	2.85	2.75	2.68	2.61	2.08	2.00	1.91
50	5.34	3.97	3.39	3.05	2.83	2.67	2.55	2.46	2.38	2.32	1.75	1.66	1.54
100	5.18	3.83	3.25	2.92	2.70	2.54	2.42	2.32	2.24	2.18	1.59	1.48	1.37
∞	5.02	3.69	3.12	2.79	2.57	2.41	2.29	2.19	2.11	2.05	1.43	1.27	1.00

Given n and m this gives the value of f such that

$$F(f) = \int_0^f \frac{\Gamma((n+m)/2)}{\Gamma(m/2)\Gamma(n/2)} m^{m/2} n^{n/2} x^{m/2-1} (n+mx)^{-(m+n)/2}\, dx = 0.99.$$

n	$m=$ 1	2	3	4	5	6	7	8	9	10	50	100	∞
1	4052	5000	5403	5625	5764	5859	5928	5981	6022	6056	6303	6334	6336
2	98.50	99.00	99.17	99.25	99.30	99.33	99.36	99.37	99.39	99.40	99.48	99.49	99.50
3	34.12	30.82	29.46	28.71	28.24	27.91	27.67	27.49	27.35	27.23	26.35	26.24	26.13
4	21.20	18.00	16.69	15.98	15.52	15.21	14.98	14.80	14.66	14.55	13.69	13.58	13.46
5	16.26	13.27	12.06	11.39	10.97	10.67	10.46	10.29	10.16	10.05	9.24	9.13	9.02
6	13.75	10.92	9.78	9.15	8.75	8.47	8.26	8.10	7.98	7.87	7.09	6.99	6.88
7	12.25	9.55	8.45	7.85	7.46	7.19	6.99	6.84	6.72	6.62	5.86	5.75	5.65
8	11.26	8.65	7.59	7.01	6.63	6.37	6.18	6.03	5.91	5.81	5.07	4.96	4.86
9	10.56	8.02	6.99	6.42	6.06	5.80	5.61	5.47	5.35	5.26	4.52	4.41	4.31
10	10.04	7.56	6.55	5.99	5.64	5.39	5.20	5.06	4.94	4.85	4.12	4.01	3.91
11	9.65	7.21	6.22	5.67	5.32	5.07	4.89	4.74	4.63	4.54	3.81	3.71	3.60
12	9.33	6.93	5.95	5.41	5.06	4.82	4.64	4.50	4.39	4.30	3.57	3.47	3.36
13	9.07	6.70	5.74	5.21	4.86	4.62	4.44	4.30	4.19	4.10	3.38	3.27	3.17
14	8.86	6.51	5.56	5.04	4.69	4.46	4.28	4.14	4.03	3.94	3.22	3.11	3.00
15	8.68	6.36	5.42	4.89	4.56	4.32	4.14	4.00	3.89	3.80	3.08	2.98	2.87
16	8.53	6.23	5.29	4.77	4.44	4.20	4.03	3.89	3.78	3.69	2.97	2.86	2.75
17	8.40	6.11	5.18	4.67	4.34	4.10	3.93	3.79	3.68	3.59	2.87	2.76	2.65
18	8.29	6.01	5.09	4.58	4.25	4.01	3.84	3.71	3.60	3.51	2.78	2.68	2.57
19	8.18	5.93	5.01	4.50	4.17	3.94	3.77	3.63	3.52	3.43	2.71	2.60	2.49
20	8.10	5.85	4.94	4.43	4.10	3.87	3.70	3.56	3.46	3.37	2.64	2.54	2.42
25	7.77	5.57	4.68	4.18	3.85	3.63	3.46	3.32	3.22	3.13	2.40	2.29	2.17
50	7.17	5.06	4.20	3.72	3.41	3.19	3.02	2.89	2.78	2.70	1.95	1.82	1.70
100	6.90	4.82	3.98	3.51	3.21	2.99	2.82	2.69	2.59	2.50	1.74	1.60	1.45
∞	6.63	4.61	3.78	3.32	3.02	2.80	2.64	2.51	2.41	2.32	1.53	1.32	1.00

Given n and m this gives the value of f such that

$$F(f) = \int_0^f \frac{\Gamma((n+m)/2)}{\Gamma(m/2)\Gamma(n/2)} m^{m/2} n^{n/2} x^{m/2-1} (n+mx)^{-(m+n)/2}\, dx = 0.995.$$

$n \backslash m$	1	2	3	4	5	6	7	8	9	10	50	100	∞
1	16211	20000	21615	22500	23056	23437	23715	23925	24091	24224	25211	25337	25465
2	198.5	199.0	199.2	199.2	199.3	199.3	199.4	199.4	199.4	199.4	199.5	199.5	199.5
3	55.55	49.80	47.47	46.19	45.39	44.84	44.43	44.13	43.88	43.69	42.21	42.02	41.83
4	31.33	26.28	24.26	23.15	22.46	21.97	21.62	21.35	21.14	20.97	19.67	19.50	19.32
5	22.78	18.31	16.53	15.56	14.94	14.51	14.20	13.96	13.77	13.62	12.45	12.30	12.14
6	18.63	14.54	12.92	12.03	11.46	11.07	10.79	10.57	10.39	10.25	9.17	9.03	8.88
7	16.24	12.40	10.88	10.05	9.52	9.16	8.89	8.68	8.51	8.38	7.35	7.22	7.08
8	14.69	11.04	9.60	8.81	8.30	7.95	7.69	7.50	7.34	7.21	6.22	6.09	5.95
9	13.61	10.11	8.72	7.96	7.47	7.13	6.88	6.69	6.54	6.42	5.45	5.32	5.19
10	12.83	9.43	8.08	7.34	6.87	6.54	6.30	6.12	5.97	5.85	4.90	4.77	4.64
11	12.23	8.91	7.60	6.88	6.42	6.10	5.86	5.68	5.54	5.42	4.49	4.36	4.23
12	11.75	8.51	7.23	6.52	6.07	5.76	5.52	5.35	5.20	5.09	4.17	4.04	3.90
13	11.37	8.19	6.93	6.23	5.79	5.48	5.25	5.08	4.94	4.82	3.91	3.78	3.65
14	11.06	7.92	6.68	6.00	5.56	5.26	5.03	4.86	4.72	4.60	3.70	3.57	3.44
15	10.80	7.70	6.48	5.80	5.37	5.07	4.85	4.67	4.54	4.42	3.52	3.39	3.26
16	10.58	7.51	6.30	5.64	5.21	4.91	4.69	4.52	4.38	4.27	3.37	3.25	3.11
17	10.38	7.35	6.16	5.50	5.07	4.78	4.56	4.39	4.25	4.14	3.25	3.12	2.98
18	10.22	7.21	6.03	5.37	4.96	4.66	4.44	4.28	4.14	4.03	3.14	3.01	2.87
19	10.07	7.09	5.92	5.27	4.85	4.56	4.34	4.18	4.04	3.93	3.04	2.91	2.78
20	9.94	6.99	5.82	5.17	4.76	4.47	4.26	4.09	3.96	3.85	2.96	2.83	2.69
25	9.48	6.60	5.46	4.84	4.43	4.15	3.94	3.78	3.64	3.54	2.65	2.52	2.38
50	8.63	5.90	4.83	4.23	3.85	3.58	3.38	3.22	3.09	2.99	2.10	1.95	1.81
100	8.24	5.59	4.54	3.96	3.59	3.33	3.13	2.97	2.85	2.74	1.84	1.68	1.51
∞	7.88	5.30	4.28	3.72	3.35	3.09	2.90	2.74	2.62	2.52	1.60	1.36	1.00

Given n and m this gives the value of f such that

$$F(f) = \int_0^f \frac{\Gamma((n+m)/2)}{\Gamma(m/2)\Gamma(n/2)} m^{m/2} n^{n/2} x^{m/2-1} (n+mx)^{-(m+n)/2}\, dx = 0.999.$$

n	$m=1$	2	3	4	5	6	7	8	9	10	50	100	∞
2	998.5	999.0	999.2	999.2	999.3	999.3	999.4	999.4	999.4	999.4	999.5	999.5	999.5
3	167.0	148.5	141.1	137.1	134.6	132.8	131.6	130.6	129.9	129.2	124.7	124.1	123.5
4	74.14	61.25	56.18	53.44	51.71	50.53	49.66	49.00	48.47	48.05	44.88	44.47	44.05
5	47.18	37.12	33.20	31.09	29.75	28.83	28.16	27.65	27.24	26.92	24.44	24.12	23.79
6	35.51	27.00	23.70	21.92	20.80	20.03	19.46	19.03	18.69	18.41	16.31	16.03	15.75
7	29.25	21.69	18.77	17.20	16.21	15.52	15.02	14.63	14.33	14.08	12.20	11.95	11.70
8	25.41	18.49	15.83	14.39	13.48	12.86	12.40	12.05	11.77	11.54	9.80	9.57	9.33
9	22.86	16.39	13.90	12.56	11.71	11.13	10.70	10.37	10.11	9.89	8.26	8.04	7.81
10	21.04	14.91	12.55	11.28	10.48	9.93	9.52	9.20	8.96	8.75	7.19	6.98	6.76
11	19.69	13.81	11.56	10.35	9.58	9.05	8.66	8.35	8.12	7.92	6.42	6.21	6.00
12	18.64	12.97	10.80	9.63	8.89	8.38	8.00	7.71	7.48	7.29	5.83	5.63	5.42
13	17.82	12.31	10.21	9.07	8.35	7.86	7.49	7.21	6.98	6.80	5.37	5.17	4.97
14	17.14	11.78	9.73	8.62	7.92	7.44	7.08	6.80	6.58	6.40	5.00	4.81	4.60
15	16.59	11.34	9.34	8.25	7.57	7.09	6.74	6.47	6.26	6.08	4.70	4.51	4.31
16	16.12	10.97	9.01	7.94	7.27	6.80	6.46	6.19	5.98	5.81	4.45	4.26	4.06
17	15.72	10.66	8.73	7.68	7.02	6.56	6.22	5.96	5.75	5.58	4.24	4.05	3.85
18	15.38	10.39	8.49	7.46	6.81	6.35	6.02	5.76	5.56	5.39	4.06	3.87	3.67
19	15.08	10.16	8.28	7.27	6.62	6.18	5.85	5.59	5.39	5.22	3.90	3.71	3.51
20	14.82	9.95	8.10	7.10	6.46	6.02	5.69	5.44	5.24	5.08	3.77	3.58	3.38
25	13.88	9.22	7.45	6.49	5.89	5.46	5.15	4.91	4.71	4.56	3.28	3.09	2.89
50	12.22	7.96	6.34	5.46	4.90	4.51	4.22	4.00	3.82	3.67	2.44	2.25	2.06
100	11.50	7.41	5.86	5.02	4.48	4.11	3.83	3.61	3.44	3.30	2.08	1.87	1.65
∞	10.83	6.91	5.42	4.62	4.10	3.74	3.47	3.27	3.10	2.96	1.75	1.45	1.00

7.12.6   CUMULATIVE TERMS, BINOMIAL DISTRIBUTION

$$B(n, x; p) = \sum_{k=0}^{x} \binom{n}{k} p^k (1 - p)^{n-k}.$$

Note that $B(n, x; p) = B(n, n - x; 1 - p)$.

If p is the probability of success, then $B(n, x; p)$ is the probability of x or fewer successes in n independent trials. For example, if a biased coin has a probability $p = 0.4$ of being a head, and the coin is independently flipped 5 times, then there is a 68% chance that there will be 2 or fewer heads (since $B(5, 2; 0.4) = 0.6826$).

		$p =$							
n	x	0.05	0.10	0.15	0.20	0.25	0.30	0.40	0.50
2	0	0.9025	0.8100	0.7225	0.6400	0.5625	0.4900	0.3600	0.2500
	1	0.9975	0.9900	0.9775	0.9600	0.9375	0.9100	0.8400	0.7500
3	0	0.8574	0.7290	0.6141	0.5120	0.4219	0.3430	0.2160	0.1250
	1	0.9928	0.9720	0.9393	0.8960	0.8438	0.7840	0.6480	0.5000
	2	0.9999	0.9990	0.9966	0.9920	0.9844	0.9730	0.9360	0.8750
4	0	0.8145	0.6561	0.5220	0.4096	0.3164	0.2401	0.1296	0.0625
	1	0.9860	0.9477	0.8905	0.8192	0.7383	0.6517	0.4752	0.3125
	2	0.9995	0.9963	0.9880	0.9728	0.9492	0.9163	0.8208	0.6875
	3	1.0000	0.9999	0.9995	0.9984	0.9961	0.9919	0.9744	0.9375
5	0	0.7738	0.5905	0.4437	0.3277	0.2373	0.1681	0.0778	0.0312
	1	0.9774	0.9185	0.8352	0.7373	0.6328	0.5282	0.3370	0.1875
	2	0.9988	0.9914	0.9734	0.9421	0.8965	0.8369	0.6826	0.5000
	3	1.0000	0.9995	0.9978	0.9933	0.9844	0.9692	0.9130	0.8125
	4	1.0000	1.0000	0.9999	0.9997	0.9990	0.9976	0.9898	0.9688
6	0	0.7351	0.5314	0.3771	0.2621	0.1780	0.1177	0.0467	0.0156
	1	0.9672	0.8857	0.7765	0.6554	0.5339	0.4202	0.2333	0.1094
	2	0.9978	0.9841	0.9527	0.9011	0.8306	0.7443	0.5443	0.3438
	3	0.9999	0.9987	0.9941	0.9830	0.9624	0.9295	0.8208	0.6562
	4	1.0000	1.0000	0.9996	0.9984	0.9954	0.9891	0.9590	0.8906
	5	1.0000	1.0000	1.0000	0.9999	0.9998	0.9993	0.9959	0.9844
7	0	0.6983	0.4783	0.3206	0.2097	0.1335	0.0824	0.0280	0.0078
	1	0.9556	0.8503	0.7166	0.5767	0.4450	0.3294	0.1586	0.0625
	2	0.9962	0.9743	0.9262	0.8520	0.7564	0.6471	0.4199	0.2266
	3	0.9998	0.9973	0.9879	0.9667	0.9294	0.8740	0.7102	0.5000
	4	1.0000	0.9998	0.9988	0.9953	0.9871	0.9712	0.9037	0.7734
	5	1.0000	1.0000	0.9999	0.9996	0.9987	0.9962	0.9812	0.9375
	6	1.0000	1.0000	1.0000	1.0000	0.9999	0.9998	0.9984	0.9922

n	x	\multicolumn{8}{c}{p =}
		0.05	0.10	0.15	0.20	0.25	0.30	0.40	0.50
8	0	0.6634	0.4305	0.2725	0.1678	0.1001	0.0576	0.0168	0.0039
	1	0.9428	0.8131	0.6572	0.5033	0.3671	0.2553	0.1064	0.0352
	2	0.9942	0.9619	0.8948	0.7969	0.6785	0.5518	0.3154	0.1445
	3	0.9996	0.9950	0.9787	0.9437	0.8862	0.8059	0.5941	0.3633
	4	1.0000	0.9996	0.9971	0.9896	0.9727	0.9420	0.8263	0.6367
	5	1.0000	1.0000	0.9998	0.9988	0.9958	0.9887	0.9502	0.8555
	6	1.0000	1.0000	1.0000	0.9999	0.9996	0.9987	0.9915	0.9648
	7	1.0000	1.0000	1.0000	1.0000	1.0000	0.9999	0.9993	0.9961
9	0	0.6302	0.3874	0.2316	0.1342	0.0751	0.0403	0.0101	0.0019
	1	0.9288	0.7748	0.5995	0.4362	0.3003	0.1960	0.0705	0.0195
	2	0.9916	0.9470	0.8591	0.7382	0.6007	0.4628	0.2318	0.0898
	3	0.9994	0.9917	0.9661	0.9144	0.8343	0.7297	0.4826	0.2539
	4	1.0000	0.9991	0.9944	0.9804	0.9511	0.9012	0.7334	0.5000
	5	1.0000	0.9999	0.9994	0.9969	0.9900	0.9747	0.9006	0.7461
	6	1.0000	1.0000	1.0000	0.9997	0.9987	0.9957	0.9750	0.9102
	7	1.0000	1.0000	1.0000	1.0000	0.9999	0.9996	0.9962	0.9805
	8	1.0000	1.0000	1.0000	1.0000	1.0000	1.0000	0.9997	0.9980
10	0	0.5987	0.3487	0.1969	0.1074	0.0563	0.0283	0.0060	0.0010
	1	0.9139	0.7361	0.5443	0.3758	0.2440	0.1493	0.0464	0.0107
	2	0.9885	0.9298	0.8202	0.6778	0.5256	0.3828	0.1673	0.0547
	3	0.9990	0.9872	0.9500	0.8791	0.7759	0.6496	0.3823	0.1719
	4	0.9999	0.9984	0.9901	0.9672	0.9219	0.8497	0.6331	0.3770
	5	1.0000	0.9999	0.9986	0.9936	0.9803	0.9526	0.8338	0.6230
	6	1.0000	1.0000	0.9999	0.9991	0.9965	0.9894	0.9452	0.8281
	7	1.0000	1.0000	1.0000	0.9999	0.9996	0.9984	0.9877	0.9453
	8	1.0000	1.0000	1.0000	1.0000	1.0000	0.9999	0.9983	0.9893
	9	1.0000	1.0000	1.0000	1.0000	1.0000	1.0000	0.9999	0.9990
11	0	0.5688	0.3138	0.1673	0.0859	0.0422	0.0198	0.0036	0.0005
	1	0.8981	0.6974	0.4922	0.3221	0.1971	0.1130	0.0302	0.0059
	2	0.9848	0.9104	0.7788	0.6174	0.4552	0.3127	0.1189	0.0327
	3	0.9984	0.9815	0.9306	0.8389	0.7133	0.5696	0.2963	0.1133
	4	0.9999	0.9972	0.9841	0.9496	0.8854	0.7897	0.5328	0.2744
	5	1.0000	0.9997	0.9973	0.9883	0.9657	0.9218	0.7535	0.5000
	6	1.0000	1.0000	0.9997	0.9980	0.9924	0.9784	0.9006	0.7256
	7	1.0000	1.0000	1.0000	0.9998	0.9988	0.9957	0.9707	0.8867
	8	1.0000	1.0000	1.0000	1.0000	0.9999	0.9994	0.9941	0.9673
	9	1.0000	1.0000	1.0000	1.0000	1.0000	1.0000	0.9993	0.9941
	10	1.0000	1.0000	1.0000	1.0000	1.0000	1.0000	1.0000	0.9995

n	x	p = 0.05	0.10	0.15	0.20	0.25	0.30	0.40	0.50
12	0	0.5404	0.2824	0.1422	0.0687	0.0317	0.0138	0.0022	0.0002
	1	0.8816	0.6590	0.4435	0.2749	0.1584	0.0850	0.0196	0.0032
	2	0.9804	0.8891	0.7358	0.5584	0.3907	0.2528	0.0834	0.0193
	3	0.9978	0.9744	0.9078	0.7946	0.6488	0.4925	0.2253	0.0730
	4	0.9998	0.9957	0.9761	0.9274	0.8424	0.7237	0.4382	0.1938
	5	1.0000	0.9995	0.9954	0.9806	0.9456	0.8821	0.6652	0.3872
	6	1.0000	1.0000	0.9993	0.9961	0.9858	0.9614	0.8418	0.6128
	7	1.0000	1.0000	0.9999	0.9994	0.9972	0.9905	0.9427	0.8062
	8	1.0000	1.0000	1.0000	0.9999	0.9996	0.9983	0.9847	0.9270
	9	1.0000	1.0000	1.0000	1.0000	1.0000	0.9998	0.9972	0.9807
	10	1.0000	1.0000	1.0000	1.0000	1.0000	1.0000	0.9997	0.9968
	11	1.0000	1.0000	1.0000	1.0000	1.0000	1.0000	1.0000	0.9998
13	0	0.5133	0.2542	0.1209	0.0550	0.0238	0.0097	0.0013	0.0001
	1	0.8646	0.6213	0.3983	0.2336	0.1267	0.0637	0.0126	0.0017
	2	0.9755	0.8661	0.6920	0.5017	0.3326	0.2025	0.0579	0.0112
	3	0.9969	0.9658	0.8820	0.7473	0.5843	0.4206	0.1686	0.0461
	4	0.9997	0.9935	0.9658	0.9009	0.7940	0.6543	0.3530	0.1334
	5	1.0000	0.9991	0.9925	0.9700	0.9198	0.8346	0.5744	0.2905
	6	1.0000	0.9999	0.9987	0.9930	0.9757	0.9376	0.7712	0.5000
	7	1.0000	1.0000	0.9998	0.9988	0.9943	0.9818	0.9023	0.7095
	8	1.0000	1.0000	1.0000	0.9998	0.9990	0.9960	0.9679	0.8666
	9	1.0000	1.0000	1.0000	1.0000	0.9999	0.9993	0.9922	0.9539
	10	1.0000	1.0000	1.0000	1.0000	1.0000	0.9999	0.9987	0.9888
	11	1.0000	1.0000	1.0000	1.0000	1.0000	1.0000	0.9999	0.9983
	12	1.0000	1.0000	1.0000	1.0000	1.0000	1.0000	1.0000	0.9999

7.12.7   CUMULATIVE TERMS, POISSON DISTRIBUTION

$$F(x; \lambda) = \sum_{k=0}^{x} e^{-\lambda} \frac{\lambda^k}{k!}.$$

If λ is the rate of Poisson arrivals, then $F(x; \lambda)$ is the probability of x or fewer arrivals occurring in a unit of time. For example, if customers arrive at the rate of $\lambda = 0.5$ customers per hour, then the probability of having no customers in any specified hour is 0.61 (the probability of one or fewer customers is 0.91).

λ	x = 0	1	2	3	4	5	6	7	8	9
0.02	0.980	1.000								
0.04	0.961	0.999	1.000							
0.06	0.942	0.998	1.000							
0.08	0.923	0.997	1.000							
0.10	0.905	0.995	1.000							
0.15	0.861	0.990	1.000	1.000						
0.20	0.819	0.983	0.999	1.000						
0.25	0.779	0.974	0.998	1.000						
0.30	0.741	0.963	0.996	1.000						
0.35	0.705	0.951	0.995	1.000						
0.40	0.670	0.938	0.992	0.999	1.000					

λ	\multicolumn{10}{c}{x =}
	0	1	2	3	4	5	6	7	8	9
0.45	0.638	0.925	0.989	0.999	1.000					
0.50	0.607	0.910	0.986	0.998	1.000					
0.55	0.577	0.894	0.982	0.998	1.000					
0.60	0.549	0.878	0.977	0.997	1.000					
0.65	0.522	0.861	0.972	0.996	0.999	1.000				
0.70	0.497	0.844	0.966	0.994	0.999	1.000				
0.75	0.472	0.827	0.960	0.993	0.999	1.000				
0.80	0.449	0.809	0.953	0.991	0.999	1.000				
0.85	0.427	0.791	0.945	0.989	0.998	1.000				
0.90	0.407	0.772	0.937	0.987	0.998	1.000				
0.95	0.387	0.754	0.929	0.984	0.997	1.000				
1.00	0.368	0.736	0.920	0.981	0.996	0.999	1.000			
1.1	0.333	0.699	0.900	0.974	0.995	0.999	1.000			
1.2	0.301	0.663	0.879	0.966	0.992	0.999	1.000			
1.3	0.273	0.627	0.857	0.957	0.989	0.998	1.000			
1.4	0.247	0.592	0.834	0.946	0.986	0.997	0.999	1.000		
1.5	0.223	0.558	0.809	0.934	0.981	0.996	0.999	1.000		
1.6	0.202	0.525	0.783	0.921	0.976	0.994	0.999	1.000		
1.7	0.183	0.493	0.757	0.907	0.970	0.992	0.998	1.000		
1.8	0.165	0.463	0.731	0.891	0.964	0.990	0.997	0.999	1.000	
1.9	0.150	0.434	0.704	0.875	0.956	0.987	0.997	0.999	1.000	
2.0	0.135	0.406	0.677	0.857	0.947	0.983	0.996	0.999	1.000	
2.2	0.111	0.355	0.623	0.819	0.927	0.975	0.993	0.998	1.000	
2.4	0.091	0.308	0.570	0.779	0.904	0.964	0.988	0.997	0.999	1.000
2.6	0.074	0.267	0.518	0.736	0.877	0.951	0.983	0.995	0.999	1.000
2.8	0.061	0.231	0.469	0.692	0.848	0.935	0.976	0.992	0.998	0.999
3.0	0.050	0.199	0.423	0.647	0.815	0.916	0.967	0.988	0.996	0.999
3.2	0.041	0.171	0.380	0.603	0.781	0.895	0.955	0.983	0.994	0.998
3.4	0.033	0.147	0.340	0.558	0.744	0.871	0.942	0.977	0.992	0.997
3.6	0.027	0.126	0.303	0.515	0.706	0.844	0.927	0.969	0.988	0.996
3.8	0.022	0.107	0.269	0.473	0.668	0.816	0.909	0.960	0.984	0.994
4.0	0.018	0.092	0.238	0.433	0.629	0.785	0.889	0.949	0.979	0.992
4.2	0.015	0.078	0.210	0.395	0.590	0.753	0.868	0.936	0.972	0.989
4.4	0.012	0.066	0.185	0.359	0.551	0.720	0.844	0.921	0.964	0.985
4.6	0.010	0.056	0.163	0.326	0.513	0.686	0.818	0.905	0.955	0.981
4.8	0.008	0.048	0.142	0.294	0.476	0.651	0.791	0.887	0.944	0.975
5.0	0.007	0.040	0.125	0.265	0.441	0.616	0.762	0.867	0.932	0.968
5.2	0.005	0.034	0.109	0.238	0.406	0.581	0.732	0.845	0.918	0.960
5.4	0.004	0.029	0.095	0.213	0.373	0.546	0.702	0.822	0.903	0.951
5.6	0.004	0.024	0.082	0.191	0.342	0.512	0.670	0.797	0.886	0.941
5.8	0.003	0.021	0.071	0.170	0.313	0.478	0.638	0.771	0.867	0.929
6.0	0.003	0.017	0.062	0.151	0.285	0.446	0.606	0.744	0.847	0.916
6.2	0.002	0.015	0.054	0.134	0.259	0.414	0.574	0.716	0.826	0.902

λ	x = 0	1	2	3	4	5	6	7	8	9
6.4	0.002	0.012	0.046	0.119	0.235	0.384	0.542	0.687	0.803	0.886
6.6	0.001	0.010	0.040	0.105	0.213	0.355	0.511	0.658	0.780	0.869
6.8	0.001	0.009	0.034	0.093	0.192	0.327	0.480	0.628	0.755	0.850
7.0	0.001	0.007	0.030	0.082	0.173	0.301	0.450	0.599	0.729	0.831
7.2	0.001	0.006	0.025	0.072	0.155	0.276	0.420	0.569	0.703	0.810
7.4	0.001	0.005	0.022	0.063	0.140	0.253	0.392	0.539	0.676	0.788
7.6	0.001	0.004	0.019	0.055	0.125	0.231	0.365	0.510	0.648	0.765
7.8	0.000	0.004	0.016	0.049	0.112	0.210	0.338	0.481	0.620	0.741
8.0	0.000	0.003	0.014	0.042	0.100	0.191	0.313	0.453	0.593	0.717
8.5	0.000	0.002	0.009	0.030	0.074	0.150	0.256	0.386	0.523	0.653
9.0	0.000	0.001	0.006	0.021	0.055	0.116	0.207	0.324	0.456	0.587
9.5	0.000	0.001	0.004	0.015	0.040	0.088	0.165	0.269	0.392	0.522
10.0	0.000	0.001	0.003	0.010	0.029	0.067	0.130	0.220	0.333	0.458
10.5	0.000	0.000	0.002	0.007	0.021	0.050	0.102	0.178	0.279	0.397
11.0	0.000	0.000	0.001	0.005	0.015	0.037	0.079	0.143	0.232	0.341
11.5	0.000	0.000	0.001	0.003	0.011	0.028	0.060	0.114	0.191	0.289
12.0	0.000	0.000	0.001	0.002	0.008	0.020	0.046	0.089	0.155	0.242
12.5	0.000	0.000	0.000	0.002	0.005	0.015	0.035	0.070	0.125	0.201
13.0	0.000	0.000	0.000	0.001	0.004	0.011	0.026	0.054	0.100	0.166
13.5	0.000	0.000	0.000	0.001	0.003	0.008	0.019	0.042	0.079	0.135
14.0	0.000	0.000	0.000	0.001	0.002	0.005	0.014	0.032	0.062	0.109
14.5	0.000	0.000	0.000	0.000	0.001	0.004	0.011	0.024	0.048	0.088
15.0	0.000	0.000	0.000	0.000	0.001	0.003	0.008	0.018	0.037	0.070

λ	x = 10	11	12	13	14	15	16	17	18	19
2.8	1.000									
3.0	1.000									
3.2	1.000									
3.4	0.999	1.000								
3.6	0.999	1.000								
3.8	0.998	0.999	1.000							
4.0	0.997	0.999	1.000							
4.2	0.996	0.999	1.000							
4.4	0.994	0.998	0.999	1.000						
4.6	0.992	0.997	0.999	1.000						
4.8	0.990	0.996	0.999	1.000						
5.0	0.986	0.995	0.998	0.999	1.000					
5.2	0.982	0.993	0.997	0.999	1.000					
5.4	0.978	0.990	0.996	0.999	1.000					
5.6	0.972	0.988	0.995	0.998	0.999	1.000				
5.8	0.965	0.984	0.993	0.997	0.999	1.000				
6.0	0.957	0.980	0.991	0.996	0.999	1.000	1.000			
6.2	0.949	0.975	0.989	0.995	0.998	0.999	1.000			
6.4	0.939	0.969	0.986	0.994	0.997	0.999	1.000			
6.6	0.927	0.963	0.982	0.992	0.997	0.999	1.000	1.000		

	$x =$									
λ	10	11	12	13	14	15	16	17	18	19
6.8	0.915	0.955	0.978	0.990	0.996	0.998	0.999	1.000		
7.0	0.901	0.947	0.973	0.987	0.994	0.998	0.999	1.000		
7.2	0.887	0.937	0.967	0.984	0.993	0.997	0.999	1.000		
7.4	0.871	0.926	0.961	0.981	0.991	0.996	0.998	0.999	1.000	
7.6	0.854	0.915	0.954	0.976	0.989	0.995	0.998	0.999	1.000	
7.8	0.835	0.902	0.945	0.971	0.986	0.993	0.997	0.999	1.000	
8.0	0.816	0.888	0.936	0.966	0.983	0.992	0.996	0.998	0.999	1.000
8.5	0.763	0.849	0.909	0.949	0.973	0.986	0.993	0.997	0.999	1.000
9.0	0.706	0.803	0.876	0.926	0.959	0.978	0.989	0.995	0.998	0.999
9.5	0.645	0.752	0.836	0.898	0.940	0.967	0.982	0.991	0.996	0.998
10.0	0.583	0.697	0.792	0.865	0.916	0.951	0.973	0.986	0.993	0.997
10.5	0.521	0.639	0.742	0.825	0.888	0.932	0.960	0.978	0.989	0.994
11.0	0.460	0.579	0.689	0.781	0.854	0.907	0.944	0.968	0.982	0.991
11.5	0.402	0.520	0.633	0.733	0.815	0.878	0.924	0.954	0.974	0.986
12.0	0.347	0.462	0.576	0.681	0.772	0.844	0.899	0.937	0.963	0.979
12.5	0.297	0.406	0.519	0.628	0.725	0.806	0.869	0.916	0.948	0.969
13.0	0.252	0.353	0.463	0.573	0.675	0.764	0.836	0.890	0.930	0.957
13.5	0.211	0.304	0.409	0.518	0.623	0.718	0.797	0.861	0.908	0.942
14.0	0.176	0.260	0.358	0.464	0.570	0.669	0.756	0.827	0.883	0.923
14.5	0.145	0.220	0.311	0.412	0.518	0.619	0.711	0.790	0.853	0.901
15.0	0.118	0.185	0.268	0.363	0.466	0.568	0.664	0.749	0.820	0.875

	$x =$									
λ	20	21	22	23	24	25	26	27	28	29
8.5	1.000									
9.0	1.000									
9.5	0.999	1.000								
10.0	0.998	0.999	1.000							
10.5	0.997	0.999	0.999	1.000						
11.0	0.995	0.998	0.999	1.000						
11.5	0.993	0.996	0.998	0.999	1.000					
12.0	0.988	0.994	0.997	0.999	0.999	1.000				
12.5	0.983	0.991	0.995	0.998	0.999	0.999	1.000			
13.0	0.975	0.986	0.992	0.996	0.998	0.999	1.000			
13.5	0.965	0.980	0.989	0.994	0.997	0.998	0.999	1.000		
14.0	0.952	0.971	0.983	0.991	0.995	0.997	0.999	0.999	1.000	
14.5	0.936	0.960	0.976	0.986	0.992	0.996	0.998	0.999	1.000	1.000
15.0	0.917	0.947	0.967	0.981	0.989	0.994	0.997	0.998	0.999	1.000

	$x =$									
λ	5	6	7	8	9	10	11	12	13	14
16	0.001	0.004	0.010	0.022	0.043	0.077	0.127	0.193	0.275	0.367
17	0.001	0.002	0.005	0.013	0.026	0.049	0.085	0.135	0.201	0.281
18	0.000	0.001	0.003	0.007	0.015	0.030	0.055	0.092	0.143	0.208
19	0.000	0.001	0.002	0.004	0.009	0.018	0.035	0.061	0.098	0.150
20	0.000	0.000	0.001	0.002	0.005	0.011	0.021	0.039	0.066	0.105
21	0.000	0.000	0.000	0.001	0.003	0.006	0.013	0.025	0.043	0.072
22	0.000	0.000	0.000	0.001	0.002	0.004	0.008	0.015	0.028	0.048
23	0.000	0.000	0.000	0.000	0.001	0.002	0.004	0.009	0.017	0.031

λ	5	6	7	8	9	10	11	12	13	14
					$x =$					
24	0.000	0.000	0.000	0.000	0.000	0.001	0.003	0.005	0.011	0.020
25	0.000	0.000	0.000	0.000	0.000	0.001	0.001	0.003	0.006	0.012
26	0.000	0.000	0.000	0.000	0.000	0.000	0.001	0.002	0.004	0.008
27	0.000	0.000	0.000	0.000	0.000	0.000	0.000	0.001	0.002	0.005
28	0.000	0.000	0.000	0.000	0.000	0.000	0.000	0.001	0.001	0.003
29	0.000	0.000	0.000	0.000	0.000	0.000	0.000	0.000	0.001	0.002
30	0.000	0.000	0.000	0.000	0.000	0.000	0.000	0.000	0.000	0.001

λ	15	16	17	18	19	20	21	22	23	24
						$x =$				
16	0.467	0.566	0.659	0.742	0.812	0.868	0.911	0.942	0.963	0.978
17	0.371	0.468	0.564	0.655	0.736	0.805	0.862	0.905	0.937	0.959
18	0.287	0.375	0.469	0.562	0.651	0.731	0.799	0.855	0.899	0.932
19	0.215	0.292	0.378	0.469	0.561	0.647	0.726	0.793	0.849	0.893
20	0.157	0.221	0.297	0.381	0.470	0.559	0.644	0.721	0.787	0.843
21	0.111	0.163	0.227	0.302	0.384	0.471	0.558	0.640	0.716	0.782
22	0.077	0.117	0.169	0.233	0.306	0.387	0.472	0.556	0.637	0.712
23	0.052	0.082	0.123	0.175	0.238	0.310	0.389	0.472	0.555	0.635
24	0.034	0.056	0.087	0.128	0.180	0.243	0.314	0.392	0.473	0.554
25	0.022	0.038	0.060	0.092	0.134	0.185	0.247	0.318	0.394	0.473
26	0.014	0.025	0.041	0.065	0.097	0.139	0.191	0.252	0.321	0.396
27	0.009	0.016	0.027	0.044	0.069	0.102	0.144	0.195	0.256	0.324
28	0.005	0.010	0.018	0.030	0.048	0.073	0.106	0.148	0.200	0.260
29	0.003	0.006	0.011	0.020	0.033	0.051	0.077	0.110	0.153	0.204
30	0.002	0.004	0.007	0.013	0.022	0.035	0.054	0.081	0.115	0.157

λ	25	26	27	28	29	30	31	32	33	34
						$x =$				
16	0.987	0.993	0.996	0.998	0.999	0.999	1.000			
17	0.975	0.985	0.991	0.995	0.997	0.999	0.999	1.000		
18	0.955	0.972	0.983	0.990	0.994	0.997	0.998	0.999	1.000	
19	0.927	0.951	0.969	0.981	0.988	0.993	0.996	0.998	0.999	0.999
20	0.888	0.922	0.948	0.966	0.978	0.987	0.992	0.995	0.997	0.999
21	0.838	0.883	0.917	0.944	0.963	0.976	0.985	0.991	0.995	0.997
22	0.777	0.832	0.877	0.913	0.940	0.960	0.974	0.983	0.990	0.994
23	0.708	0.772	0.827	0.873	0.908	0.936	0.956	0.971	0.981	0.988
24	0.632	0.704	0.768	0.823	0.868	0.904	0.932	0.953	0.969	0.979
25	0.553	0.629	0.700	0.763	0.818	0.863	0.900	0.928	0.950	0.966
26	0.474	0.552	0.627	0.697	0.759	0.813	0.859	0.896	0.925	0.947
27	0.398	0.474	0.551	0.625	0.694	0.755	0.809	0.855	0.892	0.921
28	0.327	0.400	0.475	0.550	0.623	0.690	0.751	0.805	0.851	0.888
29	0.264	0.330	0.401	0.475	0.549	0.621	0.687	0.748	0.801	0.847
30	0.208	0.267	0.333	0.403	0.476	0.548	0.619	0.684	0.744	0.797

λ	35	36	37	38	39	40	41	42	43	44
						$x =$				
16	1.000									
17	1.000									
18	1.000									
19	1.000									
20	0.999	1.000								

λ	x =									
	35	36	37	38	39	40	41	42	43	44
21	0.998	0.999	1.000	1.000						
22	0.996	0.998	0.999	0.999	1.000					
23	0.993	0.996	0.997	0.999	0.999	1.000				
24	0.987	0.992	0.995	0.997	0.998	0.999	1.000	1.000		
25	0.978	0.985	0.991	0.994	0.997	0.998	0.999	0.999	1.000	
26	0.964	0.976	0.984	0.990	0.994	0.996	0.998	0.999	0.999	1.000
27	0.944	0.961	0.974	0.983	0.989	0.993	0.996	0.997	0.998	0.999
28	0.918	0.941	0.959	0.972	0.981	0.988	0.992	0.995	0.997	0.998
29	0.884	0.914	0.938	0.956	0.970	0.980	0.986	0.991	0.994	0.997
30	0.843	0.880	0.911	0.935	0.954	0.968	0.978	0.985	0.990	0.994

7.12.8   CRITICAL VALUES, KOLMOGOROV–SMIRNOV TEST

One-sided test	$p = 0.90$	0.95	0.975	0.99	0.995
Two-sided test	$p = 0.80$	0.90	0.95	0.98	0.99
$n = 1$	0.900	0.950	0.975	0.990	0.995
2	0.684	0.776	0.842	0.900	0.929
3	0.565	0.636	0.708	0.785	0.829
4	0.493	0.565	0.624	0.689	0.734
5	0.447	0.509	0.563	0.627	0.669
6	0.410	0.468	0.519	0.577	0.617
7	0.381	0.436	0.483	0.538	0.576
8	0.358	0.410	0.454	0.507	0.542
9	0.339	0.387	0.430	0.480	0.513
10	0.323	0.369	0.409	0.457	0.489
11	0.308	0.352	0.391	0.437	0.468
12	0.296	0.338	0.375	0.419	0.449
13	0.285	0.325	0.361	0.404	0.432
14	0.275	0.314	0.349	0.390	0.418
15	0.266	0.304	0.338	0.377	0.404
20	0.232	0.265	0.294	0.329	0.352
25	0.208	0.238	0.264	0.295	0.317
30	0.190	0.218	0.242	0.270	0.290
35	0.177	0.202	0.224	0.251	0.269
40	0.165	0.189	0.210	0.235	0.252
Approximation for $n > 40$:	$\dfrac{1.07}{\sqrt{n}}$	$\dfrac{1.22}{\sqrt{n}}$	$\dfrac{1.36}{\sqrt{n}}$	$\dfrac{1.52}{\sqrt{n}}$	$\dfrac{1.63}{\sqrt{n}}$

7.12.9   CRITICAL VALUES, TWO SAMPLE KOLMOGOROV–SMIRNOV TEST

The value of D listed below is so large that the hypothesis H_0, the two distributions are the same, is to be rejected at the indicated level of significance. Here, n_1 and n_2 are assumed to be large, and $D = \max \left| F_{n_1}(x) - F_{n_2}(x) \right|$.

Level of significance	Value of D
$\alpha = 0.10$	$1.22\sqrt{\frac{n_1+n_2}{n_1 n_2}}$
$\alpha = 0.05$	$1.36\sqrt{\frac{n_1+n_2}{n_1 n_2}}$
$\alpha = 0.025$	$1.48\sqrt{\frac{n_1+n_2}{n_1 n_2}}$
$\alpha = 0.01$	$1.63\sqrt{\frac{n_1+n_2}{n_1 n_2}}$
$\alpha = 0.005$	$1.73\sqrt{\frac{n_1+n_2}{n_1 n_2}}$
$\alpha = 0.001$	$1.95\sqrt{\frac{n_1+n_2}{n_1 n_2}}$

7.12.10 CRITICAL VALUES, SPEARMAN'S RANK CORRELATION

Spearman's coefficient of rank correlation, ρ_s, measures the correspondence between two rankings. Let d_i be the difference between the ranks of the ith pair of a set of n pairs of elements. Then Spearman's rho is defined as

$$\rho_s = 1 - \frac{6\sum_{i=1}^{n} d_i^2}{n^3 - n} = 1 - \frac{6S_r}{n^3 - n}$$

where $S_r = \sum_{i=1}^{n} d_i^2$. The table below gives critical values for S_r when there is complete independence.

n	$p = 0.90$	$p = 0.95$	$p = 0.99$	$p = 0.999$
4	0.8000	0.8000	–	–
5	0.7000	0.8000	0.9000	–
6	0.6000	0.7714	0.8857	–
7	0.5357	0.6786	0.8571	0.9643
8	0.5000	0.6190	0.8095	0.9286
9	0.4667	0.5833	0.7667	0.9000
10	0.4424	0.5515	0.7333	0.8667
11	0.4182	0.5273	0.7000	0.8364
12	0.3986	0.4965	0.6713	0.8182
13	0.3791	0.4780	0.6429	0.7912
14	0.3626	0.4593	0.6220	0.7670
15	0.3500	0.4429	0.6000	0.7464
20	0.2977	0.3789	0.5203	0.6586
25	0.2646	0.3362	0.4654	0.5962
30	0.2400	0.3059	0.4251	0.5479

7.13   SIGNAL PROCESSING

7.13.1   ESTIMATION

Let $\{e_t\}$ be a white noise process (so that $\mathrm{E}[e_t] = \mu$, variance$(e_t) = \sigma^2$, and covariance$(e_t, e_s) = 0$ for $s \neq t$). Suppose that $\{X_t\}$ is a time series. A nonantici-pating linear model presumes that $\sum_{u=0}^{\infty} h_u X_{t-u} = e_t$, where the $\{h_u\}$ are constants. This can be written $H(z)X_t = e_t$ where $H(z) = \sum_{u=0}^{\infty} h_u z^u$ and $z^n X_t = X_{t-n}$. Alternately, $X_t = H^{-1}(z)e_t$. In practice, several types of models are used:

- AR(k), autoregressive model of order k: This assumes that $H(z) = 1 + a_1 z + \cdots + a_k z_k$ and so

$$X_t + a_1 X_{t-1} + \ldots a_k X_{t-k} = e_t. \tag{7.13.1}$$

- MA(l), moving average of order l: This assumes that $H^{-1}(z) = 1 + b_1 z + \cdots + b_k z_k$ and so

$$X_t = e_t + b_1 e_{t-1} + \ldots b_l e_{t-l}. \tag{7.13.2}$$

- ARMA(k, l), mixed autoregressive/moving average of order (k, l): This assumes that $H^{-1}(z) = \frac{1 + b_1 z + \cdots + b_k z_k}{1 + a_1 z + \cdots + a_k z_k}$ and so

$$X_t + a_1 X_{t-1} + \ldots a_k X_{t-k} = e_t + b_1 e_{t-1} + \ldots b_l e_{t-l}. \tag{7.13.3}$$

7.13.2   FILTERS

1. Butterworth filter of order n: $\qquad |H_a(j\Omega)|^2 = \dfrac{1}{1 + (j\Omega/j\Omega_c)^{2n}}$.

2. Chebyshev filter of order n: $\qquad |H_a(j\Omega)|^2 = \dfrac{1}{1 + \epsilon^2 T_n(\Omega/\Omega_c)}$.

7.13.3   MATCHED FILTERING (WEINER FILTER)

Let $X(t)$ represent a signal to be recovered, let $N(t)$ represent noise, and let $Y(t) = X(t) + N(t)$ represent the observable signal. A prediction of the signal is

$$X_p(t) = \int_0^{\infty} K(z)Y(t - z)\,dz,$$

where $K(z)$ is a filter. The mean square error is $\mathrm{E}\left[(X(t) - X_p(t))^2\right]$; this is mini-mized by the optimal (Weiner) filter $K_{\mathrm{opt}}(z)$.

When X and Y are stationary, define their autocorrelation functions as $R_{XX}(t - s) = E[X(t)X(s)]$ and $R_{YY}(t - s) = E[Y(t)Y(s)]$. If $\mathcal{F}$ represents the Fourier transform (see page 530), then the optimal filter is given by

$$\mathcal{F}\left[K_{opt}(t)\right] = \frac{1}{2\pi} \frac{\mathcal{F}[R_{XX}(t)]}{\mathcal{F}[R_{YY}(t)]}. \tag{7.13.4}$$

For example, if X and N are uncorrelated, then

$$\mathcal{F}\left[K_{opt}(t)\right] = \frac{1}{2\pi} \frac{\mathcal{F}[R_{XX}(t)]}{\mathcal{F}[R_{XX}(t)] + \mathcal{F}[R_{NN}(t)]}. \tag{7.13.5}$$

In the case of no noise, $\mathcal{F}\left[K_{opt}(t)\right] = \frac{1}{2\pi}$, $K_{opt}(t) = \delta(t)$, and $S_p(t) = Y(t)$.

7.13.4   KALMAN FILTERING

Kalman filtering is a linear least squares recursive estimator. It is used when the state space has a higher dimension than the observation space. For example, in some airport radars the distance to aircraft is measured and the velocity of each aircraft is inferred. The general case covered by Kalman filtering is

$$\begin{aligned} \mathbf{x}_n &= F_n \mathbf{x}_{n-1} + G_n \mathbf{w}_n \\ \mathbf{y}_n &= H_n \mathbf{x}_n + J_n \mathbf{v}_n, \end{aligned} \tag{7.13.6}$$

where $\mathbf{x}_n$ is the state to be estimated and $\mathbf{y}_n$ is the observable. Here, F_n, G_n, H_n, and J_n are matrices (F_n is required to be non-singular), $\{\mathbf{x}_n\}$ is real-valued with $\mathbf{x}_{-1} = 0$, and $\{\mathbf{w}_n\}$ and $\{\mathbf{v}_n\}$ are uncorrelated white Gaussian noise processes with $E[\mathbf{w}_n] = E[\mathbf{v}_n] = \mathbf{0}$, $E\left[\mathbf{w}_n \mathbf{w}_n^T\right] = \sigma_w^2$, and $E\left[\mathbf{v}_n \mathbf{v}_n^T\right] = \sigma_v^2$.

Consider the simpler system

$$\begin{aligned} \mathbf{x}_n &= F \mathbf{x}_{n-1} + G \mathbf{w}_n \\ \mathbf{y}_n &= \mathbf{x}_n + \mathbf{v}_n. \end{aligned} \tag{7.13.7}$$

Here, F and G are constant matrices (F is also nonsingular). If $\hat{\mathbf{x}}_{n,m}$ is the predictor of $\mathbf{x}_n$ using the values $\{\mathbf{y}_0, \dots, \mathbf{y}_m\}$, then the Kalman predictor for $\mathbf{x}_{n,n-1}$ is

$$\hat{\mathbf{x}}_{n,n-1} = F\left[\hat{\mathbf{x}}_{n-1,n-2} + K_{n-1}\left(\mathbf{y}_{n-1} - \hat{\mathbf{x}}_{n-1,n-2}\right)\right] \tag{7.13.8}$$

and the Kalman predictor for $\mathbf{x}_{n,n}$ (called the Kalman filter) is

$$\hat{\mathbf{x}}_{n,n} = F\hat{\mathbf{x}}_{n-1,n-1} + K_n\left(\mathbf{y}_n - F\hat{\mathbf{x}}_{n-1,n-1}\right) \tag{7.13.9}$$

with $\hat{\mathbf{x}}_{-1,-1} = 0$. Here K_n is the Kalman gain matrix.

Define the error $\tilde{\mathbf{x}}_n = \hat{\mathbf{x}}_{n,n-1} - \mathbf{x}_n$ and its covariance matrix $\epsilon_n = E\left[\tilde{\mathbf{x}}_n \tilde{\mathbf{x}}_n^T\right]$. Then

$$K_n = \epsilon_n \left(\epsilon_n + \sigma_v^2\right)^{-1}, \quad \text{and} \quad \epsilon_n = F\epsilon_{n-1}\left[I - K_{n-1}^T\right]F^T + G\sigma_w^2 G^T,$$

which can be solved simultaneously.

For example, consider the system $\{x_n = 0.9x_{n-1} + w_n, \ y_n = x_n + v_n\}$ with $x_{-1} = 0$, $\sigma_w^2 = 0.19$, and $\sigma_v^2 = 1$. In this case $K_n = \epsilon_n/(1 + \epsilon_n)$, and $\epsilon_n = (0.19 + \epsilon_{n-1})/(1 + \epsilon_n)$. In the limit, $\epsilon_\infty = 0.436\dots$, and $K_\infty = 0.304\dots$. Hence, for large values of n, $\hat{\mathbf{x}}_{n,n} = 0.626\hat{\mathbf{x}}_{n-1,n-1} + 0.304\mathbf{y}_n$.

7.13.5   WALSH FUNCTIONS

The Rademacher functions are defined by $r_k(x) = \text{sgn} \sin \left(2^{k+1}\pi x\right)$. If the binary expansion of n has the form $n = 2^{i_1} + 2^{i_2} + \cdots + 2^{i_m}$, then the Walsh function of order n is $W_n(x) = r_{i_1}(x)r_{i_2}(x)\ldots r_{i_m}(x)$.

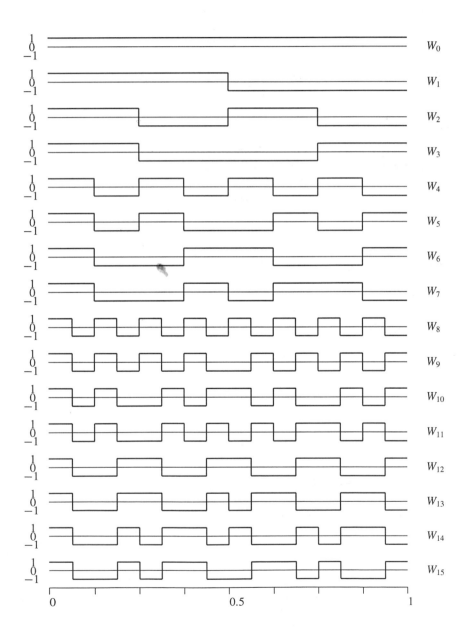

7.13.6   WAVELETS

The *Haar wavelet* is $H(x) = 1$ if $0 \leq x < 1/2$, -1 if $1/2 \leq x < 1$, and 0 otherwise. Define $H_{j,k}(x) = 2^{j/2} H(2^j x - k)$. Then the *Haar system*, $\{H_{j,k}\}_{j,k=-\infty}^{+\infty}$, forms an orthonormal basis for the Hilbert space, $L^2(\mathbb{R})$, consisting of functions f with finite energy, i.e., $\int_{-\infty}^{+\infty} |f(x)|^2 \, dx < \infty$.

Definitions

The construction of other wavelet orthonormal bases $\{\psi_{j,k}\}_{j,k=-\infty}^{+\infty}$ begins by choosing real coefficients $h_0, \ldots, h_n$ which satisfy the following conditions (we set $h_k = 0$ if $k < 0$ or $k > n$):

- Normalization: $\sum_k h_k = \sqrt{2}$.

- Orthogonality: $\sum_k h_k h_{k-2j} = 1$ if $j = 0$ and 0 if $j \neq 0$.

- Accuracy p: $\sum_k (-1)^k k^j h_k = 0$ for $j = 0, \ldots, p - 1$ with $p > 0$.

- Cohen–Lawton Criterion: A technical condition only rarely violated by coefficients which satisfy the normalization, orthogonality, and accuracy p conditions.

The terms *order of approximation* or *Strang–Fix conditions* are often used in place of "accuracy". The orthogonality condition implies that n is odd.

The four conditions above imply the existence of a solution $\varphi \in L^2(\mathbb{R})$, called the *scaling function*, to the following *refinement equation*:

$$\varphi(x) = \sqrt{2} \sum_{k=0}^{n} h_k \varphi(2x - k).$$

The scaling function has a nonvanishing integral which we normalize to $\int \varphi(x) \, dx = 1$. Then $\varphi(x)$ is unique, and it vanishes outside of the interval $[0, n]$. The maximum possible accuracy is $p = (n+1)/2$. Thus, increasing the accuracy requires increasing the number of coefficients h_k. High accuracy is desirable, as it implies that each of the polynomials $1, x, \ldots, x^{p-1}$ can be written as an infinite linear combination of the integer translates $\varphi(x - k)$. In particular, $\sum_k \varphi(x - k) = 1$. Also, the smoothness of φ is limited by the accuracy; φ can have at most $n - 2$ derivatives, although in practice it usually has fewer.

For each fixed integer j, let V_j be the closed subspace of $L^2(\mathbb{R})$ spanned by the functions, $\{\varphi_{j,k}\}_{k=-\infty}^{+\infty}$, where $\varphi_{j,k}(x) = 2^{j/2} \varphi(2^j x - k)$. The sequence of subspaces $\{V_j\}_{j=-\infty}^{+\infty}$ forms a *multiresolution analysis* for $L^2(\mathbb{R})$, meaning that:

- The subspaces are nested: $\cdots \subset V_{-1} \subset V_0 \subset V_1 \cdots$.

- They are obtained from each other by dilation by 2: $v(x) \in V_j \iff v(2x) \in V_{j+1}$.

- V_0 is integer translation invariant: $v(x) \in V_0 \iff v(x + 1) \in V_0$.

- The V_j increase to all of $L^2(\mathbb{R})$ and decrease to zero: $\cup V_j$ is dense in $L^2(\mathbb{R})$ and $\cap V_j = \{0\}$.

- The set of integer translates $\{\varphi(x-k)\}_{k=-\infty}^{+\infty}$ forms an orthonormal basis for V_0.

The projection of $f(x)$ onto the subspace V_j is an approximation at resolution level 2^{-j}. It is given by $f_j(x) = \sum_k c_{j,k} \varphi_{j,k}(x)$ with $c_{j,k} = \langle f, \varphi_{j,k} \rangle = \int f(x) \varphi_{j,k}(x) \, dx$. The *wavelet* ψ is derived from the scaling function φ by the formula,

$$\psi(x) = \sqrt{2} \sum_{k=0}^{n} g_k \varphi(2x - k), \qquad \text{where } g_k = (-1)^k h_{n-k}.$$

The wavelet ψ has the same smoothness as φ, and the accuracy p condition implies vanishing moments for ψ: $\int x^j \psi(x) \, dx = 0$ for $j = 0, \ldots, p - 1$. The functions $\psi_{j,k}(x) = 2^{j/2} \psi(2^j x - k)$ are orthonormal, and the entire collection $\{\psi_{j,k}\}_{j,k=-\infty}^{+\infty}$ forms an orthonormal basis for $L^2(\mathbb{R})$.

With j fixed, let W_j be the closed subspace of $L^2(\mathbb{R})$ spanned by $\psi(2^j x - k)$ for integer k. Then V_j and W_j are orthogonal subspaces whose direct sum is V_{j+1}. Let f be a function and let $p_j = \sum_k d_{j,k} \varphi_{j,k}(x)$ be its projection onto W_j, where $d_{j,k} = \langle f, \psi_{j,k} \rangle$. Then the approximation f_{j+1} with resolution $2^{-(j+1)}$ is $f_{j+1} = f_j + p_j$, the sum of the approximation f_j at resolution 2^{-j} and the additional fine details p_j needed to give the next higher resolution level.

The *discrete wavelet transform* is an algorithm for computing the coefficients $c_{j,k}$ and $d_{j,k}$ from the coefficients $c_{j+1,k}$. It can also be interpreted as an algorithm dealing directly with discrete data, dividing data $c_{j+1,k}$ into a *low-pass* part $c_{j,k}$ and a *high-pass* part $d_{j,k}$. Specifically,

$$c_{j,l} = \sum_k h_{k-2l} \, c_{j+1,k} \qquad \text{and} \qquad d_{j,l} = \sum_k g_{k-2l} \, c_{j+1,k}.$$

The inverse transform is

$$c_{j+1,k} = \sum_l h_{k-2l} \, c_{j,l} + \sum_l g_{k-2l} \, d_{j,l}.$$

The discrete wavelet transform is closely related to engineering techniques known as *sub-band coding* and *quadrature mirror filtering*.

Example: *the Daubechies family*. For each *even* integer $N > 0$, there is a unique set of coefficients $h_0, \ldots, h_{N-1}$ which satisfy the normalization and orthogonality conditions with maximal accuracy $p = N/2$. The corresponding φ and ψ are the *Daubechies scaling function* D_N and *Daubechies wavelet* W_N. The Haar wavelet H is the same as the Daubechies wavelet W_2. For the Haar wavelet, the coefficients are $h_0 = h_1 = 1/\sqrt{2}$ and the subspace V_j consists of all functions which are piecewise constant on each interval $[k2^{-j}, (k+1)2^{-j})$. The coefficients for D_4 are: $h_0 = (1 + \sqrt{3})/(4\sqrt{2})$, $h_1 = (3 + \sqrt{3})/(4\sqrt{2})$, $h_2 = (3 - \sqrt{3})/(4\sqrt{2})$, and $h_3 = (1 - \sqrt{3})/(4\sqrt{2})$.

Generalizations

For a given number of coefficients, the Daubechies wavelet has the highest accuracy. Other wavelets reduce the accuracy in exchange for other properties. In the *Coiflet* family the scaling function and the wavelet possesses vanishing moments, leading to simple one-point quadrature formulas. The "least asymmetric" wavelets are close to being symmetric or antisymmetric (perfect symmetry is incompatible with orthogonality, except for Haar).

Wavelet packets are libraries of basis functions defined recursively from the scaling functions ϕ and ψ. The *Walsh functions* are wavelet packets based on the Haar wavelet.

Allowing infinitely many coefficients results in wavelets supported on the entire real line. The *Meyer wavelet* is band-limited, possesses infinitely many derivatives, and has accuracy $p = \infty$. The *Battle–Lemarié* wavelets are piecewise splines and have exponential decay.

M-band wavelets replace the ubiquitous dilation factor 2 by another integer M. *Multiwavelets* replace the coefficients h_k by $r \times r$ matrices and the scaling function and wavelet by vector-valued functions $(\varphi_1, \ldots, \varphi_r)$ and $(\psi_1, \ldots, \psi_r)$, resulting in an orthonormal basis for $L^2(\mathbb{R})$ generated by the several wavelets $\psi_1, \ldots, \psi_r$.

For higher dimensions, a *separable* wavelet basis is constructed via a tensor product, with scaling function $\varphi(x)\varphi(y)$ and three wavelets $\varphi(x)\psi(y)$, $\psi(x)\varphi(y)$, $\psi(x)\psi(y)$. *Nonseparable wavelets* replace the dilation factor 2 by a *dilation matrix*.

Biorthogonal wavelets allow greater flexibility of design by relaxing the requirement that the wavelet system $\{\psi_{j,k}\}$ form an orthonormal basis to requiring only that it form a Riesz basis. The *Cohen–Daubechies–Feauveau wavelets* are symmetric and their coefficients h_k are dyadic rationals. The *Chui–Wang–Aldroubi–Unser semiorthogonal wavelets* are splines with explicit analytic formulas.

The basis condition may be further relaxed by allowing $\{\psi_{j,k}\}$ to be a *frame*, an overcomplete system with basis-like properties. Introducing further redundancy, the *continuous wavelet transform* uses all possible dilates and translates $a^{1/2}\psi(ax+b)$.

Wavelet coefficients and figures

Coefficients for Daubechies scaling functions[1]

D_2 :	h_0:	0.707106781187		D_8 :	h_0:	0.230377813309
	h_1:	0.707106781187			h_1:	0.714846570553
					h_2:	0.630880767930
D_4 :	h_0:	0.482962913145			h_3:	-0.027983769417
	h_1:	0.836516303738			h_4:	-0.187034811719
	h_2:	0.224143868042			h_5:	0.030841381836
	h_3:	-0.129409522551			h_6:	0.032883011667
					h_7:	-0.010597401785
D_6 :	h_0:	0.332670552950				
	h_1:	0.806891509311				
	h_2:	0.459877502118				
	h_3:	-0.135011020010				
	h_4:	-0.085441273882				
	h_5:	0.035226291886				

---

[1] The tables and figures are taken in part from Table 6.1 and Figure 6.3 of Ingrid Daubechies' book *Ten Lectures on Wavelets*, published by SIAM Press and used with permission.

D_{10} :

h_0:	0.160102397974
h_1:	0.603829269797
h_2:	0.724308528438
h_3:	0.138428145901
h_4:	−0.242294887066
h_5:	−0.032244869585
h_6:	0.077571493840
h_7:	−0.006241490213
h_8:	−0.012580751999
h_9:	0.003335725285

D_{12} :

h_0:	0.111540743350
h_1:	0.494623890398
h_2:	0.751133908021
h_3:	0.315250351709
h_4:	−0.226264693965
h_5:	−0.129766867567
h_6:	0.097501605587
h_7:	0.027522865530
h_8:	−0.031582039317
h_9:	0.000553842201
h_{10}:	0.004777257511
h_{11}:	−0.001077301085

D_4

W_4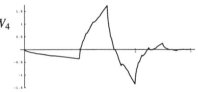

D_6

W_6

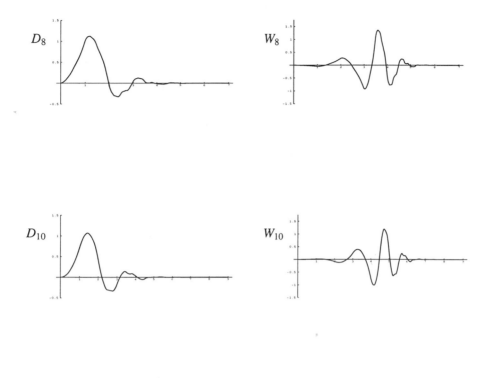

References

1. W. H. Beyer, *CRC Standard Probability and Statistics: Tables and Formulae*, CRC Press, Boca Raton, FL, 1991.

2. I. Daubechies, *Ten Lectures on Wavelets*, SIAM Press, Philadelphia, 1992.

3. W. Feller, *An Introduction to Probability Theory and Its Applications*, Volume 1, John Wiley & Sons, New York, 1968.

4. S. K. Park and K. W. Miller, "Random number generators: good ones are hard to find," *Comm. ACM*, October 1988, 31, 10, pages 1192–1201.

5. G. Strang and T. Nguyen, *Wavelets and Filter Banks*, Wellesley–Cambridge Press, Wellesley, MA, 1995.

Chapter  8

Scientific Computing

0-8493-2479-3/96/$0.00+$.50
© 1996 CRC Press, Inc.

The text *Numerical Analysis*, Fifth Edition, Prindle, Weber & Schmidt (Boston) 1993, by R. L. Burden and J. D. Faires, was the primary reference for most of the information presented in this chapter.

8.1   BASIC NUMERICAL ANALYSIS

8.1.1   APPROXIMATIONS AND ERRORS

Numerical methods involve finding approximate solutions to mathematical problems. Errors of approximation can result from two sources: error inherent in the method or formula used and round off error. *Round off error* results when a calculator or computer is used to perform real-number calculations with a finite number of significant digits. All but the first specified number of digits are either *chopped* or *rounded* to that number of digits.

If p^* is an approximation to p, the *absolute error* is defined to be $|p - p^*|$ and the *relative error* is $|p - p^*|/|p|$, provided that $p \neq 0$.

Iterative techniques often generate sequences that (ideally) converge to an exact solution. It is sometimes desirable to describe the *rate of convergence*.

DEFINITION 8.1.1

Suppose $\lim \beta_n = 0$ *and* $\lim \alpha_n = \alpha$. *If a positive constant K exists with* $|\alpha_n - \alpha| < K\,|\beta_n|$ *for large n, then* $\{\alpha_n\}$ *is said to converge to α with a rate of convergence* $O(\beta_n)$. *This is read "big oh of β_n" and written* $\alpha_n = \alpha + O(\beta_n)$.

DEFINITION 8.1.2

Suppose $\{p_n\}$ *is a sequence that converges to p. If positive constants λ and α exist with*
$$\lim_{n \to \infty} \frac{|p_{n+1} - p|}{|p_n - p|^{\alpha}} = \lambda,\ \textit{then}\ \{p_n\}\ \textit{is said to}\ \text{converge to } p \text{ of order } \alpha,\ \textit{with asymptotic}$$
error constant λ.

In general, a higher order of convergence yields a more rapid rate of convergence. A sequence has *linear convergence* if $\alpha = 1$ and *quadratic convergence* if $\alpha = 2$.

Aitken's $\triangle^2$ method

DEFINITION 8.1.3

Given the sequence $\{p_n\}_{n=0}^{\infty}$, *define the* forward difference $\triangle p_n$ *by* $\triangle p_n = p_{n+1} - p_n$, *for n ≥ 0. Higher powers $\Delta^k p_n$ are defined recursively by $\Delta^k p_n = \Delta(\Delta^{k-1} p_n)$ for $k \geq 2$. In particular, $\Delta^2 p_n = \Delta(p_{n+1} - p_n) = p_{n+2} - 2p_{n+1} + p_n$.*

If a sequence $\{p_n\}$ converges linearly to p, the new sequence $\{\hat{p}_n\}$ generated by

$$\hat{p}_n = p_n - \frac{(\Delta p_n)^2}{\Delta^2 p_n} \tag{8.1.1}$$

for all $n \geq 0$, called *Aitken's Δ^2 method*, satisfies $\lim_{n\to\infty} \dfrac{\hat{p}_n - p}{p_n - p} = 0$.

Richardson's extrapolation

Improved accuracy can be achieved by combining *extrapolation* with a low-order formula. Suppose the unknown value M is approximated by a formula $N(h)$ for which

$$M = N(h) + K_1 h + K_2 h^2 + K_3 h^3 + \cdots \tag{8.1.2}$$

for some unspecified constants $K_1, K_2, K_3, \ldots$ To apply extrapolation, set $N_1(h) = N(h)$, and generate new approximations $N_j(h)$ by

$$N_j(h) = N_{j-1}\left(\frac{h}{2}\right) + \frac{N_{j-1}\left(\frac{h}{2}\right) - N_{j-1}(h)}{2^{j-1} - 1}. \tag{8.1.3}$$

Then $M = N_j(h) + O(h^j)$. A table of the following form is generated, one row at a time:

$$
\begin{array}{llll}
N_1(h) & & & \\
N_1(\frac{h}{2}) & N_2(h) & & \\
N_1(\frac{h}{4}) & N_2(\frac{h}{2}) & N_3(h) & \\
N_1(\frac{h}{8}) & N_2(\frac{h}{4}) & N_3(\frac{h}{2}) & N_4(h).
\end{array}
$$

Extrapolation can be applied whenever the truncation error for a formula has the form $\sum_{j=1}^{m-1} K_j h^{\alpha_j} + O(h^{\alpha_m})$ for constants K_j and $\alpha_1 < \alpha_2 < \cdots < \alpha_m$. In particular, if $\alpha_j = 2j$, the following computation can be used:

$$N_j(h) = N_{j-1}\left(\frac{h}{2}\right) + \frac{N_{j-1}(\frac{h}{2}) - N_{j-1}(h)}{4^{j-1} - 1}, \tag{8.1.4}$$

where the entries in the jth column of the table have order $O(h^{2j})$.

8.1.2 SOLUTION TO ALGEBRAIC EQUATIONS

Iterative methods generate sequences $\{p_n\}$ that converge to a solution p of an equation.

DEFINITION 8.1.4

A solution p of $f(x) = 0$ is a zero of multiplicity m if $f(x)$ can be written as $f(x) = (x - p)^m q(x)$, for $x \neq p$, where $\lim_{x \to p} q(x) \neq 0$. A zero is called simple *if $m = 1$.*

Fixed point iteration

A *fixed point* p for a function g satisfies $g(p) = p$. Given p_0, generate $\{p_n\}$ by

$$p_{n+1} = g(p_n) \quad \text{for } n \geq 0. \tag{8.1.5}$$

If $\{p_n\}$ converges, then it will converge to a fixed point of g and the value p_n can be used as an approximation for p. The following theorem gives conditions that guarantee convergence.

THEOREM 8.1.1   *(Fixed point theorem)*

Let $g \in C[a, b]$ and suppose that $g(x) \in [a, b]$ for all x in $[a, b]$. Suppose, in addition, that g' exists on (a, b) with $\left| g'(x) \right| \leq k < 1$, for all $x \in (a, b)$. If p_0 is any number in $[a, b]$, then the sequence defined by Equation (8.1.5) converges to the (unique) fixed point p in $[a, b]$, and $|p_n - p| \leq \frac{k^n}{1-k} |p_0 - p_1|$ for all $n \geq 1$.

The iteration sometimes converges even if all the conditions are not satisfied.

THEOREM 8.1.2

Suppose g is a function that satisfies the conditions of Theorem 8.1.1 and g' is also continuous on (a, b). If $g'(p) \neq 0$, then for any number p_0 in $[a, b]$, the sequence generated by Equation (8.1.5) converges only linearly to the unique fixed point p in $[a, b]$.

THEOREM 8.1.3

Let p be a solution of the equation $x = g(x)$. Suppose that $g'(p) = 0$ and g'' is continuous and strictly bounded by M on an open interval I containing p. Then there exists a $\delta > 0$ such that, for $p_0 \in [p - \delta, p + \delta]$, the sequence defined by Equation (8.1.5) converges at least quadratically to p.

Steffensen's method

For a linearly convergent fixed point iteration, convergence can be accelerated by applying Aitken's Δ^2 method. This is called *Steffensen's method*. Define $p_0^{(0)} = p_0$,

FIGURE 8.1.1

Illustration of Newton's method.[1]

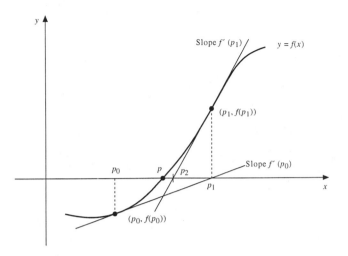

compute $p_1^{(0)} = g(p_0^{(0)})$ and $p_2^{(0)} = g(p_1^{(0)})$. Set $p_0^{(1)} = \hat{p}_0$ which is computed using Equation (8.1.1) applied to $p_0^{(0)}$, $p_1^{(0)}$ and $p_2^{(0)}$. Use fixed point iteration to compute $p_1^{(1)}$ and $p_2^{(1)}$ and then Equation (8.1.1) to find $p_0^{(2)}$. Continuing, generate $\{p_0^{(n)}\}$.

THEOREM 8.1.4

Suppose that $x = g(x)$ has the solution p with $g'(p) \neq 1$. If there exists a $\delta > 0$ such that $g \in C^3[p - \delta, p + \delta]$, then Steffensen's method gives quadratic convergence for the sequence $\{p_0^{(n)}\}$ for any $p_0 \in [p - \delta, p + \delta]$.

Newton–Raphson method (Newton's method)

To solve $f(x) = 0$, given an initial approximation p_0, generate $\{p_n\}$ using

$$p_{n+1} = p_n - \frac{f(p_n)}{f'(p_n)}, \quad \text{for } n \geq 0 \tag{8.1.6}$$

Figure 8.1.1 describes the method geometrically. Each value p_{n+1} represents the x-intercept of the tangent line to the graph of $f(x)$ at the point $[p_n, f(p_n)]$.

THEOREM 8.1.5

Let $f \in C^2[a, b]$. If $p \in [a, b]$ is such that $f(p) = 0$ and $f'(p) \neq 0$, then there exists a $\delta > 0$ such that Newton's method generates a sequence $\{p_n\}$ converging to p for any initial approximation $p_0 \in [p - \delta, p + \delta]$.

---

[1]From R.L. Burden and J.D. Faires, *Numerical Analysis*, 5th ed., Prindle, Weber & Schmidt, Boston, 1993. With permission.

Note:

1. Generally the conditions of the theorem cannot be checked. Therefore one usually generates the sequence $\{p_n\}$ and observes whether or not it converges.

2. An obvious limitation is that the iteration terminates if $f'(p_n) = 0$.

3. For *simple* zeros of f, Theorem 8.1.3 implies that Newton's method converges quadratically. Otherwise, the convergence is much slower.

Modified Newton's method

Newton's method converges only linearly if p has multiplicity larger that one. However, the function $u(x) = \frac{f(x)}{f'(x)}$ has a simple zero at p. Hence, the Newton iteration formula applied to $u(x)$ yields quadratic convergence to a root of $f(x) = 0$. The iteration simplifies to

$$p_{n+1} = p_n - \frac{f(p_n)f'(p_n)}{[f'(p_n)]^2 - f(p_n)f''(p_n)}, \qquad \text{for } n \geq 0. \qquad (8.1.7)$$

Secant method

To solve $f(x) = 0$, the secant method uses the x-intercept of the secant line passing through $(p_n, f(p_n))$ and $(p_{n-1}, f(p_{n-1}))$. The derivative of f is not needed. Given p_0 and p_1, generate the sequence with

$$p_{n+1} = p_n - f(p_n)\frac{(p_n - p_{n-1})}{f(p_n) - f(p_{n-1})}, \qquad \text{for } n \geq 1. \qquad (8.1.8)$$

Root bracketing methods

Suppose $f(x)$ is continuous on $[a, b]$ and $f(a)f(b) < 0$. The intermediate value theorem guarantees a number $p \in [a, b]$ exists with $f(p) = 0$. A *root bracketing method* constructs a sequence of nested intervals $[a_n, b_n]$, each containing a solution of $f(x) = 0$. At each step, compute $p_n \in [a_n, b_n]$ and proceed as follows:

If $f(p_n) = 0$, stop the iteration and $p = p_n$.
Else,

if $f(a_n)f(p_n) < 0$, then set $a_{n+1} = a_n, b_{n+1} = p_n$.
Else, set $a_{n+1} = p_n, b_{n+1} = b_n$.

Bisection method

This is a special case of the root bracketing method. The values p_n are computed by

$$p_n = a_n + \frac{b_n - a_n}{2} = \frac{a_n + b_n}{2}, \qquad \text{for } n \geq 1. \qquad (8.1.9)$$

Clearly, $|p_n - p| \leq (b - a)/2^n$ for $n \geq 1$. The rate of convergence is $O(2^{-n})$. Although convergence is slow, the exact number of iterations for a specified accuracy ϵ can be determined. To guarantee that $|p_N - p| < \epsilon$, use

$$N > \log_2 \left(\frac{b - a}{\epsilon} \right) = \frac{\ln(b - a) - \ln \epsilon}{\ln 2}. \qquad (8.1.10)$$

False position (*regula falsi*)

$$p_n = b_n - f(b_n) \frac{b_n - a_n}{f(b_n) - f(a_n)}, \qquad \text{for } n \geq 1. \qquad (8.1.11)$$

Both methods converge, provided the initial criteria are satisfied.

Horner's method with deflation

If Newton's method is used to solve for roots of the polynomial $P(x) = 0$, then the polynomials P and P' are repeatedly evaluated. Horner's method efficiently evaluates a polynomial of degree n using only n multiplications and n additions.

Horner's algorithm

To evaluate $P(x) = a_n x^n + a_{n-1} x^{n-1} + \cdots + a_0$ and its derivative at x_0 ($y = P(x_0)$, $z = P'(x_0)$),

> INPUT: degree n, coefficients $\{a_0, a_1, \ldots, a_n\}$; x_0,
> OUTPUT: $y = P(x_0)$; $z = P'(x_0)$.
> Algorithm
>
> 1. Set $y = a_n$; $z = a_n$.
> 2. For $j = n - 1, n - 2, \ldots, 1$,
>   set $y = x_0 y + a_j$; $z = x_0 z + y$.
> 3. Set $y = x_0 y + a_0$.
> 4. OUTPUT (y, z). STOP.

When satisfied with the approximation $\hat{x}_1$ for a root x_1 of P, use synthetic division to compute $Q_1(x)$ so that $P(x) \approx (x - \hat{x}_1) Q_1(x)$. Estimate a root of $Q_1(x)$ and write $P(x) \approx (x - \hat{x}_1)(x - \hat{x}_2) Q_2(x)$, and so on. Eventually, $Q_{n-2}(x)$ will be a quadratic, and the quadratic formula can be applied. This procedure, finding one root at a time, is called *deflation*.

Note: Care must be taken since $\hat{x}_1$ is an *approximation* for x_1. Some inaccuracy occurs when computing the coefficients of $Q_1(x)$, etc. Although the estimate x_2 of a root of $Q_2(x)$ can be very accurate, it may not be as accurate when estimating a root of $P(x)$.

8.1.3   INTERPOLATION

Interpolation involves fitting a function to a set of data points (x_0, y_0), (x_1, y_1), ..., (x_n, y_n). The x_i are unique and the y_i may be regarded as the values of some function $f(x)$, that is, $y_i = f(x_i)$ for $i = 0, 1, \ldots, n$. Polynomial interpolation methods are discussed below.

Lagrange interpolation

The *Lagrange interpolating polynomial*, denoted $P_n(x)$, is the unique polynomial of degree at most n for which $P_n(x_k) = f(x_k)$ for $k = 0, 1, \ldots, n$. It is given by

$$P(x) = \sum_{k=0}^{n} f(x_k) L_{n,k}(x) \tag{8.1.12}$$

where $\{x_0, \ldots, x_n\}$ are called *node points*.

$$
\begin{aligned}
L_{n,k}(x) &= \frac{(x - x_0)(x - x_1) \cdots (x - x_{k-1})(x - x_{k+1}) \cdots (x - x_n)}{(x_k - x_0)(x_k - x_1) \cdots (x_k - x_{k-1})(x_k - x_{k+1}) \cdots (x_k - x_n)}, \\
&= \prod_{i=0, i \neq k}^{n} \frac{(x - x_i)}{(x_k - x_i)}, \qquad \text{for } k = 0, 1, \ldots, n.
\end{aligned}
\tag{8.1.13}
$$

THEOREM 8.1.6   *(Error formula)*

If $x_0, x_1, \ldots, x_n$ are distinct numbers in $[a, b]$ and $f \in C^{n+1}[a, b]$, then, for each x in $[a, b]$, a number $\xi(x)$ in (a, b) exists with

$$f(x) = P(x) + \frac{f^{(n+1)}(\xi(x))}{(n+1)!} (x - x_0)(x - x_1) \cdots (x - x_n),$$

where P is the interpolating polynomial given in Equation (8.1.12).

Although the Lagrange polynomial is unique, it can be expressed and evaluated in several ways. Equation (8.1.12) is tedious to evaluate, and including more nodes affects the *entire* expression. *Neville's method* evaluates the Lagrange polynomial at a single point *without* explicitly finding the polynomial and adapts easily to the addition of nodes.

Neville's method

Let $P_{m_1, m_2, \ldots, m_k}$ denote the Lagrange polynomial using distinct nodes $\{x_{m_1}, x_{m_2}, \ldots, x_{m_k}\}$. If $P(x)$ denotes the Lagrange polynomial using nodes $\{x_0, x_1, \ldots, x_k\}$ and x_i and x_j are two distinct numbers in this set, then

$$P(x) = \frac{(x - x_j) P_{0,1,\ldots,j-1,j+1,\ldots,k}(x) - (x - x_i) P_{0,1,\ldots,i-1,i+1,\ldots,k}(x)}{(x_i - x_j)}. \tag{8.1.14}$$

Neville's algorithm

Generate a table of entries $Q_{i,j}$ for $j \geq 0$ and $0 \leq i \leq j$ where $Q_{i,j} = P_{i-j,i-j+1,...,i-1,i}$. Calculations use Equation (8.1.14) for a specific value of x as shown:

$$
\begin{array}{llll}
x_0 & Q_{0,0} = P_0, \\
x_1 & Q_{1,0} = P_1, & Q_{1,1} = P_{0,1}, \\
x_2 & Q_{2,0} = P_2, & Q_{2,1} = P_{1,2}, & Q_{2,2} = P_{0,1,2}, \\
x_3 & Q_{3,0} = P_3, & Q_{3,1} = P_{2,3}, & Q_{3,2} = P_{1,2,3}, & Q_{3,3} = P_{0,1,2,3}.
\end{array}
$$

Note that $P_k = P_k(x) = f(x_k)$ and $\{Q_{i,i}\}$ represents successive estimates of $f(x)$ using Lagrange polynomials. Nodes may be added until $|Q_{i,i} - Q_{i-1,i-1}| < \epsilon$ as desired.

Some interpolation formulae involve *divided differences*. Given a sequence $\{x_i\}$ and corresponding function values $f(x_i)$, the *zero*[th] *divided difference* is $f[x_i] = f(x_i)$. The *first divided difference* is defined by

$$
f[x_i, x_{i+1}] = \frac{f(x_{i+1}) - f(x_i)}{x_{i+1} - x_i} = \frac{f[x_{i+1}] - f[x_i]}{x_{i+1} - x_i}. \tag{8.1.15}
$$

The kth *divided difference* is defined by

$$
f[x_i, x_{i+1}, \ldots, x_{i+k-1}, x_{i+k}]
$$
$$
= \frac{f[x_{i+1}, x_{i+2}, \ldots, x_{i+k}] - f[x_i, x_{i+1}, \ldots, x_{i+k-1}]}{x_{i+k} - x_i}. \tag{8.1.16}
$$

Divided differences are usually computed by forming a triangular table.

Divided differences

x	$f(x)$	First divided differences	Second divided differences	Third divided differences
x_0	$f[x_0]$			
		$f[x_0, x_1]$		
x_1	$f[x_1]$		$f[x_0, x_1, x_2]$	
		$f[x_1, x_2]$		$f[x_0, x_1, x_2, x_3]$
x_2	$f[x_2]$		$f[x_1, x_2, x_3]$	
		$f[x_2, x_3]$		
x_3	$f[x_3]$			

Newton's interpolatory divided-difference formula

(also known as the Newton polynomial)

$$
P_n(x) = f[x_0] + \sum_{k=1}^{n} f[x_0, x_1, \ldots, x_k](x - x_0) \cdots (x - x_{k-1}). \tag{8.1.17}
$$

Labeling the nodes as $\{x_n, x_{n-1}, \ldots, x_0\}$, a formula similar to Equation (8.1.17) results in *Newton's backward divided-difference formula*,

$$P_n(x) = f[x_n] + f[x_{n-1}, x_n](x - x_n)$$
$$+ f[x_{n-2}, x_{n-1}, x_n](x - x_n)(x - x_{n-1})$$
$$+ \cdots + f[x_0, x_1, \ldots, x_n](x - x_n) \cdots (x - x_1). \quad (8.1.18)$$

If the nodes are equally-spaced (that is, $x_i - x_{i-1} = h$), define the parameter s by the equation $x = x_0 + sh$. The following formulae evaluate $P_n(x)$ at a single point:

1. Newton's interpolatory divided-difference formula,

$$P_n(x) = P_n(x_0 + sh) = \sum_{k=0}^{n} \binom{s}{k} k! h^k f[x_0, x_1, \ldots, x_k].$$
$$(8.1.19)$$

2. Newton's forward-difference formula (Newton–Gregory),

$$P_n(x) = P_n(x_0 + sh) = \sum_{k=0}^{n} \binom{s}{k} \Delta^k f(x_0). \quad (8.1.20)$$

3. Newton–Gregory backward formula (fits nodes x_{-n} to x_0),

$$P_n(x) = f(x_0) + \binom{s}{1} \Delta f(x_{-1}) + \binom{s+1}{2} \Delta^2 f(x_{-2}) +$$
$$\cdots + \binom{s+n-1}{n} \Delta^n f(x_{-n}). \quad (8.1.21)$$

4. Newton's backward-difference formula,

$$P_n(x) = \sum_{k=0}^{n} (-1)^k \binom{-s}{k} \nabla^k f(x_n), \quad (8.1.22)$$

where $\nabla^k f(x_n)$ is the kth *backward difference* defined by $\nabla p_n = p_n - p_{n-1}$ for $n \geq 1$. Higher powers are defined recursively by $\nabla^k p_n = \nabla(\nabla^{k-1} p_n)$ for $k \geq 2$.

5. Stirling's formula (for equally-spaced nodes $x_{-m}, \ldots, x_{-1}, x_0, x_1, \ldots, x_m$),

$$P_n(x) = P_{2m+1}(x) = f[x_0] + \frac{sh}{2}(f[x_{-1}, x_0] + f[x_0, x_1]) +$$
$$s^2 h^2 f[x_{-1}, x_0, x_1] + \frac{s(s^2 - 1)h^3}{2}(f[x_{-1}, x_0, x_1, x_2] + f[x_{-2}, x_{-1}, x_0, x_1])$$
$$+ \cdots + s^2(s^2 - 1)(s^2 - 4) \cdots (s^2 - (m-1)^2)h^{2m} f[x_{-m}, \ldots, x_m]$$
$$+ \frac{s(s^2 - 1) \cdots (s^2 - m^2)h^{2m+1}}{2}(f[x_{-m}, \ldots, x_{m+1}] + f[x_{-m-1}, \ldots, x_m]).$$

Use the entire formula if $n = 2m + 1$ is odd, and omit the last term if $n = 2m$ is even. The following table identifies the desired divided differences used in Stirling's formula:

x	$f(x)$	First divided differences	Second divided differences	Third divided differences
x_{-2}	$f[x_{-2}]$			
		$f[x_{-2}, x_{-1}]$		
x_{-1}	$f[x_{-1}]$		$f[x_{-2}, x_{-1}, x_0]$	
		$f[x_{-1}, x_0]$		$f[x_{-2}, x_{-1}, x_0, x_1]$
x_0	$f[x_0]$		$f[x_{-1}, x_0, x_1]$	
		$f[x_0, x_1]$		$f[x_{-1}, x_0, x_1, x_2]$
x_1	$f[x_1]$		$f[x_0, x_1, x_2]$	
		$f[x_1, x_2]$		
x_2	$f[x_2]$			

Inverse interpolation

Any method of interpolation which does not require the nodes to be equally-spaced may be applied by simply interchanging the nodes (x values) and the function values (y values).

Hermite interpolation

Given node points $\{x_0, x_1, \ldots, x_n\}$, the *Hermite interpolating polynomial* for a function f is the unique polynomial $H(x)$ of degree at most $2n + 1$ that satisfies $H(x_i) = f(x_i)$ and $H'(x_i) = f'(x_i)$ for each $i = 0, 1, \ldots, n$.

A technique and formula similar to Equation (8.1.17) can be used. For distinct nodes $\{x_0, x_1, \ldots, x_n\}$, define $\{z_0, z_1, \ldots, z_{2n+1}\}$ by $z_{2i} = z_{2i+1} = x_i$ for $i = 0, 1, \ldots, n$. Construct a divided difference table for the ordered pairs $(z_i, f(z_i))$ using $f'(x_i)$ in place of $f[z_{2i}, z_{2i+1}]$, which would be undefined. Denote the Hermite polynomial by $H_{2n+1}(x)$.

Hermite interpolating polynomial

$$
\begin{aligned}
H_{2n+1}(x) &= f[z_0] + \sum_{k=1}^{2n+1} f[z_0, z_1, \ldots, z_k](x - z_0) \cdots (x - z_{k-1}) \\
&= f[z_0] + f[z_0, z_1](x - x_0) + f[z_0, z_1, z_2](x - x_0)^2 \\
&\quad + f[z_0, z_1, z_2, z_3](x - x_0)^2(x - x_1) \\
&\quad + \cdots + f[z_0, \ldots, z_{2n+1}](x - x_0)^2 \cdots (x - x_{n-1})^2(x - x_n).
\end{aligned}
$$

(8.1.23)

THEOREM 8.1.7 *(Error formula)*

If $f \in C^{(2n+2)}[a, b]$, then

$$
f(x) = H_{2n+1}(x) + \frac{f^{(2n+2)}(\xi(x))}{(2n+2)!}(x - x_0)^2 \cdots (x - x_n)^2
$$

for some $\xi \in (a, b)$ and where $x_i \in [a, b]$ for each $i = 0, 1, \ldots, n$.

8.1.4   FITTING EQUATIONS TO DATA

Piecewise polynomial approximation

An interpolating polynomial has large degree and tends to oscillate greatly for large data sets. *Piecewise polynomial approximation* divides the interval into a collection of subintervals and constructs an approximating polynomial on each subinterval. *Piecewise linear interpolation* consists of simply joining the data points with line segments. This collection is continuous but not differentiable at the node points. Hermite polynomials would require derivative values. *Cubic spline interpolation* is popular since no derivative information is needed.

DEFINITION 8.1.5

Given a function f defined on $[a, b]$ and a set of numbers $a = x_0 < x_1 < \cdots < x_n = b$, a cubic spline interpolant, S, for f is a function that satisfies

1. *S is a piecewise cubic polynomial; denoted S_j on $[x_j, x_{j+1}]$ for each $j = 0, 1, \ldots, n - 1$.*

2. *$S(x_j) = f(x_j)$ for each $j = 0, 1, \ldots, n$.*

3. *$S_{j+1}(x_{j+1}) = S_j(x_{j+1})$ for each $j = 0, 1, \ldots, n - 2$.*

4. *$S'_{j+1}(x_{j+1}) = S'_j(x_{j+1})$ for each $j = 0, 1, \ldots, n - 2$.*

5. *$S''_{j+1}(x_{j+1}) = S''_j(x_{j+1})$ for each $j = 0, 1, \ldots, n - 2$.*

6. *One of the following sets of boundary conditions is satisfied:*

   - *$S''(x_0) = S''(x_n) = 0$ (free or natural boundary),*

   - *$S'(x_0) = f'(x_0)$ and $S'(x_n) = f'(x_n)$ (clamped boundary).*

If a function f is defined at all node points, then f has a unique natural spline interpolant. If, in addition, f is differentiable at a and b, then f has a unique clamped spline interpolant. To construct a cubic spline, set

$$S_j(x) = a_j + b_j(x - x_j) + c_j(x - x_j)^2 + d_j(x - x_j)^3$$

for each $j = 0, 1, \ldots, n - 1$. The constants $\{a_j, b_j, c_j, d_j\}$ are found by solving a triadiagonal system of linear equations which is included in the following algorithms.

Algorithm for natural cubic splines

INPUT: n, $\{x_0, x_1, \ldots, x_n\}$,
$\quad a_0 = f(x_0), a_1 = f(x_1), \ldots, a_n = f(x_n)$.
OUTPUT: $\{a_j, b_j, c_j, d_j\}$ for $j = 0, 1, \ldots, n - 1$.

Algorithm

1. For $i = 0, 1, \ldots, n - 1$, set $h_i = x_{i+1} - x_i$.
2. For $i = 1, 2, \ldots, n - 1$, set $\alpha_i = \frac{3}{h_i}(a_{i+1} - a_i) - \frac{3}{h_{i-1}}(a_i - a_{i-1})$.
3. Set $l_0 = 1$, $\mu_0 = 0$, $z_0 = 0$.
4. For $i = 1, 2, \ldots, n - 1$,
   set $l_i = 2(x_{i+1} - x_{i-1}) - h_{i-1}\mu_{i-1}$,
   set $\mu_i = \frac{h_i}{l_i}$, $z_i = \frac{(\alpha_i - h_{i-1}z_{i-1})}{l_i}$.
5. Set $l_n = 1$, $z_n = 0$, $c_n = 0$.
6. For $j = n - 1, n - 2, \ldots, 0$,
   set $c_j = z_j - \mu_j c_{j+1}$, $b_j = \frac{(a_{j+1} - a_j)}{h_j} - \frac{h_j(c_{j+1} + 2c_j)}{3}$,
   set $d_j = \frac{(c_{j+1} - c_j)}{3h_j}$.
7. OUTPUT $(a_j, b_j, c_j, d_j$ for $j = 0, 1, \ldots, n - 1)$.   STOP.

Algorithm for clamped cubic splines

INPUT: n, $\{x_0, x_1, \ldots, x_n\}$,
   $a_0 = f(x_0), a_1 = f(x_1), \ldots, a_n = f(x_n)$,
   $F_0 = f'(x_0), F_n = f'(x_n)$.
OUTPUT: $\{a_j, b_j, c_j, d_j\}$ for $j = 0, 1, \ldots, n - 1$.
Algorithm

1. For $i = 0, 1, \ldots, n - 1$, set $h_i = x_{i+1} - x_i$.
2. Set $\alpha_0 = \frac{3(a_1 - a_0)}{h_0} - 3F_0$, $\alpha_n = 3F_n - \frac{3(a_n - a_{n-1})}{h_{n-1}}$.
3. For $i = 1, 2, \ldots, n - 1$, set $\alpha_i = \frac{3}{h_i}(a_{i+1} - a_i) - \frac{3}{h_{i-1}}(a_i - a_{i-1})$.
4. Set $l_0 = 2h_0$, $\mu_0 = 0.5$, $z_0 = \frac{\alpha_0}{l_0}$.
5. For $i = 1, 2, \ldots, n - 1$,
   set $l_i = 2(x_{i+1} - x_{i-1}) - h_{i-1}\mu_{i-1}$,
   set $\mu_i = \frac{h_i}{l_i}$, $z_i = \frac{(\alpha_i - h_{i-1}z_{i-1})}{l_i}$.
6. Set $l_n = h_{n-1}(2 - \mu_{n-1})$, $z_n = \frac{(\alpha_n - h_{n-1}z_{n-1})}{l_n}$; $c_n = z_n$.
7. For $j = n - 1, n - 2, \ldots, 0$,
   set $c_j = z_j - \mu_j c_{j+1}$, $b_j = \frac{(a_{j+1} - a_j)}{h_j} - \frac{h_j(c_{j+1} + 2c_j)}{3}$,
   set $d_j = \frac{(c_{j+1} - c_j)}{3h_j}$.
8. OUTPUT $(a_j, b_j, c_j, d_j$ for $j = 0, 1, \ldots, n - 1)$. STOP.

Discrete least squares approximation

Another approach to fit a function to a set of data points $\{(x_i, y_i) \mid i = 1, 2, \ldots, m\}$ is *least squares approximation*. If a polynomial of degree n is used, the polynomial $P_n(x) = \sum_{k=0}^{n} a_k x^k$ is found that minimizes the *least squares error* $E = \sum_{i=1}^{m} [y_i - P_n(x_i)]^2$.

To find $\{a_0, a_1, \ldots, a_n\}$, solve the linear system, called the *normal equations*, created by setting partial derivatives of E taken with respect to each a_k equal to zero. The coefficient of a_0 in the first equation is actually the number of data points m.

Normal equations

$$a_0 \sum_{i=1}^{m} x_i^0 + a_1 \sum_{i=1}^{m} x_i^1 + a_2 \sum_{i=1}^{m} x_i^2 + \cdots + a_n \sum_{i=1}^{m} x_i^n = \sum_{i=1}^{m} y_i x_i^0,$$

$$a_0 \sum_{i=1}^{m} x_i^1 + a_1 \sum_{i=1}^{m} x_i^2 + a_2 \sum_{i=1}^{m} x_i^3 + \cdots + a_n \sum_{i=1}^{m} x_i^{n+1} = \sum_{i=1}^{m} y_i x_i^1,$$

$$\vdots$$

$$a_0 \sum_{i=1}^{m} x_i^n + a_1 \sum_{i=1}^{m} x_i^{n+1} + a_2 \sum_{i=1}^{m} x_i^{n+2} + \cdots + a_n \sum_{i=1}^{m} x_i^{2n} = \sum_{i=1}^{m} y_i x_i^n.$$

Note: $P_n(x)$ can be replaced by a function f of specified form. Unfortunately, to minimize E, the resulting system is generally *not* linear. Although these systems can be solved, one technique is to "linearize" the data. For example, if $y = f(x) = be^{ax}$, then $\ln y = \ln b + ax$. The least squares method applied to the data points $(x_i, \ln y_i)$ produces a linear system. Note that this technique does *not* find the least squares approximation for the original problem but, instead, approximates the "linearized" data.

Best fit line

Given the points $P_1(x_1, y_1)$, $P_2(x_1, y_1)$, ... $P_n(x_1, y_1)$ the line of best fit is given by $y - \bar{y} = m(x - \bar{x})$ where

$$\bar{x} = \frac{1}{n} \sum_{i=1}^{n} x_i = \frac{(x_1 + x_2 + \cdots + x_n)}{n},$$

$$\bar{y} = \frac{1}{n} \sum_{i=1}^{n} y_i = \frac{(y_1 + y_2 + \cdots + y_n)}{n},$$

$$m = \frac{(x_1 y_1 + x_2 y_2 + \cdots + x_n y_n) - n\bar{x}\,\bar{y}}{(x_1^2 + x_2^2 + \cdots + x_n^2) - n\bar{x}^2} = \frac{\overline{xy} - \bar{x}\,\bar{y}}{\overline{x^2} - \bar{x}^2}.$$

8.2   NUMERICAL LINEAR ALGEBRA

8.2.1   SOLVING LINEAR SYSTEMS

The solution of systems of linear equations using *Gaussian elimination with backward substitution* is described in Section 8.2.2. The algorithm is highly sensitive to round off error. *Pivoting strategies* can reduce round off error when solving an $n \times n$ system.

For a linear system $\mathbf{Ax} = \mathbf{b}$, assume that the equivalent matrix equation $\mathbf{A}^{(k)}\mathbf{x} = \mathbf{b}^{(k)}$ has been constructed. Call the entry, $a_{k,k}^{(k)}$, the *pivot element*.

8.2.2 GAUSSIAN ELIMINATION

To solve the system $A\mathbf{x} = \mathbf{b}$, Gaussian elimination creates the augmented matrix

$$A' = [A \vdots \mathbf{b}] = \begin{bmatrix} a_{11} & \cdots & a_{1n} & b_1 \\ \vdots & & \vdots & \vdots \\ a_{n1} & \cdots & a_{nn} & b_n \end{bmatrix}.$$

This matrix is turned into an upper triangular matrix by a sequence of (1) row permutations, and (2) subtracting a multiple of one row from another. The result is a matrix of the form (the primes denote that the quantities have been modified)

$$\begin{bmatrix} a'_{11} & a'_{12} & \cdots & a'_{1n} & b'_1 \\ 0 & a'_{22} & \cdots & a'_{2n} & b'_2 \\ \vdots & \ddots & \ddots & \vdots & \vdots \\ 0 & \cdots & 0 & a'_{nn} & b'_n \end{bmatrix}.$$

This matrix represents a system of linear equations (just as A' did), equivalent to the original system. Back substitution can be used to determine, successively, $\{x_n, x_{n-1}, \dots\}$.

8.2.3 GAUSSIAN ELIMINATION ALGORITHM

INPUT: number of unknowns and equations n, matrix A, and vector $\mathbf{b}$.
OUTPUT: solution to linear system $\mathbf{x} = (x_1, \dots, x_n) = A^{-1}\mathbf{b}$,
  or message that system does not have a unique solution.
Algorithm

1. Construct the augmented matrix $A' = [A \vdots \mathbf{b}] = (a'_{ij})$
2. For $i = 1, 2, \dots, n - 1$ do the following: *(Elimination process)*
    (a) Let p be the least integer with $i \le p \le n$ and $a'_{pi} \ne 0$
        If no integer can be found, then
        OUTPUT("no unique solution exists"). STOP.
    (b) If $p \ne i$ interchange rows p and i in A'. Call the new matrix A'.
    (c) For $j = i + 1, \dots, n$ do the following:
        i. Set $m_{ij} = a'_{ji}/a'_{ii}$.
        ii. Subtract from row j the quantity (m_{ij} times row i).

3. If $a'_{nn} = 0$ then OUTPUT ("no unique solution exists"). STOP.
4. Set $x_n = a'_{n,n+1}/a'_{nn}$. *(Start backward substitution)*

5. For $i = n - 1, \ldots, 2, 1$ set $x_i = \left[a'_{i,n+1} - \sum_{j=i+1}^{n} a'_{ij} x_j \right] / a'_{ii}$.

6. OUTPUT $(x_1, \ldots, x_n)$, *(Procedure completed successfully)*. STOP.

8.2.4   PIVOTING

Maximal column pivoting

Maximal column pivoting (often called *partial pivoting*) finds, at each step, the element in the same column as the pivot element that lies on or below the main diagonal having the largest magnitude and moves it to the pivot position. Determine the least $p \geq k$ such that $\left| a_{p,k}^{(k)} \right| = \max_{k \leq i \leq n} \left| a_{i,k}^{(k)} \right|$ and interchange the kth equation with the pth equation before performing the elimination step.

Scaled-column pivoting

Scaled-column pivoting sometimes produces better results, especially when the elements of A differ greatly in magnitude. The desired pivot element is chosen to have the largest magnitude *relative* to the other values in its row. For each row define a *scale factor* s_i by $s_i = \max_{1 \leq j \leq n} \left| a_{i,j} \right|$. The desired pivot element at the kth step is determined by choosing the smallest integer p with $\dfrac{\left| a_{p,k}^{(k)} \right|}{s_p} = \max_{k \leq j \leq n} \dfrac{\left| a_{j,k}^{(k)} \right|}{s_j}$.

Maximal (or complete) pivoting

The desired pivot element at the kth step is the entry of largest magnitude among $\{a_{i,j}\}$ with $i = k, k + 1, \ldots, n$ and $j = k, k + 1, \ldots, n$. Both row and column interchanges are necessary and additional comparisons are required, resulting in additional execution time.

8.2.5   EIGENVALUE COMPUTATION

Power method

Assume that the $n \times n$ matrix A has n eigenvalues $\{\lambda_1, \lambda_2, \ldots, \lambda_n\}$ with independent eigenvectors $\{\mathbf{v}^{(1)}, \mathbf{v}^{(2)}, \ldots, \mathbf{v}^{(n)}\}$. Assume further that A has a unique dominant eigenvector λ_1, where $|\lambda_1| > |\lambda_2| \geq |\lambda_3| \geq \cdots \geq |\lambda_n|$. For any $\mathbf{x} \in \mathbb{R}^n$, $\mathbf{x} = \sum_{j=1}^{n} \alpha_j \mathbf{v}^{(j)}$.

The algorithm is called the *power method* because powers of the input matrix are taken: $\lim_{k \to \infty} A^k \mathbf{x} = \lim_{k \to \infty} \lambda_1^k \alpha_1 \mathbf{v}^{(1)}$. However, this sequence converges to zero, if $|\lambda_1| < 1$, and diverges, if $|\lambda_1| \geq 1$, provided $\alpha_1 \neq 0$. Appropriate scaling of $A^k \mathbf{x}$ is necessary to obtain a meaningful limit. Begin by choosing a unit vector $\mathbf{x}^{(0)}$ having a component $x_{p_0}^{(0)}$ so that $x_{p_0}^{(0)} = 1 = \left\| \mathbf{x}^{(0)} \right\|_\infty$.

The algorithm inductively constructs sequences of vectors $\{\mathbf{x}^{(m)}\}_{m=0}^{\infty}$ and $\{\mathbf{y}^{(m)}\}_{m=0}^{\infty}$ and a sequence of scalars $\{\mu^{(m)}\}_{m=1}^{\infty}$ by

$$\mathbf{y}^{(m)} = A\mathbf{x}^{(m-1)}, \qquad \mu^{(m)} = y_{p_m}^{(m)}, \qquad \mathbf{x}^{(m)} = \frac{\mathbf{y}^{(m)}}{y_{p_m}^{(m)}}, \qquad (8.2.1)$$

where, at each step, p_m represents the least integer for which $\left|y_{p_m}^{(m)}\right| = \left\|\mathbf{y}^{(m)}\right\|_{\infty}$.

The sequence of scalars satisfies $\lim_{m\to\infty} \mu^{(m)} = \lambda_1$, provided $\alpha_1 \neq 0$, and the sequence of vectors $\{\mathbf{x}^{(m)}\}_{m=0}^{\infty}$ converges to an eigenvector of L_{∞} associated with λ_1.

Power method algorithm

INPUT: dimension n, matrix A, vector $\mathbf{x}$, tolerance TOL, and
   maximum iterations N.
OUTPUT: approximate eigenvalue μ,
   approximate eigenvector $\mathbf{x}$ (with $\|\mathbf{x}\|_{\infty} = 1$),
   or a message that the maximum number of iterations was exceeded.
Algorithm

1. Set $k=1$.

2. Find an integer p with $1 \leq p \leq n$ and $\left|x_p\right| = \|\mathbf{x}\|_{\infty}$.

3. Set $\mathbf{x} = \frac{1}{x_p}\mathbf{x}$.

4. While $(k \leq N)$ do the following:

   (a) Set $\mathbf{y} = A\mathbf{x}$.

   (b) Set $\mu = y_p$.

   (c) Find an integer p with $1 \leq p \leq n$ and $\left|y_p\right| = \|\mathbf{y}\|_{\infty}$.

   (d) If $y_p = 0$ then OUTPUT ("Eigenvector", $\mathbf{x}$);
         OUTPUT ("corresponds to eigenvalue 0;
         select a new vector $\mathbf{x}$ and restart"). STOP.

   (e) Set $ERR = \left\|\mathbf{x} - \frac{1}{y_p}\mathbf{y}\right\|_{\infty}$; $\mathbf{x} = \frac{1}{y_p}\mathbf{y}$.

   (f) If $ERR < TOL$ then OUTPUT $(\mu, \mathbf{x})$
         (procedure successful). STOP.

   (g) Set $k = k + 1$.

5. OUTPUT ("Maximum number of iterations exceeded"). STOP.

Notes:

1. The method does not really require that λ_1 be unique. If the multiplicity is greater than one, the eigenvector obtained depends on the choice of $\mathbf{x}^{(0)}$.

2. The sequence constructed converges linearly, so that Aitken's Δ^2 method (Equation (8.1.1)) can be applied to accelerate convergence.

Inverse power method

The *inverse power method* modifies the power method to yield faster convergence by finding the eigenvalue of A that is closest to a specified number q. Assume that A satisfies the conditions as before. If $q \neq \lambda_i$, for $i = 1, 2, \ldots, n$, the eigenvalues of $(A - qI)^{-1}$ are $\frac{1}{\lambda_1 - q}, \frac{1}{\lambda_2 - q}, \ldots, \frac{1}{\lambda_n - q}$ with the same eigenvectors $\mathbf{v}^{(1)}, \ldots, \mathbf{v}^{(n)}$. Apply the power method to $(A - qI)^{-1}$. At each step, $\mathbf{y}^{(m)} = (A - qI)^{-1}\mathbf{x}^{(m-1)}$. Generally, $\mathbf{y}^{(m)}$ is found by solving $(A - qI)\mathbf{y}^{(m)} = \mathbf{x}^{(m-1)}$ using Gaussian elimination with pivoting. Choose the value q from an initial approximation to the eigenvector $\mathbf{x}^{(0)}$ by $q = \mathbf{x}^{(0)T}A\mathbf{x}^{(0)}/\mathbf{x}^{(0)T}\mathbf{x}^{(0)}$.

The only changes in the algorithm for the power method (see page 685) are in setting an initial value q as described (do this prior to step 1), determining $\mathbf{y}$ by solving the linear system $(A - qI)\mathbf{y}^{(m)} = \mathbf{x}^{(m-1)}$ in step (4a), deleting step (4d), and replacing step (4f) with

$$\text{if} \quad ERR < TOL \text{ then set } \mu = \frac{1}{\mu} + q; \qquad \text{OUTPUT}(\mu, \mathbf{x}); \qquad \text{STOP.}$$

Wielandt deflation

Once the dominant eigenvalue has been found, remaining eigenvalues can be found by using *deflation techniques*. A new matrix B is formed having the same eigenvalues as A, except that the dominant eigenvalue of A is replaced by 0. One method is *Wielandt deflation* which defines $\mathbf{x} = \frac{1}{\lambda_1 v_i^{(1)}}[a_{i1} \; a_{i2} \; \ldots \; a_{in}]^T$, where $v_i^{(1)}$ is a coordinate of $\mathbf{v}^{(1)}$ that is nonzero, and the values $\{a_{i1}, a_{i2}, \ldots, a_{in}\}$ are the entries in the ith row of A. Then the matrix $B = A - \lambda_1 \mathbf{v}^{(1)}\mathbf{x}^T$ has eigenvalues $0, \lambda_2, \lambda_3, \ldots, \lambda_n$ with associated eigenvectors $\{\mathbf{v}^{(1)}, \mathbf{w}^{(2)}, \mathbf{w}^{(3)}, \ldots, \mathbf{w}^{(n)}\}$, where

$$\mathbf{v}^{(i)} = (\lambda_i - \lambda_1)\mathbf{w}^{(i)} + \lambda_1(\mathbf{x}^T\mathbf{w}^{(i)})\mathbf{v}^{(1)}$$

for $i = 2, 3, \ldots, n$. The ith row of B consists entirely of zero entries and B may be replaced with an $(n - 1) \times (n - 1)$ matrix B' obtained by deleting the ith row and i^{th} column of B. The power method can be applied to B' to find *its* dominant eigenvalue and so on.

8.2.6   HOUSEHOLDER'S METHOD

DEFINITION 8.2.1

Two $n \times n$ matrices A and B are said to be similar *if a nonsingular matrix S exists with $A = S^{-1}BS$.*

Householder's method constructs a symmetric tridiagonal matrix B that is similar to a given symmetric matrix A. After applying this method, the *QR algorithm* can be used efficiently to approximate the eigenvalues of the resulting symmetric tridiagonal matrix.

Algorithm for Householder's method

To construct a symmetric tridiagonal matrix $A^{(n-1)}$ similar to the symmetric matrix $A = A^{(1)}$, construct matrices $A^{(2)}, A^{(3)}, \ldots, A^{(n-1)}$, where $A^{(k)} = (a_{ij}^{(k)})$ for $k = 1, 2, \ldots, n-1$.

> INPUT: dimension n, matrix A.
> OUTPUT: $A^{(n-1)}$.   *(At each step, A can be overwritten.)*
> Algorithm
>
> 1. For $k = 1, 2, \ldots, n-2$ do the following steps:
>   - (a) Set $q = \sum_{j=k+1}^{n} (a_{jk}^{(k)})^2$.
>
>   - (b) If $a_{k+1,k}^{(k)} = 0$, then set $\alpha = -q^{\frac{1}{2}}$; else, set $\alpha = -\dfrac{q^{\frac{1}{2}} a_{k+1,k}^{(k)}}{\left| a_{k+1,k}^{(k)} \right|}$.
>
>   - (c) Set $RSQ = \alpha^2 - \alpha a_{k+1,k}^{(k)}$.
>
>   - (d) Set $v_k = 0$. (Note: $v_1 = \cdots = v_{k-1} = 0$, but are not needed.)
>   Set $v_{k+1} = a_{k+1,k}^{(k)} - \alpha$. For $j = k+2, \ldots, n$, set $v_j = a_{jk}^{(k)}$.
>
>   - (e) For $j = k, k+1, \ldots, n$, set $u_j = \dfrac{1}{RSQ} \sum_{i=k+1}^{n} a_{ji}^{(k)} v_i$.
>
>   - (f) Set $PROD = \sum_{i=k+1}^{n} v_i u_i$.
>
>   - (g) For $j = k, k+1, \ldots, n$, set $z_j = u_j - (\frac{PROD}{2RSQ}) v_j$.
>
>   - (h) For $l = k+1, k+2, \ldots, n-1$ do the following steps:
>   - i. For $j = l+1, \ldots, n$, set $a_{jl}^{(k+1)} = a_{jl}^{(k)} - v_l z_j - v_j z_l$;
> $a_{lj}^{(k+1)} = a_{jl}^{(k+1)}$.
>   - ii. Set $a_{ll}^{(k+1)} = a_{ll}^{(k)} - 2v_l z_l$.
>
>   - (i) Set $a_{nn}^{(k+1)} = a_{nn}^{(k)} - 2v_n z_n$.
>
>   - (j) For $j = k+2, \ldots, n$, set $a_{kj}^{(k+1)} = a_{jk}^{(k+1)} = 0$.
>
>   - (k) Set $a_{k+1,k}^{(k+1)} = a_{k+1,k}^{(k)} - v_{k+1} z_k$; $a_{k,k+1}^{(k+1)} = a_{k+1,k}^{(k+1)}$.
>   (Note: The other elements of $A^{(k+1)}$ are the same as $A^{(k)}$.)
>
> 2. OUTPUT $A^{(n-1)}$. STOP.
>   ($A^{(n-1)}$ is symmetric, tridiagonal, similar to A.)

8.2.7 QR ALGORITHM

The *QR algorithm* is generally used (instead of deflation) to determine all of the eigenvalues of a symmetric matrix. The matrix must be symmetric and in tridiagonal form. If necessary, first apply Householder's method. Suppose the matrix A has the form

$$A = \begin{bmatrix} a_1 & b_2 & 0 & \cdots & 0 & 0 & 0 \\ b_2 & a_2 & b_3 & & 0 & 0 & 0 \\ 0 & b_3 & a_3 & & 0 & 0 & 0 \\ \vdots & & & \ddots & & & \vdots \\ 0 & 0 & 0 & & a_{n-2} & b_{n-1} & 0 \\ 0 & 0 & 0 & & b_{n-1} & a_{n-1} & b_n \\ 0 & 0 & 0 & \cdots & 0 & b_n & a_n \end{bmatrix}.$$

If $b_2 = 0$ or $b_n = 0$, then A has the eigenvalue a_1 or a_n, respectively. If $b_j = 0$ for some j, $2 < j < n$, the problem is reduced to considering, instead of A, the smaller matrices,

$$\begin{bmatrix} a_1 & b_2 & 0 & \cdots & & 0 \\ b_2 & a_2 & b_3 & & & 0 \\ 0 & b_3 & a_3 & & & 0 \\ \vdots & & & & & \\ 0 & 0 & & a_{j-2} & b_{j-1} \\ 0 & 0 & & b_{j-1} & a_{j-1} \end{bmatrix} \quad \text{and} \quad \begin{bmatrix} a_j & b_{j+1} & 0 & \cdots & & 0 \\ b_{j+1} & a_{j+1} & b_{j+2} & & & 0 \\ 0 & b_{j+2} & a_{j+2} & & & 0 \\ \vdots & & & & & \\ 0 & 0 & & a_{n-1} & b_n \\ 0 & 0 & & b_n & a_n \end{bmatrix}.$$

If none of the b_j are zero, the QR algorithm forms $\{A^{(1)} = A, A^{(2)}, A^{(3)}, \ldots, \}$ as follows:

1. $A^{(1)} = A$ is factored as $A^{(1)} = Q^{(1)}R^{(1)}$, with $Q^{(1)}$ orthogonal and $R^{(1)}$ upper triangular.

2. $A^{(2)} = R^{(1)}Q^{(1)}$ and is factored as $A^{(2)} = Q^{(2)}R^{(2)}$, with $Q^{(2)}$ orthogonal and $R^{(2)}$ upper triangular.

In general, $A^{(i+1)} = R^{(i)}Q^{(i)} = (Q^{(i)^T}A^{(i)})Q^{(i)} = Q^{(i)^T}A^{(i)}Q^{(i)}$. Note that $A^{(i+1)}$ is symmetric and tridiagonal with the same eigenvalues as $A^{(i)}$ and, hence, has the same eigenvalues as A.

Algorithm for QR

To obtain eigenvalues of the symmetric tridiagonal $n \times n$ matrix

$$A \equiv A_1 = \begin{bmatrix} a_1^{(1)} & b_2^{(1)} & 0 & \cdots & 0 & 0 & 0 \\ b_2^{(1)} & a_2^{(1)} & b_3^{(1)} & & 0 & 0 & 0 \\ 0 & b_3^{(1)} & a_3^{(1)} & & 0 & 0 & 0 \\ \vdots & & & \ddots & & & \vdots \\ 0 & 0 & 0 & & a_{n-2}^{(1)} & b_{n-1}^{(1)} & 0 \\ 0 & 0 & 0 & & b_{n-1}^{(1)} & a_{n-1}^{(1)} & b_n^{(1)} \\ 0 & 0 & 0 & \cdots & 0 & b_n^{(1)} & a_n^{(1)} \end{bmatrix}.$$

INPUT: n; $a_1^{(1)}, \ldots, a_n^{(1)}, b_2^{(1)}, \ldots, b_n^{(1)}$, tolerance TOL, and maximum iterations M.

OUTPUT: eigenvalues of A, or recommended splitting of A,
or a message that the maximum number of iterations was exceeded.
Algorithm

1. Set $k = 1$, $SHIFT = 0$. (Accumulated shift)

2. While $k \leq M$, do steps 3–8.

3. Test for success

   (a) If $\left|b_n^{(k)}\right| \leq TOL$, then set $\lambda = a_n^{(k)} + SHIFT$;
       OUTPUT λ; set $n = n - 1$;

   (b) If $\left|b_j^{(k)}\right| \leq TOL$ for $3 \leq j \leq n - 1$, then
       OUTPUT ("split into", $\{a_1^{(k)}, \ldots, a_{j-1}^{(k)}, b_2^{(k)}, \ldots, b_{j-1}^{(k)}\}$,
       and $\{a_j^{(k)}, \ldots, a_n^{(k)}, b_{j+1}^{(k)}, \ldots, b_n^{(k)}\}$, $SHIFT$); STOP.

   (c) If $\left|b_2^{(k)}\right| \leq TOL$ then, set $\lambda = a_1^{(k)} + SHIFT$;
       OUTPUT (λ);
       Set $n = n - 1$; $a_1^{(k)} = a_2^{(k)}$;
       For $j = 2, \ldots, n$, set $a_j^{(k)} = a_{j+1}^{(k)}$; $b_j^{(k)} = b_{j+1}^{(k)}$.

4. Compute shift.
   - Set $b = -(a_{n-1}^{(k)} + a_n^{(k)})$, $c = a_n^{(k)} a_{n-1}^{(k)} - [b_n^{(k)}]^2$, and
     $d = (b^2 - 4c)^{\frac{1}{2}}$.
   - If $b > 0$, then set $\mu_1 = \frac{-2c}{(b+d)}$, $\mu_2 = \frac{-(b+d)}{2}$.
     Else, set $\mu_1 = \frac{(d-b)}{2}$ and $\mu_2 = \frac{2c}{(d-b)}$.
   - If $n = 2$, then set $\lambda_1 = \mu_1 + SHIFT$.
     $\lambda_2 = \mu_2 + SHIFT$; OUTPUT (λ_1, λ_2). STOP.
   - Choose s so that $\left|s - a_n^{(k)}\right| = \min\left(\left|\mu_1 - a_n^{(k)}\right|, \left|\mu_2 - a_n^{(k)}\right|\right)$.

5. Accumulate shift. Set $SHIFT = SHIFT + s$.

6. Perform shift. For $j = 1, \ldots, n$, set $d_j = a_j^{(k)} - s$.

7. Compute $R^{(k)}$.

   (a) Set $x_1 = d_1$; $y_1 = b_2$;

   (b) For $j = 2, \ldots, n$,
       set $z_{j-1} = (x_{j-1}^2 + [b_j^{(k)}]^2)^{\frac{1}{2}}$, $c_j = \frac{x_{j-1}}{z_{j-1}}$,
       set $S_j = \frac{b_j^{(k)}}{z_{j-1}}$, $q_{j-1} = c_j y_{j-1} + S_j d_j$, and
       set $x_j = -S_j y_{j-1} + c_j d_j$.

   (c) If $j \neq n$ then, set $r_{j-1} = S_j b_{j+1}^{(k)}$, $y_j = c_j b_{j+1}^{(k)}$.

   $(A_j^{(k)} = P_j A_{j-1}^{(k)}$ has been computed (P_j is a rotation matrix) and
   $R^{(k)} = A_n^{(k)}$.)

8. Compute $A^{(k+1)}$.

   (a) Set $z_n = x_n$, $a_1^{(k+1)} = s_2 q_1 + c_2 z_1$, $b_2^{(k+1)} = s_2 z_2$.

(b) For $j = 2, 3 \ldots, n - 1$,

set $a_j^{(k+1)} = s_{j+1} q_j + c_j c_{j+1} z_j$, and

set $b_{j+1}^{(k+1)} = s_{j+1} z_{j+1}$.

(c) Set $a_n^{(k+1)} = c_n z_n$, $k = k + 1$.

9. OUTPUT ("Maximum iterations exceeded");
   (Procedure unsuccessful.) STOP.

8.2.8   NONLINEAR SYSTEMS AND NUMERICAL OPTIMIZATION

Newton's method

Many iterative methods exist for solving systems of nonlinear equations. *Newton's method* is a natural extension of his method for solving a single equation in one variable. Convergence is generally quadratic but usually requires an initial approximation that is near the true solution. Assume $\mathbf{F}(\mathbf{x}) = \mathbf{0}$ where $\mathbf{x}$ is an n-dimensional vector, $\mathbf{F} : \mathbb{R}^n \to \mathbb{R}^n$, and $\mathbf{0}$ is the zero vector, that is,

$$\mathbf{F}(x_1, x_2, \ldots, x_n) = (f_1(x_1, x_2, \ldots, x_n), \ldots, f_n(x_1, x_2, \ldots, x_n))^{\mathrm{T}}.$$

A fixed point iteration is performed on $\mathbf{G}(\mathbf{x}) = \mathbf{x} - (J(\mathbf{x}))^{-1} \mathbf{F}(\mathbf{x})$ where $\mathbf{J}(\mathbf{x})$ is the *Jacobian matrix*,

$$\mathbf{J}(\mathbf{x}) = \begin{vmatrix} \dfrac{\partial f_1(\mathbf{X})}{\partial x_1} & \dfrac{\partial f_1(\mathbf{X})}{\partial x_2} & \cdots & \dfrac{\partial f_1(\mathbf{X})}{\partial x_n} \\ \dfrac{\partial f_2(\mathbf{X})}{\partial x_1} & \dfrac{\partial f_2(\mathbf{X})}{\partial x_2} & \cdots & \dfrac{\partial f_2(\mathbf{X})}{\partial x_n} \\ \vdots & & & \vdots \\ \dfrac{\partial f_n(\mathbf{X})}{\partial x_1} & \dfrac{\partial f_n(\mathbf{X})}{\partial x_2} & \cdots & \dfrac{\partial f_n(\mathbf{X})}{\partial x_n} \end{vmatrix}. \tag{8.2.2}$$

The iteration is given by

$$\mathbf{x}^{(k)} = \mathbf{G}(\mathbf{x}^{(k-1)}) = \mathbf{x}^{(k-1)} - \left[\mathbf{J}(\mathbf{x}^{(k-1)}) \right]^{-1} \mathbf{F}(\mathbf{x}^{(k-1)}). \tag{8.2.3}$$

The algorithm avoids calculating $\mathbf{J}(\mathbf{x})^{-1}$ at each step. Instead, it finds a vector $\mathbf{y}$ so that $\mathbf{J}(\mathbf{x}^{(k-1)})\mathbf{y} = -\mathbf{F}(\mathbf{x}^{(k-1)})$, and then it sets $\mathbf{x}^{(k)} = \mathbf{x}^{(k-1)} + \mathbf{y}$.

For the special case of a two-dimensional system (the equations $f(x, y) = 0$ and $g(x, y) = 0$ are to be satisfied), Newton's iteration becomes:

$$x_{n+1} = x_n - \left. \frac{f g_y - f_y g}{f_x g_y - f_y g_x} \right|_{x=x_n, y=y_n},$$

$$y_{n+1} = y_n - \left. \frac{f_x g - f g_x}{f_x g_y - f_y g_x} \right|_{x=x_n, y=y_n}.$$

Method of steepest descent

The method of *steepest descent* determines the *local minimum* for a function of the form $g : \mathbb{R}^n \to \mathbb{R}$. It can also be used to solve a system $\{f_i\}$ of nonlinear equations. The system has a solution $\mathbf{x} = (x_1, x_2, \ldots, x_n)^{\mathrm{T}}$ when the function,

$$g(x_1, x_2, \ldots, x_n) = \sum_{i=1}^{n} [f_i(x_1, x_2, \ldots, x_n)]^2,$$

has the minimal value zero.

This method converges only linearly to the solution but it usually converges even for poor initial approximations. It can be used to locate initial approximations that are close enough so that Newton's method will converge. Intuitively, a local minimum for a function $g : \mathbb{R}^n \to \mathbb{R}$ can be found as follows:

1. Evaluate g at an initial approximation $\mathbf{x}^{(0)} = (x_1^{(0)}, \ldots, x_n^{(0)})^{\mathrm{T}}$.

2. Determine a direction from $\mathbf{x}^{(0)}$ that results in a decrease in the value of g.

3. Move an appropriate distance in this direction and call the new vector $\mathbf{x}^{(1)}$.

4. Repeat steps 1 through 3 with $\mathbf{x}^{(0)}$ replaced by $\mathbf{x}^{(1)}$.

The direction of greatest decrease in the value of g at $\mathbf{x}$ is the direction given by $-\nabla g(\mathbf{x})$ where $\nabla g(\mathbf{x})$ is the *gradient* of g.

DEFINITION 8.2.2

If $g : \mathbb{R}^n \to \mathbb{R}$, the gradient *of g at $\mathbf{x} = (x_1, x_2, \ldots, x_n)$, denoted $\nabla g(\mathbf{x})$, is*

$$\nabla g(\mathbf{x}) = \left(\frac{\partial g}{\partial x_1}(\mathbf{x}), \frac{\partial g}{\partial x_2}(\mathbf{x}), \ldots, \frac{\partial g}{\partial x_n}(\mathbf{x}) \right).$$

Thus, set $\mathbf{x}^{(1)} = \mathbf{x}^{(0)} - \alpha \nabla g(\mathbf{x}^{(0)})$ for some constant $\alpha > 0$. Ideally the value of α minimizes the function $h(\alpha) = g(\mathbf{x}^{(0)} - \alpha \nabla g(\mathbf{x}^{(0)}))$. Instead of tedious direct calculation, the method interpolates h using a quadratic polynomial P and three numbers α_1, α_2, and α_3 that are hopefully close to the minimum value of h.

Algorithm for steepest descent

To approximate a solution $\mathbf{p}$ to the minimization problem $g(\mathbf{p}) = \min_{\mathbf{x} \in \mathbb{R}^n} g(\mathbf{x})$, given an initial approximation $\mathbf{x}$,

> INPUT: number n of variables, initial $\mathbf{x} = (x_1, x_2, \ldots, x_n)^{\mathrm{T}}$,
> tolerance TOL, and maximum iterations N.
> OUTPUT: approximate solution $\mathbf{x} = (x_1, x_2, \ldots, x_n)^{\mathrm{T}}$
> or a message of failure.

Algorithm

1. Set $k = 0$.

2. While $(k \leq N)$, do the following steps:

    (a) Set: $g_1 = g(x_1, \ldots, x_n)$ (Note: $g_1 = g(\mathbf{x}^{(k)})$.);
    $\mathbf{z} = \nabla g(x_1, \ldots, x_n)$ (Note: $\mathbf{z} = \nabla g(\mathbf{x}^{(k)})$.);
    $z_0 = \|\mathbf{z}\|_2$.

    (b) If $z_0 = 0$ then OUTPUT ("Zero gradient");
    OUTPUT $(x_1, \ldots, x_n, g_1)$
    (procedure completed, may have a minimum). STOP.

    (c) Set $\mathbf{z} = \frac{\mathbf{z}}{z_0}$. Make $\mathbf{z}$ a unit vector.
    Set $\alpha_1 = 0$, $\alpha_3 = 1$, $g_3 = g(\mathbf{x} - \alpha_3 \mathbf{z})$.

    (d) While $(g_3 \geq g_1)$, do the following steps:

        i. Set $\alpha_3 = \frac{\alpha_3}{2}$, $g_3 = g(\mathbf{x} - \alpha_3 \mathbf{z})$.

        ii. If $\alpha_3 < \frac{TOL}{2}$, then
        OUTPUT ("no likely improvement");
        OUTPUT $(x_1, \ldots, x_n, g_1)$
        (procedure completed, may not have a
        minimum). STOP.

    (e) Set $\alpha_2 = \frac{\alpha_3}{2}$, $g_2 = g(\mathbf{x} - \alpha_2 \mathbf{z})$.

    (f) Set $h_1 = \frac{(g_2 - g_1)}{\alpha_2}$, $h_2 = \frac{(g_3 - g_2)}{(\alpha_3 - \alpha_2)}$, $h_3 = \frac{(h_2 - h_1)}{\alpha_3}$.

    (g) Set $\alpha_0 = \frac{1}{2}(\alpha_2 - \frac{h_1}{h_3})$ (critical point occurs at α_0).
    set $g_0 = g(\mathbf{x} - \alpha_0 \mathbf{z})$.

    (h) Find α from $\{\alpha_0, \alpha_3\}$ so that $g = g(\mathbf{x} - \alpha \mathbf{z}) = \min\{g_0, g_3\}$.

    (i) Set $\mathbf{x} = \mathbf{x} - \alpha \mathbf{z}$.

    (j) If $|g - g_1| < TOL$ then OUTPUT $(x_1, \ldots, x_n, g)$
    (procedure completed successfully). STOP.

    (k) Set $k = k + 1$.

3. OUTPUT ("maximum iterations exceeded");
   (procedure unsuccessful). STOP.

8.3 NUMERICAL INTEGRATION AND DIFFERENTIATION

8.3.1 NUMERICAL INTEGRATION

Numerical quadrature involves estimating $\int_a^b f(x)\,dx$ using a formula of the form

$$\int_a^b f(x)\,dx \approx \sum_{i=0}^n c_i f(x_i). \qquad (8.3.1)$$

Newton–Cotes formulae

A *closed Newton–Cotes formula* uses nodes $x_i = x_0 + ih$ for $i = 0, 1, \ldots, n$, where $h = (b - a)/n$. Note that $x_0 = a$ and $x_n = b$.

An *open Newton–Cotes formula* uses nodes $x_i = x_0 + ih$ for $i = 0, 1, \ldots, n$, where $h = (b - a)/(n + 2)$. Here $x_0 = a + h$ and $x_n = b - h$. Set $x_{-1} = a$ and $x_{n+1} = b$. The nodes actually used lie in the *open interval* (a, b).

In all formulae, ξ is a number for which $a < \xi < b$ and f_i denotes $f(x_i)$.

Closed Newton–Cotes formulae

1. ($n = 1$) trapezoidal rule

$$\int_a^b f(x)\,dx = \frac{h}{2}[f(x_0) + f(x_1)] - \frac{h^3}{12}f''(\xi).$$

2. ($n = 2$) Simpson's rule

$$\int_a^b f(x)\,dx = \frac{h}{3}[f(x_0) + 4f(x_1) + f(x_2)] - \frac{h^5}{90}f^{(4)}(\xi).$$

3. ($n = 3$) Simpson's three-eighths rule

$$\int_a^b f(x)\,dx = \frac{3h}{8}[f(x_0) + 3f(x_1) + 3f(x_2) + f(x_3) - \frac{3h^5}{80}f^{(4)}(\xi).$$

4. ($n = 4$) Milne's rule

$$\int_a^b f(x)\,dx = \frac{2h}{45}[7f_0 + 32f_1 + 12f_2 + 32f_3 + 7f_4] - \frac{8h^7}{945}f^{(6)}(\xi).$$

5. ($n = 5$)

$$\int_a^b f(x)\,dx = \frac{5h}{288}[19f_0 + 75f_1 + 50f_2 + 50f_3 + 75f_4 + 19f_5] - \frac{275h^7}{12096}f^{(6)}(\xi).$$

6. ($n = 6$) Weddle's rule

$$\int_a^b f(x)\,dx = \frac{h}{140}[41 f_0 + 216 f_1 + 27 f_2 + 272 f_3 + 27 f_4 + 216 f_5 + 41 f_6]$$

$$- \frac{9h^9}{1400} f^{(8)}(\xi).$$

Open Newton–Cotes formulae

1. ($n = 0$) midpoint rule

$$\int_a^b f(x)\,dx = 2hf(x_0) + \frac{h^3}{3} f''(\xi).$$

2. ($n = 1$)

$$\int_a^b f(x)\,dx = \frac{3h}{2}[f(x_0) + f(x_1)] + \frac{3h^3}{4} f''(\xi).$$

3. ($n = 2$)

$$\int_a^b f(x)\,dx = \frac{4h}{3}[2f(x_0) - f(x_1) + 2f(x_2)] + \frac{14h^5}{45} f^{(4)}(\xi).$$

4. ($n = 3$)

$$\int_a^b f(x)\,dx = \frac{5h}{24}[11 f(x_0) + f(x_1) + f(x_2) + 11 f(x_3)] + \frac{95h^5}{144} f^{(4)}(\xi).$$

Composite rules

Some Newton–Cotes formulae extend to *composite formulae*. In the following note that $a < \mu < b$.

1. Composite trapezoidal rule for n subintervals: If $f \in C^2[a, b]$, $h = \frac{b-a}{n}$, and $x_j = a + jh$, for $j = 0, 1, \ldots, n$, then

$$\int_a^b f(x)\,dx = \frac{h}{2}\left[f(a) + 2\sum_{j=1}^{n-1} f(x_j) + f(b)\right] - \frac{b-a}{12} h^2 f''(\mu).$$

2. Composite Simpson's rule for n subintervals: If $f \in C^4[a, b]$, n is even, $h = \frac{b-a}{n}$, and $x_j = a + jh$, for $j = 0, 1, \ldots, n$, then

$$\int_a^b f(x)\,dx = \frac{h}{3}\left[f(a) + 2\sum_{j=1}^{(n/2)-1} f(x_{2j}) + 4\sum_{j=1}^{n/2} f(x_{2j-1}) + f(b)\right]$$

$$- \frac{b-a}{180} h^4 f^{(4)}(\mu).$$

3. Composite midpoint rule for $(\frac{n}{2}) + 1$ subintervals: If $f \in C^2[a, b]$, n is even, $h = \frac{b-a}{n+2}$, and $x_j = a + (j + 1)h$, for $j = -1, 0, 1, \ldots, n + 1$, then

$$\int_a^b f(x)\,dx = 2h \sum_{j=0}^{n2} f(x_{2j}) + \frac{b-a}{6}h^2 f''(\mu).$$

Method H.2.1.2 Romberg integration

Romberg integration uses the composite trapezoidal rule beginning with $h_1 = b - a$ and $h_k = \frac{b-a}{2^{k-1}}$, for $k = 1, 2, \ldots$, to give preliminary estimates for $\int_a^b f(x)\,dx$ and improves the estimates with Richardson's extrapolation. However, since many function evaluations would be repeated, the first column of the extrapolation table (with entries $R_{i,j}$) can be more efficiently determined by the following recursion formula:

$$R_{1,1} = \frac{h_1}{2}[f(a) + f(b)] = \frac{b-a}{2}[f(a) + f(b)]$$

$$R_{k,1} = \frac{1}{2}\left[R_{k-1,1} + h_{k-1} \sum_{i=1}^{2^{k-2}} f(a + (2i - 1)h_k) \right], \tag{8.3.2}$$

for $k = 2, 3, \ldots$. Now apply Equation (8.1.4) to complete the extrapolation table.

Gaussian quadrature

A quadrature formula, whose nodes (abscissas) x_i and coefficients w_i are chosen to achieve a maximum order of accuracy, is called a *Gaussian quadrature formula*. The integrand usually involves a *weight function w*. An integral in t on an interval (a, b) must be converted into an integral in x over the interval (α, β) specified for the weight function involved. This can be accomplished by the transformation $x = \frac{(b\alpha - a\beta)}{(b-a)} + \frac{(\beta - \alpha)t}{(b-a)}$. Gaussian quadrature formulae generally take the form

$$\int_\alpha^\beta w(x)f(x)\,dx = \sum_i w_i f(x_i) + E_n \tag{8.3.3}$$

where $E_n = K_n f^{(2n)}(\xi)$ for some $\alpha < \xi < \beta$. Many popular weight functions and their associated intervals are summarized in the following table:

Formulae for Integration Rules with Various Weight Functions

$w(x)$	Interval (α, β)	Abscissas are zeros of	x_i	w_i	K_n
1	$(-1,1)$	$P_n(x)$	See table on page 697	$\dfrac{-2}{(n+1)P_{n+1}(x_i)P_n'(x_i)}$	$\dfrac{2^{2n+1}(n!)^4}{(2n+1)[(2n)!]^3}$
e^{-x}	$(0,\infty)$	$L_n(x)$	See table on page 698	$\dfrac{(n!)^2 x_i}{(n+1)^2 L_{n+1}^2(x_i)}$	$\dfrac{(n!)^2}{(2n)!}$
e^{-x^2}	$(-\infty,\infty)$	$H_n(x)$	See table on page 699	$\dfrac{2^{n-1}n!\sqrt{\pi}}{n^2 H_{n-1}^2(x_i)}$	$\dfrac{n!\sqrt{\pi}}{2^n(2n)!}$
$\dfrac{1}{\sqrt{1-x^2}}$	$(-1,1)$	$T_n(x)$	$\cos\dfrac{(2i-1)\pi}{2n}$	$\dfrac{\pi}{n}$	$\dfrac{2\pi}{2^{2n}(2n)!}$
$\sqrt{1-x^2}$	$(-1,1)$	$U_n(x)$	$\cos\left(\dfrac{i\pi}{n+1}\right)$	$\dfrac{\pi}{n+1}\sin^2\left(\dfrac{i\pi}{n+1}\right)$	$\dfrac{\pi}{2^{2n+1}(2n)!}$
$\sqrt{\dfrac{x}{1-x}}$	$(0,1)$	$\dfrac{T_{2n+1}(\sqrt{x})}{\sqrt{x}}$	$\cos^2\left(\dfrac{(2i-1)\pi}{4n+2}\right)$	$\dfrac{2\pi}{2n+1}\cos^2\left(\dfrac{(2i-1)\pi}{4n+2}\right)$	$\dfrac{\pi}{2^{4n+1}(2n)!}$
$\sqrt{\dfrac{1-x}{1+x}}$	$(0,1)$	$J_n\left(x,\dfrac{1}{2},-\dfrac{1}{2}\right)$	$\cos\left(\dfrac{2i\pi}{2n+1}\right)$	$\dfrac{4\pi}{2n+1}\sin^2\left(\dfrac{i\pi}{2n+1}\right)$	$\dfrac{\pi}{2^{2n}(2n)!}$
$\dfrac{1}{\sqrt{x}}$	$(0,1)$	$P_n(\sqrt{x})$	$(x_i^+)^2$	$2h_i$	$\dfrac{2^{4n+1}[(2n)!]^3}{(4n+1)[(4n)!]^2}$
$\sqrt{x}$	$(0,1)$	$\dfrac{P_{2n+1}(\sqrt{x})}{\sqrt{x}}$	$(x_i^+)^2$	$2h_i\,(x_i^+)^2$	$\dfrac{2^{4n+3}[(2n+1)!]^4}{(4n+3)[(4n+2)!]^2(2n)!}$

In this table, P_n, L_n, H_n, T_n, U_n, and J_n denote the nth Legendre, Laguerre, Hermite, Chebyshev (first kind T_n, second kind U_n), and Jacobi polynomials, respectively. Also, x_i^+ denotes the ith positive root of $P_{2n+1}(x)$ and h_i denotes the corresponding weight for x_i^+ in the Gauss–Legendre formula ($w(x)=1$).

The following tables give abscissas and weights for selected formulae. If some x_i are specified (such as one or both end points), then the formulae of Radau and Lobatto may be used.

Gauss–Legendre quadrature

Weight function is $w(x) = 1$.
$$\int_{-1}^{1} f(x)\,dx \approx \sum_{i=1}^{n} w_i\, f(x_i).$$

n	Nodes $\{\pm x_i\}$	Weights $\{w_i\}$	n	Nodes $\{\pm x_i\}$	Weights $\{w_i\}$
2	0.5773502692	1	9	0	0.3302393550
				0.3242534234	0.3123470770
3	0	0.8888888889		0.6133714327	0.2606106964
	0.7745966692	0.5555555556		0.8360311073	0.1806481607
				0.9681602395	0.0812743883
4	0.3399810436	0.6521451549			
	0.8611363116	0.3478548451	10	0.1488743390	0.2955242247
				0.4333953941	0.2692667193
5	0	0.5688888889		0.6794095683	0.2190863625
	0.5384693101	0.4786286705		0.8650633667	0.1494513492
	0.9061798459	0.2369268851		0.9739065285	0.0666713443
6	0.2386191861	0.4679139346	11	0	0.2729250868
	0.6612093865	0.3607615730		0.2695431560	0.2628045445
	0.9324695142	0.1713244924		0.5190961292	0.2331937646
				0.7301520056	0.1862902109
7	0	0.4179591837		0.8870625998	0.1255803695
	0.4058451514	0.3818300505		0.9782286581	0.0556685671
	0.7415311856	0.2797053915			
	0.9491079123	0.1294849662	12	0.1252334085	0.2491470458
				0.3678314990	0.2334925365
8	0.1834346425	0.3626837834		0.5873179543	0.2031674267
	0.5255324099	0.3137066459		0.7699026742	0.1600783285
	0.7966664774	0.2223810345		0.9041172564	0.1069393260
	0.9602898565	0.1012285363		0.9815606342	0.0471753363

Gauss–Laguerre quadrature

Weight function is $w(x) = e^{-x}$.

$$\int_0^\infty e^{-x} f(x)\, dx \approx \sum_{i=1}^n w_i f(x_i).$$

n	Nodes $\{x_i\}$	Weights $\{w_i\}$
2	0.5857864376	0.8535533905
	3.4142135623	0.1464466094
3	0.4157745567	0.7110930099
	2.2942803602	0.2785177335
	6.2899450829	0.0103892565
4	0.3225476896	0.6031541043
	1.7457611011	0.3574186924
	4.5366202969	0.0388879085
	9.3950709123	0.0005392947
5	0.2635603197	0.5217556105
	1.4134030591	0.3986668110
	3.5964257710	0.0759424496
	7.0858100058	0.0036117586
	12.6408008442	0.0000233699
6	0.2228466041	0.4589646739
	1.1889321016	0.4170008307
	2.9927363260	0.1133733820
	5.7751435691	0.0103991974
	9.8374674183	0.0002610172
	15.9828739806	0.0000008985

n	Nodes $\{x_i\}$	Weights $\{w_i\}$
7	0.1930436765	0.4093189517
	1.0266648953	0.4218312778
	2.5678767449	0.1471263486
	4.9003530845	0.0206335144
	8.1821534445	0.0010740101
	12.7341802917	0.0000158654
	19.3957278622	0.0000000317
8	0.1702796323	0.3691885893
	0.9037017767	0.4187867808
	2.2510866298	0.1757949866
	4.2667001702	0.0333434922
	7.0459054023	0.0027945362
	10.7585160101	0.0000907650
	15.7406786412	0.0000008485
	22.8631317368	0.0000000010

Gauss–Hermite quadrature

Weight function is $w(x) = e^{-x^2}$.

$$\int_{-\infty}^{\infty} e^{-x^2} f(x)\,dx \approx \sum_{i=1}^{n} w_i f(x_i).$$

n	Nodes $\{\pm x_i\}$	Weights $\{w_i\}$
2	0.7071067811	0.8862269254
3	0	1.1816359006
	1.2247448713	0.2954089751
4	0.5246476232	0.8049140900
	1.6506801238	0.0813128354
5	0	0.9453087204
	0.9585724646	0.3936193231
	2.0201828704	0.0199532420
6	0.4360774119	0.7246295952
	1.3358490740	0.1570673203
	2.3506049736	0.0045300099
7	0	0.8102646175
	0.8162878828	0.4256072526
	1.6735516287	0.0545155828
	2.6519613568	0.0009717812

n	Nodes $\{\pm x_i\}$	Weights $\{w_i\}$
8	0.3811869902	0.6611470125
	1.1571937124	0.2078023258
	1.9816567566	0.0170779830
	2.9306374202	0.0001996040
9	0	0.7202352156
	0.7235510187	0.4326515590
	1.4685532892	0.0884745273
	2.2665805845	0.0049436242
	3.1909932017	0.0000396069
10	0.3429013272	0.6108626337
	1.0366108297	0.2401386110
	1.7566836492	0.0338743944
	2.5327316742	0.0013436457
	3.4361591188	0.0000076404

Radau quadrature

$$\int_{-1}^{1} f(x)\, dx \approx \frac{2}{n(n-1)} [f(-1) + f(1)] + \sum_{i=1}^{n-1} w_i f(x_i) + \frac{2^{2n-1}[n(n-1)!]^4}{[(2n-1)!]^3} f^{(2n-1)}(\xi),$$

where x_i is the ith root of $\frac{P_{n-1}(x)+P_n(x)}{x+1}$ and $w_i = \frac{1-x_i}{n^2[P_{n-1}(x_i)]^2}$ for $i = 1, \ldots, n-1$.

n	Nodes $\{\pm x_i\}$	Weights $\{w_i\}$
3	0	1.3333333333
	1	0.3333333333
4	0.4472135954	0.8333333333
	1	0.1666666666
5	0	0.7111111111
	0.6546536707	0.5444444444
	1	0.1000000000
6	0.2852315164	0.5548583770
	0.7650553239	0.3784749562
	1	0.0666666666
7	0	0.4876190476
	0.4688487934	0.4317453812
	0.8302238962	0.2768260473
	1	0.0476190476
8	0.2092992179	0.4124587946
	0.5917001814	0.3411226924
	0.8717401485	0.2107042271
	1	0.0357142857
9	0	0.3715192743
	0.3631174638	0.3464285109
	0.6771862795	0.2745387125
	0.8997579954	0.1654953615
	1	0.0277777777

n	Nodes $\{\pm x_i\}$	Weights $\{w_i\}$
10	0.1652789576	0.3275397611
	0.4779249498	0.2920426836
	0.7387738651	0.2248893420
	0.9195339081	0.1333059908
	1	0.0222222222
11	0	0.3002175954
	0.2957581355	0.2868791247
	0.5652353269	0.2480481042
	0.7844834736	0.1871698817
	0.9340014304	0.1096122732
	1	0.0181818181
12	0.1365529328	0.2714052409
	0.3995309409	0.2512756031
	0.6328761530	0.2125084177
	0.8192793216	0.1579747055
	0.9448992722	0.0916845174
	1	0.0151515151
13	0	0.2519308493
	0.2492869301	0.2440157903
	0.4829098210	0.2207677935
	0.6861884690	0.1836468652
	0.8463475646	0.1349819266
	0.9533098466	0.0778016867
	1	0.0128205128

Lobatto quadrature

$$\int_{-1}^{1} f(x)\,dx \approx w_1 f(-1) + w_n f(1)$$

$$+ \sum_{i=2}^{n-1} w_i f(x_i) - \frac{n(n-1)^3 2^{2n-1}[(n-2)!]^4}{(2n-1)[(2n-2)!]^3} f^{(2n-2)}(\xi)$$

where x_i is the $(i-1)^{st}$ root of $P'_{n-1}(x)$ and $w_i = \frac{2}{n(n-1)[P_{n-1}(x_i)]^2}$ for $i = 1, \ldots, n-2$.
Note that $w_1 = w_n = \frac{1}{n^2}$.

n	Nodes	Weights $\{w_i\}$
3	−0.2898979485	1.0249716523
	0.6898979485	0.7528061254
4	−0.5753189235	0.6576886399
	0.1810662711	0.7763869376
	0.8228240809	0.4409244223
5	−0.7204802713	0.4462078021
	−0.1671808647	0.6236530459
	0.4463139727	0.5627120302
	0.8857916077	0.2874271215
6	−0.8029298284	0.3196407532
	−0.3909285467	0.4853871884
	0.1240503795	0.5209267831
	0.6039731642	0.4169013343
	0.9203802858	0.2015883852
7	−0.8538913426	0.2392274892
	−0.5384677240	0.3809498736
	−0.1173430375	0.4471098290
	0.3260306194	0.4247037790
	0.7038428006	0.3182042314
	0.9413671456	0.1489884711

n	Nodes	Weights $\{w_i\}$
8	−0.8874748789	0.1853581548
	−0.6395186165	0.3041306206
	−0.2947505657	0.3765175453
	0.0943072526	0.3915721674
	0.4684203544	0.3470147956
	0.7706418936	0.2496479013
	0.9550412271	0.1145088147
9	−0.9107320894	0.1476540190
	−0.7112674859	0.2471893782
	−0.4263504857	0.3168437756
	−0.0903733696	0.3482730027
	0.2561356708	0.3376939669
	0.5713830412	0.2863866963
	0.8173527842	0.2005532980
	0.9644401697	0.0907145049
10	−0.9274843742	0.1202966705
	−0.7638420424	0.2042701318
	−0.5256460303	0.2681948378
	−0.2362344693	0.3058592877
	0.0760591978	0.3135824572
	0.3806648401	0.2906101648
	0.6477666876	0.2391934317
	0.8512252205	0.1643760127
	0.9711751807	0.0736170054

Chebyshev quadrature

$$\int_{-1}^{1} f(x)\,dx \approx \frac{2}{n}\sum_{i=1}^{n} f(x_i).$$

n	Nodes $\{\pm x_i\}$
2	0.5773502691
3	0
	0.7071067811
4	0.1875924740
	0.7946544722
5	0
	0.3745414095
	0.8324974870
6	0.2666354015
	0.4225186537
	0.8662468181
7	0
	0.3239118105
	0.5296567752
	0.8838617007

Monte–Carlo methods

Monte–Carlo methods, in general, involve the generation of random numbers (actually *pseudorandom* when computer-generated) to represent independent, uniform random variables over [0, 1]. A simulation can provide insight into the solutions of very complex problems. Refer to Section 7.5 for terminology and notation.

Monte–Carlo methods are generally not competitive with other numerical methods of this section. However, if the function fails to have continuous derivatives of moderate order, those methods may not be applicable. Monte–Carlo methods can be extended to multidimensional integrals quite easily although here only a few techniques for one-dimensional integrals $I = \int_a^b g(x)\,dx$ are given.

Hit or miss method

Suppose $0 \le g(x) \le c$, $a \le x \le b$, and $\Omega = \{(x, y) \mid a \le x \le b, 0 \le y \le c\}$. If (X, Y) is a random vector which is uniformly distributed over Ω, then the probability p that (X, Y) lies in S (see Figure 8.3.2) is $p = \frac{I}{c(b-a)}$.

If N independent random vectors $\{(X_i, Y_i)\}_{i=1}^{N}$ are generated, the parameter p can be estimated by $\hat{p} = \frac{N_H}{N}$ where N_H is the number of times $Y_i \le g(X_i)$, $i = 1, 2, \ldots, N$, called the number of "hits." (Likewise $N - N_H$ is the number

FIGURE 8.3.2

Illustration of Monte–Carlo method.[2]

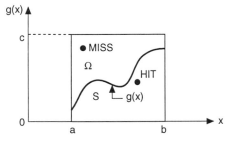

of "misses.") The value of I is then estimated by the unbiased estimator $\theta_1 = c(b-a)N_H/N$.

Hit or miss algorithm

1. Generate a sequence $\{U_j\}_{j=1}^{2N}$ of $2N$ random numbers, uniformly distributed in $[0, 1)$.
2. Arrange the sequence into N pairs $(U_1, U_1'), (U_2, U_2'), \ldots, (U_N, U_N')$, so that each U_j is used exactly once.
3. Compute $X_i = a + U_i(b-a)$ and $g(X_i)$ for $i = 1, 2, \ldots, N$.
4. Count the number of cases N_H for which $g(X_i) > cU_i'$.
5. Compute $\theta_1 = c(b-a)N_H/N$. (Estimate I.)

The number of trials N necessary for $P(|\theta_1 - I| < \epsilon) \geq \alpha$ is given by

$$N \geq \frac{(1-p)p[c(b-a)]^2}{(1-\alpha)\epsilon^2}. \tag{8.3.4}$$

Using the usual notation z_α for the value of the standard normal random variable Z for which $P(Z > z_\alpha) = \alpha$, a confidence interval for I with confidence level $1 - \alpha$ is

$$\theta_1 \pm z_{\frac{\alpha}{2}} \frac{\sqrt{\hat{p}(1-\hat{p})}(b-a)c}{\sqrt{N}}. \tag{8.3.5}$$

The sample-mean Monte–Carlo method

Write the integral $I = \int_a^b g(x)\,dx$ as $\int_a^b \frac{g(x)}{f_X(x)} f_X(x)\,dx$. Then $I = E\left[\frac{g(X)}{f_X(X)}\right]$ where the random variable X is distributed according to $f_X(x)$. Values from this distribution

[2]From R.Y. Rubinstein, *Simulation and the Monte–Carlo Method,* John Wiley & Sons, New York, 1981. With permission.

can be generated by the methods discussed in Section 7.5. For the case where $f_X(x)$ is the uniform distribution on $[0, 1]$, $I = (b - a)\mathrm{E}[g(X)]$. An unbiased estimator of I is its sample mean

$$\theta_2 = (b - a)\frac{1}{N}\sum_{i=1}^{N} g(X_i). \tag{8.3.6}$$

It follows that the variance of θ_2 is less than or equal to the variance of θ_1. In fact,

$$\mathrm{var}\,\theta_1 = \frac{I}{N}[c(b - a) - I], \quad \text{and} \quad \mathrm{var}\,\theta_2 = \frac{1}{N}\left[(b - a)\int_a^b g^2(x)\,dx - I^2\right].$$

Note that to estimate I with θ_1 or θ_2, $g(x)$ is not needed explicity. It is only necessary to evaluate $g(x)$ at any point x.

Sample-mean algorithm

1. Generate a sequence $\{U_i\}_{i=1}^{N}$ of N random numbers, uniformly distributed in $[0, 1)$
2. Compute $X_i = a + U_i(b - a)$, for $i = 1, 2, \ldots, N$.
3. Compute $g(X_i)$ for $i = 1, 2, \ldots, N$.
4. Compute θ_2 according to Equation (8.3.6) (this is an estimate of I).

Integration in the presence of noise

Suppose $g(x)$ is measured with some error: $\tilde{g}(x_i) = g(x_i) + \epsilon_i$, for $i = 1, 2, \ldots, N$, where ϵ_i are independent identically distributed random variables with $\mathrm{E}[\epsilon_i] = 0$, $\mathrm{var}(\epsilon) = \sigma^2$, and $|\epsilon_i| < k < \infty$.

If (X, Y) is uniformly distributed on the rectangle $a \leq x \leq b, 0 \leq y \leq c_1$, where $c_1 \geq g(x) + k$, set $\tilde{\theta}_1 = c_1(b - a)N_H/N$ as in the hit or miss method. Similarly, set $\tilde{\theta}_2 = \frac{1}{N}(b - a)\sum_{i=1}^{N}\tilde{g}(X_i)$ as in the sample-mean method. Then both $\tilde{\theta}_1$ and $\tilde{\theta}_2$ are unbiased and converge almost surely to I. Again, $\mathrm{var}\,\tilde{\theta}_2 \leq \mathrm{var}\,\tilde{\theta}_1$.

Weighted Monte–Carlo integration

Estimate the integral $I = \int_0^1 g(x)\,dx$ according to the following algorithm:

1. Generate numbers $\{U_1, U_2, \ldots, U_N\}$ from the uniform distribution on $[0, 1)$.
2. Arrange $U_1, U_2, \ldots, U_N$ in the increasing order $U_{(1)}, U_{(2)}, \ldots, U_{(N)}$.
3. Compute $\theta_3 = \frac{1}{2}\left[\sum_{i=0}^{N}(g(U_{(i)}) + g(U_{(i+1)})(U_{(i+1)} - U_{(i)})\right]$, where $U_{(0)} \equiv 0$, $U_{(N+1)} \equiv 1$. This is an estimate of I.

If $g(x)$ has a continuous second derivative on $[0, 1]$, then the estimator θ_3 satifies variance $\theta_3 = E(\theta_3 - I)^2 \leq k/N^4$, where k is some positive constant.

8.3.2   NUMERICAL DIFFERENTIATION

Derivative estimates

Selected formulae to estimate the derivative of a function at a single point, with error terms, are given. Nodes are equally spaced with $x_i - x_{i-1} = h$; h may be positive or negative and, in the error formulae, ξ lies between the smallest and largest nodes. To shorten some of the formulae, f_j is used to denote $f(x_0 + jh)$ and some error formulae are expressed as $O(h^k)$.

1. Two-point formula for $f'(x_0)$

$$f'(x_0) = \frac{1}{h}(f(x_0 + h) - f(x_0)) - \frac{h}{2}f''(\xi). \tag{8.3.7}$$

   This is called a *forward-difference formula* if $h > 0$ and a *backward-difference formula* if $h < 0$.

2. Three-point formulae for $f'(x_0)$

$$f'(x_0) = \frac{1}{2h}[-3f(x_0) + 4f(x_0 + h) - f(x_0 + 2h)] + \frac{h^2}{3}f^{(3)}(\xi)$$

$$= \frac{1}{2h}[f(x_0 + h) - f(x_0 - h)] - \frac{h^2}{6}f^{(3)}(\xi). \tag{8.3.8}$$

3. Four-point formulae for $f'(x_0)$

$$f'(x_0) = \frac{1}{12h}[f_{-2} - 8f_{-1} + 8f_1 - f_2] + \frac{h^4}{30}f^{(5)}(\xi). \tag{8.3.9}$$

4. Five-point formulae for $f'(x_0)$

$$f'(x_0) = \frac{1}{12h}[-25f_0 + 48f_1 - 36f_2 + 16f_3 - 3f_4] + \frac{h^4}{5}f^{(5)}(\xi). \tag{8.3.10}$$

5. Formulae for the second derivative

$$f''(x_0) = \frac{1}{h^2}[f_{-1} - 2f_0 + f_1] - \frac{h^2}{12}f^{(4)}(\xi),$$

$$= \frac{1}{h^2}[f_0 - 2f_1 + f_2] + \frac{h^2}{6}f^{(4)}(\xi_1) - hf^{(3)}(\xi_2). \tag{8.3.11}$$

6. Formulae for the third derivative

$$f^{(3)}(x_0) = \frac{1}{h^3}[f_3 - 3f_2 + 3f_1 - f_0] + O(h),$$

$$= \frac{1}{2h^3}[f_2 - 2f_1 + 2f_{-1} - f_{-2}] + O(h^2). \tag{8.3.12}$$

7. Formulae for the fourth derivative

$$f^{(4)}(x_0) = \frac{1}{h^4}[f_4 - 4f_3 + 6f_2 - 4f_1 + f_0] + O(h),$$

$$= \frac{1}{h^4}[f_2 - 4f_1 + 6f_0 - 4f_{-1} + f_{-2}] + O(h^2). \quad (8.3.13)$$

Richardson's extrapolation can be applied to improve estimates. The error term of the formula must satisfy Equation (8.1.2) and an extrapolation procedure must be developed. As a special case, however, Equation (8.1.4) may be used when first-column entries are generated by Equation (8.3.8).

Numerical solution of differential equations

Numerical methods to solve differential equations depend on whether small changes in the statement of the problem cause small changes in the solution.

DEFINITION 8.3.1

The initial value problem ,

$$\frac{dy}{dt} = f(t, y), \quad a \le t \le b, \quad y(a) = \alpha, \quad (8.3.14)$$

is said to be well-posed *if*

1. *A unique solution, $y(t)$, to the problem exists.*
2. *For any $\epsilon > 0$, there exists a positive constant $k(\epsilon)$ with the property that, whenever $|\epsilon_0| < \epsilon$ and $\delta(t)$ is continuous with $|\delta(t)| < \epsilon$ on $[a, b]$, a unique solution, $z(t)$, to the problem,*

$$\frac{dz}{dt} = f(t, z) + \delta(t), \quad a \le t \le b, \quad z(a) = \alpha + \epsilon_0,$$

exists with $|z(t) - y(t)| < k(\epsilon)\epsilon$ for all $a \le t \le b$.

This is called the *perturbed problem* associated with the original problem. Although other criteria exist, the following result gives conditions that are easy to check to guarantee that a problem is well-posed.

THEOREM 8.3.1   *(Well-posed condition)*

Suppose that f and f_y (its first partial derivative with respect to y) are continuous for t in $[a, b]$. Then the initial value problem given by Equation (8.3.14) is well-posed.

Using Taylor's theorem, numerical methods for solving the well-posed, first-order differential equation given by Equation (8.3.14) can be derived. Using equally-spaced *mesh points* $t_i = a + ih$ (for $i = 0, 1, 2, \ldots, N$) and w_i to denote an approximation to $y_i \equiv y(t_i)$, then the different methods use *difference equations* of the form

$$w_0 = \alpha, \qquad w_{i+1} = w_i + h\phi(t_i, w_i),$$

for each $i = 0, 1, 2, \ldots, N - 1$. The difference method has *local truncation error* given by

$$\tau_{i+1}(h) = \frac{y_{i+1} - y_i}{h} - \phi(t_i, y_i),$$

for each $i = 0, 1, 2, \ldots, N - 1$. The following formulae are called *Taylor methods*. Each has local truncation error $\frac{h^n}{(n+1)!} f^{(n)}(\xi_i, y(\xi_i))$ for each $i = 0, 1, 2, \ldots, N - 1$, where $\xi_i \in (t_i, t_{i+1})$.

1. Euler's method ($n = 1$):

$$w_{i+1} = w_i + hf(t_i, w_i). \tag{8.3.15}$$

2. Taylor method of order n:

$$w_{i+1} = w_i + hT^{(n)}(t_i, w_i), \tag{8.3.16}$$

where $T^{(n)}(t_i, w_i) = f(t_i, w_i) + \frac{h}{2} f'(t_i, w_i) + \cdots + \frac{h^{n-1}}{n!} f^{(n-1)}(t_i, w_i)$. The *Runge–Kutta methods* below are derived from the nth degree Taylor polynomial in two variables.

3. Midpoint method:

$$w_{i+1} = w_i + h\left[f\left(t_i + \frac{h}{2}, w_i + \frac{h}{2} f(t_i, w_i)\right)\right]. \tag{8.3.17}$$

If all second-order partial derivatives of f are bounded, this method has local truncation error $O(h^2)$, as do the following two methods.

4. Modified Euler method:

$$w_{i+1} = w_i + \frac{h}{2}\{f(t_i, w_i) + f[t_{i+1}, w_i + hf(t_i, w_i)]\}. \tag{8.3.18}$$

5. Heun's method:

$$w_{i+1} = w_i + \frac{h}{4}\left\{f(t_i, w_i) + 3f\left[t_i + \frac{2}{3}h, w_i + \frac{2}{3}hf(t_i, w_i)\right]\right\} \tag{8.3.19}$$

6. Runge–Kutta method of order four:

$$w_{i+1} = w_i + \frac{1}{6}(k_1 + 2k_2 + 2k_3 + k_4), \tag{8.3.20}$$

where

$$k_1 = hf(t_i, w_i),$$

$$k_2 = hf\left(t_i + \frac{h}{2}, w_i + \frac{1}{2}k_1\right),$$

$$k_3 = hf\left(t_i + \frac{h}{2}, w_i + \frac{1}{2}k_2\right),$$

$$k_4 = hf(t_{i+1}, w_i + k_3).$$

The local truncation error is $O(h^4)$ if the solution $y(t)$ has five continuous derivatives.

Multistep methods and predictor-corrector methods

A *multistep method* is a technique whose difference equation to compute w_{i+1} involves more prior values than just w_i. An *explicit method* is one in which the computation of w_{i+1} does not depend on $f(t_{i+1}, w_{i+1})$ whereas an *implicit method* does involve $f(t_{i+1}, w_{i+1})$. For each formula, $i = n - 1, n, \ldots, N - 1$.

Adams–Bashforth n-step (explicit) methods

1. ($n = 2$):
   $w_0 = \alpha$, $w_1 = \alpha_1$, $w_{i+1} = w_i + \frac{h}{2}[3f(t_i, w_i) - f(t_{i-1}, w_{i-1})]$.
   The local truncation error is $\tau_{i+1}(h) = \frac{5}{12} y^{(3)}(\mu_i)h^2$, for some $\mu_i \in (t_{i-1}, t_{i+1})$.

2. ($n = 3$):
   $w_0 = \alpha$, $w_1 = \alpha_1$, $w_2 = \alpha_2$, $w_{i+1} = w_i + \frac{h}{12}[23f(t_i, w_i) - 16f(t_{i-1}, w_{i-1}) + 5f(t_{i-2}, w_{i-2})]$.
   The local truncation error is $\tau_{i+1}(h) = \frac{3}{8} y^{(4)}(\mu_i)h^3$, for some $\mu_i \in (t_{i-2}, t_{i+1})$.

3. ($n = 4$):
   $w_0 = \alpha$, $w_1 = \alpha_1$, $w_2 = \alpha_2$, $w_3 = \alpha_3$, $w_{i+1} = w_i + \frac{h}{24}[55f(t_i, w_i) - 59f(t_{i-1}, w_{i-1}) + 37f(t_{i-2}, w_{i-2}) - 9f(t_{i-3}, w_{i-3})]$.
   The local truncation error is $\tau_{i+1}(h) = \frac{251}{720} y^{(5)}(\mu_i)h^4$, for some $\mu_i \int_{i-3}, t_{i+1})$.

4. ($n = 5$):
   $w_0 = \alpha$, $w_1 = \alpha_1$, $w_2 = \alpha_2$, $w_3 = \alpha_3$, $w_4 = \alpha_4$, $w_{i+1} = w_i + \frac{h}{720}[1901f(t_i, w_i) - 2774f(t_{i-1}, w_{i-1}) + 2616f(t_{i-2}, w_{i-2}) - 1274f(t_{i-3}, w_{i-3}) + 251f(t_{i-4}, w_{i-4})]$.
   The local truncation error is $\tau_{i+1}(h) = \frac{95}{288} y^{(6)}(\mu_i)h^5$, for some $\mu_i \in (t_{i-4}, t_{i+1})$.

Adams–Moulton n-step (implicit) methods

1. ($n = 2$):
   $w_0 = \alpha$, $w_1 = \alpha_1$, $w_{i+1} = w_i + \frac{h}{12}[5f(t_{i+1}, w_{i+1}) + 8f(t_i, w_i) - f(t_{i-1}, w_{i-1})]$.
   The local truncation error is $\tau_{i+1}(h) = -\frac{1}{24} y^{(4)}(\mu_i)h^3$, for some $\mu_i \in (t_{i-1}, t_{i+1})$.

2. ($n = 3$):
   $w_0 = \alpha$, $w_1 = \alpha_1$, $w_2 = \alpha_2$, $w_{i+1} = w_i + \frac{h}{24}[9f(t_{i+1}, w_{i+1}) + 19f(t_i, w_i) - 5f(t_{i-1}, w_{i-1}) + f(t_{i-2}, w_{i-2})]$.
   The local truncation error is $\tau_{i+1}(h) = \frac{19}{720} y^{(5)}(\mu_i)h^4$, for some $\mu_i \in (t_{i-2}, t_{i+1})$.

3. ($n = 4$):
   $w_0 = \alpha$, $w_1 = \alpha_1$, $w_2 = \alpha_2$, $w_3 = \alpha_3$, $w_{i+1} = w_i + \frac{h}{720}[251f(t_{i+1}, w_{i+1}) + 646f(t_i, w_i) - 264f(t_{i-1}, w_{i-1}) + 106f(t_{i-2}, w_{i-2}) - 19f(t_{i-3}, w_{i-3})]$.
   The local truncation error is $\tau_{i+1}(h) = -\frac{3}{160} y^{(6)}(\mu_i)h^5$, for some $\mu_i \in (t_{i-3}, t_{i+1})$.

In practice, implicit methods are not used by themselves. They are used to improve approximations obtained by explicit methods. An explicit method *predicts* an approximation and the implicit method *corrects* this prediction. The combination is called a *predictor-corrector method*. For example, the Adams–Bashforth method with $n = 4$ might be used with the Adams–Moulton method with $n = 3$ since both have comparable errors. Initial values may be computed, say, by the Runge–Kutta method of order four, Equation (8.3.20).

Higher order differential equations and systems

An mth-*order system* of first-order initial value problems can be expressed in the form

$$\frac{du_1}{dt} = f_1(t, u_1, u_2, \ldots, u_m),$$

$$\frac{du_2}{dt} = f_2(t, u_1, u_2, \ldots, u_m),$$

$$\vdots$$

$$\frac{du_m}{dt} = f_m(t, u_1, u_2, \ldots, u_m).$$

Generalizations of methods for solving first-order equations can be used to solve such systems. An example here uses the Runge-Kutta method of order four.

Partition $[a, b]$ as before, and let $w_{i,j}$ denote the approximation to $u_i(t_j)$ for $j = 0, 1, \ldots, N$ and $i = 1, 2, \ldots, m$. For the initial conditions, set $w_{1,0} = \alpha_1$, $w_{2,0} = \alpha_2, \ldots, w_{m,0} = \alpha_m$. From the values $\{w_{1,j}, w_{2,j}, \ldots, w_{m,j}\}$ previously computed, obtain $\{w_{1,j+1}, w_{2,j+1}, \ldots, w_{m,j+1}\}$ from

$$k_{1,i} = hf_i\left(t_j, w_{1,j}, w_{2,j}, \ldots, w_{m,j}\right),$$

$$k_{2,i} = hf_i\left(t_j + \frac{h}{2}, w_{1,j} + \frac{1}{2}k_{1,1}, w_{2,j} + \frac{1}{2}k_{1,2}, \ldots, w_{m,j} + \frac{1}{2}k_{1,m}\right),$$

$$k_{3,i} = hf_i\left(t_j + \frac{h}{2}, w_{1,j} + \frac{1}{2}k_{2,1}, w_{2,j} + \frac{1}{2}k_{2,2}, \ldots, w_{m,j} + \frac{1}{2}k_{2,m}\right),$$

$$k_{4,i} = hf_i\left(t_j + h, w_{1,j} + k_{3,1}, w_{2,j} + k_{3,2}, \ldots, w_{m,j} + k_{3,m}\right),$$

$$w_{i,j+1} = w_{i,j} + \frac{1}{6}[k_{1,i} + 2k_{2,i} + 2k_{3,i} + k_{4,i}],$$

where $i = 1, 2, \ldots, m$ for each of the above.

A differential equation of high order can be converted into a *system* of first-order equations. Suppose that a single differential equation has the form

$$y^{(m)} = f(t, y, y', y'', \ldots, y^{(m-1)}), \quad a \le t \le b$$

with initial conditions $y(a) = \alpha_1, y'(a) = \alpha_2, \ldots, y^{(m-1)}(a) = \alpha_m$. All derivatives are with respect to t. That is, $y^{(k)} = \frac{d^k y}{dt^k}$. Define $u_1(t) = y(t)$, $u_2(t) = y'(t), \ldots,$ $u_m(t) = y^{(m-1)}(t)$. This yields first-order equations

$$\frac{du_1}{dt} = u_2, \quad \frac{du_2}{dt} = u_3, \quad \cdots \quad \frac{du_{m-1}}{dt} = u_m, \quad \frac{du_m}{dt} = f(t, u_1, u_2, \ldots, u_m),$$

with initial conditions $u_1(a) = \alpha_1, \ldots, u_m(a) = \alpha_m$.

Partial differential equations

To develop difference equations for partial differential equations, one needs to estimate the partial derivatives of a function, say, $u(x, y)$. For example,

$$\frac{\partial u}{\partial x}(x, y) = \frac{u(x+h, y) - u(x, y)}{h} - \frac{h}{2}\frac{\partial^2 u(\xi, y)}{\partial x^2} \quad \text{for } \xi \in (x, x+h), \quad (8.3.21)$$

$$\frac{\partial^2 u}{\partial x^2}(x, y) = \frac{1}{h^2}[u(x+h, y) - 2u(x, y) + u(x-h, y)] - \frac{h^2}{12}\frac{\partial^4 u(\xi, y)}{\partial x^4}, \quad (8.3.22)$$
$$\text{for } \xi \in (x-h, x+h).$$

Notes:

1. Equation (8.3.21) is simply Equation (8.3.7) applied to estimate the partial
   derivative. It is given here to emphasize its application for forming difference equations for partial differential equations. A similar formula applies for
   $\partial u/\partial y$, and others could follow from the formulae in Section 8.3.2.
2. An estimate of $\partial^2 u/\partial y^2$ is similar. A formula for $\partial^2 u/\partial x \partial y$ could be given.
   However, in practice, a change of variables is generally used to eliminate this
   mixed second partial derivative from the problem.

If a partial differential equation involves partials with respect to only one of the
variables, the methods described for ordinary differential equations can be used. If,
however, the equation involves partial derivatives with respect to both variables, the
approximation of the partial derivatives require increments in both variables. The
corresponding difference equations form a *system* of linear equations that must be
solved.

Two specific forms of partial differential equations with popular methods of
solution are given. The domains are assumed to be rectangular. Otherwise, additional
considerations must be made for the boundary conditions.

Poisson equation

This elliptic partial differential equation has the form

$$\nabla^2 u(x, y) = \frac{\partial^2 u}{\partial x^2}(x, y) + \frac{\partial^2 u}{\partial y^2}(x, y) = f(x, y) \quad (8.3.23)$$

for $(x, y) \in R = \{(x, y) \mid a < x < b, c < y < d\}$, with $u(x, y) = g(x, y)$ for
$(x, y) \in S$, where $S = \partial R$.

Partition $[a, b]$ and $[c, d]$ by first choosing integers n and m, define step sizes
$h = (b-a)/n$ and $k = (d-c)/m$, and set $x_i = a + ih$ for $i = 0, 1, \ldots, n$ and
$y_j = c + jk$ for $j = 0, 1, \ldots, m$. The lines $x = x_i$, $y = y_j$, are called *grid lines*
and their intersections are called *mesh points*. Estimates $w_{i,j}$ for $u(x_i, y_j)$ can be
generated using Equation (8.3.22) to estimate $\frac{\partial^2 u}{\partial x^2}$ and $\frac{\partial^2 u}{\partial y^2}$.

Central difference method

Start with the values

$$w_{0,j} = g(x_0, y_j), \quad w_{n,j} = g(x_n, y_j), \quad w_{i,0} = g(x_i, y_0), \quad w_{i,m} = g(x_i, y_m),$$

and then solve the system of linear algebraic equations

$$2\left[\left(\frac{h}{k}\right)^2 + 1\right] w_{i,j} - (w_{i+1,j} + w_{i-1,j}) - \left(\frac{h}{k}\right)^2 (w_{i,j+1} + w_{i,j-1}) = -h^2 f(x_i, y_j),$$

for $i = 1, 2, \ldots, n - 1$ and $j = 1, 2, \ldots, m - 1$. The local truncation error is $O(h^2 + k^2)$.

If the interior mesh points are relabeled $P_l = (x_i, y_j)$ when $w_l = w_{i,j}$ where $l = i + (m - 1 - j)(n - 1)$, $i = 1, 2, \ldots, n - 1$, and $j = 1, 2, \ldots, m - 1$, then the two-dimensional array of values is now a one-dimensional array. This results in a banded linear system. The case $n = m = 4$ yields $l = (n - 1)(m - 1) = 9$. Using the relabeled grid points, $f_l = f(P_l)$, the equations at the points P_i are

$$
\begin{array}{rrcl}
P_1: & 4w_1 - w_2 - w_4 & = & w_{0,3} + w_{1,4} - h^2 f_1, \\
P_2: & 4w_2 - w_3 - w_1 - w_5 & = & w_{2,4} - h^2 f_2, \\
P_3: & 4w_3 - w_2 - w_6 & = & w_{4,3} + w_{3,4} - h^2 f_3, \\
P_4: & 4w_4 - w_5 - w_1 - w_7 & = & w_{0,2} - h^2 f_4, \\
P_5: & 4w_5 - w_6 - w_4 - w_2 - w_8 & = & 0 - h^2 f_5, \\
P_6: & 4w_6 - w_5 - w_3 - w_9 & = & w_{4,2} - h^2 f_6, \\
P_7: & 4w_7 - w_8 - w_4 & = & w_{0,1} + w_{1,0} - h^2 f_7, \\
P_8: & 4w_8 - w_9 - w_7 - w_5 & = & w_{2,0} - h^2 f_8, \\
P_9: & 4w_9 - w_8 - w_6 & = & w_{3,0} + w_{4,1} - h^2 f_9,
\end{array}
$$

where the right-hand sides of the equations are obtained from the boundary conditions.

Heat or diffusion equation

This parabolic partial differential equation has the form

$$\frac{\partial u}{\partial t}(x, t) = \alpha^2 \frac{\partial^2 u}{\partial x^2}(x, t), \quad 0 < x < \ell, \quad t > 0. \tag{8.3.24}$$

One common set of intial and boundary conditions is $u(0, t) = 0$ and $u(\ell, t) = 0$ for $t > 0$, and $u(x, 0) = f(x)$ for $0 \le x \le \ell$.

Select mesh constants h and k so that $m = \ell/h$ is an integer. The difference equation for the *Crank–Nicolson method* is

$$
\frac{w_{i,j+1} - w_{i,j}}{k}
$$
$$
- \frac{\alpha^2}{2}\left[\frac{w_{i+1,j} - 2w_{i,j} + w_{i-1,j}}{h^2} + \frac{w_{i+1,j+1} - 2w_{i,j+1} + w_{i-1,j+1}}{h^2}\right] = 0.
$$

This has local truncation error $O(k^2 + h^2)$ The difference equations can be represented in the matrix form $A\mathbf{w}^{(j+1)} = B\mathbf{w}^{(j)}$, for each $j = 0, 1, 2, \ldots$, where $\lambda = \alpha^2 k/h^2$, $\mathbf{w}^{(j)} = (w_{1,j}, w_{2,j}, \ldots, w_{m-1,j})^T$, and the matrices A and B are given by

$$A = \begin{bmatrix} (1+\lambda) & -\frac{\lambda}{2} & 0 & 0 & \cdots & 0 & 0 \\ -\frac{\lambda}{2} & (1+\lambda) & -\frac{\lambda}{2} & 0 & \cdots & 0 & 0 \\ 0 & -\frac{\lambda}{2} & (1+\lambda) & -\frac{\lambda}{2} & & 0 & 0 \\ 0 & 0 & -\frac{\lambda}{2} & (1+\lambda) & & 0 & 0 \\ \vdots & & & \vdots & \ddots & & \\ 0 & 0 & 0 & 0 & & (1+\lambda) & -\frac{\lambda}{2} \\ 0 & 0 & 0 & 0 & & -\frac{\lambda}{2} & (1+\lambda) \end{bmatrix}$$

$$B = \begin{bmatrix} (1-\lambda) & \frac{\lambda}{2} & 0 & 0 & \cdots & 0 & 0 \\ \frac{\lambda}{2} & (1-\lambda) & \frac{\lambda}{2} & 0 & \cdots & 0 & 0 \\ 0 & \frac{\lambda}{2} & (1-\lambda) & \frac{\lambda}{2} & & 0 & 0 \\ 0 & 0 & \frac{\lambda}{2} & (1-\lambda) & & 0 & 0 \\ \vdots & \vdots & & & \ddots & & \\ 0 & 0 & 0 & 0 & & (1-\lambda) & \frac{\lambda}{2} \\ 0 & 0 & 0 & 0 & & \frac{\lambda}{2} & (1-\lambda) \end{bmatrix}$$

8.3.3   SCHEMES FOR THE ODE: $y' = f(x, y)$

Adams–Bashforth, order 2:	$v_n - v_{n-1} = \frac{1}{2}h\left[3f_{n-1} - f_{n-2}\right]$
Adams–Bashforth, order 4:	
$v_n - v_{n-1} = \frac{1}{24}h\left[55f_{n-1} - 59f_{n-2} + 37f_{n-3} - 9f_{n-4}\right]$	
Adams–Moulton, order 4:	
$v_n - v_{n-1} = \frac{1}{24}h\left[9f_n + 19f_{n-1} - 5f_{n-2} + f_{n-3}\right]$	
Backward Euler:	$v_n - v_{n-1} = hf_n$
Euler's method:	$v_n - v_{n-1} = hf_{n-1}$
Explicit leapfrog:	$v_{n+1} - v_{n-1} = hf_n$
Implicit leapfrog:	$v_n - v_{n-1} = \frac{1}{2}h(f_n + f_{n-1})$
Simpson's rule:[a]	$v_n - v_{n-2} = \frac{1}{3}h(f_n + 4f_{n-1} + f_{n-2})$
Trapezoidal rule:[b]	$v_n - v_{n-1} = \frac{1}{2}h(f_n + f_{n-1})$

[a] Also known as Milne's method.
[b] Also known as Heun's method and as the Adams–Moulton method of order 2.

8.3.4 EXPLICIT SCHEMES FOR THE PDE: $au_x + u_t = 0$

Below are explicit difference formulas for the PDE, $au_x + u_t = 0$. Here, h is the uniform x spacing, and k is the uniform t spacing. The approximation to $u(x_n, t_j) = u(x_0 + nh, t_0 + jk)$ is represented by $u_{n,j}$.

Forward in time, forward in space (FTFS):

$$a\frac{u_{n+1,j} - u_{n,j}}{h} + \frac{u_{n,j+1} - u_{n,j}}{k} = 0.$$

Forward in time, centered in space (FTCS) (unstable):

$$a\frac{u_{n+1,j} - u_{n-1,j}}{2h} + \frac{u_{n,j+1} - u_{n,j}}{k} = 0.$$

Forward in time, backward in space (FTBS):

$$a\frac{u_{n,j} - u_{n-1,j}}{h} + \frac{u_{n,j+1} - u_{n,j}}{k} = 0.$$

Lax–Friedrichs method:

$$a\frac{u_{n+1,j} - u_{n-1,j}}{2h} + \frac{u_{n,j+1} - \frac{1}{2}\left(u_{n-1,j} - u_{n+1,j}\right)}{k} = 0.$$

Lax–Wendroff method:

$$u_{n,j+1} = u_{n,j} - \frac{ak}{2h}\left(u_{n+1,j} - u_{n-1,j}\right)$$
$$+ \frac{a^2 k^2}{2h^2}\left(u_{n-1,j} - 2u_{n,j} + u_{n+1,j}\right).$$

8.3.5 IMPLICIT SCHEMES FOR THE PDE: $au_x + u_t = S(x, t)$

Below are implicit difference formulas for the PDE, $au_x + u_t = S(x, t)$. Here, h is the uniform x spacing, and k is the uniform t spacing. The approximation to $u(x_n, t_j) = u(x_0 + nh, t_0 + jk)$ is represented by $u_{n,j}$, and $S_{n,j}$ is used to represent $S(x_n, t_j)$.

Backward in time, backward in space (BTBS):

$$a\frac{u_{n+1,j+1} - u_{n,j+1}}{h} + \frac{u_{n+1,j+1} - u_{n+1,j}}{k} = S_{n+1,j+1}.$$

Backward in time, centered in space (BTCS):

$$a\frac{u_{n+1,j+1} - u_{n-1,j+1}}{2h} + \frac{u_{n,j+1} - u_{n,j}}{k} = S_{n,j+1}.$$

Crank–Nicolson:

$$\frac{1}{2}\left(a\frac{u_{n+1,j+1} - u_{n-1,j+1}}{2h} + a\frac{u_{n+1,j} - u_{n-1,j}}{2h}\right)$$
$$+ \frac{u_{n,j+1} - u_{n,j}}{k} = S_{n,j+1/2}.$$

Wendroff method:

$$\frac{1}{2}\left(a\frac{u_{n+1,j+1} - u_{n,j+1}}{h} + a\frac{u_{n+1,j} - u_{n,j}}{h}\right)$$
$$+ \frac{1}{2}\left(\frac{u_{n+1,j+1} - u_{n+1,j}}{k} + \frac{u_{n,j+1} - u_{n,j}}{k}\right) = S_{n+1/2,j+1/2}.$$

8.3.6   SCHEMES FOR THE PDE: $F(u)_x + u_t = 0$

Below are difference formulas for the PDE, $F(u)_x + u_t = 0$. Here, h is the uniform x spacing, k is the uniform t spacing, and the ratio of these is $s = k/h$. The approximation to $u(x_n, t_j) = u(x_0 + nh, t_0 + jk)$ is represented by $u_{n,j}$ and $F_{m,n} = F(u_{m,n})$. A star superscript indicates an intermediate result, and $F_n^* = F(u_n^*)$. Finally, $a_n = F_n' = F'(u_n)$.

Centered in time, centered in space (unstable):

$$u_{n,j+1} = u_{n,j} - \tfrac{1}{2}s \left(F_{n+1,j} - F_{n-1,j} \right).$$

Lax–Friedrichs method:

$$u_{n,j+1} = \tfrac{1}{2} \left(u_{n+1,j} + u_{n-1,j} \right) - \tfrac{1}{2}s \left(F_{n+1,j} + F_{n-1,j} \right).$$

Lax–Wendroff method:

$$u_{n,j+1} = u_{n,j} - \tfrac{1}{2}s \left(F_{n+1,j} - F_{n-1,j} \right)$$
$$+ \tfrac{1}{2}s^2 \left[a_{n+1/2,j} \left(F_{n+1,j} - F_{n,j} \right) - a_{n-1/2,j} \left(F_{n,j} - F_{n-1,j} \right) \right].$$

Richtmeyer method:

$$u_{n+1/2}^* = \tfrac{1}{2} \left(u_{n+1,j} + u_{n,j} \right) - \tfrac{1}{2} \left(F_{n+1,j} - F_{n,j} \right)$$

$$u_{n,j+1} = u_{n,j} - s \left(F_{n+1/2}^* - F_{n-1}^* \right).$$

MacCormack method:

$$u_n^* = u_{n,j} - s \left(F_{n+1,j} - F_{n,j} \right)$$

$$u_{n,j+1} = \tfrac{1}{2} \left[u_{n,j} + u_n^* - s \left(F_n^* - F_{n-1}^* \right) \right].$$

FTBS upwind method (use when $F'(u) > 0$):

$$u_{n,j+1} = u_{n,j} + s \left(F_{n-1,j} - F_{n,j} \right).$$

FTFS upwind method (use when $F'(u) < 0$):

$$u_{n,j+1} = u_{n,j} - s \left(F_{n+1,j} - F_{n,j} \right).$$

8.3.7   SCHEMES FOR THE PDE: $u_x = u_{tt}$

Below are difference formulas for the PDE, $u_x = u_{tt}$. Here, h is the uniform x spacing, k is the uniform t spacing, and ρ is defined to be $\rho = h/k^2$. The approximation to $u(x_n, t_j) = u(x_0 + nh, t_0 + jk)$ is represented by $u_{n,j}$.

Classic explicit approximation:

$$u_{n+1,j} = (1 - 2\rho)u_{n,j} + \rho\left(u_{n,j+1} + u_{n,j-1}\right).$$

DuFort–Frankel explicit approximation:

$$(1 + 2\rho)u_{n+1,j} = 2\rho\left(u_{n,j+1} + u_{n,j-1}\right) + (1 - 2\rho)u_{n-1,j}.$$

Richardson explicit approximation:

$$u_{n+1,j} - u_{n-1,j} - 2\rho\left(u_{n,j+1} + u_{n,j-1}\right) + 4\rho u_{n,j} = 0.$$

Backward implicit approximation:

$$(1 + 2\rho)u_{n+1,j} - \rho\left(u_{n+1,j+1} + u_{n+1,j-1}\right) = u_{n,j}.$$

Crank–Nicolson implicit approximation:

$$2(\rho + 1)u_{n+1,j} - \rho\left(u_{n+1,j+1} + u_{n+1,j-1}\right) = 2(1 - \rho)u_{n,j}$$
$$+ \rho\left(u_{n,j+1} + u_{n,j-1}\right).$$

Variable weighted implicit approximation (with $0 \le \theta \le 1$):

$$(1 + 2\rho\theta)u_{n+1,j} = \rho(1 - \theta)\left(u_{n,j+1} + u_{n,j-1}\right)$$
$$+ \rho\theta\left(u_{n+1,j+1} + u_{n+1,j-1}\right) + [1 - 2\rho(1 - \theta)]u_{n,j}.$$

8.3.8   NUMERICAL SUMMATION

A sum of the form $\sum_{j=0}^{n} f(x_0 + jh)$ (n may be infinite) can be approximated by the *Euler–Maclaurin sum formula*,

$$\sum_{j=0}^{n} f(x_0 + jh) = \frac{1}{h}\int_{x_0}^{x_0+nh} f(y)\,dy + \frac{1}{2}[f(x_0 + nh) + f(x_0)]$$

$$+ \sum_{k=1}^{m} \frac{B_{2k}}{(2k)!}h^{2k-1}[f^{(2k-1)}(x_0 + nh) - f^{(2k-1)}(x_0)] + E_m \quad (8.3.25)$$

where $E_m = \frac{nh^{2m+2}B_{2m+2}}{(2m+2)!}f^{(2m+2)}(\xi)$, and $x_0 < \xi < x_0 + nh$. The B_n here are *Bernoulli numbers* (see Section 1.2.8).

The above formula is useful even when n is infinite, although the error can no longer be expressed in this form. A useful error estimate (which also holds when n is finite) is that the error is less than the magnitude of the first neglected term in the summation on the right-hand side of Equation (8.3.25) if $f^{(2m+2)}(x)$ and $f^{(2m+4)}(x)$ do not change sign and are of the same sign for $x_0 < x < x_0 + nh$. If just $f^{(2m+2)}(x)$ does not change sign in the interval, then the error is less than twice the first neglected term.

Quadrature formulae result from Equation (8.3.25) using estimates for the derivatives.

Gregory's formula

Using f_j to represent $f(x_0 + jh)$,

$$\int_{x_0}^{x_0+nh} f(y)\,dy = h(\frac{1}{2}f_0 + f_1 + \cdots + f_{n-1} + \frac{1}{2}f_n)$$

$$+ \frac{h}{12}(\Delta f_0 - \Delta f_{n-1}) - \frac{h}{24}(\Delta^2 f_0 + \Delta^2 f_{n-2})$$

$$+ \frac{19h}{720}(\Delta^3 f_0 - \Delta^3 f_{n-3}) - \frac{3h}{160}(\Delta^4 f_0 + \Delta^4 f_{n-4}) + \cdots. \quad (8.3.26)$$

where Δ represents forward differences. The first expression on the right in Equation (8.3.26) is the composite trapezoidal rule, and additional terms provide improved approximations. Care must be taken not to carry this process too far because Gregory's formula is only asymptotically convergent in general and round off error can be significant when computing higher differences.

8.4 PROGRAMMING TECHNIQUES

Efficiency and accuracy is the ultimate goal when solving any problem. Listed here are several suggestions to consider when developing algorithms and computer programs.

1. *Every algorithm must have an effective stopping rule.* For example, popular stopping rules for iteration methods described in Section 8.1.2 are based on the estimate of the absolute error, relative error, or function value. One might choose to stop when a combination of the following conditions are satisfied:

$$|p_n - p_{n-1}| < \epsilon_1, \quad \frac{|p_n - p_{n-1}|}{|p_n|} < \epsilon_2, \quad |f(p_n)| < \epsilon_3,$$

   where each ϵ_i represents a prescribed tolerance. However, since some iterations are not guaranteed to converge, or converge very slowly, it is *recommended* that an *upper bound*, say N, *is specified for the number of iterations* to be performed (see algorithm on page 685). This will avoid infinite loops.

2. *Avoid the use of arrays whenever possible.* Subscripted values often do not require the use of an array. For example, in Newton's method (see page 673) the calculations may be performed using $p = p_0 - \frac{f(p_0)}{f'(p_0)}$. Then check the stopping rule, say, if $|p - p_0| < \epsilon$, and update the current value by setting $p_0 = p$ before computing the next value of the sequence.

3. *Limit the use of arrays when forming tables.* A two-dimensional array can often be avoided. For example, a divided difference table can be formed and printed as a lower triangular matrix. The entries of any row depend only on the entries of the preceding row. Thus, one-dimensional arrays may be used to save the preceding row and the current row being calculated. It is important to note that usually the *entire array need not be saved*. For example, only special values in the table are needed for the coefficients of an interpolating polynomial.

4. *Avoid using formulae that may be highly susceptible to round off error.* Exercise caution when computing quotients of extremely small values as in Equation (8.3.7) with a very small value of h.

5. *Alter formulae* for iterations to obtain a "small correction" to an approximation. For example, writing $\frac{a+b}{2}$ as $a + \frac{b-a}{2}$ in the bisection method (see page 674) is recommended. Many of the iteration formulae in this chapter have this form.

6. *Pivoting strategies* are recommended when solving linear systems to reduce round off error.

7. *Eliminate unnecessary steps* that may increase execution time or round off error.

8. Some methods converge very rapidly, when they do converge, but rely on reasonably close initial approximations. A weaker, but reliable, method (such as the bisection method) to obtain such an approximation can be combined with a more powerful method (such as Newton's method). The weaker method might converge slowly and, by itself, is not very efficient. The powerful method might not converge at all. The combination, however, might remedy both difficulties.

References

1. R. L. Burden and J. D. Faires, *Numerical Analysis*, 5th ed., Prindle, Weber & Schmidt, Boston, 1993.

2. G. H. Golub and C. F. Van Loan, *Matrix Computations*, 2nd ed., The Johns Hopkins Press, Baltimore, 1989.

3. W. H. Press et al., *Numerical Recipies: The Art of Scientific Computing,* Cambridge University Press, New York, 1989.

Chapter 9

Financial Analysis

9.1 FINANCIAL FORMULAE

9.1.1 DEFINITION OF FINANCIAL TERMS

A amount that P is worth, after n time periods, with i percent interest per period

B total amount borrowed

P principal to be invested (equivalently, present value)

a future value multiplier after one time period

i percent interest per time period (expressed as a decimal)

m amount to be paid each time period

n number of time periods

Note that the units of A, B, P, and m must all be the same, for example, dollars.

0-8493-2479-3/96/$0.00+$.50

© 1996 CRC Press, Inc.

9.1.2 FORMULAE CONNECTING FINANCIAL TERMS

Interest: Let the principal amount P be invested at an interest rate of $i\%$ per time period (expressed as a decimal), for n time periods. Let A be the amount that this is worth after n time periods. Then

- Simple interest:

$$A = P(1 + ni) \quad \text{and} \quad P = \frac{A}{(1+ni)} \quad \text{and} \quad i = \frac{1}{n}\left(\frac{A}{P} - 1\right) \tag{9.1.1}$$

- Compound interest (see tables beginning on page 723):

$$A = P(1 + i)^n \quad \text{and} \quad P = \frac{A}{(1+i)^n} \quad \text{and} \quad i = \left(\frac{A}{P}\right)^{1/n} - 1. \tag{9.1.2}$$

When interest is compounded q times per time period for n time periods, it is equivalent to an interest rate of $(i/q)\%$ per time period for nq time periods.

$$A = P\left(1 + \frac{i}{q}\right)^{nq}, \tag{9.1.3}$$

$$P = A\left(1 + \frac{i}{q}\right)^{-nq}, \tag{9.1.4}$$

$$i = q\left[\left(\frac{A}{P}\right)^{1/nq} - 1\right]. \tag{9.1.5}$$

Continous compounding occurs when the interest is compounded infinitely often in each time period (i.e., $q \to \infty$). In this case: $A = Pe^{in}$.

Present value: If A is to be received after n time periods of $i\%$ interest per time period, then the present value P of such an investment is given by (from Equation (9.1.2)) $P = A(1 + i)^{-n}$.

Annuities: Suppose that the amount B (in dollars) is borrowed, at a rate of $i\%$ per time period, to be repaid at a rate of m (in dollars) per time period, for a total of n time periods. Then (see tables beginning on page 723):

$$m = Bi\frac{(1+i)^n}{(1+i)^n - 1}, \tag{9.1.6}$$

$$B = \frac{m}{i}\left(1 - \frac{1}{(1+i)^n}\right). \tag{9.1.7}$$

Using $a = (1 + i)$, these equations can be written more compactly as

$$m = Bi\frac{a^n}{a^n - 1} \quad \text{and} \quad B = \frac{m}{i}\left(1 - \frac{1}{a^n}\right). \tag{9.1.8}$$

9.1.3 EXAMPLES

1. **Question**: If $100 is invested at 5% per year, compounded for 10 years, what is the resulting amount?

   - **Analysis**: Using Equation (9.1.2), we identify

     Principal invested, $P = 100$ (the units are dollars)

     Time period, 1 year

     Interest rate per time period, $i = 5\% = 0.05$

     Number of time periods, $n = 10$

   - **Answer**: $A = P(1 + i)^n$ or $A = 100(1 + 0.05)^{10} = \$162.89$. (Or, see tables starting on page 726.)

2. **Question**: If $100 is invested at 5% per year and the interest is compounded 4 times a year for 10 years, what is the final amount?

   - **Analysis**: Using Equation (9.1.4) we identify

     Principal invested, $P = 100$ (the units are dollars)

     Time period, 1 year

     Interest rate per time period, $i = 5\% = 0.05$

     Number of time periods, $n = 10$

     Number of compounding time periods, $q = 4$

   - **Answer**: $A = P\left(1 + \frac{i}{q}\right)^{nq}$ or $A = 100(1 + \frac{0.05}{4})^{4 \cdot 10} = 100(1.0125)^{40} = \$164.36$.

   - **Alternate analysis**: Using Equation (9.1.2), we identify

     Principal invested, $P = 100$ (the units are dollars)

     Time period, quarter of a year

     Interest rate per time period, $i = \frac{5\%}{4} = \frac{0.05}{4} = 0.0125$

     Number of time periods, $n = 10 \cdot 4 = 40$

   - **Alternate answer**: $A = P(1 + i)^n$ or $A = 100(1.0125)^{40} = \$164.36$. (Or, see tables starting on page 723.)

3. **Question**: If $100 is invested now, and we wish to have $200 at the end of 10 years, what yearly compound interest rate must we receive?

- **Analysis**: Using Equation (9.1.2), we identify

  Principle invested, $P = 100$ (the units are dollars)

  Final amount, $A = 200$

  Time period, 1 year

  Number of time periods, $n = 10$

- **Answer**: $i = \left(\frac{A}{P}\right)^{1/n} - 1$ or $i = \left(\frac{200}{100}\right)^{1/10} - 1 = 0.0717$. (Or, see tables starting on page 724.) Hence, we must receive an annual interest rate of 7.2%.

4. **Question**: An investment returns $10,000 in 10 years time. If the interest rate will be 10% per year, what is the present value (that is, how much money would have to be invested now to obtain this amount in ten years)?

   - **Analysis**: Using Equation (9.1.2), we identify

     Final amount, $A = 10,000$ (the units are dollars)

     Time period, 10 years

     Interest rate per time period, $i = 10\% = 0.1$

     Number of time periods, $n = 10$

   - **Answer**: $P = A(1 + i)^{-n} = 10000(1.1)^{-10} = \$3855.43$ (Or, see tables starting on page 723.) The present value of this investment is $3,855.43.

5. **Question**: A mortgage of $100,000 is obtained with which to buy a house. The mortgage will be repaid at an interest rate of 9% per year, compounded monthly, for 30 years. What is the monthly payment?

   - **Analysis**: Using Equation (9.1.8), we identify

     Amount borrowed, $B = 100,000$ (the units are dollars)

     Time period, 1 month

     Interest rate per time period, $i = 0.09/12 = 0.0075$

     Number of time periods, $n = 30 \cdot 12 = 360$

   - **Answer**: $a = 1 + i = 1.0075$ and $m = Bi\frac{a^n}{a^n - 1} = (100,000)(.0075)$ $\times \frac{(1.0075)^{360}}{(1.0075)^{360} - 1} = \$755.63$. (Or, see tables starting on page 726.) The monthly payment is $755.63.

6. **Question**: Suppose that interest rates on 15-year mortgages are currently 6%, compounded monthly. By spending $600 per month, what is the largest mortgage obtainable?

   - **Analysis**: Using Equation (9.1.8), we identify

     Time period, 1 month

     Payment amount, $m = 600$ (the units are dollars)

Interest rate per time period, $i = 0.06/12 = 0.005$

Number of time periods, $n = 15 \cdot 12 = 180$

- **Answer**: $a = 1+i = 1.005$ and $B = m\,(1 - 1/a^n)\,/i = \frac{800}{0.005}\left(1 - \frac{1}{1.005^{180}}\right)$ $= 94802.81$. (Or, see tables starting on page 726.) The largest mortgage amount obtainable is $94,802.81.

9.2 FINANCIAL TABLES

Compound interest: find final value

These tables use Equation (9.1.2) to determine the final value in dollars (A) when one dollar ($P = 1$) is invested at an interest rate of i per time period, the length of investment time being n time periods. For example, if $1 is invested at a return of 3% per time period, for 50 time periods, then the final value would be $4.38 (see following table). Analogously, if $10 had been invested, then the final value would be $43.84.

n	1.00%	1.50%	2.00%	2.50%	3.00%	3.50%
			$i =$			
5	1.0510	1.0773	1.1041	1.1314	1.1593	1.1877
10	1.1046	1.1605	1.2190	1.2801	1.3439	1.4106
15	1.1610	1.2502	1.3459	1.4483	1.5580	1.6753
20	1.2202	1.3469	1.4859	1.6386	1.8061	1.9898
25	1.2824	1.4509	1.6406	1.8539	2.0938	2.3632
30	1.3478	1.5631	1.8114	2.0976	2.4273	2.8068
35	1.4166	1.6839	1.9999	2.3732	2.8139	3.3336
40	1.4889	1.8140	2.2080	2.6851	3.2620	3.9593
45	1.5648	1.9542	2.4379	3.0379	3.7816	4.7024
50	1.6446	2.1052	2.6916	3.4371	4.3839	5.5849

n	4.00%	4.50%	5.00%	5.50%	6.00%	6.50%
			$i =$			
5	1.2167	1.2462	1.2763	1.3070	1.3382	1.3701
10	1.4802	1.5530	1.6289	1.7081	1.7908	1.8771
15	1.8009	1.9353	2.0789	2.2325	2.3966	2.5718
20	2.1911	2.4117	2.6533	2.9178	3.2071	3.5236
25	2.6658	3.0054	3.3864	3.8134	4.2919	4.8277
30	3.2434	3.7453	4.3219	4.9840	5.7435	6.6144
35	3.9461	4.6673	5.5160	6.5138	7.6861	9.0623
40	4.8010	5.8164	7.0400	8.5133	10.2857	12.4161
45	5.8412	7.2482	8.9850	11.1266	13.7646	17.0111
50	7.1067	9.0326	11.4674	14.5420	18.4202	23.3067

n	7.00%	7.50%	8.00%	8.50%	9.00%	9.50%
			$i =$			
5	1.4026	1.4356	1.4693	1.5037	1.5386	1.5742
10	1.9672	2.0610	2.1589	2.2610	2.3674	2.4782
15	2.7590	2.9589	3.1722	3.3997	3.6425	3.9013
20	3.8697	4.2479	4.6610	5.1120	5.6044	6.1416
25	5.4274	6.0983	6.8485	7.6868	8.6231	9.6684
30	7.6123	8.7550	10.0627	11.5583	13.2677	15.2203
35	10.6766	12.5689	14.7853	17.3796	20.4140	23.9604
40	14.9745	18.0442	21.7245	26.1330	31.4094	37.7194
45	21.0025	25.9048	31.9204	39.2951	48.3273	59.3793
50	29.4570	37.1897	46.9016	59.0863	74.3575	93.4773

n	10.00%	10.50%	11.00%	11.50%	12.00%	12.50%
			$i =$			
5	1.6105	1.6474	1.6851	1.7234	1.7623	1.8020
10	2.5937	2.7141	2.8394	2.9699	3.1058	3.2473
15	4.1772	4.4713	4.7846	5.1183	5.4736	5.8518
20	6.7275	7.3662	8.0623	8.8206	9.6463	10.5451
25	10.8347	12.1355	13.5855	15.2010	17.0001	19.0026
30	17.4494	19.9926	22.8923	26.1967	29.9599	34.2433
35	28.1024	32.9367	38.5749	45.1461	52.7996	61.7075
40	45.2593	54.2614	65.0009	77.8027	93.0510	111.1990
45	72.8905	89.3928	109.5302	134.0816	163.9876	200.3842
50	117.3909	147.2699	184.5648	231.0699	289.0022	361.0989

n	13.00%	13.50%	14.00%	14.50%	15.00%	15.50%
			$i =$			
5	1.8424	1.8836	1.9254	1.9680	2.0114	2.0555
10	3.3946	3.5478	3.7072	3.8731	4.0456	4.2249
15	6.2543	6.6825	7.1379	7.6222	8.1371	8.6842
20	11.5231	12.5869	13.7435	15.0006	16.3665	17.8501
25	21.2305	23.7081	26.4619	29.5214	32.9190	36.6902
30	39.1159	44.6556	50.9502	58.0985	66.2118	75.4153
35	72.0685	84.1115	98.1002	114.3384	133.1755	155.0135
40	132.7816	158.4289	188.8835	225.0191	267.8635	318.6246
45	244.6414	298.4103	363.6791	442.8401	538.7693	654.9216
50	450.7359	562.0735	700.2330	871.5139	1083.6574	1346.1678

Compound interest: find interest rate

These tables use Equation (9.1.2) to determine the compound interest rate i that must be obtained from an investment of one dollar ($P = 1$) to yield a final value of A (in dollars) when the initial amount is invested for n time periods. For example, if $1 is invested for 50 time periods, and the final amount obtained is $4.00, then the actual interest rate has been 2.81% per time period (see following table). Analogously, if $100 had been invested, and the final amount was $400, then the interest rate would also be 2.81% per time period.

n	A = 2.0	2.5	3.0	3.5	4.0	4.5
1	100.00	150.00	200.00	250.00	300.00	350.00
2	41.42	58.11	73.21	87.08	100.00	112.13
3	25.99	35.72	44.22	51.83	58.74	65.10
4	18.92	25.74	31.61	36.78	41.42	45.65
5	14.87	20.11	24.57	28.47	31.95	35.10
10	7.18	9.60	11.61	13.35	14.87	16.23
20	3.53	4.69	5.65	6.46	7.18	7.81
30	2.34	3.10	3.73	4.26	4.73	5.14
50	1.40	1.85	2.22	2.54	2.81	3.05

n	A = 5.0	5.5	6.0	6.5	7.0	7.5
1	400.00	450.00	500.00	550.00	600.00	650.00
2	123.61	134.52	144.95	154.95	164.58	173.86
3	71.00	76.52	81.71	86.63	91.29	95.74
4	49.53	53.14	56.51	59.67	62.66	65.49
5	37.97	40.63	43.10	45.41	47.58	49.63
10	17.46	18.59	19.62	20.58	21.48	22.32
20	8.38	8.90	9.37	9.81	10.22	10.60
30	5.51	5.85	6.15	6.44	6.70	6.95
50	3.27	3.47	3.65	3.81	3.97	4.11

n	A = 8.0	8.5	9.0	9.5	10.0	10.5
1	700.00	750.00	800.00	850.00	900.00	950.00
2	182.84	191.55	200.00	208.22	216.23	224.04
3	100.00	104.08	108.01	111.79	115.44	118.98
4	68.18	70.75	73.21	75.56	77.83	80.01
5	51.57	53.42	55.18	56.87	58.49	60.04
10	23.11	23.86	24.57	25.25	25.89	26.51
20	10.96	11.29	11.61	11.91	12.20	12.48
30	7.18	7.39	7.60	7.79	7.98	8.15
50	4.25	4.37	4.49	4.61	4.71	4.82

n	A = 11.0	12.0	13.0	14.0	15.0	16.0
1	1000.00	1100.00	1200.00	1300.00	1400.00	1500.00
2	231.66	246.41	260.56	274.17	287.30	300.00
3	122.40	128.94	135.13	141.01	146.62	151.98
4	82.12	86.12	89.88	93.43	96.80	100.00
5	61.54	64.38	67.03	69.52	71.88	74.11
10	27.10	28.21	29.24	30.20	31.10	31.95
20	12.74	13.23	13.68	14.11	14.50	14.87
30	8.32	8.64	8.93	9.20	9.45	9.68
50	4.91	5.10	5.26	5.42	5.57	5.70

n	$A =$					
	17.0	18.0	19.0	20.0	25.0	30.0
1	1600.00	1700.00	1800.00	1900.00	2400.00	2900.00
2	312.31	324.26	335.89	347.21	400.00	447.72
3	157.13	162.07	166.84	171.44	192.40	210.72
4	103.05	105.98	108.78	111.47	123.61	134.03
5	76.23	78.26	80.20	82.06	90.37	97.44
10	32.75	33.51	34.24	34.93	37.97	40.51
20	15.22	15.55	15.86	16.16	17.46	18.54
30	9.90	10.11	10.31	10.50	11.33	12.00
50	5.83	5.95	6.07	6.17	6.65	7.04

Compound interest: find annuity

These tables use Equation (9.1.6) to determine the annuity (or mortgage) payment that must be paid each time period, for n time periods, at an interest rate of $i\%$ per time period, to pay off a loan of one dollar ($B = 1$). For example, if $1 is borrowed at 3% interest per time period, and the amount is to be paid back in equal amounts over 10 time periods, then the amount paid back per time period is $0.12 (see following table). Analogously, if $100 had been borrowed, then the mortgage amount would be $11.72.

n	$i =$					
	2.00%	2.25%	2.50%	2.75%	3.00%	3.25%
1	1.0200	1.0225	1.0250	1.0275	1.0300	1.0325
2	0.5150	0.5169	0.5188	0.5207	0.5226	0.5245
3	0.3468	0.3484	0.3501	0.3518	0.3535	0.3552
4	0.2626	0.2642	0.2658	0.2674	0.2690	0.2706
5	0.2122	0.2137	0.2152	0.2168	0.2184	0.2199
6	0.1785	0.1800	0.1815	0.1831	0.1846	0.1861
7	0.1545	0.1560	0.1575	0.1590	0.1605	0.1620
8	0.1365	0.1380	0.1395	0.1410	0.1425	0.1440
9	0.1225	0.1240	0.1255	0.1269	0.1284	0.1299
10	0.1113	0.1128	0.1143	0.1157	0.1172	0.1187
15	0.0778	0.0793	0.0808	0.0823	0.0838	0.0853
20	0.0612	0.0626	0.0641	0.0657	0.0672	0.0688
30	0.0446	0.0462	0.0478	0.0494	0.0510	0.0527

n	i =					
	3.50%	3.75%	4.00%	4.25%	4.50%	4.75%
1	1.0350	1.0375	1.0400	1.0425	1.0450	1.0475
2	0.5264	0.5283	0.5302	0.5321	0.5340	0.5359
3	0.3569	0.3586	0.3603	0.3621	0.3638	0.3655
4	0.2723	0.2739	0.2755	0.2771	0.2787	0.2804
5	0.2215	0.2231	0.2246	0.2262	0.2278	0.2294
6	0.1877	0.1892	0.1908	0.1923	0.1939	0.1954
7	0.1635	0.1651	0.1666	0.1682	0.1697	0.1713
8	0.1455	0.1470	0.1485	0.1501	0.1516	0.1532
9	0.1314	0.1330	0.1345	0.1360	0.1376	0.1391
10	0.1202	0.1218	0.1233	0.1248	0.1264	0.1279
15	0.0868	0.0884	0.0899	0.0915	0.0931	0.0947
20	0.0704	0.0720	0.0736	0.0752	0.0769	0.0786
30	0.0544	0.0561	0.0578	0.0596	0.0614	0.0632

n	i =					
	5.00%	5.25%	5.50%	5.75%	6.00%	6.25%
1	1.0500	1.0525	1.0550	1.0575	1.0600	1.0625
2	0.5378	0.5397	0.5416	0.5435	0.5454	0.5473
3	0.3672	0.3689	0.3707	0.3724	0.3741	0.3758
4	0.2820	0.2837	0.2853	0.2869	0.2886	0.2902
5	0.2310	0.2326	0.2342	0.2358	0.2374	0.2390
6	0.1970	0.1986	0.2002	0.2018	0.2034	0.2050
7	0.1728	0.1744	0.1760	0.1775	0.1791	0.1807
8	0.1547	0.1563	0.1579	0.1594	0.1610	0.1626
9	0.1407	0.1423	0.1438	0.1454	0.1470	0.1486
10	0.1295	0.1311	0.1327	0.1343	0.1359	0.1375
15	0.0963	0.0980	0.0996	0.1013	0.1030	0.1047
20	0.0802	0.0820	0.0837	0.0854	0.0872	0.0890
30	0.0651	0.0669	0.0688	0.0707	0.0726	0.0746

n	i =					
	6.50%	6.75%	7.00%	7.25%	7.50%	7.75%
1	1.0650	1.0675	1.0700	1.0725	1.0750	1.0775
2	0.5493	0.5512	0.5531	0.5550	0.5569	0.5588
3	0.3776	0.3793	0.3811	0.3828	0.3845	0.3863
4	0.2919	0.2936	0.2952	0.2969	0.2986	0.3002
5	0.2406	0.2423	0.2439	0.2455	0.2472	0.2488
6	0.2066	0.2082	0.2098	0.2114	0.2130	0.2147
7	0.1823	0.1839	0.1856	0.1872	0.1888	0.1904
8	0.1642	0.1658	0.1675	0.1691	0.1707	0.1724
9	0.1502	0.1519	0.1535	0.1551	0.1568	0.1584
10	0.1391	0.1407	0.1424	0.1440	0.1457	0.1474
15	0.1064	0.1081	0.1098	0.1115	0.1133	0.1151
20	0.0908	0.0926	0.0944	0.0962	0.0981	0.1000
30	0.0766	0.0786	0.0806	0.0826	0.0847	0.0867

	$i =$					
n	8.00%	8.25%	8.50%	8.75%	9.00%	9.25%
1	1.0800	1.0825	1.0850	1.0875	1.0900	1.0925
2	0.5608	0.5627	0.5646	0.5665	0.5685	0.5704
3	0.3880	0.3898	0.3915	0.3933	0.3951	0.3968
4	0.3019	0.3036	0.3053	0.3070	0.3087	0.3104
5	0.2505	0.2521	0.2538	0.2554	0.2571	0.2588
6	0.2163	0.2180	0.2196	0.2213	0.2229	0.2246
7	0.1921	0.1937	0.1954	0.1970	0.1987	0.2004
8	0.1740	0.1757	0.1773	0.1790	0.1807	0.1824
9	0.1601	0.1617	0.1634	0.1651	0.1668	0.1685
10	0.1490	0.1507	0.1524	0.1541	0.1558	0.1575
15	0.1168	0.1186	0.1204	0.1222	0.1241	0.1259
20	0.1019	0.1038	0.1057	0.1076	0.1095	0.1115
30	0.0888	0.0909	0.0931	0.0952	0.0973	0.0995

	$i =$					
n	9.50%	10.00%	10.50%	11.00%	11.50%	12.00%
1	1.0950	1.1000	1.1050	1.1100	1.1150	1.1200
2	0.5723	0.5762	0.5801	0.5839	0.5878	0.5917
3	0.3986	0.4021	0.4057	0.4092	0.4128	0.4163
4	0.3121	0.3155	0.3189	0.3223	0.3258	0.3292
5	0.2604	0.2638	0.2672	0.2706	0.2740	0.2774
6	0.2263	0.2296	0.2330	0.2364	0.2398	0.2432
7	0.2020	0.2054	0.2088	0.2122	0.2157	0.2191
8	0.1840	0.1874	0.1909	0.1943	0.1978	0.2013
9	0.1702	0.1736	0.1771	0.1806	0.1841	0.1877
10	0.1593	0.1627	0.1663	0.1698	0.1734	0.1770
15	0.1277	0.1315	0.1352	0.1391	0.1429	0.1468
20	0.1135	0.1175	0.1215	0.1256	0.1297	0.1339
30	0.1017	0.1061	0.1105	0.1150	0.1196	0.1241

	$i =$					
n	12.50%	13.00%	13.50%	14.00%	14.50%	15.00%
1	1.1250	1.1300	1.1350	1.1400	1.1450	1.1500
2	0.5956	0.5995	0.6034	0.6073	0.6112	0.6151
3	0.4199	0.4235	0.4271	0.4307	0.4343	0.4380
4	0.3327	0.3362	0.3397	0.3432	0.3467	0.3503
5	0.2809	0.2843	0.2878	0.2913	0.2948	0.2983
6	0.2467	0.2502	0.2536	0.2572	0.2607	0.2642
7	0.2226	0.2261	0.2296	0.2332	0.2368	0.2404
8	0.2048	0.2084	0.2120	0.2156	0.2192	0.2229
9	0.1913	0.1949	0.1985	0.2022	0.2059	0.2096
10	0.1806	0.1843	0.1880	0.1917	0.1955	0.1993
15	0.1508	0.1547	0.1588	0.1628	0.1669	0.1710
20	0.1381	0.1424	0.1467	0.1510	0.1554	0.1598
30	0.1288	0.1334	0.1381	0.1428	0.1475	0.1523

n	15.50%	16.00%	16.50%	17.00%	17.50%	18.00%
			$i =$			
1	1.1550	1.1600	1.1650	1.1700	1.1750	1.1800
2	0.6190	0.6230	0.6269	0.6308	0.6348	0.6387
3	0.4416	0.4453	0.4489	0.4526	0.4562	0.4599
4	0.3538	0.3574	0.3609	0.3645	0.3681	0.3717
5	0.3019	0.3054	0.3090	0.3126	0.3162	0.3198
6	0.2678	0.2714	0.2750	0.2786	0.2823	0.2859
7	0.2440	0.2476	0.2513	0.2549	0.2586	0.2624
8	0.2265	0.2302	0.2339	0.2377	0.2415	0.2452
9	0.2133	0.2171	0.2209	0.2247	0.2285	0.2324
10	0.2031	0.2069	0.2108	0.2147	0.2186	0.2225
15	0.1752	0.1794	0.1836	0.1878	0.1921	0.1964
20	0.1642	0.1687	0.1732	0.1777	0.1822	0.1868
30	0.1571	0.1619	0.1667	0.1715	0.1764	0.1813

9.3 OPTION PRICING

Let S represent the price of a share of stock, and presume that S follows a geometric Brownian motion $dS = \mu S\,dt + \sigma S\,d\omega$, where t is time, μ is a constant, and σ is a constant called the volatility. Let $V(S, t)$ be the value of a derivative security whose payoff is solely a function of S and t. We construct a portfolio consisting of V and Δ shares of stock. The value P of this portfolio is $P = V + S\Delta$. The random component of the portfolio increment (dP) can be removed by choosing $\Delta = -\partial V/\partial S$. The concept of arbitrage says that $dP = rP\,dt$, where r is the (constant) risk-free bank interest rate. Together this results in the classical Black–Scholes equation for option pricing (note that no transaction costs are included):

$$\frac{\partial V}{\partial t} + rS\frac{\partial V}{\partial S} + \frac{1}{2}\sigma^2 S^2\frac{\partial^2 V}{\partial S^2} - rV = 0. \tag{9.3.1}$$

If the asset pays a continuous dividend of $DS\,dt$ (i.e., this is proportional to the asset value S during the time period dt) then the modified equation is

$$\frac{\partial V}{\partial t} + (r - D)S\frac{\partial V}{\partial S} + \frac{1}{2}\sigma^2 S^2\frac{\partial^2 V}{\partial S^2} - rV = 0. \tag{9.3.2}$$

If E is the exercise price of the option, and T is the only date on which the option can be exercised (T is called the expiry date), then the solution of the modified Black–Scholes equation is

$$V(S, t) = e^{-D(T-t)}S\Phi(d_1) - Ee^{-r(T-t)}\Phi(d_2) \tag{9.3.3}$$

where

$$d_1 = \frac{\log(S/E) + (r - D + \sigma^2/2)(T - t)}{\sigma\sqrt{T - t}}, \qquad d_2 = d_1 - \sigma\sqrt{T - t},$$

and Φ is the cumulative probability distribution for the normal distribution.

Chapter 10

Miscellaneous

0-8493-2479-3/96/$0.00+$.50
© 1996 CRC Press, Inc.

10.1   UNITS

10.1.1   SI SYSTEM OF MEASUREMENT

SI, the abbreviation of the French words "Systeme Internationale d'Unites", is the accepted abbreviation for the International Metric System. It has seven base units.

- Base units

Quantity measured	Unit	Symbol
Length	Meter	m
Mass	Kilogram	kg
Time	Second	s
Electric current	Ampere	A
Temperature	Degrees Kelvin	K
Luminous intensity	Candela	cd
Amount of substance	Mole	mol

- Derived units

Quantity	SI Name	Symbol	Combination of SI units
Absorbed dose	Gray	Gy	J/kg
Activity (radiation source)	Becquerel	Bq	1/s
Capacitance	Farad	F	C/V
Conductance	Siemens	S	A/V
Electric charge	Coulomb	C	A-s
Electric potential	Volt	V	W/A
Electric resistance	Ohm	Ω	V/A
Energy	Joule	J	N-m
Force	Newton	N	$kg\text{-}m/s^2$
Frequency	Hertz	Hz	1/s
Illuminance	Lux	lx	lm/m^2
Inductance	Henry	H	Wb/A
Luminous flux	Lumen	lm	cd-sr
Magnetic flux density	Tesla	T	Wb/m^2
Magnetic flux	Weber	Wb	V-s
Power	Watt	W	J/s
Pressure or stress	Pascal	Pa	N/m^2

- Supplementary units

Quantity measured	Unit	Symbol
Plane angle	Radian	rad
Solid angle	Steradian	sr

10.1.2 DIMENSIONAL ANALYSIS/BUCKINGHAM PI

The units of the parameters in a system constrain all the derivable quantities, regardless of the equations describing the system. In particular, all derived quantities are functions of dimensionless combinations of parameters. The number of dimensionless parameters and their forms are given by the Buckingham pi theorem.

In a system, the quantity $u = f(W_1, W_2, \ldots, W_n)$ is to be determined in terms of the n measurable variables and parameters $\{W_i\}$ where f is an unknown function. Let the quantities $\{u, W_i\}$ involve m fundamental dimensions labeled by $L_1, L_2, \ldots, L_m$ (such as length, mass, time, or charge). The dimensions of any of the $\{u, W_i\}$ is given by a product of powers of the fundamental dimensions. For example, the dimensions of W_i are $L_1^{b_{i1}} L_2^{b_{i2}} L_3^{b_{i3}} \cdots L_m^{b_{im}}$ where the $\{b_{ij}\}$ are real and called the dimensional exponents. A quantity is called dimensionless if all of its dimensional exponents are zero. Let $\mathbf{b}_i = \begin{bmatrix} b_{i1} & b_{i2} & \ldots & b_{im} \end{bmatrix}^{\mathrm{T}}$ be the dimension vector of W_i and let $B = \begin{bmatrix} \mathbf{b}_1 & \mathbf{b}_2 & \ldots & \mathbf{b}_n \end{bmatrix}$ be the $m \times n$ dimension matrix of the system. Let $\mathbf{a} = \begin{bmatrix} a_1 & a_2 & \ldots & a_m \end{bmatrix}^{\mathrm{T}}$ be the dimension vector of u and let $\mathbf{y} = \begin{bmatrix} y_1 & y_2 & \ldots & y_n \end{bmatrix}^{\mathrm{T}}$ represent a solution of $B\mathbf{y} = -\mathbf{a}$. Then,

1. The number of dimensionless quantities is $k + 1 = n + 1 - \mathrm{rank}(B)$, and
2. The measurable quantity u can be expressed in terms of dimensionless parameters as

$$u = W_1^{-y_1} W_2^{-y_2} \cdots W_n^{-y_n} g(\pi_1, \pi_2, \ldots, \pi_k) \qquad (10.1.1)$$

where g is an unknown function of its parameters and the $\{\pi_i\}$ are the dimensionless quantities, $\pi_i = W_1^{x_{1i}} W_2^{x_{2i}} \cdots W_n^{x_{ni}}$, and $\mathbf{x}^{(i)} = \begin{bmatrix} x_{1i} & x_{2i} & \ldots & x_{ni} \end{bmatrix}^{\mathrm{T}}$ (for $i = 1, 2, \ldots, k$) represent the $k = n - r(B)$ linearly independent solutions of the system $B\mathbf{x} = \mathbf{0}$.

10.1.3   UNITS OF PHYSICAL QUANTITIES

In the following, read "kilograms" for the mass M, "meters" for the length L, and "seconds" for the time T. For example, acceleration is measured in units of LT^{-2}, or meters per second squared.

Quantity	Dimensions
Acceleration	LT^{-2}
Angular acceleration	T^{-2}
Angular momentum	ML^2T^{-1}
Angular velocity	T^{-1}
Area	L^2
Displacement	L
Energy or work	ML^2T^{-2}
Force	MLT^{-2}
Frequency	T^{-1}
Gravitational field strength	LT^{-2}
Gravitational potential	L^2T^{-2}
Length	L
Mass	M
Momentum	MLT^{-1}
Power	ML^2T^{-3}
Pressure	$ML^{-1}T^{-2}$
Rotational inertia	ML^2
Time	T
Torque	ML^2T^{-2}
Velocity	LT^{-1}
Volume	L^3

10.1.4 CONVERSION: METRIC TO ENGLISH

Multiply	By	To obtain
Centimeters	0.3937008	Inches
Meters	3.280840	Feet
Meters	1.093613	Yards
Kilometers	0.6213712	Miles
Grams	0.03527396	Ounces
Kilograms	2.204623	Pounds
Liters	0.2641721	Gallons (US)
Milliliters (cc)	0.03381402	Fluid ounces
Square centimeters	0.1550003	Square inches
Square meters	10.76391	Square feet
Square meters	1.195990	Square yards
Milliliters (cc)	0.06102374	Cubic inches
Cubic meters	35.31467	Cubic feet
Cubic meters	1.307951	Cubic yards

10.1.5 CONVERSION: ENGLISH TO METRIC

Multiply	By	To obtain
Mils	25.4	Microns
Inches	2.540000	Centimeters
Feet	0.3048000	Meters
Yards	0.9144000	Meters
Miles	1.609344	Kilometers
Ounces	28.34952	Grams
Pounds	0.4535924	Kilograms
Gallons (US)	3.785412	Liters
Fluid ounces	29.57353	Milliliters (cc)
Square inches	6.451600	Square centimeters
Square feet	0.09290304	Square meters
Square yards	0.8361274	Square meters
Cubic inches	16.38706	Milliliters (cc)
Cubic feet	0.02831685	Cubic meters
Cubic yards	0.7645549	Cubic meters

10.1.6 TEMPERATURE CONVERSION

If T_F is the temperature in degrees Fahrenheit and T_C is the temperature in degrees Celsius, then

$$T_C = \frac{5}{9}(T_F - 32) \quad \text{and} \quad T_F = \frac{9}{5}T_C + 32. \qquad (10.1.2)$$

10.1.7 MISCELLANEOUS CONVERSIONS

To obtain	Multiply	By
Atmospheres	Feet of water at 4°C	2.950×10^{-2}
Atmospheres	Inches of mercury at 4°C	3.342×10^{-2}
Atmospheres	Pounds per square inch	6.804×10^{-2}
BTU	Foot-pounds	1.285×10^{-3}
BTU	Joules	9.480×10^{-4}
Cubic feet	Cords	128
Degree (angle)	Radian	57.29578
Ergs	Foot-pounds	1.356×10^{7}
Feet	Miles	5280
Feet of water at 4°C	Atmospheres	33.90
Foot-pounds	Horsepower-hours	1.98×10^{6}
Foot-pounds	Kilowatt-hours	2.655×10^{6}
Foot-pounds per minute	Horsepower	3.3×10^{4}
Horsepower	Foot-pounds per second	1.818×10^{-3}
Inches of mercury at 0°C	Atmospheres	2.036
Joules	BTU	1.055060×10^{3}
Joules	Foot-pounds	1.35582
Kilowatts	BTU per minute	1.758×10^{-2}
Kilowatts	Foot-pounds per minute	2.26×10^{-5}
Kilowatts	Horsepower	0.7457
Knots	Miles per hour	0.8689762
Miles	Feet	1.893939×10^{-4}
Nautical miles	Miles	0.8689762
Radians	Degrees	1.745329×10^{-2}
Square feet	Acres	43560
Watts	BTU per minute	17.5796

10.1.8 PHYSICAL CONSTANTS

Equatorial radius of the earth = 6378.388 km = 3963.34 statute miles.
Polar radius of the earth = 6356.912 km = 3949.99 statute miles.
1 degree of latitude at 40° = 69 miles.
1 international nautical mile = 1.15078 statute miles = 1852 m = 6076.115 ft.
Mean density of the earth = 5.522 g/cm^3 = 344.7 lb/ft^3.
G (gravitational constant) = $(6.673 \pm 0.003) \times 10^{-8}$ cm^3/g-sec^2.
Acceleration, sea level, latitude 45° = 980.6194 cm/sec^2 = 32.1726 ft/sec^2.
Length of seconds pendulum, sea level, 45° = 99.3575 cm = 39.1171 in.
1 knot (international) = 101.269 ft/min = 1.6878 ft/sec = 1.1508 statute miles/hr.
1 micron = 10^{-4} cm.
1 angstrom = 10^{-8} cm.
Mass of hydrogen atom = $(1.67339 \pm 0.0031) \times 10^{-24}$ g.
Density of mercury, at 0°C = 13.5955 g/ml.
Density of water (maximum), at 3.98°C = 1.000000 g/ml.
Density of water, at 0°C = 0.999973 g/ml.
Density of dry air, at 0°C, 760 mm = 1.2929 g/liter.
Velocity of sound, dry air, at 0°C = 331.36 m/sec = 1087.1 ft/sec.
c (speed of light) = 299, 792, 458 m/sec (exact).
Heat of fusion of water, at 0°C = 79.71 cal/g.
Heat of vaporization of water, at 100°C = 539.55 cal/g.
Electrochemical equivalent of silver = 0.001118 g/sec international amp.
Absolute wavelength of red cadmium light, air at 15°C, 760 mm = 6438.4696 A.
Wavelength of orange-red line of krypton 86 = 6057.802 A.
e (charge of electron) = 1.602192×10^{-19} coul.
Avogadro's number = 6.022169×10^{23}.
1 astronomical unit = 1.495979×10^{11} m.

10.2 CALENDAR COMPUTATIONS

10.2.1 LEAP YEARS

If a year is divisible by 4, then it will be a leap year, unless the year is divisible by 100 (when it will not be a leap year), unless the year is divisible by 400 (when it will be a leap year). Hence the list of leap years include {..., 1896, 1904, 1908, ..., 1992, 1996, 2000, ...} and the list of nonleap years includes {..., 1900, ..., 1998, 1999, 2001, ...}.

10.2.2 DAY OF WEEK FOR ANY GIVEN DAY

The following formula gives the day of the week for the Gregorian calendar (i.e., for any date after 1582):

$$W \equiv \left(k + \lfloor 2.6m - 0.2 \rfloor - 2C + Y + \left\lfloor \frac{Y}{4} \right\rfloor + \left\lfloor \frac{C}{4} \right\rfloor \right) \quad \mathrm{mod}\ 7 \tag{10.2.1}$$

where

- The "mod" function returns a nonnegative value.

- $\lfloor \cdot \rfloor$ denotes the integer floor function.

- k is the day of the month (1 to 31).

- m is the month ($1 = $ March, ... , $10 = $ December, $11 = $ January, $12 = $ February). (January and February are treated as months of the preceding year).

- C is century (1997 has $C = 19$).

- Y is the year (1997 has $Y = 97$ except $Y = 96$ for January and February).

- W is the day of the week ($0 = $ Sunday, ... , $6 = $ Saturday).

   For example, consider the date 16 March 1997 (for which $k = 16$, $m = 1$, $C = 19$, and $Y = 97$). From Equation (10.2.1), we compute $W \equiv 16 + \lfloor 2.4 \rfloor - 38 + 97 + \lfloor \frac{97}{4} \rfloor + \lfloor \frac{19}{4} \rfloor$ (mod 7) $\equiv 2 + 2 - 3 + 6 + 3 + 4$ (mod 7) $\equiv 0$ (mod 7). So this date will be a Sunday.

   Because 7 does not divide 400, January 1 occurs more frequently on some days than others! In a cycle of 400 years, January 1 and March 1 occur on the following days with the following frequencies:

	Sun	Mon	Tue	Wed	Thu	Fri	Sat
January 1	58	56	58	57	57	58	56
March 1	58	56	58	56	58	57	57

10.2.3   NUMBER OF EACH DAY OF THE YEAR

Day	Jan	Feb	Mar	Apr	May	Jun	Jul	Aug	Sep	Oct	Nov	Dec
1	1	32	60	91	121	152	182	213	244	274	305	335
2	2	33	61	92	122	153	183	214	245	275	306	336
3	3	34	62	93	123	154	184	215	246	276	307	337
4	4	35	63	94	124	155	185	216	247	277	308	338
5	5	36	64	95	125	156	186	217	248	278	309	339
6	6	37	65	96	126	157	187	218	249	279	310	340
7	7	38	66	97	127	158	188	219	250	280	311	341
8	8	39	67	98	128	159	189	220	251	281	312	342
9	9	40	68	99	129	160	190	221	252	282	313	343
10	10	41	69	100	130	161	191	222	253	283	314	344
11	11	42	70	101	131	162	192	223	254	284	315	345
12	12	43	71	102	132	163	193	224	255	285	316	346
13	13	44	72	103	133	164	194	225	256	286	317	347
14	14	45	73	104	134	165	195	226	257	287	318	348
15	15	46	74	105	135	166	196	227	258	288	319	349
16	16	47	75	106	136	167	197	228	259	289	320	350
17	17	48	76	107	137	168	198	229	260	290	321	351
18	18	49	77	108	138	169	199	230	261	291	322	352
19	19	50	78	109	139	170	200	231	262	292	323	353
20	20	51	79	110	140	171	201	232	263	293	324	354
21	21	52	80	111	141	172	202	233	264	294	325	355
22	22	53	81	112	142	173	203	234	265	295	326	356
23	23	54	82	113	143	174	204	235	266	296	327	357
24	24	55	83	114	144	175	205	236	267	297	328	358
25	25	56	84	115	145	176	206	237	268	298	329	359
26	26	57	85	116	146	177	207	238	269	299	330	360
27	27	58	86	117	147	178	208	239	270	300	331	361
28	28	59	87	118	148	179	209	240	271	301	332	362
29	29	*	88	119	149	180	210	241	272	302	333	363
30	30		89	120	150	181	211	242	273	303	334	364
31	31		90		151		212	243		304		365

*In leap years, after February 28, add 1 to the tabulated number.

10.3   AMS CLASSIFICATION SCHEME

00	General	45	Integral equations
01	History and biography	46	Functional analysis
03	Mathematical logic and foundations	47	Operator theory
04	Set theory	49	Calculus of variations and optimal control; optimization
05	Combinatorics	51	Geometry
06	Order, lattices, ordered algebraic structures	52	Convex and discrete geometry
08	General algebraic systems	53	Differential geometry
11	Number theory	54	General topology
12	Field theory and polynomials	55	Algebraic topology
13	Commutative rings and algebras	57	Manifolds and cell complexes
14	Algebraic geometry	58	Global analysis, analysis on manifolds
15	Linear and multilinear algebra; matrix theory	60	Probability theory and stochastic processes
16	Associative rings and algebras	62	Statistics
17	Nonassociative rings and algebras	65	Numerical analysis
18	Category theory, homological algebra	68	Computer science
19	K-theory	70	Mechanics of particles and systems
20	Group theory and generalizations	73	Mechanics of solids
22	Topological groups, Lie groups	76	Fluid mechanics
26	Real functions	78	Optics, electromagnetic theory
28	Measure and integration	80	Classical thermodynamics, heat transfer
30	Functions of a complex variable	81	Quantum theory
31	Potential theory	82	Statistical mechanics, structure of matter
32	Several complex variables and analytic spaces	83	Relativity and gravitational theory
33	Special functions	85	Astronomy and astrophysics
34	Ordinary differential equations	86	Geophysics
35	Partial differential equations	90	Economics, operations research, programming, games
39	Finite differences and functional equations	92	Biology and other natural sciences, behavioral sciences
40	Sequences, series, summability	93	Systems theory; control
41	Approximations and expansions	94	Information and communication, circuits
42	Fourier analysis		
43	Abstract harmonic analysis		
44	Integral transforms, operational calculus		

10.4 GREEK ALPHABET

For each Greek letter, we illustrate the form of the capital letter and the form of the lower case letter. In some cases, there is a popular variation of the lower case letter.

Greek letter			Greek name	English equivalent	Greek letter			Greek name	English equivalent
A	α		Alpha	a	N	ν		Nu	n
B	β		Beta	b	Ξ	ξ		Xi	x
Γ	γ		Gamma	g	O	o		Omicron	o
Δ	δ		Delta	d	Π	π	ϖ	Pi	p
E	ϵ	ε	Epsilon	e	P	ρ	ϱ	Rho	r
Z	ζ		Zeta	z	Σ	σ	ς	Sigma	s
H	η		Eta	e	T	τ		Tau	t
Θ	θ	ϑ	Theta	th	Υ	υ		Upsilon	u
I	ι		Iota	i	Φ	ϕ	φ	Phi	ph
K	κ		Kappa	k	X	χ		Chi	ch
Λ	λ		Lambda	l	Ψ	ψ		Psi	ps
M	μ		Mu	m	Ω	ω		Omega	o

10.5 PROFESSIONAL MATHEMATICAL ORGANIZATIONS

- **American Mathematical Society (AMS)**
  P.O. Box 6248, Providence, RI 02940-6248
  Telephone: 401/455-4000, 800/321-4AMS
  Electronic mail: ams@math.ams.org

- **American Mathematical Association of Two-Year Colleges**
  North Lake College, 5001 MacArthur Blvd, Irving, TX 75038-3899
  Telephone: 214/659-5328
  Electronic mail: memays@dcccd.edu

- **American Statistical Association**
  1429 Duke Street, Alexandria, VA 22314-3402
  Telephone: 703/684-1221

- **Association for Symbolic Logic**
  Department of Mathematics, University of Illinois,
  1409 West Green Street, Urbana, IL 61801
  Telephone: 217/244-7902
  Electronic mail: asl@symcom.math.uiuc.edu

- **Association for Women in Mathematics**
  4114 Computer & Space Sciences Building, University of Maryland,
  College Park, MD 20742-2461
  Telephone: 301/405-7892
  Electronic mail: awm@math.umd.edu

- **Canadian Applied Mathematics Society**
  Department of Mathematics and Statistics, Simon Fraser University,
  Burnaby, British Columbia, Canada V5A 1S6
  Telephone: 604/291-3337, 604/291-3332
  Electronic mail: gac@cs.sfu.ca

- **Canadian Mathematical Society**
  577 King Edward, Suite 109, P.O. Box 450, Station A,
  Ottawa, Ontario, Canada K1N 6N5
  Telephone: 613/564-2223
  Electronic mail: exsmc@acadvm1.uottawa.ca

- **Casualty Actuarial Society**
  1100 North Glebe Road, Suite 600, Arlington, VA 22201
  Telephone: 703/276-3100

- **Conference Board of the Mathematical Sciences**
  1529 Eighteenth Street, N.W., Washington, DC 20036
  Telephone: 202/293-1170
  Electronic mail: ronrosier@guvax.georgetown.edu

- **Consortium for Mathematics and Its Applications (COMAP)**
  57 Bedford Street, Suite 210, Lexington, MA 02173
  Telephone: 617/862-7878
  Electronic mail: info@comap.com

- **Council on Undergraduate Research: Mathematical and Computer Sciences Division**
  University of North Carolina at Asheville, One University Heights,
  Asheville, NC 28804-3299
  Telephone: 704/251-6006

- **Fibonacci Association**
  Department of Computer Science, Box 2201,
  South Dakota State University, Brookings, SD 57007-0194
  Telephone: 605/688-5719

- **Industrial Mathematics Society**
  P.O. Box 159, Roseville, MI 48066
  Telephone: 313/771-0403

- **Institute for Operations Research and the Management Sciences (INFORMS)**
  940-A Elkridge Landing Road, Linthicum, MD 21090-2909
  Telephone: 410/850-0300, 800/4IN-FORMS
  Electronic mail: informs@jhuvms.hcf.jhu.edu

- **Institute of Mathematical Statistics**
  3401 Investment Boulevard #7, Hayward, CA 94545-3819
  Telephone: 510/783-8141
  Electronic mail: ims@stat.berkeley.edu

- **International Mathematics Union (IMPA)**
  Estrada Dona Castorina, 110, Jardim Botánico,
  Rio de Janeiro – RJ, 22460 Brazil
  Telephone: 55-21-294 9032, 55-21-5111749
  Electronic mail: imu@impa.br

- **Joint Policy Board for Mathematics**
  1529 Eighteenth Street, N.W., Washington, DC 20036
  Telephone: 202/234-9570
  Electronic mail: jpbm@math.umd.edu

- **Kappa Mu Epsilon** ($\kappa\mu\epsilon$)
  National Mathematics Honor Society, Department of Mathematics,
  Niagara University, Niagara Falls, NY 14109

- **Mathematical Association of America (MAA)**
  Dolciani Mathematical Center, 1529 Eighteenth Street, N.W.,
  Washington, DC 20036
  Telephone: 202/387-5200
  Electronic mail: maahq@maa.org

- **Mathematical Programming Society**
  Department of Mathematics and Computer Science, Eindhoven
  University of Technology, 5600 MB Eindhoven, The Netherlands
  Telephone: +31-40-474770
  Electronic mail: jkl@win.tue.nl

- **Mu Alpha Theta** ($\mu\alpha\theta$)
  University of Oklahoma, 610 Elm Avenue, Room 423, Norman, OK 73019-
  0315
  Telephone: 405/325-4489
  Electronic mail: seliason@uoknor.edu

- **National Association of Mathematicians**
  Box 959, Elizabeth City State University, Elizabeth City, NC 27909
  Telephone: 919/335-3326
  Electronic mail: nam@ecsvax.uncecs.edu

- **National Council of Teachers of Mathematics**
  1906 Association Drive, Reston, VA 22091
  Telephone: 703/620-9840

- **ORSA** (see *INFORMS*)

- **Pi Mu Epsilon** ($\pi\,\mu\epsilon$)
  National Mathematics Honorary Society, Department of Mathematics,
  East Carolina University, Greenville, NC 27858
  Telephone: 919/328-6414

- **Rocky Mountain Mathematics Consortium**
  Arizona State University, Box 871904, Tempe, AZ 85287-1904
  Telephone: 602/965-3788

- **Society of Industrial and Applied Mathematics (SIAM)**
  3600 University City Science Center, Philadelphia, PA 19104-2688
  Telephone: 215/382-9800
  Electronic mail: `siam@siam.org`

- **Society for Mathematical Biology, Inc.**
  P.O. Box 11283, Boulder, CO 80301
  Telephone: 303/499-0510

- **Society of Actuaries**
  475 North Martingale Road, Suite 800, Schaumburg, IL 60173-2226
  Telephone: 708/706-3500

- **Statistical Society of Canada**
  Department of Mathematics and Statistics, University of Victoria,
  Victoria, British Columbia, Canada V8W 3P4
  Telephone: 604/721-7470
  Electronic mail: `roger@uvvm.uvic.ca`

10.6   ELECTRONIC MATHEMATICAL RESOURCES

The following is a list of Uniform Resource Locators (URL). These are the addresses
of Web sites, gopher pages, FTP sites, etc.

`http://www.yahoo.com/Science/Mathematics/`
> A very large list of useful sites relating to mathematics. It is perhaps the best place to
> start researching an arbitrary mathematical question not covered elsewhere in this list.

`http://daisy.uwaterloo.ca/~alopez-o/math-faq/math-faq.html`
> The *FAQ* (frequently asked questions) listing from the news group `sci.math`.

`http://e-math.ams.org/`
> The American Mathematical Society home page, with information about AMS-TEX,
> the Combined Membership List of the AMS, Math Reviews subject classifications,
> preprints, etc.

`gopher://gopher.maa.org/`
> The Mathematics Association of America, available using gopher.

`http://www.siam.org/`
> The Society for Industrial and Applied Mathematics.

`http://netlib2.cs.utk.edu/master/`
> The master listing for Netlib, containing many standard programs, including linpack, eispack, hompack, SPARC packages, and ODEpack.

`http://www.netlib.org/liblist.html`
> An alternative site for Netlib.

`http://gams.cam.nist.gov/`
> The Guide to Available Mathematical Software.

`http://www.nag.co.uk:70/`
> The home page of the Numerical Algorithms Group.

`http://www.math.hmc.edu/codee/home.html`
> The Consortium of Ordinary Differential Equation Experiments, maintained by Harvey Mudd College.

`http://www.ima.umn.edu/`
> The Institute for Mathematics and its Applications at the University of Minnesota.

`http://cam.cornell.edu/~driscoll/research/drums.html`
> A famous question posed by mathematical physicist M. Kac is, "Can one hear the shape of a drum?" In 1991, Gordon, Webb, and Wolpert found two different shaped drums with the same sequence of eigenvalues. This site contains some details of the calculations.

`http://www.utm.edu:80/departments/math/largest.html`
> Information about primes, including largest known primes of various types.

`http://www.geom.umn.edu/docs/snell/chance/sources.html`
> A listing of interesting sites, primarily related to statistics.

`http://aleph0.clarku.edu/~djoyce/julia/explorer.html`
> Useful for exploring the Mandelbrot and Julia sets.

`ftp://megrez.math.u-bordeaux.fr/pub/numberfields/`
> The Computational Number Theory group in Bordeaux has announced the availability (by anonymous ftp at the above URL) of extensive tables of number fields (almost 550000 number fields). For the number fields belonging to tables of reasonable length, this site contains the signature, the Galois group of the Galois closure of the field, the discriminant of the number field, the class number, the structure of the class group as a product of cyclic groups, an ideal in the class for each class generating these cyclic groups, the regulator, the number of roots of unity in the field, a generator of the torsion part of the unit group, and a system of fundamental units.

`ftp://netlib.att.com/netlib/att/math/index.html.Z`
> The AT&T Bell Laboratories Math Archive.

`gopher://ejde.math.unt.edu`
> The Electronic Journal of Differential Equations. Available via telnet at `ejde.math.unt.edu` with login ejde, and also available at `ejde.math.swt.edu`.

`http://nyjm.albany.edu:8000/nyjm.html`
> The New York Journal of Mathematics, the first electronic journal devoted to general mathematics. Also available via gopher at `gopher nyjm.albany.edu 1070` and via FTP at `nyjm.albany.edu` in directory `/pub/nyjm`.

`http://www.math.scarolina.edu/~wavelet/`
> The Wavelet Digest is an electronic information service on the Internet at `wavelet@math.scarolina.edu`, containing questions and answers, and announcements of papers, books, journals, software, and conferences.

`http://www.math.ohio-state.edu/JAT`
> The Journal of Approximation Theory.

`http://ejc.math.gatech.edu:8080/Journal/ejc-wce.html`
> The World Combinatorics Exchange and The Electronic Journal of Combinatorics.

`http://www.cs.indiana.edu/cstr/search`
   Unified Computer Science TR Index.

`http://www.c3.lanl.gov/laces`

   LACES is a database of preprints, papers, abstracts, and related documents in areas involving discrete mathematics. This includes combinatorics, graph theory, geometry, algorithms, etc. If you have preprints in any of these areas you are invited to send them to LACES. Submissions are made available to the public immediately. Submission instructions and facilities can be found at this site.

   Features of LACES include full search capabilities, including approximate search and relevance feedback, comment and reference links, revision, abstract and comment processing (anyone can add comments to documents in the database), and more. Documents are permanently archived, and copyrights remain with the authors.

`ftp://rattler.cameron.edu`

   The Southwest Journal of Pure and Applied Mathematics.

`http://www.mag-browse.com/`

   Tables of contents of various magazines. As of the summer of 1995, 25 scientific magazines were included.

`Sloane's sequence identifier`

   To identify a sequence, send electronic mail to `sequences@research.att.com`, saying (for example) `lookup 1 11 21 1211 111221`.

10.7 COMPUTER LANGUAGES

The following is a sampling of the computer languages used by scientists and engineers:

- Numerical languages
   Ada
   APL
   C
   C++
   Fortran
   Lisp
   Matlab
   Pascal

- Statistical languages
   SPSS
   Minitab

- Optimization languages
   GAMS (AMPL)
   MINOS
   MINTO

- Symbolic languages
   Axiom
   Derive
   Macsyma
   Maple
   Mathematica
   Reduce

10.7.1 CONTACT INFORMATION

1. AXIOM	`http://www.nag.co.uk/1h/symbolic/AX.html`
2. Fortran	`http://www.nag.co.uk:70/CGI/Forms/Tools/` `imagemap.cgi/NAG`
3. Macsyma	`http://www.macsyma.com`
4. Maple	`http://www.maplesoft.com/Maple/index.html`
5. MathCad	`http://www.mathsoft.com/index.html`
6. Matlab	`http://www.mathworks.com`
7. Mathematica	`http://www.wri.com`

10.8 FIELDS' MEDALS

The Fields' medal is the most prestigious award that can be bestowed upon a mathematician. It is usually awarded to someone no more than 40 years of age; the ages of the recipients are listed below.

• 1936	Ahlfors, Lars	29	Harvard University
• 1936	Douglas, Jesse	39	MIT
• 1950	Schwartz, Laurent	35	Universite de Nancy
• 1950	Selberg, Atle	33	Princeton/Inst. for Advanced Studies
• 1954	Kodaira, Kunihiko	39	Princeton University
• 1954	Serre, Jean-Pierre	27	College de France
• 1958	Roth, Klaus	32	University of London
• 1958	Thom, Rene	35	University of Strasbourg
• 1962	Hormander, Lars	31	University of Stockholm
• 1962	Milnor, John	31	Princeton University
• 1966	Atiyah, Michael	37	Oxford University
• 1966	Cohen, Paul	32	Stanford University
• 1966	Grothendieck, Alexander	38	University of Paris
• 1966	Smale, Stephen	36	University of California at Berkeley
• 1970	Baker, Alan	31	Cambridge University
• 1970	Hironaka, Heisuke	39	Harvard University
• 1970	Novikov, Serge	32	Moscow University
• 1970	Thompson, John	37	University of Chicago

- 1974 Bombieri, Enrico   33   Univeristy of Pisa

- 1974 Mumford, David   37   Harvard University

- 1978 Deligne, Pierre   33   IHES

- 1978 Fefferman, Charles   29   Princeton University

- 1978 Margulis, Gregori   32   InstPrblmInfTrans

- 1978 Quillen, Daniel   38   MIT

- 1982 Connes, Alain   35   IHES

- 1982 Thurston, William   35   Princeton University

- 1982 Yau, Shing-Tung   33   IAS

- 1986 Donaldson, Simon   27   Oxford University

- 1986 Faltings, Gerd   32   Princeton University

- 1986 Freedman, Michael   35   University of California at San Diego

- 1990 Drinfeld, Vladimir   36   Phys. Inst. Kharkov

- 1990 Jones, Vaughan   38   University of California at Berkeley

- 1990 Mori, Shigefumi   39   University of Kyoto

- 1990 Witten, Edward   38   Princeton/Inst. for Advanced Studies

- 1994 Lions, Pierre-Louis   38   Universite de Paris-Dauphine

- 1994 Yoccoz, Jean-Chrisophe   36   Universite de Paris-Sud

- 1994 Bourgain, Jean   40   Princeton/Inst. for Advanced Studies

- 1994 Zelmanov, Efim   39   University of Wisconsin

10.9   BIOGRAPHIES OF MATHEMATICIANS

Ah'mose *(c. 1650 B.C.E.)* was the scribe responsible for copying the *Rhind Papyrus*, the most detailed original document still extant on ancient Egyptian mathematics. The papyrus contains some 87 problems with solutions dealing with what we consider first-degree equations, arithmetic progressions, areas and volumes of rectangular and circular regions, proportions, and several other topics. It also contains a table of the results of the division of 2 by every odd number from 3 to 101.

Euclid *(c. 300 B.C.E.)* is responsible for the most famous mathematics text of all time, the *Elements*. Not only does this work deal with the standard results of plane geometry, but it also contains three chapters on number theory, one long chapter on irrational quantities, and three chapters on solid geometry, culminating with the construction of the five regular solids. The axiom-definition-theorem-proof style of Euclid's work has become the standard for formal mathematical writing up to the present day.

Archimedes *(287–212 B.C.E.)* not only wrote several works on mathematical topics more advanced than Euclid, but also was the first mathematician to derive quantitative results from the creation of mathematical models of physical problems on earth. In several of his books, he described the reasoning process by which he arrived at his results in addition to giving formal proofs. For example, he showed how to calculate the areas of a segment of a parabola and the region bounded by one turn of a spiral, and the volume of a paraboloid of revolution.

Ptolemy *(C. 100–178 C.E.)* is most famous for the *Almagest*, a work in thirteen books, which contains a complete mathematical description of the Greek model of the universe with parameters for the various motions of the sun, moon, and planets. The first book provides the strictly mathematical material detailing the plane and spherical trigonometry, all based solely on the chord function, necessary for astronomical computations.

Hypatia *(c. 370–415)*, the first woman mathematician on record, lived in Alexandria. She was given a very thorough education in mathematics and philosophy by her father Theon and was responsible for detailed commentaries on several important Greek works, including Ptolemy's *Almagest*, Apollonius's *Conics*, and Diophantus's *Arithmetica*.

Brahmagupta *(c. 598–670)*, from Rajasthan in India, is most famous for his *Brahmasphutasiddhanta (Correct Astronomical System of Brahma)*, an astronomical work which contains many chapters on mathematics. Among the mathematical problems he considered and gave solution algorithms for were systems of linear congruences, quadratic equations, and special cases of the Pell equation $Dx^2 \pm 1 = y^2$. He also gave the earliest detailed treatment of rules for operating with positive and negative numbers.

Bhaskara *(1114–1185)*, the most famous of medieval Indian mathematicians, gave a complete algorithmic solution to the Pell equation. In addition, he dealt with techniques of solving systems of linear equations with more unknowns than equations and was familiar with the basic combinatorial formulas, giving many examples, though no proofs, of their use.

Qin Jiushao *(1202–1261)*, born in Sichuan, published a general procedure for solving systems of linear congruences—the Chinese remainder theorem—in his *Shushu jiuzhang (Mathematical Treatise in Nine Sections)* in 1247, a procedure which makes essential use of the Euclidean algorithm. He also gave a complete description of a method for solving numerically polynomial equations of any degree. Qin's method was developed in China over a period of a thousand years or more and is very similar to what is now called the Horner method of solution, published by William Horner in 1819.

Muhammad al-Khwarizmi *(c. 780–850)*, originally from Khwarizm in what is now Uzbekistan, was one of the first scholars called to the House of Wisdom in Baghdad by the caliph al-Ma'mun. He is best known for his algebra text, in which he gave a careful treatment of solution methods for quadratic equations. This Arabic text, after being translated into Latin in the twelfth century, provided Europeans with an introduction to algebra, a subject not considered by the ancient Greeks. Al-Khwarizmi's book on arithmetic provided Europe with one of its earliest looks at the Hindu-Arabic number system.

Abu Ali ibn al-Haytham *(965–1039)*, who spent much of his life in Egypt, is most famous for his work on optics, a work read and commented on for many centuries in Europe. In pure mathematics, he developed an inductive procedure for calculating formulas for the sums of integral powers of the first n integers, and used the formula for fourth powers to calculate the volume of the solid formed by revolving a parabola about a line perpendicular to its axis.

Nasir al-Din al-Tusi *(1201–1274)* was the head of a large group of astronomers at the observatory in Maragha, in what is now Iran. He computed a new set of very accurate astronomical tables and developed some new ideas on planetary motion which may have influenced Copernicus in working out his heliocentric system. In pure mathematics, al-Tusi's attempted proof of the parallel postulate was modified by his son and later published in Rome, where it influenced European work on non-Euclidean geometry. Al-Tusi also wrote the first systematic work on plane and spherical trigonometry, independent of astronomy, and gave the earliest proof of the theorem of sines.

Leonardo of Pisa *(1170–1240)*, often known today as Fibonacci, is most famous for his *Liber Abbaci (Book of Calculation)*, which contains the earliest publication of the Fibonacci numbers in the problem of how many pairs of rabbits can be bred in one year from one pair. Many of the sources of the book are in the Islamic world, where Leonardo spent much of his early life. The work contains the rules for computing with the new Hindu–Arabic numerals, many practical problems in such topics as calculation of profits and currency conversions, and topics now standard in algebra texts such as motion problems, mixture problems, and quadratic equations.

Levi ben Gerson *(1288–1344)* was a French rabbi and also an astronomer, philosopher, biblical commentator, and mathematician. His most famous mathematical work is the *Maasei Hoshev (The Art of the Calculator)*, which contains detailed proofs of the standard combinatorial formulas, some of which use the principle of mathematical induction.

Gerolamo Cardano *(1501–1576)*, a physician and gambler as well as a mathematician, wrote one of the earliest works containing systematic probability calculations, not all of which were correct. He is most famous, however, for his *Ars Magna (The Great Art,* 1545*)*, an algebra text which contained the first publication of the rules for solving cubic equations algebraically. Some of the rules had been discovered earlier in the sixteenth century by Scipione del Ferro and Niccoló Tartaglia.

François Viète *(1540–1603)*, a lawyer and advisor to two kings of France, was one of the earliest cryptanalysts and successfully decoded intercepted messages for his patrons. Although a mathematician only by avocation, he made important contributions to the development of algebra. In particular, he introduced letters to stand for numerical constants, thus enabling him to break away from the style of verbal algorithms of his predecessors and treat general examples by formulas rather than by giving rules for specific problems.

Simon Stevin *(1548–1620)* spent much of his life in the service of Maurice of Nassau, the Stadhouder of Holland, as a military engineer, advisor in finance and navigation, and quartermaster general of the Dutch army. In his book *De Thiende (The Art of Tenths)*, Stevin introduced decimal fractions to Europe, although they had previously been used in the Islamic world. Stevin's notation is different from our own, but he had a clear understanding of the advantage of decimals and advocated their use in all forms of measurement.

John Napier *(1550–1617)* was a Scottish laird who worked for years on the idea of producing a table which would enable one to multiply any desired numbers together by performing additions. These tables of logarithms first appeared in his 1614 book *Mirifici Logarithmorum Canonis Descriptio (Description of the Wonderful Canon of Logarithms)*. Napier's logarithms are different from, but related to, natural logarithms. His ideas were soon adapted by Henry Briggs, who eventually created the first table of common logarithms by 1628.

René Descartes *(1596–1650)* published the *Geometry* in 1637 as a supplement to his philosophical work, the *Discourse on the Method for Rightly Directing One's Reason and Searching for Truth in the Sciences*. In it, he developed the principles of analytic geometry, showing how to derive algebraic equations which represented geometric curves. The *Geometry* also contained methods for solving polynomial equations, including the modern factor theorem and Descartes' rule of signs.

Pierre de Fermat *(1601–1665)* was a French lawyer who spent his spare time doing mathematics. Not only was he a coinventor of analytic geometry, although his methods were somewhat different from those of Descartes, but he also was instrumental in the early development of probability theory and made many contributions to the theory of numbers. He is most remembered for the statement of his so-called "last theorem", that the equation $x^n + y^n = z^n$ has no nontrivial integral solution if $n > 2$, a theorem whose proof was finally completed by Andrew Wiles in 1994.

Blaise Pascal *(1623–1662)* showed his mathematical precocity with his *Essay on Conics* of 1640 in which he stated his theorem that the opposite sides of a hexagon inscribed in a conic section always intersect in three collinear points. Pascal is better known, however, for his detailed study of what is now called Pascal's triangle of binomial coefficients, the basic facts of which had been known in the Islamic and Chinese worlds for centuries. He also introduced the differential triangle in his *Treatise on the Sines of a Quadrant of a Circle*, an idea adopted by Leibniz in his calculus.

Isaac Newton *(1642–1727)*, the central figure in the Scientific Revolution, is most famous for his *Philosophiae Naturalis Principia Mathematica (Mathematical Principles of Natural Philosophy,* 1687*)*, in which he derived his system of the world based on his laws of motion and his law of universal gravitation. Over 20 years earlier, however, Newton had consolidated and generalized all the material on tangents and areas worked out by his predecessors into the magnificent problem solving tool of the calculus. He also developed the power series as a method of investigating various transcendental functions, stated the general binomial theorem, and, although never establishing his methods with the rigor of Greek geometry, did demonstrate an understanding of the concept of limit quite sufficient for him to apply the calculus to solve many important mathematical and physical problems.

Gottfried Wilhelm Leibniz *(1646–1716)*, born in Leipzig, developed his version of the calculus some ten years after Isaac Newton, but published it much earlier. Leibniz based his calculus on the inverse relationship of sums and differences, generalized to infinitesimal quantities called differentials. By clever manipulation of differentials, based in part on the geometrical model of the differential triangle, Leibniz was able to derive all of the basic rules of the differential and integral calculus and apply them to solve physical problems expressible in terms of differential equations. Leibniz's d and $\int$ notation for differentials and integrals turned out to be much more flexible and useful than Newton's dot notation and remains the notation of calculus to the present day.

Johann Bernoulli *(1667–1748)*, one of a number of prominent mathematicians of his Swiss family, was one of the earliest proponents of Leibniz's differential and integral calculus. Bernoulli helped to stimulate the development of the new techniques by proposing challenge problems to mathematicians, the most important probably being that of describing the brachistochrone, the curve representing the path of descent of a body between two given points in the shortest possible time. Many of the problems he posed required the solution of differential equations, and Bernoulli developed many techniques useful toward this end, including the calculus of the logarithmic and exponential functions.

Leonhard Euler *(1707–1783)*, a student of Johann Bernoulli in Basel who became one of the earliest members of the St. Petersburg Academy of Sciences founded by Peter the Great of Russia, was the most prolific mathematician of all time. His series of analysis texts, *Introduction to Analysis of the Infinite, Methods of the Differential Calculus*, and *Methods of the Integral Calculus*, established many of the notations and methods still in use today. Among his numerous contributions to every area of mathematics and physics are his development of the calculus of the trigonometric functions, the establishment of the theory of surfaces in differential geometry, and the creation of the calculus of variations.

Maria Agnesi *(1718–1799)*, the eldest child of a professor of mathematics at the University of Bologna, in 1748 published the clearest text on calculus up to that point. Based on the work of Leibniz and his followers, the work explained concepts lucidly and provided numerous examples, including some that have become standard in calculus texts to this day. Curiously, her name is often attached to a small item in her book not even original with her, a curve whose equation was $y = \pm\frac{a\sqrt{a-x}}{\sqrt{x}}$. This curve was called *la versiera*, derived from the Latin meaning "to turn"; unfortunately the word also was the abbreviation of the Italian word meaning "wife of the devil" and so was translated into English as "witch". The curve has ever since been known as the "witch of Agnesi."

Joseph Lagrange *(1736–1813)*, was born in Turin, becoming at age 19 a professor of mathematics at the Royal Artillery School there. He is most famous for his *Analytical Mechanics* (1788), a work which extended the mechanics of Newton and Euler, and demonstrated how problems in mechanics can generally be reduced to solutions of ordinary or partial differential equations. In 1797 he published his *Theory of Analytic Functions*, which attempted to reduce the ideas of calculus to those of algebraic analysis by assuming that every function could be represented as a power series. Although his central idea was incorrect, many of the proofs of basic theorems of calculus in this work were subsequently adapted by Cauchy into the forms still in use today.

Benjamin Banneker *(1731–1806)*, the first American black to achieve distinction in science, taught himself sufficient mathematics and astronomy to publish a series of well-regarded almanacs in the 1790s. He also assisted Andrew Ellicott in the survey of the boundaries of the District of Columbia. He was fond of solving mathematical puzzles and problems and recorded many of these in his notebooks.

Augustin-Louis Cauchy *(1789–1857)*, the most prolific mathematician of the nineteenth century, wrote several textbooks in analysis for use at the École Polytechnique, textbooks which became the model for calculus texts for the next hundred years. In his texts, Cauchy based the calculus on the notion of limit, using, for the first time, a definition which could be applied arithmetically to give proofs of some of the important results. Among numerous other subjects to which he contributed important ideas were complex analysis, in which he gave the first proof of the Cauchy integral theorem, the theory of matrices, in which he demonstrated that every symmetric matrix can be diagonalized by use of an orthogonal substitution, and the theory of permutations, in which he was the earliest to consider these from a functional point of view.

William Rowan Hamilton *(1805–1865)* became the Astronomer Royal of Ireland in 1827 because of his original work in optics accomplished during his undergraduate years at Trinity College, Dublin. In 1837, he showed how to introduce complex numbers into algebra axiomatically by considering $a + ib$ as a pair (a, b) of real numbers with appropriate computational rules. After many years of seeking an appropriate definition for multiplication rules for triples of numbers which could be applied to vector analysis in three-space, he discovered that it was in fact necessary to consider quadruplets of numbers. It was out of the natural definition of multiplication of these quaternions that the modern notions of dot product and cross product of vectors evolved.

Arthur Cayley *(1821–1895)*, although graduating from Trinity College, Cambridge, as Senior Wrangler, became a lawyer because there was no suitable mathematics position available in England. He produced nearly 300 mathematical papers during his 14 years as a lawyer, however, and finally secured a professorship at Cambridge in 1863. Among his numerous mathematical achievements are the earliest abstract definition of a group in 1854, out of which he was able to calculate all possible groups of order up to eight and the basic rules for operating with matrices, including a statement (without rigorous proof) of the Cayley–Hamilton theorem that every matrix satisfies its characteristic equation.

Richard Dedekind *(1831–1916)* solved the problem of the lack of unique factorization in rings of algebraic integers by introducing ideals and their arithmetic and demonstrating that every ideal is either prime or can be expressed uniquely as a product of prime ideals. During his teaching at Zurich in the late 1850s, he realized that, although differential calculus deals with continuous magnitudes, there was no satisfactory definition available of what it means for the set of real numbers to be continuous. He therefore worked out a definition of irrational numbers through his idea of what is now called a Dedekind cut in the set of rational numbers. Somewhat later Dedekind also considered the basic ideas of set theory and gave a set theoretic characterization of the natural numbers.

Carl Friedrich Gauss *(1777–1855)* published his important work on number theory, the *Disquisitiones Arithmeticae*, when he was only 24, a work containing not only an extensive discussion of the theory of congruences, culminating in the quadratic reciprocity theorem, but also a detailed treatment of cyclotomic equations in which he showed how to construct regular n-gons by Euclidean techniques whenever n is prime and $n - 1$ is a power of 2. Gauss also made fundamental contributions to the differential geometry of surfaces in his *General Investigations of Curved Surfaces* in 1827, as well as to complex analysis, astronomy, geodesy, and statistics during his long tenure as a professor at the University of Göttingen. Many ideas later published by others, including the basics of non-Euclidean geometry, were found in his notebooks after his death.

Karl Weierstrass *(1815–1897)* taught for many years at German gymnasia before producing a series of brilliant mathematical papers in the 1850s which resulted in his appointment to a professorship at the University of Berlin. It was in his lectures there that he insisted on defining every concept of analysis arithmetically, including such ideas as uniform convergence and uniform continuity, thus completing the transformation away from the use of terms such as "infinitely small". Since he himself never published many of these ideas, his primary influence was through the work of his numerous students.

Georg Bernhard Riemann *(1826–1866)*, in his 1854 inaugural lecture at the University of Göttingen entitled "On the Hypotheses which Lie at the Foundation of Geometry", discussed the general notion of an n-dimensional manifold, developed the idea of a metric relation on such a manifold, and gave criteria which would determine whether a three-dimensional manifold is Euclidean, or "flat". This lecture had enormous influence on the development of geometry, including non-Euclidean geometry, as well as on the development of a new concept of our physical space ultimately necessary for the theory of general relativity. Among his other achievements, Riemann's work on complex functions and their associated Riemann surfaces became one of the foundations of combinatorial topology.

Sofia Kovalevskaya *(1850–1891)* was the first European woman since the Renaissance to earn a Ph.D. in mathematics (1874), a degree based on her many new results in the theory of partial differential equations. Because women were generally not permitted to study mathematics officially in European universities, Kovalevskaya had been forced to study privately with Weierstrass. Her mathematical talents eventually earned her a professorship at the University of Stockholm, an editorship of the journal *Acta Mathematica*, and the Prix Bordin of the French Academy of Sciences for her work on the revolution of a solid body about a fixed point. Unfortunately, her career was cut short by her untimely death from pneumonia at the age of 41.

Henri Poincaré *(1854–1912)*, one of the last of the universal mathematicians, contributed to virtually every area of mathematics, including physics and theoretical astronomy. Among his many contributions was the introduction of the idea of homology into topology, the creation of a model of Lobachevskian geometry which helped to convince mathematicians that this non-Euclidean geometry was as valid as Euclid's, and a detailed study of the nonlinear partial differential equations governing planetary motion aimed at answering questions about the stability of the solar system. Toward the end of his life, Poincaré wrote several popular books emphasizing the importance of science and mathematics.

David Hilbert *(1862–1943)* is probably most famous for his lecture at the International Congress of Mathematicians in Paris in 1900 in which he presented a list of 23 problems which he felt would be of central importance for 20th century mathematics. Most of the problems have now been solved, while significant progress has been achieved in the remainder. Hilbert himself made notable contributions to the study of algebraic forms, algebraic number theory, the foundations of geometry, integral equations, theoretical physics, and the foundations of mathematics.

Leonard Eugene Dickson *(1874–1954)* was the first recipient of a doctorate in mathematics at the University of Chicago, where he ultimately spent most of his mathematical career. Dickson helped to develop the abstract approach to algebra by developing sets of axioms for such constructs as groups, fields, and algebras. Among his important books was his monumental three volume *History of the Theory of Numbers*, which traced the evolution of every important concept in that field.

Emmy Noether *(1882–1935)* received her doctorate from the University of Erlangen in 1908, a few years later moving to Göttingen to assist Hilbert in the study of general relativity. During her 18 years there, she was extremely influential in stimulating a new style of thinking in algebra by always emphasizing its structural rather than computational aspects. She is most famous for her work on what are now called Noetherian rings, but her inspiration of others is still evident in today's textbooks in abstract algebra.

Alan Turing *(1912–1954)* developed the concept of a "Turing machine" in 1936 to answer the questions of what a computation is and whether a given computation can in fact be carried out. This notion today lies at the basis of the modern all-purpose computer, a machine which can be programmed to do any desired computation. During World War II, Turing led the successful effort in England to crack the German "Enigma" code, an effort central to the defeat of Nazi Germany.

10.10 ASCII CHARACTER CODES

Left\right	American Standard Code for Information Exchange									
digits	0	1	2	3	4	5	6	7	8	9
0	nul	soh	stx	etx	eot	enq	ack	bel	bs	ht
1	nl	vt	np	cr	so	si	dle	dc1	dc2	dc3
2	dc4	nak	syn	etb	can	em	sub	esc	fs	gs
3	rs	us	sp	!	"	#	$	%	&	'
4	(	)	*	+	,	-	.	/	0	1
5	2	3	4	5	6	7	8	9	:	;
6	<	=	>	?	@	A	B	C	D	E
7	F	G	H	I	J	K	L	M	N	O
8	P	Q	R	S	T	U	V	W	X	Y
9	Z	[	\	]	^	_	`	a	b	c
10	d	e	f	g	h	i	j	k	l	m
11	n	o	p	q	r	s	t	u	v	w
12	x	y	z	{	||	}	~	del		

References

1. C. C. Gillispie, Ed., *Dictionary of Scientific Biography*, Scribners, New York, 1970–1990.

2. AMS, *Mathematical Sciences Professional Directory*, American Mathematical Society, Providence, 1995.

3. H. S. Tropp, "The Origins and History of the Fields Medal", *Historia Mathematica*, 1976, 3, 167–181.

4. E. T. Bell, *Men of Mathematics,* Dover, New York, 1945.

List of Notations

$E(u, v)$	first fundamental metric coefficient, 324
$e(u, v)$	second fundamental metric coefficient, 324
$E[\,]$	expectation, 573
$ecc(v)$	eccentricity of a vertex, 183, 186
$\mathbf{e}_i$	unit vector, 117
$e_{i_1 \cdots i_n}$	permutation symbol, 437
$\mathbf{E}_{ij}$	elementary matrix, 118
E_k	Erlang-k service time, 587
E_n	Euler numbers, 19
$E_n(x)$	Euler polynomial, 18
$E_n(x)$	exponential integral, 504
$\epsilon_{i_1 \cdots i_n}$	Levi–Civita symbol, 437
erf	error function, 498
erfc	complementary error function, 498
η	power of a test, 604
$\eta(x, y)$	component of infinitesimal generator, 414
exsec	trigonometric function, 453
$\mathcal{F}$	Fourier transform, 530
F	farad, 732
$F(a, b; c; z)$	hypergeometric function, 507
$F(u, v)$	first fundamental metric coefficient, 324
$f(u, v)$	second fundamental metric coefficient, 324
$F(x)$	Dawson's integral, 500
$F(x)$	probability distribution function, 573
$\hat{F}(x)$	sample distribution function, 601
$\hat{f}(x)$	sample density function, 601
$f(x)$	probability density function, 573
F_c	Fourier cosine transform, 535
FCFS	first come, first served, 587
FFT	fast Fourier transform, 538
FIFO	first in, first out, 587
F_n	Fibonacci numbers, 19
$\mathcal{F}_N$	discrete Fourier transform, 536
$\mathcal{F}_n$	Farey sequence, 92
F_{p^n}	Galois field, 144
F_s	Fourier sine transform, 535
$f_{X(t)}$	density function, 416
G	general service time distribution, 587
G	generating matrix, 218
G	graph, 182
G	gravitational constant, 737

r	modulus of a complex number, 51
r	radius (inscribed circle), 271, 461
r	shearing factor, 303
$R(\mathbf{A})$	range space, 128
R.M.S.	root mean square, 603
rad	radian, 732
$\mathrm{rad}(G)$	radius of graph, 183, 188
Re	real part of a complex number, 51
ρ	server utilization, 588
$\rho(\mathbf{A})$	spectral radius, 132
$\rho(s)$	radius of curvature, 322
ρ_{ij}	correlation coefficient, 576
r_i	replication number, 204
$r_k(x)$	Rademacher functions, 662
$\mathbb{R}^n$	real n element vectors, 111
$\mathbb{R}^{n \times m}$	real $n \times m$ matrices, 116
RSS	random service, 587
S	sample space, 571
S	torsion tensor, 434
s	arc length parameter, 321
s	sample standard deviation, 603
s	semiperimeter, 461
s	second, 732
S	siemens, 732
$\mathcal{S}(T)$	symmetric part of a tensor, 432
$S(x)$	Fresnel integral, 500
sec	trigonometric function, 452
sgn	signum function, 72, 122
SI	Systeme Internationale d'Unites, 732
$\mathrm{Si}(z)$	sine integral, 503
σ	standard deviation, 573
$\sigma(n)$	sum of divisors, 107
σ^2	variance, 573
σ_{ii}	variance, 576
σ_{ij}	covariance, 576
$\sigma_k(n)$	sum of kth powers of divisors, 107
sin	trigonometric function, 452
S_k	area of circumscribed polygon, 277
s_k	area of inscribed polygon, 277
s_k	elementary symmetric functions, 77
$SL(n, \mathbb{C})$	matrix group, 146

Index

N

S

X

x-intercept, 267

Y

y-intercept, 267
yards, 735
year
      day of, 739
      leap, 737

Z

$\mathbb{Z}$ (integers), 3
Z-transform, 232, 543
zenith, 297
zero
      matrix, 119
      of Bessel functions, 518
      of complex function, 54
      simple, 672
zeta function, 22, 33